Principles of
Mass Transfer
Separation Processes

Binay K. Dutta

West Bengal Pollution Control Board
Kolkata

PHI Learning Private Limited

New Delhi-110001
2012

₹ 495.00

PRINCIPLES OF MASS TRANSFER AND SEPARATION PROCESSES
Binay K. Dutta

Cover photo — Courtesy: Haldia Petrochemicals Limited

ISBN-978-81-203-2990-4

The export rights of this book are vested solely with the publisher.

Fifth Printing   ...   ...   **January, 2012**

Published by Asoke K. Ghosh, PHI Learning Private Limited, M-97, Connaught Circus, New Delhi-110001 and Printed by Rajkamal Electric Press, Plot No. 2, Phase IV, HSIDC, Kundli-131028, Sonepat, Haryana.

To the memory of
My parents Gouri Dutta and Baneswar Dutta
and
My father-in-law Debabrata Majumder

Contents

Preface

'Mass transfer and separation processes' constitutes a core course of undergraduate programmes in chemical engineering. I started teaching it at the University of Calcutta more than thirty years ago. In the process of sharing with the students the joy and hardship of studying the subject, I felt that some inadequacies remain in the available texts despite the fact that some of them are excellent treatises. Ideally, a text in this area should present a balanced mix of fundamentals and applications with a flavour of recent developments and trends. This will give the students a sense of completeness and help them in their comfortable and confident transition to a chemical engineer. This volume—a new book on an old subject—is an attempt towards this direction.

Mass transfer deals with transport of a species in a mixture in a single phase or across a phase boundary in the presence of a concentration driving force. The application of the principles of mass transfer is ubiquitous in both non-living and living world, and the concepts involved cut smoothly across the fading interdisciplinary boundaries. The concept of mass transfer and separation processes as well as the organization of the book has been briefly outlined in the first chapter that essentially serves as an introduction. The basic principles of mass transfer have been discussed in Chapters 2 to 4 citing numerous examples from diverse areas to elucidate the theory with due emphasis on physical understanding and to impress upon the readers the vast scope of the subject. The remainder of the book is mostly devoted to separation processes although several fundamental principles that could not be elaborated in Chapters 2 to 4 have been taken up in the latter chapters depending upon the needs. An attempt has been made to cover most of the topics of the subject in this sixteen-chapter book. Descriptions of construction and operation of separation equipment, which are not adequately covered in the available texts on the subject, are strewn throughout the book. An entire chapter has been devoted to gas–liquid contacting equipment. Principles and methodologies of design of separation equipment have been illustrated. Recent developments in both theory and applications have been covered selectively and references have been cited.

Assimilation of solved examples and working out solutions to exercise problems are perhaps the best ways of placing one's understanding of a subject on a solid foundation. Keeping this in mind, about one hundred and fifty numerical examples have been used to illustrate the principles and applications. More than twice that number constitutes chapter-end problems, many of which relate to practical situations and applications. More than five hundred short and multiple choice questions have been designed to provoke the thought process and enhance the understanding of the students. In deviation from other similar texts, hints to the solutions to many chapter-end problems have been provided. These should provide the students with substantial activation energy to venture into problem-solving. The problems have been superscripted 1, 2 or 3 depending upon the degree of difficulty. The crux of a problem has been indicated at the beginning of the problem statement. Complete solutions to the problems are available in the *Solutions Manual* for the instructors.

The manuscript has been checked thoroughly, but mistakes may still be there. I shall greatly appreciate if the readers kindly bring those to my notice. Suggestions for improvement are always welcome. Although the book is primarily intended for undergraduate students, it will also be useful to both postgraduate students and practising engineers.

It is my great pleasure to put on record my indebtedness to my students for the stimulus I received from them over the years. I am thankful to Professor P. Ray, Dr. Sampa Chakrabarti, Dr. Basab Chaudhuri and Professor Sekhar Bhattacharjee, my colleagues (the last three are my former students as well) to name a few, who all helped me in many ways in course of preparation of the manuscript. I am grateful to a number of organizations who allowed me to use pictures of their products and relevant information. I thank my former students Mr. Abhijitbikash Pal, Dr. Basudeb Saha, Professor Ajay K. Ray and Dr. Swapan Dhara, for various kinds of help offered by them. Dr. Dhara provided a few pictures of the operating units of Haldia Petrochemicals Limited. Finally, the encouragement I received from Ratna, my wife, and Joyita, my daughter, proved invaluable in all stages of this work.

Binay K. Dutta

1 | Introduction

Separation of mixtures constitutes a major class of operations in the chemical process industry (CPI) and allied industries. Some mixtures are amenable to separation by purely mechanical techniques. Typical examples comprise separation of suspended solids from a liquid by filtration, settling or centrifugation; separation of a mixture of solid particles of different sizes/densities by elutriation; separation of suspended small particles from a gas by a cyclone or a bag filter; or separation of two immiscible liquids by phase separation followed by decantation. But there are many other mixtures, like gas and liquid mixtures (or solutions) in general, which cannot be separated by any of the above techniques. The strategy of separation of such a mixture is based on the use of either an externally supplied agent (for example, water is used to separate ammonia from a mixture with another gas by absorption, or, say, the separation of an organic vapour from a mixture with other gases by adsorption in active carbon) or by an input of energy (for example, distillation wherein the thermal energy is used to separate the more volatile component from a solution). The separation processes of this kind are based on the principles of mass transfer and have traditionally been called *mass transfer operations*.

Before going into a brief overview of the separation processes commonly used in chemical and allied industries, it will be pertinent to make an attempt at defining mass transfer and to cite a few examples to establish how the phenomenon of mass transfer is inherent to a variety of natural processes including the life processes. Mass transfer is the transport of a species from one point to another in a single phase or from one phase to another *generally* in the presence of a *difference* in concentration (or partial pressure), called the 'driving force'. There are numerous examples of this phenomenon. Aquatic life uses oxygen dissolved in water for survival and the supply of oxygen mostly comes from air. The concentration of oxygen in natural water is less than what it should be at saturation or at equilibrium. As a result, oxygen gets absorbed in the water of lakes, rivers and oceans. The phenomenon of transport of oxygen from air to water is a 'mass transfer' process since it is caused by a concentration driving force. The driving force gives a measure of how far a system is away from equilibrium. The larger the departure of a system from equilibrium, the greater is the driving force and the higher is the rate of transport. Water exposed to air will absorb oxygen faster if it has a low concentration of oxygen. If a limited volume of water eventually gets saturated with oxygen, it loses its ability to absorb gas any further.

1

Absorption of oxygen of air into blood occurs in the lungs of an animal in the process of respiration. The absorbed oxygen is supplied to the tissues through blood circulation. Oxygen is consumed and carbon dioxide that is generated remains dissolved in the blood. As the blood is pumped back into the lungs, the carbon dioxide gets 'desorbed' and leaves with the exhaled air. Thus the absorption of oxygen and the elimination of carbon dioxide occur simultaneously in the lungs. An 'artificial heart-lung machine' does the same job of oxygenation of blood and purging it of carbon dioxide when a patient undergoes a heart operation. Hydrolyzed food materials get absorbed in the intestine by mass transfer. So does a drug orally administered to a patient. An ointment externally applied diffuses through the minute pores in the skin. In fact, the mass transfer principles play a major role in a physiological system in diverse ways. Let us take a look at a few other applications. Consider the case of removal of moisture from food grains by drying. The moisture present in a grain diffuses through it, reaches the surface and gets desorbed into the surrounding air. This continues till the vapour pressure exerted by water present in a grain is higher than the partial pressure of moisture in the surrounding gas; and the drying process stops when these two pressures become equal. This is again a process of mass transfer. A solid dissolves in a liquid by a mass transfer process till the liquid becomes saturated. But a supersaturated solution rejects the excess solute in the form of crystals since the driving force is now reversed. A variety of substances like CO_2, CO, unburnt hydrocarbons, particulates, etc. issuing from a stack as a plume get dispersed in the ambient air by 'eddy diffusion', which is a mass transfer phenomenon. The process of *doping* the junctions of a silicon semiconductor device by a substance like gallium, boron, arsenic, etc. is based on the principles of mass transfer. The dispersion of a pollutant discharged at a point in flowing water is a mass transfer phenomenon. Since all of these phenomena are caused by a concentration driving force, we may call them 'mass transfer'. However, a mechanical transfer or shifting of a mass or a body from one place to another is *not* a mass transfer phenomenon since it is not caused by a concentration driving force. For the same reason, the separation of a solid from a liquid by filtration or centrifugation, or the separation of liquid droplets from a vapour in a knockout drum are not mass transfer phenomena but are definitely examples of mechanical separation processes.

Mass transfer may be *diffusional* or *convective*. A purely diffusional mass transfer phenomenon occurs in the absence of any macroscopic motion in the medium. The migration of moisture within a grain during drying is purely diffusional. The transport of a reactant or a product through the pores of a catalyst pellet occurs by diffusion. When mass transfer occurs in a fluid medium which is in some sort of motion, the rate of mass transfer increases greatly. This is convective mass transfer although molecular diffusion has an inherent role to play. The stronger the flow field and mixing and turbulence in a medium, the higher is the rate of mass transfer.

Mass transfer is a *transport process*. It is one of the three major transport processes central to chemical engineering operations. The other two transport processes are momentum transport and heat transport. Similar physical laws govern the rates of transport of momentum, heat and mass. But studies of heat transfer and of mass transfer have more in common and similar approaches are made for analyses of many mass and heat transport problems. However, one notable difference between the two is that practical heat transfer operations mostly occur through indirect contact. The two phases exchanging heat are kept separated by a thermally conductive medium. In an evaporator, for example, the latent heat of steam is transferred through a tube wall to the solution boiling on the other side. On the other hand, most mass transfer operations occur through direct contact. The phases exchanging mass through direct contact are immiscible or partially miscible. If the phases are miscible, a selectively permeating barrier (like the tube wall in heat transfer) may be placed between them to effect mass transfer without physical mixing of the phases. Membrane gas separation is an example of selective transport through a permeating barrier and is an indirect contact process. Another important difference is the fact that the two phases in thermal equilibrium have the same temperature, but the two phases in equilibrium in respect of mass transfer do not necessarily have the same concentration of the solute. In fact, in most cases, they do not have the same concentration. The concentrations of the species in the two phases bear a thermodynamic relation called the 'equilibrium relation'. The simplest equilibrium relation is a linear relation of Henry's law type. It is to be noted that the driving force in mass transfer is expressed in a number of different ways depending upon convenience, whereas in heat transfer the driving force is always expressed in terms of temperature difference. Further, mass transfer is likely to affect the flow rates of the phases as well as the molecular motion near the phase boundary. All these factors together make the principles of mass transfer and their applications seemingly a bit more involved than their heat transfer counterparts.

The principles of mass transfer, both diffusional and convective, form the basis of most of the *separation processes* used in the chemical industries. Here we define a separation process as a technique that transforms a mixture of substances into two or more products differing in composition (King, 1980). In this text we shall deal with concentration-driven separation processes only and not with the mechanical separation processes. As a prerequisite to understand the individual separation processes, the principles of mass transfer—basically the principles of diffusion and convective mass transfer—have been discussed in Chapters 2, 3, and 4. Chapter 4, in fact, deals with the elementary principles of mass transfer from one phase to another and these principles are applied to quite a few separation processes described in the latter chapters. Many separation processes or mass transfer operations are carried out in a stage-wise fashion and this concept of a stage-wise process has been introduced in Chapter 4. Chapters 6 to 9 and 11 to 14 describe the more common separation processes used in the chemical industries.

Separation of mixtures accounts for about 40 to 70% of both capital and operating costs of a chemical industry (Humphrey and Keller, 1997). The cost of separation of high-value products from a dilute solution (as in the case of recovery and concentration of bioproducts) may entail even 90% of the operating cost of a plant. Some kind of separation process is necessary almost in every stage from purification of raw materials to product separation and treatment of effluent streams. This is schematically shown in Figure 1.1. The core separation processes in the chemical industry are: gas absorption and stripping, distillation, liquid–liquid and solid–liquid extraction, drying of a wet solid, adsorption, crystallization, membrane separation and separation of multicomponent mixtures. All these separation processes involve mass transfer from one phase to another. Such two-phase systems may be categorized as gas (or vapour)–liquid, liquid–liquid, gas–solid, and liquid–solid.

Gas or (Vapour)–liquid contact

Separation of a soluble species from a gas mixture by using a solvent is called 'gas absorption'. This is a gas–liquid contacting operation. A typical application is the separation of CO_2 from the ammonia synthesis gas using a solvent like aqueous ethanolamine or carbonate–bicarbonate buffer (Chapter 6). The absorbed gas is recovered by 'stripping' when the solvent also gets regenerated and fit for reuse. The most common technique of separation of a liquid mixture is fractional distillation. This technique (Chapter 7) relies upon the difference in volatility of a

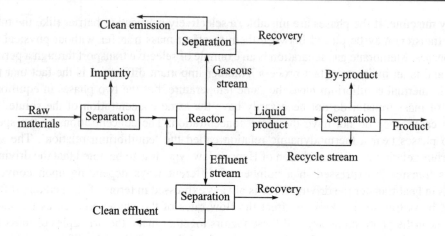

Figure 1.1 The role of separation processes in a chemical industry.

component over another in the mixture. Heat is supplied to vaporize a part of the liquid which flows up through a properly designed column and gets into intimate contact with a down-flowing liquid when the exchange of the component occurs. The more volatile components migrate into the vapour phase and the less volatile ones get transferred into the liquid phase. The concentration of the more volatiles increases up the column and that of the less volatiles increases down the column. The top product, which comes up as a vapour, is condensed. The less volatile part is taken out as the bottom product.

Liquid–liquid contact

If some or all of the components have low volatility and are thermally unstable in a liquid mixture or solution, it becomes convenient to introduce a suitable liquid, called solvent, into the separation device to extract the target compounds. This is liquid–liquid extraction (Chapter 8). The desired species is recovered from the extract by using another separation technique, say distillation or crystallization. Thus, penicillin is extracted from the fermentation broth by using an ester like butyl acetate and the final product recovery is done by crystallization.

Solid–liquid contact

One type of solid–liquid contact operation aims at solubilizing or extracting a target substance from a solid matrix. This is 'solid–liquid extraction' or 'leaching' (Chapter 9). Some typical examples are acid-leaching of ores or extraction of oil from flaked oil seeds or fragrance from flowers. Another type of solid–liquid operation involves simultaneous separation and purification of a substance from a supersaturated solution by 'crystallization'. A dissolved solute, particularly at a low concentration, can be conveniently separated by using a solid 'agent' that adsorbs the target substance. The solid adsorbent loaded with the solute is now further treated to recover the product. Here the adsorbent plays the same role as a solvent does in gas absorption. Another important case of solid–liquid contact is the separation of an ionic species from a solution by a solid ion exchange resin.

Gas–solid contact

Separation of a solute from a gas mixture can sometimes be done by adsorption in a solid material. The adsorbed solute is recovered frequently by thermal stripping. Another important application of gas–solid contacting is for drying of a moist solid using a drying gas. The hot gas is brought in intimate contact with the solid when the moisture leaves the solid and migrates into the gas as a vapour. A common application is the separation of organic vapours present in low concentration in a gaseous emission by using a bed of active carbon. Gas–solid contact also occurs in a less common separation like gas chromatography.

From the above description, it appears that a separation process needs some kind of a separating agent to split a mixture into more than two streams of different compositions. For example, a gas mixture gets separated when it is in contact with a solvent that selectively or preferentially absorbs one or more components. Here the solvent is the separating agent. The separating agent is left out after a job is completed. Thermal energy is the separating agent in distillation. It is supplied for vaporization of a liquid mixture and is removed from the top vapour when it is condensed. In liquid–liquid extraction, the externally added solvent is the separating agent. It is removed from the extract to recover the product. A hot gas is the common separating agent in drying and an adsorbent is the agent for separation by adsorption. Table 1.1 gives a list of the separating agents for the common separation processes.

Table 1.1 Separation processes, separating agents and typical applications (after Humphrey, 1995)

Separation process	Separating agent	Typical applications
Gas absorption and stripping	Solvent	Removal of CO_2 from synthesis gas; removal of CO_2 and H_2S from natural gas; stripping volatile substances from wastewater by steam.
Distillation	Heat	Fractionation of crude oil; separation of air.
Liquid–liquid extraction	Solvent	Removal of aromatics (benzene, toluene and xylene) from gasoline reformate; recovery of penicillin from fermentation broth.
Solid–liquid extraction	Solvent	Extraction of caffein from coffee; extraction of herbal products from barks and leaves.
Drying	Heat/drying gas	Drying of fruits; drying of polymer beads; drying of ceramic items before firing.
Adsorption	Adsorbent solid	Separation of organics from a gas or an aqueous solution; drying of air
Ion exchange	Ion exchange resin	Demineralization of water; separation of salts.
Crystallization	Heat (removal)	Production of salt, sugar, etc.
Membrane separation	Membranes	Desalination of water; preparation of absolute alcohol; concentration of fruit juice; air separation.

A good understanding of the construction and operating principles of separation equipment is essential for an overall grasp of the area. Considerable space has been devoted in respective chapters to address these aspects. Recent developments in equipment have been included as far as possible. The selection criteria for an equipment, from several available alternatives for a particular separation job, have also been discussed. The procedure of equipment design and sizing has been illustrated by simple examples. Since gas–liquid and vapour–liquid contacting, particularly distillation, is more frequent in process industries, an entire chapter (Chapter 5) has been devoted to the description of the basic features of the relevant equipment including the recent modifications.

Separation using a membrane as the separating agent or a separating barrier is now an established strategy. Spectacular developments have taken place in membrane casting and module design to exploit the separation capability of membranes for a variety of applications. An overview of different applications and aspects of membrane separation have both been discussed in Chapter 14.

Humidification and water cooling is necessary in every process industry. This operation cannot be considered a separation process since the basic objective is not the separation of a stream. However, it is a very useful practical example of simultaneous heat and mass transfer. It has been discussed in Chapter 10.

Unsteady state diffusion occurs in many natural processes relevant to applications in chemical engineering and allied areas. It is a vast area and an in-depth discussion cannot be made in a textbook of this size. Similarly, mass transfer accompanied by a chemical reaction is common to many gas absorption processes and quite a few liquid extraction processes. Elementary principles of these topics have been dealt with in Chapter 16.

Besides the separation processes described above, there are less common techniques such as electrophoresis, electrodialysis, zone messing, etc. used for specific separations. The first two are typical processes in which the major driving force is electrical (difference in voltage). These techniques have been kept out of scope of this text.

During the last few decades spectacular developments have taken place in several new areas such as materials, biotechnology, pharmaceuticals, and alternative fuels. These developments are accompanied by challenging separation problems often beyond the scope of the traditional mass transfer operations. Improving selectivity of separation by using better separating agents (for example, better solvents), concentration of high-value products from dilute solutions, improving efficiency and reducing equipment size, reducing energy requirements are a few of these challenges. In addition, growing concern for environment and rising energy costs are the two major factors having significant influence on reshaping separation processes. Some of these issues have been discussed very recently by Noble and Agrawal (2005).

On a broader perspective, the two important present-day criteria of evaluation of a process, new or conventional, are whether it is 'sustainable' and 'green'. Alongside development and adoption of green technologies, has come up the idea of 'green separation processes'. A few of their attributes have been mentioned above. So far as the chemical process industries are concerned, green technologies and green separation processes are complementary. A recent monograph by Afonoso and Crespo (2005) is devoted to reviewing and exploring the potentials of such processes.

REFERENCES

Afonoso, C.A.M., and J.G. Crespo, *Green Separation Processes—Fundamentals and Applications*, Wiley VCH, 2005.

Humphrey, J.L., 'Separation processes: Playing a critical role', *Chem. Eng. Progr.*, Dec. 1995, 31–41.

Humphrey, J.L., and G.E. Keller, *Separation Process Technology*, McGraw-Hill, New York, 1997.

King, C.J., *Separation Processes*, 2nd ed., McGraw-Hill, New York, 1980.

Noble, R.D., and R. Agrawal, 'Separation research needs for the 21st century', *Ind. Eng. Chem. Res., 44*(2005) 2887–2892.

2 | Molecular Diffusion

It is a matter of common experience that the molecules of a species move from a region of higher concentration to that of a lower concentration tending to make the concentration in the medium uniform. Thus a drop of ink released in the water in a glass gradually spreads to make the water uniformly coloured; the fragrance of a bunch of roses kept on the centre table of the drawing room reaches out even to a remote corner of the room; or the smell of petrol is felt when a car is being fuelled. All these observations are attributed to a basic natural phenomenon called 'diffusion'. The transport of molecules from a higher concentration to a lower concentration in a stagnant medium occurs by a mechanism called 'molecular diffusion', while in a turbulent medium the phenomenon called 'eddy diffusion' or 'turbulent diffusion' has the major role to play. This latter process occurs through random motion of the fluid elements and is much faster than molecular diffusion. The tendency of equalization of concentration occurs since there is a difference in concentration (or partial pressure) of the species between two points, and this difference in concentration is called the 'concentration driving force' in mass transfer.

The transport of a species from a point of higher concentration to a point of lower concentration in a medium by molecular diffusion becomes important if the medium is stagnant or in laminar motion. But molecular diffusion does not have a significant role to play in mass transfer in a turbulent medium except in a region very close to the phase boundary. Consider, for example, vaporization of a layer of water. If the surrounding air is stagnant, vaporization occurs rather slowly since water molecules escape from the surface by molecular diffusion which is a slow process. If there is flow of air over the water layer, the rate of vaporization becomes faster. However, the air velocity remains low in a narrow region adjacent to the water surface where transport by molecular diffusion plays an important role.

Since the mass transfer operations mentioned in Chapter 1 are based on diffusional phenomena, the study of molecular diffusion is essential for understanding these phenomena. In this chapter, we shall explain the theoretical framework of the analysis of diffusion and develop suitable equations to calculate the rate of transport of a species in a medium by molecular diffusion under a given set of conditions. The rate of molecular diffusion is intimately connected with molecular velocity and concentration difference (or driving force). The concentration, the molecular velocity and the flux of a species in a mixture can be expressed in a number of ways as described below.

2.1   CONCENTRATION, VELOCITY AND FLUX

2.1.1   Concentration

The concentration of a species in a solution is generally expressed in terms of one of the following:

ρ_i = 'mass concentration' of the species i (i.e. mass of i per unit volume of the solution or mixture), in kg/m^3 (or lb/ft^3)

ρ = 'total mass concentration' of all the species in a solution, in kg/m^3 (or lb/ft^3); the total mass concentration ρ is nothing but the density of the solution

$w_i = \rho_i/\rho$ = mass fraction of the species i in a solution

C_i = molar concentration of the species i in a solution, in $kmol/m^3$ (or $lbmol/ft^3$)

C = total molar concentration of the solution, in $kmol/m^3$ (or $lbmol/ft^3$)

$x_i = C_i/C$ = mole fraction of the species i in a solution.

If there are n species in a solution, we have the following relations.

$$\sum_{i=1}^{n} \rho_i = \rho; \qquad \sum_{i=1}^{n} C_i = C; \qquad \sum_{i=1}^{n} w_i = 1; \qquad \sum_{i=1}^{n} x_i = 1$$

In a gas mixture, the 'concentration' of a species is more commonly expressed in terms of its partial pressure p_i, or the mole fraction, $y_i = p_i/P$, where P is the total pressure. It is customary to denote the mole fraction of a species i by x_i in a solution (liquid) and by y_i in a gas mixture.

2.1.2   Velocity

In a liquid solution or in a gaseous mixture, the various components or species move with different velocities. By 'velocity' we mean both the molecular velocity in the microscopic scale and the bulk motion. By bulk motion we mean the motion in a fluid caused by a pressure difference. A diffusing species moves with a velocity greater than the average velocity of the medium. Two types of average velocities with respect to a 'stationary observer' are defined in this connection.

Mass average velocity

In an n-component mixture, the mass average velocity[†] u is defined as

$$u = \frac{\sum_{i=1}^{n} \rho_i u_i}{\sum_{i=1}^{n} \rho_i} = \frac{1}{\rho} \sum_{i=1}^{n} \rho_i u_i \tag{2.1}$$

where u_i is the linear velocity of the ith species in the concerned direction. The quantity u_i does not mean the instantaneous velocity of a molecule of the component. It is rather a statistical mean of the velocities of the molecules of component i in the given direction.

[†]This is the velocity which we can measure by a flow measuring device such as an anemometer.

Molar average velocity

Similarly, the molar average velocity of a mixture, U, is defined as

$$U = \frac{\sum_{i=1}^{n} C_i u_i}{\sum_{i=1}^{n} C_i} = \frac{1}{C} \sum_{i=1}^{n} C_i u_i \tag{2.2}$$

If the concentration of a solute in a solution is small, the contribution of the motion of the solute molecules to the average velocity also remains small. So the average velocity becomes virtually equal to the velocity of the medium or the solvent. Again, if the molecular weights of all the species are equal, the mass and the molar average velocities are the same (this is very simple to prove).

2.1.3 Mass Flux and Molar Flux

In the study of mass transfer, the term 'flux' means the net rate at which a species in a solution passes through a unit area, which is normal to the direction of diffusion, in unit time. It is expressed in kg/m$^2 \cdot$s, kmol/m$^2 \cdot$s, or lbmol/ft$^2 \cdot$h.

2.1.4 Frames of Reference

Three frames of reference (or coordinate systems) are commonly defined for expressing the flux of a diffusing species (Skelland, 1974). We imagine that in any frame of reference there is an 'observer' who 'observes' or 'measures' the velocity or flux of the species in a mixture. In a 'stationary frame of reference' ('stationary' means stationary with respect to the earth), the observer notes a velocity u_i of the ith species. If the observer is seated in a frame of reference that moves with the mass average velocity u, he will note a velocity, $(u_i - u)$, of the species i. This, in fact, is the relative velocity of the species with respect to the observer who himself has a velocity u in the same direction. Similarly, if the observer is seated in a coordinate system moving with the molar average velocity U, he finds that the molecules of the species i have a velocity $(u_i - U)$. The relative velocities in the three frames of reference are shown in Figure 2.1.

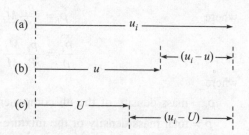

Figure 2.1 Relative velocities of species i in the three frames of reference: (a) The observer is stationary; (b) the observer is moving with the mass average velocity; (c) the observer is moving with the molar average velocity.

The mass and molar fluxes in the three frames of reference are expressed as

Mass flux

Relative to a stationary observer : $n_i = \rho_i u_i$ (2.3)
Relative to an observer moving with the mass average velocity : $i_i = \rho_i(u_i - u)$ (2.4)
Relative to an observer moving with the molar average velocity : $j_i = \rho_i(u_i - U)$ (2.5)

Molar flux

Relative to a stationary observer $\qquad$: $N_i = C_i u_i$ $\qquad$ (2.6)

Relative to an observer moving with the mass average velocity : $I_i = C_i(u_i - u)$ $\qquad$ (2.7)

Relative to an observer moving with the molar average velocity : $J_i = C_i(u_i - U)$ $\qquad$ (2.8)

EXAMPLE 2.1 (*Calculation of average velocities*) A gas mixture ($N_2 = 5\%$, $H_2 = 15\%$, $NH_3 = 76\%$ and $Ar = 4\%$) flows through a pipe, 25.4 mm in diameter, at 4.05 bar total pressure. If the velocities of the respective components are 0.03 m/s, 0.035 m/s, 0.03 m/s and 0.02 m/s, calculate the mass average, molar average and volume average velocities of the mixture.

Solution

Let us call N_2: 1, H_2: 2, NH_3: 3, and Ar: 4.

The volume average velocity (= molar average velocity) is given by

$$U = \frac{1}{C}(C_1 u_1 + C_2 u_2 + C_3 u_3 + C_4 u_4) = y_1 u_1 + y_2 u_2 + y_3 u_3 + y_4 u_4$$

Here y_i is the mole fraction of component i in the gas mixture. Putting the values, we get

$$U = (0.05)(0.03) + (0.15)(0.035) + (0.76)(0.03) + (0.04)(0.02)$$

$$= \boxed{0.0303 \text{ m/s}}$$

The mass average velocity is given by

$$u = \frac{1}{\rho}(\rho_1 u_1 + \rho_2 u_2 + \rho_3 u_3 + \rho_4 u_4) \qquad \text{(i)}$$

where $\qquad$ $\rho_i = \dfrac{p_i}{RT} M_i$ $\qquad$ and $\qquad$ $\rho = \dfrac{P}{RT} M$

$\Rightarrow$ $\qquad$ $\dfrac{\rho_i}{\rho} = \dfrac{p_i}{P}\dfrac{M_i}{M} = y_i \dfrac{M_i}{M}$ $\qquad$ (ii)

where

ρ_i = mass density of the ith component

ρ = total mass density of the mixture

M_i = molecular weight of the ith component

M = average molecular weight of the mixture.

Now, $\qquad$ $M = y_1 M_1 + y_2 M_2 + y_3 M_3 + y_4 M_4$

$$= (0.05)(28) + (0.15)(2) + (0.76)(17) + (0.04)(40) = 16.22$$

$\Rightarrow$ $\qquad$ $u = \dfrac{1}{M}\displaystyle\sum_{i=1}^{4} y_i M_i u_i$

$$= \frac{(0.05)(28)(0.03) + (0.15)(2)(0.035) + (0.76)(17)(0.03) + (0.04)(40)(0.02)}{16.22}$$

$$= \boxed{0.029 \text{ m/s}}$$

2.2 FICK'S LAW

The basic law of diffusion, called the 'Fick's law', was enunciated by Adolf Eugen Fick, a physiologist, in 1885.[†] The law states that *the molar flux of a species relative to an observer moving with the molar average velocity is proportional to the concentration gradient of the species*. If *A* diffuses in a binary mixture of *A* and *B*, then according to Fick's law, the flux of *A* is expressed as

$$J_A \propto \frac{dC_A}{dz} \quad \Rightarrow \quad J_A = -D_{AB}\frac{dC_A}{dz} \tag{2.9}$$

Here D_{AB} is the proportionality constant called the 'diffusion coefficient' or the 'diffusivity' of *A* in a mixture of *A* and *B*. The diffusional flux J_A is a positive quantity by convention. Since diffusion occurs spontaneously in the direction of decreasing concentration $[(dC_A/dz) < 0]$, the negative sign is incorporated in Eq. (2.9) to make it *consistent* with respect to sign. Equation (2.9) is the mathematical representation of Fick's law for diffusion in a binary mixture.

Here it will be pertinent to point out the similarity of Fick's law of diffusion given by Eq. (2.9) with the two other basic laws of transport, i.e. the Fourier's law of heat conduction and the Newton's law of viscosity. In heat conduction (also called 'diffusion of heat') the flux of thermal energy is proportional to the temperature gradient, i.e.

$$q_z = -k\frac{dT}{dz} \tag{2.10}$$

Here q_z is the heat flux in the *z*-direction and the temperature decreases in that direction.

The shear stress in a viscous fluid in laminar motion can be shown to be equivalent to the flux of momentum from a faster-moving layer to an adjacent slower-moving layer. The Newton's law of viscosity states that the shear stress or the momentum flux is proportional to the velocity gradient, i.e.

$$\tau_{zx} = -\mu\frac{du_x}{dz} \tag{2.11}$$

Here u_x is the velocity in the *x*-direction which is a function of *z*. Transport of momentum occurs in the *z*-direction (which is normal to the direction of liquid velocity).

It appears from Eqs. (2.9), (2.10) and (2.11) that the three processes of diffusive transport of mass, heat and momentum are governed by similar laws. The transport of mass occurs in the direction of decreasing concentration, the transport of heat occurs in the direction of decreasing temperature, and that of momentum occurs in the direction of decreasing velocity (or momentum). The same sign convention applies to all the three laws as well. The analogy among these laws is of considerable importance in chemical engineering and is discussed in further details in Section 3.8.

The Fick's law given by Eq. (2.9) expresses the molar flux J_A with respect to an observer moving with the molar average velocity. In practice, however, the molar flux N_A in a stationary frame of reference is more useful. An expression for N_A can be developed by using Eqs. (2.8) and (2.9).

[†] For more details of Fick's work, see Cussler (1997).

Molar average velocity [from Eqs. (2.2) and (2.6)] is

$$U = \frac{1}{C}(N_A + N_B) \tag{2.12}$$

Fluxes of A and B [from Eq. (2.6)] are

$$N_A = C_A u_A \quad \text{and} \quad N_B = C_B u_B \tag{2.13}$$

Therefore, using Eqs. (2.8) and (2.9),

$$
\begin{aligned}
J_A = -D_{AB}\frac{dC_A}{dz} &= C_A(u_A - U) \\
&= C_A u_A - C_A U \\
&= N_A - \frac{C_A}{C}(C_A u_A + C_B u_B) \\
&= N_A - \frac{C_A}{C}(N_A + N_B)
\end{aligned}
$$

$$\Rightarrow \qquad N_A = (N_A + N_B)\frac{C_A}{C} - D_{AB}\frac{dC_A}{dz} \tag{2.14}$$

The molar flux of A in a binary mixture with respect to a stationary observer is given by Eq. (2.14) on the basis of Fick's law. The flux N_A can be viewed as consisting of two terms as follows:

(i) The term representing bulk flow, i.e.

$$(N_A + N_B)\frac{C_A}{C} \tag{2.15}$$

and (ii) the term representing molecular diffusion, i.e.

$$-D_{AB}\frac{dC_A}{dz} \tag{2.16}$$

If the concentration of A in a mixture is small (dilute solution), the contribution of the bulk flow term given in Eq. (2.15) becomes small too. In such a case, we may write

$$N_A \approx J_A = -D_{AB}\frac{dC_A}{dz} \tag{2.17}$$

The diffusing molecules move at a velocity greater than the molar average velocity. The relative velocity of a molecular species with respect to an observer moving with the molar average velocity U is sometimes called the 'diffusion velocity'.

Diffusion velocity of species A,

$$v_{A,d} = u_A - U = \frac{J_A}{C_A} = -\frac{D_{AB}}{C_A}\frac{dC_A}{dz} \tag{2.18}$$

For gas phase diffusion, Eq. (2.14) may be written in terms of partial pressure too. If the gas mixture is assumed to behave ideally, $C_A = p_A/RT$ and $C = P/RT$, where T is the uniform temperature of the gas (in K),

$$\Rightarrow \qquad N_A = (N_A + N_B)\frac{p_A}{P} - \frac{D_{AB}}{RT}\frac{dp_A}{dz} \tag{2.19}$$

Although Eqs. (2.9) and (2.14) are the commonly used expressions for J_A and N_A, it has been argued (see, for example, Hines and Maddox, 1985) that these quantities should be expressed in terms of the gradient of mole fraction rather than the gradient of concentration or partial pressure. This point may be explained by taking an example. Let us consider a volume of air in a rectangular enclosure with the top surface hot (Figure 2.2). Air in contact with this surface is at a higher temperature (say T_1). The concentration (in kmol/m^3, say) of any of the constituents of air, say N$_2$, at the hot surface is $[C_{N_2}]_1 = [p_{N_2}]_1/RT_1$; its concentration at the cold bottom

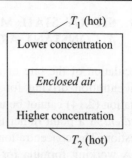

Figure 2.2 Air in an enclosure with hot top surface and cold bottom surface.

surface is $[C_{N_2}]_2 = [p_{N_2}]/RT_2$. Here T_2 is the bottom temperature. The total pressure of air and the partial pressures of the components are uniform throughout the enclosure, i.e. $[p_{N_2}]_1 = [p_{N_2}]_2$. Also $T_1 > T_2 \Rightarrow [C_{N_2}]_1 < [C_{N_2}]_2$, which means that there is a concentration gradient of N$_2$ in the chamber. But does nitrogen diffuse from the 'higher concentration region' near the bottom to the 'lower concentration region' near the top? No, because there is no difference in mole fraction of nitrogen between the top and the bottom regions.[†] So the use of concentration gradient in expressing the Fick's law and the descendant equations may sometimes be misleading and erroneous. It is therefore necessary to write down the equations in the following forms [Eqs. (2.20) and (2.21)] in order to take care of the situations like above. However, we shall use Eqs. (2.9) and (2.14) wherever these are applicable.

$$J_A = -CD_{AB} \frac{dy_A}{dz} \tag{2.20}$$

$$N_A = (N_A + N_B)y_A - CD_{AB} \frac{dy_A}{dz} \tag{2.21}$$

Here C is the average total molar concentration of the mixture.

If the gas mixture is ideal, the mutual diffusivities of A and B are equal. It is rather easy to prove this result. The flux of B in the mixture can be written following Eq. (2.14), i.e.

$$N_B = (N_A + N_B) \frac{C_B}{C} - D_{BA} \frac{dC_B}{dz}$$

Adding the preceding equation to Eq. (2.14),

$$(N_A + N_B) = (N_A + N_B)\left(\frac{C_A + C_B}{C}\right) - D_{AB}\frac{dC_A}{dz} - D_{BA}\frac{dC_B}{dz} = \text{constant}$$

Noting that

$$C = C_A + C_B \quad \text{and} \quad \frac{dC_A}{dz} = -\frac{dC_B}{dz}, \tag{2.22}$$

we get the result

$$D_{AB} = D_{BA} \tag{2.23}$$

[†] Here we neglect the coupling effects of concentration and temperature gradients on diffusion. The coupling effects are dealt with in irreversible thermodynamics (see, for example, Prigogine, 1967).

2.3   STEADY STATE MOLECULAR DIFFUSION THROUGH A CONSTANT AREA IN A BINARY GAS MIXTURE

Calculation of the rate of molecular diffusion from one point to another in the presence of a concentration driving force becomes necessary in numerous practical situations. The flux equation (2.14) cannot be used directly since it expresses the flux in terms of the *concentration gradient* at a point rather than the concentrations of the diffusing species at the two points in question. The concentration gradient is not an easily measurable quantity, but the concentration is. A working formula for the diffusion rate in terms of the concentration difference can be developed by integrating Eqs. (2.14), (2.19) or (2.21). This will be done in two practically important *limiting situations* given below for a binary mixture of A and B. It is *assumed* that (i) the area through which diffusion occurs is constant (i.e. the area does not depend upon the distance in the direction of diffusion), (ii) the gas mixture is ideal, (iii) the temperature is uniform, and (iv) diffusion occurs at steady state. The term *steady state* deserves an explanation.

If a system is at steady state, the variables and parameters associated with it do not change with time. Or, in other words, the 'state' of the system does not change with time. For example, if diffusion of A occurs from point 1 to point 2 in a medium at steady state, the concentration distribution of A (and of the other species in the medium as well) and the rate of transport remain invariant with time.[†]Another term called *pseudo-steady state* is often used in connection with the analysis of transport problems. It will be explained later in Section 2.5.1.

In this section we shall consider diffusion through a constant area. The flux of the diffusing species does not change with position at steady state. But in the case of diffusion through a *variable area*, the flux changes with position even when the system is at steady state. For example, in the case of evaporation from the surface of a liquid drop in an ambient medium, the flux of the vapour decreases with the radial position, i.e. it becomes less and less as the radial distance increases. Diffusion through a variable area will be discussed in Section 2.7.

2.3.1   Diffusion of A Through Non-diffusing B

This situation can be illustrated using an example. Dry air is required for burning of sulphur in a sulphuric acid plant. Air is dried in contact with concentrated sulphuric acid in a 'packed tower'(see Chapter 5). Moisture(A) diffuses through a *film* or layer of air(B), reaches the acid surface and gets absorbed in it. But air (we consider air a single substance or component) being virtually insoluble in sulphuric acid, will not diffuse. In other words, the moisture has a 'source' (the bulk of air is the source) and a 'sink' (the acid), but 'dry' air has a 'source' but no 'sink'. So air is 'non-diffusing'. There are numerous other real-life examples of this limiting situation.

The component B being non-diffusing, its flux $N_B = 0$. So, Eq. (2.19) reduces to

$$N_A = N_A \frac{p_A}{P} - \frac{D_{AB}}{RT} \frac{dp_A}{dz} \tag{2.24}$$

$$\Rightarrow \qquad N_A dz = -\frac{D_{AB}P}{RT(P - p_A)} dp_A \tag{2.25}$$

[†] 'Steady state' should not be confused with 'equilibrium'. In a system at equilibrium, no *net* transport of a species from one point to another occurs.

It may be noted that for diffusion through a constant area at steady state, N_A = constant. If diffusion occurs from a point $z = 0$ (where the partial pressure of A is $p_A = p_{A0}$) to the point $z = l$ (where $p_A = p_{Al}$), integration of Eq. (2.25) over the 'length l of the diffusion path' yields

$$N_A \int_0^l dz = -\frac{D_{AB}\,P}{RT} \int_{p_{A0}}^{p_{Al}} \frac{dp_A}{P - p_A} \quad \Rightarrow \quad N_A = \frac{D_{AB}\,P}{RTl}\ln\frac{P - p_{Al}}{P - p_{A0}} \tag{2.26}$$

Since the total pressure in the medium is uniform,

$$P = p_{A0} + p_{B0} = p_{Al} + p_{Bl} \quad \Rightarrow \quad P - p_{A0} = p_{B0},$$

$$P - p_{Al} = p_{Bl} \quad \text{and} \quad p_{A0} - p_{Al} = p_{Bl} - p_{B0}$$

Using the above results, we can rearrange Eq. (2.26) to the following form.

$$N_A = \frac{D_{AB}\,P}{RTl}\frac{p_{A0} - p_{Al}}{p_{A0} - p_{Al}}\ln\frac{p_{Bl}}{p_{B0}} = \frac{D_{AB}\,P}{RTl}\frac{p_{A0} - p_{Al}}{(p_{Bl} - p_{B0})/\ln(p_{Bl}/p_{B0})}$$

$$\Rightarrow \qquad N_A = \frac{D_{AB}\,P}{RTl}\frac{p_{A0} - p_{Al}}{p_{BM}} \tag{2.27}$$

where

$$p_{BM} = (p_{Bl} - p_{B0})/\ln(p_{Bl}/p_{B0})$$

We call p_{BM} the 'log mean partial pressure of B' between the locations $z = 0$ and $z = l$.

Also, if we consider diffusion of A from the point $z = 0$ to any point $z = z$ where the partial pressure of A is p_A, we have

$$N_A = \frac{D_{AB}\,P}{RT\,z}\ln\frac{P - p_A}{P - p_{A0}} \tag{2.28}$$

The molar flux of the species A in a mixture of A and B can be calculated using Eq. (2.26) or (2.27). Equation (2.27) expresses the flux in terms of the driving force of the species A, i.e. $p_{A0} - p_{Al}$. Once the flux N_A is known, we can use Eq. (2.28) to calculate the partial pressure p_A of A at any intermediate point and the distribution of the partial pressure of A along the diffusion path can also be determined. The partial pressure of the other component B at any point is $p_B = P - p_A$. Typical distributions of the partial pressures of the components along the diffusion path are shown in Figure 2.3.

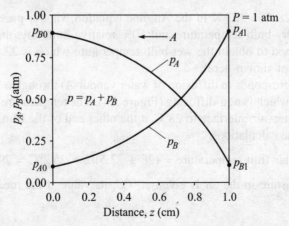

Figure 2.3 Partial pressure distribution of A and B for diffusion of A through non-diffusing B.

The component A diffuses from the location $z = 0$ towards the location $z = l$ because it has a non-zero gradient of partial pressure at each point of the diffusion path. The component B also has a gradient of partial pressure, although of the opposite sign [see Eq. (2.22)]. So it is expected that B will diffuse in the opposite direction. But we have started with the basic assumption that B is non-diffusing! Why is it so? To explain the apparent contradiction, we take the help of an example. Consider a flock of fish swimming against the water current of a river such that the absolute velocities of the fish and the water are equal in magnitude but opposite in direction. To a stationary observer on the bank of the river, the flock of fish appears to be non-moving while the river water appears to flow. The 'flux' of the fish is therefore zero. But a fisherman on a boat freely floating on the water (that is, the boat is moving with the velocity of the current) will definitely observe a 'flux' of the fish in the direction opposite to that of the current. Similarly, in the case of diffusion of A through non-diffusing B, the flux of B to a stationary observer appears to be zero ($N_B = 0$) because the diffusing molecules of B are 'swept away' by the molecules of A (very much like the fish being swept away by the current). But an observer imagined to be fixed to an avearge molecule of A (like the fisherman on the boat) will note a flux of B in the opposite direction.

EXAMPLE 2.2 (*Diffusion of A through non-diffusing B*)   There is a 2 mm thick layer of water on the floor of a room. The water vaporizes and diffuses through a stagnant film of air of estimated thickness of 2.5 mm on the water surface. Under the condition of evaporation, the water temperature is essentially equal to its wet-bulb temperature. If the ambient temperature is 28°C, calculate the time required for the water layer to disappear completely for the following cases: (a) the ambient air has a relative humidity of 60%; and (b) the floor has micropores and water penetrates the floor at a constant rate of 0.1 kg/m^2·h, the ambient air having a humidity as in part (a).

Read the wet-bulb temperature from the humidity chart and calculate the vapour pressure of water using the Antoine equation given below. The diffusivity of water vapour in air is 0.853 ft^2/h at 1 atm and 0°C.

Vapour pressure, p_v (in bar), of water is given by: $\ln p_v = 13.8573 - 5160.2/T$, where T is the temperature in K.

Solution

(a) Substituting $T = 28°C = 301$ K in the Antoine equation, vapour pressure, $p_v = 0.0374$ bar.

For air of 28°C dry-bulb temperature and 60% relative humidity, the psychrometric chart (Chapter 8) may be used to obtain the wet-bulb temperature which is 22.5°C (the procedure of reading the chart is not shown here).

The given case corresponds to diffusion of water vapour(A) through a 2.5 mm thick stagnant layer or film of air(B) which is non-diffusing (Figure 2.4). The temperature in this gas-film varies from 22.5°C at the water–air interface to 28°C at the other end of the film. So we take the mean film temperature in the calculations.

$$\text{Mean air-film temperature} = (28 + 22.5)/2 = 25.2°C = 298.2 \text{ K}$$

The diffusivity of moisture in the air is given at 0°C; its value at the mean film temperature is [see Eq. (2.57)]

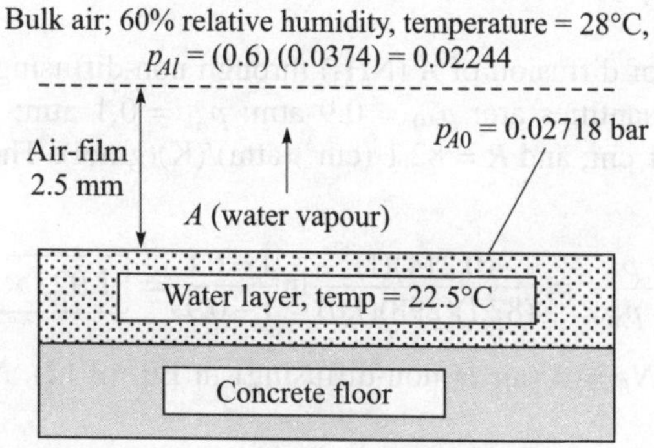

Bulk air; 60% relative humidity, temperature = 28°C,
$p_{Al} = (0.6)(0.0374) = 0.02244$

$p_{A0} = 0.02718$ bar

Air-film
2.5 mm

A (water vapour)

Water layer, temp = 22.5°C

Concrete floor

Figure 2.4   The water layer and the air-film.

$$D_{AB} = \left(0.853 \frac{\text{ft}^2}{\text{h}} \times (30.48)^2 \frac{\text{cm}^2}{\text{ft}^2} \times \frac{1}{3600} \frac{\text{h}}{\text{s}} \right) \left(\frac{298.2}{273} \right)^{1.75} = 0.2567 \text{ cm}^2/\text{s} = 2.567 \times 10^{-5} \text{ m}^2/\text{s}$$

Use Eq. (2.26) to calculate the steady-state flux of water vapour. Here, $T = 298.2°C$; $l = 2.5$ mm $= 2.5 \times 10^{-3}$ m; $P = 1.013$ bar; p_{A0} = vapour pressure of water at the wet-bulb temperature, 22.2°C (i.e. 295.2 K) = 0.02718 bar; $p_{Al} = (0.6)p_v = (0.6)(0.0374) = 0.02244$ bar. Substituting these values in Eq. (2.26), the flux of water vapour is

$$N_A = \frac{(2.567 \times 10^{-5})(1.013)}{(0.08317)(298.2)(2.5 \times 10^{-3})} \left(\ln \frac{1.013 - 0.02244}{1.013 - 0.02718} \right) = 2.01 \times 10^{-6} \frac{\text{kmol}}{\text{m}^2 \cdot \text{s}}$$

$$= 3.623 \times 10^{-5} \text{ kg/m}^2 \cdot \text{s}$$

The water layer on the floor is 2 mm thick in the beginning. The amount of water per m² of floor area

$$= 2 \times 10^{-3} \text{ m} \times 1 \text{ m}^2 = 0.002 \text{ m}^3 \qquad \text{i.e.} \qquad 2 \text{ kg}$$

Time for complete evaporation $= \dfrac{2 \text{ kg/m}^2}{3.623 \times 10^{-5} \text{ kg/m}^2 \cdot \text{s}} = 5.52 \times 10^4 \text{ s} = \boxed{15.3 \text{ h}}$

(b) The combined rate of loss of water by penetration in the floor and by vaporization
$= 0.1$ kg/m²·h (penetration) $+ 3.623 \times 10^{-5}$ kg/m²·s (vaporization) $= 0.2304$ kg/m²·h

Time for disappearance of water $= \dfrac{2 \text{ kg/m}^2}{0.2304 \text{ kg/m}^2 \cdot \text{h}} = \boxed{8.68 \text{ h}}$

EXAMPLE 2.3 (*Calculation of flux and velocity*)   Ammonia(*A*) diffuses through a stagnant layer of air(*B*), 1 cm thick, at 25°C and 1 atm total pressures. The partial pressures of NH_3 on the two sides of the air layer are $p_{A0} = 0.9$ atm and $p_{Al} = 0.1$ atm respectively. Air is non-diffusing. Calculate (a) the molar flux of NH_3, (b) the velocities of the individual components with respect to a stationary observer, (c) the molar and the mass average velocities of the components, and (d) the molar flux of NH_3 with respect to an observer moving with the mass average velocity. Also prepare the plots of partial pressure distributions of ammonia and air along the diffusion path. *Given:* $D_{AB} = 0.214$ cm²/s.

Solution

(a) This again is a case of diffusion of A (NH_3) through non-diffusing B (air), i.e. $N_B = 0$. The values of the relevant quantities are: $p_{A0} = 0.9$ atm; $p_{Al} = 0.1$ atm; $D_{AB} = 0.214$ cm^2/s; $T = 298$ K; $P = 1.0$ atm; $l = 1$ cm; and $R = 82.1$ (cm^3)(atm)/(K)(gmol). The molar flux of ammonia [see Eq. (2.26)] is

$$N_A = \frac{D_{AB}P}{RTl}\ln\frac{P-p_{Al}}{P-p_{A0}} = \frac{(0.214)(1)}{(82.1)(298)(1.0)}\ln\frac{1-0.1}{1-0.9} = \boxed{1.922\times10^{-5}\,\text{gmol/cm}^2\cdot\text{s}}$$

(b) and **(c)** Substituting $N_B = 0$ (air is non-diffusing) in Eq. (2.12), $N_A = UC \Rightarrow U = N_A/C = N_A/(P/RT)$

$$\Rightarrow \qquad U = \frac{1.922\times10^{-5}\,\text{gmol/cm}^2\cdot\text{s}}{1/(82.1)(298)\,\text{gmol/cm}^3} = \boxed{0.47\text{ cm/s} = \text{molar average velocity}}$$

Also, $N_A = u_A C_A \Rightarrow u_A = N_A/C_A = UC/C_A = U/y_A$, y_A is the mole fraction of A.

Since C_A varies along the diffusion path, u_A also varies. We calculate the values at the end where NH_3 concentration is higher,

$$p_{A0} = 0.9 \text{ atm and } y_{A0} = p_{A0}/P = 0.9 \Rightarrow u_{A0} = U/y_{A0} = 0.47/0.9 = 0.522 \text{ cm/s}$$

and

$$u_B = 0 \text{ (since } N_B = 0)$$

Mass average velocity [see Eq. (2.1)], $u = \dfrac{u_A\rho_A + u_B\rho_B}{\rho} = \dfrac{u_A\rho_A}{\rho} = \dfrac{(u_A)(p_A M_A/RT)}{(PM/RT)}$

$$= \frac{u_A y_A M_A}{M}$$

where

$$M_A = 17$$

$$M = M_A y_A + M_B y_B = (17)(0.9) + (29)(0.1) = 18.2$$

The mass average velocity of A is

$$u = \frac{(0.522)(0.9)(17)}{18.2} = \boxed{0.439\text{cm/s}}$$

(d) Use Eq. (2.7) directly to calculate the molar flux of NH_3 *relative to* an observer moving with the mass average velocity (i.e. 0.439 cm/s),

$$I_A = C_A(u_A - u)$$

$$= \frac{p_A}{RT}(u_A - u)$$

$$= \frac{0.9}{(82.1)(298)}(0.522 - 0.439)$$

$$= \boxed{3.05\times10^{-6}\,\text{gmol/cm}^2\cdot\text{s}}$$

The above flux occurs at the high NH_3-concentration end of the diffusion path where $y_A = 0.9$.

In order to find out the partial pressure distribution of A and B along the diffusion path, use Eq. (2.28).

$$\Rightarrow \qquad N_A = 1.922 \times 10^{-5}\,\frac{\text{gmol}}{\text{cm}^2 \cdot \text{s}} = \frac{(0.214)(1.0)}{(82.1)(298)(z)}\ln\frac{1-p_A}{1-0.9}$$

$$\Rightarrow \qquad p_A = 1 - (0.1)\,\exp(2.197z)\ \text{atm}$$

The plots of p_A vs. z (in cm) and p_B ($= P - p_A$) vs. z may be prepared from the above equation. These plots are presented in Figure 2.3.

EXAMPLE 2.4 (*Flux, velocity and pressure gradient*)   A test tube, 1.5 cm in diameter and 12 cm tall, is partly filled with a solution of alkaline pyrogallate. The depth of the empty space above the solution is 5 cm. The temperature is 25°C and the total pressure is 1 atmosphere. Air may be assumed to contain 21% O_2 and 79% N_2. The diffusivity of O_2 in N_2 at the given condition is 0.21 cm²/s.

(a)   Calculate the rate of absorption of oxygen from air in the solution at steady state if air flows gently over the open end of the test tube. Make plots of the distribution of partial pressures of the gases along the diffusion path.
(b)   Calculate the partial pressure gradient of oxygen midway in the diffusion path.
(c)   Calculate the molar average velocity of the mixture and the 'diffusion velocity' of the two components (O_2 and N_2) at the top end, at the middle and at the liquid surface.
(d)   Calculate the flux of the components midway of the diffusion path with respect to an observer moving with twice the molar average velocity at the location in the direction away from the liquid surface.

Solution

The system is sketched in Figure 2.5. Oxygen(A) is absorbed quickly in an alkaline pyrogallate solution. Nitrogen(B) is virtually insoluble in it. So the partial pressure of O_2 at the liquid surface is $p_{A1} = 0$, that at the open mouth of the tube is $p_{A0} = 0.21$ atm $= (0.21)(1.013)$ $= 0.213$ bar; length of the diffusion path $l = 5$ cm $= 0.05$ m; $D_{AB} = 2.1 \times 10^{-5}$ m²/s; $R = 0.08317$ (m³)(bar)/(kmol)(K).

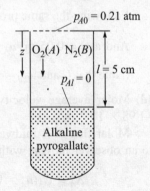

Figure 2.5 Diffusion of oxygen through non-diffusing nitrogen.

(a) Use Eq. (2.26) and put the values of the different quantities to calculate the flux.

$$N_A = \frac{(2.1 \times 10^{-5})(1.013)}{(0.08317)(298)(0.05)}\ln\frac{1.013 - 0}{1.013 - 0.213}$$

$$= 4.05 \times 10^{-6}\,\frac{\text{kmol}}{\text{m}^2 \cdot \text{s}} = 1.3 \times 10^{-4}\,\frac{\text{kg}\ O_2}{\text{m}^2 \cdot \text{s}}$$

Area of diffusion = cross-section of the test tube, $a = (\pi/4)(0.015)^2 = 1.767 \times 10^{-4}$ m²

Rate of diffusion of oxygen = $aN_A = (1.767 \times 10^{-4})(4.05 \times 10^{-6}) = \boxed{7.16 \times 10^{-10}\ \text{kmol/s}}$

The partial pressure distribution of A along the diffusion path can be calculated after putting the value of N_A ($= 4.05 \times 10^{-6}$) and other quantities in Eq. (2.28).

(b) The partial pressure gradient (dp_A/dz) of oxygen at any point on the diffusion path can be calculated from Eq. (2.24) using the steady-state flux of O_2 (i.e. N_A) calculated before. Thus midway in the diffusion path, $z = 0.025$, and $p_A = 0.113$ bar. We rearrange Eq. (2.24) and put $p_A = 0.113$ bar.

$$\frac{dp_A}{dz} = -\frac{RT(P - p_A)}{D_{AB}P}N_A = -\frac{(0.08317)(298)(1.013 - 0.113)}{(2.1 \times 10^{-5})(1.013)}(4.05 \times 10^{-6}) = \boxed{-4.15 \text{ bar/m}}$$

(c) Let us first calculate the quantities *midway in the diffusion path* ($z = 0.025$; $p_A = 0.113$ bar). The velocities of the species *with respect to a stationary observer* can be obtained from Eq. (2.13).

Oxygen: $\quad u_A = \dfrac{N_A}{C_A} = N_A\left(\dfrac{RT}{p_A}\right) = (4.05 \times 10^{-6})\dfrac{(0.08317)(298)}{0.113} = 8.88 \times 10^{-4}$ m/s

Nitrogen: $\quad u_B = \dfrac{N_B}{C_B} = \dfrac{0}{C_B} = 0$ (B is non-diffusing; hence $N_B = 0$)

The molar average velocity in the z-direction [see Eq. (2.12)] is

$$U = \frac{1}{C}(u_A C_A + u_B C_B) = \frac{C_A}{C}u_A = \frac{p_A}{P}u_A = \frac{(0.113)(8.88 \times 10^{-4})}{1.013} = \boxed{9.9 \times 10^{-5} \text{ m/s}}$$

The diffusion velocity of oxygen [Eq. (2.18)] is

$$v_{A,d} = u_A - U = 8.88 \times 10^{-4} - 9.9 \times 10^{-5} = \boxed{7.9 \times 10^{-4} \text{ m/s}}$$

The diffusion velocity of nitrogen, $v_{B,d} = u_B - U = 0 - 9.9 \times 10^{-5} = \boxed{-9.9 \times 10^{-5} \text{ m/s}}$

Following the same procedure, at $z = 0$, $v_{A,d} = \boxed{3.72 \times 10^{-4} \text{ m/s}}$; $\boxed{v_{B,d} = -9.9 \times 10^{-5} \text{ m/s}}$

And at $z = 0.05$ m, $u_A = N_A/C_A = \infty$; $v_{A,d} = \boxed{\infty}$; $v_{B,d} = \boxed{-9.9 \times 10^{-5} \text{ m/s}}$

(Note that U and $v_{B,d}$ — but not $v_{A,d}$ — remain constant over the length of the diffusion path.)

(d) Molar average velocity, $U = 9.9 \times 10^{-5}$ m/s; velocity of the observer, $V = -2U = -1.98 \times 10^{-4}$ m/s.

Molar flux of A midway in the diffusion path ($z = 0.025$ m, $p_A = 0.113$ bar) with respect to an observer moving with a velocity V is

$$N_A' = C_A(u_A - V) = N_A - V\frac{p_A}{RT} = 4.05 \times 10^{-6} - \frac{(-1.98 \times 10^{-4})(0.113)}{(0.08317)(298)}$$

$$= \boxed{4.95 \times 10^{-6} \text{ kmol/m}^2 \cdot \text{s}}$$

The corresponding flux of B (with respect to an observer moving with a velocity $V = -1.98 \times 10^{-4}$ m/s) is

$$N_B' = C_B(u_B - V) = 0 - \frac{p_B}{RT}V = -\frac{(1.013 - 0.113)}{(0.08317)(298)}(-1.98 \times 10^{-4})$$

$$= \boxed{7.2 \times 10^{-6} \text{ kmol/m}^2 \cdot \text{s}}$$

EXAMPLE 2.5 (*Diffusion with changing bulk[†] concentration*)   A reagent bottle containing 3 kg of *iso*-propanol is accidentally dropped on the floor of an empty room adjacent to a laboratory causing a spill of the entire liquid. The liquid quickly spreads on the floor of the room (3 m × 4 m, 3 m high), and starts vaporizing. Although the temperature of the vaporizing liquid will be lower than that of the ambient air, for simplicity it may be assumed that both are at the same temperature, 27°C. The pressure is atmospheric.

(a)   Two exhaust fans are switched on immediately after the spill to ventilate the room. It takes 5 minutes for the liquid to vaporize completely. If it is assumed that the concentration of *iso*-propanol in the air of the room remains *small* (because of efficient ventilation), and the alcohol vapour diffuses out from the liquid surface through a stagnant film of air, calculate the thickness of the air-film.

(b)   If the exhaust fans do not work and the vapour continues to accumulate in the air in the room, how long will it take for the evaporation of the liquid? The thickness of the air-film is the same as that calculated in part (a) and the concentration of the organic vapour in the room remains fairly uniform at any time.

(c)   If the TLV[††] (*threshold limit value*) of *iso*-propanol is 400 ppm, determine the minimum rate of ventilation in the room necessary to ensure that the concentration of the organic vapour does not exceed the TLV. The air-film thickness over the liquid remains the same as that calculated in part (a).

Given: vapour pressure of *iso*-proponal at 27°C = 0.065 bar and its diffusivity in air = 0.0995 cm^2/s.

Solution

This is a case of diffusion of A (*iso*-propanol) through non-diffusing B (air).

$$\text{Area of the floor} = 3 \text{ m} \times 4 \text{ m} = 12 \text{ m}^2$$

$$\text{Mass of } \textit{iso}\text{-propanol per unit floor area} = 3 \text{ kg}/12 \text{ m}^2 = 0.25 \text{ kg/m}^2$$

If the thickness of the stagnant film of air over the liquid is δ, the diffusion flux of the alcohol vapour through the air-film [see Eq. (2.26)] is

$$N_A = \frac{D_{AB}P}{RT\delta} \ln \frac{P - p_{A\delta}}{P - p_{A0}}$$

(a) Here P = total pressure = 1.013 bar; D_{AB} = 0.0995 cm^2/s = 9.95 × 10^{-6} m^2/s; R = 0.08317 (m^3)(bar)/(K)(kmol); T = 273 + 27 = 300 K; p_{A0} = partial pressure of the organic vapour on the liquid surface = 0.065 bar; $p_{A\delta}$ = 0 (since the organic concentration in the bulk air is small); molecular weight of *iso*-propanol = 60.

$$N_A = \frac{(9.95 \times 10^{-6})(1.013)}{(0.08317)(300)\,\delta} \ln \frac{1.013 - 0}{1.013 - 0.065} = \frac{2.679 \times 10^{-8}}{\delta} \frac{\text{kmol}}{\text{m}^2 \cdot \text{s}}$$

[†] Bulk of medium or phase means the region 'far away' from a phase boundary.

[††] The TLV of a substance is an indicator of the level of exposure that a person can experience without an unreasonable risk of disease or injury. It suggests a guideline but does not amount to a standard. The TLV may be of more than one kind. *Iso*-propanol has a short term exposure limit (STEL) of 400 ppm according to the 'material safety data sheet' (MSDS) of Mallinckrodt Chemicals.

$$= \frac{2.679 \times 10^{-8}}{\delta} \frac{kmol}{m^2 \cdot s} \times 60 \frac{kg}{kmol} = \frac{1.607 \times 10^{-6}}{\delta} \frac{kg}{m^2 \cdot s}$$

Since the liquid evaporates completely in 5 minutes, the flux value can be directly calculated.

$$\text{Flux} = \frac{0.25}{5 \times 60} \frac{kg/m^2}{s} = 8.333 \times 10^{-4} \frac{kg}{m^2 \cdot s}$$

$$\Rightarrow \qquad \text{Flux} = \frac{1.607 \times 10^{-6}}{\delta} \frac{kg}{m^2 \cdot s} = 8.333 \times 10^{-4} \frac{kg}{m^2 \cdot s}$$

$$\Rightarrow \qquad \text{The air-film thickness, } \delta = 0.00193 \text{ m} = \boxed{1.93 \text{ mm}}$$

(b) If there is no ventilation in the room, the organic vapour continues to accumulate in the air and the driving force for mass transfer through the air-film gradually decreases. The rate of evaporation of the alcohol at any time is equal to the rate of diffusion through the film.

Volume of air in the room = 3 m × 4 m × 3 m = 36 m³. If p_A is the partial pressure of accumulated organic in the room at any time t, the total moles of alcohol is

$$m_A = \frac{p_A V}{RT} = \frac{(p_A)(36)}{(0.08317)(300)} = 1.443 p_A$$

The time rate of change of the amount of alcohol in the room $= \dfrac{dm_A}{dt} = 1.443 \dfrac{dp_A}{dt}$

Assuming *pseudo-steady state* diffusion through the air-film,

Rate of diffusion of alcohol at the time $t = (\text{Area})(N_A)$

$$= (12 \, m^2) \frac{D_{AB} P}{RT \delta} \ln \frac{P - p_A}{P - p_{A0}}$$

$$= \frac{(12)(9.95 \times 10^{-6})(1.013)}{(0.08317)(300)(0.00193)} \ln \frac{1.013 - p_A}{1.013 - 0.065}$$

$$= 0.002512 [\ln(1.013 - p_A) + 0.0534]$$

$$\Rightarrow \qquad \frac{dm_A}{dt} = 1.443 \frac{dp_A}{dt} = 0.002512 [\ln(1.013 - p_A) + 0.0534] \qquad \text{(i)}$$

The above equation is to be integrated in order to calculate the time of complete evaporation of the liquid. It is to be noted that the initial partial pressure of the organic in the room, $p_{Ai} = 0$, and the final partial pressure, p_{Af} (when the 3 kg liquid, mol. wt. = 60, vaporizes completely) is given by

$$p_{Af} = \left(\frac{3}{60} \right) \frac{RT}{V} = \left(\frac{3}{60} \right) \frac{(0.08317)(300)}{36} = 0.03465 \text{ bar}$$

Integrating Eq. (i) above within the appropriate limits,

$$\int_{p_A = 0}^{p_A = 0.03465} \frac{dp_A}{\ln(1.013 - p_A) + 0.0534} = \frac{0.002512}{1.443} \int_0^t dt$$

The integral on the left cannot be integrated analytically. Numerical integration using the Simpson's rule gives

$$0.7653 = \frac{0.002512}{1.443} t \quad \Rightarrow \quad t = \boxed{440 \text{ s}}$$

The time required is considerably more than that in case (a). This is because of the gradual fall in the flux as a result of the reduced driving force for mass transfer.

(c) This part is left as an exercise.

2.3.2 Equimolar Counterdiffusion of *A* and *B*

This is a situation in which the components *A* and *B* both diffuse at equal rates but in opposite directions. Like the previous case, there are many real-life examples of this limiting case as well. Take the example of a particle of carbon burning in air. We visualize that the particle is surrounded by an 'air-film' through which the molecules of oxygen diffuse and reach the surface of the particle to sustain combustion. If a molecule of O_2 diffuses to the surface, a molecule of CO_2 is formed which diffuses out through the 'air-film' (provided that CO_2 is the only product of combustion) at steady state. So oxygen and carbon dioxide undergo 'equimolar counterdiffusion'. Separation of a liquid mixture containing the components *A* and *B* by distillation may be cited as another practical example. In distillation (see Chapter 7), the vapour rising through the distillation column remains in intimate contact with the down-flowing liquid. Exchange of mass occurs between the phases—the more volatile component moves from the liquid to the vapour phase and the less volatile one gets transported from the vapour to the liquid phase (see Example 2.7). If the column is perfectly insulated against heat loss and the molar heats of vaporization of the components are equal, the mass exchange between the phases will occur in equimolar counterdiffusion mode. For equimolar counterdiffusion of *A* and *B*, we may write $N_A = -N_B^{\dagger}$, i.e. $N_A + N_B = 0$. Substituting this relation in Eq. (2.19),

$$N_A = -\frac{D_{AB}}{RT} \frac{dp_A}{dz} \tag{2.29}$$

Since N_A remains constant for steady-state diffusion through a constant area, integration of Eq. (2.29) from the point $z = 0$ (where $p_A = p_{A0}$) to the point $z = l$ (where $p_A = p_{Al}$) yields

$$N_A \int_0^l dz = -\frac{D_{AB}}{RT} \int_{p_{A0}}^{p_{Al}} dp_A \quad \Rightarrow \quad N_A = \frac{D_{AB}(p_{A0} - p_{Al})}{RTl} \tag{2.30}$$

The distributions of the partial pressures of *A* and *B* along the diffusion path in this case are linear as shown in Figure 2.6.

---

† The fluxes N_A and N_B are vector quantities and occur in the direction of decreasing concentration of the species concerned.

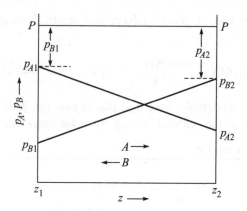

Figure 2.6   Equimolar counterdiffusion of A and B—variation of p_A and p_B with position (total pressure = P).

2.3.3   Non-equimolar Counterdiffusion of A and B

There are many practical situations where the molecules of A and B diffuse in opposite directions at different molar rates. Let us consider a case where oxygen diffuses through a gas-film to reach the surface of a hot char particle and the product is carbon monoxide only. For each mole of $O_2(A)$ diffusing towards the particle, two moles of $CO(B)$ diffuse in the opposite direction. So it is a case of non-equimolar counterdiffusion, and $N_A = -N_B/2$. The flux of A (or of B) in such a problem can be determined by integrating Eq. (2.19) after substituting N_B in terms of N_A. Examples 2.6 and 2.7 illustrate two cases of equimolar counterdiffusion of A and B.

EXAMPLE 2.6 (*Equimolar counterdiffusion*)   Two large vessels are connected by a tube 5 cm in diameter and 15 cm in length. Vessel 1 contains 80% $N_2(A)$ and 20% $O_2(B)$; vessel 2 contains 20% N_2 and 80% O_2. The temperature is 20°C and the total pressure is 2 atmosphere. Calculate (a) the steady-state flux and the rate of transport of N_2 from vessel 1 to vessel 2, (b) the same quantities for O_2, (c) the partial pressure of N_2 and its gradient in the tube 0.05 m from vessel 1, and (d) the net mass flux with respect to a stationary observer. *Given:* the diffusivity of N_2–O_2 pair is 0.23 cm²/s at 316 K and 1 atm.

Solution
The system is schematically shown in Figure 2.7. The diffusivity value at the given condition (2 atm and 20°C) is [use Eq. (2.57)]

$$D_{AB} = (0.23)\left(\frac{1}{2}\right)\left(\frac{273+20}{316}\right)^{1.75} \text{cm}^2/\text{s} = 1.01 \times 10^{-5} \text{ m}^2/\text{s}$$

Also the partial pressures are: $p_{A1} = (2 \text{ atm})(0.8) = 1.6$ atm; $p_{A2} = (2 \text{ atm})(0.2) = 0.4$ atm

(a) This is a case of steady-state equimolar counterdiffusion. Use Eq. (2.30) to calculate the flux of nitrogen. The length of the diffusion path is 15 cm = 0.15 m.

$$N_A = \frac{D_{AB}}{RTl}(p_{A1} - p_{A2})$$

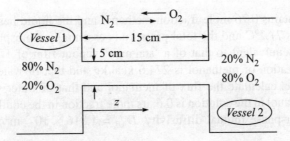

Figure 2.7 Equimolar counterdiffusion between two large vessels.

$$= \frac{1.01 \times 10^{-5}}{(0.0821)(293)(0.15)} (1.6 - 0.4)$$

$$= \boxed{3.36 \times 10^{-6} \text{ kmol/m}^2 \cdot \text{s}}$$

Area of cross-section of the tube, $a = (\pi/4)(0.05)^2 = 1.963 \times 10^{-3} \text{ m}^2$

The rate of transport of N_2 from vessel 1 to 2 $= aN_A = (1.963 \times 10^{-3})(3.36 \times 10^{-6})$

$$= \boxed{6.6 \times 10^{-9} \text{ kmol/s}}$$

(b) The flux and the rate of transport of oxygen will be the same in magnitude as those of nitrogen but will occur in the opposite direction, i.e.

$$N_B = \boxed{-3.36 \times 10^{-6} \text{ kmol/m}^2 \cdot \text{s}}$$

(c) For steady-state equimolar counterdiffusion through a constant area, the partial pressure changes linearly along the diffusion path. Therefore the gradient of partial pressure of A along z is

$$\frac{dp_A}{dz} = \frac{p_{A2} - p_{A1}}{l} = \frac{0.4 - 1.6}{0.15} = -8 \text{ atm/m}$$

Partial pressure at a point 0.05 m from vessel 1 is

$$p_A = p_{A1} + \left(\frac{dp_A}{dz}\right)\Delta z = 1.6 - (8)(0.05) = \boxed{1.2 \text{ atm}}$$

(d) Net or total mass flux,

$$n_T = M_A N_A + M_B N_B = (28 - 32)(3.36 \times 10^{-6})$$

$$= \boxed{-1.344 \times 10^{-5} \text{ kmol/m}^2 \cdot \text{s}}$$

EXAMPLE 2.7 (*Non-equimolar counterdiffusion in distillation of a binary mixture*)   An aqueous solution of methanol is being separated by distillation in a column. Methanol(A), which is the more volatile component, moves from the liquid phase to the vapour phase while water(B), the less volatile component, gets transported in the opposite direction. At a section of the column, the vapour phase contains 0.76 mole fraction methanol and the liquid has 0.6 mole fraction of it. The temperature is 71.2°C and the total pressure is essentially atmospheric. The diffusional resistance offered is equivalent to that of a 'stagnant' vapour film of 1 mm thickness. If the latent heat of vaporization of methanol is 274.6 kcal/kg and that of water is 557.7 kcal/kg at the given temperature, calculate the flux of methanol and that of water vapour. *Given:* if the mole fraction of methanol in the solution is 0.6, its mole fraction in the equilibrium vapour would be 0.825. The vapour-phase mutual diffusivity, $D_{AB} = 1.816 \times 10^{-5}$ m²/s.

Solution

Methanol being more volatile, it vaporizes during distillation and diffuses from the liquid surface to the vapour phase whereas water molecules diffuse in the opposite direction (Figure 2.8). The latent heat of vaporization of methanol molecules is compensated by the heat of condensation released by the water molecules. If the molar latent heats of the components are equal, the process of transport through the film would be of equimolar counterdiffusion type.

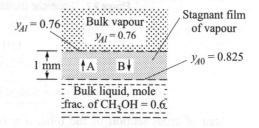

Figure 2.8   Non-equimolar counterdiffusion of components through a vapour film of CH₃OH(*A*) and H₂O(*B*).

Otherwise it will be of non-equimolar counterdiffusion type. Since the molar heats of phase change of methanol and water are not equal, non-equimolar counterdiffusion occurs in the given case.

Methanol: Mol. wt. = 32 (= M_A); molar latent heat, $\Delta H_A^v = (274.6)(32) = 8787$ kcal/kmol

Water: Mol. wt. = 18 (=M_B); molar latent heat, $\Delta H_B^v = (557.7)(18) = 10039$ kcal/kmol

The counterdiffusion fluxes are related as

$$N_A \, \Delta H_A^v = - N_B \, \Delta H_B^v \quad \Rightarrow \quad N_B = - \frac{8787}{10039} N_A = -0.8753 N_A$$

From Fick's law, Eq. (2.19), for diffusion in a binary gas mixture, we may write

$$N_A = (N_A - 0.8753 N_A) \frac{p_A}{P} - \frac{D_{AB}}{RT} \frac{dp_A}{dz}$$

Rearranging and integrating over the vapour-film thickness *l* (Figure 2.8),

$$N_A \frac{RT}{PD_{AB}} \int_{z=0}^{l} dz = - \int_{y_{A0}}^{y_{Al}} \frac{dy_A}{1 - 0.1247 y_A} \quad \Rightarrow \quad N_A = \frac{D_{AB} P}{(0.1274) RT l} \ln \frac{1 - 0.1247 y_{Al}}{1 - 0.1247 y_{A0}} \qquad \text{(i)}$$

Now the flux of methanol can be calculated from Eq. (i) above. The mole fraction of methanol in the vapour is $y_{Al} = 0.76$; the mole fraction of methanol in the liquid = 0.6 and the corresponding equilibrium mole fraction of methanol in the vapour at the liquid–vapour interface (obtained from the *vapour–liquid equilibrium data* of the methanol–water system; see Example 7.15) is $y_{A0} = 0.825$. Also, $P = 1$ atm, $l = 1.0$ mm (1×10^{-3} m); $T = 71.2$°C = 344.2 K.

Methanol flux,

$$N_A = \frac{(1.816 \times 10^{-5})(1)}{(0.1247)(0.0821)(344.2)(1 \times 10^{-3})} \ln \frac{1 - (0.1247)(0.76)}{1 - (0.1247)(0.825)} = \boxed{4.65 \times 10^{-5} \text{ kmol/m}^2 \cdot \text{s}}$$

Water flux, $N_B = -0.8753 N_A = -(0.8753)(4.65 \times 10^{-5}) = \boxed{-4.07 \times 10^{-5} \text{ kmol/m}^2 \cdot \text{s}}$

EXAMPLE 2.8 (*Equimolar counterdiffusion in an interconnected system*) Two glass vessels of volumes 3 litre and 4 litre respectively are connected with a 5 mm diameter and 4 cm long tube fitted with a plug valve. Vessel 2 has a side tube, 3 mm in diameter and 2 cm long (this tube too has a plug valve), which connects vessel 2 to a 'large' vessel (we call it vessel 3). Vessels 1 and 3 are initially filled with nitrogen and vessel 2 with ammonia, all at atmospheric pressure and 25°C. The valves in the connecting tubes are opened and diffusion starts. Calculate the partial pressure of nitrogen in vessel 1 after 5 hours if diffusion through the connecting tubes is assumed to occur at pseudo-steady state. The diffusivity of ammonia in nitrogen is 0.23 cm²/s at 25°C and 1 atm pressure. The assembly is schematically shown in Figure 2.9 (the plug valves in the connective tubes are not shown).

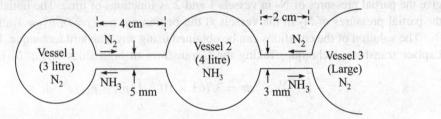

Figure 2.9 Equimolar counterdiffusion in a three-vessel system.

Solution
Equimolar counterdiffusion will occur between vessels 1 and 2 as well as between vessels 2 and 3, the total pressure in each of the vessels remaining constant at 1 atm. The partial pressures of the two components [$N_2(A)$ and $NH_3(B)$] in vessels 1 and 2 will change with time. But the gas in vessel 3 will essentially contain N_2 only since it is 'large'. Let us use the following notations (Figure 2.9).

V_1, V_2: volumes of the vessels 1 and 2; p_{A1}, p_{A2}: partial pressures of $N_2(A)$ in the vessels at any time t; p_{A3} = partial pressure of N_2 in vessel 3 (= 1 atm, constant); d_1, l_1: diameter and length of the tube connecting vessels 1 and 2; d_2, l_2: diameter and length of the tube connecting vessels 2 and 3.

We assume that diffusion occurs at *pseudo-steady state*. The time rate of change of the partial pressure of A in vessel 1 as a result of its mass exchange with vessel 2 can be written as [also see Section 2.5.1]

$$-\frac{d}{dt}\left(\frac{p_{A1}V_1}{RT}\right) = -\frac{V_1}{RT}\frac{dp_{A1}}{dt} = \frac{D_{AB}}{RT l_1}(p_{A1} - p_{A2})\left(\frac{\pi}{4}d_1^2\right) \tag{i}$$

Similarly, the time rate of change of the partial pressure of A in vessel 2, that exchanges mass with both vessels 1 and 3, is given by (note the signs of the terms)

$$\frac{d}{dt}\left(\frac{p_{A2}V_2}{RT}\right) = \frac{V_2}{RT}\frac{dp_{A2}}{dt} = \frac{D_{AB}}{RTl_1}(p_{A1} - p_{A2})\left(\frac{\pi}{4}d_1^2\right) + \frac{D_{AB}}{RTl_2}(p_{A3} - p_{A2})\left(\frac{\pi}{4}d_2^2\right) \qquad \text{(ii)}$$

The numerical values of the different quantities in Eqs. (i) and (ii) are:

$V_1 = 3$ litre $= 3000$ cm^3, $V_2 = 4$ litre $= 4000$ cm^3; $D_{AB} = D_{BA} = 0.23$ cm^2/s; $l_1 = 4$ cm, $d_1 = 5$ mm $= 0.5$ cm; $l_2 = 2$ cm, $d_2 = 3$ mm $= 0.3$ cm; and $p_{A3} = 1$ atm. Substituting these values in Eqs. (i) and (ii), we get

$$-\frac{dp_{A1}}{dt} = \frac{0.23}{(3000)(4)}\left(\frac{\pi}{4}\right)(0.5)^2\,(p_{A1} - p_{A2}) = 3.763 \times 10^{-6}(p_{A1} - p_{A2}) \qquad \text{(iii)}$$

$$\frac{dp_{A2}}{dt} = \frac{0.23}{(4000)(4)}\left(\frac{\pi}{4}\right)(0.5)^2\,(p_{A1} - p_{A2}) + \frac{0.23}{(4000)(2)}\left(\frac{\pi}{4}\right)(0.3)^2\,(1 - p_{A2})$$

$$= 2.032 \times 10^{-6} + 2.823 \times 10^{-6}p_{A1} - 4.855 \times 10^{-6}p_{A2} \qquad \text{(iv)}$$

The solution of the simultaneous linear first-order ordinary differential equations (iii) and (iv) will give the partial pressures of N_2 in vessels 1 and 2 as functions of time. The initial conditions (i.e. the partial pressures of N_2 in the vessels at the beginning) are: $t = 0$; $p_{A1} = 1$ atm, and $p_{A2} = 0$.

The solution of the equations can be obtained using any standard technique. Here we use the Laplace transform technique. Taking the L-transform of both sides of Eq. (iii), we have

$$-\int_0^\infty \frac{dp_{A1}}{dt}\,e^{-st}dt = 3.763 \times 10^{-6}\int_0^\infty (p_{A1} - p_{A2})\,e^{-st}dt$$

or $\quad -([e^{-st}p_{A1}]_{t=0, p_{A1}=1}^{t=\infty}) - s\int_0^\infty p_{A1}\,e^{-st}\,dt \quad$ i.e. $\quad 1 - s\bar{p}_{A1} = 3.763\times 10^{-6}(\bar{p}_{A1} - \bar{p}_{A2}) \qquad \text{(v)}$

where $\bar{p}_{A1} = \int_0^\infty p_{A1}\,e^{-st}dt$ is the Laplace transform of p_{A1}, s = L-transform parameter.

Next we take the L-transform of both sides of Eq. (iv).

$$\int_0^\infty \frac{dp_{A2}}{dt}\,e^{-st}dt = 2.032\times 10^{-6}\int_0^\infty e^{-st}dt + 2.823\times 10^{-6}\int_0^\infty p_{A1}\,e^{-st}dt - 4.855\times 10^{-6}\int_0^\infty p_{A2}\,e^{-st}dt$$

Integrating and using the initial condition on p_{A2} [$t = 0$, $p_{A2} = 0$; there was pure NH_3 in vessel 2 initially],

$$sp_{A2} = (2.032 \times 10^{-6}/s) + 2.823 \times 10^{-6}\bar{p}_{A1} - 4.855 \times 10^{-6}\bar{p}_{A2} \qquad \text{(vi)}$$

Solving the simultaneous algebraic equations (v) and (vi), we get the following expression for the L-transform of p_{A2} (which is then split into partial fractions).

$$\bar{p}_{A2} = \frac{4.855\times 10^{-6}(s + 1.575\times 10^{-6})}{s(s + 7.615\times 10^{-6})(s + 1.154\times 10^{-6})} = \frac{1}{s} - \frac{0.583}{(s + 7.615\times 10^{-6})} - \frac{0.417}{(s + 1.005\times 10^{-6})}$$

On inversion of the transform by the usual technique, we get the partial pressure of N_2 in vessel 2 as a function of time.

$$p_{A2}(t) = 1 - 0.583 \exp(-7.615 \times 10^{-6}\, t) - 0.416 \exp(-1.005 \times 10^{-6}\, t); \; t \text{ is in seconds.}$$

Similarly, the L-transform of p_{A1} can be obtained as

$$\bar{p}_{A1} = \frac{1}{s} - (0.57)\left[\frac{1}{(s + 1.005 \times 10^{-6})} - \frac{1}{(s + 7.615 \times 10^{-6})} \right]$$

when, $\qquad p_{A1}(t) = 1 - 0.57[\exp(-1.005 \times 10^{-6}t) - \exp(-7.615 \times 10^{-6}t)]$

At time $t = 5$ h $= 18,000$ seconds, $p_{A1}(t) = \boxed{0.937 \text{ atm}}$

It is interesting to trace the concentration history in the vessels. The partial pressure of nitrogen in vessel 2 is a monotonically increasing function of time. But in vessel 1, the partial pressure of nitrogen decreases for some time while that of NH_3 increases because of mass exchange with vessel 2. Ammonia (A) simultaneously diffuses from vessel 2 to vessel 3. When the partial pressure of NH_3 decreases considerably in vessel 2, NH_3 starts diffusing back from vessel 1 to vessel 2 and therefrom to the large vessel 3. As a result, the partial pressure of N_2 in vessel 1 starts increasing. Thus the partial pressure of N_2 in vessel 1 goes through a minimum. The proof of this as well as the calculation of the minimum partial pressure of N_2 in vessel 1 are left as an exercise. (**Ans.** The lowest value of p_{A1} is 0.637 atm that occurs at 91.3 h)

EXAMPLE 2.9 (*Equimolar counterdiffusion with changing bulk concentration*) A 5-litre vessel has two side tubes, each 4 cm long, as shown in Figure 2.10. At the end of the 2 cm diameter tube (tube 1) is a plug soaked in a nonvolatile acid solution. The 1 cm diameter tube (call it tube 2) is kept open to the ambient. The vessel is initially filled with a mixture of 60% ammonia and 40% air at 1 atm total pressure and then transport of the gases through the tubes is allowed to occur. Ammonia will diffuse at a faster rate through the larger diameter tube and will get absorbed as soon as it reaches the acid-soaked plug. Air will diffuse into the vessel through the other tube (which is open to the ambient) so as to maintain the total pressure constant. Calculate the time after which NH_3 concentration in the vessel drops down to 20%. Pseudo-steady state condition may be assumed to prevail. The temperature is 25°C. *Given:* diffusivity of ammonia in air is 0.198 cm²/s at 0°C and 1 atm pressure.

Hints: Let V = volume of the vessel; p_{AV} = the partial pressure of NH_3 in the vessel at any time t; N_{A1} and N_{A2} are the fluxes of $NH_3(A)$ through the tubes (Figure 2.10). Diffusion of $NH_3(A)$ through non-diffusing air(B) occurs through tube 1. *Non-equimolar* counterdiffusion occurs through tube 2, and the magnitude of the flux of air through it will be larger than that of NH_3 so that the lowering of total pressure in the vessel because of transport of NH_3 through both the tubes together is compensated.

The total pressure P will thereby remain constant at all time. Let N_{B2} be the flux of air through tube 2 and a_1 and a_2 be the cross-sections of the tubes. N_{B2} is related to the NH_3 fluxes (N_{A1} and N_{A2}) as

$$a_2 |N_{B2}| = a_1 |N_{A1}| + a_2 |N_{A2}| \tag{i}$$

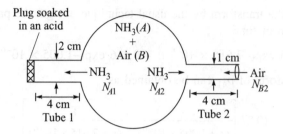

Figure 2.10   A sketch of the vessel with side tubes.

Fick's law applied to the ammonia flux in tube 2: $N_{A2} = (N_{A2} + N_{B2})\dfrac{p_A}{P} - \dfrac{D_{AB}}{RT}\dfrac{dp_A}{dz}$ (ii)

Here p_A is the local partial pressure of NH_3 in tube 2. Note that at $z = 0$ (vessel-side end), $p_A = p_{AV}$ (p_{AV} is the partial pressure of NH_3 in the vessel at any instant t) and at $z = l_2$ (open end of tube 2), $p_A = 0$. Put $N_{B2} = -(a_1/a_2)N_{A1} - N_{A2}$ [in consideration of Eq. (i) and the direction of the flux of ammonia leaving a tube being taken as positive] in Eq. (ii) and rearrange to get

$$\int_{p_{AV}}^{0} \frac{dp_A}{\left(N_{A2} + \dfrac{a_1}{a_2}\dfrac{p_A}{P} N_{A1} \right)} = -\frac{RT}{D_{AB}}\int_{0}^{l_2} dz$$

On integration and rearrangement, we have

$$a_1 N_{A1} + a_2 N_{A2} = a_1 N_{A1}\left[1 + \frac{p_{AV}/P}{\exp\left(\dfrac{RT l_2}{D_{AB}}\dfrac{a_1}{a_2}\dfrac{N_{A1}}{P} \right) - 1} \right]$$ (iii)

The flux N_{A1} can be written straightaway as

$$N_{A1} = \frac{D_{AB}P}{RT l_1} \ln \frac{P - 0}{P - p_{AV}}$$ (iv)

The time rate of change of the partial pressure of NH_3 in the vessel, p_{AV}, is given by

$$-\frac{V}{RT}\frac{dp_{AV}}{dt} = a_1 N_{A1} + a_2 N_{A2}$$ (v)

Substitution for $a_1 N_{A1} + a_2 N_{A2}$ from Eqs. (iii) and (iv) in (v) and integration from $p_{AV} = 0.6$ atm (beginning) to $p_{AV} = 0.2$ (end) gives the required time. The integration has to be done numerically.

Ans. time, $t =$ $\boxed{6.25\ \text{h}}$

2.4   MULTICOMPONENT DIFFUSION

Though multicomponent diffusion is a more complex process, a simple analysis can be done following the Maxwell–Stefan approach (Taylor and Krishna, 1993). We will first use this approach for the analysis of diffusion of a species A in a binary mixture and then extend it to the case of a multicomponent mixture. The method basically assumes that in a non-uniform binary mixture of A and B in which A is diffusing at steady state, the difference in the partial pressure of A (Δp_A) over a small distance Δz is proportional to

(a) the molar concentrations of A and B (i.e. C_A and C_B),
(b) the length of the diffusion path (Δz), and
(c) the difference in the velocities of A and B (i.e. $u_A - u_B$).

Then, at constant temperature and pressure,

$$-\Delta p_A \propto C_A C_B \Delta z (u_A - u_B)$$

$$\Rightarrow \qquad -\Delta p_A = K' C_A C_B \Delta z (u_A - u_B) \qquad \text{where } K' \text{ is the proportionality constant.}$$

Taking limit $\Delta z \to 0$,

$$-\frac{dp_A}{dz} = K' C_A C_B (u_A - u_B) = K' C_B C_A u_A - K' C_A C_B u_B = K' C_B N_A - K' C_A N_B \qquad (2.31)$$

Putting $C_A + C_B = C$ (= total molar concentration), and $C_A = p_A/RT$,

$$-RT \frac{dC_A}{dz} = K'(C - C_A)N_A - K' C_A N_B = K' C N_A - K'(N_A + N_B)C_A$$

$$\Rightarrow \qquad N_A = (N_A + N_B)\frac{C_A}{C} - \frac{RT}{K'C}\frac{dC_A}{dz}$$

If we call $\dfrac{RT}{K'C} = D_{AB}$ = diffusivity of A in a mixture of A and B,

$$N_A = (N_A + N_B)\frac{C_A}{C} - D_{AB}\frac{dC_A}{dz}$$

The above equation is identical to Eq. (2.14) obtained from Fick's law. Thus, the Fick's law can be derived theoretically by the Maxwell–Stefan approach.

Now we consider a multicomponent mixture containing n components. For component i, we can generalize Eq. (2.31) by summing up the contributions of all possible binaries containing this component [there are $(n - 1)$ such binaries]. Thus,

$$-RT \frac{dC_i}{dz} = \sum_{\substack{j=1 \\ j \neq i}}^{n} K'_{ij}(C_j N_i - C_i N_j)$$

Dividing both sides by the uniform total molar concentration C, and by RT,

$$-\frac{dy_i}{dz} = \sum_{\substack{j=1 \\ j \neq i}}^{n} \frac{K'_{ij}}{RT}(y_j N_i - y_i N_j) = \sum_{\substack{j=1 \\ j \neq i}}^{n} \frac{1}{CD_{ij}}(y_j N_i - y_i N_j) \qquad (2.32)$$

where

$$D_{ij} = \frac{RT}{CK'_{ij}} = \text{diffusivity of the component } i \text{ in a binary mixture of } i \text{ and } j.$$

Again, extending Eq. (2.21) for diffusion of A in a multicomponent mixture, we can write

$$N_i = y_i \sum_{j=1}^{n} N_j - CD_{im} \frac{dy_i}{dz} \tag{2.33}$$

where D_{im} is the diffusivity of i in the mixture. Comparing Eq. (2.32) with (2.33), an expression for D_{im} is obtained as

$$D_{im} = \frac{N_i - y_i \sum\limits_{j=1}^{n} N_j}{\sum\limits_{\substack{j=1 \\ j \neq i}}^{n} \frac{1}{D_{ij}} (y_j N_i - y_i N_j)} \tag{2.34}$$

According to the above equation, the diffusivity D_{im} of molecules of component i in the mixture, depends upon the mole fractions and fluxes of all the components. As a result, integration of Eq. (2.33) is not straightforward. This makes the solution of multicomponent diffusion problems pretty complicated. Simple results can, however, be obtained in certain limiting cases. For example, if all the components except i are non-diffusing or 'inert' (i.e. $N_j = 0$, $j \neq i$), we see from Eq. (2.34) that the diffusivity of i in the mixture is independent of the flux. That is,

$$D_{im} = \frac{1 - y_i}{\sum\limits_{\substack{j=1 \\ j \neq i}}^{n} \frac{y_j}{D_{ij}}} = \frac{1}{\sum\limits_{\substack{j=1 \\ j \neq i}}^{n} \frac{y_j'}{D_{ij}}} \tag{2.35}$$

where y_j' is the mole fraction of the component j in the mixture on 'i-free basis'. For this case, Eq. (2.33) can be directly integrated between $z = 0$ to $z = l$ to yield an expression for the flux N_i. That is,

$$N_i = \frac{D_{im} C}{l} \ln \frac{1 - y_{il}}{1 - y_{i0}} \tag{2.36}$$

Equation (2.36) is analogous to Eq. (2.26) for diffusional flux of A in non-diffusing B.

In the general case, Eq. (2.33) is not directly useful for the calculation of the diffusional flux (since the diffusivity of any of the components depends upon the fluxes in turn) and it is necessary to solve Eq. (2.32). For diffusion in an n-component mixture, Eq. (2.32) represents a set of $(n - 1)$ independent, simultaneous, first-order, linear, ordinary differential equations that can be solved for a given situation. The general solution is quite involved. Here we discuss the solution methodology for the case of diffusion in a ternary mixture only.

If the components in the mixture are called 1, 2 and 3, Eq. (2.32) may be written as

Component 1: $\qquad -C \frac{dy_1}{dz} = N_1 \left(\frac{y_2}{D_{12}} + \frac{y_3}{D_{13}} \right) - y_1 \left(\frac{N_2}{D_{12}} + \frac{N_3}{D_{13}} \right) \tag{2.37}$

Component 2: $\qquad -C \frac{dy_2}{dz} = N_2 \left(\frac{y_1}{D_{21}} + \frac{y_3}{D_{23}} \right) - y_2 \left(\frac{N_1}{D_{21}} + \frac{N_3}{D_{23}} \right) \tag{2.38}$

Component 3: $\qquad -C \frac{dy_3}{dz} = N_3 \left(\frac{y_1}{D_{31}} + \frac{y_2}{D_{32}} \right) - y_3 \left(\frac{N_1}{D_{31}} + \frac{N_2}{D_{32}} \right) \tag{2.39}$

If we make use of the relation, $D_{ij} = D_{ji}$ for an ideal gas mixture, any one of the above three equations can be obtained by adding the remaining equations because the sum of the mole fractions is unity.

$$y_1 + y_2 + y_3 = 1 \tag{2.40}$$

Thus, there are only two *independent,* simultaneous, first-order, linear, ordinary differential equations (there will be $n - 1$ equations for an n-component mixture as stated before) which may be solved for a given set of concentrations of the species at the two ends of the diffusion path. Toor (1964), Krishna and Standardt (1976), among others, developed a matrix method of solution of the coupled equations for an n-component system. Simpler solution techniques may be adopted in some special cases and here we show one such solution.

Let us consider a ternary mixture of ideal gases in which (i) components 1 and 2 diffuse while component 3 is non-diffusing (i.e. $N_3 = 0$), and (ii) diffusion occurs through a path length l. Equations (2.37) and (2.38) may be written as

Component 1:
$$-C\frac{dy_1}{dz} = N_1\left(\frac{y_2}{D_{12}} + \frac{y_3}{D_{13}}\right) - y_1\frac{N_2}{D_{12}} \tag{2.41}$$

Component 2:
$$-C\frac{dy_2}{dz} = N_2\left(\frac{y_1}{D_{21}} + \frac{y_3}{D_{23}}\right) - y_2\frac{N_1}{D_{12}} \tag{2.42}$$

Equations (2.41) and (2.42) may be combined into a single equation after considerable algebraic manipulation and using the relations $D_{12} = D_{21}$ and $D_{32} = D_{23}$. For this purpose, we define a quantity

$$\xi = \frac{(1/D_{12}) - (1/D_{13})}{(1/D_{12}) - (1/D_{23})} = \frac{D_{23}}{D_{13}}\left(\frac{D_{13} - D_{12}}{D_{23} - D_{12}}\right)$$

Now we divide both sides of Eq. (2.41) by N_1, multiply both sides of Eq. (2.42) by ξ/N_2 and subtract the resulting equations to get

$$-C\left(\frac{1}{N_1}\frac{dy_1}{dz} - \frac{\xi}{N_2}\frac{dy_2}{dz}\right) = -\frac{N_2}{N_1}\frac{y_1}{D_{12}} + \left(\frac{y_2}{D_{12}} + \frac{y_3}{D_{13}}\right) + \xi\frac{N_1}{N_2}\frac{y_2}{D_{12}} - \xi\left(\frac{y_1}{D_{12}} + \frac{y_3}{D_{23}}\right) \tag{2.43}$$

or
$$-\frac{C}{N_1 + N_2}\left(\frac{N_1 + N_2}{N_1}\frac{dy_1}{dz} - \xi\frac{N_1 + N_2}{N_2}\frac{dy_2}{dz}\right)$$

$$= -\frac{N_2}{N_1}\frac{y_1}{D_{12}} - \frac{y_1}{D_{12}} + \xi\left(\frac{N_1}{N_2}\frac{y_2}{D_{12}} + \frac{y_2}{D_{12}}\right) + \left(\frac{y_2}{D_{12}} + \frac{y_3}{D_{13}}\right) - \xi\left(\frac{y_1}{D_{12}} + \frac{y_3}{D_{23}}\right) + \frac{y_1}{D_{12}} - \frac{\xi y_2}{D_{12}}$$

$$= -\frac{y_1}{D_{12}}\left(\frac{N_1 + N_2}{N_1}\right) + \frac{\xi y_2}{D_{12}}\left(\frac{N_1 + N_2}{N_2}\right) - \frac{y_2}{D_{12}}(\xi - 1) - \frac{y_1}{D_{12}}(\xi - 1) + \frac{y_3}{D_{12}}\left(\frac{D_{12}}{D_{13}} - \frac{D_{12}}{D_{23}}\xi\right)$$

The above equation can be rearranged to the following form

$$D_{12}C\frac{d\left[\dfrac{N_1 + N_2}{N_1}y_1 - \xi\dfrac{N_1 + N_2}{N_2}y_2\right]}{\dfrac{N_1 + N_2}{N_1}y_1 - \xi\dfrac{N_1 + N_2}{N_2}y_2 + (\xi - 1)} = (N_1 + N_2)dz$$

Let the mole fractions of the components at the two ends of the diffusion path (i.e. the boundary conditions) be

$$\text{at } z = 0, \quad y_1 = y_{10} \quad \text{and} \quad y_2 = y_{20}$$
$$\text{at } z = l, \quad y_1 = y_{1l} \quad \text{and} \quad y_2 = y_{2l}$$

On integration between these limits followed by rearrangement,

$$(N_1 + N_2) = \frac{D_{12}C}{l} \ln \frac{\dfrac{N_1 + N_2}{N_1} y_{1l} - \dfrac{N_1 + N_2}{N_2} \xi\, y_{2l} + (\xi - 1)}{\dfrac{N_1 + N_2}{N_1} y_{10} - \dfrac{N_1 + N_2}{N_2} \xi\, y_{20} + (\xi - 1)} \tag{2.44}$$

The two fluxes N_1 and N_2 cannot be calculated from the single equation (2.44). In order to have another relation, we turn to Eq. (2.39). Putting $N_3 = 0$ (since the component 3 is non-diffusing in the particular case under consideration), $D_{31} = D_{13}$ and $D_{32} = D_{23}$ in Eq. (2.39), we get

$$-C\frac{dy_3}{dz} = -y_3 \left(\frac{N_1}{D_{13}} + \frac{N_2}{D_{23}} \right)$$

Integrating from $z = 0$, $y_3 = y_{30}$ to $z = l$, $y_3 = y_{3l}$,

$$\frac{N_1}{D_{13}} + \frac{N_2}{D_{23}} = \frac{C}{l} \ln \frac{y_{3l}}{y_{30}} \tag{2.45}$$

Now we have two equations [Eqs. (2.44) and (2.45)] in the two unknown fluxes N_1 and N_2. The solution of these simultaneous *nonlinear* algebraic equations gives the fluxes N_1 and N_2.

In many practical situations, we come across 'non-equimolar counterdiffusion'. To deal with such a case, we need to relate the fluxes of the components and use these relations in Eqs. (2.37) and (2.38) and then proceed with the solution. This is illustrated in Example 2.11.

EXAMPLE 2.10 (*Diffusion of only one component in a three-component mixture*)   A mixture of 60% hydrogen and 40% oxygen is blowing over a pan of water at 1 atm pressure. The bulk gas temperature is 30°C and the water temperature is 20°C. The vapour pressure of water at this temperature is 17.53 mm Hg. If the concentration of moisture in the bulk gas is negligible, calculate the steady-state flux of water vapour through a stagnant film of estimated thickness 1.5 mm on the water surface. The diffusivity values are: $D_{O_2-H_2O} = 0.357$ cm^2/s at 79°C; $D_{H_2-H_2O} = 0.972$ cm^2/s at 34°C; $D_{H_2-O_2} = 0.891$ cm^2/s at 43°C (all at 1 atm pressure). Assume that the volume ratio of H_2 and O_2 remains constant along the diffusion path.

Hints: Here water vapour(1) diffuses through *non-diffusing* hydrogen(2) and oxygen(3). We assume that the composition of the mixture on moisture-free basis remains unchanged over the film, so that Eq. (2.35) may be used to calculate D_{1m}. At the mean gas-film temperature (298 K), the diffusivities are $D_{12} = 0.923$ and $D_{13} = 0.267$ cm^2/s (calculated from the values given at other temperatures). The mole fractions of H_2 and O_2 on H_2O-free basis can be found to be $y_2' = 0.6$ and $y_3' = 0.4$. From Eq. (2.35), $D_{1m} = 0.465$ cm^2/s. Put $y_{1l} = 0$ (dry air) and $y_{10} = (17.53/760) = 0.023$, $l = 1.5$ mm, $C = P/RT = 0.0409$ kmol/m^3 in Eq. (2.36) and obtain flux of water vapour, $N_1 = 2.96 \times 10^{-5}$ kmol/m$^2 \cdot$ s.

EXAMPLE 2.11 (*Multicomponent diffusion*)   In an experimental reactor for the study of catalytic cracking of ethane(1) to ethylene(2) and hydrogen(3), the bulk gas composition is 60% ethane and 20% each of ethylene and hydrogen. The mole fraction of the gases at the catalyst surface are: $y_1 = 0.4$, $y_2 = 0.3$ and $y_3 = 0.3$. Diffusion of ethane to the catalyst surface occurs through a stagnant gas film of thickness 1.5 mm and the products diffuse back. The temperature is 720°C and the pressure is 1.0 atm gauge. Calculate the flux of ethane through the gas film. The diffusivities of the species at the given condition can be estimated using the Chapman–Enskog equation.

Solution
Estimation of the diffusivities D_{13} and D_{23} using Eq. (2.54) in Section 2.5.3:

The molecular weights of the components are: $M_1 = 30$; $M_2 = 28$; $M_3 = 2$. $T = 720°C = 993$ K

The Lennard–Jones parameters are (Table 2.2):

$$C_2H_6: \quad \sigma_1 = 4.443 \text{ Å}, \; \varepsilon_1/k = 215.7$$
$$C_2H_4: \quad \sigma_2 = 4.163 \text{ Å}, \; \varepsilon_2/k = 224.7$$
$$H_2: \quad \sigma_3 = 2.827 \text{ Å}, \; \varepsilon_3/k = 59.7$$

Ethane(1)–Hydrogen(3) pair: $\sigma_{13} = (\sigma_1 + \sigma_3)/2 = (4.443 + 2.827)/2 = 3.63$ Å

$$\frac{\varepsilon_{13}}{k} = \left(\frac{\varepsilon_1}{k}\frac{\varepsilon_3}{k}\right)^{1/2} = [(215.7)(59.7)]^{1/2} = 113.5; \qquad \frac{kT}{\varepsilon_{13}} = \frac{993}{113.5} = 8.75$$

From the collision integral (Table 2.3), $[\Omega_D]_{13} = 0.76$

From Eq. (2.54), $\qquad D_{13} = \dfrac{(0.001858)(993)^{3/2}[(1/30) + (1/2)]^{1/2}}{(2)(3.63)^2(0.76)} = 2.12$ cm^2/s[†]

Ethylene(2)–Hydrogen(3) pair: $\sigma_{23} = (\sigma_2 + \sigma_3)/2 = (4.163 + 2.827)/2 = 3.5$

$$\frac{kT}{\varepsilon_{23}} = \left(\frac{kT}{\varepsilon_2}\frac{kT}{\varepsilon_3}\right)^{1/2} = \left(\frac{993}{224.7}\frac{993}{59.7}\right)^{1/2} = 8.57; \qquad [\Omega_D]_{23} = 0.762$$

$$D_{23} = \frac{(0.001858)(993)^{3/2}[(1/28) + (1/2)]^{1/2}}{(2)(3.5)^2(0.762)} = 2.28 \text{ cm}^2/\text{s}$$

Now consider the reaction on the catalyst surface: $C_2H_6 \rightarrow C_2H_4 + H_2$
$$\qquad\qquad (1) \qquad\quad (2) \quad\;\; (3)$$

Flux relation: $N_1 = -N_2 = -N_3$
Substituting in Eqs. (2.37) and (2.38),

$$-C\frac{dy_1}{dz} = N_1\left(\frac{y_2}{D_{12}} + \frac{y_3}{D_{13}}\right) + N_1 y_1\left(\frac{1}{D_{12}} + \frac{1}{D_{13}}\right) \tag{i}$$

$$-C\frac{dy_2}{dz} = -N_1\left(\frac{y_1}{D_{21}} + \frac{y_3}{D_{23}}\right) - N_1 y_2\left(\frac{1}{D_{21}} - \frac{1}{D_{23}}\right) \tag{ii}$$

[†] The diffusivity of C_2H_6–H_2 pair is given in Perry's (1984), at 273 K and 1 atm: $D_{13} = 0.459$ cm^2/s. So, at 2 atm and 720°C (993 K) the diffusivity should be: $D_{13} = (0.459)(1/2)(993/273)^{3/2} = 1.6$ cm^2/s. This roughly matches with the estimated value of 2.12 cm^2/s.

Equations (i) and (ii) have to be solved subject to the given values of the mole fractions of the components at the boundaries of the gas film (boundary conditions), i.e.

at $z = 0$ (bulk gas): $\qquad y_{10} = 0.6, \qquad y_{20} = 0.2, \qquad y_{30} = 0.2$

at $z = l$ (catalyst surface): $\qquad y_{1l} = 0.4, \qquad y_{2l} = 0.3, \qquad y_{3l} = 0.3$

Equations (i) and (ii) may be solved by Laplace transform or by matrix method. Here we make some approximations and obtain a simplified solution. Adding Eqs. (i) and (ii) and putting $D_{12} = D_{21}$, $D_{23} = D_{32}$,

$$-C\frac{d}{dz}(y_1 + y_2) = N_1 y_3 \left(\frac{1}{D_{13}} - \frac{1}{D_{23}} \right) + N_1 \left(\frac{y_1}{D_{13}} + \frac{y_2}{D_{23}} \right)$$

The estimated diffusivities $D_{13} = 2.12$ cm²/s and $D_{23} = 2.28$ cm²/s are reasonably close. The solution of the above equation can be simplified by assuming $D_{13} \approx D_{23}$ when the first term on the r.h.s. vanishes.

i.e.
$$-C\frac{d}{dz}(y_1 + y_2) = N_1 \left(\frac{y_1}{D_{13}} + \frac{y_2}{D_{23}} \right)$$

Using the average value of the diffusivities, $(D_{13} + D_{23})/2 = D$, and integrating the above equation,

$$-\int_{(y_{10}+y_{20})}^{(y_{1l}+y_{2l})} \frac{d(y_1 + y_2)}{(y_1 + y_2)} = \frac{N_1}{DC} \int_0^l dz \qquad \Rightarrow \qquad N_1 = \frac{DC}{l} \ln \left(\frac{y_{10} + y_{20}}{y_{1l} + y_{2l}} \right)$$

Given: $\qquad l = 1.5$ mm $= 0.15$ cm; $\qquad D = (2.12 + 2.28)/2 = 2.2$ cm²/s;

$\qquad C = (P/RT) = 2/(82.1)(993) = 2.45 \times 10^{-5}$ gmol/cm³; and the y values as given above.

Flux of ethane, $N_1 = \dfrac{(2.2)(2.45 \times 10^{-5})}{0.15} \ln \left(\dfrac{0.6 + 0.2}{0.4 + 0.3} \right) = \boxed{4.804 \times 10^{-5} \text{ gmol/cm}^2 \cdot \text{s}}$

Detailed treatment of multicomponent diffusion is available in Cussler (1976), Wesselingh and Krishna (1990) and Taylor and Krishna (1993). A derivation of Fick's law from the kinetic theory has been given by Haynes (1986)[#].

2.5 GAS-PHASE DIFFUSION COEFFICIENT: MEASUREMENT AND PREDICTION

The experimental values of binary diffusion coefficients for several gas mixtures are given in Table 2.1. It is seen that for many small gas molecules, the values lie between 0.1 cm²/s (10^{-5} m²/s or 0.4 ft²/h) and 1 cm²/s (10^{-4} m²/s or 4 ft²/h) at atmospheric pressure and room temperature. The gas-phase diffusivity generally varies with the absolute temperature raised to the power 1.5 to 1.75, and inversely to the total pressure up to about 10 atm [$D_{AB} \propto T^{1.5 \text{ to } 1.75}$; $D_{AB} \propto (1/P)$]. It depends significantly also on the molecular weight of a species. As expected intuitively, a large molecule diffuses slowly compared to a small molecule, and also hinders

---

[#] In an interesting article, Kraaijeveld and Wesselingh (1993) showed that in some cases the diffusion coefficients of ions in a mixture of electrolytes or in an ion-exchange can even be negative.

Table 2.1 Experimental diffusivity values for selected gas pairs at 1.013 bar pressure

Gas pair A–B	Temperature (K)	$D_{AB} \times 10^5$ (m^2/s)	Gas pair A–B	Temperature (K)	$D_{AB} \times 10^5$ (m^2/s)
Air–CH$_4$	273	1.96	Air–C$_2$H$_5$OH	273	1.02
Air–CO$_2$	276.2	1.42	Air–H$_2$	273	6.11
Air–H$_2$O	298.2	2.6	Air–O$_2$	273	1.775
Air–Benzene	298.2	0.9	Air–NH$_3$	333	2.53
Air–*n*-Butanol	299.1	0.87	CH$_4$–Ar	298	2.02
CH$_4$–He	298	6.75	CH$_4$–H$_2$	298	7.26
CO–N$_2$	295.8	2.12	CO–H$_2$	295.6	7.43
CO$_2$–H$_2$	298	6.46	CO$_2$–N$_2$	298.2	1.65
CO$_2$–O$_2$	273	1.39	CO$_2$–CO	273	1.37
CO$_2$–H$_2$O	307.5	2.02	H$_2$–N$_2$	297.2	7.73
H$_2$–N$_2$	297	7.79	H$_2$–O$_2$	273.2	6.97
H$_2$–He	298.2	11.32	H$_2$–SO$_2$	285.5	5.25
H$_2$–H$_2$O	307.1	9.15	H$_2$–NH$_3$	298	7.83
N$_2$–SO$_2$	263	1.04	O$_2$–H$_2$O	308.1	2.82
O$_2$–CO	273	1.85	He–H$_2$O	298.2	9.08
He–Benxene	298.2	3.84	Ar–NH$_3$	295.1	2.32

diffusion of other molecules. For example, the diffusivity of hydrogen in *n*-butane is 0.272 cm^2/s at 0°C and 1 atm compared to 0.674 cm^2/s in nitrogen. The diffusivity strongly depends upon the intermolecular forces in a mixture and is also governed by collisions of the diffusing molecules with others present in the mixture. The rate of collision increases as the mean free path decreases. This is favoured at a higher pressure, and hence the diffusivity of a gas decreases with increasing pressure.

There are a few methods of experimental determination of the gas-phase diffusion coefficient. Two simple methods are described here.

2.5.1 Twin-bulb Method

The apparatus used in this method consists of two reasonably large bulbs or chambers of volumes V_1 and V_2, connected by a narrow tube fitted with a plug-type valve or a stopcock. There should be a suitable arrangement for stirring the contents of the bulbs in order to keep the concentrations in them uniform (the bulbs are said to be 'well-mixed'). The entire assembly should be maintained at a constant temperature. A schematic sketch of the apparatus is shown in Figure 2.11.

Initially, the valve in the connecting tube is kept closed. The two bulbs are evacuated. One of the bulbs is repeatedly flushed with pure *A* and the other with pure *B* and then filled with the gases at the same pressure, *P*. The valve is then opened to allow diffusion to start and continue undisturbed for some time, at the end of which the valve is closed. Samples of the gases from the bulbs are taken and analyzed for their composition.

Because the total pressures in the bulbs remain constant and equal, equimolar counter-diffusion through the connecting tube occurs. The bulbs being large, the concentrations or partial pressures of the components in the bulbs will change rather slowly. A theoretical analysis of

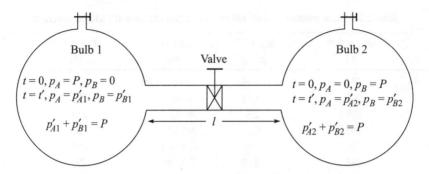

Figure 2.11 The twin-bulb apparatus—a schematic sketch.

diffusion in the system can be made with the pseudo-steady state[†] approximation. This means that, at any instant, diffusion through the connecting tube occurs at steady state. As the concentrations in the bulbs change a little, a new steady state of diffusion is attained *simultaneously*. The assumption is correct if the 'time scale' for the change of the concentrations in the bulbs is considerably larger than the time scale for the attainment of steady-state diffusion through the connecting tube. The working equation for the calculation of the diffusion coefficient from the concentration changes in the bulbs is derived below.

If a is the inner cross-section of the connecting tube, l is its length, and p_{A1} and p_{A2} ($p_{A1} > p_{A2}$) are the partial pressures of A in the bulbs at any time t, the steady-state rate of transport of A from bulb 1 to bulb 2 can be written as [see Eq. (2.30)]

$$aN_A = \frac{aD_{AB}(p_{A1} - p_{A2})}{RTl} = -aN_B \tag{2.46}$$

If C_{A1} and C_{A2} are the instantaneous concentrations of A in the bulbs, the rates of change of these concentrations are given by the following equations:

$$-V_1 \frac{dC_{A1}}{dt} = aN_A \qquad \Rightarrow \qquad -\frac{V_1}{RT}\frac{dp_{A1}}{dt} = aN_A \tag{2.47}$$

and

$$V_2 \frac{dC_{A2}}{dt} = aN_A \qquad \Rightarrow \qquad \frac{V_2}{RT}\frac{dp_{A2}}{dt} = aN_A \tag{2.48}$$

Here C_{A1} decreases with time but C_{A2} increases. Hence the negative sign in Eq. (2.46). Also, we have used the relations $C_{A1} = p_{A1}/RT$ and $C_{A2} = p_{A2}/RT$ applicable to ideal gases. Combining Eqs. (2.47) and (2.48),

$$-\frac{d}{dt}(p_{A1} - p_{A2}) = aRT\left(\frac{1}{V_1} + \frac{1}{V_2}\right)N_A = \frac{aD_{AB}(p_{A1} - p_{A2})}{l}\left(\frac{1}{V_1} + \frac{1}{V_2}\right)$$

$$\Rightarrow \qquad -\frac{d(p_{A1} - p_{A2})}{(p_{A1} - p_{A2})} = \frac{aD_{AB}}{l}\left(\frac{1}{V_1} + \frac{1}{V_2}\right)dt \tag{2.49}$$

We use the following conditions:

$$t = 0, \ p_{A1} - p_{A2} = P - 0 = P \qquad \text{and} \qquad t = t', \ p_{A1} - p_{A2} = p'_{A1} - p'_{A2} \ \text{(say)}$$

[†] The pseudo-steady state approximation is used in a number of exercises and examples in this chapter.

Integration of Eq. (2.49) within the above limits gives the working equation for the calculation of D_{AB}. That is,

$$\ln \frac{P}{p'_{A1} - p'_{A2}} = \frac{aD_{AB}}{l}\left(\frac{1}{V_1} + \frac{1}{V_2}\right)t' \tag{2.50}$$

The quantities to be measured in this experiment are the initial pressure in the vessels and the partial pressures of one of the components (say A) in the vessels at the end of the experiment. The mutual diffusion coefficient D_{AB} can be directly determined from Eq. (2.50).

2.5.2 Use of the Stefan Tube

This method is suitable if, under the given set of experimental conditions, one of the components (say A) is available as a volatile liquid and the other component (B) is a gas which is *not soluble* in A. The apparatus is very simple. A vertical glass tube, sealed at the bottom, is joined to a larger diameter horizontal tube to form a tee (T) as shown in Figure 2.12. The liquid A is taken in the narrow vertical tube and the gas B is forced through the horizontal tube. Evaporated A diffuses through the mixture of A and B in the vertical tube, reaches the top and is swept away by the flowing stream of B. As B is insoluble in A, it will not diffuse and the situation will conform to *diffusion of A through non-diffusing B*. The liquid level in the vertical tube will drop very slowly and *pseudo-steady state assumption* (i.e. A diffuses through the tube virtually at steady-state at all time) is reasonable. This means that as the liquid level falls by a small amount, a new steady-state rate of diffusion is established simultaneously. The drop in the liquid level over a period of time is noted.

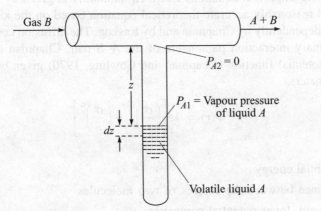

Figure 2.12 A schematic of the Stefan tube.

Let, at any time t, the liquid level be at a distance z from the top of the vertical tube, p_{A1} be the partial pressure of A at the liquid surface and p_{A2} that at the top. The diffusional flux of A through this distance z is given as follows [see Eq. (2.27)].

$$N_A = \frac{D_{AB}P(p_{A1} - p_{A2})}{RTzp_{BM}} \tag{2.51}$$

If the fall in the liquid level is dz in a small time dt, the number of moles of A that diffuse out is $a\,dz(\rho_A/M_A)$. By a material balance over the time dt,

$$\frac{a\,dz\,\rho_A}{M_A} = a N_A\,dt = \frac{a D_{AB}\,P(p_{A1} - p_{A2})}{RT\,p_{BM}\,z}\,dt$$

Here a is the inner cross-section of the vertical tube, ρ_A and M_A are the density (of the liquid) and molecular weight of A respectively. If at time $t = 0$, the liquid level is at z_0 from the top, and at time t' (i.e. at the end of the experiment) the liquid level is at z', integration of the above equation and rearrangement gives

$$D_{AB} = \frac{RT\,p_{BM}\,\rho_A\,(z'^2 - z_0^2)}{2\,P\,M_A\,(p_{A1} - p_{A2})\,t'} \tag{2.52}$$

The partial pressure of A at the liquid surface, p_{A1}, is equal to its vapour pressure at the prevailing temperature. At the open top of the tube, the partial pressure of A is virtually zero ($p_{A2} = 0$) because A is greatly diluted by the gas B flowing at a high rate. All the quantities being known, D_{AB} can be calculated.

2.5.3   Predictive Equations for the Gas-phase Diffusivity

Although experimental diffusivity values for a large number of binary gas mixtures are available, we often come across mixtures for which no experimental data have been reported. In such a case, we take the help of a suitable predictive equation or correlation for the estimation of diffusivity. Many such predictive equations—theoretical, semi-empirical or empirical—are available. A detailed account of the more important equations and their suitability is given by Poling et al. (2001).

A useful and reasonably accurate theoretical equation based on the kinetic theory of gases was suggested independently by Chapman and by Enskog. The diffusion coefficient D_{AB} strongly depends upon binary interaction parameters of the A–B pair. Chapman and Enskog used the Lennard–Jones potential function (Chapman and Cowling, 1970) given below to calculate the interaction parameters.

$$\Phi(r) = 4\varepsilon\left[\left(\frac{\sigma}{r}\right)^{12} - \left(\frac{\sigma}{r}\right)^{6}\right] \tag{2.53}$$

where

   $\Phi(r)$ = potential energy

      r = distance between the centres of two molecules

   ε and σ = Lennard–Jones potential parameters.

The Chapman–Enskog equation is given by

$$D_{AB} = \frac{1.858 \times 10^{-7}\,T^{3/2}(1/M_A + 1/M_B)^{1/2}}{P\,\sigma_{AB}^2\,\Omega_D}\ \text{m}^2/\text{s} \tag{2.54}$$

Here

         T = absolute temperature, in K

   M_A, M_B = molecular weights of the components A and B

P = total pressure, in atm

σ_{AB} = a characteristic length parameter of the binary, in Å

Ω_D = collision integral which is a function of kT/ε_{AB} (where k is the Boltzmann's constant and ε_{AB} is another characteristic binary parameter).

The following equations can be used to calculate σ_{AB} and ε_{AB}.

$$\sigma_{AB} = (\sigma_A + \sigma_B)/2; \qquad \varepsilon_{AB} = [\varepsilon_A \varepsilon_B]^{1/2} \tag{2.55}$$

The values of σ and ε are listed for a number of common substances in Table 2.2 and the collision integral, Ω_D, is given in Table 2.3. The values of σ and ε for substances not listed in Table 2.2 can be calculated from the following approximate relations:

$$\varepsilon/k = 0.75 T_c \qquad \text{and} \qquad \sigma = (5/6)V_c^{1/3} \tag{2.56}$$

Table 2.2 Lennard–Jones potential parameters for selected compounds

Compound	σ (Å)	ε/k (K)	Compound	σ (Å)	ε/k (K)
He	2.551	10.22	Air	3.711	78.6
CCl_4	5.947	322.7	$CHCl_3$	5.389	340.2
CH_3Cl	4.182	350.0	CH_3OH	3.626	481.8
CH_4	3.758	148.6	CS_2	4.483	467.0
C_2H_4	4.163	224.7	C_2H_6	4.443	215.7
C_2H_5Cl	4.898	300.0	C_2H_5OH	4.530	362.6
Propylene	4.678	298.9	Acetone	4.600	560.2
n-Butane	4.687	531.4	Di-ethyl ether	5.678	313.8
n-Hexane	5.949	399.3	Cl_2	4.217	316.0
Ethyl acetate	5.205	521.3	HCl	3.339	344.7
HBr	3.353	449.0	H_2	2.827	59.7
H_2O	2.641	809.1	H_2S	3.623	301.1
NH_3	2.900	558.3	NO	3.492	116.7
N_2	3.798	71.4	O_2	3.467	106.7
SO_2	4.112	335.4	Benzene	5.349	412.3

where T_c is the critical temperature (K) and V_c is the critical volume (cm^3/gmol) of a component. Use of the Chapman–Enskog equation has been illustrated in Example 2.11.

An empirical equation suggested by Fuller, Schettler and Giddings (1966) is not only simple to use but also reasonably accurate in predicting binary gas-phase diffusivity up to moderate pressures.

$$D_{AB} = \frac{1.0133 \times 10^{-7} T^{1.75}}{P[(\Sigma v)_A^{1/3} + (\Sigma v)_B^{1/3}]^2} \left[\frac{1}{M_A} + \frac{1}{M_B} \right]^{1/2} \text{ m}^2/\text{s} \tag{2.57}$$

Here

T = temperature, in K

M_A and M_B = molecular weights of A and B respectively

P = total pressure, in bar.

Table 2.3   Numerical values of the collision integral, Ω_D

kT/ε	Ω_D	kT/ε	Ω_D	kT/ε	Ω_D
0.30	2.662	0.95	1.476	1.90	1.094
0.35	2.476	1.00	1.439	2.00	1.075
0.40	2.318	1.05	1.406	2.5	0.9996
0.45	2.184	1.10	1.375	3.0	0.949
0.50	2.066	1.15	1.346	3.5	0.912
0.55	1.966	1.20	1.320	4.0	0.8836
0.60	1.877	1.25	1.296	4.5	0.861
0.65	1.798	1.30	1.273	5.0	0.8422
0.70	1.729	1.40	1.233	7.0	0.7896
0.75	1.667	1.50	1.198	10.0	0.7424
0.80	1.612	1.60	1.167	30	0.6232
0.85	1.562	1.70	1.140	50	0.5756
0.90	1.517	1.80	1.116	70	0.5464

In order to use Eq. (2.57), one has to estimate (Σv) for each of the components by adding atomic diffusion volumes listed in Table 2.4 for selected molecules and structural groups. The error in the prediction remains within 5% for many binaries. As an example, let us estimate the diffusivity of *cyclo*-hexane(A) in nitrogen(B) at 15°C and 1 atm pressure.

Cyclo-hexane (C_6H_{12}) has one ring. From Table 2.4, the volume terms of A and B are

$$\Sigma v_A = (6)(16.5) + (12)(2.31) - 20.1 = 106.5; \qquad \Sigma v_B = 17.9$$

Table 2.4   Atomic and diffusion volumes (Fuller et al., 1966)

C	16.5	H_2	7.07	CO_2	26.9
H	2.31	He	2.88	N_2O	35.9
O	5.48	N_2	17.9	NH_3	14.9
N	5.69	O_2	16.6	H_2O	12.7
Cl	19.5	Air	20.1	Cl_2	37.7
S	17.0	Ar	16.1	SO_2	41.1
Aromatic ring	−20.2	Kr	22.8		
Heterocyclic ring	−20.2	CO	18.9		

Also, $M_A = 84$, $M_B = 28$, $T = 15°C = 288$ K, $P = 1.013$ bar. Substituting the values in the Fuller's equation [Eq. (2.57)], $D_{AB} = 8.12 \times 10^{-6}$ m²/s = 0.0812 cm²/s. The experimental value (Perry, 1997) at the given condition is 0.076 cm²/s; therefore the error in prediction = 7%.

2.6   MOLECULAR DIFFUSION IN LIQUIDS

Here we describe the equations for the calculation of diffusional flux of a species in solution, the experimental determination and estimation of liquid-phase diffusion coefficients.

2.6.1 Flux Equations

The flux Eq. (2.14) is valid for both gas and liquid phases. However, unlike ideal gases, the total molar concentration of a liquid is expected to vary from one point to another. While integrating Eq. (2.14) for liquid-phase diffusion from point 1 to point 2, use of an average total molar concentration is justified. Putting $x_A = C_A/C$ in Eq. (2.14), we get

$$N_A = (N_A + N_B)x_A - D_{AB}\left(\frac{\rho}{M}\right)_{av} \frac{dx_A}{dz} \qquad (2.58)$$

Here ρ = density and M = molecular weight of the solution; $(\rho/M)_{av}$ is the average molar concentration of the liquid.

Equation (2.58) may be integrated between the points 1 and 2 as we did in the case of gas-phase diffusion. The integrated equations are given below.

(a) For the diffusion of A through non-diffusing B,

$$N_A = \frac{D_{AB}(\rho/M)_{av}}{l\,x_{BM}}(x_{A0} - x_{Al}), \qquad \text{where } x_{BM} = \frac{x_{Bl} - x_{B0}}{\ln(x_{Bl}/x_{B0})} \qquad (2.59)$$

(b) For equimolar counterdiffusion of A and B,

$$N_A = \frac{D_{AB}(\rho/M)_{av}}{l}(x_{A0} - x_{Al}) \qquad (2.60)$$

Here x_{A0} and x_{Al} are the mole fractions of A at points 1 and 2 separated by a distance l. It is to be remembered that very often diffusion in the liquid phase occurs at low concentrations. As a result, it is reasonable to assume $x_{BM} \cong 1$, so that $N_A = J_A$.

EXAMPLE 2.12 (*Liquid-phase diffusion*)   In a slurry reactor the gas(A) is sparged in an agitated suspension of catalyst particles, 1 mm in average diameter, in a liquid(B). The gas dissolves in the liquid and is transported to the surface of the catalyst particles where it undergoes an *instantaneous reaction*. In a particular case the concentration of A in the liquid is 1.0 kmol/ m^3, the rate of reaction is 3.15×10^{-6} kmol/m$^2 \cdot$s based on the external surface area of the catalyst particles, and the diffusivity of A in the liquid is 7×10^{-10} m^2/s. If the diffusion of dissolved A to the catalyst surface occurs through a stagnant film surrounding a particle, calculate the thickness of the liquid-film.

Solution

Consider a stagnant liquid-film of thickness δ surrounding a catalyst particle. If r is the radial distance of any point in the liquid-film from the centre of the catalyst particle, we have (for the details of the derivation of the following equation, see Section 2.7.1)

$$4\pi r^2 N_A = \text{constant} = W \qquad \text{and} \qquad N_A = -D\,dC_A/dr \text{ (if the concentration is low).}$$

We combine the above two equations and integrate from $r = r_c$ (the radius of the catalyst particle), $C_A = 0$ to $r = r_c + \delta$ (i.e. the other boundary of the liquid-film), $C_A = C_{Ab}$ (bulk liquid concentration, see Figure 2.13).

$$\int_0^{C_{Ab}} dC_A = -\frac{W}{4\pi D}\int_{r_c}^{r_c+\delta}\frac{dr}{r^2} = \frac{W}{4\pi D}\left(\frac{1}{r_c} - \frac{1}{r_c+\delta}\right) \quad \Rightarrow \quad W = 4\pi D C_{Ab}\frac{r_c(r_c+\delta)}{\delta}$$

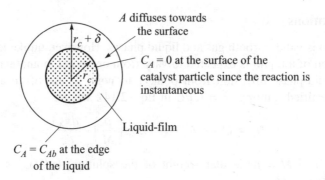

Figure 2.13   Diffusion through the film on a spherical pellet.

Given: $r_c = 0.5$ mm $= 5 \times 10^{-4}$ m; $D = 7 \times 10^{-10}$ m²/s; $C_{Ab} = 1.0$ kmol/m³; and the rate of reaction = the flux of the reactant to the surface of the catalyst particle, $N_A = 3.15 \times 10^{-6}$ kmol/m²·s.

$$\Rightarrow \qquad W = 4\pi r_c^2 N_A = 4\pi D C_{Ab} \frac{r_c(r_c + \delta)}{\delta}$$

$$\Rightarrow \qquad 1 + \frac{r_c}{\delta} = \frac{N_A r_c}{D C_{Ab}} = \frac{(3.15 \times 10^{-6})(5 \times 10^{-4})}{(7 \times 10^{-10})(1.0)}$$

$$\Rightarrow \qquad 1 + (5 \times 10^{-4})/\delta = 2.25. \text{ The liquid-film thickness, } \delta = 0.0004 \text{ m} = \boxed{0.4 \text{ mm}}$$

2.6.2   Experimental Determination of Liquid-phase Diffusion Coefficient

There are a number of methods for the determination of the liquid-phase diffusion coefficient. Here we describe a common method that uses a 'diaphragm cell' (Dullien and Shemilt, 1961).

The diaphragm cell is a two-compartment cell, as shown in Figure 2.14, separated by a porous diaphragm usually of sintered glass. Solutions of the species A in the solvent B at two different concentrations are taken in the two compartments. Diffusion is allowed to occur through the narrow passageways of the pores from the higher concentration cell to the lower concentration cell for some time. At the end of a run, samples of the solutions are taken from the cells and analyzed for the concentrations of A. The contents of the compartments are always kept well-stirred. If the area of cross-section of the diaphragm is a and ε is its porosity, then the effective area available for diffusion is $a\varepsilon$. However, the length of the diffusion path is not equal to the thickness of the diaphragm since the pores are not straight. Many of the pores are interconnected and some may even have dead ends. A simple method to take into account this characteristic of the pores is to introduce an empirical parameter called 'tortuosity factor', τ. It is the ratio of the average length of the diffusion path (through the diaphragm) to the thickness of the diaphragm.

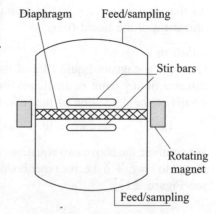

Figure 2.14   The diaphragm cell.

The working equation for the calculation of the diffusion coefficient from the data collected with a diaphragm cell can be derived following the procedure adopted in the case of the twin-bulb method (Section 2.5.1). For diffusion in the liquid phase, particularly at low concentrations [see Eq. (2.17)], it is reasonable to neglect the bulk flow term in Eq. (2.14). The approximate form of Fick's law is

$$N_A = -D_{AB} \frac{dC_A}{dz} \tag{2.61}$$

Equation (2.61) can be integrated at steady state to give

$$N_A = \frac{D_{AB}(C_{A1} - C_{A2})}{l\tau}; \qquad C_{A1} > C_{A2} \tag{2.62}$$

Here l is the thickness of the diaphragm, and $l\tau$ is the *effective length* of the diffusion path. If V_1 and V_2 are the volumes of the solutions in the two cells and C_{A1} and C_{A2} are the concentrations therein at time t, then by invoking the arguments given in Section 2.5.1 (the *pseudo-steady state approximation*),

$$-V_1 \frac{dC_{A1}}{dt} = a\varepsilon N_A \qquad \text{and} \qquad V_2 \frac{dC_{A2}}{dt} = a\varepsilon N_A \tag{2.63}$$

Adding the above two equations and substituting N_A from Eq. (2.62),

$$-\frac{d}{dt}(C_{A1} - C_{A2}) = a\varepsilon \frac{D_{AB}(C_{A1} - C_{A2})}{l\tau} \left(\frac{1}{V_1} + \frac{1}{V_2} \right) \tag{2.64}$$

If $C_{A1,0}$ and $C_{A2,0}$ are the initial concentrations and $C_{A1,f}$ and $C_{A2,f}$ are the final concentrations in the compartments at time t_f, integration and rearrangement of Eq. (2.64) yields

$$D_{AB} = \frac{l\tau}{a\varepsilon t_f} \left(\frac{1}{V_1} + \frac{1}{V_2} \right)^{-1} \ln\left(\frac{C_{A1,0} - C_{A2,0}}{C_{A1,f} - C_{A2,f}} \right) \tag{2.65a}$$

Equation [2.65(a)] can be used to calculate the diffusion coefficient from the measured concentrations and time. However, it is not easy to determine the effective porosity ε and the tortuosity factor τ of the diaphragm. It is more convenient to carry out separate measurements for a solute of known diffusion coefficient in the given solvent to *calibrate* the cell. Then the quantity

$$\frac{a\varepsilon}{\tau l} \left(\frac{1}{V_1} + \frac{1}{V_2} \right) = \beta \text{ (say)} \tag{2.65b}$$

can be calculated for a particular diaphragm cell. The quantity β is called the 'cell constant'. Once the cell constant is determined, the diffusivity of any species in any solvent can be measured. Potassium chloride–water is a common system used to determine the cell constant. Sample calculations are illustrated in Example 2.13.

An apparatus based on similar principles, called the 'Wilke-Kallanbach diffusion cell', is used for the determination of effective diffusivity of a gas in a porous solid (for example, a catalyst pellet).

EXAMPLE 2.13 (*Diffusivity determination—diaphragm cell*)   A two-compartment diaphragm cell is used to measure the diffusion coefficient of propionic acid in water at 18.5°C. The cell has a 1.8 mm thick and 3.5 cm diameter glass frit diaphragm. The volumes of the two compartments are 60.2 cm³ and 59.3 cm³ respectively. A calibration experiment is done by filling the large compartment with 0.3 molar aqueous solution of KCl and the smaller compartment with water. Molecular diffusion of the solute occurs through the pores of the diaphragm. The concentration of KCl reduces to 0.215 molar at the end of 55.2 h runtime. The diffusivity of KCl is known to be 1.51×10^{-5} cm²/s at the experimental temperature of 18.5°C. Calculate the cell constant from these data.

The cell is then thoroughly washed and the larger compartment is filled with 0.4 molar aqueous propionic acid. The smaller compartment is filled with water as before. At the end of 56.4 h, a sample from the larger compartment is found to contain 0.32 molar acid. Calculate the diffusivity of propionic acid in water. If the average porosity of the diaphragm is 0.39, what is the tortuosity of the pores?

Solution
Equations [2.65(a) and (b)] are the working equations for this problem. The end concentration in the smaller compartment has to be obtained by material balance in each case.

Diffusion of KCl: $V_1 C_{A1,0} + V_2 C_{A2,0} = V_1 C_{A1,f} + V_2 C_{A2,f}$

Given: $V_1 = 60.2$ cm³; $V_2 = 59.3$ cm³; $C_{A1,0} = 0.3$; $C_{A2,0} = 0$; $C_{A1,f} = 0.215$

$\Rightarrow$ $C_{A2,f} = 0.0863$ molar
Other quantities given are: $D = 1.51 \times 10^{-5}$ cm²/s; time, $t_f = 55.2$ h $= 55.2 \times 3600$ s
The cell constant can be calculated from Eq. [2.65(a)].

$$\beta = \frac{1}{D t_f} \ln \frac{C_{A1,0} - C_{A2,0}}{C_{A1,f} - C_{A2,f}} = \frac{1}{(1.51 \times 10^{-5})(55.2 \times 3600)} \ln \frac{0.3 - 0}{0.215 - 0.0863} = \boxed{0.282 \text{ cm}^{-2}}$$

Diffusion of propionic acid:

Given: $C_{A1,0} = 0.4$; $C_{A2,0} = 0$; $C_{A1,f} = 0.32$; then by material balance as above, $C_{A2,f} = 0.0812$; also the time allowed is $t_f = 56.4$ h $= 56.4 \times 3600$ s. Substituting these values in Eq. [2.65(a)],

$$D = \frac{1}{\beta t_f} \ln \frac{C_{A1,0} - C_{A2,0}}{C_{A1,f} - C_{A2,f}} = \frac{1}{(0.282)(56.4 \times 3600)} \ln \frac{0.4 - 0}{0.32 - 0.0812} = \boxed{9.01 \times 10^{-6} \text{ cm}^2/\text{s}}$$

(This value compares well with the literature value, 8.74×10^{-6} cm²/s)

Calculation of the tortuosity factor:

$$\text{Cell constant, } \beta = \frac{a \varepsilon}{\tau l} \left(\frac{1}{V_1} + \frac{1}{V_2} \right)$$

Given: area of the diaphragm, $a = (\pi/4)(3.5)^2 = 9.621$ cm²; $\varepsilon = 0.39$; $l = 0.18$ cm; $\beta = 0.282$.

$\Rightarrow$ Tortuosity factor, $\tau = \frac{(9.621)(0.39)}{(0.282)(0.18)} \left(\frac{1}{60.2} + \frac{1}{59.3} \right) = \boxed{2.5}$

2.6.3 Predictive Equations for Liquid-phase Diffusivity

The magnitude of the liquid-phase diffusivity is much smaller than that of the gas-phase diffusivity. From the brief list of experimental liquid-phase diffusivity values of several common substances given in Table 2.5, it is apparent that for diffusion of small solute molecules in water, the value generally lies between 0.5×10^{-5} cm^2/s and 2×10^{-5} cm^2/s. A larger molecule has a smaller diffusivity.

Table 2.5   Liquid-phase diffusivities of selected compounds at infinite dilution at 25°C

Solute	Solvent	$D_{AB}^0 \times 10^{-9}$ (m^2/s)	Solute	Solvent	$D_{AB}^0 \times 10^{-9}$ (m^2/s)
Carbon dioxide	Water	1.92	Benzoic acid	Water	1.00
Chlorine	Water	1.25	Acetone	Water	1.16
Nitric oxide	Water	2.60	Acetone	Chloroform	2.35
Oxygen	Water	2.10	Benzene	Chloroform	2.89
Ammonia	Water	1.64	Acetic acid	Benzene	2.09
Hydrogen sulphide	Water	1.41	Benzoic acid	Benzene	1.38
Sulphuric acid	Water	1.73	Water	Acetone	4.56
Nitric acid	Water	2.60	Benzene	Ethyl alcohol	1.81
Methanol	Water	1.6	Iodine	Ethyl alcohol	1.32
Ethanol	Water	1.28	Water	Ethyl alcohol	1.24
Formic acid	Water	1.50	n-Butyl alcohol	Water	0.988
Acetic acid	Water	1.21	Water	Ethyl acetate	3.20

A number of semi-empirical equations and correlations are available for the prediction of the liquid-phase diffusivity. But generally the accuracy of prediction is not as good as in the case of gases. This is because the theory of the liquid state is less clearly understood. The more important equations for the estimation of the liquid-phase coefficient are described by Poling et al. (2001). Hayduk and Minhas (1982) proposed a simple and useful correlation. Here we cite the Wilke–Chang equation (1955) which is simple to use but not always good in prediction.

$$D_{AB}^0 = \frac{1.173 \times 10^{-16} \, (\varphi \, M_B)^{1/2} \, T}{\mu \, v_A^{0.6}} \tag{2.66}$$

Here D_{AB}^0 is the diffusivity of the solute A in solvent B in m^2/s; the superscript '0' refers to an infinitely dilute solution. The different quantities involved are: M_B = molecular weight of B (the solvent); φ = association factor for the solvent [water: $\varphi = 2.26$; methanol: $\varphi = 1.5$; ethanol: $\varphi = 1.5$; non-associated solvents: $\varphi = 1.0$]; T = absolute temperature, in K; μ = solution viscosity, in kg/m·s; v_A = solute molar volume at the normal boiling point, in m^3/kmol.

Let us estimate the diffusivity of acetic acid(A) in water(B) using the Wilke–Chang equation at 293 K.

Molar volume of the solute (acetic acid) at its normal boiling point, $v_A = 0.0641$ m^3/kmol (Poling et al., p. 54); viscosity of the solvent (water) at 293 K (Poling et al., p. 441), $\mu = 1.0121 \times 10^{-3}$ kg/m·s; $\varphi = 2.26$ for water, $M_B = 18$. Substituting the values of different quantities in Eq. (2.66), $D_{AB} = 1.116 \times 10^{-5}$ cm^2/s. This value would be a little larger at 298 K.

Experimental value (Table 2.5) is $D_{AB} = 1.19 \times 10^{-5}$ cm^2/s. Error in prediction = -6.2%.

Certain characteristics of the liquid diffusivity may be noted in Eq. (2.66). The diffusivity, D_{AB}, varies linearly with the absolute temperature T and inversely as the viscosity of the medium, μ, which is approximately true for many solute-solvent pairs. The well-known Stokes–Einstein equation given below also shows this type of dependence.

$$\frac{D_{AB}\,\mu}{T} = \text{constant} \tag{2.67}$$

From the nature of dependence of D_{AB} on v_A given in Eq. (2.66), it again appears that larger molecules have lower diffusivities. Thus the diffusivity of *iso*-propanol in water is less than that of methanol. A more viscous medium offers greater hindrance to the movement of solute molecules. As a result, liquid-phase diffusivity decreases as the viscosity of the solvent increases.

A detailed account of many available correlations and their suitability is given by Poling et al. (2001) and in Perry's Handbook (7th edition; Chapter 5).

2.6.4 Concentration Dependence of the Liquid Diffusivity

Diffusivity of a solute in a concentrated solution may sometimes be substantially different from that in a dilute solution. The reason is that a concentrated solution is more non-ideal and will have a more complex solute-solvent interaction. The change in the viscosity with concentration has also some effect on the diffusivity. Sometimes the diffusivity in a binary solution shows a maximum or minimum with change in the concentration. Here we cite an important equation proposed by Leffler and Cullinan (1970) for the determination of diffusivity in a concentrated solution.

$$D_{AB}\,\mu = (D_{BA}^0\,\mu_A)^{x_A}\,(D_{AB}^0\,\mu_B)^{1-x_A}\left[1 + \frac{d\ln\gamma_A}{d\ln x_A}\right] \tag{2.68}$$

where D_{AB}^0 is the diffusivity of A in an infinitely dilute solution in B, and D_{BA}^0 is the same for B in an infinitely dilute solution in A. The activity coefficient of A (i.e. γ_A) is expressed by the following equation at ordinary pressure (where the vapour phase is rather ideal), i.e.

$$\gamma_A = \frac{y_A\,P}{x_A\,P_A^v} \tag{2.69}$$

Here P_A^v is the vapour pressure of A at the given temperature. The derivative $(d\ln\gamma_A/d\ln x_A)$ can be obtained from the above equation. Details of the concentration dependence of diffusivity and also the phenomenon of diffusion in electrolytes (where the ions present in the solution greatly influence diffusivity) are given by Poling et al. (2001).

2.7 DIFFUSION THROUGH A VARIABLE AREA

So far we have analyzed problems in which the cross-sectional area of diffusion remains constant. This is true for a flat geometry. However, there are many situations where the area of diffusion changes along the direction of diffusion, or changes with time even. Two common geometries that involve diffusion through a variable area are the cylindrical and the spherical geometries. Diffusion in a tapered or conical geometry is also encountered in some cases. A few typical cases are analyzed in this section.

2.7.1 Diffusion in Spherical Geometry

Evaporation of a drop of water in stagnant air will be analyzed here as a model case. Let us consider an evaporating drop that has radius r_s at any instant t. Imagine a thin spherical shell of inner radius r and thickness Δr around the drop as shown in Figure 2.15. This is a binary system involving diffusion of water vapour(A) through air(B). Then

Rate of input of A into the thin shell (at $r = r$) $\qquad \therefore (4\pi r^2)N_A|_r$

Rate of output of A from the thin shell (at $r = r + \Delta r$) : $(4\pi r^2)N_A|_{r+\Delta r}$

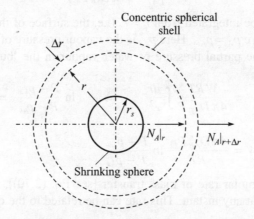

Figure 2.15 A sketch indicating shell balance for mass transfer from a sphere.

The notation $|_r$ means that the quantity is evaluated at the position r.

By a steady-state mass balance (note that the rate of accumulation = 0),

$$(4\pi r^2)N_A|_r - (4\pi r^2)N_A|_{r+\Delta r} = 0$$

$$\text{Input} \qquad \text{Output} \qquad \text{Accumulation}$$

Dividing both sides by Δr and taking the limit $\Delta r \to 0$,

$$\lim_{\Delta r \to 0} \frac{(4\pi r^2)N_A|_r - (4\pi r^2)N_A|_{r+\Delta r}}{\Delta r} = 0 \Rightarrow -\frac{d}{dr}(4\pi r^2 N_A) = 0$$

$$\Rightarrow \qquad\qquad 4\pi r^2 N_A = \text{constant} = W \text{ (say)} \qquad\qquad (2.70)$$

Equation (2.70) is a very important result for *steady state* diffusion through a variable area and can be generalized as

$$(\text{Area})(\text{Flux}) = \text{Constant} \qquad\qquad (2.71)$$

In this case water vapour diffuses out, but air does not diffuse because it is not soluble in water. So the case corresponds to diffusion of A through non-diffusing B. Since diffusion occurs in the radial direction, we replace z by r in Eq. (2.19) to get

$$N_A = (N_A + N_B)\frac{p_A}{P} - \frac{D_{AB}}{RT}\frac{dp_A}{dr}$$

Putting $N_B = 0$ and rearranging,

$$N_A = - \frac{D_{AB}P}{RT(P - p_A)}\frac{dp_A}{dr} \tag{2.72}$$

From Eqs. (2.70) and (2.72),

$$-\frac{dp_A}{P - p_A} = \frac{WRT}{4\pi D_{AB}P}\frac{dr}{r^2} \tag{2.73}$$

The above equation can be integrated from $r = r_s$ (i.e. the surface of the drop) to $r = \infty$ (i.e. far away from the drop) where $p_A = p_{A\infty}$. Here p_{As} is the vapour pressure of water at the temperature of the drop and $p_{A\infty}$ is the partial pressure of water vapour in the 'bulk air'.

$$-\int_{p_{As}}^{p_{A\infty}} \frac{dp_A}{P - p_A} = \frac{WRT}{4\pi D_{AB}P}\int_{r_s}^{\infty}\frac{dr}{r^2} \quad \Rightarrow \quad \ln\frac{P - p_{A\infty}}{P - p_{As}} = \frac{WRT}{4\pi D_{AB}P}\frac{1}{r_s}$$

$$\Rightarrow \qquad W = \frac{4\pi D_{AB}Pr_s}{RT}\ln\frac{P - p_{A\infty}}{P - p_{As}} \tag{2.74}$$

Since W is the constant molar rate of mass transfer [see Eq. (2.70)], it is equal to the rate of vaporization of the drop at any instant. This rate can be related to the change in the drop radius by the following equation.

$$W = -\frac{d}{dt}\left(\frac{4}{3}\pi r_s^3\frac{\rho_A}{M_A}\right) = -4\pi\frac{\rho_A}{M_A}r_s^2\frac{dr_s}{dt} \tag{2.75}$$

The negative sign is incorporated because the size of the drop decreases with time. Equating Eqs. (2.74) and (2.75),

$$-4\pi\frac{\rho_A}{M_A}r_s^2\frac{dr_s}{dt} = \frac{4\pi D_{AB}Pr_s}{RT}\ln\frac{P - p_{A\infty}}{P - p_{As}}$$

Here again we have made use of the 'pseudo-steady state' assumption, that the drop size changes so slowly that the diffusion of water vapour through the surrounding air occurs virtually at steady state at all time. The change in the drop size over a considerable period of time can be determined by integrating the above equation. If at time $t = 0$, the radius of the drop is r_{s0} and at time t' it is r_s',

$$-\int_{r_{s0}}^{r_s'} r_s\,dr_s = \frac{D_{AB}PM_A}{RT\rho_A}\ln\frac{P - p_{A\infty}}{P - p_{As}}\int_0^{t'}dt \quad \Rightarrow \quad r_{s0}^2 - r_s'^2 = \frac{2D_{AB}PM_At'}{RT\rho_A}\ln\frac{P - p_{A\infty}}{P - p_{As}} \tag{2.76}$$

How much time is required for complete evaporation of the drop? The answer is obtained by substituting $r'_s = 0$ in Eq. (2.76).

$$\Rightarrow \qquad t' = \frac{RT\rho_A\, r_{s0}^2}{2D_{AB}\,PM_A\,\ln\left[(P - p_{A\infty})/(P - p_{As})\right]} \tag{2.77}$$

Diffusion in the spherical geometry is encountered in many situations. Typical examples are diffusion in a spherical catalyst pellet, evaporation of droplets in a spray drier, etc. The rate of steady-state diffusion in the cylindrical geometry can be determined by a similar approach (see Example 2.14).

EXAMPLE 2.14 (*Diffusion from a sphere*)   Calculate the time required for the sublimation of 3 g of naphthalene from a naphthalene ball of mass 4 g kept suspended in a large volume of stagnant air at 45°C and 1.013 bar pressure. Diffusivity of naphthalene in air under the given conditions is 6.92×10^{-6} m²/s, its density is 1140 kg/m³, and its sublimation pressure at 45°C is 0.8654 mm Hg.

Hints: Equation (2.76) can be used directly. Initial mass of the ball = 4 g, radius, $r_{s0} = 0.943$ cm; final mass of the ball = 1 g, radius, $r'_s = 0.594$ cm. Other parameters: $D_{AB} = 0.0692$ cm²/s; $P = 1$ atm; $T = 318$ K; M_A = molecular wt. of naphthalene = 128; $p_{A\infty}$ = partial pressure of naphthalene in the bulk air = 0; p_{As} = sublimation pressure of naphthalene at 318 K = 0.8654 mm Hg = 0.00114 atm.

Substituting the values of the various quantities in Eq. (2.76), the time required, $t' = \boxed{219.5\,\text{h}}$

EXAMPLE 2.15 (*Diffusion from a cylinder*)   Sublimation of a 20 cm long naphthalene cylinder of mass 10 g occurs in a large volume of air in a room at 45°C and 1 atm pressure. The vapour diffuses through a stagnant film of air of thickness 3 mm surrounding the cylinder. The air beyond the film is well-mixed. Calculate the time required for sublimation of half of the naphthalene. Loss of mass because of sublimation from the flat ends may be neglected (as their combined area is considerably smaller than that of the cylindrical surface). The data given in Example 2.13 may be used.

Solution

This is a case of diffusion of A (naphthalene) through non-diffusing B (air) through a variable area. Taking the help of Eq. (2.71) together with Eq. (2.72), we may write

$$(2\pi rL)N_A = (2\pi rL)\left(-\frac{D_{AB}P}{RT(P - p_A)}\right)\frac{dp_A}{dr} = W \text{ (constant)}; \qquad L = \text{length of the cylinder}$$

Here r is the radial distance of any point within the surrounding air-film (thickness of the film = δ) from the axis of the cylinder; W is the molar rate of sublimation. The distance r varies from r_c (the radius of the cylinder) to the outer edge of the air-film, i.e. ($r_c + \delta$). The corresponding values of the partial pressure of naphthalene are: at $r = r_c$, $p_A = p_{As}$ (the sublimation pressure); at $r = r_c + \delta$, $p_A = 0$ (as there is no naphthalene in the bulk air). To calculate the rate of sublimation, we have to integrate the above equation.

$$-\int_{p_{As}}^{0}\frac{dp_A}{P - p_A} = \frac{RTW}{2\pi D_{AB}PL}\int_{r_c}^{r_c+\delta}\frac{dr}{r} \qquad \Rightarrow \qquad W = \frac{2\pi D_{AB}PL\ln[P/(P - p_{As})]}{RT\ln(1 + \delta/r_c)} \tag{i}$$

In order to calculate the required time of sublimation, we make the usual pseudo-steady state approximation. If at any time t, the mass of the cylinder is m $(= \pi r_c^2 L \rho_A)$, the rate of sublimation (neglecting the end losses) can be expressed as (M_A = mol. wt.)

$$W = -\frac{d(m/M_A)}{dt} = -\frac{d}{dt}(\pi r_c^2 L \rho_A / M_A) = -2\pi L (\rho_A / M_A) r_c \frac{dr_c}{dt} \qquad \text{(ii)}$$

From (i) and (ii),

$$\frac{2\pi D_{AB} P L}{RT \ln(1 + \delta/r_c)} \ln[P/(P - p_{As})] = -2\pi L (\rho_A / M_A) r_c \frac{dr_c}{dt}$$

Integrating,

$$-\int_{r_{c1}}^{r_{c2}} r_c \ln\left(1 + \frac{\delta}{r_c}\right) dr_c = \frac{D_{AB} P}{RT} \frac{M_A}{\rho_A} \ln\left(\frac{P}{P - p_{As}}\right) \int_0^t dt$$

$$\Rightarrow \quad \frac{1}{2} r_{c1}^2 \ln\left(1 + \frac{\delta}{r_{c1}}\right) - \frac{1}{2} r_{c2}^2 \ln\left(1 + \frac{\delta}{r_{c2}}\right) + \frac{\delta}{2}\left[(r_{c1} - r_{c2}) - \delta \ln \frac{r_{c1} + \delta}{r_{c2} + \delta}\right]$$

$$= \frac{D_{AB} P}{RT} \frac{M_A}{\rho_A}\left(\ln \frac{P}{P - p_{As}}\right) t$$

Initial volume of the cylinder = 10 g/(1.14 g/cm^3) = 8.772 cm^3 = $\pi r_{c1}^2 L$; $\Rightarrow r_{c1} = 0.3736$ cm
Final volume of the cylinder = 8.772/2 = 4.386 cm^3 = $\pi r_{c2}^2 L$; $\Rightarrow r_{c2} = 0.2642$ cm
$\delta = 3$ mm = 0.3 cm; $D_{AB} = 0.0692$ cm^2/s; $P = 1$ atm; $p_{As} = 0.00114$ atm.
Substituting the values of the various quantities in the above equation, the required time,

$$t = \boxed{10.35 \text{ h}}$$

EXAMPLE 2.16 (*Diffusion to a sphere, changing bulk concentration*)   A 1 cm diameter spherical pellet of a strongly basic oxide is held at the centre of a closed vessel of 5 litre volume. Initially the vessel is evacuated and then filled with an equimolar mixture of H$_2$S and N$_2$ at 25°C and 1 atm total pressure. As the molecules of H$_2$S reach the surface of the pellet, they get absorbed instantaneously so that the concentration of H$_2$S at the surface remains zero at all time. Diffusion of H$_2$S occurs through a stagnant film of estimated thickness of 4 mm surrounding the pellet. The *bulk* of the gas may be assumed to have a uniform composition at any time. Calculate the time of absorption of 95% of the H$_2$S gas. The temperature remains at 25°C and the diffusivity of H$_2$S in nitrogen is 1.73×10^{-5} m^2/s at this temperature and 1 atm pressure. (Figure 2.16 gives a sketch of the system.)

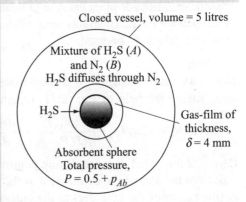

Figure 2.16   Absorption of H$_2$S in a pellet.

Solution

At the time t, let the partial pressure of H$_2$S(A) in the bulk gas be p_{Ab}. The initial partial pressure of N$_2$(B), which is not absorbed, is 0.5 atm. This value remains constant all through.

Total pressure at any instant, $P = 0.5 + p_{Ab}$

Diffusion of H_2S occurs through non-diffusing N_2 through a spherical gas-film of i.d. $= r_1$ and o.d. $= r_1 + \delta$. The thickness of the film is δ. Diffusion is assumed to occur at *pseudo-steady state*.

For diffusion in the spherical geometry at steady state, we have from Eqs. (2.70) and (2.72),

$$4\pi r^2 N_A = W \text{ (constant),} \qquad \text{where } N_A = \frac{D_{AB}P}{RT(P - p_A)}\frac{dp_A}{dr}$$

Here p_A is the partial pressure of A at any radial position r within the gas-film (thickness $= \delta$) surrounding the adsorbent sphere. Since p_A increases with r, no negative sign is used in the expression for flux, N_A. At the surface of the sphere, $r = r_1$ and $p_A = 0$; at the outer edge of the spherical film, $r = r_1 + \delta$, $p_A = p_{Ab}$. Integrating the above equation [see Eq. (2.74)],

$$\frac{4\pi D_{AB}P}{RT}\int_0^{p_{Ab}} \frac{dp_A}{P - p_A} = W\int_{r_1}^{r_1+\delta} \frac{dr}{r^2} = W\left(\frac{1}{r_1} - \frac{1}{r_1 + \delta}\right) = W\frac{\delta}{(r_1)(r_1 + \delta)}$$

$$\Rightarrow \quad W = \frac{4\pi D_{AB}P}{RT}\left[\ln\frac{P}{P - p_{Ab}}\right]\left[\frac{r_1(r_1 + \delta)}{\delta}\right] = \text{the rate of absorption of } H_2S \text{ at time } t.$$

If V is the volume of the vessel, we may write the following transient mass balance equation.

$$-\frac{V}{RT}\frac{dp_{Ab}}{dt} = W = \frac{4\pi D_{AB}P}{RT}\left[\ln\frac{0.5 + p_{Ab}}{0.5}\right]\left[\frac{r_1(r_1 + \delta)}{\delta}\right]$$

At a constant temperature, $D_{AB}P = $ constant. The above equation has to be integrated over a period of time during which the partial pressure of A changes from the initial value ($p_{Ab} = 0.5$ atm) to 0.05% of it [i.e. $p_{Ab} = (0.05)(0.5) = 0.025$ atm].

$$-\int_{0.5}^{0.025} \frac{dp_{Ab}}{\ln(1 + 2p_{Ab})} = \frac{4\pi(D_{AB}P)}{V}\frac{(r_1)(r_1 + \delta)}{\delta}\int_0^t dt$$

The integral has to be evaluated numerically. The values of the different quantities are: $V = 0.005 \text{ m}^3$; $D_{AB}P = (1.73 \times 10^{-5} \text{ m}^2/\text{s})(1 \text{ atm})$ and remains constant; $r_1 = 0.5 \text{ cm} = 0.005 \text{ m}$; $\delta = 4 \text{ mm} = 0.004 \text{ m}$.

Using the Simpson's 1/3rd rule, the integral is evaluated to be 1.755.

$$\text{Required time, } t = \frac{(1.755)(0.005)(0.004)}{4\pi(1.73 \times 10^{-5})(1)(0.005)(0.005 + 0.004)} \text{ s} = \boxed{1 \text{ h}}$$

2.7.2 Diffusion Through a Tapered Tube

Let us consider two 'large' vessels connected by a tapered tube of length L. The end radii of the tubes are r_1 (at vessel 1) and r_2 (at vessel 2). The vessels contain mixtures of the gases A and B at the same total pressure P and temperature T. The partial pressures of A in the vessels are p_{A1} and p_{A2}, respectively. Since the vessels are 'large', the compositions of the gases in the two vessels are assumed to remain fairly constant in spite of the diffusional transport occurring through the connecting tube. It is required to determine the rate of diffusion through the tube at steady state.

A sketch of the system is shown in Figure 2.17. The z-axis coincides with the axis of the tube and $z = 0$ is taken at the vessel 1 end. Because $p_{A1} > p_{A2}$, component A diffuses from vessel 1 to vessel 2, while B diffuses in the reverse direction. Thus there will be equimolar counterdiffusion of A and B through the tapered tube. Considering a thin section of the tube of thickness Δz at a position z where the local radius is r, we can write

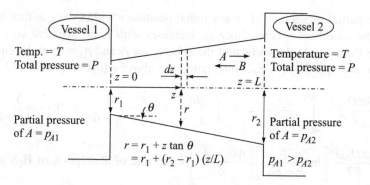

Figure 2.17   Equimolar counterdiffusion through a tapered tube.

Rate of input of A into the section at $z = (\pi r^2)N_A\big|_z$

Rate of output of A from the thin section at $z + \Delta z = (\pi r^2)N_A\big|_{z+\Delta z}$

Since there is no accumulation within the section at steady state,

$$(\pi r^2)N_A\big|_z - (\pi r^2)N_A\big|_{z+\Delta z} = 0$$

Dividing by Δz throughout and taking the limit $\Delta z \to 0$,

$$\lim_{\Delta z \to 0} \frac{(\pi r^2)N_A\big|_z - (\pi r^2)N_A\big|_{z+\Delta z}}{\Delta z} = 0$$

$$\Rightarrow \qquad -\frac{d}{dz}(\pi r^2 N_A) = 0 \quad \text{i.e.} \quad \pi r^2 N_A = \text{constant} = W_1 \text{ (say)}^\dagger \tag{2.78}$$

Following Eq. (2.29), the local flux for equimolar counterdiffusion is given by

$$N_A = -\frac{D_{AB}}{RT}\frac{dp_A}{dz} \quad \text{i.e.} \quad \pi r^2 N_A = W_1 = -\pi r^2 \frac{D_{AB}}{RT}\frac{dp_A}{dz}$$

The local radius r can be related to the axial position z by using the property of similar triangles, i.e.

$$r = r_1 + \left(\frac{r_2 - r_1}{L}\right)z$$

Substituting for N_A and r in Eq. (2.78), rearranging and integrating within the limits $z = 0$, $p_A = p_{A1}$ and $z = L$, $p_A = p_{A2}$,

---

† Equation (2.78) can be written directly by using the generalization of Eq. (2.71), i.e. the product of flux and area of diffusion remains constant.

$$-\int_{p_{A1}}^{p_{A2}} dp_A = \frac{W_1 RT}{\pi D_{AB}} \int_0^L \frac{dz}{r_1 + \left(\dfrac{r_2 - r_1}{L}\right)z} \quad \Rightarrow \quad W_1 = \frac{\pi D_{AB}}{RT} \frac{r_1 r_2}{L} (p_{A1} - p_{A2}) \qquad (2.79)$$

The constant W_1 is, in fact, the constant rate of diffusional transport of A through the tube. So the rate of transport can be calculated from Eq. (2.79). It is interesting to note that the rate of diffusion is equal to that through a 'uniform diameter tube' of radius $(r_1 r_2)^{1/2}$. So the 'effective radius' of the tapered tube in respect of diffusion is the geometric mean of the end radii.

EXAMPLE 2.17 (*Diffusion through a tapered region*)   Test tubes of tapered shape are sometimes used in the laboratories. Consider a 15 cm tall tapered test tube, open at the top. Half of the tube (to a depth of 7.5 cm) is full of ethyl acetate (A) at 25°C. The diameter of the tube at the top is 20 mm and that at the bottom is 12 mm. Calculate the rate of evaporation loss of the ester at the beginning. And also calculate the time of fall of the level by 2 cm. The ambient temperature is 25°C and the pressure is 1.013 bar. The data for the ester are given as follows: mol. wt. = 88; density = 900 kg/m^3; vapour pressure at 25°C = 0.1264 bar; diffusivity in air = 8.66×10^{-6} m^2/s.

Hints: At any time t, the liquid level is at a depth z (from the open top) where the radius is r. At the bottom of the tube, $z = L = 15$ cm, where $r = r_2 = 12$ mm; at the top, $z = 0$ and $r = r_1 = 20$ mm (neglect the curvature at the bottom of the tube).

If N_A is the local flux of ethyl acetate vapour(A) through air(B),

$$\pi r^2 N_A = \text{constant} = W \text{ (say)} \tag{i}$$

The local flux can be written as [diffusion of A through non-diffusing B, see Eq. (2.72)]

$$N_A = \frac{D_{AB} P}{RT (P - p_A)} \frac{dp_A}{dz} \quad \text{and} \quad r = r_1 - \frac{r_1 - r_2}{L} z \tag{ii}$$

Substituting (ii) in (i) and integrating,

$$\frac{\pi D_{AB} P}{RT} \int_0^{p_A^v} \frac{dp_A}{P - p_A} = W \int_0^z \frac{dz}{[r_1 - (r_1 - r_2)z/L]^2}$$

On integration and simplification,

$$W = \frac{\pi D_{AB} P}{RT} \frac{r_1}{z} \left[r_1 - (r_1 - r_2)\left(\frac{z}{L}\right) \right] \ln \frac{P}{P - p_A^v} \tag{iii}$$

The initial rate of vaporization loss (when $z = 7.5$ cm), $W = \boxed{1.58 \times 10^{-10} \text{ kmol/s}}$

If the fall in the level of the liquid in time dt is dz, then

$$\left(\pi r^2 \frac{dz}{dt} \right) \frac{\rho_A}{M_A} = W \tag{iv}$$

Equation (ii) gives r in terms of z. Substituting for r and W in Eq. (iv), we get

$$\int_{z_1}^{z_2} z \left[r_1 - \frac{r_1 - r_2}{L} z \right] dz = \frac{D_{AB} P}{RT} \frac{M_A}{\rho_A} r_1 \ln \frac{P}{P - p_A^v} t$$

Integrate and put the values of the different quantities ($r_1 = 0.01$ m; $r_2 = 0.006$ m; $z_1 = 0.075$ m; $z_2 = 0.095$ m; $L = 0.15$ m; $P = 1.013$ bar; $p_A^v = 0.1264$ bar, etc.), and evaluate the integral and calculate the time.

Ans. $\boxed{79 \text{ h}}$

EXAMPLE 2.18 (*Diffusion through a converging-diverging region*)   Two 'large' vessels containing mixtures of $O_2(A)$ and $CO_2(B)$ are connected by a tube having converging and diverging sections as shown in Figure 2.18. The partial pressure of oxygen in vessel 1 is $p_{A1} = 0.3$ bar and that in vessel 2 is $p_{A2} = 0.1$ bar. The total pressure is 1.013 bar in both the vessels and the temperature is 20°C. Calculate the rate of diffusion of oxygen through the tube at steady state. What would be the partial pressure of carbon dioxide and its gradient at the neck (i.e. at the point of the smallest cross-section) of the connecting tube? *Given:* $D_{AB} = 0.153$ cm²/s; $r_1 = 5$ cm; $r_2 = 10$ cm; throat radius, $r = 2.5$ cm; length of the two sections, $l_1 = 12$ cm, $l_2 = 20$ cm.

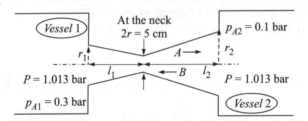

Figure 2.18   Equilmolar counterdiffusion through a converging-diverging section connecting two 'large' vessels.

Hints: The arrangement is shown in Figure 2.18. At steady state, equimolar counterdiffusion occurs through the tapered connecting tube. Also the rate of transport of oxygen from the cross-section 1 to the neck(n) is the same as that from the neck to cross-section 2. Recall Eq. (2.79). If p_{An} is the partial pressure of O_2 at the neck, we can use the condition of *continuity of the rate of transport* at that point at steady state.

$$W = \frac{\pi D_{AB}}{RT} \frac{r_1 r}{l_1} (p_{A1} - p_{An}) = \frac{\pi D_{AB}}{RT} \frac{r_2 r}{l_2} (p_{An} - p_{A2})$$

$$\Rightarrow \qquad p_{An} = \frac{r_1 l_2 p_{A1} + r_2 l_1 p_{A2}}{r_1 l_2 + r_2 l_1}$$

$$\Rightarrow \qquad W = \frac{\pi D_{AB}}{RT} \frac{r_1 r_2 r}{r_1 l_2 + r_2 l_1} (p_{A1} - p_{A2})$$

and

$$\left[\frac{dp_B}{dz} \right]_n = - \left[\frac{dp_A}{dz} \right]_n = \left[\frac{W}{\pi r^2} \frac{RT}{D_{AB}} \right]_n$$

2.8   KNUDSEN DIFFUSION, SURFACE DIFFUSION AND SELF-DIFFUSION

The kind of diffusion phenomena discussed so far relate to transport in the presence of a concentration (or partial pressure) gradient in a continuum. Knudsen diffusion and surface diffusion are two other important diffusional phenomena different from the above. These are illustrated in Figure 2.19. A simple illustration of diffusion in a continuum is also shown for comparison.

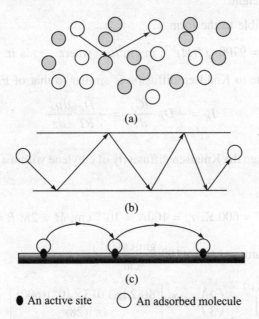

(a)

(b)

(c)

● An active site   ○ An adsorbed molecule

Figure 2.19   Illustration of (a) diffusion in a continuum, (b) Knudsen diffusion, and (c) surface diffusion.

2.8.1   Knudsen Diffusion

The movement of molecules in a mixture is governed by molecular velocity as well as collision with other molecules. Collision of the diffusing molecules with others present in the mixture offers the resistance to diffusion. If gas diffusion occurs in a very fine pore, particularly at a low pressure, the 'mean free path' of the molecules may be larger than the diameter of the passage. Then collision with the wall becomes much more frequent than collision with other molecules. The rate of diffusional transport of a species is now governed by its molecular velocity, the diameter of the passage and, of course, the gradient of concentration or partial pressure. This is called 'Knudsen diffusion' and becomes important if the pore size is normally below 50 nm. Such a situation commonly occurs for intra-particle transport in a catalyst containing fine pores.

A few models have been proposed to describe and quantify Knudsen diffusion. A simple approach based on the kinetic theory of gases yields the following expression for Knudsen diffusivity.

$$D_K = \left(\frac{2}{3}\right) r_p v_T \qquad\qquad (2.80)$$

where

r_p = radius of the passage or capillary

$v_T = \left(\dfrac{8RT}{\pi M} \right)^{1/2}$ = average velocity of the molecules by virtue of their thermal energy

T = temperature, in K

M = molecular weight.

Equation (2.80) is reducible to the form

$$D_k = 9700 r_p (T/M)^{1/2}, \text{ in cm}^2/\text{s}; \quad \text{where} \quad r_p \text{ is in cm} \tag{2.81}$$

The equation for flux due to Knudsen diffusion is similar to that of Fick's law.

$$J_K = -D_K \frac{dC_A}{dz} = -\frac{D_K}{RT} \frac{dp_A}{dz} \tag{2.82}$$

EXAMPLE 2.19   Estimate the Knudsen diffusivity of ethylene within a 100 Å pore of a catalyst at 600 K.

Solution

Use Eq. (2.80). *Given:* T = 600 K; r_p = 100Å = 10^{-6} cm; M = 28; R = 82.1 cm^3.atm/K.gmol.

$$1 \text{ atm} = 1.013 \times 10^6 \frac{\text{gm.cm/s}^2}{\text{cm}^2}$$

$$\Rightarrow \quad D_K = \frac{2}{3} r_p \left(\frac{8RT}{\pi M} \right)^{1/2} = \left(\frac{2}{3} \right)(10^{-6}) \left[\frac{8(82.1)(1.013 \times 10^6)(600)}{(\pi)(28)} \right]^{1/2} = \boxed{0.045 \text{ cm}^2/\text{s}}$$

2.8.2   Surface Diffusion

Surface diffusion is the transport of adsorbed molecules on a surface in the presence of a concentration gradient. Molecules adsorbed on a surface remain anchored to the active sites. If the fractional surface coverage (it is the ratio of the actual amount adsorbed to that required to form a monolayer) is less than unity, some of the active sites remain vacant. An adsorbed molecule tends to migrate to an adjacent empty site if it has sufficient energy to jump the energy barrier. Since the active sites are discrete, the migration or surface diffusion is visualized to occur by a 'hopping' or 'leap-frog' mechanism [Figure 2.19(c)]. Several models of surface diffusion have been proposed in the literature. The flux due to surface diffusion is given by a Fick's law-type equation, i.e.

$$J_s = -D_s \frac{dC_s}{dz} \tag{2.83}$$

where

D_s = surface diffusion coefficient, in m^2/s

C_s = surface concentration of the adsorbed molecules, in kmol/m^2.

The surface diffusion flux J_s is the number of moles transported across unit distance on the surface normal to the direction of transport (mol/m·s). The experimental values of D_s normally range between 10^{-4} and 10^{-5} cm²/s.

A brief review of Knudsen diffusion and surface diffusion is available in Do (1998).

2.8.3 Self-diffusion

The molecules of a gas or a liquid continuously move from one position to another. As a result of this continual motion, the molecules in a mixture of uniform composition also diffuse but the net rate of transport across any plane over a macroscopic time scale is zero. Self-diffusion refers to the diffusion of the molecules in a pure substance; the corresponding diffusion coefficient is called the 'self-diffusion coefficient' or 'self-diffusivity'. An approximate value of the self-diffusivity, D_{AA}, can be obtained by measuring the diffusivity of molecules of A having an atom substituted by its isotope in an otherwise pure A. Expectedly, the self-diffusion coefficient of a molecule is close to that in a mixture with similar molecules. For example, the self-diffusivity of liquid benzene is 2.2×10^{-9} m²/s at 25°C [Easteal et al., *AIChE J.*; *30* (1984) 641–642].

2.9   APPLICATIONS OF THE PRINCIPLES OF MOLECULAR DIFFUSION

The principles of molecular diffusion discussed in this chapter are used in a variety of scientific and engineering calculations. It is particularly important if the transport of a species occurs in a medium which is rather stagnant or in laminar motion. Even when the medium is turbulent, a laminar layer of fluid exists at the phase boundary in which transport by molecular diffusion has a dominating role to play. Transport in a porous medium occurs primarily by molecular diffusion. A very important example is the diffusion of reactants and products in a porous catalyst pellet. Besides normal pore diffusion, Knudsen diffusion and surface diffusion often play a very important role in determining the performance of a catalyst (Worstell, 2004). Above all, the principles of molecular diffusion form the basis of the study of fundamentals of mass transport.

NOTATIONS

The units mentioned against the following notations used in this book are not exclusive.

a	: cross-section of diffusion, m²
C_i	: molar concentration of the species i in a mixture, kmol/m³
C	: total molar concentration, kmol/m³
D_{AB}	: diffusivity of A in B, m²/s
D_{im}	: diffusivity of the ith species in a mixture, m²/s
J	: molar flux with respect to an observer moving with the molar average velocity, kmol/m²·s
L, l	: length of the diffusion path, m
M	: molecular weight

N_A	: molar flux of A with respect to a stationary observer, $kmol/m^2 \cdot s$
P	: total pressure, bar or atm
p_i	: partial pressure of the species i in a mixture, bar or atm
p_{BM}	: log mean partial pressure of B, bar or atm
r	: radial position, m
r_s	: radius of a sphere, m
r_s'	: radius of a sphere at time t', m
R	: universal gas constant, 0.08317 $(m^3)(bar)/(kmol)(K)$, 0.0821 $(m^3)(atm)/(kmol)(K)$
t	: time, s
T	: temperature, K
u_i	: molecular velocity of the species i with respect to a stationary observer, m/s
u	: mass average velocity of the components in a mixture, m/s
U	: molar average velocity of the components in a mixture, m/s
$v_{A,d}$	: diffusion velocity of species A [Eq. (2.18)], m/s
V	: volume of liquid/gas/vessel/compartment, m^3
x_i	: mole fraction of the species i in a (liquid) solution
y_i	: mole fraction of the species i in a gas mixture
z	: the longitudinal coordinate (in the direction of diffusion)
β	: cell constant of a diaphragm cell
δ	: thickness of a stagnant film, m
ε	: porosity of a medium, m^3 pore volume/m^3 of the medium; Lennard–Jones potential parameter
μ	: viscosity, cP, kg/m·s
τ	: tortuosity factor

Subscripts

1, 2	: locations 1 and 2 in a mixture
A, B	: components A or B in a mixture
i	: the ith component in a mixture
s	: surface

SHORT AND MULTIPLE CHOICE QUESTIONS

1. Give a few examples of occurrence of purely molecular diffusion in industrial processes.

2. Under what conditions are the mass average velocity and the molar average velocity of the components of a mixture equal?

3. Identify the vector and the scalar quantities from the following: (i) concentration, (ii) length of the diffusion path, (iii) concentration gradient, (iv) molar flux, (v) mass average velocity, (vi) partial pressure, and (vii) radial diffusional flux during vaporization of a droplet.

4. Give the English units of (i) diffusivity, (ii) molar flux, and (iii) concentration gradient.

5. Under what condition is the approximate form of Fick's law, Eq. (2.17), valid?

6. For what kind of solution/mixture we may take $D_{AB} = D_{BA}$?

7. Give a few practical situations (for example, in industries) that involve: (a) diffusion of A through non-diffusing B, (b) equimolar counterdiffusion.

8. Consider loss of ethanol vapour by diffusion from a half-filled open test tube. At what point in the diffusion path will the contribution of the bulk flow term to the molar flux be maximum?

9. Consider diffusion of A in non-diffusing B through a constant area from $z = z_1$, $p_A = p_{A1}$ to $z = z_2$, $p_A = p_{A2}$ ($p_{A1} > p_{A2}$). At which point in the diffusion path is the magnitude of the partial pressure gradient maximum?

10. Under what condition does the diffusivity of the component i in a multicomponent gas mixture (D_{im}) remain constant over the length of the diffusion path?

11. The species A is diffusing through non-diffusing B in a gas mixture. The terminal partial pressures of A are p_{A1} and p_{A2}. Does a point exist on the diffusion path of length L where the partial pressure gradient is $(p_{A1} - p_{A2})/L$?

12. Consider two cases of diffusion of A through a gaseous mixture of A and B: (i) B is non-diffusing, (ii) B undergoes equimolar counterdiffusion. All the parameters (P, T, D_{AB}, L, etc.) as well as the terminal partial pressures of A are the same in both the cases. In which case is the flux of A larger? Can you give a qualitative explanation?

13. How does the binary gas-phase diffusivity depend upon the total pressure and temperature? Can you give qualitative explanations?

14. A student attempts to measure the diffusivity of A in air by using the Stefan tube. The boiling point of A is only several degrees higher than the experimental temperature. Do you think that the pseudo-steady state approximation is valid in this case? Give a qualitative explanation.

15. How does the liquid-phase diffusivity of a solute depend upon the temperature and the viscosity of the medium?

16. Identify the correct answer to the following:

    (a) The molar average velocity of the components in a binary mixture in which they are in equimolar counterdiffusion is

        (i) equal to the mass average velocity

        (ii) zero

        (iii) always negative

        (iv) always positive.

    (b) Which of the following relations is correct for a gas mixture containing 40% CO_2, 50% C_3H_8 and 10% CH_3CHO at 1 atm and 40°C?

        (i) $u > U$ (ii) $u = U$ (iii) $u < U$

(c) The breathing process within the lungs involves
   (i) diffusion of A through non-diffusing B
   (ii) equimolar counterdiffusion
   (iii) multicomponent non-equimolar counterdiffusion.

(d) The gas-phase reaction $2A + B = C + D$ occurs on the surface of a catalyst pellet at steady state. What is the value of the flux ratio N_A/N_C?
   (i) -2 (ii) -0.5 (iii) 2

(e) A mixture of benzene(A) and chlorobenzene(B) is being separated by fractional distillation. If the heats of vaporization are $\Delta H_A^v = 94$ kcal/kg and $\Delta H_B^v = 78$ kcal/kg, what is the ratio of N_A/N_B across the vapour film?
   (i) -0.83 (ii) -1.0 (iii) -1.2

(f) Equimolar counterdiffusion of A and B occurs between points 1 ($y_{A1} = 0.3$) and 2 ($y_{A2} = 0.1$) through a distance of 1 cm. *Given:* $P = 1$ atm and $D_{AB} = 0.2$ cm^2/s, what is the 'diffusion velocity' of A halfway in the diffusion path?
   (i) 2 mm/s   (ii) 2 cm/s   (iii) 0.2 m/s

(g) The gas A diffuses through non-diffusing B from point 1 to point 2. *Given:* $P = 2$ atm; $y_{A1} = 0.1$; $y_{A2} = 0$. Then the ratio $(dp_A/dz)_1/(dp_A/dz)_2$ is
   (i) 10   (ii) 1.11   (iii) 0.9

(h) Consider the preceding problem (g). The length of the diffusion path is 5 mm and the partial pressure gradient of A midway in the film is $dp_A/dz = -7$ atm/m. What is the partial pressure gradient of B at that point?
   (i) -14 atm/m   (ii) -7 atm/m   (iii) 7 atm/m

(i) Two glass bulbs (volume of bulb 1 is 5 lit; bulb 2, 10 lit) are connected by a narrow tube. Bulb 1 is filled with gas A, and bulb 2 with gas B, both at 1 atm pressure. Equimolar counterdiffusion of A and B starts. The initial flux of A is $(N_A)_I$. After 10 hours, half of A diffuses out from bulb 1 to bulb 2 and the flux becomes $(N_A)_{II}$. Pseudo-steady state prevails. The ratio $(N_A)_I/(N_A)_{II}$ is
   (i) 0.5   (ii) 2.0   (iii) 4.0

(j) Consider steady-state equimolar counterdiffusion through the converging-diverging tube shown in Figure 2.18. *Given:* $r_1 = 1$ cm; $r_2 = 2$ cm; $N_A = 10^{-6}$ kmol/m^2·s at the vessel 1 end of the tube. The rate of transport of B at the vessel 2 end of the tube is
   (i) 2×10^{-6} kmol/s, towards vessel 1
   (ii) 2.5×10^{-7} kmol/s, towards vessel 1
   (iii) 5×10^{-7} kmol/s, towards vessel 2.

(k) Two large vessels containing gaseous mixtures of A and B at different concentrations but at the same total pressure are connected by a tapered tube of length 15 cm and end diameters 1 cm and 4 cm. What should be the diameter of a cylindrical tube of the same length that allows the same rate of transport of A?
   (i) 2.5 cm   (ii) 2 cm   (iii) 3 cm

(l) At which of the following locations in the tapered tube of the preceding problem (k) is the magnitude of flux of B maximum?

   (i) At the larger diameter end

   (ii) At the smaller diameter end

   (iii) Midway in the tube

(m) Equimolar counterdiffusion of A and B occurs through a spherical film of i.d. $= r_i$ and thickness δ. The flux of A is $(N_A)_I$ at $r = r_i$. The flux through a flat film of the same thickness is $(N_A)_{II}$. If $(N_A)_I$ is larger than $(N_A)_{II}$ by 5%, the film thickness δ is

   (i) $0.025r_i$ (ii) $0.05r_i$ (iii) $0.1r_i$.

(n) A naphthalene hemisphere is placed on a glass plate and a naphthalene ball of identical diameter is kept suspended in the stagnant air in two large rooms. The respective shapes of the balls are maintained while they sublime and reduce in size. Which of the following statements are true in this connection?

   (i) They take the same time for complete sublimation.

   (ii) The sphere disappears first.

   (iii) The hemisphere disappears first.

(o) Sublimation of a *long* cylinder made of naphthalene occurs in a large volume of stagnant air. The time required for its complete sublimation is

   (i) infinite

   (ii) half the time of sublimation of a sphere of the same mass

   (iii) twice the time of sublimation of a cylinder of the same mass and length/diameter = 1.

(p) Which of the following is a probable value of D_{AB} for CO_2–N_2 binary at 50°C, 2 atm?

   (i) $20 \ cm^2/s$ (ii) $2.25 \ ft^2/h$ (iii) $10^{-5} \ m^2/s$

(q) Which of the following is a probable value of the diffusivity of ethanol in chloroform vapour at 15°C and 1 atm pressure?

   (i) $8.5 \times 10^{-5} \ ft^2/h$ (ii) $1.1 \times 10^6 \ mm^2/h$ (iii) $0.136 \ cm^2/s$

(r) Which of the following solutes has the highest diffusivity in water?

   (i) *tert*-butanol   (ii) *iso*-propanol   (iii) methanol

(s) Which of the following gas pairs has the lowest mutual diffusivity?

   (i) CH_3OH–Air   (ii) CH_3OH–CO_2 (iii) CH_3OH–H_2

(t) The species A diffuses in a gaseous A–B binary from point $z = 0$, $y_A = y_{A0}$ to $z = l$, $y_A = y_{Al}$ at temperature T and total pressure P. The total pressure is now doubled, but the mole fractions of A at the two locations and the temperature of the medium remain the same as before. What would be the fractional increase in the flux of A?

   (i) It will be doubled.

   (ii) It will be halved.

   (iii) It will remain unchanged.

(u)   The diffusivity of acetone in water at a low concentration at 25°C is 1.16×10^{-9} m^2/s. What would be the diffusivity at 60°C? The viscosity values of the solvent (water) are 0.9 cP at 25°C, and 0.48 cP at 60°C.

   (i) 2.34×10^{-9} m^2/s (ii) 1.95×10^{-9} m^2/s (iii) 6.9×10^{-10} m^2/s

(v)   The diffusivity of argon in nitrogen at 20°C and 1 atm pressure is 0.194 cm^2/s. What would be the diffusivity of N_2 in Ar at 50°C and 2.5 atm?

   (i) 0.194 cm^2/s (ii) 0.09 cm^2/s (iii) 0.535 cm^2/s

(w)   How does the velocity of the gas–liquid interface in a Stefan tube change with the depth of the gas space above the interface?

   (i)   Changes directly
   (ii)   Changes inversely
   (iii)   Is independent of depth

(x)   Which of the following diffusion phenomenon can be explained by a hopping mechanism?

   (i)   Surface diffusion
   (ii)   Knudsen diffusion
   (iii)   Multicomponent diffusion

(y)   Which of the following is an approximate range of surface diffusion coefficient?

   (i) $1–10$ cm^2/s (ii) $0.01–0.001$ cm^2/s (iii) $10^{-4}–10^{-5}$ cm^2/s

(z)   In which of the following situations the Knudsen diffusion is expected to be important?

   (i)   Liquid-phase diffusion in large pores
   (ii)   Gas-phase diffusion in a very fine capillary at a low pressure
   (iii)   Diffusion in a molten metal

PROBLEMS

2.1   **(*Diffusion of A through non-diffusing B*)**[1]   Water is evaporating from the placid surface of a lake and the vapour(A) diffuses through a stagnant film of air(B) of estimated thickness 3 mm. The water temperature is 23°C and the air temperature is 27°C. The relative humidity of air is 65%. If the diffusivity of water vapour through air is 0.257 cm^2/s at 23°C and 0.262 cm^2/s at 27°C, calculate the rate of evaporation. The vapour pressure of water can be calculated using the Antoine equation given in Example 2.2.

2.2   **(*Diffusion of A through non-diffusing B*)**[1]   The water level in a large concrete reservoir is found to drop by 20 mm over a period of 10 days. The average temperature of water is 23°C and the average humidity of the bulk air is 0.0135 kg per kg dry air. Permeation through the concrete may be neglected. If loss of vapour occurs through a stagnant film of air, calculate the thickness of this film. The diffusivity of moisture in air under the given condition is 1.0 ft^2/h and the vapour pressure of water can be calculated using the Antoine equation given in Problem 2.1.

2.3 (*Diffusion of A through non-diffusing B*)[1]   In a sulphuric acid plant, the air used for burning sulphur must be dry. Drying of air is done by countercurrent contact with concentrated sulphuric acid in a packed tower. At a particular section of the tower, the relative humidity of air is 30% and the temperature is 35°C. If moisture in the air diffuses to the surface of the acid through a stagnant film of thickness 1.2 mm, calculate the flux of moisture at the given section. The partial pressure of moisture at the acid surface is zero because the concentrated acid has an extremely high affinity for moisture. The diffusivity value is given in Table 2.1, and the vapour pressure equation is given in Example 2.2.

2.4 (*Flux and partial pressure gradient in diffusion of A through non-diffusing B*)[1]
Ammonia is being absorbed from an ammonia(*A*)–air(*B*) mixture in sulphuric acid. The concentration of ammonia in the air 10 mm from the acid surface is 40% by volume and that at the acid surface is negligible. The total pressure in the system is 400 mm Hg and the temperature is 300 K. Calculate (a) the rate of absorption of ammonia across 0.1 m^2 gas liquid contact area, (b) the partial pressure gradient of ammonia at 4 mm from the acid surface, and (c) the rate of mass transfer of ammonia by molecular transport and that by bulk flow at the two ends of the film.

2.5 (*Diffusion of A through non-diffusing B*)[1]   A test tube, 1.5 cm in diameter and 12 cm long, has 0.4 g camphor in it. How long will it take for the camphor to disappear? The pressure is atmospheric and the temperature is 20°C. The sublimation pressure of camphor at this temperature is 97.5 mm Hg, and the diffusivity of camphor can be estimated by using the Fuller's equation, Eq. (2.57).

2.6 (*Diffusion of A through non-diffusing B, spherical film*)[2]   An absorbent sphere of a basic oxide is kept suspended in a large volume of a mixture of 70% air and 30% CO_2 at 40°C and 1 atmosphere total pressure. The bulk gas is well-stirred and diffusion of CO_2 to the surface of the absorbent occurs through a stagnant gas-film of 3.5 mm thickness surrounding the sphere. The radius of the sphere is much larger than the thickness of the gas-film. Because CO_2 is quickly absorbed on reaching the surface of the sphere, its concentration there is essentially zero. Calculate the flux of CO_2 and its diffusion velocity midway in the gas-film. The diffusivity of CO_2 in air at 25°C and 1 atm is 1.62×10^{-5} m^2/s.

2.7 (*Equimolar counter-diffusion, variable area*)[2]   Two well-mixed vessels of volume V_1 and V_2 are connected by a tube, 1 cm in diameter and 6 cm in length, fitted with a plug valve. The vessels are filled with mixtures of N_2 and CO_2 at 30°C and 1.013 bar total pressure. The partial pressures of N_2 in the vessels are 10^4 Pa and 8×10^4 Pa respectively. The valve is opened and the gases are allowed to diffuse through the connecting tube.

(a) Calculate the molar flux of N_2 with respect to a stationary observer if the vessels are very large. Also calculate the molar flux midway in the tube with respect to an observer moving at the average velocity of the N_2 molecules in the direction from vessel 1 to vessel 2.

(b) Calculate the rate of transport if the connecting tube is tapered having end diameters 10 mm (vessel 1 side) and 20 mm (vessel 2 side) and is 6 cm in length.

(c)   Recalculate the change in the rate of transport in part (b) if the tube joins the vessels in the reverse way (i.e. the 20 mm end is connected to vessel 1).

(d)   Consider case (a). If the vessels have limited volumes ($V_1 = 5$ litres and $V_2 = 3$ litres), calculate the time required for the partial pressure of N_2 in vessel 1 to be doubled. Also calculate the partial pressure of N_2 midway of the connecting tube after 20 hours. Pseudo-steady state diffusion may be assumed.

2.8   (*Non-equimolar counterdiffusion*)[1]   Determine the rates of the following reactions (based on unit surface area of the catalyst) occurring on a flat catalyst surface at a temperature T and total pressure P.

(a)   Isomerization reaction of the type $A \rightarrow B$

(b)   Dimerization reaction of the type $2A \rightarrow B$

(c)   Decomposition reaction of the type $2A \rightarrow 3B$

It is assumed that (a) the reactions are all diffusion-controlled, i.e. the concentration of A at the catalyst surface is negligibly small, (b) the diffusion of the gases occurs through a stagnant gas-film of thickness δ, and (c) the partial pressure of B in the bulk gas is p_{B0}.

2.9   (*Equimolar counterdiffusion at pseudo-steady state*)[2]   A 2-litre bulb contains carbon dioxide gas at atmospheric pressure and 25°C. The bulb has a side tube, 3 cm long and 5 mm in diameter, open to the ambient (Figure 2.20) at the same temperature and pressure. How long will it take for half of the gas to diffuse out of the bulb if the transport occurs at pseudo-steady state? The temperature is 25°C and the pressure is atmospheric. The diffusivity of CO_2 in air is 1.62×10^{-5} m^2/s.

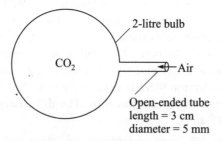

Figure 2.20   Diffusion of CO_2 from a bulb.

2.10   (*Multicomponent diffusion*)[3]   In an experiment on the kinetics of catalytic oxidation of carbon monoxide to carbon dioxide on the surface of a noble metal catalyst, the composition of the bulk gas is 20% CO, 20% O_2 and 60% CO_2, the temperature is 250°C and the total pressure is atmospheric. The reaction being very fast, the concentration of carbon monoxide is negligible at the surface of the catalyst. If the gases diffuse through a stagnant film, 0.8 mm thick, at the surface of the catalyst, calculate the rate of formation of carbon dioxide. Take the binary diffusivity values from Table 2.1.

2.11   (*Multicomponent diffusion*)[3]   A mixture of NH_3 and N_2 having 10 mole % NH_3 at 1 atm total pressure and 450°C flows over a hot surface coated with CuO. The flow rate of the gas is large enough so that the concentration of moisture in the bulk gas is negligible. If the reaction is diffusion-controlled

$$3CuO + 2NH_3(1) \quad \rightarrow \quad N_2(2) + 3H_2O(3) + Cu$$

and diffusion of NH_3 to the solid surface occurs through a gas-film 2 mm thick, calculate the rate of reaction of NH_3. The binary diffusivities at the given condition are:

$$D_{12} = 0.953, \ D_{23} = 1.107, \text{ and } D_{13} = 1.484 \text{ cm}^2/\text{s}.$$

2.12 (*Multicomponent diffusion*)[3] In an experimental apparatus CO_2 and H_2S are being absorbed in an alkaline solution from a gas mixture containing 20% CO_2(1), 10% H_2S(2) and 70% CH_4(3) at 30°C and 5 atm total pressure. The diffusion of the solutes occurs through a stagnant gas-film of 2 mm thickness. The concentrations of the solutes (CO_2 and H_2S) at the gas–liquid interface are negligibly small. Calculate the rates of absorption of the gases. The following binary diffusivity values are given:

$$D_{12} = 0.0303, \ D_{23} = 0.0417, \text{ and } D_{13} = 0.0367 \text{ cm}^2/\text{s}.$$

2.13 (*Multicomponent diffusion*)[2] Carbon dioxide is being absorbed in a strongly alkaline solution from a gas mixture containing 12% CO_2(1), 22% N_2(2) and 66% H_2(3). Nitrogen and hydrogen are virtually insoluble. Calculate the rate of absorption through a gas-film of 1.5 mm thickness if the ratio of volume fractions of N_2 and H_2 remains constant over the diffusion path. The temperature is 50°C and the total pressure is 5 bar. Assume that CO_2 reaching the solution is absorbed instantaneously.

2.14 (*Diffusion of A through non-diffusing B, pseudo-steady state*)[1] A test tube, 15 mm in diameter and 15 cm tall, half-full of ethyl acetate(*A*) has been kept open to air(*B*) in the laboratory. What is the diffusion flux of the ester at the beginning if pseudo-steady state condition prevails? How long will it take for the level to drop down to 7 cm measured from the bottom of the test tube? The temperature is 25°C and the ambient pressure is 1.013 bar. *Given:* the vapour pressure of ethyl acetate at 25°C = 0.1264 bar, its diffusivity in air at the given condition is $D_{AB} = 0.0866 \text{ cm}^2/\text{s}$ and the density of the liquid is 900 kg/m^3. [*Hints:* Equation (2.52) may be directly used.]

2.15 (*Gas-phase diffusivity, twin-bulb technique*)[2] In an attempt to measure the diffusivity of ammonia in nitrogen by the twin-bulb method, a student filled the two bulbs (each of volume 5 litre and connected by a tube 8 cm long and 3 cm in diameter) with mixtures of the gases. The initial partial pressures of NH_3 in the bulbs were 0.725 and 0.275 atm. At the end of 5.7 hours, he took samples of the gases from the bulbs. The analysis of the samples showed that the mole fractions of ammonia in the bulbs were 0.543 and 0.457 respectively. The total pressures in the bulbs were maintained at 1 atm and the temperature was 30°C. Calculate the diffusivity of NH_3 in the mixture from these data and compare with the literature value of 0.237 cm^2/s at the given temperature and pressure. [*Hints:* Use the integrated form of Eq. (2.49) for the given conditions.]

2.16 (*Estimation of gas-phase diffusivity*)[1] Estimate the diffusivities in the following cases:

(a) Mutual diffusivity of (i) NH_3 and H_2O vapour at 100°C and 1 atm, (ii) H_2S and N_2 at 25°C and 1 atm, and (iii) ethylene oxide and air at 25°C and 1 atm (use the Fuller's equation)

(b)   Mutual diffusivity of n-hexane and O_2 at 1 atm and 50°C (use the Chapman–Enskog equation) and compare with the experimental value of 0.0753 cm²/s at 0°C and 1 atm (Perry, 1997).

2.17 (*Liquid-phase diffusion at a low concentration*)[1]   Oxygen(A) diffuses through a stagnant film of water(B), 0.5 mm thick, at 25°C. The concentrations of dissolved oxygen on two sides of the film are 0.0144 kg/m³ and 0.008 kg/m³ respectively. Calculate the flux of oxygen using (a) the integrated form of Eq. (2.14) and (b) the integrated form of Eq. (2.18), i.e. neglecting the bulk flow term. Comment on the values you calculate. The diffusivity of O_2 in water is given in Table 2.5.

2.18 (*Concentration-dependent diffusivity*)[2]   The solute A diffuses through the liquid B from point 1 to 2, distance l apart. The concentrations of the solute at the two points are C_{A1} and C_{A2} respectively. Determine the diffusional flux if the diffusivity of A in B depends upon its concentration in the form $D_{AB} = K_1 + K_2 C_A$. Consider both the cases of diffusion of (a) A through non-diffusing B and (b) equimolar counterdiffusion of A and B.

2.19 (*Estimation of liquid-phase diffusivity*)[1]   Estimate the diffusivity of (a) methanol in water, (b) ethylene oxide in water, and (c) benzene in ethanol at 25°C using the Wilke–Chang equation. Compare with the experimental values given in Table 2.5. Estimate the molar volume (cm³/gmol) of the solute at the normal boiling point using the Tyn and Clous correlation, $V_b = 0.285 V_c^{1.048}$, where V_c is the critical volume, cm³/gmol (get the necessary data from Poling et al., 2001).

2.20 (*Liquid-phase diffusivity by diaphragm cell*)[2]   A diaphragm cell has two compartments of volumes 45.2 cm³ and 46 cm³, and the fritted glass diaphragm is 2.8 cm in diameter and 1.8 mm thick. In an experiment for calibration of the cell, the smaller compartment is filled with 1.0 molar KCl solution and the larger compartment with water. Diffusion is allowed to occur at 25°C. At the end of 44 h 30 min, the concentration of KCl in the smaller compartment drops down to 0.80 molar.

Now the cell is thoroughly washed and the smaller compartment is filled with 1.0 molar methanol while water is taken in the other compartment. Diffusion occurs at the same temperature for the same period of time. If the concentration of methanol at the end is 0.815 molar in the smaller compartment, calculate its diffusivity in water. The diffusivity of KCl in water is known to be 1.86×10^{-9} m²/s at 25°C.

2.21 (*Liquid-phase diffusion in a diaphragm cell*)[2]   The following data on a diaphragm cell are available: compartment volumes—50.2 and 51 cm³; diaphragm diameter = 2.1 cm; thickness = 0.18 cm. At the beginning of an experiment, the larger compartment is filled with 0.9 molar aqueous acetic acid at 25°C and the smaller one with water. At the end of 50 h, the concentration in the smaller compartment is 0.0816 molar. The diffusivity of acetic acid in water at 25°C is 1.2×10^{-5} cm²/s. If the porosity of the diaphragm is 0.35, calculate the tortuosity of the pores.

2.22 (*Diffusion through a spherical film*)[2]   Redo Problem 2.8 for the case of a spherical catalyst pellet of radius r_s. All other quantities including the gas-film thickness remain the same. Explain qualitatively why the rate of reaction in each case is different for the two geometries although the parameters remain unchanged.

2.23 (*Equimolar counterdiffusion through a spherical film*)[2]   A sphere of pure carbon, 12 mm in diameter, burns in a flowing stream of oxygen gas. The sphere is surrounded by a stagnant film of gas of an estimated thickness of 3 mm. The average temperature of the gas-film is 1300°C and the total pressure is 1 atmosphere. The product of combustion is assumed to be CO_2 only and its partial pressure in the bulk gas is 0.2 atmosphere. Calculate (a) the initial rate of combustion and (b) the time required for the size of the carbon sphere to get reduced to 8 mm. The diffusivity of CO_2 in O_2 at the given condition = 3.4 cm²/s; density of the carbon sphere = 900 kg/m³. Assume that diffusion occurs at pseudo-steady state and that the thickness of the stagnant gas-film remains unchanged even when the size of the carbon sphere decreases.

2.24 (*Sublimation time of a volatile solid*)[2]   Calculate the time of sublimation of 80% of the mass of a 15 mm diameter sphere of naphthalene in air if the sphere is always surrounded by a 4 mm thick stagnant film of air. The temperature is 35°C and the pressure is 1 atm. The diffusivity of naphthalene vapour in air under the given conditions is 0.0892 cm²/s, the density of solid naphthalene is 1140 kg/m³, and its vapour pressure at 35°C is 0.4303 mm Hg.

2.25 (*Vaporization of a drop in a stagnant medium*)[2]   A drop of ethanol, 2 mm in diameter, suspended at the end of a thin wire, vaporizes in the ambient air (1.013 bar, 30°C). The temperature of the drop undergoing vaporization is estimated to be 18°C. The thickness of the stagnant air-film surrounding the drop is estimated to be 1.5 mm under the prevailing condition. Assuming that the thickness of the film remains unchanged, calculate the time required for the drop size to reduce to 1 mm. Also calculate the time required for disappearance of the drop if the ambient air is totally stagnant. Vapour pressure of ethanol at 18°C is 0.0516 bar; liquid density = 789 kg/m³; molecular weight = 46. The diffusivity of ethanol in air is 0.102 cm²/s at 0°C.

2.26 (*Diffusion through a cylindrical film*)[3]   In the solvent recovery system of a film coating unit, toluene vapour is recovered from a nitrogen stream by condensation followed by adsorption in an active carbon bed. The 19 mm diameter tubes (i.d. = 15.8 mm) of the vertical condenser used for the purpose are cooled by DM (*demineralized*) chilled water flowing through the shell. The gas flows through the tubes and condensation occurs on the inner surfaces of the tubes.

At a particular section of a condenser tube, the temperature of the film of liquid toluene is 6.5°C and the temperature of the gas is 15°C. The partial pressure of toluene in the bulk gas is 25 mm Hg and transport of toluene from the bulk gas to the surface of the falling condensate film occurs by molecular diffusion through a stagnant gas layer of 3 mm thickness. If the total pressure is 1.2 bar, calculate the rate of condensation per metre length of the tube. The vapour pressure of toluene at 6.5°C is 10 mm Hg and the thickness of the condensate film is small. The diffusivity of toluene in N_2 at the mean film temperature may be estimated using the Fuller's equation.

2.27 (*Vapour loss from a spherical vessel*)[3]   A spherical container, 0.8 m in diameter, is half-full of benzene. The cap of the 70 mm diameter opening at the top of the tank was not put in place by mistake causing vapour loss through the opening (Figure 2.21). Calculate the rate of loss of benzene by molecular diffusion if the pseudo-steady state condition is assumed to apply. The temperature is 25°C and the pressure is 1 atmosphere. The cap is very short and diffusion through the open space within the vessel needs only to be considered. The vapour pressure of benzene at 25°C is 0.127 bar.

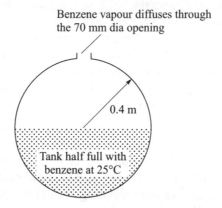

Figure 2.21   Loss of benzene vapour through the opening at the top of a tank.

2.28   (*Diffusion through a spherical film*)[3]   Consider diffusion of A in a binary mixture of A and B to the surface of a sphere of radius r through a surrounding stagnant gas-film of thickness δ. Calculate the range of values of δ/r for which the rate of transport is within 95% of that calculated by neglecting the curvature of the stagnant gas-film. Repeat the calculation for a long cylinder of radius r.

2.29   (*Diffusion and vapour loss in a carrier gas*)[3]   A cylindrical 6-litre vessel (vessel 1) is half-full of ethanol at 20°C and 1 atm pressure. The vessel is connected by a tubing to another large vessel (vessel 2) containing the same liquid (Figure 2.22) so that the liquid depth in it remains unchanged even if some evaporation loss occurs (this means that the volume of the open space in the vessel remains constant). The upper-half of vessel 1 contains N_2 *saturated with ethanol* vapour at the given temperature. Nitrogen gas at 20°C is now passed through the vessel (see the figure) at a rate of 4 litre per minute. Vaporization of ethanol occurs simultaneously by diffusion through a stagnant gas-film on the liquid surface of estimated thickness 2.5 mm. The diameter of the vessel is 0.16 m, the vapour pressure of ethanol at 20°C is 0.058 bar, and the diffusivity of ethanol in N_2 is 1.02×10^{-5} cm^2/s.

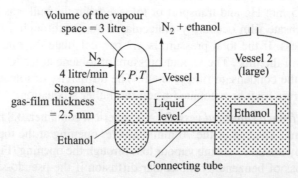

Figure 2.22   Ethanol vapour is carried away by passing N_2 through the vapour space of vessel 1.

(a) How long will it take (assuming pseudo-steady state) for the partial pressure of ethanol in the gas space to drop to 0.045 bar? (b) Calculate the partial pressure of ethanol in the gas space in the vessel at steady state.

2.30 (*Pseudo-steady state diffusion*)[3] Two bulbs of volume 1 litre each are joined by a 3 cm long and 2 cm diameter tube provided with a plug valve. Bulb 1 is filled with pure $N_2(B)$ and bulb 2 with N_2 containing 5% $NH_3(A)$. At time $t = 0$, nitrogen gas with 10% ammonia in it starts flowing through bulb 1 at a rate of 2 litre per hour and the plug valve is simultaneously opened to allow diffusion to start. The bulbs are well-mixed all the time and diffusion through the connecting tube occurs at pseudo-steady state. When does the flux through the connective tube become zero? What happens after that? The temperature is 25°C and the total pressure is always atmospheric. The arrangement is shown in Figure 2.23. The diffusivity of NH_3 in N_2 is 2.3×10^{-5} m²/s.

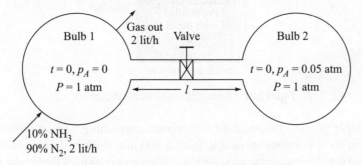

Figure 2.23 A sketch of the two-bulb assembly.

2.31 (*Non-equimolar counterdiffusion*)[2] Carbon monoxide gas reacts with metallic nickel at nearly room temperature to form nickel carbonyl, $Ni(CO)_4$. Reduced nickel is very active.

$$Ni + 4CO = Ni(CO)_4$$

Carbon monoxide diffuses to a nickel sheet through a gas-film of thickness 2 mm at 40°C and 1 atm. The carbonyl forms instantly and diffuses to the bulk gas that contains 60% CO nad 40% $Ni(CO)_4$ by volume. If the diffusivity of $Ni(CO)_4$ in CO is 1.91×10^{-5} m²/s, calculate the rate of formation of the compound per unit gas–solid contact area.

2.32 Consider Example 2.6 and calculate (a) the velocity of the observer who finds a zero mass flux and (b) the velocity of the observer at midway in the tube who finds oxygen molecules non-diffusing.

2.33. (*Diffusion of a hydrocarbon through contaminated soil*)[2] Evaporation of volatile organics from soil is important in connection with 'remediation' of contaminated soils. An example is evaporation of gasoline or diesel from soils contaminated with such substances by leakage from underground storage tanks. The pores of soil get filled by the leaking liquid. Kang and Oulman [*J. Environ. Eng.*, *122* (May 1996) 384–386] tested evaporation of *n*-heptane, gasoline and diesel from soils contaminated with these liquids separately. They observed that with progress of evaporation from a contaminated soil exposed to air, the interface between the liquid in the pores and the gas gradually recedes within the soil. Further, the movement of the interface was found to follow the equation for the drop in liquid level in the Stefan tube [Eq. (2.52), for example]. The phenomenon is sketched in Figure 2.24.

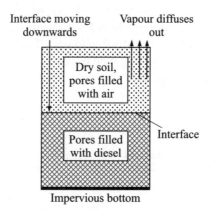

Figure 2.24   Transport of diesel vapour through soil.

A sample of soil contaminated with diesel, containing 143 kg diesel per m³ soil, is spread on an impervious surface to form a 100 mm thick bed exposed to air. Given the following data, calculate the time for complete vaporization of the liquid. Equation (2.52) may be used after necessary modification.

Data: porosity of the soil = 0.4; temperature = 25°C (assumed constant); pressure = 1 atm; vapour pressure of diesel at 25°C = 0.268 mm Hg; average molecular weight of diesel = 200; the diffusivity of diesel vapour in air = 6.28 mm²/s.

REFERENCES

Chapman, S., and T.G. Cowling, *The Mathematical Theory of Nonuniform Gases*, 3rd ed., Cambridge University Press, 1970.

Cussler, E.L., *Diffusion: Mass Transfer in Fluid Systems*, 2nd ed., Cambridge University Press, New York, 1997.

Cussler, E.L., *Multicomponent Diffusion*, Elsevier, Amsterdam, 1976.

Do, D.D., *Adsorption Analysis: Equilibria and Kinetics*, Imperial College Press, London, 1998.

Dullien, F.A.L., and L.W. Shemilt, 'Diffusion coefficient for the liquid system ethanol–water', *Canad. J. Chem. Eng.*, *39*(1961) 242–247.

Fuller, E.N., P.D. Schettler, and J.C. Giddings, *Ind. Eng. Chem.*, *58*(1966) 19.

Hayduk, W., and B.S. Minhas, *Canad. J. Chem. Eng.*, *60*(1982) 295.

Haynes, H.W., 'A note on diffusive mass transport', *Chem. Eng. Education*, Winter 1986, 22–27.

Hines, A.L., and R.N. Maddox, *Mass Transfer—Fundamentals and Applications*, Prentice Hall, 1985.

Kraaijeveld G., and J.A. Wesselingh, 'Negative Maxwell–Stefan diffusion coefficients', *Ind. Eng. Chem. Res., 32*(1973) 738–742.

Krishna, R., and G.L. Standardt, *AIChE J., 1*(1976) 383–389.

Leffler, J., and H.T. Cullinan, *Ind. Eng. Chem. Fundamantals, 9*(1970) 84, 88.

Perry's *Chemical Engineers' Handbook*, 7th ed., McGraw-Hill, New York, 1997.

Poling, E.B., J.M. Prausnitz, and J.P. O'Connell, *The Properties of Gases and Liquids*, 5th ed., McGraw-Hill, New York, 2001.

Prigogine, I., *Introduction to Thermodynamics of Irreversible Processes*, 3rd ed., Interscience, New York, 1967.

Skelland, A.H.P., *Diffusional Mass Transfer*, John Wiley, New York, 1974.

Taylor, R., and R. Krishna, *Multicomponent Mass Transfer*, Wiley, New York, 1993.

Toor, H.L., *AIChE J., 10*(1964) 460–465.

Wesselingh, J.A., and R. Krishna, *Mass Transfer*, Ellis Horwood, 1990.

Wilke, C.R., and P. Chang, *AIChE J., 1*(1955) 264.

Worstell, J.H., 'Improve fixed-bed reactor performance', *Chem. Eng. Prog.*, Jan 2004, 51–57.

3 | Convective Mass Transfer and Mass Transfer Coefficient

While preparing a cup of black coffee you take a spoonful of sugar and a little instant coffee in a cup, add hot water and stir it with the spoon for about fifteen seconds. The coffee is ready for you. The crystals of sugar and the particles of coffee have dissolved quickly and the content is homogeneous. But if the water is left unstirred, it takes more time for the sugar to dissolve and a much longer time for the liquid to be uniform in concentration. What message does this convey to us? Dissolution of a solid occurs slowly in a stagnant medium—molecular diffusion having a major or sometimes the governing role in the process. But the rate of dissolution or, in other words, the rate of mass transfer increases dramatically if there is motion in the medium. This occurs because of convection. Mass transfer occurring under the influence of motion in a fluid medium is called 'convective mass transfer'. We may try to *visualize* a simple *mechanism* of dissolution of the sugar crystals in a stirred cup of water. The water just in contact with a crystal (or, in other words, the liquid at the 'solid–liquid interface') gets saturated with sugar almost instantly. Here 'interface' means the contact surface between the two phases. The dissolved sugar diffuses from the interface to the bulk liquid through a thin layer or 'film' of the solution adhering to the crystal. More sugar dissolves in the liquid simultaneously at the interface. The 'thickness' of the film that we visualize decreases if the stirring rate is more rapid. The more brisk the motion of the liquid is, the thinner is the film and the quicker is the rate of dissolution or the rate of mass transfer. The picture we visualize is schematically represented in Figure 3.1.

In the previous chapter, we discussed the methods of calculation of the rate of mass transfer due to molecular diffusion. Now we are faced with another question: how to calculate the mass transfer rate when there is bulk motion, particularly turbulent motion, in the medium? And, how can we calculate the rate of 'convective mass transfer'? In this chapter, we shall address these questions.

Before we go further into this issue, let us discuss a little the modes of convective mass transfer. Similar to the case of convective heat transfer, convective mass transfer may be of two types—*forced convection mass transfer* and *free convection* (or natural convection) *mass transfer*. In the former case, the motion or flow in the medium is caused by an external agency (for example, a pump, a blower, an agitator, etc.). In free convection mass transfer, on the other hand, the motion in the medium is caused by a difference in the density. Let us elaborate this point

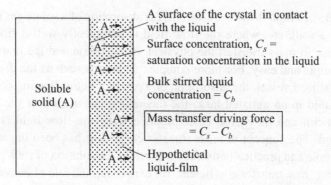

Figure 3.1 Visualization of the dissolution process of a solid.

a little further. Consider a sugar cube suspended in a glass of water [Figure 3.2(a)]. Sugar dissolves, the concentration of the liquid near the surface increases and its density increases as a result. But the density of the liquid below the sugar cube is less. Thus, a *density difference* is created. This causes a motion in the medium in the form of free convection currents and thereby enhances the rate of mass transfer. However, if the sugar cube rests at the bottom, the density of the liquid at the bottom will be more than that at the top. No buoyancy force comes into play in this case and there is no free convection mass transfer [Figure 3.2(b)]. Free convection mass transfer will not be dealt with in this text. The interested readers are referred to Skelland (1974).

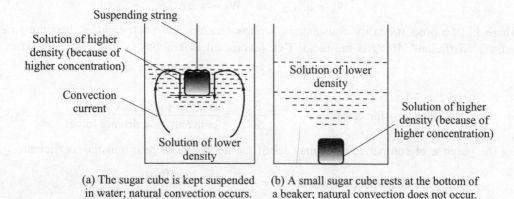

(a) The sugar cube is kept suspended in water; natural convection occurs.

(b) A small sugar cube rests at the bottom of a beaker; natural convection does not occur.

Figure 3.2 (a) Natural convection occurs due to adverse density gradient; (b) higher density at the bottom, no natural convection.

The mechanism is similar to that in the case of free convection heat transfer in which the density difference is caused by a temperature difference. In free convection mass transfer, it is the concentration difference that creates the density difference.

Convective mass transfer is strongly influenced by the flow field. If the flow field is 'well-defined', it is possible to calculate the mass transfer rate by solving the differential equations obtained from mass and momentum balance. Typical examples are (i) the dissolution of a solid coated on a flat plate in a fluid flowing over it, (ii) the absorption of a solute gas in a laminar liquid-film falling down a wall, etc. where the flow field is sufficiently well-defined. However, to a beginner of a course in mass transfer, the physical visualization and the mathematical exercise may not appear simple and easy. For more complex situations such as the dissolution of a solid in a mechanically stirred vessel, the absorption of a gas in a liquid flowing down the packing in a tower or in a liquid in an agitated tank, the theoretical calculation of the mass transfer rate becomes very difficult and may even be impossible since the flow field is complex and not properly understood. The concept of *mass transfer coefficient* has been introduced with a view to developing a simple and practically useful approach to the solution of such problems. The idea is similar to defining 'heat transfer coefficient' for expressing the rate of convective heat transfer between a surface and a fluid in motion.

3.1 THE MASS TRANSFER COEFFICIENT

The mass transfer coefficient is defined on the following 'phenomenological basis'.

> Rate of mass transfer $\propto$ Concentration driving force (i.e. the difference in concentration)
> Rate of mass transfer $\propto$ Area of contact between the phases

If W_A is the rate of mass transfer (kmol/s) of the solute A, ΔC_A is the concentration driving force between two points, and a is the area of mass transfer,

$$W_A \propto a\Delta C_A \quad \Rightarrow \quad W_A \propto k_c a\Delta C_A \tag{3.1}$$

where k_c, the proportionality constant, is a phenomenological coefficient[†] called the 'mass transfer coefficient'. If N_A is the molar flux (expressed as kmol/m$^2\cdot$s, say), we may write

$$W_A = aN_A = k_c a \Delta C_A \quad \Rightarrow \quad N_A = k_c \Delta C_A$$

$$\Rightarrow \qquad \text{Mass transfer coefficient, } k_c = \frac{N_A}{\Delta C_A} = \frac{\text{molar flux}}{\text{concentration driving force}} \tag{3.2}$$

For the purpose of comparison, we may recall the definition of heat transfer coefficient:

$$\text{Heat transfer coefficient, } h = \frac{\text{heat flux}}{\text{temperature driving force, } \Delta T}$$

The inverse of mass transfer coefficient is a measure of the 'mass transfer resistance'. If the driving force is expressed as the difference in concentration (kmol/m^3, say), the unit of mass transfer coefficient is m/s (or cm/s, ft/s, etc. which is the same as the unit of velocity).

If the mass transfer coefficient is expressed as the ratio of the local flux and the local driving force, it is called the 'local mass transfer coefficient'. When it is expressed as the ratio of the average flux (over a surface) and the average driving force, it is known as the 'average mass transfer coefficient'.

---

† The word 'phenomenological' implies that the definition of mass transfer coefficient (k_c) given by Eq. (3.1) or (3.2) is based on the 'phenomenon', that k_c is proportional to the driving force ΔC_A and area a.

3.2 TYPES OF MASS TRANSFER COEFFICIENTS

Convective mass transfer can occur in a gas or a liquid medium. A few choices of the driving force (difference in concentration, partial pressure, mole fraction, etc.) are available unlike in the case of heat transfer where the temperature difference is the only driving force. Different types of mass transfer coefficients have been defined depending upon: (i) whether mass transfer occurs in the gas phase or in the liquid phase, (ii) the choice of the driving force, and (iii) whether it is a case of diffusion of *A* through non-diffusing *B* or a case of counterdiffusion.

Convective heat transfer is often visualized to occur through a "stagnant film" adhering to the surface. The transport of heat through the film is assumed to occur purely by conduction. In the study of mass transfer too, this concept is frequently used. This will be discussed in more detail in Section 3.9.1. If the transport of mass occurs through a stagnant film of thickness δ, we may write down the following expressions for the mass transfer flux as the product of a mass transfer coefficient and the appropriate driving force.

3.2.1 Diffusion of *A* Through Non-diffusing *B*

Mass transfer in the gas phase: $\quad N_A = k_G(p_{A1} - p_{A2}) = k_y(y_{A1} - y_{A2}) = k_c(C_{A1} - C_{A2})$ (3.3)

Mass transfer in the liquid phase: $N_A = k_x(x_{A1} - x_{A2}) = k_L(C_{A1} - C_{A2})$ (3.4)

Here k_G, k_y, and k_c are the gas-phase mass transfer coefficients, and k_x and k_L are the liquid-phase mass transfer coefficients; the subscripts 1 and 2 refer to two positions in a medium. The units of the mass transfer coefficients can be obtained from the definitions above. For example, a unit of k_y is (kmol)/(m^2)(s)(Δy), where Δy stands for the driving force in mole fraction unit. If the gas phase is ideal, the concentration term in Eq. (3.3) is given by $C_A = p_A/RT$, where p_A is the partial pressure of *A*. Supposing that the distance between the two locations 1 and 2 is δ (the *film thickness*), the expressions for the mass transfer coefficients can be obtained by comparing Eq. (3.3) with Eq. (2.27) and Eq. (3.4) with Eq. (2.59).

Gas phase: $\qquad k_G = \dfrac{D_{AB}P}{RT\delta\, p_{BM}}; \qquad k_y = \dfrac{D_{AB}P^2}{RT\delta\, p_{BM}}; \qquad k_c = \dfrac{D_{AB}P}{\delta\, p_{BM}}$ (3.5a)

Liquid phase: $\qquad k_x = \dfrac{D_{AB}(\rho/M)_{av}}{\delta\, x_{BM}}; \qquad k_L = \dfrac{D_{AB}}{\delta\, x_{BM}}$ (3.5b)

The relations among the three types of gas-phase mass transfer coefficients (i.e. k_G, k_y, and k_c) can be easily obtained from [Eq. 3.5(a)]. Similarly, the relation between the two types of liquid-phase mass transfer coefficients, k_x and k_L, can be obtained from Eq. [3.5(b)].

$$k_c = RTk_G; \qquad k_y = Pk_G; \qquad k_x = (\rho/M)_{av}k_L$$ (3.6)

3.2.2 Equimolar Counterdiffusion of *A* and *B*

The set of notations for mass transfer coefficients are used here with a prime (′) to differentiate them from the case of diffusion of *A* through non-diffusing *B*.

Gas phase: $\qquad N_A = k'_G(p_{A1} - p_{A2}) = k'_y(y_{A1} - y_{A2}) = k'_c(C_{A1} - C_{A2})$ (3.7)

Liquid phase: $\qquad N_A = k'_x(x_{A1} - x_{A2}) = k'_L(C_{A1} - C_{A2})$ (3.8)

Comparing Eq. (3.7) with Eq. (2.30) for gas-phase transport, and Eq. (3.8) with Eq. (2.60) for liquid-phase transport, we can have the following expressions for the mass transfer coefficients in this case:

Gas phase: $\quad k_G' = \dfrac{D_{AB}}{RT\delta}; \qquad k_y' = \dfrac{D_{AB}P}{RT\delta}; \qquad k_c' = \dfrac{D_{AB}}{\delta}$ (3.9a)

Liquid phase: $\quad k_x' = \dfrac{D_{AB}(\rho/M)_{av}}{\delta}; \qquad k_L' = \dfrac{D_{AB}}{\delta}$ (3.9b)

Conversion: $\quad k_c' = \dfrac{RT}{P}k_y' = RTk_G'; \qquad k_x' = (\rho/M)_{av}k_L' = C_{av}k_L'$ (3.10)

If the concentration of A is expressed in the mole ratio unit (moles A per mole of A-free medium), the mass transfer coefficients k_Y and k_X are expressed in the following way.

Conversion: $\qquad N_A = k_Y(Y_{A1} - Y_{A2}), \qquad$ for the gas phase   (3.11)

and $\qquad\qquad N_A = k_X(X_{A1} - X_{A2}), \qquad$ for the liquid phase   (3.12)

Here Y_A and X_A are the concentrations of A in the gas or in the liquid phase in mole ratio unit [note that similar expressions can be written using the mass ratio (mass A/mass B) unit as well]. Note that $Y_A = y_A/(1 - y_A)$ and $X_A = x_A/(1 - x_A)$. The types of mass transfer coefficients defined above and their interrelations are given in Table 3.1. In order to calculate the mass transfer flux of a species, we need to know the mass transfer coefficient and the existing driving force.

Table 3.1   Different types of mass transfer coefficients

Diffusion of A through non-diffusing B		Equimolar counterdiffusion of A and B		Unit of the mass transfer coefficient
Flux, N_A	Mass transfer coefficient	Flux, N_A	Mass transfer coefficient	
Gas-phase mass transfer				
$k_G(p_{A1} - p_{A2})$	$k_G = \dfrac{D_{AB}P}{RT\delta\, p_{BM}}$	$k_G'(p_{A1} - p_{A2})$	$k_G' = \dfrac{D_{AB}}{\delta RT}$	$\dfrac{mol}{(time)(area)(\Delta p_A)}$
$k_y(y_{A1} - y_{A2})$	$k_y = \dfrac{D_{AB}P^2}{RT\delta p_{BM}}$	$k_y'(y_{A1} - y_{A2})$	$k_y' = \dfrac{D_{AB}P}{\delta RT}$	$\dfrac{mol}{(time)(area)(\Delta y_A)}$
$k_c(C_{A1} - C_{A2})$	$k_c = \dfrac{D_{AB}P}{\delta\, p_{BM}}$	$k_c'(C_{A1} - C_{A2})$	$k_c' = \dfrac{D_{AB}}{\delta}$	$\dfrac{mol}{(time)(area)(\Delta C_A)}$
Liquid-phase mass transfer.				
$k_L(C_{A1} - C_{A2})$	$k_L = \dfrac{D_{AB}}{\delta\, x_{BM}}$	$k_L'(C_{A1} - C_{A2})$	$k_L' = \dfrac{D_{AB}}{\delta}$	$\dfrac{mol}{(time)(area)(\Delta C_A)}$
$k_x(x_{A1} - x_{A2})$	$k_x = \dfrac{CD_{AB}}{\delta\, x_{BM}}$	$k_x'(x_{A1} - x_{A2})$	$k_x' = \dfrac{CD_{AB}}{\delta}$	$\dfrac{mol}{(time)(area)(\Delta x_A)}$
Conversion				
$k_G RT = \dfrac{RT}{P}k_y = k_c;\ k_L = \dfrac{k_x}{C_{av}}$		$k_c' = k_G'RT = \dfrac{RT}{P}k_y';\ k_L' = \dfrac{k_x'}{C_{av}}$		

The fundamental difference between the types of mass transfer coefficients defined in Eqs. (3.3) to (3.5) and the types of coefficients defined in Eqs. (3.7) to (3.9) has to be carefully noted. The former class of coefficients (k_G, k_y, k_c, k_x, and k_L) are inherently associated with the log mean concentration of the other species (B) which is 'non-diffusing'. Accordingly, this type of mass transfer coefficient has a dependence on concentration because of the term p_{BM} or x_{BM} (this dependence can however be ignored at low concentrations of A). On the contrary, the coefficients k'_G, k'_y, k'_c, k'_x, k'_L do not have dependence on concentration. The second type of coefficient, k_c', is called 'Colburn-Drew mass transfer coefficient'.

Another type of mass transfer coefficient, called the 'F-type coefficient', has been proposed (Treybal, 1980; Benitez, 2002). This coefficient, akin to the Colburn-Drew mass transfer coefficient, is not concentration dependent even in the case of 'diffusion of A through non-diffusing B'. If we integrate Eq. (2.19) over a film thickness δ, we get

$$N_A = \frac{N_A}{N_A + N_B} \frac{D_{AB} P}{RT\delta} \ln \frac{\left[N_A/(N_A + N_B)\right] - y_{A2}}{\left[N_A/(N_A + N_B)\right] - y_{A1}} = \frac{N_A}{N_A + N_B} F_G \ln \frac{\left[N_A/(N_A + N_B)\right] - y_{A2}}{\left[N_A/(N_A + N_B)\right] - y_{A1}}$$

(3.13)

where $y_A = p_A/P$ and $DP/RT\delta = F_G$ is the F-type mass transfer coefficient which is independent of the concentration of the diffusing species. If we compare Eq. (3.13) with Eq. (3.5) for the case of diffusion of A through non-diffusing B, it is easy to find out that

$$F_G = k_G p_{BM}$$

(3.14)

However, for equimolar counterdiffusion, F_G and k'_G are related as $F_G = k'_G P$ which is independent of partial pressure of the diffusing species. The F-type coefficients are rarely used in practice.

EXAMPLE 3.1 Determine the relation between the gas-phase mass transfer coefficients, k_G and k_Y.

Solution

The driving force in the mole ratio unit, Y, between two points 1 and 2 can be written as

$$Y_{A1} - Y_{A2} = \frac{p_{A1}}{P - p_{A1}} - \frac{p_{A2}}{P - p_{A2}} = \frac{P p_{A1} - p_{A1} p_{A2} - P p_{A2} + p_{A2} p_{A1}}{(P - p_{A1})(P - p_{A2})} = \frac{P(p_{A1} - p_{A2})}{p_{B1} p_{B2}}$$

$$\Rightarrow \qquad p_{A1} - p_{A2} = (Y_{A1} - Y_{A2}) \frac{p_{B1} p_{B2}}{P}$$

Now, we have

$$N_A = k_G(p_{A1} - p_{A2}) = \frac{D_{AB} P}{RT\delta\, p_{BM}}(p_{A1} - p_{A2}) = \frac{D_{AB} P}{RT\delta\, p_{BM}}(Y_{A1} - Y_{A2}) \frac{p_{B1} p_{B2}}{P} = k_Y(Y_{A1} - Y_{A2})$$

Since $N_A = k_Y(Y_{A1} - Y_{A2})$, we may write

$$k_Y = \frac{D_{AB}\, p_{B1} p_{B2}}{RT\,\delta\, p_{BM}} = k_G \frac{p_{B1} p_{B2}}{P}$$

A similar relation between k'_G and k'_Y (in the case of equimolar counterdiffusion) applies.

EXAMPLE 3.2 (*Calculation of the gas-phase mass transfer coefficient for an evaporating drop*)   The gas-phase mass transfer coefficient for the evaporation of a drop of ethyl alcohol in a stream of air at 300 K and 1.2 bar pressure is $k_G = 2.4 \times 10^{-6}$ kmol/(s)(m^2)(mm Hg).

(a)   Calculate the values of the mass transfer coefficient if the driving force is expressed in terms of difference in: (i) mole fraction of alcohol in the gas phase, (ii) mole ratio of alcohol, and (iii) concentration of alcohol in kmol/m^3. Also calculate the coefficient, F_G.

(b)   Express k_G in (i) lbmol/(ft^2)(s)(psi), (ii) lbmol/(ft^2)(h)(atm), and (iii) lbmol/(ft^2)(h) (inch Hg).

If the diffusivity of alcohol in air is 0.102 cm^2/s at 0°C, estimate the thickness of the stagnant gas-film. Vapour pressure of alcohol = 0.0877 bar at 300 K.

Solution

In this case, diffusion of A(alcohol vapour) occurs through non-diffusing B(air).

(a) *Given:* $P = 1.2$ bar $= 1.2/1.013 = 1.185$ atm $= 900.3$ mm Hg; $R = 0.08317$ (m^3)(bar)/(kmol)(K); $T = 300$ K

(i) From Eq. (3.6), $k_y = Pk_G = 2.4 \times 10^{-6} \dfrac{\text{kmol}}{(\text{m}^2)(\text{s})(\text{mm Hg})} \times (900.3 \text{ mm Hg})$

$$= \boxed{2.161 \times 10^{-3} \dfrac{\text{kmol}}{(\text{s})(\text{m}^2)(\Delta y)}}$$

(ii) At the surface of the drop, p_{A1} = vapour pressure of alcohol at 300 K = 0.0877 bar

i.e. $p_{B1} = P - p_{A1} = 1.2 - 0.0877 = 1.1123$ bar $= 834.5$ mm Hg

Also, $p_{A2} = 0$, i.e. $p_{B2} = P = 1.2$ bar $= 900.3$ mm Hg

From Example 3.1,

$$k_Y = k_G \frac{p_{B1} p_{B2}}{P} = 2.4 \times 10^{-6} \frac{(834.5)(900.3)}{(900.3)} = \boxed{2.003 \times 10^{-3} \frac{\text{kmol}}{(\text{s})(\text{m}^2)(\Delta Y)}}$$

(iii) $k_c = k_G RT = 2.4 \times 10^{-6} \dfrac{\text{kmol}}{(\text{m}^2)(\text{s})(\text{mm Hg})} \times \dfrac{760 \text{ mm Hg}}{1.013 \text{ bar}} \times 0.08317 \dfrac{\text{m}^3 \text{ bar}}{\text{kmol K}} \times 300 \text{ K}$

$$= \boxed{0.0449 \text{ m/s}}$$

Calculation of F_G:

From Eq. (3.14),

$$F_G = k_G p_{BM} = 2.4 \times 10^{-6} \cdot \frac{p_{B2} - p_{B1}}{\ln(p_{B2}/p_{B1})} = 2.4 \times 10^{-6} \times \frac{900.3 - 834.5}{\ln(900.3/834.5)}$$

$$= \boxed{2.081 \times 10^{-3} \text{ kmol/m}^2 \cdot \text{s}}$$

(b)

(i) $k_G = 2.4 \times 10^{-6} \dfrac{\text{kmol}}{(\text{m}^2)(\text{s})(\text{mm Hg})}$

$$= 2.4 \times 10^{-6} \dfrac{\text{kmol}}{(\text{m}^2)(\text{s})(\text{mm Hg})} \times \frac{2.2046 \text{ lbmol}}{\text{kmol}} \times \frac{1 \text{ m}^2}{10.764 \text{ ft}^2} \times \frac{51.7 \text{ mm Hg}}{\text{psi}}$$

$\Rightarrow$ $\qquad$ $k_G = \boxed{2.541 \times 10^{-5} \dfrac{\text{lbmol}}{(\text{s})(\text{ft}^2)(\text{psi})}}$

(ii) Similarly, $k_G = \boxed{1.345 \dfrac{\text{lbmol}}{(\text{ft}^2)(\text{h})(\text{atm})}}$ and (iii) $k_G = \boxed{4.55 \times 10^{-2} \dfrac{\text{lbmol}}{(\text{ft}^2)(\text{h})(\text{inch Hg})}}$

Thickness of the stagnant film:

From Eq. [3.5(a)], film thickness, $\delta = \dfrac{D_{AB}P}{k_G\, RT\, \ln p_{BM}}$

The diffusivity value is given at 1 atm and 0°C. At 1.2 bar (= 1.185 atm) and 300 K the diffusivity is

$$D_{AB} = (0.102)\left(\frac{1.013}{1.185}\right)\left(\frac{300}{273}\right)^{1.75} = 0.103 \text{ cm}^2/\text{s} = 1.03 \times 10^{-5} \text{ m}^2/\text{s}$$

Also, $\qquad p_{BM} = \dfrac{p_{B2} - p_{B1}}{\ln(p_{B2}/p_{B1})} = \dfrac{1.2 - 1.1123}{\ln(1.2/1.1123)} = 1.1556$ bar

$$k_G = 2.4 \times 10^{-6} \text{ kmol/(m}^2)(\text{s})(\text{mm Hg}) = (2.4 \times 10^{-6})(760 \text{ mm Hg}/1.013 \text{ bar})$$

$$= 1.8 \times 10^{-3} \text{ kmol/(m}^2)(\text{s})(\text{bar})$$

$\therefore$ $\quad \delta = \dfrac{(1.03 \times 10^{-5}\, \text{m}^2/\text{s})(1.2\, \text{bar})}{[1.8 \times 10^{-3}\, \text{kmol/(m}^2)(\text{s})(\text{bar})]\,[0.08317\,(\text{m}^3)(\text{bar})/(\text{kmol})(\text{K})]\,(300\,\text{K})(1.1556\,\text{bar})}$

$$= 2.4 \times 10^{-4} \text{ m} = \boxed{0.24 \text{ mm}}$$

3.2.3 Typical Magnitudes of Mass Transfer Coefficients and Film Thickness

It will be relevant here to mention the 'order of magnitude'[†] of gas- and liquid-phase mass transfer coefficients occurring in a typical separation equipment.

Gas-phase mass transfer coefficient, $k_c \sim 10^{-2}$ m/s; film thickness, $\delta \sim 1$ mm

Liquid-phase mass transfer coefficient, $k_L \sim 10^{-5}$ m/s; film thickness, $\delta \sim 0.1$ mm

Once these typical values are noted, it is rather easy to determine the orders of magnitude of other types of mass transfer coefficients. For example, at $T = 298$ K and at a 'low concentration',

$$k_G = \frac{k_c}{RT} \sim \frac{10^{-2} \text{ m/s}}{0.08317\,[(\text{m}^3)(\text{bar})/(\text{kmol})(\text{K})]\,(298\,\text{K})} \Rightarrow k_G \sim 4 \times 10^{-4} \text{ kmol/(m}^2)(\text{s})(\Delta p, \text{ bar})$$

[†] The concept of 'order of magnitude' is sometimes used in the analysis of physical systems to identify quantities which are small enough to be neglected compared to other quantities. The boundary layer approximation of equations of motion is a common example of order of magnitude analysis. Here we use the term to imply an *approximate* range of value of a quantity. Thus if we say 'α is of order β' (sometimes written as $\alpha \sim \beta$), we mean that α and β differ by less than a factor of ten.

For liquid-phase mass transfer in a 'dilute' aqueous solution,

$$k_x = k_L(\rho/M)_{av} \sim (10^{-5} \text{ m/s})(1000/18 \text{ kmol/m}^3) \quad \Rightarrow \quad k_x \sim 5 \times 10^{-4} \text{ kmol/(m}^2)(\text{s})(\Delta x)$$

Since the liquid-phase diffusivity of common solutes, $D \sim 10^{-9}$ m^2/s,

$$\text{liquid film thickness, } \delta \sim D/k_L \quad \Rightarrow \quad \delta \sim 10^{-4} \text{ m or 0.1 mm}$$

Typical values of gas–liquid mass transfer coefficients in industrial equipment are given in Chapter 5 (Table 5.1).

3.3   DIMENSIONLESS GROUPS IN MASS TRANSFER

In many cases it is convenient to express the transport coefficients and other important parameters (such as the fluid properties, velocity, etc.) in terms of meaningful dimensionless groups. In the study of heat transfer, for example, the heat transfer coefficient h is often expressed in terms of the Nusselt number (Nu). The other important parameters and properties influencing the heat transfer coefficient are taken care of through two other dimensionless groups—namely the Reynolds number (Re) and the Prandtl number (Pr). Experimental forced convection heat transfer data are frequently correlated as Nu = Φ(Re, Pr) and the resulting correlation may be used to estimate the heat transfer coefficient for any other set of process conditions and system parameters. The most important of such correlations is the Dittus–Boelter equation.

A similar approach is followed in the study of mass transfer too. Here we have the two most important dimensionless groups—the Sherwood number, Sh (which is the mass transfer analogue of the Nusselt number) and the Schmidt number, Sc (which is the mass transfer analogue of the Prandtl number). In fact, the origin of Sh and Sc can be traced to their analogy with Nu and Pr respectively. Let us discuss this analogy here.

In *heat transfer*, the Nusselt number is

$$\text{Nu} = \frac{\text{convective heat flux}}{\text{heat flux for conduction through a stagnant medium of thickness } l \text{ for the same } \Delta T}$$

$$= \frac{h\,\Delta T}{(k/l)\,\Delta T} = \frac{hl}{k} \qquad [k = \text{thermal conductivity}] \tag{3.15}$$

Similarly, in *mass transfer*, the Sherwood number is

$$\text{Sh} = \frac{\text{convective mass (molar) flux}}{\substack{\text{mass (molar) flux for molecular diffusion through a stagnant medium of} \\ \text{thickness } l \text{ under the driving force } \Delta p_A}}$$

If we consider the gas-phase mass transfer of A through a binary mixture of A and B (B is non-diffusing),

$$\text{Convective mass flux [see Eq. (3.3)]} = k_G\,\Delta p_A$$

$$\text{Mass flux due to molecular diffusion of } A \text{ through non-diffusing } B = \frac{D_{AB}P}{RT\,l\,p_{BM}}\,\Delta p_A$$

Then,
$$\text{Sh} = \frac{k_G \Delta p_A}{(D_{AB} P / RT l \, p_{BM}) \Delta p_A} = \frac{k_G p_{BM} RT l}{D_{AB} P} = \frac{k_c l}{D_{AB}} \frac{p_{BM}}{P} \tag{3.16}$$

If we consider transport of A in a solution at a rather low concentration ($x_{BM} = 1$),

$$\text{Convective mass flux, } N_A = k_L \Delta C_A$$

Diffusive flux of A through a stagnant liquid layer of thickness $l = \frac{D_{AB}}{l} \Delta C_A$

[from Eq. (2.60)]

Then, the Sherwood number,
$$\text{Sh} = \frac{k_L \Delta C_A}{(D_{AB}/l) \Delta C_A} = \frac{k_L l}{D_{AB}} \tag{3.17}$$

Here l is a 'characteristic length'. The commonly used characteristic lengths are: for a sphere—diameter, d; for a cylinder—diameter, d; for a flat plate—distance from the leading edge, x (say).[†]

Now let us turn to the Schmidt number which is the mass transfer analogue of the Prandtl number. We define the Prandtl number as

$$\text{Pr} = \frac{\text{momentum diffusivity}}{\text{thermal diffusivity}} = \frac{\mu/\rho}{k/\rho c_p} = \frac{c_p \mu}{k}$$

Analogously, we define the Schmidt number as

$$\text{Sc} = \frac{\text{momentum diffusivity}}{\text{molecular diffusivity}} = \frac{\mu/\rho}{D_{AB}} = \frac{\mu}{\rho D_{AB}} = \frac{\nu}{D_{AB}} \tag{3.18}$$

There are a few more dimensionless groups commonly used in the study of mass transfer. A list of the important groups along with their physical significances are given in Table 3.2. The heat transfer analogues of the groups are also given alongside for comparison. It will be useful to have a look into the orders of magnitude of the above two dimensionless groups, Sh and Sc. Take the case of gas-phase mass transfer for flow past a sphere, 1 cm in diameter, at low partial pressure of the solute (i.e. $p_{BM}/P \sim 1$). The Sherwood number and the Schmidt number may be found to be

$$\text{Sh} = \frac{k_c d}{D_{AB}} \frac{p_{BM}}{P} \sim \frac{(10^{-2} \text{ m/s})(10^{-2} \text{ m})}{10^{-5} \text{ m}^2/\text{s}} \Rightarrow \text{Sh} \sim 10$$

$$\text{Sc} = \frac{\nu}{D_{AB}} = \frac{10^{-5} \text{ m}^2/\text{s}}{10^{-5} \text{ m}^2/\text{s}} \Rightarrow \text{Sc} \sim 1$$

For liquid-phase mass transport in a similar geometry,

$$\text{Sh} = \frac{k_L d}{D_{AB}} \sim \frac{(10^{-5} \text{ m/s})(10^{-2} \text{ m})}{10^{-9} \text{ m}^2/\text{s}} \Rightarrow \text{Sh} \sim 100$$

$$\text{Sc} = \frac{\nu}{D_{AB}} = \frac{10^{-6} \text{ m}^2/\text{s}}{10^{-9} \text{ m}^2/\text{s}} \Rightarrow \text{Sc} \sim 1000$$

[†] The location of a point in the boundary layer is often indicated by the coordinates (x, y). These notations should not be confused with mole fractions.

Table 3.2 Important dimensionless groups in mass transfer

Dimensionless groups and their physical significance	Analogous groups in heat transfer
Reynolds number, $Re = \dfrac{lv\rho}{\mu} = \dfrac{lv}{\nu} = \dfrac{\text{inertial forces}}{\text{viscous forces}}$	The same
Schmidt number, $Sc = \dfrac{\mu}{\rho D} = \dfrac{\nu}{D} = \dfrac{\text{momemntum diffusivity}}{\text{molecular diffusivity}}$	$Pr = \dfrac{c_p \mu}{k} = \dfrac{\mu/\rho}{k/\rho c_p} = \dfrac{\nu}{\alpha} = \dfrac{\text{momentum diffusivity}}{\text{thermal diffusivity}}$
Sherwood number*, $Sh = \dfrac{k_L l}{D} = \dfrac{k_L \Delta C}{(D/l)\Delta C} = \dfrac{\text{convective mass flux}}{\text{diffusive flux across a layer of thickness } l}$	$Nu = \dfrac{hl}{k} = \dfrac{\text{convective heat flux}}{\text{conduction heat flux across a layer of thickness } l}$
Stanton number, $St_M = \dfrac{Sh}{(Re)(Sc)} = \dfrac{k_L}{v} = \dfrac{k_L \Delta C}{v\Delta C} = \dfrac{\text{convective mass flux}}{\text{flux due to bulk flow of the medium}}$	$St_H = \dfrac{Nu}{(Re)(Pr)} = \dfrac{h\Delta T}{v\Delta T} = \dfrac{\text{convective heat flux}}{\text{heat flux due to bulk flow}}$
Peclet number, $Pe_M = (Re)(Sc) = \dfrac{lv}{D} = \dfrac{v\Delta C}{(1/D)\Delta C} = \dfrac{\text{flux due to bulk flow of the medium}}{\text{diffusive flux across a layer of thickness } l}$	$Pe_H = (Re)(Pr) = \dfrac{(v\rho c_p)\Delta T}{(k/l)\Delta T} = \dfrac{\text{heat flux due to bulk flow}}{\text{conduction flux across a thickness } l}$
Colburn factor, $j_D = St_M(Sc)^{2/3} = \dfrac{Sh}{(Re)(Sc)^{1/3}}$	$j_H = St_H(Pr)^{2/3} = \dfrac{Nu}{(Re)(Pr)^{1/3}}$
Grashof number, $Gr = \dfrac{l^3 \Delta\rho g}{\mu \nu}$	The same
Lewis number, $Le = Sc/Pr$	See Chapter 10

* The Sherwood number for gas-phase mass transfer is defined in Eq. (3.16). The suffix M or D refers to mass transfer, H to heat transfer. The Grashof number is the analogue of Reynolds number in free convection mass transfer. Pr = Prandtl number; Nu = Nusselt number; l = characteristic length; $\nu = \mu/\rho$ = momentum diffusivity; $\alpha = k/\rho c_p$ = thermal diffusivity; $\Delta\rho$ = difference in density because of a difference in concentration or temperature.

3.4 CORRELATIONS FOR THE CONVECTIVE MASS TRANSFER COEFFICIENT

As stated before, we need to know the mass transfer coefficient for calculating the rate of convective mass transfer. In practice the mass transfer coefficient in a typical situation may be obtained from a suitable correlation if an experimental value is not available. A large number of mass transfer correlations, covering a wide variety of practical situations and geometries, exist in the literature. These correlations have been developed by researchers on the basis of large volumes of experimental data. A few important correlations for the convective mass transfer coefficient in terms of dimensionless groups are listed in Table 3.3. A comprehensive compilation of mass transfer correlations covering a wide range of systems is available in Perry's Handbook (7th ed., 1997, Ch. 5).

Table 3.3 Correlations for the mass transfer coefficient in a few simple situations

Description	Range of application	Correlation
Laminar flow through a circular tube	Re ≤ 2,100	$Sh = k_L d/D = 1.62[(Re)(Sc)(d/L)]^{1/3}$
Turbulent flow through a tube	4,000 ≤ Re ≤ 60,000; 0.6 ≤ Sc ≤ 3,000	$Sh = 0.023\,(Re)^{0.83}\,(Sc)^{0.33}$
Boundary layer flow over a flat plate	$Re_l < 80,000$ // $Re_l > 5\times10^5$	$j_D = 0.664(Re_l)^{-0.5}$ // $j_D = 0.037(Re_l)^{-0.2}$
Flow through a wetted-wall tower	3,000 < Re′ < 40,000; 0.5 < Sc < 3	$j_D = 0.0328(Re')^{-0.23}$
Gas-phase flow through a packed bed	10 ≤ Re″ ≤ 2500	$j_D = 1.17(Re'')^{-0.415}$
Liquid flow through a packed bed	Re″ < 55	$j_D = 1.09(Re'')^{-2/3}$
	3 < Re″ <10,000	$Sh = 2 + 1.1(Re)^{0.6}(Sc)^{0.33}$

d = tube diameter; $Re_l = lv\rho/\mu$, l = characteristic length; $Re' = dv'\rho/\mu$, v' = gas velocity relative to the surface of the falling film; $Re'' = d_p v''\rho/\mu$, d_p = diameter of the sphere, v'' = superficial velocity of the fluid (i.e. velocity based on the bed cross-section).

But how do we collect and correlate mass transfer data in a given situation or geometry? Let us illustrate this point by taking a simple example. Suppose we want to develop a correlation for the mass transfer coefficient for transport from a sphere in convective flow. We take a ball of naphthalene, suspend it in a flowing stream of gas (say, air) at a temperature T (Figure 3.3). Let the change in mass of the ball over a period of time Δt be Δm. The partial pressure of naphthalene *at the surface* of the ball is p_{As} which is equal to the vapour pressure (or sublimation pressure) of naphthalene at the experimental temperature. The partial pressure is zero in the bulk gas. If M_w is the molecular weight of naphthalene, we have

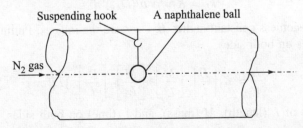

Figure 3.3 A simple experimental arrangement for measurement of mass transfer coefficient in flow past a sphere.

$$\text{Average molar flux, } N_A = \frac{\Delta m}{M_w \Delta t (\pi d_p^2 / 4)} \, p_{As}$$

$$\text{Driving force, } \Delta p = p_{As} - 0 = p_{As}$$

where d_p is the average diameter of the ball over the time Δt (if the change in mass is small, the average diameter can be used to calculate the area of the ball).

Therefore, the gas-phase mass transfer coefficient is

$$k_G = \frac{N_A}{\Delta p_A} = \frac{\Delta m}{M_w \Delta t (\pi d_p^2 / 4) \, p_{As}} \tag{3.19}$$

In a particular experiment, k_G can be calculated by using the above equation. The experiment can be repeated using (i) different fluids (liquids and gases), (ii) different flow rates, and (iii) spheres of different materials (which sublime or dissolve in the flowing fluids) and sizes. In this way, a large volume of data on k_G and k_L against the corresponding Reynolds number (Re) and Schmidt number (Sc) can be collected. The k_G and k_L values are converted into Sherwood numbers. The resulting set of data can be correlated in the form

$$\text{Sh} = a(\text{Re})^b \, (\text{Sc})^c \tag{3.20}$$

The values of the constants a, b, and c can be obtained by a nonlinear least square fitting or a graphical procedure. Then we arrive at a correlation that gives the Sherwood number as a function of Re and Sc. Such a correlation is useful for estimation of the mass transfer coefficient and the mass transfer rate in any other situation involving transport to a fluid flowing past a sphere. The ranges of Re and Sc for which a correlation is valid should be clearly mentioned.

But how do we identify the dimensionless groups or numbers used for correlating the mass transfer data? The answer may obtained by 'dimensional analysis'. One technique is to use the 'Buckingham Pi theorem' (see, for example, Dutta, 2001). This technique, applied to the case of mass transfer for flow past a sphere, tells us that the Sherwood number, Sh, is a function of Re and Sc as given in Eq. (3.20).

An alternative and simpler technique of dimensional analysis is based on the assumption of power law dependence of the mass transfer coefficient on the relevant important system parameters and properties. Let us illustrate this technique for developing the general relation given by Eq. (3.20) for dissolution of a sphere of material (A) in a flowing liquid (B). The mass transfer coefficient k_L is expected to depend upon the following major quantities: the diameter of the sphere, d; the velocity of the liquid, v; the density of the liquid, ρ; its viscosity, μ; and the diffusivity of the solute, D_{AB}. We assume a power-law dependence of k_L on these quantities.

$$k_L = K_1 v^\alpha \rho^\beta \mu^\gamma (D_{AB})^\delta d^\varepsilon \tag{3.21}$$

where K_1 is a dimensionless constant and α, β, ..., ε are the indices. Putting the dimensions of the various quantities on both sides,

$$\frac{L}{t} = K_1 \left[\frac{L}{t}\right]^\alpha \left[\frac{M}{L^3}\right]^\beta \left[\frac{M}{Lt}\right]^\gamma \left[\frac{L^2}{t}\right]^\delta [L]^\varepsilon$$

Equating the powers of L (length), M (mass), and t (time) on both sides,

$$L: \qquad 1 = \alpha - 3\beta - \gamma + 2\delta + \varepsilon \tag{3.22}$$

$$M: \quad 0 = \beta + \gamma \tag{3.23}$$

$$t: \quad -1 = -\alpha - \gamma - \delta \tag{3.24}$$

From Eq. (3.23), $\beta = -\gamma$, and from Eq. (3.24), $\delta = 1 - \alpha - \gamma$. Substituting these in Eq. (3.22),

$$1 = \alpha + 3\gamma - \gamma + 2 - 2\alpha - 2\gamma + \varepsilon \quad \Rightarrow \quad \varepsilon = \alpha - 1$$

Putting these results in Eq. (3.21),

$$k_L = K_1 v^\alpha \rho^{-\gamma} \mu^\gamma (D_{AB})^{1-\gamma-\alpha} d^{\alpha-1}$$

$$\Rightarrow \quad \frac{k_L d}{D_{AB}} = K_1 v^\alpha \rho^{-\gamma} \mu^\gamma (D_{AB})^{-\gamma-\alpha} d^\alpha = K_1 \left(\frac{d \rho v}{\mu} \right)^\alpha \left(\frac{\mu}{\rho D_{AB}} \right)^{\alpha+\gamma}$$

$$\Rightarrow \quad Sh = K_1 (Re)^\alpha (Sc)^{\alpha'} \quad \text{where } \alpha' = \alpha + \gamma \tag{3.25}$$

So the experimental mass transfer coefficient data can be correlated in the form of Eq. (3.25), which is identical to Eq. (3.20), in terms of dimensionless groups. If enough data on Sh, Re and Sc for various systems are available or collected, the values of the constants α and α' can be determined by 'nonlinear regression'. The resulting equation or correlation can be used for calculating the mass transfer coefficient in any other similar system.

EXAMPLE 3.3 (*Mass transfer in flow past a sphere*)   A naphthalene ball of 1 cm diameter is suspended in a stream of air flowing at a velocity of 5 m/s at 45°C and 1 atm total pressure. Calculate the time required for its diameter to be halved. The following correlation for the Sherwood number may be used.

$$Sh = 2 + 0.6 (Re)^{0.5} (Sc)^{0.33}$$

Sublimation pressure of naphthalene at 45°C is 0.8654 mm Hg. The other relevant physicochemical properties are: $D_{AB} = 6.92 \times 10^{-6}$ m²/s; the density of naphthalene at 45°C = 1140 kg/m³; $\rho_{air} = 1.1$ kg/m³; $\mu_{air} = 1.92 \times 10^{-5}$ kg/m·s. Assume that the ball retains the spherical shape all through. (Is this assumption correct?)

Solution

Naphthalene vapour (A) is transported through non-diffusing air (B). The mass transfer coefficient can be obtained from the given correlation. The Reynolds number and, therefore, the Sherwood number and the mass transfer coefficient depend upon the radius of the ball which decreases with time. If r is the radius of the naphthalene ball at any time t, the Reynolds number is

$$Re = \frac{2r\rho v}{\mu} = r \frac{(2)(1.1)(5)}{1.92 \times 10^{-5}} = 5.73 \times 10^5 r \text{ (the maximum value of Re is 2864)}$$

$$\text{Schmidt number, } Sc = \frac{\mu}{\rho D_{AB}} = \frac{1.92 \times 10^5}{(1.1)(6.92 \times 10^{-6})} = 2.522$$

$$\Rightarrow \quad Sh = 2 + 0.6 (Re)^{0.5} (Sc)^{1/3} = 2 + (0.6)(5.73 \times 10^5 r)^{0.5} (2.522)^{1/3} = 2 + 618 (r)^{1/2}$$

Given: Temperature, $T = 45°C = 318$ K; since the vapour pressure of naphthalene is small, $P/p_{BM} \approx 1$

Then, $\text{Sh} = \dfrac{k_G \, p_{BM} \, RT \, 2r}{P D_{AB}} = \dfrac{k_G \, (0.08317)(318)(2r)}{6.92 \times 10^{-6}} = 7.644 \times 10^6 \, r k_G$

$\Rightarrow$ $7.644 \times 10^6 \, r k_G = 2 + 618(r)^{1/2}$ $\Rightarrow$ $k_G = \dfrac{2.616 \times 10^{-7}}{r} + \dfrac{8.085 \times 10^{-5}}{\sqrt{r}}$

Now we have to relate the rate of change of the size of the ball with the mass transfer rate. At time t, the rate of sublimation can be expressed as

$$-\frac{d}{dt}\left(\frac{4}{3}\pi r^3 \frac{\rho}{M}\right) = (4\pi r^2) k_G (p_{Av} - p_{Ab})   \quad \text{i.e.} \quad   -\frac{dr}{dt} = \left(\frac{M}{\rho}\right) k_G \, p_{Av} \qquad \text{(i)}$$

where

  ρ = density of solid naphthalene at 45°C = 1140 kg/m^3
  M = molecular weight = 128
  p_{Av} = vapour pressure of naphthalene at 45°C = 0.8654 mm Hg = 0.001153 bar
  p_{Ab} = partial pressure of naphthalene in the bulk air = 0.

Putting the values of various quantities in Eq. (i), we have

$$-\frac{dr}{dt} = \left(\frac{128}{1140}\right)\left(\frac{2.616 \times 10^{-7}}{r} + \frac{8.085 \times 10^{-5}}{\sqrt{r}}\right)(0.001153)$$

$$= \frac{3.3867 \times 10^{-11}}{r} + \frac{1.0467 \times 10^{-8}}{\sqrt{r}}$$

In order to calculate the required time, the above equation has to be integrated from the initial radius, $r_i = 0.5$ cm (= 0.005 m) to the final radius, $r_i/2 = 0.25$ cm (= 0.0025 m).

$$t = -\int_{0.005}^{0.0025} \frac{dr}{\dfrac{3.3867 \times 10^{-11}}{r} + \dfrac{1.0467 \times 10^{-8}}{\sqrt{r}}} = -\int_{0.005}^{0.0025} \frac{r \, dr}{3.3867 \times 10^{-11} + 1.0467 \times 10^{-8} \sqrt{r}}$$

The integral is of the form $I = \displaystyle\int \frac{r \, dr}{a + b\sqrt{r}}$;   put $\sqrt{r} = x$ $\Rightarrow$ $dr = 2x\,dx$

$\Rightarrow$ $I = 2\displaystyle\int \frac{x^3 \, dx}{a + bx}$; make another substitution $\xi = \alpha + \beta x$ $\Rightarrow$ $x = (\xi - \alpha)/\alpha$; $dx = d\xi/\beta$

$$I = 2\int \frac{[(\xi - \alpha)/\beta]^3 \cdot (d\xi/\beta)}{\xi} = \frac{2}{\beta^4}\int \frac{(\xi - \alpha)^3}{\xi} \, d\xi = \frac{2}{\beta^4}\left[\frac{\xi^3}{3} - \frac{3\xi^2 \alpha}{2} + 3\xi\alpha^2 - \alpha^3 \ln\xi\right]$$

Put the limits and calculate the integral, $I = 13{,}820$ s = $\boxed{3.84 \text{ h}}$

If there is no convection, i.e. if sublimation occurs in a stagnant medium by purely molecular diffusion, it can be shown (see Example 2.13) that it takes 76.9 h for the radius to be reduced to half of the initial value [note that we get the same result by discarding the second term on the r.h.s. of Eq. (ii) above and integrating the function]. This again shows that convective mass transfer is a much faster process than transport by molecular diffusion alone.

EXAMPLE 3.4 (*Solid dissolution in an agitated vessel*)   A solution of $K_2Cr_2O_7$ is to be prepared by dissolving crystals of the solid in an agitated vessel. Twenty kilograms of the solid is charged into a vessel containing 500 kg water. The vessel is provided with a flat-bladed turbine that rotates at 120 rpm. Following data are given: density of the solid = 2690 kg/m³; average particle size = 0.6 mm; solubility of the solid in water at the given temperature = 8 wt%; average viscosity of the solution over the concentration range involved = 0.98 cP; density of the liquid = 1000 kg/m³ (assumed constant); diffusivity of potassium dichromate in water = 1.5×10^{-5} cm²/s. Calculate the time required for complete dissolution of the solid.

The following correlation for Sherwood number can be used to calculate the solid–liquid mass transfer coefficient.

$$\text{Sh} = \frac{k_L d_p}{D} = 2 + 0.44(\text{Re}_s)^{0.504}\ (\text{Sc})^{0.355}$$

where

$$\text{Re}_s = \text{stirrer Reynolds number} = \frac{N d_p^2 \rho}{\mu}\ ;\ \text{Sc} = \frac{\mu}{\rho D}\ ;\ d_p = \text{particle diameter.}$$

Hints: Let at any time t, the mass of the undissolved solid in the vessel be m kg. Mass of solid already dissolved = $20 - m$. Mass of solution = $500 + (20 - m)$, volume = $(520 - m)/1000$ m³. Instantaneous concentration of the solution, $C = (20 - m)/[(520 - m)/1000]$ kg/m³. Solubility, $C_s = 80$ kg/m³.

Now we express the quantities k_L and a (the total area of the particles at the time, t) in terms of m.

If $d_0 = 0.6$ mm (the initial diameter of a particle), the number of particles = 6.574×10^7. Mass of a single particle at the time $t = m/(6.574 \times 10^7)$; instantaneous diameter, $d_p = 2.211 \times 10^{-4}(m)^{1/3}$; area of a particle = $\pi d_p^2 = (\pi)[2.211 \times 10^{-4}(m)^{1/3}]^2$; total area of the particles, $a = (10.1)m^{2/3}$. Schmidt number, $\text{Sc} = \mu/\rho D = 653$.

Instantaneous Reynolds number, $\text{Re}_s = N d_p^2 \dfrac{\rho}{\mu} = (0.09976)(m)^{2/3}$

$$\text{Sh} = 2 + (0.44)(0.09976 \times m^{2/3})^{0.504}(653)^{0.385} = 2 + 1.67m^{0.336} = \frac{k_L d_p}{D}$$

$$k_L = (6.784 \times 10^{-6})(2 + 1.67m^{0.336})(m)^{-1/3}$$

The rate of dissolution of the crystals can be written as

$$-\frac{dm}{dt} = k_L a(C_s - C)$$

$$= [(6.784 \times 10^{-6})(2 + 1.67m^{0.336})m^{-1/3}](10.1m^{2/3})\left(80 - \frac{(20 - m)(1000)}{520 - m}\right) = \phi(m)$$

Numerical integration of the above equation (from $m = 20$ to $m = 0$) gives the time of dissolution.

Ans. $\boxed{15\ \text{min}}$

3.5 TURBULENT OR EDDY DIFFUSION

Turbulent motion of a fluid is characterized by rapid and highly irregular fluctuation of the velocity at any point in the fluid. Experimental evidences indicate that in a turbulent medium, tiny fluid elements move about randomly and are responsible for a high rate of transport of momentum, heat or mass. These fluid elements, not necessarily of the same size, are called *eddies*. It is visualized that eddies are continually formed and they break up by interaction among themselves or even may disappear in the process. Eddies are, therefore, short-lived.

Mass or heat transfer in a turbulent medium is a result of the mixing process caused by the movement of the eddies. This is illustrated in Figure 3.4 for transport of a soluble substance from a pipe wall to a flowing fluid. For the sake of simplicity it may be visualized that the effect of turbulence does not reach the wall. Transport of momentum, mass or heat occurs by diffusion through a thin layer, called the *laminar sublayer*, at the wall. Beyond this layer, transport occurs predominantly by eddies. However, the motion of eddies and the phenomenon of eddy transport are not well-understood despite the extensive theoretical and experimental research done on these phenomena[†]. To simplify the analysis of the phenomenon, the physical laws of transport (of heat, mass and momentum) are very often extended to the case of eddy transport by replacing the molecular transport coefficient by an 'eddy transport coefficient' (also see Section 3.10). For example, in the case of mass transfer from the tube wall we can write

$$J_{A,\text{turb}} = -E_D \frac{dC_A}{dr} \qquad (3.26)$$

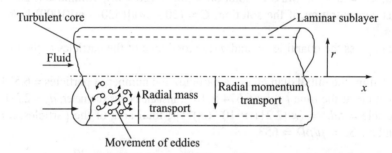

Figure 3.4   Momentum and mass transport in turbulent flow by eddy diffusion.

where E_D is the 'eddy diffusivity' of mass. This equation is identical to Eq. (2.9) except that D_{AB} is replaced by E_D. The 'total flux' is, therefore, obtained by adding the fluxes due to molecular diffusion and eddy diffusion (Sherwood et al., 1975).

$$J_{A,\text{total}} = -(D_{AB} + E_D)\frac{dC_A}{dr} \qquad (3.27)$$

The eddy diffusivity E_D is not as simple a quantity as the molecular diffusivity D_{AB}. It depends upon the intensity of the local turbulence. The intensity of turbulence decreases as one approaches the wall. Therefore, the contribution of eddy diffusion towards the rate of mass transfer is substantially less than that by molecular diffusion very near the wall. The situation is just the opposite in the bulk of the turbulent medium. The phenomenon of eddy diffusion and a few models have been described by Deen (1998).

[†] Advanced softwares for computational fluid dynamics (CFD) are now in routine use for the numerical solution of transport problems in many complicated geometries and flow situations.

3.6 THE WETTED-WALL COLUMN

Mass transfer from a flowing gas to a falling liquid-film (or vice versa) is encountered in a number of practical situations (for example, gas absorption or stripping in a packed tower). The wetted-wall tower is a classical model experimental set-up for measuring the mass transfer coefficient. The mass transfer data obtained in such a column also throw light on the mechanism of mass transfer in a system of similar geometry and flow conditions. The wetted-wall column is a vertical tube or pipe provided with an arrangement for liquid feeding and withdrawal (Figure 3.5). The gas flows up through the column and the liquid flows down as a film (which may have a calm or rippling surface depending upon the 'film Reynolds number'; see Rosenhow et al., 1985) over a section of the column. Most of the experiments reported on the wetted-wall column involve evaporation of pure liquids in flowing streams of air and other gases. In an experiment on evaporation of water in air, for example, the average mass flux

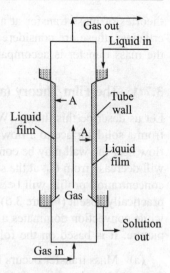

Figure 3.5 Schematic of a wetted-wall column.

can be calculated from the known area of the wetted section of the wall, the total rate of mass transfer (calculated from the flow rate of air and the moisture content at the inlet and at the exit of the column), and the average driving force. The driving force at any section is the difference between the vapour pressure of water at the prevailing temperature and the partial pressure of moisture in the bulk air. Since the area of gas–liquid contact is known and the liquid-film is visible (it can be photographed), this apparatus has also been used for study of mans transfer in distillation and in chemically reactive gas–liquid systems. A large number of mass transfer correlations for the wetted-wall column is available. One such commonly used correlation is cited in Table 3.3. A simple calculation of mass transfer in a wetted-wall column is illustrated in Example 3.9.

The wetted-wall column has been used widely for determination of diffusivity of a dissolved gas in a liquid. If the flow of the liquid is laminar and ripple-free, the mass transfer coefficient can be obtained using the penetration theory (see Section 3.7.2). The diffusivity can be calculated from the experimentally measured rate of absorption and the area of gas–liquid contact (Davies et al., 1967)

3.7 THEORIES OF MASS TRANSFER

At the beginning of this chapter, we defined the mass transfer coefficient just as a phenomenological quantity to be determined experimentally. No attempt was made to have an insight of the physical mechanism of convective mass transfer at a phase boundary. However, there are a number of theories of mass transfer which aim at visualizing the mechanism and developing the expressions for the mass transfer coefficient theoretically. In fact, any such theory is based on a conceptual model[†] for mass transfer. We shall now discuss the more important and simple

[†]A 'model' is an idealized picture of a physical phenomenon or of an object that makes the phenomenon or the object amenable to theoretical analysis using mathematical equations and tools.

theories of mass transfer at a phase boundary. These theories are old and rather simple. Nevertheless, these are considered very important in the study of mass transfer, particularly when the mass transfer is accompanied by a chemical reaction.

3.7.1   The Film Theory (also called 'Film Model')

Let us describe this theory (Whitman, 1923) through an illustration. We consider mass transfer from a solid surface to a flowing liquid. Even though the bulk liquid is in turbulent motion, the flow near the wall may be considered to be laminar. The concentration of the dissolved solid (A) will decrease from C_{Ai} at the solid–liquid interface[#] to C_{Ab} at the bulk of the liquid. In reality the concentration profile will be very steep near the solid surface where the effect of turbulence is practically absent (Figure 3.6). Molecular diffusion is responsible for mass transfer near the wall while convection dominates a little away from it. The film theory, however, visualizes a simpler picture. It is based on the following assumptions.

   (a)   Mass transfer occurs by purely molecular diffusion through a stagnant fluid layer at the phase boundary (here the wall is the phase boundary). Beyond this film, the fluid is well-mixed having a concentration which is the same as that of the bulk fluid (i.e. C_{Ab}).

   (b)   Mass transfer through the film occurs at steady state.

   (c)   The bulk flow term [i.e. $(N_A + N_B)C_A/C$, see Eq. (2.15)] in the expression for the Fick's law is small. So the flux can be written as $N_A = -D_{AB}(dC_A/dz)$. As stated before, this is valid when: (i) the flux is low and (ii) the mass transfer occurs at low concentrations [or the mass transfer occurs by equimolar counterdiffusion]. For many practical situations this assumption is satisfactory.

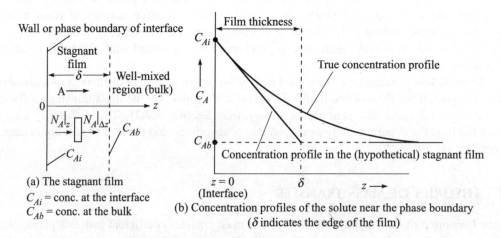

(a) The stagnant film
C_{Ai} = conc. at the interface
C_{Ab} = conc. at the bulk

(b) Concentration profiles of the solute near the phase boundary
(δ indicates the edge of the film)

Figure 3.6   The stagnant film and the concentration profiles.

The underlying concept of the film theory of mass transfer is analogous to that of heat transfer (the heat transfer coefficient is frequently called the 'film coefficient'). Figure 3.6 shows

---

[#] It is generally assumed that equilibrium prevails at the interface or the phase boundary. So, C_{Ai} is, in fact, the solubility of the solid in the liquid.

the stagnant film. We consider an elementary volume of thickness Δz and of unit area normal to the z-direction (i.e. the direction of mass transfer). We make a steady state mass balance over this element located at position z.

Rate of input[†] of the solute at $z = N_A|_z$

Rate of output of the solute at $z + \Delta z = N_A|_{z+\Delta z}$

Rate of accumulation = 0 (at steady state)

$$\Rightarrow \qquad N_A|_z - N_A|_{z+\Delta z} = 0$$

Dividing by Δz throughout and taking the limit $\Delta z \to 0$, we get

$$- dN_A/dz = 0$$

Putting $N_A = -D_{AB}\dfrac{dC_A}{dz}$ in the preceding equation, we have

$$D_{AB}\frac{d^2C_A}{dz^2} = 0 \qquad \text{i.e.} \qquad \frac{d^2C_A}{dz^2} = 0 \tag{3.28}$$

Integrating Eq. (3.28) and using the following boundary conditions (i) and (ii),

(i) $z = 0$ (i.e. the wall or the phase boundary or the interface), $C_A = C_{Ai}$

(ii) $z = \delta$ (i.e. the other end of the film of thickness, δ), $C_A = C_{Ab}$,

we get

$$C_A = C_{Ai} - (C_{Ai} - C_{Ab})\frac{z}{\delta} \tag{3.29}$$

The above equation indicates that the theoretical concentration profile, according to the film theory, is linear as shown in Figure 3.6(b) (where the 'true' concentration profile is also shown). The mass transfer flux through the film is constant at steady state and is given as

$$N_A = -D_{AB}\left[\frac{dC_A}{dz}\right]_{z=0} = \frac{D_{AB}}{\delta}(C_{Ai} - C_{Ab}) \tag{3.30}$$

Comparing with Eq. (3.3), the mass transfer coefficient is

$$k_L = \frac{D_{AB}}{\delta} \tag{3.31}$$

Thus the mass transfer coefficient can be calculated from the film theory if the diffusivity and the film thickness are known. Whereas the former can possibly be obtained from the literature or may be estimated by using a suitable correlation, the latter (i.e. the film thickness δ) is unknown. So this theory does not help us in reality to predict the mass transfer coefficient. However, the film theory, like two other theories described below, has been extremely useful in the analysis of mass transfer accompanied by a chemical reaction (as we shall see in Chapter 16).

The film thickness, however, can be attributed a physical significance. It is the thickness of the stagnant layer of fluid that offers a mass transfer resistance equal to the actual resistance to mass transfer offered by the fluid in motion. The film theory predicts linear dependence of k_L

[†] The notation $|_z$ means 'evaluated at z' (see Section 2.7.2).

upon the diffusivity D_{AB}. Unfortunately, experimental data for diverse systems show that the coefficient of mass transfer to a turbulent fluid varies as $(D_{AB})^n$ where n may have any value from zero to about 0.8.

The film theory is simple indeed and that is why it has got wide acceptance. Nevertheless, it does not visualize a realistic physical picture regarding the mechanism of mass transfer at the phase boundary. Two other classical but more realistic models are described below.

3.7.2 The Penetration Theory

Before going into the details of this theory, let us have a close look at the phenomenon of mass transfer from a rising gas bubble—for example, absorption of oxygen from an air bubble in a fermenter. As the bubble rises, the liquid elements from the bulk reach the top of the bubble, move along its spherical surface, reach its bottom and then get detached from it. The detached liquid elements eventually get mixed up with the bulk liquid (Figure 3.7). Absorption of oxygen in a small liquid element occurs as long as the element remains at the gas–liquid interface (i.e. in contact with the gas). Similar phenomena occur in a large number of other situations involving mass transfer at a phase boundary. Thus, we may generalize the

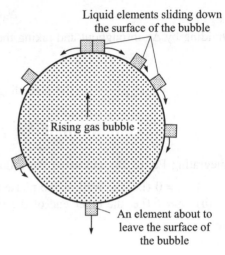

Liquid elements sliding down the surface of the bubble

Rising gas bubble

An element about to leave the surface of the bubble

Figure 3.7 The penetration model illustrated.

picture by arguing that in the case of mass transfer at a phase boundary, an element of liquid reaches the interface (by any mechanism whatsoever) and stays there for a short while when it receives some solute from the other phase. At the end of its stay at the interface, the liquid element moves back into the bulk liquid carrying with it the solute it picked up during its brief stay at the interface. In the process, the liquid element makes room for another liquid element, fresh from the bulk, on the surface of the bubble. The above visualization (or 'model') of the process of mass transfer at a phase boundary forms the basis of the 'Penetration Theory' proposed by Higbie (1935). The following are the basic assumptions of the penetration theory.

(a) Unsteady state mass transfer occurs to a liquid element so long as it is in contact with the bubble (or the other phase).

(b) Equilibrium exists at the gas–liquid interface.

(c) Each of the liquid elements stays in contact with the gas (or the other phase) for the same period of time.

If we confine our attention to mass transfer to a gas bubble of diameter d_b rising at a velocity u_b, the contact time of a liquid element with the gas is $t_c = d_b/u_b$, Unsteady state mass transfer to a liquid element during this period of time can be described by a partial differential equation given below (this equation can be derived by using an approach very similar to that used in the case of unsteady heat conduction to a semi-infinite medium, as discussed Chapter 15). The equation is

$$\frac{\partial C_A}{dt} = D_{AB} \frac{\partial^2 C_A}{\partial z^2} \tag{3.32}$$

The appropriate initial and boundary conditions are:

Initial condition   : $t = 0$, $z \geq 0$; $C_A = C_{Ab}$

Boundary condition 1 : $t > 0$, $z = 0$; $C_A = C_{Ai}$ (3.33)

Boundary condition 2 : $t > 0$, $z = \infty$; $C_A = C_{Ab}$

The initial condition implies that in a fresh liquid element coming from the bulk, the concentration is uniform and is equal to the bulk concentration. The boundary condition 1 assumes that 'interfacial equilibrium' exists at all time. The last condition means that if the contact time of an element with the gas is small, the 'depth of penetration' of the solute in the element should also be small and effectively the element can be considered to be of 'infinite thickness' in a relative sense. Equation (3.32), subject to the initial and boundary conditions (3.33), can be solved for the transient concentration distribution of the solute in the element by introducing a 'similarity variable' η, as in the case of unsteady state heat conduction (see Dutta, 2001). The solution is

$$\frac{C_A - C_{Ab}}{C_{Ai} - C_{Ab}} = 1 - \mathrm{erf}\eta; \qquad \text{where } \eta = \frac{z}{2\sqrt{D_{AB}t}} \qquad (3.34)$$

The mass flux to the element at any time t can be derived from the equation

$$N_A(t) = -D_{AB}\left[\frac{\partial C_A}{\partial z}\right]_{z=0} = \sqrt{\frac{D_{AB}}{\pi t}}(C_{Ai} - C_{Ab}) \qquad (3.35)$$

The flux decreases with time because of a gradual build-up of the solute concentration within the element and the resulting decrease in the driving force. At a large time, the element becomes nearly saturated and the flux becomes vanishingly small.

The average mass flux over the contact time t_c is given by

$$N_{A,\mathrm{av}} = \frac{1}{t_c}\int_0^{t_c} N_A(t)\,dt = 2\sqrt{\frac{D_{AB}}{\pi t_c}}(C_{Ai} - C_{Ab}) \qquad (3.36)$$

Comparing Eqs. (3.35) and (3.36) with Eq. (3.3),

$$\text{Instantaneous mass transfer coefficient, } k_L = \sqrt{\frac{D_{AB}}{\pi t}} \qquad (3.37)$$

$$\text{Average mass transfer coefficient, } k_{L,\mathrm{av}} = 2\sqrt{\frac{D_{AB}}{\pi t_c}} \qquad (3.38)$$

The above equations show that the mass transfer coefficient is proportional to the square root of diffusivity. Although this is again not in conformity with experimental observations in general, this is definitely an improvement over the film theory for a more realistic visualization. Here the contact time t_c is the model parameter like the film thickness δ in the film theory.

3.7.3 The Surface Renewal Theory

One of the major drawbacks of the penetration theory is the assumption that the contact time or the 'age' of the liquid elements is the same for all. In a turbulent medium it is much more probable that some of the liquid elements are swept away, while still young, from the interface by eddies while some others, unaffected by the eddies for the time being, may continue to be in contact with the gas for longer times. As a result, there will be a 'distribution of age' of the liquid elements present at the interface at any moment. This is how Danckwert (1951) visualized the phenomenon. He assumed that (i) the liquid elements at the interface are being randomly replaced by fresh elements from the bulk, (ii) at any moment each of the liquid elements at the surface has the same probability of being replaced by a fresh element, (iii) unsteady state mass transfer occurs to an element during its stay at the interface. The Danckwert's theory is thus called the *surface renewal theory*. The model parameter is the fractional rate of surface renewal (s, the fraction of the surface area renewed in unit time). The equation for the mass transfer coefficient according to the Danckwert's theory is as follows (the derivation is shown in Chapter 16).

$$k_L = \sqrt{D_{AB}\,s} \tag{3.39}$$

It may be noted that the surface renewal theory also predicts the square root dependence of the mass transfer coefficient k_L on the diffusivity. It also has similar dependence on the fractional rate of surface renewal, s. Increasing turbulence in the medium causes more brisk surface renewal (i.e. larger s) thereby increasing the mass transfer coefficient. The expressions for the mass transfer coefficient obtained from the above three theories and the boundary layer theory described below are listed in Table 3.4.

Table 3.4   Mass transfer coefficients from the different theories of mass transfer

Theory	Steady/unsteady state	Expression for the coefficient, k_L	Dependence on diffusivity	Model parameter (unit)
Film theory	Steady state	$k_L = D/\delta$	$k_L \propto D$	δ (m)
Penetration theory	Unsteady state	$k_{L,inst} = [D/\pi t]^{1/2}$	$k_L \propto D^{1/2}$	
		$k_{L,av} = 2[D/\pi t_c]^{1/2}$	$k_L \propto D^{1/2}$	t_c (s)
Surface renewal theory	Unsteady state	$k_{L,av} = [Ds]^{1/2}$	$k_L \propto D^{1/2}$	s (s^{-1})
Boundary layer theory	Steady state	Eqs. (3.40), (3.41)	$k_L \propto D^{2/3}$	

inst.—instantaneous;   av. — average

3.7.4   The Boundary Layer Theory

The foregoing theories of mass transfer have been built up on the basis of idealized pictures of the way mass transfer occurs at a phase boundary. As such, these theories, though fit well in some particular cases, do not reflect the real picture in general. The major reason is that none of these theories explicitly takes into account the hydrodynamics or flow field that characterizes a system, although the flow field greatly influences the rate of convective mass transfer. What the foregoing theories do is to use a model parameter (the film thickness, the contact time or the surface renewal rate) to take into account the effect of fluid motion *implicitly*. For example, more intense fluid velocity or a high degree of turbulence in the medium is associated with a decrease in the film thickness or the contact time or an increase in the fractional rate of surface renewal. The boundary layer theory (see, for example, Bird et al., 2002), on the other hand, gives a far more realistic picture of the way mass transfer takes place at a phase boundary.

Before dealing with mass transfer in boundary layer flow, let us recapitulate the formation of boundary of layer on an immersed surface in a viscous fluid in motion. For simplicity, we take the case of flow past a flat plate (Figure 3.8) oriented along the direction of flow (zero angle of incidence). The fluid velocity is zero at the surface of the plate (the no-slip condition) but increases with distance from the plate. At a rather short distance away from the surface, the fluid velocity almost reaches the velocity of the bulk fluid along the direction of orientation of the plate (called the 'free stream velocity', V_∞). The region above the plate within which the fluid velocity changes from zero at the surface to the free stream velocity is called the 'velocity boundary thickness', δ. To be more precise, this region is called the 'velocity boundary layer' (or the 'momentum boundary layer' or the 'hydrodynamic boundary layer'). The boundary layer thickness increases gradually along the plate. It is expressed as a function of the distance from the leading edge, i.e. $\delta = \delta(x)$. Theoretically, the free stream velocity is reached at a large distance from the plate. However, in reality the velocity reaches nearly the free stream value at a rather small distance away from the plate. Typically, the boundary layer thickness at any point on the plate is defined *arbitrarily* as the transverse distance from the plate where 99% of the free stream velocity is attained.

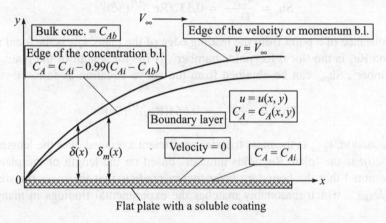

Figure 3.8 Momentum and concentration boundary layers on a flat plate for Sc > 1. V_∞ = free stream velocity; C_{Ab} = bulk concentration; C_{Ai} = surface concentration or the solubility of the coated solid in the liquid. Since Sc > 1, the momentum diffusivity is larger than the molecular diffusivity ($v_\infty > D_{AB}$), and the momentum boundary layer is thicker than the concentration boundary layer as a result.

If the flow occurs at *zero angle of incidence* and the plate is 'wide', the motion in the boundary is two-dimensional, $u = u(x, y)$. The general equation of motion of a viscous fluid, called the *Navier–Stokes equation*, can be simplified and approximated to write down the equations of motion for two-dimensional boundary layer flow, which can be solved to get the velocity field in the laminar boundary layer (Dutta, 2001). The characteristics of the boundary layer depends upon the Reynolds number defined as $\text{Re}_x = \rho V_\infty x/\mu$, where Re_x is the local Reynolds number as it is based on the distance x from the leading edge. Boundary layer flow remains laminar if the Reynolds number is less than about 3×10^5, above which the flow turns turbulent. This value of the Reynolds number is called the 'critical Reynolds number'.

Mass transfer in boundary layer flow occurs in a way similar to that of heat transfer. If the plate is coated with a soluble substance and the liquid (or gas) flows over it, two boundary layers are formed—the 'velocity boundary layer' and the 'concentration' or 'mass boundary layer' (Figure 3.8). It may be recalled that in boundary layer flow over a heated plate, a thermal boundary layer is formed along with the velocity or momentum boundary layer (thickness = δ). The concentration distribution in the boundary layer is a function of position, $C_A = C_A(x, y)$, and its thickness is a function of the distance from the leading edge, $\delta = \delta_m(x)$. The thickness of the concentration boundary layer δ_m is defined as the distance over which the solute concentration drops by 99% of the concentration difference between the wall and the bulk liquid. The relative thicknesses of the velocity and the concentration boundary layers depend upon the value of the Schmidt number, Sc (which is the ratio of the momentum diffusivity to the molecular diffusivity). If the Schmidt number is greater than unity, the thickness of the momentum boundary layer at any location on the plate is more than the concentration boundary layer. It can be shown that $\delta/\delta_m = \text{Sc}^{1/3}$ (Deen, 1998; Bird et al., 2002).

Theoretical analysis of mass transfer in a laminar boundary can be done following the same approach as adopted in the case of heat transfer, and the following equation for the local Sherwood number, Sh_x, can be developed.

$$\text{Sh}_x = \frac{k_{L,x}x}{D_{AB}} = 0.332(\text{Re}_x)^{1/2}(\text{Sc})^{1/3} \qquad (3.40)$$

Here x is the distance of a point from the leading edge of the plate, $k_{L,x}$ is the local mass transfer coefficient, and Re_x is the 'local Reynolds number'. If l is the length of the plate, the 'average Sherwood number', Sh_{av}, can be obtained from the above equation as follows:

$$\text{Sh}_{av} = \frac{k_{L,av}l}{D_{AB}} = 0.664(\text{Re}_l)^{1/2}(\text{Sc})^{1/3} \qquad (3.41)$$

In the above equation, $k_{L,av}$ is the mass transfer coefficient averaged over the length of the plate, and $\text{Re}_l = \rho V_\infty l/\mu$ is the 'plate Reynolds number' based on the length of the plate, l.

It is to be noted that the boundary layer theory predicts that the mass transfer coefficient k_L varies as $(D_{AB})^{2/3}$ which reasonably matches the experimental findings in many cases.

3.7.5   Other Theories

Quite a few other theories were proposed at different times to describe mass transfer at a phase boundary (for example the film-penetration theory). Theories based on eddy diffusivity have also been proposed. Although the theories of mass transfer provide an insight into the mechanism of mass transfer at a phase boundary, these are not directly useful for predictive purposes (the boundary layer theory is an exception in many practical situations). However, the penetration theory and the surface renewal theory have proved to be immensely useful for mass transfer calculations when the dissolved solute undergoes a chemical reaction. Consumption of the dissolved solute reduces its concentration in the solution, increases the driving force and thereby increases the rate of absorption compared to the case where no such reaction occurs (i.e. where only the physical transport of the solute occurs). In fact, any of the above theories can be used to calculate the degree of enhancement of the rate of mass transfer as a result of chemical reaction. This aspect will be discussed in detail in Chapter 16. The penetration theory has been the basis of the Billet model of mass transfer in a packed column (as we shall see in Chapter 6).

EXAMPLE 3.5 (*Gas absorption in a laminar jet*)   Gas absorption in a laminar liquid jet is a model experimental technique for the determination of the liquid-phase diffusivity of a soluble gas and also for studying the kinetics of gas–liquid reactions. A sketch of a laminar jet apparatus is given in Figure 3.9. A liquid jet is created by forcing the liquid through a narrow vertical tube, fitted within an enclosure. If an appropriate flow rate is maintained, the liquid comes out as a jet (that very much looks like a liquid rod or cylinder). The jet is collected in a tube of a diameter marginally greater than that of the jet and having a slightly flared opening. This liquid collection tube is oriented vertically below the jet. The solute gas, diluted with a carrier if necessary, flows through the enclosure. The rate of absorption of the gas is determined either by measuring the inlet and the outlet gas flow rates or by analyzing the concentration of the dissolved gas in the exit liquid.

In an experiment for the determination of the diffusivity of hydrogen sulphide in water, pure H_2S gas is passed through the enclosure of the jet. The following data were collected in a particular experiment at steady state: temperature = 25°C; total pressure in the jet chamber = 1.03 atm; length of the jet = 5 cm; rate of flow of water = 13.2 ml/s; absorption rate of H_2S = 4.42×10^{-4} g/s. The solubility of H_2S in water at 1 atm pressure and 25°C is 0.1136 kmol/(m^3)(atm). Calculate the diffusivity of H_2S in water from the above data.

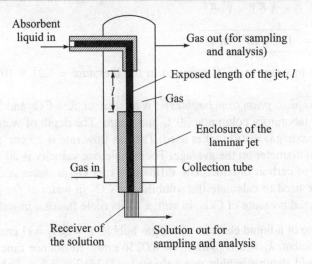

Figure 3.9   A simplified sketch of the laminar jet apparatus.

Solution

A liquid jet has a rod-like flow; it has a flat velocity profile. In other words, the velocity is uniform over a cross-section of the jet.

Let us use the following notations: r = radius of the jet; v = (uniform) velocity of the jet; Q = the liquid flow rate (= $\pi r^2 v$) = 13.2 ml/s = 1.32×10^{-5} m^3/s; l = length of the jet (= 0.05 m); t_c = contact time = l/v. Molecular weight of H_2S = 34.

The solute gas gets dissolved at the surface of the jet and penetrates into it by *unsteady state* diffusion. The situation fits in the penetration theory almost ideally. Accordingly, the average mass transfer coefficient [see Eq. (3.36)] and the gas–liquid area of contact are

$$k_{L,\text{av}} = 2\sqrt{\frac{D_{AB}}{\pi t_c}} = 2\sqrt{\frac{D_{AB}}{\pi}\frac{v}{l}}; \qquad \text{the area of contact} = 2\pi r l \qquad \text{(i)}$$

$$\text{The rate of absorption of } H_2S = (2\pi r l)(k_{L,\text{av}})(C_{Ai} - C_{Ab}) \qquad \text{(ii)}$$

where C_{Ai} = interfacial concentration of H_2S in the liquid, and C_{Ab} = H_2S concentration in the bulk of the jet. The interfacial concentration is the same as the solubility of the gas at the given temperature and pressure, and can be calculated at the given pressure (1.03 atm) using the Henry's law:

$C_{Ai} = (1.03)(0.1136) = 0.117 \text{ kmol/m}^3$

$C_{Ab} = 0$ (because of the small contact time, the depth of penetration of the solute in the jet will be small and the bulk liquid free from H_2S)

The given rate of absorption of $H_2S = 4.42 \times 10^{-4}$ g/s = $(4.42/34) \times 10^{-4} \times 10^{-3}$, i.e. 1.3×10^{-8} kmol/s.

Using Eqs. (i) and (ii) and the given rate of absorption [note that $r = (Q/\pi v)^{1/2}$],

$$1.3 \times 10^{-8} = 2\pi l \sqrt{\frac{Q}{\pi v}} \cdot 2\sqrt{\frac{D_{AB} v}{\pi l}}(0.117 - 0) = 4\sqrt{D_{AB}(1.32 \times 10^{-5})(0.05)}(0.117)$$

$$\Rightarrow \qquad D_{AB} = \boxed{1.17 \times 10^{-9} \text{ m}^2\text{/s}}$$

[Diffusivity of H_2S in water at 25°C reported in the literature = 1.21×10^{-9} m^2/s]

EXAMPLE 3.6 (*Gas absorption from bubbles*)   A mixture of 50% CO_2 and 50% N_2 is bubbling through water in a laboratory column at 30°C and 1 atm. The depth of water in the column is 30 cm. A single-nozzle gas distributor is used. The gas flow rate is 15 cm^3 per minute and the bubbles are of 1 cm diameter on the average. The bubble rise velocity is 20 cm/s. Calculate the rate of absorption of carbon dioxide. The diffusivity of CO_2 in water is 2.19×10^{-5} cm^2/s. Henry's law can be used to calculate the solubility of CO_2 in water at the given temperature, $p = 1860x^*$ (p = partial pressure of CO_2, in atm; x^* is its mole fraction in water at equilibrium).

Hints: Contact time of a liquid element with a gas bubble, $t_c = d_b/v_b = (1 \text{ cm})/(20 \text{ cm/s}) = 0.05$ s Mass transfer coefficient, $k_L = 2(D_{AB}/\pi t_c)^{1/2} = 0.0236$ cm/s. Residence time of a single bubble in the liquid = (liquid depth)/(bubble rise velocity) = 0.3/0.2 = 1.5 s. Volume of a bubble = 0.5236 cm^3; area of a bubble = 3.1416 cm^2. Solubility of CO_2 in water (from Henry's law), $C_s = 1.493 \times 10^{-5}$ gmol/cm^3 (p_{CO_2} is approximately taken as 0.5 atm). Concentration of CO_2 in the bulk water, $C_b = 0$.

Amount of CO_2 absorbed from a single bubble during its residence time of 1.5 s

$$= (k_L)(\text{area of a bubble})(C_s - C_b)(1.5 \text{ s}) = 1.66 \times 10^{-6} \text{ gmol}$$

Average number of bubbles formed per minute = 15/0.5236 = 28.65 per min.

Rate of absorption of CO_2 from the bubbles per minute

$$= (1.66 \times 10^{-6} \text{ gmol per bubble})(28.65 \text{ bubbles per min}) = 4.757 \times 10^{-5} \text{ gmol/min}$$

EXAMPLE 3.7 (*Gas absorption in an agitated vessel*)   In an experimental agitated contactor, pure carbon dioxide is being absorbed in water at 25°C and 2 atm pressure. Water is pumped into the contactor at a rate of 1 litre per minute and the carbonated water leaves the vessel continuously so that a constant volume is maintained in the contactor. The outlet water contains 2.3 g CO_2 per litre. The specific interfacial area of gas–liquid contact is 80 m²/m³ of the gas–liquid dispersion; the volume of the gas–liquid dispersion is 8 litre. The liquid phase can be assumed to be well mixed. The solubility of CO_2 in water can be calculated using the Henry's law. At 25°C, the Henry's law constant for CO_2 is 1640 atm/mol fraction and its diffusivity in water is 1.92×10^{-9} m²/s. Calculate

(a) the thickness of the liquid-film if the film theory is applicable,
(b) the contact time between a liquid element with the gas if the penetration theory is applicable, and
(c) the fractional surface renewal rate if the surface renewal theory is applicable.

The density of the liquid is 997 kg/m³ (i.e. the same as that of water at the given temperature).

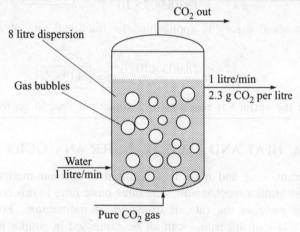

Figure 3.10 CO_2 gas bubbles through a tank.

Solution
The solubility of CO_2 at the experimental temperature is given by Henry's law, $p = 1640x^*$

At $p = 2$ atm, $x^* = 2/1640 = 0.00122$ (the superscript* is often used to indicate the equilibrium concentration). We shall first calculate the mass transfer coefficient k_L, and then use it to determine the required quantities.

Molecular weight of the solution = $(44)(0.00122) + (18)(1 - 0.00122) = 18.03 \approx 18$
Moles of solution per m³ = $(997 \text{ kg/m}^3)/(18 \text{ kg/mol}) = 55.4 \text{ kmol/m}^3$
Moles of CO_2 per m³ solution, $C_s = (55.4)(0.00122) = 0.0676 \text{ kmol/m}^3$

Concentration of the carbonated solution leaving the vessel,

$$C = 2.3 \text{ g } CO_2/\text{litre} = 2.3 \text{ kg } CO_2/\text{m}^3 = 2.3/44 = 0.0523 \text{ kmol/m}^3$$

= Concentration of CO_2 in the liquid in the vessel (since it is well-mixed).

Volume rate of input of water ≈ volume rate of output of the solution

$$= 1 \text{ litre/min} = 1.667 \times 10^{-5} \text{ m}^3/\text{s}$$

The inlet water is CO_2-free. So at steady state, the rate of absorption of CO_2 in the vessel

$$= (1.667 \times 10^{-5} \text{ m}^3/\text{s})(0.0523 \text{ kmol/m}^3) = 8.718 \times 10^{-7} \text{ kmol/s}$$

If V = the volume of the gas–liquid dispersion in the vessel (= 8 litre = 0.008 m³), $\bar{a}$ = specific interfacial area of contact between the dispersed gas and the liquid (= 80 m²/m³), and k_L = mass transfer coefficient,

Rate of absorption of CO_2 at steady state = $V \bar{a} k_L (C_s - C) = 8.718 \times 10^{-7}$ kmol/s

$\Rightarrow$ $(0.008)(80)(k_L)(0.0676 - 0.0523) = 8.718 \times 10^{-7}$; when $k_L = 8.903 \times 10^{-5}$ m/s

(a)   If the film theory is applicable, film thickness,

$$\delta = \frac{D_{AB}}{k_L} = \frac{1.92 \times 10^{-9}}{8.903 \times 10^{-5}} = \boxed{0.0216 \text{ mm}}$$

(b)   If the penetration theory is applicable, the contact time [see Eq. (3.38)] is

$$t_c = \frac{4 D_{AB}}{\pi k_L^2} = \frac{(4)(1.92 \times 10^{-9})}{(\pi)(8.903 \times 10^{-5})^2} = \boxed{0.308 \text{ s}}$$

(c)   If the surface renewal theory is applicable, the fractional rate of surface renewal [see Eq. (3.39)],

$$s = \frac{k_L^2}{D_{AB}} = \frac{(8.903 \times 10^{-5})^2}{1.92 \times 10^{-9}} = \boxed{4.13 \text{ s}^{-1}}$$

(This means that the surface is renewed 4.13 times per second on the average.)

3.8   MOMENTUM, HEAT AND MASS TRANSFER ANALOGIES

Transport of momentum, heat and mass in a medium in laminar motion are all diffusional processes and occur by similar mechanisms. The three basic laws in this connection—Newton's law of viscosity that governs the rate of transport of momentum, Fourier's law of heat conduction and Fick's law of diffusion—can all be expressed in similar forms.

Newton's Law: Momentum flux, $\tau = -\mu \dfrac{d u_x}{dz}$ $\Rightarrow$ $\tau = -v \dfrac{d}{dz}(\rho u_x)$ (3.42)

Fourier's Law: Heat flux, $q_z = -k \dfrac{dT}{dz}$ $\Rightarrow$ $q_z = -\alpha \dfrac{d}{dz}(\rho c_p T)$ (3.43)

Fick's Law: Mass flux (at a low concentration), $N_A = -D_{AB} \dfrac{dC_A}{dz}$ (3.44)

In Eq. (3.42), τ is the shear stress which is the same as momentum flux, ρu_x is the 'volumetric concentration of momentum' in the x-direction (i.e. momentum per unit volume of the liquid), and $v = \mu/\rho$, is the 'momentum diffusivity'. In Eq. (3.43), $\rho c_p T$ is the 'volumetric concentration of thermal energy' and $\alpha (= k/\rho c_p)$ is the 'thermal diffusivity'. Thus, all the above three equations state that the flux is proportional to the gradient of the quantity transported (momentum, heat energy, or mass), and the proportionality constant is the corresponding 'diffusivity' (that has the same unit, m²/s, in all the cases). A negative sign is included in each equation to indicate that transport occurs in the direction of decreasing concentration (of momentum, heat, or mass).

In turbulent flow, similar equations are used to express the rate of transport except that an 'eddy diffusivity' is included to account for the contribution of eddy transport (see Section 3.5). Thus,

$$\text{Momentum flux, } \tau = -(v + E_v)\frac{d}{dz}(\rho u_x) \tag{3.45}$$

$$\text{Heat flux, } q_z = -(\alpha + E_H)\frac{d}{dz}(\rho c_p T) \tag{3.46}$$

$$\text{Mass flux (at a low concentration), } N_A = -(D_{AB} + E_M)\frac{dC_A}{dz} \tag{3.47}$$

Here E_v, E_H and E_M are eddy diffusivities of momentum, heat and mass respectively. Since turbulent transport is a much faster process than molecular transport, all the eddy diffusivities are larger than their molecular counterparts by about two orders of magnitude (i.e. a few hundred times) or even more.

The similarity of the three transport laws has been extended to relate the appropriate dimensionless groups involving the heat transfer coefficient and the mass transfer coefficient to the friction factor. Such relations or 'analogies' (Skelland, 1974) can be used to estimate the heat transfer coefficient (h), or the mass transfer coefficients (k_G, k_L, etc.) if the friction factor of the flowing medium is known. Here we mention a few simple analogies without going into the theoretical formalism (see Skelland, 1974; Hines and Maddox, 1985; Dutta, 2001). The oldest such analogy in the case of heat transfer was proposed by Reynolds applicable to *transport in pipe flow*. Extending the analogy to the case of mass transfer, we may write

$$\text{St}_H = \frac{\text{Nu}}{\text{Re Pr}} = \frac{f}{2} \quad \text{and} \quad \text{St}_M = \frac{\text{Sh}}{\text{Re Sc}} = \frac{f}{2} \tag{3.48}$$

Here St_H is the Stanton number for heat transfer and St_M is that for mass transfer, Nu is the Nusselt number involving the heat transfer coefficient, and f is the friction factor for the fluid flowing through a pipe.

The Prandtl analogy, also applicable to transport in pipe flow, is given by

$$\text{St}_H = \frac{f/2}{1 + 5\sqrt{f/2}\,(\text{Pr} - 1)} \quad \text{and} \quad \text{St}_M = \frac{f/2}{1 + 5\sqrt{f/2}\,(\text{Sc} - 1)} \tag{3.49}$$

The Prandtl analogy reduces to the Reynolds analogy if Pr = 1 or Sc = 1.

Colburn related the mass transfer coefficient to the friction factor by proposing the well-known 'Colburn analogy'. He introduced the Colburn j-factor and suggested the following analogies for transport in pipe flow.

$$j_H = \text{St}_H\,\text{Pr}^{2/3} = \frac{\text{Nu}}{\text{Re Pr}^{1/3}} = 0.023\text{Re}^{-0.2} \tag{3.50}$$

and
$$j_D = \text{St}_M\text{Sc}^{2/3} = \frac{\text{Sh}}{\text{Re Sc}^{1/3}} = 0.023\text{Re}^{-0.2} \tag{3.51}$$

Here the subscripts 'H' and 'M' refer to heat and mass transfer respectively [the subscript 'D' in j_D means diffusion and is synonymous to the subscript M in Eq. (3.49)]. The importance of the analogies lies in the fact that if the heat transfer coefficient is known at a particular hydrodynamic condition characterized by the Reynolds number, the mass transfer coefficient in a system having similar geometry and at similar hydrodynamic condition (i.e. the same Reynolds number) can be determined just by putting $j_H = j_D$.

EXAMPLE 3.8 (*Mass transfer in a packed bed*)   Water at 25°C flows through a bed of benzoic acid spheres of size $d_p = 8$ mm at a superficial velocity of 0.022 m^3 per second per square metre of bed cross-section. The fractional void volume of the bed is 0.4 and the depth of the bed is 0.7 m. If the inlet water is free from benzoic acid, calculate the concentration of the acid in the effluent from the bed.

The following data are available: diffusivity of benzoic acid in water = 10^{-5} cm^2/s; kinematic viscosity of the liquid = 0.95 centistoke; solubility of benzoic acid in water at the given temperature = 3.01 kg/m^3. For a packed bed of sphere, the specific surface area (i.e. the area of the spheres per unit volume of the bed) is given by: $\bar{a} = 6(1 - \varepsilon)/d_p$.

Solution

The concentration of benzoic acid in the bulk liquid, C_b, increases along the bed from the inlet value of $C_{b1} = 0$. The concentration of the liquid in contact with the surface of a sphere is, $C_s = 3.01$ kg/m^3. As a result, the driving force, $C_s - C_b$, changes along the bed.

Let us use the following notations: Q = volumetric flow rate of water; a = cross-sectioal area of the bed. Then, Q/a = liquid flow rate per unit area of the bed = 0.022 m^3/m^{2}s = 2.2 cm/s (this is also the linear velocity of the liquid if the entire cross-section is available for flow and is called the 'superficial liquid velocity').

If we consider a differential thickness of the bed, dh, at a distance h from the top of the bed (see Figure 3.11), the concentration changes by dC_b and a differential mass balance at steady state over dh gives

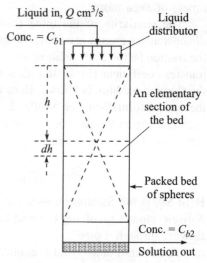

$$Q\, dC_b = (k_L \bar{a})(A\, dh)(C_s - C_b)$$

Figure 3.11   An elementary section of a packed bed.

In the above equation, $k_L \bar{a}$ is the 'volumetric mass transfer coefficient' (i.e. the amount of mass transfer per unit time per unit volume of the bed per unit concentration driving force). Integrating the above equation over the height h,

$$\int_{C_{b1}}^{C_{b2}} \frac{dC_b}{C_s - C_b} = k_L \bar{a} \frac{a}{Q} \int_0^h dh \quad \Rightarrow \quad \ln \frac{C_s - C_{b1}}{C_s - C_{b2}} = k_L \bar{a} \frac{a}{Q} h \tag{i}$$

Now we need to calculate the value of k_L at the given flow rate of the liquid through the bed. We use the correlation

$$\varepsilon j_D = 0.25 \mathrm{Re}^{-0.31}$$

Given: diameter of a sphere, $d_p = 0.8$ cm; superficial liquid velocity, $v_o = 2.2$ cm/s; the kinematic viscosity, $\nu = 0.0095$ cm^2/s; diffusivity of the solute, $D_{AB} = 10^{-5}$ cm^2/s; bed voidage, $\varepsilon = 0.4$.

$$\text{Re} = \frac{d_p v_o}{v} = \frac{(0.8)(2.2)}{(0.0095)} = 185 \quad \text{and} \quad \text{Sc} = \frac{v}{D_{AB}} = \frac{0.0095}{10^{-5}} = 950$$

$$\varepsilon j_D = \varepsilon \frac{\text{Sh}}{\text{Re Sc}^{1/3}} = 0.25(185)^{-0.31} = 0.0495 \quad \Rightarrow \quad \text{Sh} = \frac{(0.0495)(185)(950)^{1/3}}{0.4} = 225$$

$$k_L = \text{Sh}\left(\frac{D_{AB}}{d_p}\right) = 225\left(\frac{10^{-5}}{0.8}\right) = 0.00281 \text{ cm/s}$$

Specific interfacial area of contact, $\bar{a} = \dfrac{6(1-\varepsilon)}{d_p} = \dfrac{6(1-0.4)}{0.8} = 4.5 \text{ cm}^2/\text{cm}^3$

Putting the values of the different quantities in Eq. (i), the effluent concentration,

$$C_{b2} = \boxed{1 \text{ kg/m}^3}$$

EXAMPLE 3.9 (*Mass transfer in a wetted-wall column*)   As stated in Section 3.6, one of the experimental devices for the determination of the mass transfer coefficient is a wetted-wall column. In an experiment, benzene is absorbed from a stream of nitrogen in a wetted-wall column in which the absorbent is a non-volatile mineral oil. Under the conditions, the liquid-phase mass transfer resistance can be safely neglected. The mass flow rate of the feed gas is 13,500 kg/h·m^2 at 30°C and 1.013 bar pressure. Mole fractions of benzene in the inlet and outlet gases are 0.02 and 0.0052 respectively. The interfacial concentration of benzene on the gas side is negligibly small.

Calculate the gas-phase mass transfer coefficient.

Can you predict the mass transfer coefficient for the absorption of ammonia in a dilute solution of H$_2$SO$_4$ in the same wetted-wall column if the flow rate of air is 4.51 kg/m^2·s at 25°C and 1.013 bar, and the partial pressure of ammonia in the feed gas is 10 mm Hg?

Given: i.d. of the column = 3.5 cm; thickness of the liquid film is small; height of the wetted section = 3 m; viscosity: for nitrogen (at 30°C) = 0.018 cP, for air (at 25°C) = 0.0183 cP; diffusivity of benzene in N$_2$ at 30°C = 0.0973 cm^2/s, that of NH$_3$ in air at 25°C = 0.231 cm^2/s.

Since the concentration of benzene in the gas is small, the change of flow rate over the column also remains small. So calculations may be done on the basis of the average gas flow rate. It is also given that the Colburn factor j_D varies as Re$^{-0.23}$.

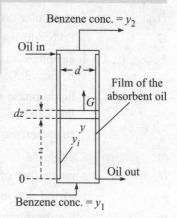

Benzene conc. = y_2

Oil in

Film of the absorbent oil

dz

G

y

y_i

z

Oil out

Benzene conc. = y_1

Figure 3.12 Gas absorption in a wetted-wall column.

Hints: Consider an elementary section of the column of thickness dz at a height z from the bottom as shown in Figure 3.12. Suppose

y = local concentration of benzene (the solute) in the bulk gas (mole fraction); y_i = interfacial concentration at the same section; G = molar gas flow rate; and d = diameter of the column.

Then the elementary area of gas–liquid contact = $(\pi d)(dz)$. If the gas concentration changes by dy over the section, a differential mass balance can be written as

$$-G dy = (\pi d)(dz)k_y(y - y_i)$$

Assuming that the gas flow rate remains reasonably constant over the column (this assumption is valid at low concentration, as in the given case, and an *average gas flow rate* may be used).

Integrating from $z = 0$, $y = y_1 = 0.02$ (bottom) to $z = L = 3$ m, $y = y_2 = 0.0052$ (top), we get

$$k_y = [G \ln(y_1/y_2)]/(\pi dL)$$

Average mol. wt. of the gas at the bottom = $(0.02)(78) + (0.98)(28) = 29$; at the top it is 28.2; average molar gas flow rate at the bottom = $(13,500/29) = 465.5$ kmol/m^2·h, that at the top = 458.6 kmol/m^2·h. Average = 462 kmol/m^2·h.

Area of the cross-section of the tube (0.035 m dia) = 9.62×10^{-4} m^2.

Actual gas flow rate through the tube,

$$G = (9.62 \times 10^{-4})(462) = 0.4448 \text{ kmol/h}$$

Then,

$$k_y = 1.786 \text{ kmol/(h)(m}^2)(\Delta y)$$

Now, if '1' denotes the N$_2$–benzene system and '2' denotes the air–NH$_3$ system, calculate Re$_1$ (= 7140), Re$_2$ (= 8630), Sc$_1$ (= 1.5) and Sc$_2$ (= 0.675). Then

$$\frac{j_{D,1}}{j_{D,2}} = \left(\frac{\text{Re}_1}{\text{Re}_2}\right)^{-0.23} \qquad \Rightarrow \qquad \frac{\text{Sh}_1}{\text{Sh}_2} = \left(\frac{\text{Re}_1}{\text{Re}_2}\right)^{0.77}\left(\frac{\text{Sc}_1}{\text{Sc}_2}\right)^{0.33}$$

Take $p_{BM} \approx P$ in Sh, calculate $k_{y2} = 4.25$ kmol/(h)(m^2)(Δy) for the air–NH$_3$ system at the given conditions.

NOTATIONS

C_A	:	molar concentration of A, kmol/m^3
d, d_p	:	diameter of a tube or sphere, or particle, m
D_{AB}	:	molecular diffusivity of A in B, m^2/s
E	:	Eddy 'diffusivity' [suffix v—momentum, H—heat, M—mass diffusion], m^2/s.
k_y, k_G, k_c, k_Y	:	gas-phase mass transfer coefficients for diffusion of A through non-diffusing B, Eq. (3.3); a prime is used to mean equimolar counterdiffusion
k_x, k_L, k_X	:	liquid-phase mass transfer coefficients for diffusion of A through stagnant B, Eq. (3.4)
l	:	characteristic length, m
m	:	mass, kg
N_A	:	molar flux of species A
p	:	partial pressure, bar, atm, etc.
p_{BM}	:	log mean partial pressure of the non-diffusing component
P	:	total pressure

s	:	fractional rate of surface renewal, s^{-1}
t, t_c	:	time, contact time, s
u, v	:	velocity (in the longitudinal or transverse direction), m/s
V_∞	:	free stream velocity ('far away' from an immersed surface), m/s
y, Y	:	mole fraction, mole ratio of a species in the gas phase
x, X	:	mole fraction, mole ratio of a species in liquid
z	:	distance, m
Re_x	:	local Reynolds number, $xV_\infty\rho/\mu$; x is the longitudinal distance
Sc	:	Schmidt number
Sh	:	Sherwood number, Eqs. (3.16), (3.17)
δ	:	film thickness; velocity boundary layer thickness, m
δ_m	:	mass transfer boundary layer thickness, m
μ	:	viscosity of a fluid, kg/m·s
ν	:	momentum diffusivity, μ/ρ
1, 2	:	positions 1 and 2.

Subscripts

b	:	bulk of a phase
i	:	interface between two phases
av	:	average value

SHORT AND MULTIPLE CHOICE QUESTIONS

1. Explain the basic difference between the mass transfer coefficients k_y and k_y'.

2. Obtain the relation between k_Y and k_Y'. Write down the units of mass transfer coefficients. Discuss when and how the mass transfer coefficients depend upon concentration.

3. Give the physical significances of the dimensionless groups in mass transfer.

4. For mass transfer from a sphere to a stagnant liquid, show that $Sh = 2$.

5. Explain the underlying assumptions of the theories of mass transfer.

6. Derive Eqs. (3.34) and (3.39).

7. The film theory gives a linear concentration profile of the solute within the stagnant film. Is there a point within the film at which the gradient of 'true concentration profile' and that of the 'theoretical concentration' profile in the film are the same?

8. Discuss the importance and applications of mass transfer analogies.

9. A gas A diffuses through a non-diffusing B across a stagnant film of thickness 2 mm. *Given:* mole fractions of A on the two sides of the film are $y_{A1} = 0.3$, $y_{A2} = 0.05$; total pressure = 1 atm; molar flux, $N_A = 5 \times 10^{-4}$ kmol/m²·s.

Calculate the Colburn-Drew mass transfer coefficient. Also calculate the molar flux if transport of A occurs through a stagnant film of B, 1 mm thick, for $y_{A1} = 0.2$ and $y_{A2} = 0.03$.

10. Make the correct choice from the alternatives given against the following questions.

   (a) Identify the quantities that have influence on the mass transfer coefficient: (i) diffusivity, (ii) solubility of the solute, (iii) molar flux, (iv) hydrodynamics of the system, (v) viscosity of the medium, (vi) interfacial concentration gradient, (vii) the interfacial area of contact.

   (b) If the mass transfer flux is expressed in terms of a mass transfer coefficient, the driving force should be

   (i) the concentration gradient at the interface
   (ii) the concentration difference between the interface and the bulk
   (iii) the interfacial concentration.

   (c) How does an increase in the liquid flow rate in a packed tower affect the rate of surface renewal of the liquid in a packed tower? The rate of surface renewal will

   (i) increase   (ii) decrease   (iii) remain unchanged.

   (d) How does an increase in the gas flow rate affect the gas-phase mass transfer coefficient in a packed tower? The mass transfer coefficient will

   (i) increase   (ii) decrease   (iii) remain unchanged.

   (e) How do you define the Stanton number for mass transfer?

   (i) $\dfrac{Sh}{Re\ Sc}$ (ii) $\dfrac{Sh}{Re\ Sc^{1/3}}$ (iii) $\dfrac{Pe}{Sc}$

   (f) How do you define the Peclet number?

   (i) $Pe = Re \cdot Sc$ (ii) $Pe = Re/Sc$ (iii) $Pe = Sh/Sc$

   (g) What is the expression for the Colburn factor, j_D?

   (i) $St\ Sc^{-1/3}$ (ii) $\dfrac{Sh}{Re\ Sc^{1/3}}$ (iii) $\dfrac{Sh}{Re\ Sc}$

   (h) The Sherwood number, Sh

   (i) increases with the friction factor, f
   (ii) increases with the Reynolds number, Re
   (iii) decreases with Re.

   (i) Air containing a solute flows over a pan containing water at a velocity of 20 ft/s. Which of the following all in $lbmol/(ft^2)(h)(atm)$, is a probable value of the average mass transfer coefficient?

   (i) 0.45   (ii) 0.00345   (iii) 562

   (j) The probable value of the Schmidt number for diffusion of NH_3 in air at 0°C may be

   (i) 40.5   (ii) 0.665   (iii) 0.0155

   The probable value of the Schmidt number for diffusion in water at 15°C may be
   (i) 5000   (ii) 0.132   (iii) 650

(k) Dissolution of a solid is being carried out in two identical stirred tanks at the same solid loading and stirrer rpm except that particles of 1 mm size are charged in tank 1 and particles of 0.5 mm size are charged in the other tank. In which tank is the dissolution of mass transfer coefficient expected to be larger?

   (i) Tank 1

   (ii) Tank 2

   (iii) The mass transfer coefficients in the tanks should be practically the same.

(l) What is the significance of 'film thickness' in mass transfer? It is

   (i) the actual thickness of the stagnant film that adheres to the phase boundary

   (ii) the depth of penetration of the solute in a liquid element

   (iii) the thickness of a stagnant film that offers the same resistance to mass transfer as is actually being offered under the given hydrodynamic condition.

(m) For gas absorption from a bubble in steady rise through a stagnant liquid, which of the following theories is most appropriate?

   (i) The film theory

   (ii) The penetration theory

   (iii) The surface renewal theory

(n) Consider a thin sheet of naphthalene placed in a stream of air. If we assume that mass transfer of naphthalene occurs through a stagnant film, then the 'thickness of the film' on the sheet will be

   (i) greater than the average thickness of the boundary layer

   (ii) less than the average thickness of the boundary layer

   (iii) equal to the average thickness of the boundary layer.

(o) A solid coated on the surface of a flat plate dissolves in a liquid flowing past the plate at zero angle of incidence. Convective transport of the solute occurs through the laminar mass transport boundary layer formed on the plate. In such a case the thickness of the momentum boundary layer is expected to be greater than the concentration boundary layer if the Schmidt number is

   (i) greater than 1   (ii) less than 1   (iii) equal to 1.

(p) Which of the following is a unit of fractional surface renewal rate?

   (i) cm/s   (ii) ft^2/h (iii) h^{-1}

(q) How does the 'age' of a liquid element at the phase boundary affect the rate of mass transfer to it? The rate of mass transfer

   (i) increases with the age of the element

   (ii) decreases with the age

   (iii) does not depend upon the age.

(r) A student measured the liquid-phase mass transfer coefficient for absorption of A in water. Applying the film theory he calculated the thickness of the liquid film, $\delta = 0.02$ mm. If the diffusivity of A in water is 1.1×10^{-5} cm^2/s, what would have been the value of the surface renewal rate (per second) if he had applied the surface renewal theory to his study?

   (i) 5.5×10^{-4} (ii) 325   (iii) 2.75

(s) Consider a bubble of a pure gas A rising steadily through a stagnant liquid B. The following data are given: diffusivity $= 3.14 \times 10^{-5}$ cm^2/s; bubble diameter $= 0.5$ cm; bubble rise velocity $= 20$ cm/s; solubility of the gas $= 0.2$ gmol/litre. What is the 'life' (in seconds) of individual liquid elements that come in contact with the bubble?

(i) 10   (ii) 0.1   (iii) 0.025

What is the average rate of surface renewal?

(i) 40 per second   (ii) 0.2 per second   (iii) 20 per second

What is the value of the average mass transfer coefficient in cm/s?

(i) 0.2   (ii) 0.04   (iii) 0.5

(t) A 10 mm diameter bubble of pure gas A rises through a quiescent liquid at a steady velocity of 25 cm/s and the average mass transfer coefficient is found to be 0.013 cm/s. What would be the average mass transfer coefficient in cm/s if bubbles of 5 mm diameter rise through the liquid at a velocity of 10 cm/s?

(i) 0.0104   (ii) 0.0116   (iii) 0.0162

(u) The mass transfer coefficient for absorption of CO_2 in water in an agitated tank is found to be 0.006 cm/s. Which of the following is a probable value of the mass transfer coefficient in cm/s for absorption of H_2S in water under identical hydrodynamic condition?

(i) 0.005   (ii) 0.05   (iii) 0.5

(v) In an experiment on mass transfer through the laminar boundary layer over a flat plate, 1 m long, the average mass transfer coefficient was found to be 0.00705 cm/s. What would be the average mass transfer coefficient in cm/s if the plate length is doubled?

(i) 0.0141   (ii) 0.0035   (iii) 0.005

(w) The Stanton number for heat transfer in a certain system is 0.0048. What would be the Stanton number for mass transfer under identical geometrical and hydrodynamic conditions if the Lewis number is 1.2?

(i) 0.00576   (ii) 0.0041   (iii) 0.00425

(x) The mass transfer coefficients obtained by the Reynolds and Prandtl analogies are the same if

(i) Sc $= 0$ (ii) Sc $= 1$ (iii) Sc $= \infty$

(y) Consider mass transfer of a solute in laminar boundary flow over a flat plate. The local mass transfer coefficient at a distance 0.2 m from the leading edge is 0.012 cm/s. What would be the local mass transfer coefficient in cm/s at a distance 0.4 m from the leading edge?

(i) 0.0085   (ii) 0.006   (iii) 0.017

(z) How does the mass transfer coefficient vary with the diffusivity according to the boundary layer theory?

(i) $D^{1/2}$ (ii) $D^{1/3}$ (iii) $D^{2/3}$

PROBLEMS

3.1 (*Calculation of mass transfer coefficients*)[1] Ammonia(A) is being absorbed in water from a mixture with nitrogen(B). The partial pressure of the solute in the bulk gas is 40 mm Hg and that at the gas–liquid interface is negligibly small. Diffusion occurs through a stagnant film of thickness 1 mm. The total pressure is 1 atm and the temperature is 25°C. Diffusivity of NH_3 in N_2 is 0.23 cm²/s. Calculate the absorption flux of NH_3 as well as the mass transfer coefficients k_G, k_y, k_c, k_Y, and F_G.

3.2 (*Interrelation among mass transfer coefficients*)[1] A stream of nitrogen containing 7.5% benzene vapour is scrubbed with a nonvolatile absorption oil in a tower at 35°C and 1.2 bar total pressure. The gas-phase mass transfer coefficient is estimated to be $k_G = 9.8 \times 10^{-4}$ kmol/(m²)(s)(bar). The mole fraction of benzene at the gas–liquid interface is $y_i = 0.01$. Calculate the gas-phase mass transfer coefficients k_y, k_c and k_Y. Also calculate the values of the mass transfer coefficient in terms of lbmol/(ft²)(h)(Δy), lbmol/(ft²)(s)(lbmol/ft³), and lbmol/(ft²)(h)(psi).

3.3 (*Dissolution of a bubble*)[2] A 0.8 cm diameter bubble of pure CO_2 is injected into an excess well-stirred liquid at 25°C. The bubble diameter shrinks to 0.2 cm after 80 s. *Given:* total pressure = 1 atm; solubility of CO_2 in water = 1.45×10^{-3} mass fraction; diffusivity of CO_2 in water = 1.9×10^{-5} cm²/s.

　　Calculate the average value of the mass transfer coefficients, k_L and k_x. How long will it take for the bubble to vanish if the mass transfer coefficients remain constant? (Is this a reasonable assumption?)

3.4 (*Mass transfer coefficient in counterdiffusion*)[2] The gas-phase reaction $A \rightarrow B$ occurs on the surface of a catalyst in the form of a wire gauge. The bulk concentration of the species A is 0.002 kmol/m³ and the rate of reaction of A is measured at 0.08 kmol per hour per m² area of the catalyst. If the reaction is instantaneous and the entire diffusional resistance to the transport of the reactive species from the bulk gas to the catalyst surface is offered by a stagnant film of the gas, calculate (a) the thickness of the film; (b) the mass transfer coefficients, k'_G, k'_y and (c) the concentration of A halfway the gas film. *Given:* total pressure = 1.5 bar; temperature = 250°C; $D_{AB} = 0.16$ cm²/s at 1 bar and 100°C.

3.5 (*Evaporative mass transfer from a drop in free fall*)[3] A raindrop of initial diameter 0.8 mm starts falling from a sufficiently high altitude. The terminal free fall velocity depends upon the properties of the medium as well as on the diameter of the drop. As the drop moves through the air, its size reduces because of evaporation. The gas-phase mass transfer coefficient for the evaporation of water changes as a result. It is required to calculate the time required for the size of the drop to reduce to 0.6 mm. The terminal velocity of fall for the given range of drop size can be calculated from the following equation:

$$v_t = \frac{180}{d}(d^{3/2} - 8.3 \times 10^{-6}); \qquad \text{the diameter } d \text{ is in metre and } v_t \text{ in m/s.}$$

The following assumptions may be made: (i) the drop is always at its terminal velocity of fall corresponding to its instantaneous diameter (this is also a kind of pseudo-steady state assumption); (ii) the ambient air is at 25°C, 1 atm total pressure and 70% relative humidity; (iii) the shape of the drop remains spherical all the time; and (iv) the drop temperature is 22°C (which is nearly equal to the wet-bulb temperature). The mass transfer coefficient can be estimated from the Ranz and Marshall correlation given by

$$Sh = 2 + 0.6(Re)^{0.5}(Sc)^{0.33}$$

The following data are available: diffusivity of moisture in air = 0.257 cm^2/s at the mean film temperature; density of air = 1.18 kg/m^3; viscosity of air = 1.8 × 10^{-5} kg/m·s; vapour pressure of water at 22°C is 0.02605 atm.

3.6 (*An application of dimensional analysis*)[2]   It has been observed experimentally that the rate of toxin removal in an artificial kidney (see Section 14.5.2) is a function of blood velocity, density, viscosity, diffusion coefficient of toxin and the diameter of the dialysis tubing. Using dimensional analysis, determine the dimensionless groups and the type of correlation that may be applicable.

3.7 (*Mass transfer in a wetted-wall column*)[1]   In a wetted-wall tower, H_2S is being absorbed from air into water at 1.6 bar total pressure and 25°C. The gas-phase mass transfer coefficient is predicted to be $k_c = 3.42$ kmol/(h)(m^2)(ΔC, kmol/m^3). At a given point in the column, the mole fraction of H_2S in the liquid at the gas–liquid interface is 1.8×10^{-5} and that in the bulk gas is 0.15. The solubility of H_2S in water at the given temperature is 0.00337 mass fraction per atmosphere pressure of the gas. Calculate the local flux.

3.8 (*Evaporation of water in a wetted-wall column*)[1]   Water is being evaporated into a counter-current stream of air in a wetted-wall column, 30 mm in diameter. Estimate the evaporative flux of water at a point in the column where the water temperature is 305 K and the mole fraction of water vapour in the bulk air is 0.0098.

   The following data and information are supplied: air rate (dry basis) = 1 kg/min; water rate = 0.2 kg/min; air temperature at the location = 38°C; air viscosity (at 38°C) = 1.85×10^{-5} lb/ft·s; total pressure = 1 atm. Vapour pressure of water at the given temperature can be obtained from Antoine equation (see Problem 2.2). The gas-phase mass transfer coefficient can be calculated using the Gilliland and Sherwood correlation given by (note that it resembles the Dittus–Boelter equation for heat transfer)

$$Sh = 0.023(Re)^{0.8}(Sc)^{0.33}$$

The Reynolds number of air may be calculated at the bulk condition (to be more precise, the air velocity should be taken relative to free surface velocity of water).

3.9 (*Gas absorption in a falling film*)[2]   Air mixed with a soluble gas flows countercurrent to water flowing down as a thin film covering the inner wall of an experimental column, 5 cm in diameter (refer to Figure 3.5). The water-film thickness is 1 mm and it flows at an average velocity, $v = 2.1$ m/s. The diffusion coefficient D of the solute is 1.7×10^{-5} cm^2/s. If the water leaving the tower is 10% saturated, calculate the height of the tower. The mass transfer coefficient for a falling film can be calculated using the correlation

$$(k_L z/D) = 0.69(zv/D)^{0.5},$$

where z is the position along the film measured from the top.

Assume that the gas flow rate is large so that the concentration of the solute in the gas remains essentially constant.

3.10 (*Mass transfer in crystal growth*)[2]   In an experiment on the growth of a single crystal of NaCl at 30°C, a supersaturated solution of the salt containing 39 g NaCl per 100 g of water flows at a velocity of 0.12 m/s past a suspended crystal of 2.5 mm size. For the sake of simplicity, the shape of the crystal may be assumed to be spherical. If the experimentally measured rate of growth of the crystal is $dr/dt = 9.5 \times 10^{-5}$ mm/s (where r is the equivalent radius of the crystal), determine whether the growth process can be considered to be 'diffusion-controlled'.

The following data are given: solubility of NaCl in water at 30°C = 36.3 g per 100 g water; density of the solution = 1300 kg/m^3; density of solid NaCl = 2160 kg/m^3; viscosity of the solution = 1.0 cP; diffusivity of NaCl in water under the given conditions = 1.4×10^{-9} m^2/s. The mass transfer coefficient at the solid surface can be calculated from the Rowe's correlation, $Sh = 2 + 0.79 Re^{1/2} Sc^{1/3}$.

3.11 (*An application of the penetration theory*)[2]   Air bubbles of 0.005 m diameter rise through an otherwise stagnant pool of 'oxygen-free' water at 30°C. The steady velocity of rise is 0.1 m/s. If the diffusivity of O_2 in water at 25°C is 2.1×10^{-9} m^2/s, calculate the liquid side coefficient and the rate of mass transfer from a single bubble. The solubility of O_2 in water at 30°C can be calculated by using the Henry's law coefficient as 4.75×10^4 atm/mol fraction. The viscosities of water are 0.911 cP and 0.817 cP at 25°C and 30°C respectively.

3.12 (*Mass transfer coefficient from the penetration theory*)[3]   For the experimental confirmation of his penetration theory, Higbie devised a small set-up comprising a narrow vertical glass tube filled with water in which pure carbon dioxide was released at the bottom at a regular frequency. The bubbles moving through the tube were of the shape of a capsule. The length of a bubble, its residence time in the water in the tube, and the velocity of rise were measured. The contact time of a liquid element on the surface of a bubble with the gas was estimated from these measurements. The CO_2 content in the exit water was determined by chemical analysis.

In an experiment to test the validity of the Higbie's theory, carbon dioxide gas (1 atm, 25°C) is introduced at the bottom of a narrow tube, 3 mm in diameter and 0.6 m long, through which water is flowing downwards slowly. The bubbles are of capsule shape, 0.05 m long. The thickness of the water film between the bubble and the tube wall is small. The bubble rise velocity is 0.2 m/s. Bubbles enter the tube at $^1/_3$ second interval and the rate of absorption of carbon dioxide is estimated to be 40 mg/min. The solubility of CO_2 in water at 1 atm and 25°C is 1.5 kg/m^3. The concentration of CO_2 in bulk water is very *small*. Does the Higbie's thoery appear to work in this case? The bubbles may be assumed cylindrical for calculation of the area.

3.13 (*Gas absorption from rising bubbles*)[3]   A 'pure gas' is being bubbled through a column of liquid. The bubbles are spherical, 6 mm average diameter (assumed constant), and rise with a constant velocity of 0.18 m/s. The volume of gas–liquid dispersion is 2.5 litre and the fractional gas hold-up (the volume fraction of gas in the dispersion) is 0.02. The liquid is well-mixed and there is no dissolved gas at the beginning. The diffusivity of the gas in the liquid is 1.8×10^{-9} m^2/s. The liquid-phase mass transfer coefficient may be calculated by using the penetration theory. Determine the time it takes for the liquid to attain 50% of the saturation concentration.

3.14 (*Boundary-layer mass transfer*)^2 A plate, 0.5 m square, coated with a layer of benzoic acid, is placed in a stream of water flowing at a velocity of 0.25 m/s at a temperature of 25°C. Calculate the average rate of dissolution of the acid per unit area of the plate and also the equivalent thickness of a stagnant liquid film that would offer the same resistance to mass transfer.

The following data are available: solubility of benzoic acid in water at 25°C = 3.01 kg/m^3; diffusivity of benzoic acid in water = 10^{-9} m^2/s and the viscosity of water at 25°C = 8.9×10^{-4} kg/m·s.

3.15 (*Boundary-layer mass transfer*)^2 A rectangular pan, 40 cm long and 30 cm wide, full of water is placed in a wind tunnel (in effect, it is a case of boundary-layer flow on a flat surface). Wind flows at a linear velocity of 5 m/s through the tunnel. Calculate the rate of evaporation of water. The resistance to mass transfer is offered only by the boundary layer on the surface of the liquid. The following data are available:

The air temperature is 300 K and has a humidity of 60%. Vapour pressure of water at 300 K = 0.0353 bar; diffusivity of moisture in air at 300 K and 1 atm = 0.262 cm^2/s; ρ_{air} = 1.16 kg/m^3; ν_{air} = 1.59×10^{-5} m^2/s. Take the water temperature as 300 K (although, in reality, it will gradually approach the wet-bulb temperature; see Chapter 10).

3.16 (*Boundary-layer mass transfer*)^2 A stream of air at 101.3 kPa pressure and 300 K flows over the top surface of a sheet of naphthalene of length 0.25 m at a velocity of 15 m/s.

Given: diffusivity of naphthalene vapour in air under the given conditions = 6×10^{-6} m^2/s; kinematic viscosity of air = 1.6×10^{-5} m^2/s; vapour pressure of naphthalene at 300 K = 0.235 mm Hg.

Calculate (a) the molar concentration of naphthalene at the plate surface, (b) the average mass transfer coefficient, and (c) the rate of loss of naphthalene from the surface per unit width.

It is known that for boundary layer heat transfer from a flat plate, the average heat transfer coefficient can be calculated from the equation: $\text{Nu} = 0.664(\text{Re}_L)^{1/2}(\text{Pr}^{1/3})$.

3.17 (*Gas absorption in a falling film*)^2 Pure chlorine gas is being absorbed in water in a small experimental wetted-wall tower, 2 cm in diameter and 30 cm in height. The free surface velocity of the water film is 40 cm/s. Under the given conditions, the solubility of chlorine in water is 0.823 g/100 g water and its diffusivity is 1.26×10^{-5} cm^2/s.

What is the rate of absorption of the gas in gmol/h?

Assume: (i) the 'depth of penetration' of the dissolved gas is small; (ii) a flat velocity profile of the liquid near the free surface.

3.18 (*Oxygen absorption in water from air bubbles*)^3 Air at 25°C and 1 atm pressure is bubbled through water in a 100-litre aquarium for oxygenation. The tank is initially filled with water having 0.001 kg/m^3 oxygen. At any time there is 1 litre of air dispersed in the water in the form of 5 mm diameter (on the average) bubbles that have a rise velocity of 0.26 m/s. The solubility of oxygen in water at the given temperature and pressure is 0.0085 kg/m^3.

(a) Calculate the average mass transfer coefficient. (b) How long should it take for the oxygen concentration in the water to reach 60% of the saturation value? (c) Calculate the maximum and the minimum oxygen flux over this time.

3.19 (*Problem 3.18 continued*)[2] Let there be a total of 50 fishes in the aquarium described in Problem 3.18. Each fish needs, on the average, 1.5×10^{-8} kg oxygen per second for healthy survival. What should be the fractional air hold-up in the tank if the oxygen content in the water is to be maintained at 60% (this is reasonable for survival of fish) of the saturation value at steady state? The average bubble size, rise velocity, physical properties are as in Problem 3.18.

3.20 (*Mass transfer in flow through a pipe*)[3] Air containing 5% CO_2 enters a tube of 40 mm i.d. at the bottom at a velocity of 4 m/s. The inner wall of the tube is irrigated with a strong solution of NaOH. The tube has a 3 m wetted section and 75% of the entering CO_2 is absorbed before the gas leaves the tube. Calculate the gas-phase mass transfer coefficient.

Make differential mass balance over a thin section of the tube taking into account the variation of the gas flow rate. Also estimate the mass transfer coefficient using the correlation $k_c d/D = 0.026 Re^{0.8} Sc^{0.33}$. Use the gas velocity relative to the free surface liquid velocity (that has a value of 0.15 m/s) in the calculation of Reynolds number. Take $D = 0.165$ cm^2/s. The pressure drop of the gas across the tube may be neglected.

3.21 (*Mass transfer in a laboratory stirred cell*)[3] The 'laboratory stirred cell' is a simple device for the study of mass transfer accompanied by a chemical reaction in a gas–liquid system (Danckwerts, P.V., *Gas Liquid Reactions*, McGraw-Hill, 1970). The apparatus is a small cylindrical vessel partly filled with the absorbent liquid or solution. A stirrer enters the cell at the top and the stirrer blades just touch the flat liquid surface. The surface of the liquid gets continuously 'renewed' as the stirrer rotates (Figure 3.13). The gas, pure or diluted with an 'inert' carrier, flows through the space above the liquid.

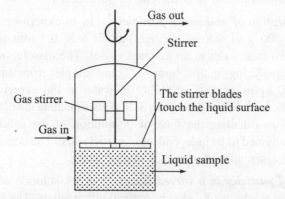

Figure 3.13 A simplified sketch of a stirred cell (gas absorption occurs at the flat gas–liquid interface).

An experiment has been conducted with such an apparatus on the absorption of pure CO_2 at 1 atm pressure in water in order to measure the rate of surface renewal at a given stirrer speed. When 100 ml of water is taken in the cell and the experiment is run for

12 minutes, the concentration of CO_2 in the liquid is found to be 0.112 mass%. The gas–liquid contact area, which is virtually the same as the cross-sectional area of the cell, is 31.5 cm^2. The temperature of the system is maintained at 25°C. The solubility of CO_2 in water at 1 atm pressure can be calculated from the Henry's law: $p_A = Hx_A^*$, where $H = 1.64 \times 10^3$ atm per unit mole fraction. The gas-phase mass transfer resistance is absent for absorption of a pure gas.

Calculate the liquid-phase mass transfer coefficient for the given experiment and the fractional rate of surface renewal.

The liquid in the cell may be assumed 'well-mixed' and the solution density may be assumed to be the same as that of water. The inlet CO_2 gas is saturated with water vapour at 25°C so that there is no evaporation of water during the experiment. The diffusion coefficient of CO_2 in water at 25°C is 1.92×10^{-5} cm^2/s.

3.22 **(*Gas-phase mass transfer coefficient in a stirred cell*)[1]**   In order to measure the gas-phase mass transfer coefficient in a stirred cell at a given stirrer speed, absorption of ammonia diluted with dry air in aqueous sulphuric acid is carried out for a given period of time. The gas mixture flows into the cell at a constant rate and the outlet gas contains 3% of ammonia by volume. The gas in the cell is 'well-stirred' and the cross-sectional area is 31.5 cm^2. If the volume of acid taken is 100 ml at 1(N) concentration and at the end of 20 minutes the liquid is found to contain 0.82 gmole ammonia per litre, calculate the gas-phase mass transfer coefficient.

3.23 **(*Mass transfer to suspended catalyst particles*)[2]**   A liquid-phase catalytic reaction $A \rightarrow B + C$ occurs on the surface of 50 g suspended catalyst particles (mean diameter = 1 mm; density = 3800 kg/m^3) in an experimental batch agitated reactor. Two litre feed solution containing 0.5 kmol of A/m^3 is taken in the reactor. Given that: (i) the reaction is *diffusion-controlled*; (ii) the catalyst is non-porous (the reaction occurs on the external surface only); and (iii) the liquid–solid mass transfer coefficient, $k_L = 3.5 \times 10^{-5}$ m/s, calculate the conversion of A at the end of 30 minutes.

3.24 **(*Time of dissolution of suspended particles*)[3]**   In an experiment on the dissolution of salt in water, 500 g of salt of average particle size 0.7 mm (assumed spherical) is suspended in 10 litre water in an agitated vessel. The dissolution rate is measured by collecting and analyzing small volumes of liquid samples from time to time. The density of salt is 2160 kg/m^3 and its solubility in water at the experimental temperature is 350 kg/m^3. If the initial dissolution rate is 20.8 g/s, calculate the dissolution mass transfer coefficient. Also, calculate the time of dissolution of the solid if the mass transfer coefficient is assumed to be independent of particle size. The density of the solution may be taken to be essentially the same as that of water.

3.25 **(*Dissolution of particles in a stirred vessel*)[3]**   A 5% solution of a reagent is required in the process of synthesis of a pharmaceutical intermediate. The solid reagent, available as crystals (density = 1580 kg/m^3) of average particle size 0.75 mm, is dissolved in a stirred vessel to prepare 1.2 m^3 solution in a batch. The requisite volume of water and the calculated quantity of the solid are charged into a 1.15 m diameter tank fitted with a 0.6 m diameter impeller.

Given: agitator rpm = 120; diffusivity of the solute = 1.5×10^{-5} cm^2/s; average viscosity of the solution = 0.98 cP; solubility of the solid in water = 7.6 g per hundred gram water.

Calculate the time required for the dissolution of the solid.

The Sherwood number correlation given in Example 3.4 can be used. (Solution density = 1000 kg/m^3.)

3.26 (*Mass transfer in a packed bed*)[3] Air at 20°C and 1 atm pressure flows through a bed of naphthalene balls, 5 mm in average diameter. *Given:* the superficial gas velocity = 0.20 m/s; fractional bed voidage = 0.65; specific surface area of the bed = 140 m^2/m^3; gas-phase mass transfer coefficient, k_c = 70 m/h; vapour pressure of naphthalene at 20°C = 1.7×10^{-4} bar. If the air leaving the bed has 0.0138 mol% naphthalene vapour in it, calculate the bed height. Also calculate the sublimation flux at the inlet and at the exit of the bed. Estimate the mass transfer coefficient using the correlation, $j_D = 1.17 \, \text{Re}^{-0.415}$ (see Table 3.3) and compare with the given value. Take $v = 1.5 \times 10^{-5}$ m^2/s for air; $D_{AB} = 5.8 \times 10^{-6}$ m^2/s.

3.27 (*Mass transfer in flow past a sphere*)[3] A 0.5 cm diameter spherical pellet is kept suspended in a flowing stream of water. If the water velocity is 1 m/s, calculate the time required for the size of the sphere to be reduced to 1 mm. The following correlations for mass transfer (Sandoval–Robles et al., 1980) may be used.

$$\text{Sh} = 0.803(\text{Re})^{0.474}(\text{Sc})^{1/3} \text{ for } 20 < \text{Re} < 2000; \; \text{Sh} = 0.3(\text{Re})^{0.593}(\text{Sc})^{1/3} \text{ for } 2000 < \text{Re} < 23,000$$

Given: solubility of the solid = 30 kg/m^3; diffusivity = 1.5×10^{-9} m^2/s; viscosity of liquid = 0.95 cP; and density of the solid = 1800 kg/m^3 . The bulk water is free from the solute. Assume that the spherical shape of the pellet is retained.

3.28 (*Diffusivity measurement by a laminar jet apparatus*)[2] In an experiment for the determination of the diffusivity of CO_2 in water, the rate of absorption of the pure gas was measured using a laminar jet apparatus (see Figure 3.9) at 1.05 atm and 25°C. The following data are given: jet length = 4 cm; gas flow rates = 30.5 cm^3/min at the inlet, and 23.5 cm^3/min at the outlet; water flow rate = 15 ml/s; Henry's law constant ($p = Hx_A^*$) was H = 1540 atm per unit mole fraction. Calculate the diffusivity of CO_2 in water.

3.29 (*Evaporation time of a liquid spill*)[2] Accidental spill of a liquid during storage or transportation may sometimes happen in a chemical plant. Prior estimation of the evaporation rate from a possible spill is necessary for an analysis of the potential hazard. The evaporation data is also used as an input to dispersion models to predict the vulnerability zone and potential hazard to the neighbouring community. Peress (*Chem. Eng. Progress*, April 2003, 32–34; also see Berry, J., *Chem. Eng. Progress*, Jan 2005, 32–39) cited the following simple correlation for the mass transfer coefficient during evaporation of a spill in air.

$$k_c = 0.67u^{0.78}(M_w/M_l)^{1/3}, \text{ in cm/s}$$

where u = wind speed (m/s), M_w = mol. wt. of water, M_l = mol. wt. of the liquid spilled.

One hundred gallons of toluene is spilled during pumping to a storage tank and spreads over an area of 75 m^2. The wind velocity is u = 12 km/h, temperature = 25°C, and pressure = 1 atm. Calculate the rate of evaporation of the liquid and the time of its complete disappearance. *Given:* vapour pressure of toluene at 25°C = 28.44 mm Hg; density of the liquid = 860 kg/m^3; 1 ft^3 = 7.48 gal.

3.30 (*Correlation of mass transfer data for pipe flow*)[2]   Dissolution of a soluble solid coated on the inner surface of a tube in a liquid flowing through it has been studied by many workers with the purpose of developing mass transfer correlations. The mass transfer coefficient k_L is expected to depend upon the following variables: tube diameter, d; liquid velocity, v; its density, ρ and viscosity, μ; and diffusivity of the solute, D. Using the 'power law technique', develop a suitable form of correlation for the mass transfer coefficient in terms of dimensionless quantities.

3.31 (*Boundary layer mass transfer covering both laminar and turbulent regimes*)[3]   A pan containing water at 80°F is placed in a wind tunnel (Figure 3.14) through which dry air flows at a velocity of 12 mile/h. The pan has a length of $x = 3$ m in the longitudinal direction and contains water at a uniform depth of 10 mm. The correlations for the 'local' Sherwood number are:

$$\text{Sh}_x = 0.332(\text{Re}_x)^{1/2}(\text{Sc})^{1/3} \quad \text{for laminar boundary layer flow, Re} < 3 \times 10^5$$
$$= 0.0292(\text{Re}_x)^{0.8}(\text{Sc}) \quad \text{for turbulent boundary layer flow, Re} \geq 3 \times 10^5$$

Calculate the time of evaporation of the water. *Given:* pressure = 1 atm; kinematic viscosity of air = 1.7×10^{-4} ft^2/s; diffusivity of moisture = 2.8×10^{-4} ft^2/s; vapour pressure of water = 26 mm Hg.

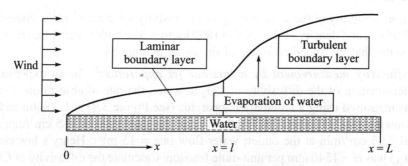

Figure 3.14   Evaporation of water in flowing air.

3.32 (*Oxygen absorption in a rotating disk device*)[3]   The 'rotating disk reactor' is a novel oxygenation device for wastewater treatment [Kim et al., *Chem. Eng. Sci.*, 40(1985) 2281–2286; Dionysiou et al., *Env. Sci. Technol.*, 36(2002) 3834–3843]. It consists of a number of closely spaced disks mounted on a rotating horizontal shaft. The disks are kept partly submerged in wastewater (Figure 3.15). The area of a disk above the water remains covered with a water-film. The time of exposure of a liquid element of the water-film depends upon the rotational speed of the disk as well as the fraction sub-merged in water. Mass transfer correlations for oxygen absorption in such a device have been proposed in the literature (see the above two and related references). However, the penetration theory provides a simple but approximate method of calculation of the mass transfer coefficient.

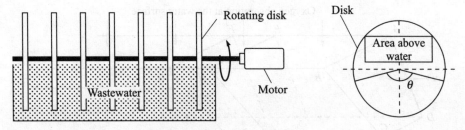

Figure 3.15 A rotating disk oxygenator.

The segment of a disk, 3 m in diameter, submerged in water forms an angle $\theta = 120°$ at its centre. The rotational speed is 30 rpm. If the water in the trough has 5 ppm of oxygen in it at steady state, calculate the theoretical rate of oxygen absorption on both sides of a disk using the penetration theory.

Given: Henry's law ($p = Hx$) constant for oxygen, $H = 4.2 \times 10^4$ atm at the given temperature, and the diffusivity of oxygen in water, $D = 2.05 \times 10^{-9}$ m^2/s.

3.33 (*DO sag in a non-tidal river*)[3] Contamination of a natural water system (rivers, lakes, for example) is partly removed by self purification processes involving dilution, sedimentation and aeration. Wastewater containing biodegradable organics is often discharged into a river and this is a very important source of contamination. The oxygen demand for bacterial degradation of organics (called biochemical oxygen demand, BOD) is met by absorption of oxygen from air. Depletion of oxygen below about 5 ppm becomes critical for the aquatic life.

A non-tidal river has a BOD load of L_0 (expressed as milligram oxygen required for biodegradation of the organics present in one litre wastewater) and a dissolved oxygen concentration w_0 (mg/l or g/m^3) at a certain position ($z = 0$) along the river where the wastewater is discharged. The cross-section of the river (a', m^2) is uniform and the average water velocity is u (m/s). The breadth of the river at the water surface is b (m). As the water flows downstream, degradation of BOD continues following a first order kinetics, $L_t = L_0 \exp(-kt)$, where L_t is the BOD in an element of water at a position z such that $z = ut$. This means that the rate of consumption of dissolved oxygen at the position $z = ut$ is $-d(L_t)/dt$. Absorption of oxygen occurs at the water surface, the mass transfer coefficient being k_L (m/s). Over a certain distance from the reference point ($z = 0$), the rate of consumption of oxygen for biodegradation of orgaincs is usually more than the rate of its absorption from air. This causes a lowering of dissolved oxygen (DO) level, called the 'DO sag'. But at a longer distance along the river, the BOD becomes lower (since much of it has already been removed), the oxygen consumption rate gets reduced, and the DO level builds up because of replenishment by absorption from air. Under such an idealized condition, a minimum DO should occur at some distance from $z = 0$. Develop a simple model for the process (called the 'Streeter-Phelp model') for the calculation of distribution of DO along the river and the point where the minimum of DO occurs (see G.M. Masters, *Introduction to Environmental Engineering and Science*, Prentice Hall, New Delhi, 1991). A sketch of the system is given in Figure 3.16.

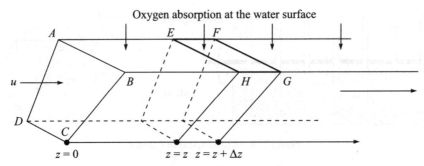

Figure 3.16   Schematic of a river subjected to a BOD load. [*ABCD* = cross-section of the river at $z = 0$; breadth of the river at the free surface, $AB = b$; *EFGH* = a differential area (=$b.dz$ on the water surface at $z = z$.]

3.34 (*A non-catalytic gas–solid reaction proceeding with the formation of an 'ash layer' — the 'shrinking core model'*)[3]   There are many industrially important gas–solid reactions of the type $A(s) + B(g) \rightarrow C(s) + D(g)$. A typical example is the roasting of zinc ore (ZnS) in air which is a major step of zinc metallurgy. A porous layer of the oxidation product, ZnO, forms on the surface of a pellet of ZnS. This is often called the 'ash layer'. Oxygen from air diffuses through an external 'gas-film' surrounding the pellet, and then through the ash layer to reach the surface of the unreacted core of ZnS. As the reaction proceeds, the size of core reduces or 'shrinks' and the thickness of the ash layer increases. The above visualization of the diffusion–reaction process, which pretty much simulates the phenomenon, is called the shrinking-core model as illustrated in Figure 3.17.

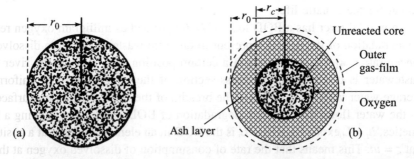

Figure 3.17   Schematic of the 'shrinking core model': (a) initial state; (b) state at time t.

Consider a non-porous spherical pellet of solid A (initial radius = r_0)[#] that undergoes reaction with gas B at the surface with the formation of a layer of the product ('ash') of porosity ε. It is assumed that the diameter of the pellet remains unchanged even with the progress of reaction (the diameter of the inner core, however, decreases). The reaction between A and B at the surface of the unreacted solid core is 'instantaneous'. There is an external gas-film resistance as well.

Develop an expression for the rate of reaction of the solid. Assume that the radius of the core is r_c at any time. The gas B diffuses through the air-film (let the corresponding mass transfer coefficient be k_c) and then through the ash layer which is of the form of a spherical shell. Since the reaction is instantaneous, the concentration or partial pressure

---

[#] In reality, the ZnS particles fed to a kiln for roasting are never spherical. A regular shape (for example, spherical) is often assumed for the sake of a simplified theoretical analysis.

of B at the core surface is virtually zero. Determine the rate of transport of B (area $\times$ flux) and equate it to the rate of reaction of A. How can the model be verified using experimental data? What is the time of complete reaction of the sphere?

3.35 The rate and time of dissolution of a drug are important pharmacological parameters. Seventy-five milligrams of fairly uniform-sized particles (diameter, $d_p = 150$ µm) of the drug *tolbutamide* was added to 1000 ml water in a stirred vessel to conduct a dissolution experiment. The amount dissolved was determined by analyzing the samples withdrawn from time to time and the results are given below.

Determine the 'dissolution rate constant' $k' = k_L C_s / d_p \rho_s$ (see Martin, A., *Physical Pharmacy*, 4th ed., 2001) of the drug under the prevailing conditions. Here k_L = dissolution mass transfer coefficient, m/s; C_s = solubility of the drug in water, kg/m³; d_p = initial diameter in metre; ρ_s = density of the solid, kg/m³. The drug concentration in the bulk water may be considered negligible.

Time, in min	0	10	20	30	40	50
Solute concentration, in mg/ml	0	0.0197	0.0374	0.0510	0.0595	0.0650

REFERENCES

Benitez, J., *Principles and Modern Applications of Mass Transfer*, Wiley Interscience, New York, 2002.

Bird, R.B., W.E. Stewart, and E.N. Lightfoot, *Transport Phenomena*, 2nd ed., Wiley, New York, 2002.

Danckwerts, P.V., 'Significance of liquid-film coefficients in gas absorption,' *Ind. Eng. Chem.*, *43*(1951) 1460–1493.

Davies, G.A., et al, 'The diffusion of carbon dioxide in organic liquid', *Canad.J. Chem. Eng.*, *45*(1967) 372–376.

Deen, W.M., *Analysis of Transport Phenomenona*, Oxford University Press, London, 1998.

Dutta, B.K., *Heat Transfer—Principles and Applications*, Prentice-Hall, New Delhi, 2001.

Higbie, R., 'The rate of absorption of a pure gas into a still liquid during short periods of exposure,' *Trans. AIChE*, *31*(1935) 365–389.

Hines, A.L., and R.N. Maddox, *Mass Transfer Fundamantals and Applications*, Prentice Hall, New Jersey, 1985.

Perry's *Chemical Engineers' Handbook*, 7th ed., McGraw-Hill, New York, 1997.

Rohsehow, W.M., J.P. Hartnett, and E.N. Ganik (Eds.), *Handbook of Heat Transfer Fundamentals*, 2nd ed., McGraw-Hill, New York, 1985.

Sandoval-Robles, J.G., J.P. Riba, and J.P. Couderc, 'Mass transfer around a sphere,' New York *Trans. Inst. Chem. Engrs.*, *58*(1980) 132–134.

Skelland, A.H.P., *Diffusional Mass transfer*, Wiley, New York, 1974.

Sherwood, T.K., R.L. Pigford, and C.R. Reid, *Mass Transfer*, McGraw-Hill, New York, 1975.

Treybal, R.E., *Mass Transfer Operations*, 3rd ed., McGraw-Hill, New York, 1980.

Whitman, W.G., *Chem. Met. Engg.*, *29*(1923) 146.

4 | Interphase Mass Transfer

We have so far discussed the theoretical principles of diffusion and mass transfer from one point to another in a *single phase* or in a homogeneous medium by using either the equations of molecular diffusion or the phenomenological mass transfer coefficients. However, most mass transfer operations in practice involve transport of one or more solute from one phase to another. Let us take a few examples. In a sulphuric acid plant, the air supplied to the sulphur burner should be moisture-free. Drying of the air is done in contact with concentrated sulphuric acid in a 'packed column' (see Chapter 5). A packed column used for this purpose consists of a cylindrical shell filled with an inert packing material irrigated with concentrated sulphuric acid at the top. The liquid trickles down the packing while the air flows up through it, and an intimate contact between the two phases occurs. Moisture from the bulk of the air diffuses to the air–H_2SO_4 interface, gets absorbed in the liquid and then diffuses further into the bulk of the liquid. In a petroleum refinery, extraction of aromatics from kerosene using sulpholane[†] as the extracting solvent proceeds by diffusion of the aromatic compounds from the bulk of the kerosene phase to the kerosene–sulpholane interface, dissolution in sulpholane followed by diffusion into the bulk of the solvent. To take a simple and familiar example, consider aeration of the pool of water in an aquarium. Oxygen from the rising air bubbles diffuses to the air–water interface, gets absorbed in water at the interface and is then transported into the bulk of water. Each of the above is a case of 'interphase mass transfer'.

How can we calculate the rate of mass transfer in a two-phase system? The theoretical principles concerned will be dealt with in this chapter. Since diffusion and mass transfer occur in both the phases, we need to make use of two mass transfer coefficients—one for each phase.

However, here the driving force is not merely the difference of the concentrations of the solute in the two phases. The driving force is rather measured by how far the phases are away from equilibrium. This is an important departure from the way we analyze the phenomenon of heat transfer from one phase to another. In heat transfer, equilibrium means that the phases are

---

[†] Sulpholane is widely used in the refineries for extraction of aromatics. It is a five-member heterogeneous ring compound, $(CH_2)_4SO_2$.

at the same temperature so that the driving force is zero. In mass transfer, on the other hand, equality of concentration of two phases does not necessarily ensure equilibrium.

4.1 EQUILIBRIUM BETWEEN PHASES

Equilibrium between two phases in contact means a state in which there is no net transfer of the solute from one phase to the other. At equilibrium, the chemical potentials of the solute in the two phases are equal. Let us consider an example in order to describe how equilibrium between phases can be studied. A small vessel (provided with side tubes and valves) contains some amount of water and an air space above it. An amount of sulphur dioxide gas is introduced into the air space (Figure 4.1) through a side tube and then the valve is closed. Sulphur dioxide, being soluble in water, will be absorbed in it. However, some SO_2 molecules will also simultaneously leave

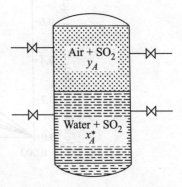

Figure 4.1 Equilibration of air–SO_2–water system.

the water phase and re-enter the gas phase but not necessarily at the same rate. The vessel is maintained at a constant temperature and this process of absorption and desorption continues. Eventually a time comes when the rate of absorption becomes equal to that of desorption. The partial pressure of SO_2 in air and its concentration in water will no longer change. Then we say that the system is at 'equilibrium'. If small samples of the phases are taken and analyzed for the SO_2 contents, we get the equilibrium partial pressure (p_A) in the gas phase and the corresponding mole fraction (x_A^*) in the liquid phase (here $A = SO_2$). If some more sulphur dioxide is fed into the vessel and sufficient time is allowed thereafter, the system will reach a new equilibrium state and we get another set of equilibrium values[#] (p_A, x_A^*). Sets of (p_A, x_A^*) values at a constant temperature and at a constant total pressure generated in this way are called the equilibrium data for a particular system at the given temperature. If we create turbulence in the gas and the liquid phases in the container, the rate of transfer of the solute from one phase to the other increases, thus reducing the time for attainment of equilibrium in an experiment. A plot of these data is called the *equilibrium line* or the *equilibrium curve*. Equilibrium data may also be expressed in mole fraction (y_A vs. x_A) or mole ratio (X_A vs. Y_A) units. Experimental equilibrium data (y vs. x^*) for the SO_2–water system at 1 atm total pressure and at different temperatures are plotted in Figure 4.2. Since the solubility of SO_2 in water decreases with temperature, the equilibrium line becomes steeper at a higher temperature (for this choice of the coordinate axes). The following facts should be noted in this connection.

(a) A particular set of equilibrium data for a system is associated with a particular temperature and pressure condition. In a system at equilibrium, the number of phases P', the number of components C', and the number of variants F', also called the *degrees of freedom*, are related by the 'phase rule'.

$$F' = C' - P' + 2$$

[#] An asterisk (for example, x_A^*) is often used to denote the value of a quantity at equilibrium.

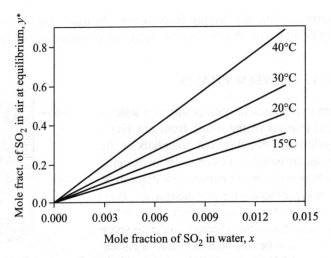

Figure 4.2   Equilibrium diagram (solubility) of SO_2 in water at different temperatures.

The application of the phase rule can be illustrated by taking the example of equilibrium in the SO_2–water system. There are three components in total (assuming the air to be a single component) and two phases (the gas and the liquid phases). So there should be three variants or degrees of freedom. These three variants should be specified to define the system completely. Let us specify two of the variants, temperature and pressure. If, in addition, we specify the mole fraction of SO_2 in the gas phase (air), the system is defined completely and the mole fraction x_A of SO_2 in water becomes automatically fixed.

(b) If the two phases are at *equilibrium*, there is no net transfer of the solute from one phase to the other. However, this does not mean that there is no transfer of solute molecules from one phase to the other at all. It rather means that if a few molecules go from phase-I to phase-II, the same number of molecules move from phase-II to phase-I in order to maintain the concentrations in the phases constant. This equilibrium is sometimes called 'dynamic equilibrium'.

(c) If the two phases are not in equilibrium, mass transfer from phase-I to phase-II occurs so long as the concentration of the solute in phase-II is lower than the equilibrium concentration (see Section 4.5). The extent of deviation from the equilibrium state is a measure of the 'driving force' for mass transfer. For a system at equilibrium, the driving force is zero. Similar arguments apply if there are more than two phases in contact.

4.2 THE RAOULT'S AND THE HENRY'S LAW

The equilibrium data or the equilibrium distribution of a solute between two immiscible (or partially miscible) phases are determined experimentally, although there have been numerous attempts with varying degrees of success to predict the equilibrium data theoretically. Equilibrium data for many systems are available in *Perry's Handbook* (1997) and other data-books (e.g. *International Critical Tables*). Two important laws of equilibrium between phases are described as follows:

4.2.1 Raoult's Law

For an *ideal* gas–liquid or vapour–liquid system, the equilibrium relationship obeys the Raoult's law. The law is mathematically expressed as

$$p_A^* = x_A P_A \qquad (4.1)$$

where

P_A = vapour pressure of A at the given temperature

x_A = mole fraction of the solute A in the liquid

p_A^* = equilibrium partial pressure exerted by the solute.

A solution behaves ideally when

(a) the solute and the solvent molecules have similar sizes and similar intermolecular forces,

(b) the excess volume of mixing is zero, and

(c) the heat of mixing is zero when both the solute and the solvent are liquids.

When the solute is a gas, the heat of mixing is equal to the heat of condensation.

Most solutions are, however, non-ideal. There are some solutions which are nearly ideal in their behaviour.

4.2.2 Henry's Law

Equilibrium data for many non-ideal gas–liquid systems at low concentrations can be expressed by the Henry's law (for more details about Henry's law, see Carroll, 1999)

$$p_A^* = Hx_A \qquad (4.2)$$

where H is the Henry's law constant, and p_A^* and x_A have significances as stated above. The constant H for a given solute–solvent pair is a strong function of temperature (it increases with temperature). There are two other common forms of this law.

$$y_A^* = mx_A \qquad (4.3)$$
$$p_A^* = H'C_A \qquad (4.4)$$

where m and H' are also Henry's law constants corresponding to the above forms of the law and C_A is the liquid-phase concentration of the solute (in $kmol/m^3$, say).

For equilibrium distribution of a solute (A) in two essentially immiscible liquid phases (L and L'), a distribution law given below is often valid.

$$C_{A,L}^* = KC_{A,L'} \qquad (4.5)$$

where $C_{A,L}^*$ is the concentration of A in the liquid L and $C_{A,L'}$ is that in the liquid L'; K is called the *distribution coefficient*. Equation (4.5) is similar to Henry's law. Yaws et al. (1999, 2005) gave a list of Henry's law constants for several gases as a function of temperature and have cited many references in this context. The temperature dependence of the Henry's law constant sometimes follows an Arrhenius-type equation, $m = m_0 \exp(- E/RT)$.

4.3 MASS TRANSFER BETWEEN TWO PHASES

A majority of industrial mass transfer operations involve two phases (fluid–fluid or fluid–solid), and sometimes even three phases. The phases usually have low mutual solubility or are practically immiscible. Consider, for example, the case of absorption of ammonia from a mixture in air by using water, or absorption of moisture from air using concentrated sulphuric acid for the purpose of air drying in a sulphuric acid plant. The two "carrier" phases involved (air and water in the former case, and air and sulphuric acid in the latter) are practically immiscible, while the solute (ammonia or moisture) diffuses from the gas phase to the liquid phase. If the carrier phases are partially miscible (this is common in liquid–liquid extraction), the mass transfer calculations may become a little more complicated.

4.3.1   Concentration Profiles Near the Interface

Mass transfer from one phase (say the gas phase, G) to another phase (say the liquid phase, L) involves the following sequential steps:

(a)   The solute(A) is transported from the bulk of the gas phase(G) to the gas–liquid interface.
(b)   The solute(A) is picked up or absorbed by the liquid phase(L) at the gas–liquid interface.
(c)   The absorbed solute(A) is transported from the interface to the bulk of the liquid(L).

The steps (a) and (c) above are facilitated by turbulence in the fluid mediums.

The term 'interface' means the geometrical plane or surface of contact between two phases. How should the concentration of solute A on either side of the interface vary in order that solute A is absorbed by the liquid? The concentration of A should be larger in the bulk of the gas than at the *gas-side of the interface* (thereby providing a positive 'driving force' for mass transfer towards the liquid). Similarly, the concentration of A should decrease from the *liquid-side of the interface* to the bulk of the liquid ensuring a favourable driving force in the liquid phase as well. A schematic of the variations of the gas-phase and the liquid-phase concentrations near the interface is shown in Figure 4.3. The gas-phase concentration of A (in mole fraction unit) decreases from y_b in the bulk gas to y_{Ai} at the gas-side of the interface. The liquid-phase concentration decreases from x_{Ai} at the liquid-side of interface to x_{Ab} in the bulk of the liquid (the subscript 'b' is used here to denote the 'bulk' of a phase). What does the term 'concentration at the interface' (i.e. the

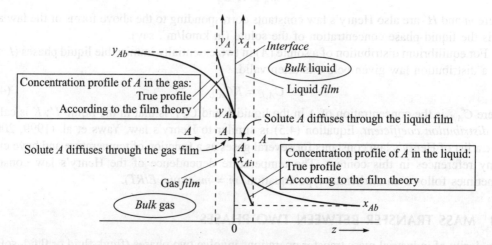

Figure 4.3   Concentration profile of the solute A on the two sides of the interface in a dilute solution.

phase boundary) or the 'interfacial concentration' (y_{Ai} or x_{Ai}) mean? In Figure 4.3, y_A and x_A are the functions of z (the abscissa indicates distance), and $z = 0$ means the interface. So we can say

$$\lim_{z \to 0-} y_A = y_{Ai} \quad \text{and} \quad \lim_{z \to 0+} x_A = x_{Ai} \qquad (4.6)$$

Physically, y_{Ai} is the mole fraction of A on the gas-side of the interface and x_{Ai} is the mole fraction of A on the liquid-side of the interface. Commonly, these are called the *interfacial concentrations*.

In most situations involving mass transfer, we assume that equilibrium exists at the interface, i.e. y_{Ai} and x_{Ai} are at equilibrium. This is sometimes written as

$$y_{Ai} = \varphi(x_{Ai}) \qquad (4.7)$$

where the function φ represents the dependence of y_A on x_A at equilibrium. This function is also called the *equilibrium relation*. If it so happens that the Henry's law is valid for this solute–solvent pair, the equilibrium relation becomes linear [see Eq. (4.3)], i.e.

$$y_{Ai} [= \varphi(x_{Ai})] = m x_{Ai} \qquad (4.8)$$

If the two phases which are not in equilibrium are brought into contact, how long may it take for the 'interfacial equilibrium' to be attained? It is a very relevant question. It can be shown by simple calculations that the time scale of attainment of the interfacial equilibrium is a fraction of a second (see Danckwerts, 1970). So the assumption of interfacial equilibrium is a valid one in most situations. However, there are cases when equilibrium does not exist at the interface, and we say that there is an 'interfacial resistance'. Gas–liquid and liquid–liquid interfaces having an accumulation of a surface active agent (for example, cetyl alcohol at an air–water interface) exhibit interfacial resistance. During crystal growth in a supersaturated solution (dealt with in Chapter 13), the solute molecules diffuse from the bulk of the solution to the crystal surface (the reverse of dissolution), but it takes a little time for the solute molecules to orient themselves into the lattices. This causes an interfacial resistance at the solid–liquid interface. A brief account of these phenomena is given by Sherwood et al. (1975).

4.3.2 The Two-film Theory

The steps involved in mass transfer from one phase to another have been described in the previous section. Since the interfacial resistance is negligible in most cases, resistances to mass transfer are offered only by the two phases in contact. Lewis and Whitman (1924) *visualized* that two stagnant fluid films exist on either side of the interface and mass transfer occurs through these films, in sequence, by purely molecular diffusion. Beyond these films the concentration in a phase is equal to the bulk concentration. This is the *two-film theory* of Lewis and Whitman. The two films and the concentration distributions are schematically shown in Figure 4.3. The idea is similar to that of *stagnant films* described in heat transfer. But, as a matter of fact, a *stagnant film* is only a visualization or imagination. It does not exist in reality. Nevertheless, the two-film model, or the two-film theory, has proved to be extremely useful in mass transfer modeling, analysis and calculations. Treybal (1980) preferred to call it the *two-resistance theory* because the existence of the mass transfer resistances is a physical reality but that of the films is not.

4.3.3 Determination of the Interfacial Concentrations

The determination of the interfacial concentrations is very often necessary in mass transfer calculations. We can do it algebraically or graphically. If mass transfer occurs from a gas phase to a liquid phase at *steady state*, the mass flux of the solute A from the bulk gas to the interface must be equal to that from the interface to the bulk liquid. This is because, at steady state, there cannot be any accumulation of the solute anywhere. In terms of the gas- and the liquid-phase coefficients (see Table 3.1), we can write

$$N_A = k_y(y_{Ab} - y_{Ai}) = k_x(x_{Ai} - x_{Ab}) \tag{4.9}$$

Gas-phase flux   Liquid-phase flux
to the interface   from the interface

Assuming interfacial equilibrium, x_{Ai} and y_{Ai} are related by Eq. (4.7).

$$y_{Ai} = \varphi(x_{Ai}) \tag{4.7}$$

If the bulk concentrations (x_{Ab} and y_{Ab}) and the mass transfer coefficients (k_x and k_y) are known, the algebraic Eqs. (4.9) and (4.7) can be solved for the two unknowns x_{Ai} and y_{Ai}, which are the interfacial concentrations. This is the algebraic procedure. However, the equilibrium data are mostly available in the tabular form rather than in the functional form such as Eq. (4.7). So a graphical procedure described below is of wider use.

Refer to Figure 4.4. Equilibrium data are plotted on the x-y plane to obtain the equilibrium curve. The point M, representing the bulk concentrations of the phases (x_{Ab}, y_{Ab}), is located on the same plane. From Eq. (4.9), we may write

$$\frac{y_{Ab} - y_{Ai}}{x_{Ab} - x_{Ai}} = -\frac{k_x}{k_y} \tag{4.10}$$

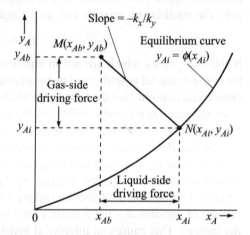

Figure 4.4 Graphical determination of interfacial concentrations.

It is now obvious that if a line of slope $-k_x/k_y$ is drawn through the point M and extended to the equilibrium line, the point N will be reached. The point N, lying on the equilibrium line, gives the interfacial concentrations.

4.4 THE OVERALL MASS TRANSFER COEFFICIENT

The calculation of the flux of interphase mass transfer by using Eq. (4.9) becomes an easy job if the interfacial and bulk concentrations of the solute in either of the phases are known. But, as a matter of fact, interfacial concentrations are not directly measurable quantities and cannot be specified as such in a practical problem. Even in an experimental set-up on mass transfer study, it is only the bulk concentrations that can be measured by taking samples of the phases and analyzing for the solute contents. In reality, the interfacial concentrations cannot be accurately measured since it is not possible to collect a sample of any phase from the interface, which is just a geometrical surface. Thus, Eq. (4.9) does not help us much for practical mass transfer calculations. It is rather necessary to develop a method of calculation of the mass transfer rate using the bulk concentrations of the phases. It may be recalled that in convective heat transfer calculations (for example, in a double-pipe heat exchanger), the rate of heat transfer is calculated using the difference of the bulk temperatures as the driving force and an 'overall heat transfer coefficient'. Similarly, for the purpose of use in mass transfer calculations, we will define an 'overall mass transfer coefficient', suitably combining the 'individual coefficients'.

At this point, we also need to consider how the 'overall driving force' should be expressed in relation to the overall mass transfer coefficient. In the case of heat transfer, the difference in the bulk temperatures of the two phases is taken as the driving force. In mass transfer, the driving force can be expressed in terms of the gas-phase concentration difference or the liquid-phase concentration difference (unlike in the case of heat transfer where the difference of the bulk temperature of the two phases is the driving force irrespective of the nature of the phases). So, depending upon how we express the overall driving force, we define two overall mass transfer coefficients as shown below (here the concentrations are expressed in the mole fraction unit).

$$N_A = K_y(y_{Ab} - y^*_{Ab}) \tag{4.11}$$
$$= K_x(x^*_{Ab} - x_{Ab}) \tag{4.12}$$

In Eq. (4.11), K_y is the 'overall gas-phase mass transfer coefficient' in which the suffix 'y' means that the corresponding driving force should be expressed in terms of gas-phase mole fraction difference. But what is y^*_{Ab}? It is the mole fraction of the solute in the gas phase *that can remain in equilibrium* with a solution having a mole fraction x_{Ab} of the solute A. By virtue of the equilibrium relation (4.7), we can write

$$y^*_{Ab} = \varphi(x_{Ab}) \tag{4.13}$$

because x_{Ab} and y^*_{Ab} are in equilibrium (as stated before, we often use an $*$ to denote the equilibrium concentration).

The quantity $(y_{Ab} - y^*_{Ab})$ is the overall driving force on the 'gas-phase basis'. We have assumed here that mass transfer occurs from the gas to the liquid phase. If it is so, the system must be away from equilibrium, and $(y_{Ab} - y^*_{Ab})$ gives a measure of how far the system is away from equilibrium.

Similarly, in Eq. (4.12), K_x is the 'overall liquid-phase mass transfer coefficient', and $(x^*_{Ab} - x_{Ab})$ is the overall driving force on liquid-phase basis. Here x^*_{Ab} is the mole fraction of A in the solution that can remain in equilibrium with a gas-phase containing solute A at a mole fraction y_{Ab}. Invoking Eq. (4.7), we can now write

$$y_{Ab} = \varphi(x^*_{Ab}) \tag{4.14}$$

It is to be noted that the mole fractions y^*_{Ab} and x^*_{Ab} do not physically exist in the system. These are merely the equilibrium concentrations corresponding to the bulk concentrations in the liquid- and the gas-phase respectively.

The next important question is: How to relate the overall coefficients, K_y and K_x, with the 'individual coefficients', k_x and k_y?[†] We will do this by taking the help of a geometrical construction on the x–y plane. The equilibrium curve for a particular system (consisting of the

---

[†] The coefficients k_y and k_x (or, for that matter, k_G, k_c, k_L, etc.) are called the individual coefficients since they pertain to transfer in a single-phase only. These are comparable to the individual coefficients (h_i or h_o) in heat transfer.

solute, the carrier gas and the solvent liquid) is drawn in Figure 4.5 on the x–y plane and the bulk concentrations (x_{Ab}, y_{Ab}) are indicated by the point M. The interfacial concentrations are indicated by the point N, and the slope of the line MN is $-k_x/k_y$ [see Eq. (4.10)]. The horizontal line through y_{Ab} meets the equilibrium curve at the point T having an abscissa x^*_{Ab}. The vertical line through M meets the equilibrium curve at the point S that has the ordinate y^*_{Ab}. Let the slope of the chord SN of the equilibrium line be m', and that of the chord NT be m''.

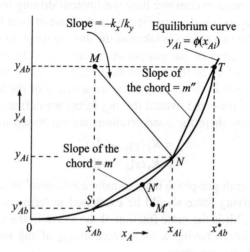

Figure 4.5   Geometrical representation of the overall driving force.

Now, at steady state, the flux is the same irrespective of whether the gas- or the liquid-phase mass transfer coefficient is used, i.e.

$$N_A = k_y(y_{Ab} - y_{Ai}) = k_x(x_{Ai} - x_{Ab}) = K_y(y_{Ab} - y^*_{Ab}) \tag{4.15}$$

or
$$(y_{Ab} - y_{Ai}) = \frac{N_A}{k_y} \tag{4.16a}$$

$$(x_{Ai} - x_{Ab}) = \frac{N_A}{k_x} \tag{4.16b}$$

and
$$(y_{Ab} - y^*_{Ab}) = \frac{N_A}{K_y} \tag{4.16c}$$

From Figure 4.5,

$$(y_{Ab} - y^*_{Ab}) = (y_{Ab} - y_{Ai}) + (y_{Ai} - y^*_{Ab}) = (y_{Ab} - y_{Ai}) + \frac{(y_{Ai} - y^*_{Ab})}{(x_{Ai} - x_{Ab})}(x_{Ai} - x_{Ab})$$

$$= (y_{Ab} - y_{Ai}) + m'(x_{Ai} - x_{Ab}) \tag{4.17}$$

From Eqs. (4.16) and (4.17),

$$\frac{N_A}{K_y} = \frac{N_A}{k_y} + \frac{m' N_A}{k_x} \quad \Rightarrow \quad \frac{1}{K_y} = \frac{1}{k_y} + \frac{m'}{k_x} \tag{4.18}$$

Equation (4.18) shows how the overall mass transfer coefficient K_y is related to the individual coefficients k_y and k_x, and the slope m' of the chord SN of the equilibrium line.

Proceeding in a similar fashion, we can express the overall liquid-phase mass transfer coefficient in terms of the individual coefficients.

$$N_A = k_y(y_{Ab} - y_{Ai}) = k_x(x_{Ai} - x_{Ab}) = K_x(x^*_{Ab} - x_{Ab})$$

i.e.

$$(x^*_{Ab} - x_{Ab}) = \frac{N_A}{K_x} \tag{4.19}$$

and

$$(x^*_{Ab} - x_{Ab}) = \frac{(x^*_{Ab} - x_{Ai})}{(y_{Ab} - y_{Ai})}(y_{Ab} - y_{Ai}) + (x_{Ai} - x_{Ab})$$

$$= \frac{1}{m''}(y_{Ab} - y_{Ai}) + (x_{Ai} - x_{Ab}) \tag{4.20}$$

From Eqs. (4.20), (4.19) and [4.16(a),(b)],

$$\frac{N_A}{K_x} = \frac{N_A}{m'' k_y} + \frac{N_A}{k_x} \quad \Rightarrow \quad \frac{1}{K_x} = \frac{1}{m'' k_y} + \frac{1}{k_x} \tag{4.21}$$

The above equation relates the overall liquid-phase mass transfer coefficient, K_x, with k_x, k_y and the slope m'' of the chord NT of the equilibrium line.

Equations (4.18) and (4.21) lead to the concept of 'controlling resistance' in mass transfer. Since K_y is the overall mass transfer coefficient, its inverse, $1/K_y$, can be considered to be the 'overall mass transfer resistance' *on the gas-phase basis* [see Eq. (4.18)]. It is the sum of the individual mass transfer resistances of the two phases described below.

$$\frac{1}{k_y} = \text{individual gas-phase mass transfer resistance}$$

$$\frac{m'}{k_x} = \text{individual liquid-phase mass transfer resistance } (\textit{on gas phase basis})$$

Similar is the message of Eq. (4.21).

$$\frac{1}{k_x} = \text{individual liquid-phase mass transfer resistance}$$

$$\frac{1}{m'' k_x} = \text{individual gas-phase mass transfer resistance } (\textit{on liquid-phase basis})$$

Also,

The fractional resistance offered by the gas-phase

$$= \frac{\text{resistance offered by the gas-phase}}{\text{total resistance of the two phases}} = \frac{1/k_y}{1/K_y} \tag{4.22}$$

The fractional mass transfer offered by the liquid-phase

$$= \frac{\text{resistance offered by the liquid-phase}}{\text{total resistance of the two phases}} = \frac{m'/k_x}{1/K_y} \tag{4.23}$$

The relative magnitudes of the resistances become immediately understandable from the preceding expressions. If the slope m' is large, the fractional liquid-phase resistance becomes high and we say that the rate of mass transfer is controlled by the liquid-phase resistance. On the other hand, if m' is very small, the rate of mass transfer is controlled by the gas-phase resistance.

It is possible to draw more direct conclusions from the above. If the gas is highly soluble, m' is small. Therefore, the absorption of a highly soluble gas is gas-phase resistance controlled. For example, absorption of ammonia in water (highly soluble) or absorption of a hydrocarbon in a non-volatile oil (a hydrocarbon is highly soluble in a mineral oil) is gas-phase resistance controlled. But the absorption of oxygen in the aqueous medium of an aerobic fermenter (the solubility of oxygen is low) is liquid-phase resistance controlled. If a gas has a moderate solubility in a liquid, both the resistances are likely to be important. However, for the absorption of a pure gas, whatever be the solubility, there is no gas-phase resistance. This is because in such a case, the solute does not have to diffuse through another gas and its partial pressure at the interface is the same as that in the bulk gas; so the gas-phase does not offer any resistance.

A few important points may be noted in this connection.

(a) In Figure 4.5, the point M (which indicates the bulk concentrations of the phases) is located above the equilibrium curve for the particular choice of the coordinates. So there is a positive driving force for mass transfer from the gas-phase to the liquid-phase. In another situation, if the bulk concentrations of the same gas–liquid system are represented by the point M' in Figure 4.5 (M and M' lie on the opposite sides of the equilibrium curve), the driving force ($y_{Ab} - y_{Ai}$) becomes negative. So there will be transfer of the solute A from the liquid-phase to the gas-phase (i.e. 'desorption' or 'stripping' of the solute, instead of absorption, will occur).

(b) In the above discussions and derivations, we have taken the example of mass transfer in a gas–liquid system. Similar treatment is valid for any other system. For example, mass transfer in a liquid–liquid system (extraction), or in a gas–solid system (adsorption).

(c) In a real mass transfer equipment, the intensity of turbulence or mixing may vary from one point to another. As a result, the individual and the overall mass transfer coefficients may not remain uniform throughout the equipment. An average coefficient is normally used in such cases.

(d) If the Henry's law ($y = mx$) is applicable for any system, the equilibrium line in Figure 4.5 becomes straight and the slopes of the chords in Eqs. (4.18) and (4.21) become equal, i.e. $m' = m'' = m$.

Other overall mass transfer coefficients may also be defined depending upon how we express the driving force. For example, if the overall driving force in gas–liquid mass transfer is expressed on gas-phase basis in terms of the difference in partial pressure of the solute A (Δp_A), or on liquid-phase basis in terms of the difference in molar concentration (ΔC_A), the overall mass transfer coefficients may be written as

$$\frac{1}{K_G} = \frac{1}{k_G} + \frac{H'}{k_L} \tag{4.24}$$

$$\frac{1}{K_L} = \frac{1}{H' k_G} + \frac{1}{k_L} \tag{4.25}$$

Here the solubility equilibrium is assumed to follow the Henry's law as given by Eq. (4.4). The conversion of one type of overall coefficient to another (for example, K_G to K_y) may be done using Eq. (3.6).

EXAMPLE 4.1 (*Overall coefficient and driving force*)   The equilibrium distribution of a solute A between air and water at low concentration at a particular temperature is given below.

$$y = 1.2x$$

At a certain point in a mass transfer device, the concentration of solute A in the bulk air is 0.04 mole fraction and that in the bulk aqueous phase is 0.025. In which direction does the transport of the solute A occur (i.e. from the gas to the liquid or from the liquid to the gas)? Calculate the overall gas-phase and the overall liquid-phase driving forces for mass transfer?

At the same point, the local individual mass transfer coefficients for the transport of A are, $k_y = 7.2$ kmol/(h)(m^2)(Δy) and $k_x = 4.6$ kmol/(h)(m^2)(Δx). Calculate (a) the interfacial concentrations in both the gas-phase and the liquid-phase; (b) the overall mass transfer coefficients, K_x and K_y; and (c) the local mass flux, N_A.

Which resistance controls the role of mass transfer?

Solution

Bulk concentration of A in the gas-phase, $y_b = 0.04$; equilibrium relation: $y = 1.2x$
The corresponding equilibrium (or saturation) liquid-phase concentration,

$$x_b^* = \frac{y_b}{1.2} = \frac{0.04}{1.2} = 0.0333$$

The actual concentration of the solute in the bulk liquid is $x_b = 0.025$ which is *less than* the equilibrium value, $x_b^* = 0.0333$. Therefore, the transport of the solute A will occur from the gas-phase to the liquid-phase.

The overall driving force:
on gas-phase basis,

$$y_b - y_b^* = 0.04 - 1.2x_b = 0.04 - (1.2)(0.025) = 0.01$$

on liquid-phase basis,

$$x_b^* - x_b = 0.0333 - 0.025 = 0.0083$$

(a) *Given:* $k_y = 7.2$ kmol/(h)(m^2)(Δy); $k_x = 4.6$ kmol/(h)(m^2)(Δx). At steady state, the local flux is

$$N_A = k_y(y_b - y_i) = k_x(x_i - x_b) \quad \Rightarrow \quad 7.2(0.04 - y_i) = 4.6(x_i - 0.025)$$

Also $y_i = 1.2x_i$ (assuming interfacial equilibrium)

Solving the above two equations, the interfacial concentrations are:

$$x_i = \boxed{0.03044} \qquad \text{and} \qquad y_i = \boxed{0.03653}$$

(b) The overall gas-phase coefficient,

$$\frac{1}{K_y} = \frac{1}{k_y} + \frac{m}{k_x} = \frac{1}{7.2} + \frac{1.2}{4.6} = 0.1389 + 0.2609 = 0.3998$$

or $K_y = \boxed{2.501 \text{ kmol/(h)(m}^2)(\Delta y)}$

Similarly, the overall liquid-phase coefficient,

$$\frac{1}{K_x} = \frac{1}{mk_y} + \frac{1}{k_x} = \frac{1}{(1.2)(7.2)} + \frac{1}{4.6} = 0.1157 + 0.2174 = 0.3331$$

or
$$K_x = \frac{1}{0.3331} = \boxed{3.002 \text{ kmol/(h)(m}^2)(\Delta x)}$$

(c) The local mass flux,

$$N_A = k_y(y_b - y_i) = 7.2(0.04 - 0.03653) = \boxed{0.025 \text{ kmol/(h)(m}^2)}$$

The controlling resistance:

Fraction of the total mass transfer resistance in the gas-phase

$$= (1/k_y)/(1/K_y) = 0.1389/0.3998 = 0.347$$

Fraction of the total mass transfer resistance in the liquid-phase

$$= (1/k_x)/(1/K_x) = 0.2174/0.3331 = 0.653$$

So the mass transfer resistances are comparable in magnitude and neither of them can be said to be controlling.

EXAMPLE 4.2 (*Interfacial resistance to mass transfer*)   The individual mass transfer coefficients for absorption of A in a solvent are: $k_y = 60$ kmol/(h)(m^2)(Δy) and $k_x = 35$ kmol/(h)(m^2)(Δx). The equilibrium relation is $y = 0.8x$. At a particular section of the equipment, the bulk compositions are $x_b = 0.03$ and $y_b = 0.08$. The local mass transfer flux is 1.2 kmol/(h)(m^2). Is there any interfacial resistance to mass transfer? If so, calculate its magnitude.

Hints: If there is no interfacial resistance, the overall mass transfer coefficient K_y can be found to be 25.3 kmol/(h)(m^2)(Δy). Theoretical flux = $K_y(y_b - y_b^*) = 25.3[0.08 - (0.8)(0.03)] = 1.417$ kmol/(h)(m^2). This is more than the actual flux of 1.2 kmol/(h)(m^2). So there is an interfacial resistance to mass transfer. The actual overall coefficient is $(K_y)_{\text{true}} = (1.2)/[0.08 - (0.8)(0.03)] = 21.43$ kmol/(h)(m^2)(Δy). The interfacial resistance

$$= [1/(K_y)_{\text{true}}] - [1/K_y] = \boxed{0.00714 \text{ (h)(m}^2)(\Delta y)\text{/kmol}}$$

EXAMPLE 4.3 (*Application to a gas–liquid system*)   In a laboratory experiment, the solute A is being absorbed from a mixture with an insoluble gas in a falling film of water at 30°C and a total pressure of 1.45 bar. The gas-phase mass transfer coefficient at the given gas velocity is estimated to be $k_c = 90.3$ kmol/(h)(m^2)(kmol/m^3). It is known that 13.6% of the total mass transfer resistance lies in the gas-phase. At a particular section of the apparatus, the mole fraction of the solute in the bulk gas is 0.065 and the interfacial concentration of the solute in the liquid is known to be $x_i = 0.00201$. The equilibrium solubility of the gas in water at the given temperature is

$$p = 3.318 \times 10^4 x^*$$

where p is the partial pressure of A in the gas in mm Hg and x^* is the solubility of A in water in mole fraction.

Calculate (a) the absorption flux of the gas at the given section of the apparatus, (b) the bulk liquid concentration at that section of the apparatus, (c) the overall liquid-phase mass transfer coefficient, and (d) the individual and overall gas-phase driving forces in terms of Δp and Δy.

Solution

The total pressure, $P = 1.45$ bar; partial pressure of the solute A in the bulk gas at the given section of the apparatus, $p_b = (1.45)(0.065) = 0.09425$ bar; temperature, $T = 303$ K. The gas-phase mass transfer coefficient is [see Eq. (3.6)]

$$k_y = \frac{P}{RT} k_c = \frac{(1.45)(90.3)}{(0.08317)(303)} = 5.196 \frac{kmol}{(h)(m^2)(\Delta y)}$$

Interfacial concentration on the liquid side, $x_i = 0.00201$, then

$$p_i = (3.318 \times 10^4)(0.00201) = 66.7 \text{ mm Hg} = (66.7)(1.013)/(760) \text{ bar} = 0.0889 \text{ bar}$$

Assuming interfacial equilibrium,

$$y_i = \frac{p_i}{P} = \frac{0.0889}{1.45} = 0.0613 = \text{mole fraction of } A \text{ on the gas-side of the interface.}$$

The equilibrium relation is: $p = 3.318 \times 10^4 x^*$. It can also be expressed as

$$y = \frac{p}{P} = \frac{(3.318 \times 10^4 \text{ mm Hg}) x^*}{(1.45 \text{ bar})(760 \text{ mm Hg}/1.013 \text{ bar})} = 30.5 x^*$$

(a) Flux of the solute, $N_A = k_y(y_b - y_i) = (5.196)(0.065 - 0.0613) = \boxed{0.01922 \text{ kmol/(h)(m}^2)}$

(b) To determine the bulk liquid concentration, we need to first calculate the liquid-phase mass transfer coefficient.

The gas-phase resistance $= 1/k_y = 1/5.196 = 0.1924$ (h)(m^2)(Δy)/kmol

$= 13.6\%$ of the total resistance

Total mass transfer resistance $= 0.1924/0.136 = 1.415$

The liquid-phase resistance $= (1.415)(1 - 0.136) = 1.2223 = \dfrac{m}{k_x}$; but $m = 30.5$

$$\Rightarrow \qquad k_x = \frac{30.5}{1.2223} = 24.95 \text{ kmol/(h)(m}^2)(\Delta x)$$

The local flux [from part(a)], $N_A = 0.01922 = k_x(x_i - x_b) = (24.95)(0.00201 - x_b)$

$$\Rightarrow \qquad x_b = \boxed{0.00124}$$

(c) The overall liquid-phase mass transfer coefficient is given by

$$\frac{1}{K_x} = \frac{1}{k_x} + \frac{1}{m k_y} = \frac{1}{24.95} + \frac{1}{(30.5)(5.195)} = 0.04639$$

$$\Rightarrow \qquad K_x = \frac{1}{0.04639} = \boxed{21.55 \text{ kmol/(h)(m}^2)(\Delta x)}$$

(d) Individual gas-phase driving force, $\Delta y = y_b - y_i = 0.065 - 0.0613 = \boxed{0.0037 \text{ mole fraction}}$

Or, in terms of difference of partial pressure, $\Delta p = P\Delta y = (1.45)(0.0037) = \boxed{0.00536 \text{ bar}}$

Overall gas-phase driving force, $\Delta y = y_b - y_b^* = y_b - m x_b = 0.065 - (30.5)(0.00124) = \boxed{0.0272}$

EXAMPLE 4.4 (*Mass transfer in a continuous-stirred cell*)   In an experimental study on absorption of SO_2 in a stirred cell, 100 ml of water is taken in the cell described in Problem 3.21 and a mixture of 14.2% SO_2 and 85.8% N_2 is passed through the cell at a rate of 1.5 litre per minute at 20°C and 1 atm pressure. Water is also passed through the cell at a rate of 27 ml per minute, the volume of solution being maintained at 100 ml. Both the gas and liquid phases are 'well stirred'. The outlet gas has 11% SO_2 in it at steady state. The gas-phase mass transfer coefficient has been measured separately (by absorbing NH_3 in a solution of H_2SO_4 under identical conditions of stirring in the cell and making the necessary diffusivity correction) and is found to be 3.8 kmol/(h)(m²)(Δy).

(a) Calculate the concentration of SO_2 in the effluent solution, the liquid-phase mass transfer coefficient and the rate of surface renewal.

(b) What must be the flow rate of water through the cell (keeping the liquid volume constant at 100 ml) so that the rate of absorption increases and the outlet gas concentration drops to 10%?

Solubility data of SO_2 in water at 20°C is given by $y = 31.3x$ in the concentration range involved; diffusivity of SO_2 in water = 1.51×10^{-5} cm²/s.

Hints: Gas flow rate (14.2% SO_2 and 85.8% air) = 1.5 litres per minute at 20°C and 1 atm.

$$Y_{in} = 0.142/(1 - 0.142) = 0.165; \qquad Y_{out} = 0.11/(1 - 0.11) = 0.1236$$

Air flow rate (on SO_2-free basis) = 0.0535 gmol/min. Rate of absorption = $(0.0535)(0.165 - 0.1236) = 0.002215$ gmol/min.

Water flow rate = 27 ml/min = 27/18 = 1.5 gmol/min; SO_2 concentration in the effluent from the cell ≈ $0.002215/1.5 = 1.476 \times 10^{-3}$ mole fraction at steady state in the cell (since the liquid is well-mixed, its concentration in the cell and at the cell exit are the same).

(a) The bulk concentrations of the liquid and the gas phases,

$$x_b = 1.476 \times 10^{-3}; \qquad y_b = 0.11 \text{ (mole fraction)}$$

Equilibrium relation: $y = mx$, $m = 31.3$ (given). Then, $y_b^* = mx_b = (31.3)(0.001476) = 0.0462$
The rate of absorption at steady state = 0.002215 gmol/min = 1.329×10^{-4} kmol/h
Area of mass transfer = 31.5 cm² = 0.00315 m² (see Problem 3.22). Therefore,

$$1.329 \times 10^{-4} = K_y(0.00315)(y_b - y_b^*) = K_y(0.00315)(0.11 - 0.0462)$$
$$\Rightarrow \qquad K_y = 0.6613 \text{ kmol/(h)(m}^2)(\Delta y)$$

Calculation of the liquid-phase mass transfer coefficient,

$$\frac{1}{K_y} = \frac{1}{k_y} + \frac{m}{k_x} \qquad \Rightarrow \qquad \frac{1}{0.6613} = \frac{1}{3.8} + \frac{31.3}{k_x}$$

$$\Rightarrow \qquad k_x = \boxed{25.06 \text{ kmol/(h)(m}^2)(\Delta x)}$$

To calculate the surface renewal rate, we need to know k_L. From Table 3.1, $k_L = k_x/C$.

Since the solution is 'dilute', total molar concentration of the solution is practically the same as the molar concentration of water, i.e. $C = 1 \text{ kmol}/(18/1000) \text{ m}^3 = 55.5 \text{ kmol/m}^3$.

$$k_L = \frac{k_x}{55.5} = \frac{25.06}{55.5} = 0.4515 \text{ m/h} = 0.0125 \text{ cm/s}$$

and the surface renewal rate,

$$s = \frac{k_L^2}{D_{AB}} = \frac{(0.0125)^2}{1.51 \times 10^{-5}} = \boxed{10.4 \text{ per second}}$$

(b) If the outlet gas concentration is 10% at the same inlet gas flow rate, absorption rate = 0.002883 mol/min. If the required water flow rate is Q ml/min,

$$0.002883 \approx \left(Q\frac{\text{ml}}{\text{min}} \right) \frac{x_b \text{ mol}}{18 \text{ ml}} = \frac{Q \cdot x_b}{18} \qquad \text{(i)}$$

Now,

$$(0.002883)(10^{-3})(60) \text{ kmol/h} = K_y(0.00315)(y_b - y_b^*); \qquad y_b = 0.1 \text{ (given)}$$

Putting the value of K_y, calculate y_b^* and then calculate

$$x_b = \frac{y_b^*}{m} = 5.42 \times 10^{-4} \qquad \text{and from Eq. (i) above} \qquad Q = \boxed{95.8 \text{ ml/min}}$$

EXAMPLE 4.5 (*Graphical determination of interfacial concentrations*) The equilibrium solubility of SO_2 in water at 30°C is given by Sherwood [*Ind. Eng. Chem.*, *17*(1925) 745]

p_{SO_2}, mm Hg	0.6	1.7	4.7	8.1	11.8	19.7	36	52	79
g SO_2 per 100 g H_2O	0.02	0.05	0.10	0.15	2.0	0.3	0.5	0.7	1.0

At a point in an absorption column operating at a total pressure of 4.5 bar, the bulk concentrations in the gas and the liquid-phases are $x = 0.0014$ and $y = 0.02$. The individual gas-phase and liquid-phase mass transfer coefficients are $k_x = 80 \text{ kmol}/(h)(m^2)(\Delta x)$ and $k_y = 15 \text{ kmol}/(h)(m^2)(\Delta y)$.

Calculate (a) the interfacial concentrations at the particular location, (b) the overall mass transfer coefficients and the rate of absorption, (c) the mass transfer coefficients k_x' and k_y', and (d) the individual and overall driving forces at the location in terms of Δx and ΔC.

What fraction of the total resistance is offered by the gas-film? What should have been the value of the coefficient k_y, if the gas-phase offered 60% of the total resistance to mass transfer (for the given liquid-phase coefficient)?

Solution
Computation of the equilibrium data in terms of x and y:
This is shown for one data set, $p = 52$ mm Hg and liquid concentration = 0.7 g SO_2 per 100 g water.

The total pressure, $\qquad P = 4.5 \text{ bar} = (4.5)(760/1.013) \text{ mm Hg}$

$$y = \frac{52 \text{ mm Hg}}{(4.5)(760/1.013) \text{ mm Hg}} = 0.0154$$

$$\text{Mol. wt. of } SO_2 = 64; \qquad x = \frac{0.7/64}{(0.7/64) + (100/18)} = 0.001965$$

The calculated equilibrium data are given below:

$10^3 x$	0.0562	0.1403	0.280	0.422	0.564	0.842	1.403	1.965	2.79
p, mm Hg	0.6	1.7	4.7	8.1	11.8	19.7	36	52	79
$10^2 y$	0.0178	0.0504	0.139	0.24	0.35	0.584	1.07	1.54	2.34

(a) The equilibrium data are plotted and the equilibrium curve is shown in Figure 4.6. The bulk concentrations of the two phases at the given locations are: $x_b = 0.0014$; $y_b = 0.02$. Locate the point $P(0.0014, 0.02)$ on the x–y plane. A line PM of slope $-k_x/k_y = -80/15 = -5.33$ is drawn through the point P so as to meet the equilibrium line at M. The point M gives the interfacial concentration of the phases, $x_i = \boxed{0.00206}$ and $y_i = \boxed{0.0164}$.

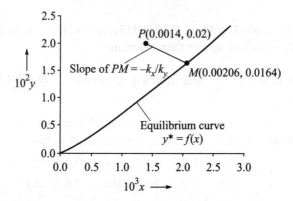

Figure 4.6 Graphical determination of interfacial concentrations. *P* is a point representing the bulk concentrations. *M* is the point representing the corresponding interfacial concentrations.

(b) *The overall coefficients:* In the region near the interfacial concentration, the equilibrium line is *almost linear* having a slope $m = 5.65$. From Eqs. (4.18) and (4.21),

$$\frac{1}{K_y} = \frac{1}{k_y} + \frac{m}{k_x} = \frac{1}{15} + \frac{5.65}{80} = 0.1373 \qquad \Rightarrow \qquad K_y = \boxed{7.28 \text{ kmol/(h)(m}^2)(\Delta y)}$$

$$\frac{1}{K_x} = \frac{1}{m k_y} + \frac{1}{k_x} = \frac{1}{(5.65)(15)} + \frac{1}{80} = 0.0243 \qquad \Rightarrow \qquad K_x = \boxed{41.1 \text{ kmol/(m}^2)(\text{h})(\Delta x)}$$

Absorption flux, $N_A = k_y(y_b - y_i) = 15(0.02 - 0.0164) = \boxed{0.054 \text{ kmol/(m}^2)(\text{h})}$

(c) *The mass transfer coefficients, k'_x and k'_y:*

$$k_y = \frac{k'_y}{(1 - y)_M} \qquad \text{and} \qquad k_x = \frac{k'_x}{(1 - x)_M}; \quad M \text{ means 'log mean'}$$

Both x and y are small and $(1 - y)_M \approx (1 - x)_M \approx 1$. Therefore, $\boxed{k'_x = k_x \text{ and } k'_y = k_y}$.

(d) This part is left as an exercise.

4.5 MATERIAL BALANCE IN A CONTACTING EQUIPMENT—THE OPERATING LINE

In a conventional mass transfer equipment such as a packed tower, spray column, etc. two phases remain in *direct contact*[†] as they pass through the equipment so that mass transfer from one phase to the other may occur. During passage through the equipment, the concentrations of the phases change continuously because of mass transfer from one phase to the other. While the construction and the operating features of important mass transfer equipment will be discussed later, here we will explore how to follow the concentration changes of the phases as they move from the inlet to the exit of an equipment.

These are dictated by the material balance equations over a section of the column. Two modes of contact between the phases will be considered—'countercurrent contact' (in which the phases move in the opposite directions) and 'cocurrent contact' (in which the phases move in the same direction). Another type of contact called the *crosscurrent contact* will be taken up later.

4.5.1 The Steady-state Countercurrent Mass Transfer

A countercurrent contacting apparatus is shown in Figure 4.7. The meanings of the various notations are also shown in the figure. The phase L is heavier and flows down the apparatus and

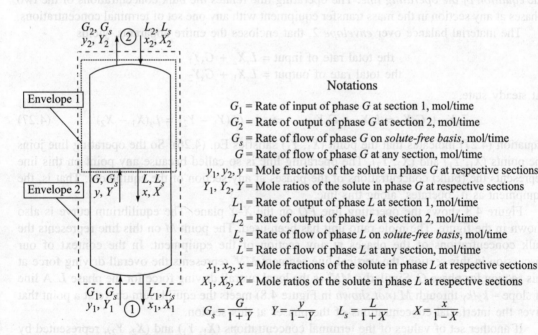

Notations

G_1 = Rate of input of phase G at section 1, mol/time
G_2 = Rate of output of phase G at section 2, mol/time
G_s = Rate of flow of phase G on *solute-free basis*, mol/time
G = Rate of flow of phase G at any section, mol/time
y_1, y_2, y = Mole fractions of the solute in phase G at respective sections
Y_1, Y_2, Y = Mole ratios of the solute in phase G at respective sections
L_1 = Rate of output of phase L at section 1, mol/time
L_2 = Rate of output of phase L at section 2, mol/time
L_s = Rate of flow of phase L on *solute-free basis*, mol/time
L = Rate of flow of phase L at any section, mol/time
x_1, x_2, x = Mole fractions of the solute in phase L at respective sections
X_1, X_2, X = Mole ratios of the solute in phase L at respective sections

$$G_s = \frac{G}{1+Y} \qquad Y = \frac{y}{1-Y} \qquad L_s = \frac{L}{1+X} \qquad X = \frac{x}{1-X}$$

Figure 4.7 Mass balance for steady state countercurrent contact.

[†] In the case of heat transfer between two fluids (for example, in a heat exchanger), the two phases are generally in 'indirect contact'; their thermal contact occurs through a separating wall like the tube wall. On the other hand, most mass transfer operations are direct-contact, except membrane separation discussed in Chapter 14.

the lighter phase G, flows up; the phases may be a liquid and a gas, a solid and a gas, or a solid and a liquid, etc. We *assume* that the phases L and G are mutually immiscible and are the 'carriers' of solute A. As a matter of convention, the bottom end of a continuous contact equipment (for example, a packed tower) will be called the end or terminal '1', the top end or terminal, '2' [we will follow a different convention for a stage-wise contact unit (see Section 4.6)]. Considering *envelope* 1 that encloses a part of the apparatus including one of the ends (Treybal, 1980),

the total rate of input of the solute (with both the phases) $= L_sX_2 + G_sY$

the total rate of output of the solute (with both the phases) $= L_sX + G_sY_2$

At steady state,   the rate of input = the rate of output

i.e. $L_sX_2 + G_sY = L_sX + G_sY_2$ $\Rightarrow$ $G_s(Y - Y_2) = L_s(X - X_2)$ (4.26)

The molar flow rates of the phases, G_s and L_s, are taken on 'solute-free basis', i.e. these are simply the flow rates of the carrier phases; G_s and L_s remain constant along the equipment since we have assumed that they are mutually immiscible. Concentrations (X and Y) are expressed in the mole ratio unit.

Equation (4.26) represents a straight line having a slope L_s/G_s and passing through the point (X_2, Y_2). Note that X_2 and Y_2 are the concentrations of the two phases at a terminal of the equipment while X and Y are their concentrations at *any* location within the equipment. This equation is called the *equation of the operating line*. The operating line relates the bulk concentrations of the two phases at any section in the mass transfer equipment with any one set of terminal concentrations.

The material balance over *envelope* 2, that encloses the entire apparatus, yields

the total rate of input $= L_sX_2 + G_sY_1$

the total rate of output $= L_sX_1 + G_sY_2$

At steady state,

$$L_sX_2 + G_sY_1 = L_sX_1 + G_sY_2 \quad \Rightarrow \quad G_s(Y_1 - Y_2) = L_s(X_1 - X_2)$$ (4.27)

Equation (4.27) indicates that the point (X_1, Y_1) satisfies Eq. (4.26). So the operating line joins the points (X_1, Y_1) and (X_2, Y_2). The operating line is so called because any point on this line represents the (bulk) concentrations of the phases at any section of the equipment. That is, the equipment as if 'operates' along this line.

Figure 4.8 shows the operating line PQ on the X–Y plane. The equilibrium curve is also shown in the figure. The mole ratio unit has been used. The point M on this line represents the bulk concentrations of the phases at any section of the equipment. In the context of our discussion in this section, the vertical line segment MN' represents the overall driving force at this section for phase G. Similarly, MN'' is the local overall driving force for the phase L. A line of slope $-k_X/k_Y$ through M (*not shown* in Figure 4.8) meets the equilibrium curve at a point that gives the interfacial concentrations of the phases at this section.

If another set of values of the terminal concentrations (X_1, Y_1) and (X_2, Y_2), represented by the points R and S, are chosen such that the operating line is represented by RS (now it lies below the equilibrium curve for the particular choice of the coordinate axes), then there will be a 'negative driving force' for the transfer of the solute from phase G to phase L. So, in effect, transfer of the solute from phase L to phase G will occur.

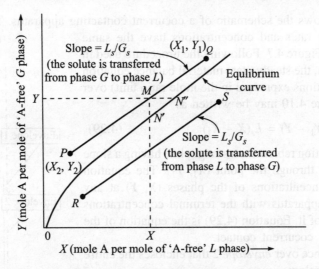

Figure 4.8   The operating line for a countercurrent contact (concentrations are in mole ratio unit).

The entire exercise can also be done using the concentrations of the phases in the mole fraction unit instead of the mole ratio unit. A material balance over *envelope* 1 yields

$$Gy + L_2x_2 = G_2y_2 + Lx \quad \Rightarrow \quad Gy - G_2y_2 = Lx - L_2x_2 \qquad (4.28)$$

There is a major difference between Eq. (4.28) and Eq. (4.26). The quantities G and L (i.e. the total flow rates of the phases—the carrier and the solute) are not constant. If transfer of the solute from the phase G to the phase L occurs, L will gradually increase because of uptake of solute and reach the value of L_1 at the bottom end of the apparatus. The flow rate of the phase G also changes likewise. So the slope of the operating line (L/G) will keep on changing along the equipment. The operating line is no longer a straight line. It will be a curve, drawn on the x–y plane, such as that shown in Figure 4.9. However, if the concentrations of the phases are *low*, the variations in the flow rates of L and G will be rather small. In such a case, the operating line will be *nearly* straight.

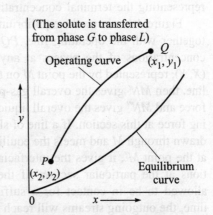

Figure 4.9   The operating curve for a countercurrent process (the concentrations expressed in mole fraction).

4.5.2   The Steady-state Cocurrent Process

In a mass transfer operation, countercurrent contact is preferred to cocurrent contact because a much greater amount of solute can be transferred for the same amount of solvent used. However, in some special cases involving mass transfer accompanied by a chemical reaction (for example, catalytic hydro-desulphurization of petroleum products in a trickle-bed reactor), the co-current mode of contact is adopted. As the name implies, the phases flow in the same direction in a cocurrent unit.

Figure 4.10 shows the schematic of a cocurrent contacting apparatus. The notations used for the phase flow rates and concentrations have the same significances as in Figure 4.7. Following the procedure used in the previous section, the steady-state material balance equation (with the concentrations expressed in the mole ratio unit) over *envelope* 1 in Figure 4.10 may be written as

$$G_s(Y_1 - Y) = L_s(X - X_1) \qquad (4.29)$$

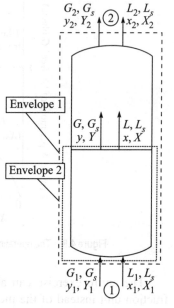

The above equation represents a straight line having a slope $-L_s/G_s$ and passing through the point (X_1, Y_1). The equation relates the bulk concentrations of the phases (X, Y) at any section inside the apparatus with the terminal concentrations (X_1, Y_1) at one end of it. Equation (4.29) is the equation of the 'operating line' for cocurrent contact.

A material balance over *envelope* 2 that encloses the entire apparatus is given below.

$$G_s(Y_1 - Y_2) = L_s(X_2 - X_1) \qquad (4.30)$$

The relation (4.30) shows that the operating line equation (4.29) is satisfied by the point (X_2, Y_2). So in the case of cocurrent contact also, the operating line joins the points representing the terminal concentrations of the two phases.

Figure 4.10   Mass balance in a steady state cocurrent process (notations as in Figure 4.7).

Figure 4.11 shows the equilibrium curve on the X–Y plane together with the operating line, PQ. If the bulk concentrations of the phases at any section are (X, Y), represented by the point M on the operating line, then MN' gives the overall gas-phase driving force and MN'' gives the overall liquid-phase driving force at this section. If a line of slope $-k_x/k_y$ is drawn through M and meets the equilibrium curve at the point M', it gives the interfacial concentrations at the particular section. If the phases are allowed to be in contact for a sufficiently long time, the outgoing streams will reach equilibrium, and the equilibrium concentrations will be given by the point F. Thus the equilibrium curve, in effect, is also the locus of the point representing the inter-facial concentration. If the point representing the concentrations of the phases at the inlet to the

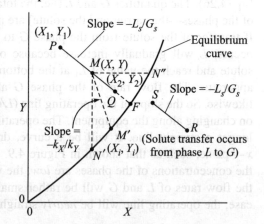

Figure 4.11   Operating lines for cocurrent contact (concentration in the mole ratio unit).

apparatus lies on the other side of the equilibrium curve, the operating line is represented by the line RS. As the sign of the driving force changes, transfer of the solute now occurs from phase L to phase G.

The material balance can also be written using the mole fraction unit instead of the mole ratio unit. By invoking arguments as in the case of countercurrent contact, we can say that the operating line will be a curve in this case as well.

4.6 MASS TRANSFER IN STAGE-WISE CONTACT OF TWO PHASES

The schematic of a countercurrent contacting apparatus presented in Figure 4.7 does not say anything about its internal construction. While we leave the details of the construction and operation of such a device for the next chapter, it will be useful to mention here how the phases are brought into intimate contact in order to achieve efficient transfer of the solute from one phase to the other. For example, in *continuous countercurrent contact* of a gas-phase and a liquid-phase, the liquid may trickle down a packed bed of inert solid while the gas flows up through it (we call it a 'packed tower'). A large area of contact of the phases is thus provided and the capacity of mass transfer of the apparatus is enhanced. In the *stage-wise contact* of the two phases (Figure 4.12), the liquid is fed at the top of a tower or column and it flows down the column from one 'tray' (or 'plate') to the next below (it is called a *tray tower* or *plate tower*). The gas flows up bubbling through the liquid on a tray to the one above.

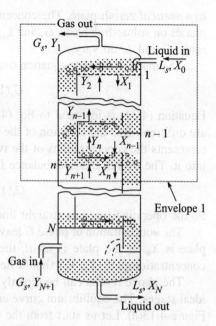

Figure 4.12 Countercurrent contact in a tray tower.

4.6.1 Stage

Any device or combination of devices in which two immiscible phases are brought into intimate contact in order to achieve mass transfer (of one or more solutes) from one phase to the other is called a *stage*. An efficient contact of the phases in a stage *tends* to bring them to equilibrium. If the contacting is so efficient that the phases reach equilibrium when they leave, the stage is called an *ideal stage*. This leads to the definition of 'stage efficiency'. The stage efficiency gives a measure of how close to the equilibrium the phases may reach in a stage. An ideal stage has 100% efficiency. A group of interconnected stages in which the phases flow from one stage to other, in sequence, is called a *cascade*.

4.6.2 Determination of the Number of Stages in Countercurrent Contact

In general, a graphical construction is the most convenient method for the purpose when a single solute is transferred. Consider an N-tray column (Figure 4.12) in which the concentrations of the gas and the liquid phases entering or leaving the different stages are shown. In the case of stage-wise contact, it is a convention that the subscript of a concentration term or a flow rate term denotes the stage from which the stream concerned comes out. For example, Y_n denotes the concentration (in mole ratio unit) of the gas phase leaving the nth plate or tray of a tower. The top tray of the column is the tray or plate number '1', and the bottom tray is the tray number 'N'. Accordingly, in Figure 4.12, the concentration of phase G entering the column is denoted by Y_{N+1} (the stream, as if, comes from the *hypothetical* $(N + 1)$th stage preceding stage N). Similarly the phase L entering plate 1 at the top is imagined as a stream coming from the *hypothetical* zeroth plate. The concentration of this stream is called $X_0{}^\dagger$. The flow rates of the phases on solute-free basis, G_s and L_s, remain constant along the column although the total flow rates, G and L, do vary.

The material balance equation over *envelope* 1 in Figure 4.12 enclosing the top n trays gives

$$G_s(Y_{n+1} - Y_1) = L_s(X_n - X_0) \qquad (4.31)$$

Equation (4.31) is identical to Eq. (4.26) except that the subscripts of the concentration terms are different. It is the equation of the operating line, and (X_n, Y_{n+1}) is any point on this line that represents the concentrations of the two phases, one leaving the nth tray and the other entering into it. The overall material balance for the entire column is

$$G_s(Y_{N+1} - Y_1) = L_s(X_N - X_0) \qquad (4.32)$$

So the operating line is a straight line joining the points (X_0, Y_1) and (X_N, Y_{N+1}).

The concentration of phase G leaving the nth plate is Y_n, and that of phase L leaving the same plate is X_n. If the plate is *ideal*, the phases reach equilibrium as they leave. Therefore, the concentration pair (X_n, Y_n) should lie on the equilibrium curve, $Y^* = \varphi(X)$.

The above results can be directly utilized for the graphical determination of the number of ideal stages. The equilibrium curve and the operating line (PQ) are drawn on the X–Y plane in Figure 4.13(a). Let us start from the point $Q(X_N, Y_{N+1}$; bottom of the column). A vertical line through Q meets the equilibrium line at point $D(X_N, Y_N)$. A horizontal line through D meets the operating line at the point E which must have an abscissa X_{N-1}. This is because (X_n, Y_{n+1}) is a point on the operating line, and putting $n = N - 1$, we see that (X_{N-1}, Y_N) should lie on this line. The region QDE stands for the Nth plate. By drawing successive vertical and horizontal line segments or steps between the operating line and the equilibrium curve, we do the graphical construction for the number of plates. This continues till the point $P(X_0, Y_1)$ is reached. The full construction is further explained under Example 4.6.

There is an obvious question in this connection. What should we do if the construction does not end up exactly at the point P? We get *fraction of a plate* in the last step of construction. This is explained in Figure 4.13(b). The idea behind expressing the number of ideal plates as a mixed fraction is that if we divide this number by the *overall plate efficiency*, we get a better estimate of the number of real trays required for the separation[††].

In the graphical construction described in this section we start at the point Q on the operating line. The construction can also start at the other terminal of the column represented by the point P on the operating line. This alternative construction gives the same number of ideal trays. Conversely, if the number of ideal trays in a column is given, the degree of removal of the solute from a phase that can be achieved in it can be determined graphically; but this will involve a *trial-and-error procedure*. A trial operating line is drawn and it is checked if the desired concentration is reached at the other terminal after the given number of trays are fitted between the equilibrium line and the operating line.

[†] In the case of a continuous contact equipment, the subscripts 1 and 2 are generally used to denote the terminal concentrations as stated in Section 4.5.1.

[††] Let the number of ideal trays be $5\frac{1}{2}$, and the overall plate efficiency be 0.5. The number of real trays = $(5\frac{1}{2})/$ $(0.5) = 11$. But, if instead, we take the next whole number (i.e. 6) as the number of ideal trays, the number of real trays would have been $6/(0.5) = 12$, which is one more than that required.

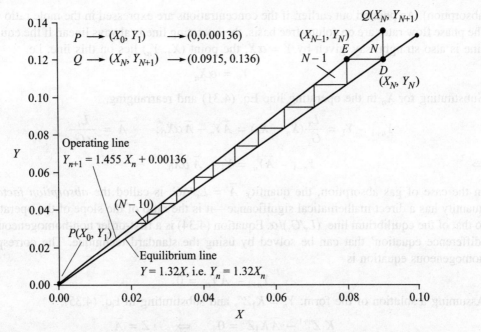

Figure 4.13 (a) Graphical construction of stages for countercurrent mass transfer (data from Example 4.5).

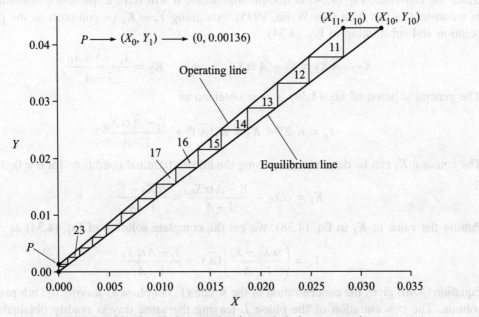

Figure 4.13(b) Graphical construction of stages in the low concentration.

4.6.3 Algebraic Determination of the Number of Ideal Stages

The number of ideal stages can be calculated algebraically if both operating and equilibrium lines are straight. We first consider the case of transfer of the solute from phase G to L (call it absorption). As pointed out earlier, if the concentrations are expressed in the mole ratio unit and the phase flow rates are on solute-free basis, the operating line is always linear. If the equilibrium line is also straight, say, given by $Y = \alpha X$, the point (X_n, Y_n) lies on this line, i.e.

$$Y_n = \alpha X_n \tag{4.33}$$

Substituting for X_n in the operating line Eq. (4.31) and rearranging,

$$Y_{n+1} - Y_1 = \frac{L_s}{G_s}(X_n - X_0) = \bar{A}Y_n - \bar{A}\alpha X_0; \qquad \bar{A} = \frac{L_s}{\alpha G_s}$$

$$\Rightarrow \qquad\qquad Y_{n+1} - \bar{A}Y_n = Y_1 - \bar{A}\alpha X_0 \tag{4.34}$$

In the case of gas absorption, the quantity $\bar{A} = L_s/\alpha G_s$ is called the *absorption factor*. This quantity has a direct mathematical significance—it is the ratio of the slope of the operating line to that of the equilibrium line, $(L_s/G_s)/\alpha$. Equation (4.34) is a first-order non-homogeneous linear 'difference equation' that can be solved by using the standard technique. The corresponding homogeneous equation is

$$Y_{n+1} - \bar{A}Y_n = 0 \tag{4.35}$$

Assuming a solution of the form: $Y_n = K_1 Z^n$, and substituting in Eq. (4.35),

$$K_1 Z^{n+1} - \bar{A}K_1 Z^n = 0 \qquad \Rightarrow \qquad Z = \bar{A} \tag{4.36}$$

Since the difference Eq. (4.34) is non-homogeneous, it will have a 'particular solution' which is a constant in this case (see Wylie, 1975). Assuming $Y_n = K_2$ (= constant) as the particular solution and substituting in Eq. (4.34),

$$K_2 - \bar{A}K_2 = Y_1 - \bar{A}\alpha X_0 \qquad \Rightarrow \qquad K_2 = \frac{Y_1 - \bar{A}\alpha X_0}{1 - \bar{A}} \tag{4.37}$$

The general solution of Eq. (4.34) is now obtained as

$$Y_n = K_1 Z^n + K_2 = K_1(\bar{A})^n + \frac{Y_1 - \bar{A}\alpha X_0}{1 - \bar{A}} \tag{4.38}$$

The constant K_1 can be determined by using the known terminal condition: for $n = 0$, $Y_0 = \alpha X_0$.

$$K_1 = \alpha X_0 - \frac{Y_1 - \bar{A}\alpha X_0}{1 - \bar{A}} = \frac{\alpha X_0 - Y_1}{1 - \bar{A}} \tag{4.39}$$

Putting the value of K_1 in Eq. (4.38), we get the complete solution of Eq. (4.34) as

$$Y_n = \left(\frac{\alpha X_0 - Y_1}{1 - \bar{A}}\right)(\bar{A})^n + \frac{Y_1 - \bar{A}\alpha X_0}{1 - \bar{A}} \tag{4.40}$$

Equation (4.40) gives the concentration of the solute (Y_n) in phase G leaving the nth plate of the column. The concentration of the phase L leaving the same tray is readily obtainable using Eq. (4.33). To determine the total number of ideal plates, we put $n = N + 1$ and $Y_n = Y_{N+1}$ in Eq. (4.40).

$$Y_{N+1} = \left(\frac{\alpha X_0 - Y_1}{1 - \bar{A}}\right)(\bar{A})^{N+1} + \frac{Y_1 - \bar{A}\alpha X_0}{1 - \bar{A}}$$

A rearrangement of the equation gives

$$\overline{A}^N = \frac{Y_{N+1}[(1/\overline{A}) - 1] - [Y_1/\overline{A} - \alpha X_0]}{\alpha X_0 - Y_1}$$

Rearranging further and taking logarithm of both sides,

$$N = \frac{\log\left[\left(\frac{Y_{N+1} - \alpha X_0}{Y_1 - \alpha X_0}\right)\left(1 - \frac{1}{\overline{A}}\right) + \frac{1}{\overline{A}}\right]}{\log \overline{A}}$$

(4.41)

The above equation is the well-known *Kremser Equation* (also called the Kremser–Brown–Souders equation) originally developed in connection with gas absorption in a plate column. However, it is applicable to other mass transfer operations as well (for example, counter-current adsorption). Charts based on Eq. (4.41) are available for ready use (see Ludwig, 1997). A typical chart is given in Figure 4.14.

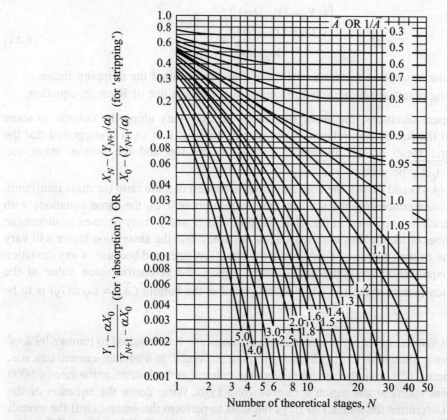

Figure 4.14 Kremser Chart [Eqs. (4.41) and (4.44)]; parameters of the chart: $\overline{A}$ for 'absorption', $1/\overline{A}$ for 'stripping'.

The solution given by Eq. (4.40), does not apply when $\overline{A} = 1$. In this case Eq. (4.34) becomes

$$Y_{n+1} - Y_n = Y_1 - \overline{A}\, \alpha X_0$$

(4.42)

If we write this equation for $n = N, N - 1, N - 2, \ldots, 1$, and add, we get

$$Y_{N+1} - Y_1 = N(Y_1 - \overline{A}\,\alpha X_0)$$

$$\Rightarrow \qquad\qquad N = \frac{Y_{N+1} - Y_1}{Y_1 - \overline{A}\,\alpha X_0} \qquad\qquad (4.43)$$

Equation (4.43) can be given a physical interpretation. When the absorption factor $\overline{A} = L_s/(\alpha G_s)$ $= 1$, the slope of the operating line becomes $L_s/G_s = \alpha$, which is the same as the slope of the equilibrium curve, Eq. (4.33). So the operating and the equilibrium lines become parallel. The change in the concentration of a phase at each stage (which is equivalent to the distance between the lines) is equal. Therefore, the number of plates will be equal to the ratio of the total concentration change over the column to the concentration change over a single plate or stage.

In the case of transfer of the solute from phase L to G (if the phase G is a gas and the phase L is a liquid, transfer of the solute from L to G is called *stripping*), and the number of theoretical plates or stages is given by

$$N = \frac{\log\left[\left(\dfrac{X_0 - (Y_{N+1}/\alpha)}{X_N - (Y_{N+1}/\alpha)}\right)(1 - \overline{A}) + \overline{A}\right]}{\log(1/\overline{A})} \qquad (4.44)$$

The inverse of the absorption factor, $\overline{S} = 1/\overline{A} = \alpha G_s/L_s$, is called the stripping factor.

The following points are to be noted in connection with the use of Kremser equation.

(a) In practical situations, the absorption factor $\overline{A}$ may vary along the column to some extent if the equilibrium relation is not strictly linear. If it is so, it is suggested that the geometric mean of the absorption factors at the top and the bottom trays, i.e. $\overline{A} = \sqrt{\overline{A}_1 \overline{A}_N}$ be used.

(b) In Eqs. (4.41) and (4.44), the concentrations are taken in mole ratio (or mass ratio) unit. If the solute concentrations are low (say, within about 7%), the same equations with concentrations expressed in the mole fraction unit (x and y) may be used to determine the number of ideal plates with reasonable accuracy. But the absorption factor will vary along the column because of changes in the total flow rates and because of any deviation of the equilibrium relation from linearity. Again, the geometric mean value of the absorption factors at the top ($\overline{A}_1 = L_1/\alpha G_1$) and at the bottom ($\overline{A}_N = L_N/\alpha G_N$) is to be used.

EXAMPLE 4.6 (*Number of trays for countercurrent contact*)   It is required to remove 99% of the solute C from a solution of C in G by using a 'pure' solvent L in a counter-current cascade. The feed containing 12% C in the mixture enters the column at the bottom at the rate of 6000 kg/h. The solvent enters at the top at a rate of 7685 kg/h. Write down the equation of the operating line. Determine the number of trays required to perform the separation if the overall tray efficiency is 40%. The equilibrium relation is linear, $Y = 1.32X$, where $Y = $ kg C per kg C-free G, and $X = $ kg C per kg C-free L.

Solution

Feed concentration = 12%; feed rate on solute-free basis, $G_s = (6000)(1 - 0.12) = 5280$ kg.

Mass of solute entering = $(6000)(0.12) = 720$ kg; fraction of the solute removed = 0.99.

Using the *mass ratio unit*, feed concentration, $Y_{N+1} = 0.12/0.88 = 0.136$; exit concentration, $Y_1 = 0.00136$ (see Figure 4.15].

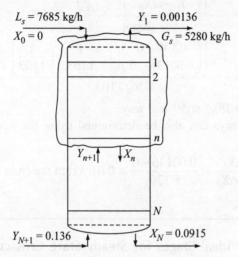

Figure 4.15 The input and output streams.

The entering solvent does not have any C in it; i.e. $X_0 = 0$. Solvent input rate, $L_s = 7685$ kg/h.

Material balance over the column: $G_s(Y_{N+1} - Y_1) = L_s(X_N - X_0)$,

i.e. $5280(0.136 - 0.00136) = 7685(X_1 - 0)$ or $X_1 = 0.0915$

Equation of the operating line:

By a material balance over the envelope, Figure 4.15,

$$G_s(Y_{n+1} - Y_1) = L_s(X_n - X_0); \text{ but } X_0 = 0$$

$\Rightarrow$ $5280(Y_{n+1} - 0.00136) = 7685X_n$ i.e. $\boxed{Y_{n+1} = 1.455X_n + 0.00136}$

This is the operating line which passes through the terminal points: top $(0, 0.00136)$, and bottom $(0.0915, 0.136)$.

Determination of the number of ideal trays:

The equilibrium line, $Y = \alpha X = 1.32X$ (slope, $\alpha = 1.32$), is drawn on the X–Y plane. The operating line, PQ, is also drawn through the terminal points as above. The number of ideal stages is obtained by the construction of steps on the diagram.

In the lower part of the diagram, the driving force is pretty small. In order to ensure accuracy, the construction of steps in this region is done separately using enlarged scales. The construction is shown in Figure 4.13(a) for the top eleven trays, and Figure 4.13(b) for the rest. The number of ideal trays is 23.8. The number of real trays is obtained by dividing this number by the fractional tray efficiency.

The number of real trays = 23.8/0.4 = 59.5, $\boxed{\text{say } 60}$.

In the given problem, both the equilibrium and operating lines are linear. So the number of ideal trays can also be calculated from the Kremser equation, Eq. (4.41) as well.

The absorption factor, $\bar{A} = L_s/\alpha G_s = 7685/(1.32)(5280) = 1.103$

$$\Rightarrow \qquad N = \frac{\log\left[\left(\dfrac{Y_{N+1} - \alpha X_0}{Y_1 - \alpha X_0}\right)\left(1 - \dfrac{1}{\bar{A}}\right) + \dfrac{1}{\bar{A}}\right]}{\log \bar{A}}$$

$$= \frac{\log\left[\left(\dfrac{0.136 - 0}{0.00136 - 0}\right)\left(1 - \dfrac{1}{1.103}\right) + \dfrac{1}{1.103}\right]}{\log 1.103} = \boxed{23.7}$$

Number of real trays = 23.7/0.4 = 59 real trays.

The number of ideal trays can also be determined using the Kremser chart, Figure 4.14. We have

$$\bar{A} = 1.103 \text{ and } \frac{Y_1 - \alpha X_0}{Y_{N+1} - \alpha X_0} = \frac{0.00136 - 0}{0.136} = 0.01. \text{ From the chart (Figure 4.14), the number}$$

of ideal stage, $N = \boxed{22.5}$.

4.6.4   The Number of Ideal Stages for Steady State Crosscurrent Contact

The arrangement of flow of the phases in this kind of contact is shown in Figure 4.16. The phase G flows from one stage to the next sequentially. An amount of fresh L phase is added to each stage and the phases are brought into intimate contact. The phases leaving a stage are then separated. The phase G flows to the next stage, and the phase L, along with the solute transferred into it, is taken out of the apparatus. The amount of phase G on solute-free basis (denoted by G_s) flowing from one stage to the next remains constant (because the carrier and the solvent phases, G and L, are assumed to be mutually immiscible). But the amounts of phase L (and also its concentrations) fed to the different stages may not be the same.

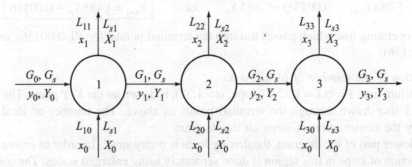

Figure 4.16   Flow arrangement in a cross-flow cascade.

It is obvious that in an individual stage of the cascade, the contact is cocurrent. So we can use the results of Section 4.6.2 in order to determine the number of ideal contact stages required to achieve a desired degree of separation. The graphical method of determination is illustrated in

Figure 4.17. The equilibrium curve is drawn on the X–Y plane. The operating line for stage 1 is drawn through the point $P_1(X_0, Y_0)$ with a slope $-L_{s1}/G_s$. The operating line is extended to meet the equilibrium curve at the point Q_1 if the stage is ideal. The operating line for stage 2 starts from P_2 (which has an ordinate $Y = Y_0$, and abscissa corresponding to the point Q_1) and will have a slope $-L_{s2}/G_s$. The operating lines for the three stages are P_1Q_1 (slope $= -L_{s1}/G_s$), P_2Q_2 (slope $= -L_{s2}/G_s$), and P_3Q_3 (slope $= -L_{s3}/G_s$). If equal amounts of phase L are supplied to the stages, the operating lines will be parallel. If all the stages are *ideal*, the construction procedure can be continued to find out the number of stages required to reduce the concentration of G phase to a specified level. Alternatively, if the number of stages in a cross-flow cascade is given, any other unknown quantity (for

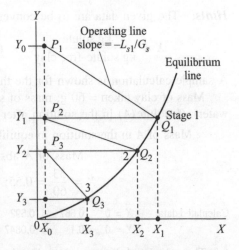

Figure 4.17 Graphical construction of a cross-current cascade (Mass transfer from phase G to phase L).

example, the flow rate of a phase, the degree of separation attainable, etc.) of the system can be determined. A trial-and-error procedure may be required. The procedure of calculation is the same if the mass transfer occurs from phase L to G.

For a system having a linear equilibrium relation (i.e. if $Y = \alpha X$), the cross-flow cascade problem can be readily solved algebraically. The operating and the equilibrium line equations in terms of the input and output concentrations for each stage are written. The resulting set of equations can be solved for any unknown or unknowns as required. An algebraic approach is also possible if the equilibrium relation, even if nonlinear, is available in the form of an equation (rather than tabulated data). The methods are illustrated in Example 4.9 for mass transfer from phase L to phase G.

EXAMPLE 4.7 (*Batch adsorption from a solution*)   An adsorbent, which is a modified clay, is used to separate an organic compound A from an aqueous solution. One kilogram of the solution containing 10% of the organic was treated with varying amounts of the clay in a number of laboratory tests. The following data were collected.

Gram clay used	15	40	60	100	135	210	325	450
% A in the solution in equilibrium	9.1	7.81	6.93	5.66	4.76	3.38	2.44	1.48

(a) Do the test data fit the Freundlich adsorption isotherm in the form $Y = aX^\beta$, where Y = gram solute per gram clay, and X = gram solute per gram solute-free solvent?

(b) How much of the adsorbent is required to recover 90% of the solute from 1000 kg of 10% solution?

(c) If 678 kg of the adsorbent is used per 1000 kg of the solution, how much of the solute is recovered if the treatment is done in two stages, using half of the clay in each stage?

Hints: The given data are to be converted to

$$X = \frac{\text{kg solute}}{\text{kg solute-free clay}} \quad \text{and} \quad Y = \frac{\text{kg solute}}{\text{kg solute-free solvent (water)}}$$

A sample calculation is shown for the third data point.

Mass of clay taken = 60 g; mass of solution taken initially = 1000 g (100 g solute + 900 g water); % solute (A) in the solution after equilibration = 6.93%.

Mass of A in the solution in equilibrium = $[(900)/(1 - 0.0693)] - 900 = 67$ g

Mass of A absorbed = $100 - 67 = 33$ g

$$X = \frac{33}{60} = 0.55; \quad Y = \frac{67}{900} = 0.0744$$

Calculated data:

$X = 0$	0.667	0.592	0.550	0.460	0.407	0.326	0.238	0.189
$Y = 0$	0.1	0.0847	0.0744	0.060	0.050	0.035	0.025	0.015

(a) The calculated data are plotted on log-log scale from which we get by fitting a straight line

$$Y = 0.173X^{1.36} \quad \text{i.e.} \quad \alpha = 0.173; \quad \beta = 1.36$$

(b) Mass of solution treated = 1000 kg (900 kg water + 100 kg solute); 90 kg solute to be removed. If M kg adsorbent is used, at equilibrium, $X = 90/M$; $Y = 10/900 = 0.0111$

Putting these equilibrium values of X and Y in the Freundlich's isotherm, we have $M = \boxed{678 \text{ kg}}$.

(c) Two stage contact—use $678/2 = 339$ kg of clay in each stage.

Mass of the aqueous phase (on *solute-free basis*), $G_s = 900$ kg; mass of clay, $L_s = 339$ kg.

Slope of the operating line = $-L_s/G_s = -339/900 = -0.376$; feed concentration, $Y_0 = 100/900 = 0.111$; the feed clay is solute-free, i.e. $X_0 = 0$.

Draw the equilibrium line $(Y = 0.173X^{1.36})$. Locate the point $P_1(0, 0.111)$ on the Y-axis; draw a line of slope -0.376 through P_1 to meet the equilibrium line at $Q_1(X_1, Y_1)$. Draw a horizontal line through Q_1 to meet the Y-axis at $P_2(0, Y_1)$. Draw the operating line for the second cross-current stage through P_2 and parallel to P_1Q_1 to meet the equilibrium line at Q_2. Then P_2Q_2 is the operating line for the second stage. At the point Q_2, the concentration of the solute (in the aqueous phase) is $Y_2 = 0.006$. Mass of solute leaving the second stage = $(900)(0.006) = 5.4$ kg. The graphical construction is left as an exercise.

EXAMPLE 4.8 (*Batch adsorption from a gas*)   The equilibrium distribution of moisture between air and a newly developed adsorbent at 25°C is given by

$$Y = 0.0337X$$

where Y = kg moisture per kg dry air, and X = kg moisture per kg dry adsorbent.

(a) In an experiment on the adsorption of moisture by this material, a cylindrical vessel, provided with a frictionless piston, is filled with 0.2 m³ of air containing moisture at a partial pressure of 20 mm Hg and then 50 g of the adsorbent is added into the vessel. The total pressure within the cylinder remains at 1 atm and the temperature is 25°C. Calculate the partial pressure of moisture in the vessel, the amount of water vapour adsorbed, and the final volume of air after equilibrium is established.

(b) How much of the adsorbent is required to remove 99% of the moisture from 100 m³ of air at 25°C, 1 atm total pressure and 80% relative humidity by (i) a single-stage batch contact, (ii) two-stage batch contact such that 60% of the total solid required is used in the first stage and the remaining 40% in the second stage?

Given: vapour pressure of water at 25°C = 23.6 mm Hg.

Hints: **(a)** Mass of dry air in the vessel = 229.2 g; mass of moisture in the vessel at the start = 3.87 g.

Let the final (i.e. after the equilibrium is attained) partial pressure of moisture in the vessel be p mm Hg, and the mass of moisture be m g. Then, at equilibrium,

$$Y = m/229.2; \qquad X = Y/0.0337 = 0.1295m$$

Also,

$$X = \text{(mass of moisture removed)/(mass of adsorbent)}$$
$$= (3.87 - m)/50 = 0.1295m \qquad \text{i.e.} \qquad m = 0.518 \text{ g}$$

If V is the final volume of air in the vessel (1 atm, 25°C), mass of air in it is 229.2 g as before, i.e.

Mass of air,
$$V\left(\frac{760 - p}{760}\right)\left(\frac{273}{298}\right)\left(\frac{28.8}{22.414}\right) = 229.2$$

Mass of moisture,
$$V\left(\frac{p}{760}\right)\left(\frac{273}{298}\right)\left(\frac{18}{22.414}\right) = 0.518$$

Solving these two equations,

$$V = \boxed{0.1954 \text{ m}^3}$$

$$p = \boxed{2.74 \text{ mm Hg}}$$

and the mass of moisture absorbed = $\boxed{3.032 \text{ g}}$.

(b)(i) Mass of dry air, $G_s = 114.8$ kg; mass of moisture = 1.83 kg; $Y_0 = 1.83/114.8 = 0.01594$ kg moisture per kg dry air. Final mass of moisture in the vessel = 1% of the initial = 0.0183 kg; $Y_1 = 0.0183/114.8 = 1.594 \times 10^{-4}$ kg/kg dry air.

$$X_0 = 0; \quad X_1 = ? \quad \text{Material balance: } G_s(Y_0 - Y_1) = L_s(X_1 - X_0)$$

Apply equilibrium relation: $Y_1 = 0.0337X_1$ to get $L_s = \boxed{383 \text{ kg}}$.

(b)(ii) Total mass of adsorbent used = $L_{s1} + L_{s2}$; $\quad L_{s1}/L_{s2} = 60/40 = 1.5; \quad X_0 = 0$.

Material balance for Stage 1: $L_{s1}(X_1 - X_0) = G_s(Y_0 - Y_1)$, i.e. $L_{s1}X_1 = 1.83 - 114.8Y_1$

Stage 2: $L_{s2}(X_2 - X_0) = G_s(Y_1 - Y_2)$, i.e. $L_{s2}(X_2 - 0) = 114.8(Y_1 - Y_2)$

Apply the equilibrium relation: $Y_1 = 0.0337X_1$; and $Y_2 = 0.0337X_2$; $Y_2 = 1.594 \times 10^{-4}$, given

Solving the above equations,

$$L_{s1} = 42.5 \text{ kg}$$
$$L_{s2} = 28.4 \text{ kg}$$

Total mass of the adsorbent = $\boxed{70.9 \text{ kg}}$

EXAMPLE 4.9 (*Multistage crosscurrent contact*)   The equilibrium distribution of a solute C between solvents A and B (up to 30% of C in solution in A) is given by

$$Y = 3.75X$$

where X and Y are the concentrations of C in A and B respectively, both in the mass ratio unit (i.e. mass of the solute per unit mass of solute-free solvent). The solvents A and B are practically immiscible.

It is required to calculate the amount of the solvent B required to separate 95% of C from 1000 kg of a 15% (by mass) solution of C in A for the following separation schemes: (a) an ideal single-stage contact; (b) an ideal three-stage crosscurrent contact, the amount of the solvent used in each stage being equal; (c) a very large number of crosscurrent contacts using an infinitesimal amount of the solvent in each stage.

Solution

Basis: 1000 kg of the feed solution containing 15% C (solute) and 85% A (carrier). Let L denote the feed solution (C in A) and G denote the extracting solvent (B) phase.

Amount of the carrier phase in the feed, $L_s = 1000(1 - 0.15) = 850$ kg

Feed concentration (on solute-free basis), $X_0 = (15$ kg $C)/(85$ kg carrier$) = 0.1765$ kg solute per kg carrier, A.

At the outlet, 95% of the solute is removed; exit concentration of the phase L is

$$(0.15)(0.05)/850 = 0.00882 \text{ kg } C \text{ per kg } A$$

(a) *Single-stage contact* [see Figure 4.18(a)]

Mass balance over the stage: $L_s(X_0 - X_1) = G_s(Y_1 - Y_0)$

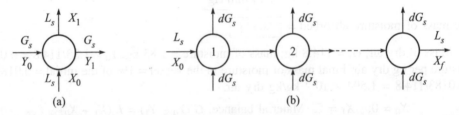

(a)   (b)

Figure 4.18   (a) Single-stage ideal contact. (b) An *infinitesimally small* quantity of phase G is added to each of the *infinite* number of crosscurrent stages.

The phases are in equilibrium as they leave the *ideal stage*. Therefore, $Y_1 = 3.75X_1$. Putting the values of various quantities, i.e.

$$X_0 = 0.1765; \ Y_1 = 3.75X_1 = (3.75)(0.00882) = 0.0331 \text{ kg } C \text{ per kg } B; \ Y_0 = 0$$

in the mass balance equation, we have

$$(850)(0.1765 - 0.00882) = G_s(0.0331 - 0)$$

or $$G_s = \frac{(850)(0.16768)}{0.0331} = \boxed{4306 \text{ kg}}$$

(b) *An ideal three-stage crosscurrent cascade* (see Figure 4.16)

The mass balance equations over the three stages are given below (equal amount of B is used for each stage).

$$\text{Stage 1:} \quad L_s(X_0 - X_1) = G_s(Y_1 - Y_0)$$
$$\text{Stage 2:} \quad L_s(X_1 - X_2) = G_s(Y_2 - Y_0)$$
$$\text{Stage 3:} \quad L_s(X_2 - X_3) = G_s(Y_3 - Y_0)$$

Given: $L_s = 850$ kg; $X_0 = 0.1765$; $X_3 = 0.00882$; $Y_0 = 0$; $Y_1 = 3.75X_1$; $Y_2 = 3.75X_2$ and $Y_3 = 3.75X_3$; $G_s = ?$

Putting the above values in the mass balance equations,

$$\text{Stage 1:} \quad 850(0.1765 - X_1) = G_s(3.75X_1)$$
$$\text{Stage 2:} \quad 850(X_1 - X_2) = G_s(3.75X_2)$$
$$\text{Stage 3:} \quad 850(X_2 - 0.00882) = G_s(3.75)(0.00882)$$

The above three mass balance equations can be solved for the three unknowns, X_1, X_2, and G_s. But the equations are nonlinear. A graphical method of solution is therefore more convenient. The procedure of graphical solution of such a problem is given below (see also Section 4.6.4).

Step 1: Draw the equilibrium line on the X-Y plane (in the given case, the line is straight).
Step 2: Locate the concentrations of the input streams to the first stage, (X_0, Y_0).
Step 3: Draw three operating lines of equal slopes (because the same amount of solvent, G_s is used in each stage). One end of such an operating line lies on the horizontal line $Y = Y_0 (= 0)$ and the other end on the equilibrium line. A *trial-and-error* construction method may have to be adopted so that the last operating line (that corresponds to the third stage) ends up at the point (X_3, Y_3) on the equilibrium line where $X_3 = 3.75Y_3$.

The construction is shown in Figure 4.19. The equal slope of the lines $= L_s/G_s = -2.187 \Rightarrow$ $G_s = 388.7$. The total amount of extracting solvent required $= 3 \times 388.7 = \boxed{1166 \text{ kg}}$.

This is substantially less than that required if the separation is done in a single stage.

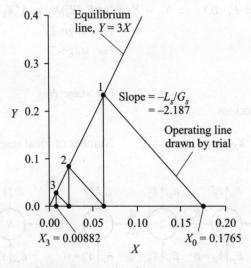

Figure 4.19 Graphical construction of three crosscurrent stages by trial.

(c) *A cascade having an infinite number of crosscurrent contact stages* [see Figure 4.18(b)]
While the feed stream moves from one stage to the next with gradually reducing concentration
of the solute in it, a small amount, dG_s, of the solvent B is added to each stage.

The material balance for the nth stage: $- L_s dX = (Y - Y_0)dG_s = Y dG_s$

Here dX is the change in the concentration of the stream L as it moves through a stage. Since
dX is negative, a *minus* sign is used in the above equation to maintain consistency of sign. Since
the stages are ideal, the phases leaving a stage are in equilibrium, i.e. $Y = 3.75X$.

$$\Rightarrow \qquad\qquad -L_s dX = (3.75X)\, dG_s$$

On integration from $X = X_0$ (the feed concentration) to $X = X_f = 0.00882$, which is the terminal
concentration,

$$-L_s \int_{X_0}^{X_f} \frac{dX}{X} = \int_0^{G_s} dG_s \quad\Rightarrow\quad L_s \ln \frac{X_0}{X_f} = 3.75 G_s$$

$$\Rightarrow \qquad\qquad 850 \ln\left(\frac{0.1765}{0.00882}\right) = 3.75 G_s \quad \text{or} \quad G_s = \boxed{679.2 \text{ kg}}$$

which is the required amount of solvent.

EXAMPLE 4.10 (*A crosscurrent extraction battery*)   A feed having X_0 kg solute per kg carrier
A is treated with a solvent B in an N-stage crosscurrent cascade. The feed rate is R_s kg/h (solute-
free basis), and an equal amount of pure solvent, E_s kg/h, is supplied to each of the stages. If
the equilibrium relation is linear ($Y = \alpha X$), determine the number of ideal stages required to reduce
the solute concentration in phase A to X_N (this phase is called the 'raffinate'; see Chapter 8).

Solution
Refer to Figure 4.20. For $Y_{1i} = Y_{2i} = \ldots = Y_{ni} = 0$, the material balance equation for the stage-1
becomes:

$$R_s(X_0 - X_1) = E_s Y_1 = E_s \cdot \alpha X_1 \Rightarrow X_0 - X_1 = (\alpha E_s/R_s)X_1 = A'X_1 \Rightarrow X_0 = (A' + 1)X_1$$

For stage-2	$X_1 = (A' + 1)X_2$
For stage-3	$X_2 = (A' + 1)X_3$
$\vdots$	$\vdots$
For stage-N	$X_{N-1} = (A' +1)X_N$

Multiplying the above equations,

$$X_0 = (A' + 1)^N X_N \qquad\Rightarrow\qquad \text{Number of ideal stages,} \quad \boxed{N = \frac{\log(X_0/X_N)}{\log(A' +1)}}$$

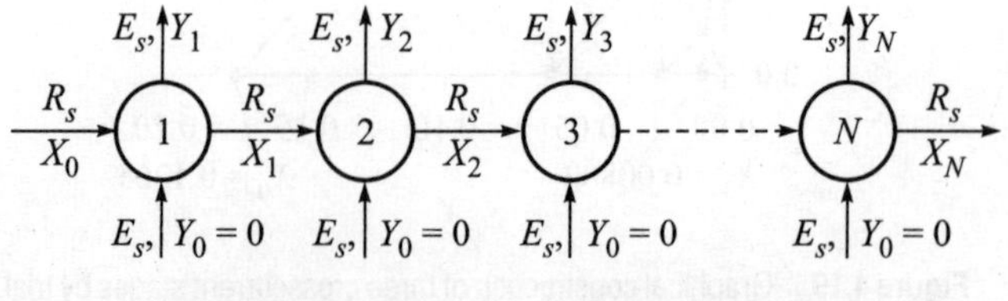

Figure 4.20   Crosscurrent extraction battery.

4.7   INTERPHASE MASS TRANSFER IN DRUG DELIVERY SYSTEMS

Controlled or sustained release drug delivery devices are very effective in administering a drug at a predetermined rate. Such a device is implanted in a patient and the drug gets released over a period of time. Common controlled release devices are 'capsule type' or 'matrix type' or their hybrid versions (Chien, 1991). Transdermal controlled release from a device applied on the skin externally is also pretty common. A controlled release device is based on the principles of diffusion and interphase mass transfer. A 'capsule type' device and the associated mass transfer principles are briefly described below.

The device consists of a mass of drug particles encapsulated in a polymeric membrane permeable to the drug. The drug molecules get 'dissolved' in the polymer at the inner surface of the capsule, diffuse through the membrane and are 'desorbed' or released at the outer surface of the membrane because of a concentration driving force. The system is schematically shown in Figure 4.21. We use the following notations:

C_{m1} = concentration of the drug at the inner surface of the polymeric membrane (this is the 'solubility' of the drug in the polymer)

C_{mi} = concentration of the drug at the outer surface of the polymer

C_{Li} = concentration of the drug in the fluid at the membrane surface

C_{Lb} = concentration at the edge of the fluid diffusion layer

l_m = membrane thickness

δ_L = fluid diffusion layer thickness

D_m = diffusivity of the drug in the membrane

D_L = diffusivity of the drug in the fluid.

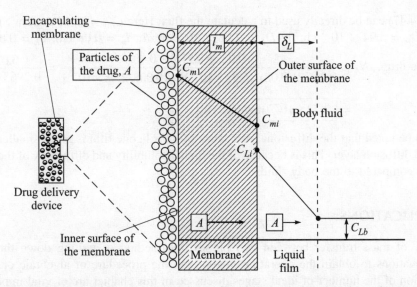

Figure 4.21   A controlled release device; the concentration profiles of the drug in the polymeric membrane and in the outer diffusion layer are shown.

Linear 'interfacial equilibrium' is assumed at the membrane-fluid interface.

$$C_{Li} = \beta C_{mi} \tag{4.45}$$

Steady-state flux of the drug, $N_A = \dfrac{D_m}{l_m}(C_{m1} - C_{mi}) = \dfrac{D_L}{\delta_L}(C_{Li} - C_{Lb})$ (4.46)

If we use the linear equilibrium relation, Eq. (4.45), and combine the two resistances in series, the above equation reduces to

$$N_A = \frac{\beta C_{m1} - C_{Lb}}{(\beta l_m/D_m) + (\delta_L/D_L)} \tag{4.47}$$

The rate of release of the drug at steady state can be calculated from the above equation if the relevant parameters are known. It is to be noted that the release rate will decrease in course of time because of a number of reasons including reduction in the amount of drug in the capsule.

EXAMPLE 4.11 (*Rate of drug delivery*)   Polydimethylsiloxane (PDMS, its structure is given in Table 14.2) is an attractive polymeric material for implants and drug delivery applications because of its good permeability to non-hydrophilic organic substances and compatibility with the human body. A quantity of progesterone, an important hormone, is encapsulated in a 0.8 mm thick silicone membrane (also called the silastine membrane) and implanted in the body of a patient. The following data are given: diffusivity of the drug in the polymer, $D_m = 5.94 \times 10^{-7}$ m^2/h; that in the body fluid, $D_L = 2.08 \times 10^{-7}$ m^2/h; partition coefficient, $\beta = 0.022$; 'solubility' of progesterone in the polymer = 0.513 mg/cm^3; estimated thickness of the diffusion fluid layer, $\delta_L = 0.08$ mm. If the drug concentration in the body fluid is essentially zero (which is a quite reasonable assumption), calculate the rate of release of the drug.

Solution

Equation (4.47) can be directly used to calculate the flux. Here $C_{m1} = 0.513$ mg/cm^3; $\beta = 0.022$; $C_{Lb} = 0$; $D_m = 5.94 \times 10^{-3}$ cm^2/h; $D_L = 2.08 \times 10^{-3}$ cm^2/h; $l_m = 0.08$ cm; $\delta_L = 0.008$ cm.

Flux of the drug, $N_A = \dfrac{(0.022)(0.513) - 0}{[(0.022)(0.08)/(5.94 \times 10^{-3})] - [0.008/2.08 \times 10^{-3}]} = \dfrac{0.0113}{0.2963 + 3.846}$

$$= \boxed{2.72 \times 10^{-3} \text{ mg/cm}^2 \cdot \text{h}}$$

It is to be noted that the diffusional resistance of the silicone film is much smaller than that of the fluid diffusion layer. This is because of the higher solubility and diffusivity of the hormone in silicone compared to the body fluid.

4.8   APPLICATIONS

The theory of mass transfer between two phases, the method of writing down the material balance equations to obtain the operating line(s), and the procedure of algebraic or graphical determination of the number of ideal stages discussed in this chapter are of vital importance in all mass transfer operations. Whether an operation involves contacting two fluids (as in gas absorption, distillation, solvent extraction, etc.), or a fluid and a solid (adsorption, drying, etc.), the above basic principles and methodologies are applicable for the calculation of the rate of mass transfer or the number of ideal stages required to perform a desired separation. The next chapters will illustrate these applications in more details.

NOTATIONS

$A, \overline{A}$	:	component A; absorption factor, Eq. (5.31); carrier phase A; solute A
B	:	carrier phase B
C	:	concentration, kmol/m^3; solute C
G, G_s	:	gas flow rate, gas flow rate on *solute-free basis*, kmol/s
$G_n(y_n)$	:	flow rate (concentration) of the stream G leaving the nth tray
H, H'	:	Henry's law constants, bar, (bar)(m^3/kmol); Eqs. (4.2), (4.4)
k_x, k_y	:	individual liquid or gas-phase mass transfer coefficient, kmol/(s)(m^2)(Δx or Δy)
K_x, K_y	:	overall liquid or gas-phase mass transfer coefficient, kmol/(s)(m^2)(Δx or Δy)
L, L_s	:	liquid flow rate, liquid flow rate on *solute-free basis*, kmol/s
$L_n(x_n)$	:	flow rate (concentration) of the stream L leaving the nth tray
m	:	Henry's law constant in the form of Eq. (4.3) or Eq. (4.8)
m', m''	:	local slopes of the chords of the equilibrium line, Eq. (4.5)
n	:	the tray numbered n
N	:	total number of trays
N_A	:	molar flux of component A
p	:	partial pressure, bar, atm, mm Hg
P	:	total pressure, kPa, bar, atm
x, y	:	solute mole fraction in the gas-phase and the liquid-phase respectively
X, Y	:	concentration in the liquid-phase or gas-phase in mole ratio (or mass ratio) unit
α	:	solubility equilibrium constant in Eq. (4.33), $Y = \alpha X$

Subscripts/Superscripts

*	:	refers to equilibrium condition
b	:	value of a quantity (concentration, partial pressure, etc.) at the bulk condition
i	:	interfacial value
M	:	log mean value
1, 2	:	values at the column terminals

SHORT AND MULTIPLE CHOICE QUESTIONS

1. Here are a few cases of gas absorption. Classify them as:
   (a) absorption of the following gases in water: O_2, CO_2, H_2S, SO_2, Cl_2, HCl, NH_3, acetaldehyde vapour, formaldehyde vapour, acetone vapour; (b) absorption of CO_2, H_2S, SO_2 in caustic solution; (c) absorption of benzene, acetylene, CS_2 in a non-volatile oil; (d) desorption of NH_3, tri-chloroethylene, benzene from a wastewater stream; (e) absorption of 8% CO_2 in an aqueous solution containing 10% mono-ethanolamine. Classify these cases as (i) gas-film resistance controlling; (ii) liquid-film resistance controlling; (iii) both gas-film and liquid-film offering comparable resistance.

2. The Henry's law constant for hydrogen sulphide in water at 25°C is 990 kPa/(gmol/litre). Calculate the value of the constant (H) in MPa $(p = Hx)$ and its dimensionless value $(m$ in $y = mx)$ at 25°C if the partial pressure of H_2S (p) is low and the total pressure is 1 atm. Also calculate the solubility of H_2S (mg/litre) in water at 25°C and a partial pressure of 50 mm Hg.

3. The solute A is absorbed from a gas (G) in a liquid (L) in a countercurrent tower. *Given:* feed gas rate = 35 kmol/h, 10 mol% A, 90 mol% carrier; liquid rate at the top (solute-free) = 40 kmol/h; equilibrium relation, $Y = 1.1X$ (Y is the concentration in the gas phase in the mole ratio unit). The overall driving force at the top, gas-phase basis, is $(\Delta Y)_{top}$ = 0.00555. What is the driving force at the bottom of the tower?

4. The operating line (PQ) and the equilibrium line (OM) for four gas–liquid systems are given on the X–Y plane in Figure 4.22. Identify them as cases representing: (a) cocurrent absorption; (b) countercurrent absorption; (c) cocurrent stripping; (d) countercurrent stripping.

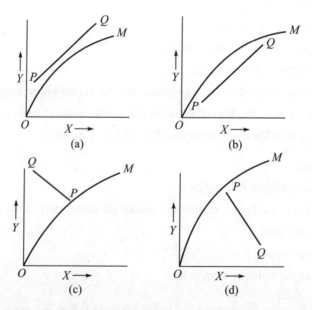

Figure 4.22 Equilibrium lines (OM) and operating lines (PQ) for a few systems.

5. Comment on the units of concentration that can be used for application of Eqs. (4.41) and (4.44) for analytical determination of the number of ideal stages. Explain how the absorption (or stripping) factor influences the number of ideal stages.

6. The equilibrium relation for a system is $y = 2.5x$. If the equilibrium relation is expressed in the form $Y = \varphi(X)$, what would be the slope of this equilibrium line at $X = 0$ and at $X = 0.1$?

   (i) 2.5, 3.46   (ii) 0, 2.5   (iii) 2.5, 4.22

7. The equilibrium relations for the gas–liquid pairs A–C and B–C (A and B are solutes; C is the solvent) follow the Henry's law: $p_A = H_A x_A$ and $p_B = H_B x_B$, $H_A > H_B$ at the same temperature. If the individual solubilities of the gases at the same temperature and pressure are S_A and S_B kmol/m^3, then

   (i) $S_A > S_B$ (ii) $S_A < S_B$ (iii) no conclusion.

8. The value of the Henry's law constant, H [as given in Eq. (4.2)]

   (i) increases with temperature
   (ii) decreases with temperature
   (iii) is independent of temperature.

9. The individual gas-phase mass transfer coefficient k_y has the same unit as

   (i) diffusivity
   (ii) molar concentration
   (iii) molar flux.

10. Which one of the following is a probable value of the mass transfer coefficient k_L for the dissolution of small KCl crystals in water in an agitated vessel?

    (i) 10^{-5} mm/s   (ii) 0.02 mm/s   (iii) 5 m/s

11. Which one of the following is a probable value of k_G for absorption of chlorine gas from air in water in a packed tower?

    (i) 0.08   (ii) 5×10^{-4} (iii) 6.5×10^{-7} kmol/(m^2)(s)(bar)

12. Absorption of oxygen from air in water is liquid-film resistance controlled. What will happen to the controlling resistance if oxygen from air is absorbed in a strong solution of alkaline pyrogallate? The controlling resistance will be offered by

    (i) the gas-phase
    (ii) the liquid-phase
    (iii) both the gas and liquid phases.

13. Which one of the following is a realistic value of the individual gas-phase mass transfer resistance [i.e. $1/k_y$, expressed as (h)(m^2)(Δy)/kmol] for absorption of pure SO$_2$ gas in water at 30°C and 0.95 bar pressure?

    (i) 200   (ii) 1.5   (iii) 0

14. Chlorine gas in mixture with N$_2$ is being *absorbed* in water at 27°C in a wetted-wall tower; temperature = 21°C; total pressure = 1.2 bar; partial pressure of chlorine in the bulk gas = 0.1 bar. The Henry's law constant for chlorine = 600 bar/mole fraction.

Which of the following *cannot be* a set of interfacial concentrations $[x_i, y_i]$ for this system?

   (i) [0.01, 0.0833]   (ii) [1.1×10^{-4}, 0.055]   (iii) [1.8×10^{-6}, 0.04]

15. The solute C is being transferred from phase A (lighter) to phase B (heavier) in a counter-current packed tower. The flow rates of the phases (solute-free basis) are $A_s = 70$ kmol/h, $B_s = 50$ kmol/h, and the equilibrium relation is linear, $Y = 0.6X$ (X and Y are concentrations in phase A and B respectively, mole ratio unit). The phase A entering at the bottom has 0.1 mol C per mol C-free A, and the phase B entering at the top is solute-free. The overall driving force at the top of the column on the A-phase basis is $(\Delta Y)_{top} = 0.001$. What is the driving force at the bottom, $(\Delta Y)_{bottom}$?

   (i) 0.012   (ii) 0.0005   (iii) 0.0169

16. The solute C is being removed from its solution in A using a pure solvent B in a three-stage crosscurrent contactor. The feed rate is 30 kmol/h containing 10 mole% C. A total of 27 kmol/h of solvent B is used. The equilibrium relation is linear. What will be the slope of the operating line $(-B_s/A_s)$ for the first stage if the maximum amount of the solute C has to be recovered?

   (i) −0.333   (ii) 3.0   (iii) −0.90

17. An aqueous solution of SO_2 containing 0.0001 mole fraction of the solute is suddenly exposed to pure SO_2 gas at 0.1 atm total pressure. The Henry's law constant is 40.7 atm/mole fraction. What would be the *instantaneous flux* of SO_2 just on exposure if interfacial equilibrium reaches immediately? Neglect evaporation of water.

   (i)   Almost zero
   (ii) 40.7×10^{-2} kmol/h·m^2
   (iii)   Extremely large

18. The equilibrium distribution of A in a gas–liquid system (G–L) is linear, $Y = \alpha X$; α is a function of temperature, $\ln \alpha = 0.3512 - (26.462/T)$, T in K. The flow rates of the phases (solute-free basis) are: $G_s = 38$ kmol/h and $L_s = 49.5$ kmol/h; the feed gas has 8% A in it. At what temperature does the absorption factor become unity?

   (i) 23°C   (ii) 55°C   (iii) 32°C

19. If 80 kmol/h of a gas mixture containing 10 mol% of the solute A is contacted with water (solute-free) in a countercurrent packed tower in order to remove 95% of the solute, answer the following questions using the mole fraction unit of concentration. The equilibrium is described by Henry's law: $y_A = (2.0)x_A$.

   (a) If 152 kmol/h water (solute-free) is fed to the top of the tower, what are the overall gas-phase driving forces at the top, $(\Delta y_A)_2$, and at the bottom, $(\Delta y_A)_1$?
       $(\Delta y_A)_1, (\Delta y_A)_2 \rightarrow$ (i) 0.1, 0.095   (ii) 0, 0.055   (iii) 0.0048, 0.00552

   (b) If 200 kmol/h water is used, what is the overall gas-phase driving force at a section of the column where 50% of the solute has been absorbed? $\Delta y_A =$

       (i) 0.05   (ii) 0.381   (iii) 0.0172

   (c) What is the slope of the operating line, dy_A/dx_A, at the section of the tower referred to in part (b) above?

       (i) 2.303   (ii) 2.685   (iii) 1.6

(d) What is the value of the absorption factor ($A = L/mG$) at the section referred to in part (b) above?

(i) 1.342 (ii) 0.584 (iii) 2.157

20. Make a sketch to show typical concentration profiles of the solute during mass transfer across an interface. Qualitatively explain the concentration profiles.

21. A gas mixture containing four components (A_1, A_2 and A_3 are soluble; B is the carrier) is equilibrated with a solvent. Apply the phase rule to decide which parameters should be specified to describe the system completely.

22. The Kremser equation can be written in the form

$$(\bar{A})^N = \left(\frac{Y_{N+1} - \alpha X_o}{Y_1 - \alpha X_o} \right)\left(1 - \frac{1}{A} \right) + \frac{1}{A}$$

The equation appears to be satisfied by $\bar{A} = 1$. Can $\bar{A} = 1$ be really considered as a solution to this equation?

23. The solubility of A in water is 0.5 kmol/m³ at a partial pressure of 60 mm Hg. If the total pressure is 1.2 atm and the Henry's law is applicable, calculate the Henry's law constant ('m' in $y = mx$).

PROBLEMS

4.1 (*The equilibrium relation in different forms*)[1] The solubility of a gaseous substance A (mol. wt. = 26) in water is given by Henry's law: $p_A = 10^5 x_A$, p_A in mm Hg. Convert the equilibrium relation to the following forms: (a) $y_A = m x_A$ if the total pressure is 10 bar; (b) $p_A = m' C_A$, C_A in gmol/litre. Also write down the equilibrium relation using the mole ratio unit. Assume that the solution is dilute and has a density equal to that of water (1000 kg/m³).

4.2 (*Calculation of the overall coefficient*)[1] At a particular section of an equipment for absorption of the solute A in a liquid, the bulk gas phase contains 9.5 mol% A and the liquid contains 2 mol% of it. The gas-film coefficient is $k_y = 10$ kmol/(h)(m²)(Δy) and 60% of the mass transfer resistance occurs in the liquid-film. The Henry's law applies, $y_A = 0.85 x_A^*$. Calculate (a) the overall mass transfer coefficient, K_x; (b) the molar flux of A; and (c) the interfacial concentrations of the solute, x_{Ai} and y_{Ai}.

4.3 (*Calculation of the interfacial concentrations*)[1] In a certain equipment used for the absorption of SO_2 from air by water, at one section, the gas and liquid phase concentrations of the solute are 10 mole% and 4 mass% respectively. The solution density is 61.8 lb/ft³. At the given temperature (40°C) and pressure (10 atm), the distribution of the SO_2 between air and water can be approximately described as $p_A = 25 x_A$, where p_A is the partial pressure of SO_2 in the gas phase in atm. The individual mass transfer coefficients are $k_x = 10$ kmol/(h)(m²)(Δx) and $k_y = 8$ kmol/(h)(m²)(Δy). Calculate the overall coefficient, K_G in kmol/(h)(m²)(Δp, mm Hg) and x_{Ai} and p_{Ai} at the gas–liquid interface.

4.4 (*Use of the two-resistance model*)[1]   Absorption of oxygen from an air bubble occurs in 'pure' water. Calculate the overall coefficients K_y and K_x for the following cases: (a) The two-film model is applicable. The air-film thickness is 2 mm, and the water-film thickness is 0.02 mm. (b) The film model is applicable for the gas-phase transport and the penetration model for transport in the liquid-phase. The contact time of a liquid element with the gas is 1 s. *Given:* diffusivity of O_2 in air = 0.176 cm²/s, in water = 2.1×10^{-9} m²/s; the equilibrium relation is $p = 4.36 \times 10^4 x$, p = partial pressure of O_2 in atm; temperature = 298 K; total pressure = 1 atm.

4.5 (*Controlling resistance in mass transfer*)[1]   Jasmone is a high-value product used in perfumery and cosmetic industries. A suspension of jasmine flowers in water is contacted with an organic solvent to recover the compound. During extraction, the compound diffuses from the aqueous phase to the dispersed organic phase. The individual mass transfer coefficients are 3.5×10^{-6} cm/s (organic phase) and 2.7×10^{-5} cm/s (aqueous phase). The solute is 175 times more soluble in the organic phase ($y = 175x$; y = mole fraction of the solute in the organic phase). The aqueous solution is dilute and the total molar concentration of the organic phase is 10 kmol/m³. Calculate the overall mass transfer coefficient K_y. Which phase resistance controls?

4.6 (*Controlling resistance*)[1]   In a liquid–liquid contacting device the equilibrium distribution of solute C in the solvents A and B can be represented as

$$y = 10.5x$$

where x and y are the concentrations of the solute C in phases A and B respectively. If the individual mass transfer resistances are

$$k_x = 10.21 \text{ lbmol/h·ft}^2 \quad \text{and} \quad k_y = 4.35 \text{ lbmol/h·ft}^2$$

which phase resistance controls the rate of mass transfer?

4.7 (*Release of a VOC from an open wastewater treatment basin*)[2]   Many volatile organic compounds (some of these are obnoxious and toxic) are formed in open wastewater treatment basins. Sadel et al. [*Environ. Progr.*, *15* (1996) 82–92] studied the release of VOCs from an open basin in the wastewater treatment facility of Ciba-Geigy Corp. at McIntosh, Alabama. The liquid-phase mass transfer coefficient for methyl-isobutyl ketone (MIBK), a VOC, under a wind velocity of 3 m/s over the basin was found to be $k_L = 3$ cm/h and the gas-phase coefficient was $k_c = 0.028$ m/s at 25°C. If the Henry's law constant ($p_A = Hx_A$) for MIBK is $H = 5.5$ atm, and its average concentration in the basin is 8.7 ppm, calculate (a) the overall mass transfer coefficients, K_L and K_G; (b) the fraction of the total resistance offered by the gas-phase; and (c) the flux of MIBK if the bulk air is assumed to be free from the VOC.

4.8 (*Use of the relative mass transfer resistance*)[1]   The overall gas-phase mass transfer coefficient in an absorption tower is $K_y = 5.35$ kmol/(h)(m²)(Δy) and 70% of the total mass transfer resistance is known to be in the gas-phase. The equilibrium relation is given by

$$y = 3.2x$$

The total pressure is 760 mm Hg. Calculate (a) the individual gas-phase and liquid-phase mass transfer coefficients; (b) the overall liquid-phase mass transfer coefficient, K_x; and

(c) the overall mass transfer coefficients, K_G and K_Y. The total molar concentration of the gas is 0.041 kmol/m^3; the bulk liquid is essentially water.

4.9 (*An application to gas absorption*)[2] Consider absorption of the solute C from a carrier gas A using the solvent B. The gas-phase mass transfer coefficient is $k_G = 0.05$ kmol/(m^2)(h) (kPa). At a particular section of the absorber, the mole fraction of C in the bulk gas is 0.15 and the total pressure is 120 kPa. The bulk liquid concentration is 0.045 mole fraction, and the local flux is known to be 0.08 kmol/m$^2 \cdot$h.

(a) Calculate the interfacial concentration of the solute and the fraction of the total resistance lying in the gas phase.

(b) If the gas-phase mass transfer coefficient increases by 50% but all other parameters remain the same, what would be the fractional increase in the molar flux of the solute?

The equilibrium solubility of the gas (i.e. the equilibrium relation) is linear $y = 2.5x$ for $y \leq 0.15$.

4.10 (*Equilibrium calculation*)[1] Equilibrium data for ammonia–water system at 20°C and 30°C are given below [Sherwood, T.K., *Ind. Eng. Chem.*, *17*(1925) 745].

kg NH$_3$ per kg water	0.02	0.03	0.04	0.05	0.075	0.10	0.15	0.20	0.25
p_{NH_3}, mm Hg at 20°C	12	18.2	24.9	31.7	50	69.5	114	166	227
p_{NH_3}, mm Hg at 30°C	19.3	29.6	40.1	51	79.5	110	169	260	352

Densities of ammonia solutions in this temperature range are given below.

Mass% NH$_3$	1	2	4	8	12	16	20	24	28
Density, kg/m^3	994	985.9	981.1	965.1	950.1	936.2	922.9	910.9	898

If the total pressure is maintained at 1 atm, calculate and plot x_A vs y_A and C_A vs y_A (A = ammonia) diagrams for the ammonia–water system.

4.11 (*Mass transfer calculations using tabular equilibrium data*)[2] Vapour pressures of H$_2$O (mm Hg) over H$_2$SO$_4$ of various concentrations at 25°C are given below:

Mass% H$_2$SO$_4$	40	45	50	55	60	65	70	75	80
Vapour pressure of H$_2$O	13.5	11.1	8.74	6.36	4.09	2.34	1.23	0.546	0.19

The relative humidity of moist air is to be reduced by contacting it with sulphuric acid in a packed tower. The absorbent, 70% H$_2$SO$_4$, is fed at the top of the column at a rate of 1000 kg/h$\cdot$m^2, and air of relative humidity of 80% enters at the bottom at a rate of 3000 kg/h$\cdot$m^2. The dry air must not have a relative humidity over 2%. The temperature is 25°C and the pressure is 1 atm. Although drying of air by highly concentrated H$_2$SO$_4$ (as done in a H$_2$SO$_4$ plant) is gas-film resistance controlled (why?), the liquid-phase mass transfer resistance is not negligible if the acid concentration is not high. In the present case, the mass transfer coefficients are estimated to be

$$k_G = 0.016 \text{ kmol/(h)(m}^2\text{)(mm Hg)} \quad \text{and} \quad k_x = 0.96 \text{ kmol/(h)(m}^2\text{)(}\Delta x\text{)}.$$

Calculate (a) the overall coefficient K_y and (b) the interfacial concentrations (x_i, y_i) at a section of the tower where the relative humidity of bulk air is 40%. The Antoine equation for water is given under Example 2.2 and also in Table 7.2.

Since absorption of moisture in H_2SO_4 is highly exothermic, there will be significant temperature variation along the column. But, for the sake of simplicity, the temperature may be assumed to remain constant at 25°C.

4.12 (*Determination of the number of ideal trays*)[1]   It is required to absorb 95% of the acetone from a mixture with nitrogen containing 1.5 mol% of the compound in a countercurrent tray tower. The total gas input is 30 kmol/h and water enters the tower at a rate of 90 kmol/h. The tower operates at 300 K and 1 atm. The equilibrium relation is $y = 2.53x$. Determine the number of ideal trays necessary for this separation. Use the graphical method as well as the Kremser analytical method.

4.13 (*An inverse problem—calculation of the fractional separation, the number of trays being given*)[2]   Acetone from a mixture with air containing 2 mol% acetone is absorbed counter-currently in water in a plate tower containing four theoretical stages. The inlet gas rate is 40 kmol/h and acetone-free water is supplied to the column at a rate of 110 kmol/h. The equilibrium relation is $y = 2.5x$. Determine the concentration of the solute in the exit liquid analytically as well as graphically.

4.14 (*Another inverse problem*)[2]   An aqueous waste stream containing a toxic volatile organic compound (VOC) has to be air-stripped in a tray tower so that the air, loaded with the VOC may flow to the flare for incineration. The waste stream has 0.1 kg of the organic per 100 kg of water and the concentration has to be reduced to 50 ppm. The equilibrium distribution of the solute between air and water is linear and can be expressed as

$$Y = 4.35X \qquad (X, Y : \text{kg VOC per kg air or water})$$

A column of suitable diameter having 20 trays that are 50% efficient is available. Can the tower meet the requirement? The air rate is 1500 kg/h and the wastewater is to be treated at a rate of 4000 kg/h.

4.15 (*The equation of the operating line*)[3]   A countercurrent absorption tower receives 100 kmol of a gas mixture per hour having 15% of a solute A. It is required to absorb 95% of the solute. 'Pure' solvent enters at a rate of 80 kmol/h at the top. (a) What is the equation of the operating line if the concentrations are expressed in the *mole ratio* unit? (b) If the *mole fraction* unit is used, what would be the slope of the operating line at a section where the bulk gas concentration is 10 mol%? What is the maximum slope of the operating line and where does it occur?

4.16 (*Overall driving force at a section of a column*)[2]   A gas mixture having 7 mol% of the solute A is to be scrubbed in a packed tower at a rate of 70 kmol/h. The solvent, water, is fed at a rate of 80 kmol/h. In the concentration range involved, the solubility of the gas is described by the equation: $y_A^* = 1.2x_A - 0.62x_A^2$. It is desired to absorb 98% of A present in the feed. Determine the equation of the operating line and the overall gas-phase driving force at a point in the column where the bulk liquid concentration is $x_A = 0.04$.

4.17 (*Adsorption from a solution*)[2]   Laboratory test data on a newly developed adsorbent material show the material to be quite attractive for the removal of colour from wastewater from a textile dying plant. The following equilibrium relation was derived from the test data.

$$Y = 0.62X^{0.48}$$

where Y = kg colouring matter adsorbed per kg of the adsorbent, and X = kg colour per 1000 kg water.

(a) What per cent of the colouring matter will be removed if 100 kg of the wastewater containing 1 part colouring matter per 100 part of water is treated with 1 kg of the adsorbent in the following ways? (i) The entire adsorbent is used in a single batch; or (ii) half of the adsorbent is used to treat the solution in a batch, the adsorbent is removed and the water is further treated with the rest of the adsorbent again.

(b) Calculate the quantity of adsorbent required to remove 99% of the colour from 100 kg solution containing 0.8% of colour by weight in (i) a single batch, (ii) an 'ideal *crosscurrent* contact' in which a differential amount of the absorbent is added to each stage (see Example 4.9).

4.18 (*An optimization problem*)[3]   A solution of C in A has to be treated with a solvent B in a two-stage crosscurrent separation unit. The liquids A and B are immiscible and the equilibrium relation is linear, $Y = \alpha X$, where X = kg C per kg A and Y = kg C per kg B. For a given total amount of solvent used for a two-stage crosscurrent contact, show that for the maximum removal of C from the feed, half of the solvent needs to be used in each stage.

4.19 (*Crosscurrent extraction*)[3]   One hundred kilogram of an aqueous solution of p-chlorophenol at a concentration of 1 g per kg water is to be treated with 2 kg of an adsorbent to recover the compound from the solution by a two-stage crosscurrent contact. Calculate the maximum percentage recovery of the solute if the equilibrium relation at the operating temperature of 298 K is given by

$$Y = 0.6X$$

where X = kg solute (here it is p-chlorophenol) per 1000 kg water and Y = kg solute per kg adsorbent.

4.20 (*Calculation of solvent requirement for crosscurrent extraction*)[3]   One thousand kilograms of an aqueous solution has 0.12 kg solute per kg water. It is treated with an organic solvent, immiscible with water, in a three-stage mixer-settler unit in order to recover 96% of the solute. In the first stage, 1200 kg of the solvent is used, and equal amounts of solvent are used in the next two stages so that the desired recovery of the solute is achieved. The equilibrium relation is $W_s = 1.25W_w$, where W_s is kg solute per kg organic solvent and W_w is kg solute per kg water. Calculate the total solvent requirement.

4.21 (*Calculation of solvent requirement*)[3]   Nicotine is to be extracted from a liquor by using a solvent in a three-stage crosscurrent device. The feed rate is 2000 kg/h, containing 10 mass% nicotine. 95% of the solute has to be recovered. The solvent has 0.001 mass% nicotine in it. The equilibrium in the system can be expressed as $W_l = 0.85W_s$, where W_l is kg nicotine per kg nicotine-free feed and W_s is kg nicotine per kg of nicotine-free solvent. If equal amounts of solvent are used in the stages, calculate the total solvent requirement for the job.

4.22 (*Comparing the modes of contact*)[3]   A solution of C in the solvent A containing 25 mol% C is fed to a multi-stage separation device at a rate of 10 kmol per hour in which it is to be treated with the extracting solvent B entering at equal molar rate. It is required to calculate and compare the performance of the separation device if (a) it is a cocurrent cascade, (b) a countercurrent cascade, (c) a crosscurrent cascade. The stages in a cascade are ideal in each case. Calculate the fraction of the solute C removed from the solution against the number of stages in each of the above three configurations. The equilibrium relation is $Y = X$.

4.23 (*Gas–solid equilibrium*)[2]   The equilibrium moisture absorption by a variety of silica gel is a linear function of the humidity in air: $W_a = 0.0344W_s$, where W_a = humidity of air, kg moisture per kg dry air, and W_s = kg moisture absorbed per kg of dry gel. In an experiment, 0.5 kg of silica gel containing 5% moisture is placed in a vessel fitted with a frictionless piston (in order to maintain the total pressure constant). The vessel contains 1 m^3 of moist air in which the partial pressure of moisture is 15 mm Hg at the beginning. The total pressure is 1 atm and the temperature is 25°C. Calculate (a) the amount of moisture picked up by the gel and (b) the final partial pressure of moisture in the vessel.

4.24 (*Mass transfer to a pellet*)[3]   A spherical adsorbent particle of diameter 10 mm and mass 0.04 gmol is kept in contact with a large volume of moist air at 25°C. The partial pressure of moisture is 15 mm Hg and the total pressure is 1 atm. The equilibrium relation is $Y = 0.1X$; Y = kmol moisture/kmol dry air, and X = kmol moisture/kmol dry adsorbent. After 3 minutes of contact, the sphere contains 0.16 kmol moisture/kmol dry adsorbent. If the size of the adsorbent particle remains unchanged, calculate the mass transfer coefficient of moisture. Resistance to moisture diffusion within the pellet is negligible.

4.25 (*Mass transfer from a falling drop*)[3]   Single uniform drops of chloroform, 6 mm in diameter, are in free fall through a large volume of a dilute aqueous solution of acetone (5 mass%) at a terminal velocity of $v_d = 0.1$ m/s at 25°C. Acetone is transported from the bulk of the aqueous phase into a drop. The depth of the pool of the aqueous layer is 1.0 m. The drops are collected at the bottom and the liquid is found to contain 1.02 mass% acetone. The distribution of acetone between chloroform and water is given by $w_d = 1.72w_c$, where w_d is the mass fraction acetone in the dispersed phase (i.e. chloroform) and w_c is the same parameter in the continuous phase (water). Calculate the overall mass transfer coefficient K_x based on the overall aqueous phase driving force. The density of the aqueous phase is $\rho_c = 990$ kg/m^3 and that of the dispersed phase is $\rho_d = 1480$ kg/m^3.

   Many semi-theoretical and empirical correlations are available in the literature for estimation of both continuous phase and dispersed phase mass transfer coefficients for extraction of a solute from falling drops (see, for example, *Perry's Handbook*, 7th ed.; Skelland, A.H.P., *Diffusional Mass Transfer*). It will be interesting to estimate the mass transfer coefficient using the available correlations and to compare with the value calculated above. Here are two such correlations applicable to falling (or rising) drops in a liquid.

Continuous phase (c): $(Sh)_c = \dfrac{(k_L)_c d_p}{D_c} = 0.6(Re)^{1/2}(Sc)_c^{1/2};$

$$Re = \frac{d_p v_d \rho_c}{\mu_c}; \qquad (Sc)_c = \frac{\mu_c}{\rho_c D_c}; \qquad (Sc)_d = \frac{\mu_d}{\rho_d D_d} \qquad (i)$$

Dispersed phase (d): $(Sh)_d = \dfrac{(k_L)_d d_p}{D_d} = 31.4\left(\dfrac{4 D_d t_f}{d_p^2}\right)^{-0.34} (Sc)_d^{-0.125} \left(\dfrac{d_p v_d^2 \rho_c}{\sigma}\right)^{0.37} \qquad (ii)$

Here d_p = drop diameter, and t_f = contact time.

Following values of the different parameters are given—diffusivity of acetone: in water, $D_c = 2 \times 10^{-9}$ m²/s, in the drop, $D_d = 4.0 \times 10^{-9}$; viscosity: water, $\mu_c = 0.88$ cP, chloroform, $\mu_d = 0.53$ cP; interfacial tension, $\sigma = 30$ dyne/cm. Also calculate the continuous-phase mass transfer coefficient using the penetration theory[#] and compare with the value obtained from correlation (i) above.

4.26 (*Selection of the mode of contact*)[3] A solution of C in the liquid L is contacted with solvent G. The flow rates of the phases (on solute-free basis) are L_s and G_s kmol/h; feed concentration is X_0 and the solvent B fed to the column is solute-free; the equilibrium relation is linear, $Y = \alpha X$. It is necessary to choose between two devices—a three-stage countercurrent device and a three-stage crosscurrent device. Which device will offer better recovery of the solute? Compare by numerical calculation for $\bar{A} = L_s/\alpha G_s = 0.9$.

4.27 (*Calculation of the overall coefficients*)[2] In a countercurrent column, the bulk concentrations of the solute at a section are $x = 0.05$(liquid), and $y = 0.17$(gas). The individual coefficients are $k_y = 2.9 \times 10^{-4}$ and $k_x = 5 \times 10^{-4}$, and the equilibrium relation can be approximated by the function: $y^* = 2.5x + 8x^2$, $0 \leq x \leq 0.2$. What is the direction of mass transfer (gas to liquid or the reverse)? Calculate the overall coefficients K_x and K_y. What fraction of the mass transfer resistance occurs in the liquid phase?

4.28 Derive Eqs. (4.43) and (4.44).

4.29 (*Number of stages in crosscurrent extraction*)[2] Reconsider Example 4.9. The same amount of solvent E_s is supplied to each stage as before. But the solvent has some residual solute in it that has a concentration of Y_0 kg per kg solute-free solvent. Show that the number of ideal contact stages required to reduce the solute concentration from X_0 to X_N is given by

$$N \cdot \log(1 + A') = \log\left[\frac{\alpha X_0 - Y_0}{\alpha X_N - Y_0}\right]; \qquad A' = \alpha E_s/R_s$$

[#] A 'small' drop is found to behave like a 'rigid' sphere; there is virtually no motion within it. But in a bigger drop the 'interfacial shear' acting on the moving drop may be sufficient to cause a circulating motion within it. This is called 'internal circulation' within a drop which significantly increases the drop-side mass transfer coefficient. Another important factor is the surface tension gradient along the drop surface that occurs during transport of a solute across the interface. These factors greatly influence the mass transfer coefficient. These points are also discussed in Chapter 8.

4.30 (**Controlled release of a drug**)[2]   The release rate of a steroid ester from an implanted capsule was determined experimentally in order to measure the relevant parameters. Following data are available (see Section 4.7 for meanings of the notations used): solubility of the steroid in the polymer = 100 mg/cm^3; partition coefficient, $\beta = 0.15$; diffusivities, $D_m = 1.083 \times 10^{-7}$ m^2/h, $D_L = 1.042 \times 10^{-6}$ m^2/h; polymer membrane thickness, $l_m = 1$ mm. If the release rate is 1 mg/cm$^2 \cdot$h, estimate the thickness of the diffusion layer of the outer fluid. Which transport resistance appears to be more prominent?

4.31 (**Drug diffusion through a dialysis membrane**)[2]   Measurement of diffusivity or permeability of a drug through a membrane is very important for determining its potential for drug delivery applications. Farng and Nelson [*J. Pharm. Sci.*, 66 (1977) 1611–1614] used a two-compartment diffusion cell (see Figure 4.23) to measure the diffusivity and permeability of sodium salicylate, a model compound, through a microporous cellophane membrane. They also studied the influence of addition of sodium carboxymethyl cellulose (CMC, a polymer) on the rate of transport of the solute. In a particular experiment, compartment-1 of the diffusion cell was filled with a solution having 8 mmol/litre of the solute in 3% CMC, while the other compartment was filled with pure water. The steady-state solute flux through the membrane was 2.18×10^{-9} gmol/cm$^2 \cdot$s.

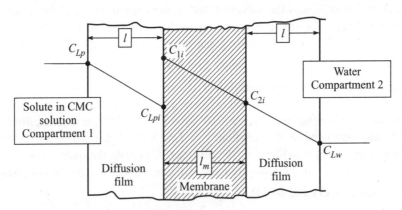

Figure 4.23   Concentration profiles of the solute in the membrane and in the liquid films on both sides (schematic).

Given the following data, calculate the 'effective' diffusivity and the permeability of sodium salicylate through the cellophane membrane: estimated thickness of the liquid diffusion layer on either side of the membrane, $l = 8.2 \times 10^{-3}$ cm (equal on both the sides); thickness of the cellophane film, $l_m = 4.66 \times 10^{-3}$ cm; diffusivity of the solute in the aqueous CMC solution, $D_1 = 1.33 \times 10^{-5}$ cm^2/s and in water, $D_2 = 1.11 \times 10^{-5}$ cm^2/s; volume fraction of water in the membrane = 0.667 (this is the same as the average fractional void volume of the membrane).

It is to be noted that the membrane is first soaked in water. When fitted in the diffusion cell, transport of the solute occurs through the pores filled with water. Physically the process is similar to transport through a porous diaphragm (see Section 2.9). However, the solubilities of sodium salicylate in CMC solution and in water being different, partitioning of the solute occurs at the upstream surface of the membrane. The partition coefficient is $\beta = C_{1i}/C_{Lp,i} = 1.16$, where $C_{Lp,i}$ is solute concentration in 3% CMC at the membrane surface, and C_{1i} is solution solute concentration in the membrane at the surface. Since the membranes pores are occupied with water, no partitioning of the solute occurs at the other surface of the membrane (in other words, the solute concentration is 'continuous' in the membrane and the compartment-2). The concentration profiles are illustrated in Figure 4.23.

REFERENCES

Carroll, J.J., 'Henry's law revisited', *Chem. Eng. Progr.*, Jan 1999, 49–56.

Chien, Y.W., *Novel Drug Delivery Systems*, Marcel Dekkar, New York, 2nd ed., 1991.

Danckwerts, P.V., *Gas Liquid Reactions*, McGraw-Hill, New York, 1970.

Lewis, W.K., and W.G. Whitman, *Ind. Eng. Chem.*, *16*(1924) 1215.

Ludwig, E.E., *Applied Process Design*, Vol. 2, 3rd ed., Gulf Publishing, Houston, Texas, 1997.

Perry's *Chemical Engineers' Handbook*, 7th ed., McGraw-Hill, New York, 1997.

Sherwood, T.K., R.L. Pigford, and C.R. Wilke, *Mass Transfer*, McGraw-Hill, New York, 1975.

Treybal, R.E., *Mass Transfer Operations*, 3rd ed., McGraw-Hill, New York, 1980.

Wylie, C.R., *Advanced Engineering Mathematics*, 4th ed., McGraw-Hill, 1975.

Yaws, C.L. et al. 'Water solubility data for 151 hydrocarbons', *Chem. Eng.*, Feb. 1993, 108–111.

Yaws, C.L. et al., 'Solubility and Henry's law constants for chlorinated compounds in water,' *Chem. Engg.*, February 2005, 50–56.

5 | Gas–Liquid Contacting Equipment

In Chapters 2–5, we discussed the basic principles of diffusion and mass transfer in a single phase or at a phase boundary. We also introduced the idea and strategy of contacting two phases in a stage-wise manner in order to transfer a solute from one phase to the other effectively and efficiently. Equipment and devices for interphase mass transfer can be broadly classified into the following categories:

- Gas–liquid or vapour–liquid contacting (gas absorption and stripping, distillation, humidification or dehumidification and water cooling)
- Liquid–liquid contacting (solvent extraction)
- Gas–solid contacting (drying and adsorption)
- Liquid–solid contacting (leaching, crystallization and ion exchange).

In many applications, the mass transfer equipment operates in the continuous mode. Batch contacting is sometimes used, particularly for low processing capacities or in small production units. The objective is to achieve an intimate contact between the phases and to ensure a high rate of mass transfer. A high degree of turbulent mixing is created to properly disperse one phase into the other. This helps in generating a large interfacial area of contact as well as in increasing the mass transfer coefficient. In a 'tray tower' (described below), for example, interfacial area is generated by passage of the gas (or vapour) into the liquid through perforations or openings; in a 'packed tower', on the other hand, interfacial area is generated by spreading the liquid on the packing surface. A gas–liquid contacting equipment may be provided with heating or cooling arrangements wherever necessary in order to maintain the desired process conditions. Mass transfer equipment is mostly 'custom-built' (i.e. designed and fabricated according to the requirements of the client; these types of equipment cannot be readily purchased from the market as 'on-the-shelf' items like pumps, valves, blowers, air-conditioners, etc.). The common types of equipment used for carrying out gas–liquid mass transfer in practice and their constructional and operational features are described in this chapter. Equipment for contacting other combinations of phases (liquid–liquid, gas–solid, etc.) mentioned above will be described in respective chapters.

5.1 INTRODUCTION TO GAS–LIQUID CONTACTING

A variety of gas–liquid contacting equipment is in use. In some of these, the gas is dispersed in the liquid in the form of bubbles (for example, tray towers, bubble columns, agitated vessels, etc.); in some others the liquid is dispersed in the form of droplets or discontinuous films in a continuous gas phase (for example, spray towers, packed towers, venturi scrubbers, etc.). Sometimes both gas and liquid phases are continuous (for example, a 'falling film contactor' which is used for certain gas–liquid reactions). Tray and packed columns are most widely used for gas–liquid contacting — namely for gas absorption, stripping, distillation. These are also used for liquid–liquid extraction (discussed in Chapter 8). The usual ranges of the two important mass transfer parameters, namely the mass transfer coefficient k_L and the specific interfacial area $\overline{a}$, attainable in common commercial gas–liquid contactors are given in Table 5.1.

Table 5.1 Common range of values of mass transfer parameters in commercial gas–liquid contactors

Contacting equipment	Superficial gas velocity (m/s at normal condition)	Mass transfer parameters		
		$k_L \times 10^4$ (m/s)	$k_y \times 10^3$ (kmol/s.m^2.Δy)	$\overline{a}$ (m^2/m^3)
Sieve tray	0.02–0.5	1–20	0.5–6.0	100–200
Packed column	0.1–1.2	1–20	0.03–2.0	10–350
Bubble column	0.1–0.3	0.4–3.0	0.5–2.0	50–600
Spray column	0.05–3.0	0.7–1.5	0.5–2.0	10–100
Mechanically agitated contactor	0.05–3.0	0.3–4.0		100–1000

5.2 TRAY OR PLATE COLUMN

A tray column primarily consists of a vertical cylindrical shell and a set of 'tower internals' that include (i) trays or plates on which the gas–liquid contact occurs, (ii) arrangements for flow of the liquid from one tray to the lower one through the downcomer, and (iii) inlet and outlet nozzles for the two phases. Figure 5.1 schematically shows a few essential parts of a 'sieve tray' column.

In a gas absorption application, the liquid enters the top tray through a nozzle. It impinges on a baffle plate, moves across the tray and flows into the lower tray through a 'downcomer'. The sieve trays shown in the figure are made of perforated metal sheets. (There are various other kinds of trays which will be described later.) The gas flows upwards and vigorously bubbles through the liquid on a tray, forming a turbulent 'gas–liquid dispersion' in which bubble breakage and coalescence occur continuously. An average depth of the dispersion is maintained on a tray. A large gas–liquid contact area and a high mass transfer coefficient are achieved. Mass transfer from the gas to the liquid (or from the liquid to the gas) phase occurs depending on the direction of the driving force. For example, in 'gas absorption', the solute gets transported from the gas to the liquid phase; the reverse occurs in stripping (discussed in Chapter 6). The gas then leaves the froth or dispersion (this is called 'gas–liquid disengagement') and enters the next upper tray. The liquid flows across a tray and then over a 'weir' to enter into the downcomer (the functions of a downcomer and a weir are discussed in Section 5.2.3). The downcomer is a region near the wall, separated by a 'downcomer plate', in which the bubbles get disengaged from the liquid.

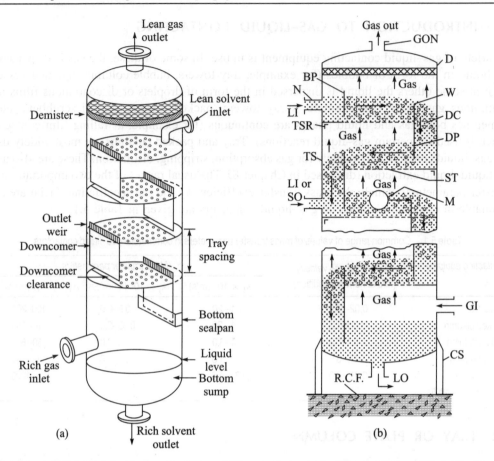

Figure 5.1 (a) Schematic of a 'sieve tray' column and (b) sectional sketch of a 'sieve tray' column [BP: baffle plate; CS: column support; D: demister; DC: downcomer; DP: downcomer plate; GI: gas inlet; GON: gas outlet nozzle; LI: liquid inlet; LI or SO: liquid inlet or side-stream outlet; M: manhole; N: nozzle; RCF: reinforced concrete foundation; ST: sieve tray; TS: tower shell; TSR: tray-support ring; W: weir].

The clear liquid flows to the next lower tray. In this way, countercurrent and stage-wise gas–liquid contact takes place in the tower. Each tray acts as a stage in which the liquid flowing down from the upper tray and the gas flowing up from the lower tray come into contact; the tower acts as a cascade (a 'stage' and a 'cascade' have been defined in Chapter 4).

The constructional and operational features of a tray tower and tower internals are briefly discussed below. Further details are available in the literature (see, for example, Kister, 1989; Ludwig, 1997; Chopey, 1997).

5.2.1 The Shell

The shell is usually made of a metal or an alloy. Plastic (for example, FRP) shells are also used sometimes. The material is selected on the basis of corrosiveness of the fluids, temperature and pressure conditions, and cost. If the shell diameter is small, it may be made of several flanged sections in order that the trays may be fitted into it and maintained, when necessary, by opening it. Tray towers of diameter less than 1 metre are rarely used. On the other extreme, towers as big as 10 metre in diametre are known to be in use.

A metal pipe may be used as the shell if the required diameter of the tower is small. Larger diameter shells are made from metal sheets by rolling. In fact, smaller sections are first made and then welded to get the shell of required diameter and length. Shell thickness is calculated by using a standard vessel design code (for example, ASME Section VIII; IS 2825; Moss, 2004). A tower may have flanged or welded ends depending upon the diameter.

Trays are bolted to tray support rings. Metal angles (L-section) rounded and welded to the shell may act as the tray support rings (the support rings also act as 'stiffeners' of the shell). Big diameter trays need support beams in addition, in order to prevent sagging of a tray under liquid load. Channels and I-section beams clamped or bolted at both ends to the support rings are used to support trays as shown later in Figure 5.11.

A tower is generally 'skirt-supported' on concrete foundations (Moss, 2004). The support should be strong enough to take the column weight, the liquid load and the wind stress. The seismic factor at the particular location is also needed to be considered during column and support design. Since the bending moment due to wind load is maximum at the tower bottom, it is a common practice to use different wall thicknesses for different sections of the shell. The bottom section has the maximum thickness and the upper sections have gradually smaller thicknesses. This strategy substantially reduces the weight, and hence the cost, of the shell. A tall tower has a ladder fixed on its wall. Small platforms with railings are fixed to the shell wall at the level of each manway for easy and safe access into the tower. Towers are insulated against heat exchange with the surroundings. A tower is erected on the foundation using a crane. Examples of erection after lifting a tower by a helicopter have been reported.

5.2.2 The Tray

A 'tray' has two major functions:

1. It allows the gas to flow through the holes or passages; the gas vigorously bubbles through the liquid to form a 'gas–liquid dispersion'. The tray holds the dispersion on it.
2. The trays separate the column into a number of compartments each of which constitutes a stage. Mass transfer between the phases occurs on a tray. Therefore, the trays as a whole constitute the heart of a column. The performance of a column depends upon the performance of the trays.

Trays are also called 'plates'. There are quite a few types of trays in use. The *bubble-cap tray* will be described first.

The bubble-cap tray

This is the oldest type of tray and is still in commercial use. A bubble cap consists of two major components—a bell-shaped 'cap' and a 'riser' (also called a 'chimney'). Figure 5.2(a) and (b) shows a typical bubble-cap design. The riser is inserted through a hole on the tray floor (or deck) and the bell-shaped cap is bolted to it. A ring gasket (not shown) is used below the nut. The riser or chimney is a piece of tube with a flared or expanded bottom end (there are other designs too). In fact, the riser acts as the vapour passage and also holds the cap.

A bubble cap has slots on its wall. The shape of the slots may be rectangular (most common), triangular, trapezoidal, or saw-tooth type. In the bell-shaped cap shown in Figure 5.2(a) and 5.2(b), the slots end a little above the bottom of the cap. The continuous portion of a cap below the slots is called the 'shroud ring'. The cap may be mechanically weak if there is no shroud ring and the slots extend up to the bottom. A bell-shaped cap rests on three short legs or tabs, integral to the cap, placed 120° apart. The open region thus provided between the tray floor and the cap bottom is called the 'skirt clearance'. Such a design helps in reducing accumulation of sediments and provides an additional area for gas flow if there is a sudden surge of the gas. Figure 5.2(c) shows a few other designs of the bubble cap.

The caps and the risers are made of low carbon steel, stainless steel or any other suitable material that can withstand the environment within the tower. Caps are arranged on a tray on equilateral triangular pitch with rows normal to the direction of liquid flow. Bubble caps generally range from 1 inch to 6 inches in diameter. The rectangular slots may be of the following size range:

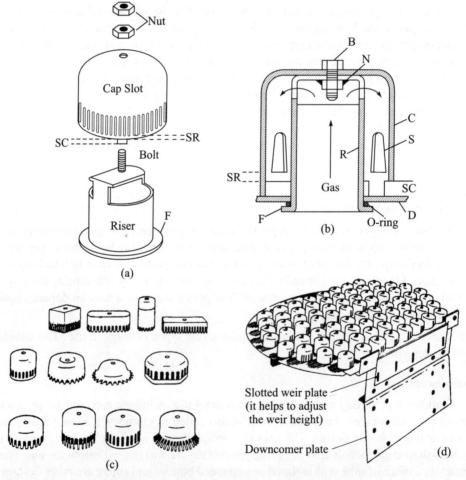

Figure 5.2   Bubble caps and a bubble-cap tray: (a) an exploded view of a bubble cap and (b) sectional diagram of a bubble cap [B: bolt; C: cap; D: tray deck; F: flared bottom of the riser; N: nut; R: riser; S: slot; SC: skirt clearance; SR: shroud ring] *Courtesy:* ACS Industries, USA; (c) different types of bubble-caps and (d) a bubble-cap tray

length ½ inch to 1½ inches, width ⅛ to ⅜ inch. Quite a few other slot geometries are used as well [Figure 5.2(c)]. The number of slots in a cap ranges from 12 to 70. For a medium-size column (4 to 10 feet), 4-inch caps are common. The cap-pitch (centre-to-centre distance) is about 1 inch to 2 inches more than the cap outer diameter. A bubble-cap tray is shown in Figure 5.2(d).

The sieve tray

This is the simplest type of tray in which the bubble caps are replaced by holes or perforations for entrance of the gas into the liquid. The holes are of relatively small diameter — usually ranging from ⅛ to ½ inch. This is why the name 'sieve tray' (also called 'perforated tray'). For clean services, use of a hole diameter of ³⁄₁₆ inch is common. However, for liquids that foul or cause deposition, a hole diameter of ½ inch may have to be used. In vacuum services, ⅛ inch hole diameter is preferred. Small holes enhance tray capacity, reduce entrainment, reduce weeping, promote froth regime operation and exhibit better mass transfer characteristics.

Holes are made by punching rather than by drilling a tray sheet (small holes may have to be made by drilling) in order to reduce the labour cost. These are arranged on an equilateral triangular pitch or a square pitch. The pitch (i.e. the centre-to-centre distance between the two adjacent holes) varies between $2.5d_H$ and $5d_H$ ($3.8d_H$ is common), where d_H is the hole diameter [as shown marked on Figure 5.12(b)]. The rows of holes are oriented normal to the direction of liquid flow. A sieve tray typically has a free area of 6 to 10% [free area fraction = hole area/tower cross-section, less the downcomer area]. The layout of a sieve tray, the downcomers and the weirs are shown in Figure 5.3(a) and (b). The assembly of a sieve tray is shown in Figure 5.3(c).

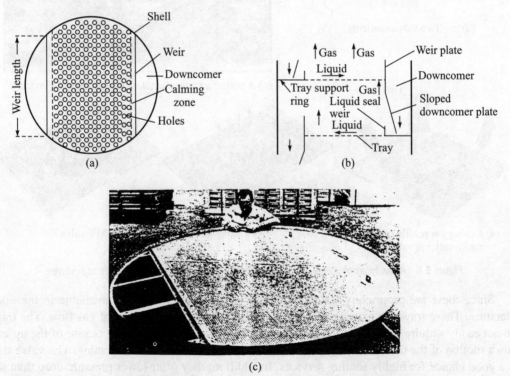

Figure 5.3 (a) Sieve tray layout, (b) downcomer, weir and the liquid seal weir, and (c) assembly of a sieve-tray.

The valve tray

The valve tray is a relatively new class of tray that provides variable area for the gas or vapour flow depending upon the flow rate or 'throughput'. This is why it is called 'valve tray'. A valve tray is a proprietary (that is patented) tray. Different types of valve trays are made by different companies.

A common valve tray has sufficiently large punched holes on the tray floor, each fitted with a movable disk, generally circular. A disk has guides that can slide vertically up or down along the thickness of the tray floor [Figure 5.4(a) and (b)]. The opening for the gas flow changes in this way, but the disk is always held in the same vertical line. As the gas flow increases, the disk is automatically raised. It settles down at a low vapour rate to prevent 'weeping'. The guides or retaining legs are bent at the end so that the disk does not pop up or gets detached even at a large vapour rate. The valve, a part of a valve tray (Koch Flexitray having 'caged valves') and the vapour flow profile through valves are all also shown in Figure 5.4(c). A valve tray offers a high 'turn down' ratio (this term will be defined later).

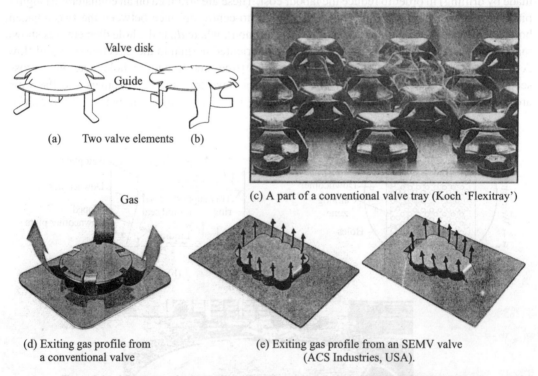

Valve disk

Guide

(a)   Two valve elements   (b)

(c) A part of a conventional valve tray (Koch 'Flexitray')

Gas

(d) Exiting gas profile from   (e) Exiting gas profile from an SEMV valve
    a conventional valve   (ACS Industries, USA).

Figure 5.4   A few types of valves, a part of a valve tray, and vapour flow profile through valves.

Since these are proprietary trays, the details of their design are not available in the open literature. These trays are extremely flexible because of the variable area of gas flow. The trays do not easily acquire deposits from dirty liquids, polymers or other solids because of the up and down motion of the disk and the guides. Valve units are, therefore, self-cleaning. The valve tray is a good choice for highly fouling services. In addition, they offer lower pressure drop than the bubble-cap type and generally they are cheaper than the latter type. A few problems common to all kinds of valve trays are (i) mechanical wear and corrosion because of continuous movement of the valve legs, and (ii) sticking of the disk on the tray if there is sticky deposition on the tray.

Excessive opening of the valves at a low gas rate causes weeping and valves should therefore be heavy enough to prevent this. On the other hand, heavy valves incur a greater pressure drop. As a compromise, alternate rows of heavy (made from 12 or 14 gauge sheets) and light (made from 16 gauge sheets) valves are used. In a common valve tray layout, 12 to 16 valves per ft^2 of tray area are accommodated. Common orifice and disk diameters are of the order of 1½ and 2 inches. The disks typically rise $\frac{3}{16}$ to $\frac{7}{16}$ inch above the tray deck. The flow area of fully open valves on a tray is about 10–15% of the active tray area (the active tray area is the tray cross-section less the downcomer area).

Because of high flexibility, high turndown ratio and relatively low cost, valve trays are now widely used for gas absorption and distillation. Various valve designs from different companies are available. Koch-Glitch makes twenty types of valves to suit a variety of services. In new installations, bubble-cap trays are rarely used; sieve trays and the valve trays are the preferred tray types. In contrast to movable or 'floating' valves described before, many companies have come up with 'fixed' valves that have properly shaped and profiled fixed covers above valve opening for better gas/vapour distribution. Typical fixed valves are shown in Figure 5.4(e) here and later on in Figure 5.14(c).

Other types of trays

There are a few other less common trays used for gas–liquid contacting. Typical examples are: Dual flow tray, Ripple tray, Leva film tray, etc. (Billet, 1979). A dual flow tray is a sieve tray without downcomers. The vapour (or gas) bubbles through the liquid and the liquid simultaneously weeps through the perforations (this is why it is called 'dual flow'). An average froth height, which is less than that on a standard sieve tray, is maintained. Since the contact time between the liquid and the vapour is small, the efficiency of a dual flow tray is less than that of a sieve tray. However, this is partly compensated by the increased active area (there is no loss of area due to the downcomers). Dual flow trays are known to be in use in a limited number of installations.

The Ripple tray (supplied by Stone and Webster) is a variation of the dual flow tray (Sloley, 1999). The tray has a corrugated deck and the liquid preferentially weeps through the troughs on the deck.

5.2.3 Downcomers and Weirs

The 'downcomer' is a passage through which the liquid flows down from one tray to the next below (Figures 5.1 and 5.3). The desired depth of the gas–liquid dispersion is maintained on a tray by using a 'weir' in the form of a vertical plate. The liquid, along with some dispersed gas or vapour bubbles, overflows the weir and enters the 'downcomer' or the 'downspout'. Disengagement of the gas as bubbles occurs in the upper region of a downcomer. The lower region contains clear liquid that enters the lower tray. The downcomer must provide sufficient residence time for gas–liquid disengagement (the residence time is the ratio of the downcomer volume and the volumetric flow rate of the clear liquid). The residence time is usually 3 to 5 seconds. However for a foaming liquid, considerably higher residence time and therefore a larger downcomer volume has to be provided. The 'clear liquid' velocity in the downcomer normally ranges between 0.3 and 0.5 ft/s. This value may vary depending upon the liquid properties.

A 'downcomer plate[†]' may be straight or inclined. The downcomer shown in Figure 5.1 or in Figure 5.7 is a straight plate which covers a constant segment of the tower cross-section. It is called a 'segmental downcomer'. In the downcomer design shown in Figure 5.3(b), the lower end of the downcomer plate is bent towards the column wall. This design, called 'inclined' or slopped downcomer, provides more downcomer space in the upper region where the gas–liquid disengagement occurs but less space in the lower region where the liquid is rather clear. In another variation, called 'stepped downcomer', the downcomer area decreases in steps [Figure 5.5(a)]. The downcomer plate is fixed to the tray from which the liquid overflows. The weir plate is bolted to the downcomer plate through a slotted bolt hole, so that the weir height can be easily adjusted [see Figure 5.2(d)]. The shape of an inclined downcomer and the layout of the perforations on a sieve tray are schematically shown in Figure 5.3. The lower edge of the downcomer plate should remain dipped into the liquid on the lower tray maintaining a clearance, (called 'downcomer clearance') of ½ to 1 inch from the tray floor. This makes a 'downcomer seal' [also shown in Figure 5.5(b) as D.S.] prevent 'short-circuiting' of some of the gas through the downcomer. An alternative is a depressed downcomer seal [Figure 5.5(c)]. The depressed region of the tray is called the 'seal pan' or 'seal pot'.

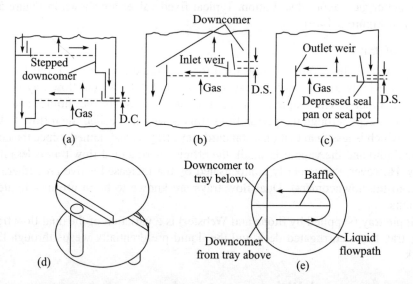

Figure 5.5   Downcomer types and seals: (a) a stepped downcomer, (b) a normal downcomer seal (D.S.), (c) a 'depressed' downcomer seal, (d) a 'pipe downcomer', and (e) the downcomer on a 'reverse-flow tray'. [D.C. = 'downcomer clearance'].

The weir length may vary from 60 to 80% of the tower diameter; the downcomer area (on one side) correspondingly varies from 5 to 15% of the tray area. A weir height of 1 to 2 inches is generally maintained. The row of bubble caps, valves or perforations (in case of a sieve tray) adjacent to the overflow weir should be about 3 to 4 inches away from it so that partial disengagement of the gas occurs before the liquid overflows the weir and enters the downcomer. This blank region on the tray deck is called the 'calming zone' [see Figure 5.3(a)]. The area of a tray that contains bubble caps, holes or valves is called the 'active tray area'.

[†] A 'downcomer plate' is just a metal plate and should not be confused with a tray.

In small columns, pipe downcomers ('downtubes') are preferred [see Figure 5.5(d)]. In a 'reverse-flow tray', the liquid entering a tray flows over half of the active tray area and then changes direction around a central baffle [see Figure 5.5(e)]. Both the downcomer and the downcomer seal are placed on the same side of such a tray. A longer liquid flow path is created this way. Such an arrangement is suitable if the liquid flow rate in the column is small.

5.2.4 Nozzles

A tower for contacting a liquid and a vapour (or a gas) should be provided with a few nozzles for feed entry (both gas and liquid), entry of reflux at the top and of the reboiler vapour return at the bottom (in a distillation column), and for product withdrawal from the tower. The primary criterion of a feed nozzle design is to ensure that the feed is introduced with minimum splashing or jetting (the velocity of liquid feed in the nozzle should not exceed 1 m/s). The feed should be evenly distributed and mixed with internal liquid or vapour. A few nozzle types for feed entry and liquid draw-off are shown in Figure 5.6. In case of a multipass tray, the feed or the reflux stream has to be proportionally balanced to the active areas of a tray.

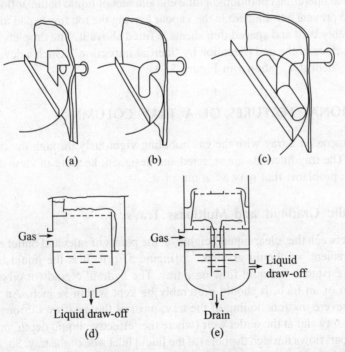

Figure 5.6   Feed entry and product draw-off nozzles: (a) an internal baffle prevents 'jetting' of the liquid feed, (b) a downward-bent feed nozzle, (c) a bifurcated feed nozzle, and (d) and (e) gas inlet and liquid draw-off nozzles [5.6(e) shows a split flow tray].

The location of the feed nozzle as per design calculations may not always be the optimum in practice. As a precautionary measure, one or two additional nozzles are sometimes provided above and below the calculated feed tray to provide some flexibility. The feed pipe may be connected to any of these adjacent nozzles if required for improved performance; otherwise these are just kept closed. A few ports or small nozzles for sampling and for instrument (temperature and pressure sensors) connection are also provided at suitable locations for the measurement of composition, temperature, and pressure. The bottom feed or the reboiler vapour return nozzle must be placed above the bottom liquid level. Viewing ports are sometimes provided for frequent inspection and testing.

'Manholes' are provided for each of 10 to 15 trays for access of a workman into the column for inspection, cleaning, and maintenance. The manhole diameter is kept in the range 16 to 24 inches. Larger manholes may be necessary for admitting a person wearing protective clothing and a breathing apparatus depending upon the environment within a tower. For towers of less than 3 ft diameter, handholes (8 to 14 inches) are provided for the purpose of cleaning. A ladder and an access platform are needed to be built for all manholes 12 ft or higher from the floor. A manhole or a handhole is covered with a gasketed manhole cover which is nothing but a 'blind flange'.

5.2.5   Mist Eliminator

Even under normal operating conditions, a little entrainment of liquid in the upflowing vapour may occur. In order to prevent entrainment in the vapour leaving the top tray, a pad made of wire mesh or a pack of suitably bent and spaced thin sheets is fitted above it. The droplets are retained after they strike the surface of the pad (retention by 'inertial impaction'). Such a device is called 'mist eliminator' or a 'demister' (shown in Figure 5.31).

5.3   OPERATIONAL FEATURES OF A TRAY COLUMN

The flow phenomena on a tray with the gas bubbling vigorously through the flowing liquid are pretty complex. The tray internals are selected and designed, keeping in view the complexity of the flow and the problems that may arise out of it.

5.3.1   Hydraulic Gradient and Multipass Trays

The difference between the 'clear liquid heights' at the points of inlet and outlet on a tray is called the 'hydraulic gradient' or 'liquid gradient'[††] [Figure 5.7(a)]. It is the liquid head required for overcoming the resistance to liquid flow on a tray. The hydraulic gradient on a tray should not exceed a fraction of an inch. It should preferably be kept within ½ inch. An excessive liquid gradient causes severe malfunctioning of the tray; most of the gas flows through the holes near the middle of the tray and at the outlet weir (where the 'effective liquid depth' on the tray is less) and only a small part flows through the holes at the liquid inlet side of the tray. Such maldistribution of the gas or the vapour (also called 'vapour channelling') severely reduces the 'tray efficiency'. In extreme cases, liquid 'dumping' or 'back-trapping' may occur through the end where the liquid enters the tray [Figure 5.7(b)]. Hydraulic gradient is a very important quantity to be checked during tray design. It remains pretty small for a sieve tray. But for a bubble-cap tray it may be significant because the bubble caps offer a larger resistance to liquid flow.

[††] The term gradient appears to be a misnomer. 'Gradient' means the rate of change of a quantity with position. But the hydraulic gradient is really the 'difference' of liquid heights.

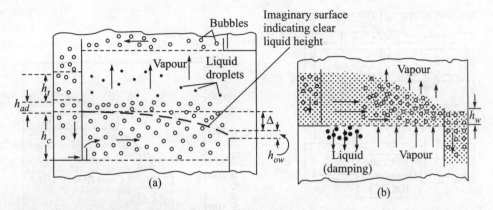

Figure 5.7 (a) Hydraulic gradient and clear liquid backup in the downcomer: h_c = clear liquid height at the tray inlet, h_{ad} = head loss for flow below the 'downcomer apron' (i.e. for flow through the 'downcomer clearance'), h_t = total tray pressure drop for flow of the gas [= $h_d + h_l$, see Eq. (5.14)], $h_{db} = h_c + h_{ad} + h_t$ = downcomer backup; (b) 'backtrapping' or 'dumping' of liquid from a tray: Δ = hydraulic gradient, h_w = weir height, h_{ow} = crest height at weir outlet.

The hydraulic gradient may be large on a cross-flow tray if either or both of tower diameter and liquid load are large. The liquid flow path should not be kept too long in order to avoid maldistribution of liquid and vapour streams. A 'split flow' or 'double pass'configuration of the tray may be adopted in such a case. The liquid load is split into two or more equal parts. More than one downcomers are provided on a split-flow tray [Figure 5.8(a) and (b)]. The design of a two-pass tray is not very difficult since it is symmetric. But the challenge becomes critical with more than two passes of the liquid. Three-pass trays are rarely used since they are inherently asymmetric. Four-pass trays [Figure 5.8(c)] are more frequently used in relatively large diameter columns. A very important design requirement is 'balancing' of the liquid flows so that the gas

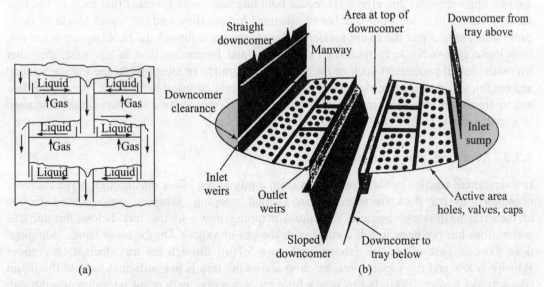

Figure 5.8(a) and (b) (a) Sketch of a 'split-flow' tray, two-pass; and (b) a two-pass sieve tray (Sloley, 1999) with sloped downcomers.

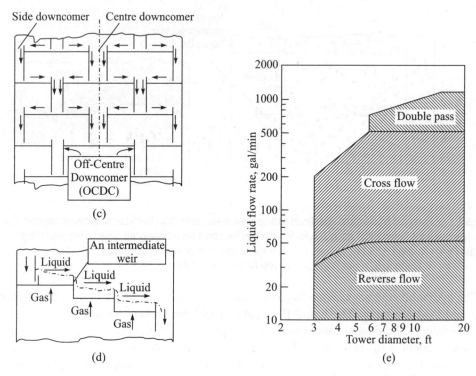

Figure 5.8(c), (d) and (e) (c) Schematic of a four-pass tray, (d) a 'cascade' or 'stepped' tray, and (e) the diagram for selection of liquid flow pattern.

and liquid flows remain uniform in all the four sections despite differences in the geometry. There are two approaches to this effect: (i) 'equal bubbling area' which means that each of the four sections should have the same number of openings for gas flow, and (ii) 'equal length of flow-path' which means that the liquid residence time is the same though the bubbling areas are not. Both these approaches have their own advantages and limitations. But in any case, the other hydraulic design parameters such as the weir shape [straight or swept-back, see Figure 5.13(c)] and height, and downcomer clearance should be properly adjusted to 'balance' the liquid flow and to ensure uniform performance of all the four sections. These issues have been discussed in a recent article (Pilling, 2005).

5.3.2 Weeping and Dumping

If a very small fraction of the liquid flows from a tray to the lower one through perforations or openings of the tray deck, the phenomenon is called 'weeping'. Weeping causes some reduction of the 'tray efficiency' because the liquid dripping down to the tray below through the perforations has not been in full contact with the gas or vapour. On the other hand, 'dumping' is an extreme case of leakage [shown in Figure 5.7(b)] through the tray deck if the vapour velocity is low and the vapour pressure drop across the tray is not sufficient to hold the liquid (Bennett and Kovac, 2000). In practice, a little bit of weeping may occur intermittently through sieve trays because of the instantaneous pressure imbalance.

5.3.3 Entrainment

When a gas bubbles through the liquid pool vigorously, droplets of liquid are formed in the vapour space by quite a few mechanisms including shearing action of the gas jet or rupture of the liquid film as a gas bubble bursts. Depending upon the size of a droplet, its velocity of projection and the drag force acting on it due to the gas velocity, the droplet may descend back into the liquid on the tray or may be carried into the tray above. The phenomenon of carry over of the suspended droplets into the upper tray is called 'entrainment'. The chances of entrainment are more if a droplet is small, if the gas velocity is large, or if the tray spacing is small.

Entrainment causes two major problems: (i) It leads to mixing of the entrained liquid from the lower tray with the liquid on the upper tray. This adversely affects the mass transfer driving force at the upper tray and reduces the 'tray efficiency'. (ii) The carry over of a substantial mass of liquid as droplets into the upper tray increases the liquid flow rate and downcomer load of that tray. In extreme cases, the second problem may lead to 'flooding' of the tower (as explained in Section 5.3.5). Entrainment is expressed as kg(droplets entrained)/s, kg per kg vapour, or kg per kg liquid flow, or kmol per kmol liquid flowing.

5.3.4 Flow Regimes on the Tray

The characteristics of gas–liquid dispersion on a tray depend upon the flow rates of the two phases, besides the tray type. A few 'flow regimes' may be identified (Lockett, 1986; Yanagi, 1990) in this connection [Figure 5.9(a)]. When the vapour (or the gas) rises through the liquid, there may be violent 'spray action' on one extreme or a 'quiescent flow' of the two-phase 'emulsion'

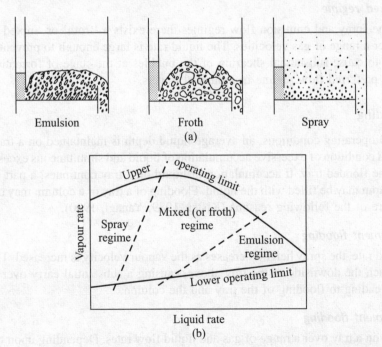

Emulsion   Froth   Spray
(a)

Liquid rate
(b)

Figure 5.9 (a) Types of gas–liquid dispersion on a tray, and (b) flow regimes and operating limits of a sieve tray (qualitative).

(or dispersion) on the other extreme, depending upon the flow rates of the two phases. In between, there occurs a 'froth regime' [Figure 5.9(a)]. In addition to the flow regimes, the flow rates of the two phases (particularly of the vapour phase) also govern phenomena such as weeping, dumping, entrainment, and flooding. A *qualitative* description of the flow regimes and their effects are shown in Figure 5.9(b).

Spray regime

It occurs at low liquid rates and high vapour velocities. The vapour enters at a high velocity into a shallow liquid layer disintegrating the liquid into droplets which are projected up in the space between two consecutive trays. The gas becomes the continuous phase, and the liquid, the dispersed. This is called the 'spray regime'. If the vapour rate is very high and the tray spacing is not sufficient, the droplets cannot settle. These are rather carried by the gas into the upper tray causing an accumulation of liquid there and eventual 'flooding' (flooding is described in Section 5.3.5). This is more likely to occur in vacuum operation since the gas velocity remains very high. A change of flow regime from froth to spray is called *phase inversion* in a tray column since the gas changes from dispersed to continuous state.

Emulsion regime

This occurs if the gas flows through the liquid at a rather low rate. The vapour bubbles formed at the nozzles are 'sheared off' by the fast-moving liquid. The bubble size and its rise velocity remain low as a result. The liquid with the slowly rising entrapped bubbles appears like an 'emulsion' and hence the name of the regime.

Froth or mixed regime

In between the spray and emulsion flow regimes there exists a 'froth' or 'mixed flow' regime extending over a range of gas velocities. The liquid rate is large enough to prevent spraying but not too large to cause substantial shearing of the bubbles at the stage of formation. The froth regime is the preferred flow regime in industrial towers.

5.3.5   Flooding

Under normal operating conditions, an average liquid depth is maintained on a tray. 'Flooding' is an abnormal condition of excessive accumulation of liquid and simultaneous excessive pressure drop across the flooded tray. If accumulation of liquid on a tray continues, a part or eventually the entire column may be filled with the liquid. Flooding of a tray or a column may occur because of one or more of the following reasons (Kister, 1989; Yanagi, 1990).

Spray entrainment flooding

At a low liquid rate, the spray height increases as the vapour velocity is increased. The spray may eventually reach the downside of the tray above, causing a substantial carry over of the liquid droplets and leading to flooding of the tray and the column.

Froth entrainment flooding

Froth appears on a tray over a range of gas and liquid flow rates. Depending upon the flow rates of the phases and the tray spacing, the froth may almost fill the entire space between two successive trays. Most of the liquid droplets suspended in the gas are then carried into the upper tray causing liquid accumulation thereon and eventual flooding of the tray. If the liquid is prone to foaming on aeration, flooding may occur even at lower gas velocities.

Downcomer flooding

When the liquid flow rate is high, the rate of flow of the gas–liquid dispersion into the downcomer also becomes high. If the downcomer cannot accommodate the dispersion load and the gas–liquid disengagement does not occur properly, the aerated frothy liquid fills the downcomer and finally backs up onto the tray above (Yanagi, 1990) leading to 'downcomer flooding'.

Let us refer to Figure 5.7(a). The static pressure exerted by the froth in the downcomer, expressed as 'clear liquid height', balances the sum of three terms (Yanagi, 1990): (i) the clear liquid height on the the tray (h_c); (ii) the head loss for liquid flow under the downcomer plate or the 'downcomer apron' (h_{ad}), which depends upon the downcomer clearance, the liquid flow rate and liquid properties; and (iii) the total gas pressure drop for flow through the liquid on the tray (h_t), which is the sum of dry tray pressure drop and the pressure drop for passage of the gas through the liquid. The sum of these three terms, all expressed as 'liquid head', is called the 'downcomer backup' (h_{db}) under stable tray operation, i.e.

$$h_{db} = h_c + h_t + h_{ad} \tag{5.1}$$

The froth height h_f over the tray floor in the downcomer is given by

$$h_f = \frac{h_{db}}{\phi_d} \tag{5.2}$$

where ϕ_d is the average relative froth density in the downcomer ($\phi_d = \rho_f/\rho_L$; ρ_f = froth density, and ρ_L = liquid density). Downcomer flooding occurs if the froth height h_f crosses the weir level of the upper tray, i.e.

$$h_f \geq S + h_w \qquad (S = \text{tray spacing}; h_w = \text{weir height}) \tag{5.3}$$

One strategy of overcoming the problem of downcomer flooding is to provide a larger tray spacing. Downcomer backup is further discussed in Section 5.5.2 and illustrated in Example 5.1.

5.3.6 The Performance Diagram

The performance of a particular type of tray depends upon the *relative* liquid and vapour throughputs. The effects of the phase flow rates on the performance of a sieve tray are qualitatively shown in Figure 5.10 (Yanagi, 1990). This is also called the *tray stability diagram*.

Let us assume that the tray operates at gas and liquid rates corresponding to point N located in the 'region of normal operation' in Figure 5.10. If we keep on increasing the gas throughput at a constant liquid rate, more liquid is entrained in the gas. At point E, the gas rate is high enough to cause excessive entrainment. The tray efficiency falls to an unacceptable level. At point F, the tray gets flooded and is inoperable.

Also, the tray does not operate satisfactorily if the gas rate is kept on decreasing. At a gas rate corresponding to point W, the gas pressure drop across the tray decreases to the extent that some liquid starts leaking through the tray holes. This is weeping of the tray as discussed before. As the gas rate is further reduced to point L, the weeping rate increases significantly causing

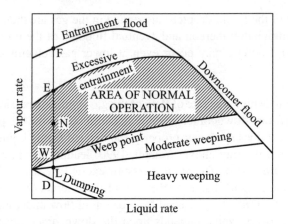

Figure 5.10   Performance diagram of a sieve tray.

deterioration of performance of the tray. The tray should be operated above this point. If the gas throughput is yet reduced to the point D, dumping of liquid starts. Under such a condition, most of the liquid passes through the tray holes and little, if any, flows into the downcomer.

The operable limits of a tray in respect of gas and liquid flow rates depend on the tray design, temperature and pressure conditions as well as the properties of the liquid and vapour phases.

5.3.7   Turndown Ratio

A column designed for a particular capacity may have to be operated at an enhanced or reduced capacity depending upon changes in the production rate in the plant due to various factors. It is, therefore, desirable that the trays have some degree of *flexibility* to operate over a range of throughput around the design capacity. Such flexibility is expressed in terms of the 'turndown ratio', which is defined as the ratio of the 'design vapour throughput' to the 'minimum operable throughput'.

Sieve trays have a low turndown ratio of about 2 (i.e. a sieve tray can normally be operated up to 50% of the design vapour throughput; at a still smaller vapour rate, severe weeping occurs). This value can be increased by reducing the fractional hole area. But this strategy is not very effective because of increased vapour pressure drop and reduced capacity. Valve trays normally have a turndown ratio of 4; bubble-cap trays have a still larger turndown ratio.

5.3.8   Tray Spacing

Tray spacing is the distance or gap between two consecutive trays in a column. An adequate tray spacing is important for quite a few reasons. The rate of entrainment (see Section 5.3.4) strongly depends upon the tray spacing. If a larger spacing is provided, most of the liquid droplets descend back to the tray reducing the entrainment. The column can operate at a greater superficial gas velocity and a smaller column diameter can be used for a given throughput. But the column height increases if the same number of trays have to be accommodated. Hence, a trade-off between a smaller column diameter and a larger height has to be struck.

Tray spacing varies over a pretty wide range of 8 to 36 inches. For a column 4 ft or larger in diameter, a tray spacing of 18 to 24 inches is adequate. If frequent inspection or maintenance is required, a larger tray spacing is convenient and advisable. A tray spacing of 30 inches or more is used in a vacuum column. In a big diameter column, the tray support beams restrict the movement of a workman on a tray for the purpose of cleaning and maintenance. So a larger spacing is necessary. If the liquid has a foaming tendency, a larger tray spacing should be allowed. A spacing less than 18 inches is not recommended for the common three tray types unless for any compelling reason.

5.3.9 Comparison of Bubble Cap and Sieve Trays

A qualitative comparison of the three commonly used trays in respect of capacity, efficiency, flexibility (turndown ratio), cost and a few other criteria is given in Table 5.2. It is to be noted that each of the criteria depends upon the particular system and operating conditions.

Table 5.2 Comparison of three common tray types (Kister, 1992)*

Parameter	Bubble-cap tray	Sieve tray	Valve tray
Capacity	Moderate	High	High to very high
Efficiency	Moderate	High	High
Entrainment	High (about three times that of a sieve tray)	Moderate	Moderate
Pressure drop	High	Moderate	Moderate
Turndown	Excellent (can operate at a very low capacity)	About 2 (not suitable to operate at variable loads)	4-5
Fouling tendency	High, tends to collect solids	Low	Low to moderate
Cost	High (about 2–3 times that of a sieve tray)	Low	About 20% more than sieve trays
Applications	Rarely used in new columns, may be used if low flow rates are anticipated	Most applications if turndown is not important	Preferred if a high turndown is anticipated
Share of market	About 5%	25%	About 70%

*Comparative assessment of trays should be done mainly on the basis of flexibility (turndown ratio), efficiency (discussed in Chapter 6), pressure drop and cost. Bubble-cap trays are more expensive and are not preferred for new installations. But they can satisfactorily operate at 50 to 120% of the design vapour velocity and 15 to 130% of the design liquid load.

5.4 A FEW MECHANICAL DETAILS

Mechanical construction of trays

It has been stated before that the trays are supported on tray-support rings welded to the shell. However, large trays are invariably made up of a few sections. Sometimes it may be necessary to take out a section through a manway for maintenance or replacement. The tray sections are screwed or bolted together to form the complete tray. The peripheral edge of a tray is bolted or clamped to the tray-support ring. Slotted bolt-holes in the ring are sometimes used for ease of assembling. If the tray and the shell have unequal expansions while operating at an elevated temperature, the slotted bolt-holes allow relative motion between the shell and the tray. Trays are also sometimes supported on brackets or clips welded to the shell. In a big diameter column, each tray has a central section as a separately bolted piece, called the 'manway section' (about 16 by 24 inches). During a maintenance job, a workman enters the column through a manway on the shell wall and opens the manway section of a tray to crawl into the next tray. Sections of a large tray and the supporting arrangements are shown in Figure 5.11(a).

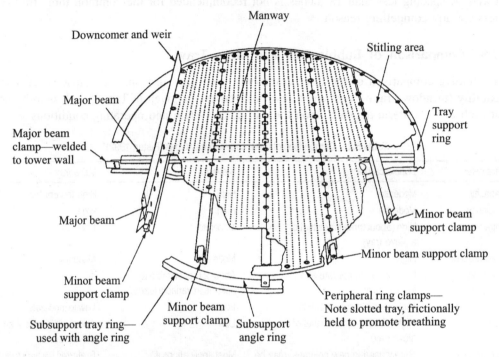

Figure 5.11(a)   Major mechanical and structural components of a tray.

The tray deck is generally fabricated from 14 gauge sheets if the material is a corrosion-resistance alloy, and 10 gauge (0.135 inch) for carbon steel. The support beams should be strong enough to keep the maximum deflection of a tray under full load to below ⅛ inch. The tray-support assembly should also be designed for a distributed load of 200 to 300 lb/ft^2 of tray area. Downcomer plates are generally ⅛ to ¼ inch thick.

Levelling and tolerance

Levelling of the trays, the weirs and the downcomer bottom edges are essential to ensure smooth operation. Inadequate levelling leads to maldistribution of the gas and the liquid, causing a drop in efficiency besides other problems. Ideally, each of these should be horizontal. But levelling a number of interconnected items is not an easy task in practice. A tolerance (or deviation) of ±⅛ inch is pretty much within the acceptable limit. Levelling is done by a level gauge and other instruments. Equally important is the verticality of the tower—the top should be within 1 inch to 2 inches from the vertical. This has to be carefully maintained at the time of installation of the tower.

Cartridge trays

Although a packed tower is preferred if the column diameter turns out to be small (< 3 ft), there are situations in which a tray tower is advantageous. Typical examples are fouling systems, certain foaming systems, and high pressure applications that demand a large turndown ratio. Since a diameter like 3 ft is too small to allow access to a workman into the column for installation of the trays, tray cartridges, rather than individual trays, are used in such a column. A tray cartridge consists of five to ten trays (sieve, valve, bubble cap or any other suitable type) fastened or pre-assembled in a bundle using four to six 'tie rods' and 'spacers'. The spacers inserted on a tie rod maintain the desired tray spacing. The cartridges are than slipped into the shell that usually has flanged sections. A support clip for the cartridge is provided in each section of the shell. Circumferential gaskets are used to prevent leakage between the trays and the column wall. The 'roundness' of the column is very important to ensure easy installation of a cartridge and a good seal. There should be enough 'head space' above the column for installation of the cartridges as well as for pulling them out for maintenance. The details of assembling trays into a cartridge and a few assembled cartridges are shown in Figure 5.11(b) and (c). Various aspects of installation of tray cartridges have been discussed in a recent article by Sands (2006).

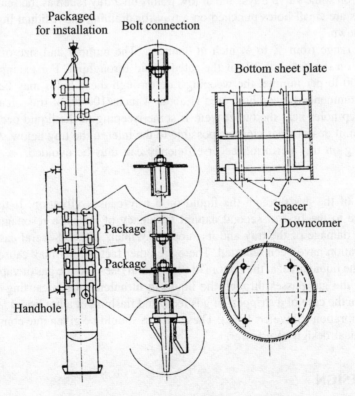

Figure 5.11(b)   The details of assembling a tray cartridge.

Figure 5.11(c) A few assembled tray cartridges (Sanda, 2006).

Weep-holes for draining of the tray

When a tower goes for shutdown, certain amount of liquid remains trapped or held up on a bubble-cap tray, on some valve trays, and at low points on a tray (such as the seal pan, inlet weir, etc). Weep-holes are small holes punched on a tray for draining the residual liquid on a tray in case of a shutdown.

Weep-holes range from ⅛ to ⅝ inch in diameter. The number and size of these holes are usually decided on the basis of 2% of the rated liquid throughput. For example, if the liquid throughput is 100 lb per minute, the weeping rate through these holes may be about 2 lb per minute. The recommended weep-hole area is about 4 inch^2/100 ft^2 of tray area. It is preferred to locate the weep-holes near the outlet weir. If some weeping of the liquid occurs even during normal operation, it descends as close as possible to the inlet to the tray below. Any undesirable effect of weeping on tray performance or efficiency can thus be avoided.

Tray vibration

Violent passage of the gas through the liquid on a tray causes vibration. If the frequency of vibration is close to the first or second natural frequency of a tray, a resonant condition may occur leading to damage of the tray and its support (Winter, 1993). Several cases of failure of trays due to vibration have been reported. There are other factors that may cause tray vibration. For example, if the liquid level at the bottom of the column rises and the gas or vapour inlet nozzle gets submerged, the gas passes through the liquid in turbulent surges causing vibration. High velocity steam (in the case of a stripper) or gas feed, and flashing of a hot liquid feed in a column also cause tray vibration (Shiveler, 1995). These factors should be given due consideration at the stage of mechanical design of a tower.

5.5 TRAY DESIGN

While designing a process plant or a part of it, complete material and energy balance calculations for every piece of equipment or device are done in order to establish the design basis in terms of the flow rate, the composition, the temperature and pressure of each stream as well as the amount of heat input, output and generation, if any. For example, before we proceed to design a tray or a packed tower, we need to know the flow rates, the compositions, and the temperatures of all the liquid and the gas (or vapour) streams entering and leaving the tower as well as the operating pressure. In addition, the physical properties of the streams such as density, viscosity, diffusivity, surface tension, etc. are required to be known or estimated for use in design calculations. Such properties of many liquids and gases are available in some standard data books (see, for example, Yaws, 1999). It is to be noted, however, that data on physical properties of gas and liquid mixtures necessary for design may not be readily available in the literature. Very often the properties have to be calculated or estimated from pure component properties of the species present in a mixture. Even the pure component properties may have to be estimated sometimes if the experimental data are not available. Fortunately, a large number of correlations have been reported in the literature (see, for example, Poling et al., 2001; see References, Chapter 2) for this purpose.

Of the three most common types of trays—namely, bubble-cap, sieve and valve trays—the design methods of the former two are pretty well-established (Kister, 1992; Ludwig, 1997). Here we give a brief outline of the procedure of design of a sieve tray (also called 'perforated tray'). Valve trays are 'proprietary' trays. Only limited information on their design is available in the open literature (Kister, 1992).

Design of a sieve tray for gas (or vapour)–liquid contact

Once the design basis (the flow rates, the compositions, the temperatures, the pressures, etc.) of the streams is established, the number of trays required for the specified degree of separation of a feed mixture is determined following the procedures described in Chapters 4, 6 and 7. The next step is the selection and design of the tray as well as of the accessories and associated items like heat exchangers (condensers and reboilers), nozzles, piping, insulation and the mechanical design of the tray and the column support. So far as the design of a sieve tray is concerned, the major items to be determined are the tray diameter (i.e. the column diameter), the size and layout of the holes, the tray spacing and tower internals such as downcomers and weir.

5.5.1 Tray (or Column) Diameter

The required diameter of a tray or the column for the given flow rates of the gas and the liquid phases is determined from flooding considerations. It has been stated before that as the gas velocity in a column is gradually increased, a limiting velocity is attained above which entrainment is high enough to cause accumulation of liquid on the trays leading to flooding. This velocity corresponds to the theoretical maximum capacity of the column. There are a few methods of calculation of the flooding velocity. Two methods are described below.

Fair's method

The method (Kister, 1992; Ludwig, 1997; Stichlmair and Fair, 1998) is based on the Souders–Brown equation that gives the flooding velocity for 'spray entrainment flooding'.

$$u_{s,fl} = C_{SB}\left(\frac{\rho_L - \rho_G}{\rho_G}\right)^{1/2} \tag{5.4}$$

Here $u_{s,fl}$ is the 'superficial velocity'[†] at flooding, and C_{SB} is called the 'Souders–Brown flooding constant' (sometimes called 'capacity factor'). Souders and Brown (1934) obtained this equation by equating the weight of a droplet with the drag force acting on it by the upflowing gas. In reality the quantity C_{SB} is not a constant; it depends upon tray spacing S, liquid load, fractional hole area on a tray and the hole diameter. Fair (1961) proposed a slightly modified form of Eq. (5.4) as given below for the determination of the flooding velocity. He also developed a chart [Figure 5.12(a)] for C_{SB} (in ft/s) given as a function of a flow parameter, F_{lv} [= $(L/G)(\rho_G/\rho_L)^{0.5}$], for different values of the plate spacing, S (inch).

$$u_{s,fl} = C_{SB}\left(\frac{\sigma}{20}\right)^{0.2}\left(\frac{\rho_L - \rho_G}{\rho_G}\right)^{0.5} , \text{ in ft/s} \tag{5.5}$$

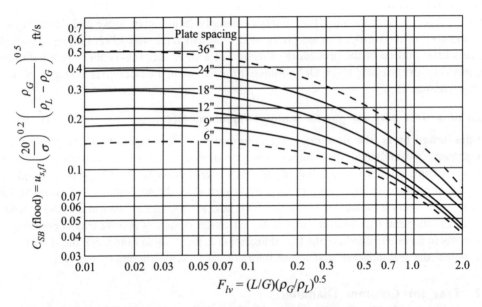

Figure 5.12(a)   Souder–Brown constant (C_{SB}) at flooding condition as a function of the flow parameter.

Here σ is the surface tension of the liquid in dyne/cm. Lygeros and Magoulas [*Hydro. Proc.*, 65 (Dec. 1986), p. 43] expressed the Souders–Brown constant in Fair's flooding chart by the following algebraic equation.

$$C_{SB} = 0.03445 + 5.421 \times 10^{-3}S^{0.755} \exp\left(-1.463 F_{lv}^{0.842}\right)$$

[S = tray spacing in inches; C_{SB} in ft/s]

At low-to-moderate pressure, $\rho_G \ll \rho_L$, and the quantity $F_s = u_s(\rho_G)^{0.5}$ is taken as a measure of the capacity factor or capacity parameter [see Figure 5.12(h)]; u_s = superficial gas velocity.

[†] 'Superficial velocity' is the linear velocity of the fluid on the basis of the cross-sectional area available for flow.

Kister and Haas method

The following correlation for the quantity C_{SB} was proposed by Kister and Haas (1990) for a sieve tray.

$$C_{SB} = 0.144 \left[\frac{d_H^2 \sigma}{\rho_L} \right]^{0.125} \left[\frac{\rho_G}{\rho_L} \right]^{0.1} \left[\frac{S}{h_{ct}} \right]^{0.5}, \text{ in ft/s} \tag{5.6}$$

where d_H = hole diameter, in inch

σ = surface tension, in dyne/cm

ρ_G, ρ_L = vapour and liquid densities, in lb/ft^3

S = tray spacing, in inch

h_{ct} = 'clear liquid height at the transition from froth to the spray regime', in inch.

The last quantity h_{ct} may be calculated from the following correlations.[†]

$$h_{ct} = (h_{ct})_w \left(\frac{62.2}{\rho_L} \right)^{0.5(1-n)} \tag{5.7}$$

$$(h_{ct})_w = \frac{0.29 f_h^{-0.791} d_H^{0.833}}{1 + 0.0036 Q_L^{-0.59} f_h^{-1.79}}; \qquad n = 0.0231 \frac{d_H}{f_h} \tag{5.8}$$

Here f_h = fractional hole area = A_h/A_a = (hole area)/(bubbling or active tray area). Another method of determination of the column diameter, called the 'Hunt method', has been described by Ludwig (1997). If the liquid and gas rates vary in different sections of a column, the diameter is calculated on the basis of the larger flow rate.

Tray area

Once C_{SB} is obtained by using one of the preceding methods, the flooding velocity is calculated from Eq. (5.5) or (5.6). The 'allowable vapour velocity' is taken as 60 to 80% of the flooding velocity to keep away safely from flooding, taking into account the uncertainties in the data or the equations and also the sudden fluctuations in flow rates. The 'active tray area' A_a may be determined by dividing the gas flow rate by the allowable velocity. The 'downcomer areas' are added to the active area and the tower cross-section A_T is calculated as

$$A_T = \frac{G_v}{(f_{fl} u_{s,fl})(1 - f_d)} = \frac{A_a}{1 - f_d} = \frac{A_a}{f_a} \tag{5.9}$$

Here

G_v = volumetric gas flow rate, in ft^3/s or m^3/s

f_{fl} = fractional approach to the flooding velocity (normally 0.6 to 0.8)

f_a = fractional active area of the tray [= $1- 2A_d/A_T$, A_d = downcomer area on one side;

$2A_d/A_T = f_d$ = fraction of tower cross-section occupied by the downcomers on *both sides*].

[†] It is seen that h_{ct} depends upon three quantities—d_H, A_f, and Q_L—which are not known before the tray is designed. So the use of the Kister and Haas equation involves 'iteration'. Reasonable values of these quantities are assumed, h_{ct} is calculated, and the column diameter is estimated. A revised value of h_{ct} is now obtained and a more accurate value of the column diameter is calculated. The 'iterative procedure' is common to many design calculations.

It is to be noted that the tray area overlapping the support ring as well as the calming sections at the inlet and at the outlet of a tray do not have any holes. These areas have to be deducted from the vapour flow area in order to get the 'effective bubbling area'.

5.5.2 Tray Layout and Hydraulics

This involves the determination of the size and the number of holes, their arrangement on the tray, the area of the downcomer, the downcomer liquid velocity, the downcomer clearance, the hydraulic gradient, the downcomer backup, weeping, entrainment, and a few other things.

Size and number of holes

The hole diameter of an industrial tray normally lies between $\frac{1}{8}$ to $\frac{1}{2}$ inch, but may be as small as $\frac{1}{16}$ inch, or as big as 1 inch in some cases. For fouling (for example, distillation of a mixture of ethyl benzene and styrene; styrene has a tendency to polymerize, thus fouling the holes) and corrosive services, larger holes are preferred. Plugged holes cause larger pressure drop for gas flow through the tray and may lead to flooding. Small holes reduce entrainment (thus improving tray capacity) and exhibit better turndown characteristics.

Perforation on a triangular pitch is preferred to a square pitch. Rows of holes should be perpendicular to the direction of liquid flow. A chart for fractional hole area (i.e. the ratio of the open area and the active tray area) has been given by Kister (1989). It can, however, be calculated using the following equation

$$\text{Fractional hole area, } f_h = K'(\text{hole diameter/hole pitch})^2 \qquad (5.10)$$

where $K' = 0.905$ for an equilateral triangular pitch, and 0.785 for a square pitch. The fractional hole area on a sieve tray ranges from 0.05 to 0.15, 0.08 to 0.12 being common.

Downcomer area

Downcomer area is calculated on the basis of allowable clear liquid velocity in the downcomer so that sufficient time is allowed for disengagement of the vapour bubbles. There are equations for the calculation of the allowable liquid velocity in the downcomer. The recommended maximum values of the downcomer liquid velocity and the minimum liquid residence time (Kister, 1992) are given in Table 5.3. The importance of downcomer design has been addressed by Biddulph et al. (1993).

Table 5.3 Maximum velocity and minimum residence time in the downcomer

Foaming tendency	Examples of systems	Clear liquid velocity (ft/s) in the downcomer for tray spacing			Residence time (s)
		S = 18-inch	24-inch	30-inch	
Low	Low pressure operation, low molecular weight hydrocarbons, alcohols, etc.	0.4–0.5	0.5–0.6	0.6–0.7	3
Medium	Crude oil distillation, absorbers, medium molecular weight hydrocarbons	0.3–0.4	0.4–0.5	0.5–0.6	4
High	Amines, glycerine solution, glycols, high pressure (>300 psi) light hydrocarbons	0.2–0.25	0.2–0.25	0.2–0.3	5–7

Stichlmair and Fair (1998) suggest the following for this purpose. Liquid velocity in the downcomer should not exceed 0.1 m/s; liquid residence time should be more than 5 s; the height of the clear liquid in the downcomer should not exceed half of the tray spacing. The downcomer area is normally taken as 10 to 12% of the column cross-section. If it is taken as 10%, the quantity f_d in Eq. (5.9) becomes $f_d = 1 - (2)(0.1) = 0.8$.

Downcomer weir length

The weir length (l_w), the area of the downcomer (A_d), and the distance of the weir from the centre line of the column (r_w) are related as in Figure 5.12(b). The charts for their evaluation are available (Kister, 1992; Ludwig, 1997). The following set of equations [Eq. (5.11)] may also be used to calculate the length of the segmental weir for a given fractional downcomer area (A_d/A_t).

$$\frac{A_d}{A_t} = \frac{\theta - \sin\theta}{2\pi}; \qquad \theta = 2\,\sin^{-1}[l_w/D_c] = 2\,\cos^{-1}[2r_w/D_c]; \tag{5.11}$$

where D_c = column diameter.

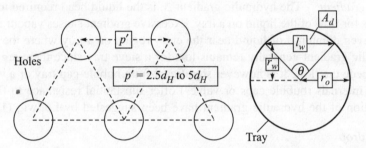

Figure 5.12(b) Hole pitch, downcomer area, and weir length.

Check for downcomer backup

Once a tower diameter is selected (on the basis of spray entrainment flooding), the 'downcomer backup' needs to be checked for possible downcomer flooding. The definition and the basis of calculation of downcomer backup as well as the related equations, Eqs. (5.1)–(5.3), have been given in Section 5.3.5. The calculation procedure and a few useful correlations and charts are described below. Downcomer backup should be sufficiently less than the tray spacing, preferably not more than half of it.

Weir height (h_w):   The clear liquid height (h_c) is the sum of weir height (h_w), the height of liquid over the weir (h_{ow}), and half the hydraulic gradient ($\Delta/2$). All these quantities are expressed as inch liquid head. A suitable weir height (generally between 1 to 2 inches for a distillation tray; up to 4 inches for absorption) is to be selected. The quantity ($h_w + h_{ow}$) is called the 'static liquid seal' of a tray.

$$h_c = h_w + h_{ow} + \Delta/2 \tag{5.12}$$

Liquid height over the weir (h_{ow}):   For segmental downcomers, Francis weir equation may be used.

$$h_{ow} = 0.48 F_w (Q_L)^{2/3} \tag{5.13}$$

where F_w is a weir correction factor for which a chart is available [Figure 5.12(c)].

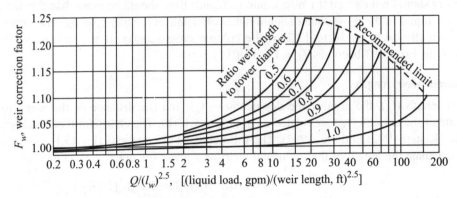

Figure 5.12(c)   Weir correction factor chart.

Hydraulic gradient: The hydraulic gradient Δ, is the liquid head required to overcome the frictional forces for flow of the liquid on a tray. Excessive gradient causes vapour maldistribution and weeping (even dumping) of liquid near the entry region on a tray where the liquid depth is higher. Hydraulic gradient generally remains low for a sieve tray since there are no submerged internals to impede the flow. It is however significant for a bubble-cap tray or a valve tray since the submerged internals (bubble caps or valves) offer substantial resistance to flow. Equations for the calculation of the hydraulic gradient have been suggested by Ludwig (1997).

Tray pressure drop

Tray pressure drop (h_t) is the sum of dry tray pressure drop (h_d) and the pressure drop for flow of the gas through the liquid (h_l)

$$h_t = h_d + h_l \tag{5.14}$$

Dry tray pressure drop: It is given by an orifice-type equation

$$h_d = K''(\rho_G/\rho_L)u_h^2; \qquad K'' = 0.186/C_o^2; \qquad u_h = \text{gas velocity through the holes} \tag{5.15a}$$

Figure 5.12(d) can be used to determine C_o. It is mainly a function of the ratio of tray thickness to hole diameter, and that of hole area to active area, f_h.

The discharge coefficient can also be calculated from the following equation [developed from Figure 5.12(d)].

$$C_o = 0.74(A_h/A_a) + \exp[0.29(t_t/d_H) - 0.56] \tag{5.15b}$$

Recommended sheet metal thickness (t_t) for the tray deck (and also for other tray parts) has been given by Kister (1989). Minimum deck thickness is 14 gauge (0.075 inch) for alloy steel, and 10 gauge (0.134 inch) for carbon steel. The ratio of tray deck thickness to hole diameter ranges from 0.1 to 1.3 for alloy steel, and 0.25 to 3 for carbon steel (Chase, 1967).

Pressure drop for flow through the liquid: The pressure drop for flow of the gas through the aerated liquid (h_l) may be calculated as a multiple of the clear liquid height (h_c).

$$h_l = \beta h_c \tag{5.16a}$$

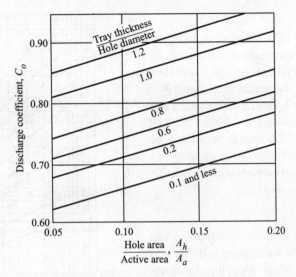

Figure 5.12(d) Hole discharge coefficient chart.

Here β is called the aeration factor as given in Figure 5.12(e). An algebraic correlation as follows is also available for β.

$$\beta = 0.0825 \ln(Q_L) - 0.269 \ln(F_{sh}) + 1.13 \tag{5.16b}$$
$$[Q_L, \text{ in gpm/in.; } F_{sh} = u_h(\rho_G)^{0.5}, \text{ in (ft/s)(lb/ft}^3)^{0.5}]$$

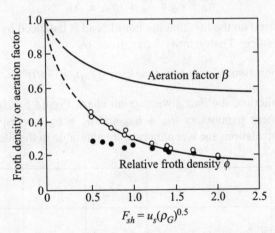

Figure 5.12(e) Sieve tray aeration factor and relative froth density.

Head loss for flow under the downcomer (h_{ad}): This can be calculated from the equation (Kister, 1992)

$$h_{ad} = 0.03(\text{GPM}/100A_{da})^2 \tag{5.17}$$

where GPM = liquid rate in gal/min; A_{da} = available area in ft^2 for flow under the segmental downcomer apron.

The possibility of downcomer flooding can now be checked using Eq. (5.3).

Entrainment

A chart for entrainment calculation given in Figure 5.12(f) has been recommended and used by many designers. Correlations for the estimation of entrainment rate are also available(Kister, 1992; Bennet et al., 1997). The entrainment rate [ψ = mol entrained per mol down flow; Figure 5.12(f)] should not exceed 10%, it should preferably be lower than that. A simple expression relating tray efficiency with fractional entrainment is available [see Eq. (6.57)].

Weeping

There are two things to be considered—weep point and weep rate. The weep point is defined as the vapour velocity when weeping becomes noticeable. For a still lower vapour velocity, weeping increases and the tray efficiency drops. The weeping tendency increases with (i) larger

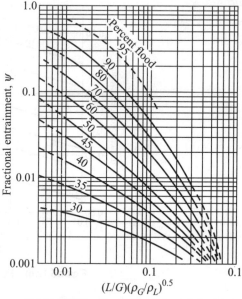

Figure 5.12(f)   Sieve tray entrainment chart.

fractional hole area, (ii) larger liquid rate, (iii) larger weir height, (iv) lower surface tension of the liquid, (v) decreasing plate thickness, and (vi) closer hole spacing or pitch.

The weep point may be calculated from the following equation obtained by force balance.

$$h_d + h_\sigma = h_w + (h_{ow} + \Delta) \qquad (5.18)$$

Equation (5.18) is based on the fact that the liquid head is balanced by dry tray pressure drop and the surface tension force. The quantity h_σ is given by

$$h_\sigma = \frac{0.04\sigma}{\rho_L d_H} \text{ inch liquid}; \qquad \sigma \text{ in dyne/cm}; \qquad \rho_L \text{ in lb/ft}^3; \qquad d_H \text{ in inch.} \qquad (5.19)$$

For a more accurate prediction, the Fair's weep point chart, Figure 5.12(g), may be used. If no weeping occurs, the system parameters ($h_w + h_{ow}$ and $h_d + h_\sigma$) correspond to a point above the weep point curve. Correlations for weeping rate are available in the literature (Lockett, 1986; Kister, 1992).

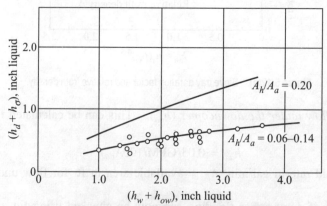

Figure 5.12(g)   The Fair's weep point chart.

Turndown check

Turndown check of the design is done in order to find out if unacceptable weeping or dumping occurs at 50–60% of the vapour and liquid load. If the tray does not admit of the reduced flows, it is preferred to revise the design in order to ensure a turndown ratio of about 2 for a sieve tray. The hole vapour velocity at which weeping starts can be calculated by trial-and-error as illustrated in Example 5.1. The upper limit of stable operation of a tray is determined by entrainment, and the lower limit by weeping (see Figure 5.10).

5.5.3 Tray Efficiency

The tray design and the hydraulics influence the 'tray efficiency' which is a very important factor in column design. Tray efficiency is discussed in Chapter 6 (Section 6.8).

The design of a sieve tray following the above procedure, equations, correlations and charts is illustrated in Example 5.1. It is to be noted that the liquid and vapour flow rates do not remain uniform at all the trays in a column. Column design is done on the basis of the highest gas or vapour rate. If the vapour flow rate varies largely, it may even be judicious to design a tower of two sections of different diameters. Tray design often involves quite a bit of trial-and-error. Trial values of the design parameters are assumed and revised if necessary after the first cycle of calculation. Example 5.1 illustrates this design procedure of a sieve tray.

EXAMPLE 5.1[†] (*Design of a sieve tray*)   Design a sieve tray for the separation of a mixture of benzene and toluene on the basis of the following data and information. The column will have 30 trays, the feed entering at the 13th tray from the top.

Liquid rate, top: $L = 14,100$ kg/h, bottom: $L = 15,300$ kg/h; vapour rate, top: $G = 23,300$ kg/h, bottom: $G = 24,500$ kg/h; liquid density, $\rho_L = 810$ kg/m^3 (50.4 lb/ft^3), average; vapour density, $\rho_G = 2.65$ kg/m^3 (0.165 lb/ft^3), average; liquid surface tension, $\sigma = 20.5$ dyne/cm; temperature, $T = 82°C$, average; pressure at the column top = 18 psia. Use the flow rates at column bottom for design calculations.

Solution

(a) *Calculation of tower diameter:*   We need to first calculate the flooding velocity. Both the Fair's method and the Kister and Haas method will be used to estimate the Souders–Brown constant C_{SB}, for the purpose of comparison.

Fair's method: Using the values of different quantities, the flow parameter is

$$F_{lv} = \left(\frac{L}{G}\right)\left(\frac{\rho_G}{\rho_L}\right)^{0.5} = \left(\frac{15,300}{24,500}\right)\left(\frac{0.165}{50.4}\right)^{0.5} = 0.0357$$

Select a tray spacing of 18 inch considering the given flow rates. From Figure 5.12(a),

$$C_{SB} = 0.285 = u_{s,fl}\left(\frac{20}{\sigma}\right)^{0.2}\left(\frac{\rho_G}{\rho_L - \rho_G}\right)^{0.5}$$

[†]Mixed units have been used in this and a few other problems, as well as in the solution. This is nothing unusual given the fact that many charts and empirical correlations are available only in British engineering units.

$$\Rightarrow \qquad u_{s,fl} = (0.285)\left(\frac{20.5}{20}\right)^{0.2}\left(\frac{50.4-0.165}{0.165}\right)^{0.5} = 5 \text{ ft/s}$$

Take the operating velocity as 70% of the flooding velocity. The operating velocity is

$$u_s = (5)(0.7) = 3.5 \text{ ft/s}$$

Volumetric flow rate of the vapour $\quad = \left(\dfrac{24{,}500}{2.65}\dfrac{\text{m}^3}{\text{h}}\right)\left(35.315\dfrac{\text{ft}^3}{\text{m}^3}\right) = 326{,}500 \text{ ft}^3/\text{h}$

Active tray area, $\qquad\qquad A_a = \dfrac{326{,}500}{(3.5)(3600)} = 25.9 \text{ ft}^2$

Take fractional downcomer area, $\quad f_d = 0.20$

Tower cross-section, $\qquad\qquad A_T = \dfrac{25.9 \text{ ft}^2}{1-f_d} = \dfrac{25.9}{1-0.2} = 32.4 \text{ ft}^2$

Tower diameter, $\qquad\qquad D_c = \left[\dfrac{(4)(32.4)}{\pi}\right]^{1/2} = \boxed{6.42 \text{ ft}}$ (= 1.96 m)

Kister and Haas method: In order to use this method, the quantities h_{ct}, d_H, A_f and Q_L are required to be known (or *to be assumed* to begin with). Since these are not known, we assume the following values which are to be checked later. Select 18-inch tray spacing.

Take hole diameter, $d_H = 3/8$ inch; fractional hole area on the tray, $A_f = 0.1$. We find out the value of Q_L on the basis of 10% of the tray area for the downcomer in a *tentatively* 6 ft dia column.

For a 6 ft dia coulmn with 10% downcomer area [i.e. $A_d = (0.1)(\pi/4)(D_c)^2$; $A_d/A_T = 0.1$], the length of the segmental weir at the downcomer entry,

$$l_w = (0.727)(D_c) = (0.727)(6) = 4.36 \text{ ft} \quad \text{[see Eq. (5.11)]}$$

Liquid rate, $\quad L = 15{,}300 \text{ kg/h} = (15{,}300)/[(0.81)(3.78)(60)] \text{ gal/min} = 83.3 \text{ gpm}$

$$Q_L = 83.3/(l_w, \text{ inch}) = (83.3)/(4.36)(12) = 1.6 \text{ gpm per inch}$$

The fractional hole area f_h is taken as 0.1 (to be checked later).
From Eqs. (5.6) to (5.8),

$$(h_{ct})_w = \frac{(0.29)(0.1)^{-0.791}(3/8)^{0.833}}{1+(0.0036)(1.6)^{-0.59}(0.1)^{-1.79}} = 0.68; \qquad n = (0.0231)\frac{3/8}{0.1} = 0.0866$$

$$h_{ct} = (h_{ct})_w\left(\frac{62.2}{50.4}\right)^{0.5(1-0.0866)} = (0.68)(1235)^{0.457} = 0.749$$

$$C_{SB} = (0.144)\left[\frac{(3/8)^2(20.5)}{50.4}\right]^{0.125}\left[\frac{0.165}{50.4}\right]^{0.1}\left[\frac{18}{0.749}\right]^{0.5} = 0.2787$$

From Eq. (5.4), flooding velocity,

$$u_{s,fl} = C_{SB}\left(\frac{\rho_L-\rho_G}{\rho_G}\right)^{0.5} = (0.2787)\left(\frac{50.4-0.165}{0.165}\right)^{0.5} = 4.86 \text{ ft/s}$$

This value is pretty close to the value of 5 ft/s obtained before by using the Fair's method.

Select a tower dia, D_c = 2 m; cross-section = 3.142 m^2 = 33.8 ft^2; bubbling area (or active area), A_a = (33.8)(0.8) = 27 ft^2.

This makes the superficial vapour velocity, u_s = (326,500)/(3600)(27) = 3.354 ft/s, which is 67% of the flooding velocity and is acceptable. We shall now check for the other important parameters.

(b) *Check of the estimated downcomer area:* The estimated tray diameter, the assumed downcomer area and fractional hole area need to be checked for their suitability. We shall first check the velocity and the residence time of the liquid in the downcomer.

Estimated downcomer area = 10% of tray cross-section = 3.38 ft^2

$$\text{The clear liquid flow rate} = \left(\frac{15{,}300}{810}\frac{\text{m}^3}{\text{h}}\right)\left(35.315\frac{\text{ft}^3}{\text{m}^3}\right) = 0.1853 \text{ ft}^3/\text{s}$$

The downcomer liquid velocity = (0.1853 ft^3/s)/(3.38 ft^2) = 0.055 ft/s

This value is considerably lower than the normal values (see Table 5.3). Let us check the residence time of the liquid in the downcomer.

$$\text{Downcomer volume} \approx (3.38 \text{ ft}^2)(18 \text{ inch, tray spacing}) = 5 \text{ ft}^3$$
$$\text{Residence time} = (5 \text{ ft}^3)/(0.1853 \text{ ft}^3/\text{s}) = 27 \text{ s}$$

The residence time is much larger than the safe accepted value of 5 s.

The above values show that we can safely reduce the downcomer area thereby reducing the column diameter. Let us take the downcomer area as 6% of the tower cross-section.

Revised tower cross-section = A_a/f_a = 25.9/[1 – (2)(0.06)] = 29.43 ft^2; tower diameter = 6.12 ft.

Select a 6.12 ft (= 185 cm) diameter column with 6% of the cross-section allowed for the downcomer.

Downcomer area = (29.43)(0.06) = 1.766 ft^2; Weir length, l_w = 3.75 ft (1140 mm); [A_d/A_t = 0.6; θ = 1.352 radian; see Eq. (5.11)]; r_w = 325 mm

The downcomer liquid velocity = 0.1853/1.766 = 0.105 ft/s, residence time = 14.3 s

These are acceptable values. So we keep the revised column diameter at D_c = $\boxed{6.12 \text{ ft}}$

(c) *Effective bubbling area and layout of the holes:* The 'effective' bubbling area is a little less than the area for gas flow (25.9 ft^2). A tray-support ring of 1.5 inches radial width appears to be suitable for a 6 ft dia column. This will cover a part of the tray area reducing the bubbling area. Also about 3 inch calming zone at the inlet as well as at the outlet weir is desirable. The total of these areas, that do not have any hole, is estimated to be about 3 ft^2.

$\Rightarrow$ 'Effective' bubbling area = 25.9 – 3 = 22.9 ft^2

Place the holes on a triangular pitch of p' = $3d_H$ $\Rightarrow$ hole dia/hole pitch = 1/3.
Using Eq. (5.10),

Fractional hole area = (0.905)(1/3)^2 = 0.101 $\Rightarrow$ 10.1% which is acceptable.
Total area of the holes = (22.9)(0.101) = 2.32 ft^2

$$\text{Number of holes} = \frac{2.32}{(\pi/4)[3/(8 \times 12)]^2} = 3025 \text{ placed on a triangular pitch.}$$

(d) *Wier height:*   Select an outlet weir height of h_w = 2 inches (50 mm) on the tray.

(e) *Pressure drop calculation:*   Vapour velocity through the holes,

$$u_h = \text{(vapour flow rate)/(hole area)} = (326,500)/(2.32)(3600) = 39.1 \text{ ft/s}$$

(i)   Dry tray pressure drop [see Eq. [5.15(a)], $h_d = (0.186/C_o^2)(\rho_G/\rho_L)u_h^2$
Select a tray thickness of 3/16 inches. Tray thickness/hole dia = (3/16)/(3/8) = 0.5.
From Figure 5.12(d), the orifice coefficient, C_o = 0.73.

$$\Rightarrow \qquad h_d = \left(\frac{0.186}{(0.73)^2}\right)\left(\frac{0.165}{50.4}\right)(39.1)^2 = 1.74 \text{ inches of liquid}$$

(ii)   *Calculation of* h_{ow}:   Revised weir length, l_w = 3.75 ft [from Eq. (5.11)]

$$Q_L = (83.3 \text{ gpm})/(3.75)(12) = 1.85 \text{ gpm per inch of weir length}$$
$$Q/(l_w \text{ in ft})^{2.5} = (83.3)/(3.75)^{2.5} = 3.1$$
weir length/tower diameter, $(l_w \text{ in ft})/D_c = 3.75/6.12 = 0.61$

From Figure 5.12(c) and Eq. (5.13),

Weir correction factor, F_w = 1.27,

and $\qquad\qquad h_{ow} = 0.48F_w(Q_L)^{2/3} = (0.48)(1.27)(1.85)^{2/3} = 0.92 \text{ inch}$

(iii)   Pressure drop for flow of the vapour through the liquid, $h_l = \beta h_c$
Neglecting hydraulic gradient (which remains small for a sieve tray of such diameter),
the clear liquid height, $h_c = h_w + h_{ow} = 2 + 0.92 = 2.92$ inches
Superficial vapour velocity based on the bubbling area,

$$u_s = \frac{326,500 \text{ ft}^3/\text{h}}{(22.9 \text{ ft}^2)(3600 \text{ s/h})} = 3.95 \text{ ft/s}; \quad u_s(\rho_G)^{1/2} = (3.95)(0.165)^{1/2} = 1.6$$

From Figure 5.12(e), β = 0.6, and h_l = (0.6)(2.92) = 1.75 inches [From Eq. (5.16a)]

(iv)   Calculation of h_{ad} (head loss for liquid flow below the downcomer apron):
Select ½ inch clearance below the downcomer. Area for liquid flow,

$$A_{da} = (1/2 \text{ inch})(3.75 \text{ ft}) = 0.156 \text{ ft}^2$$

From Eq. (5.17), $h_{ad} = (0.03)\left[\dfrac{83.3}{(100)(0.156)}\right]^2 = 0.87 \text{ inch}$

Neglect hydraulic gradient Δ, that remains small for a sieve tray of such diameter. Use
Eqs. (5.1), (5.12) and (5.13) to calculate the total pressure drop
$$= h_c + h_t + h_{ad} = (h_w + h_{ow}) + (h_d + h_l) + h_{ad}$$
$$= (2 + 0.92) + (1.74 + 1.75) + 0.87 = 7.3 \text{ inches of liquid.}$$

(f) *Check for downcomer backup:*   The clear liquid backup in the downcomer (7.3 inches) is
less than half the tray spacing of 18 inches. Hence the downcomer backup is pretty much within
the limit. There is no possibility of downcomer backup flooding.

[*Note:* The backup of aerated liquid in the downcomer (h_f) can be obtained from Eq. (5.2) if the average relative froth density (ϕ_d) is known. This rarely goes below 0.5. The relative froth density predicted by Figure 5.12(d), applicable for the gas–liquid dispersion on a tray, is much smaller than that in the downcomer. This is because of 'deaeration' of the froth in the 'calming zone' as well as in the downcomer.]

(g) *Check for entrainment:* Use Figure 5.12(f) (Fair's plot) to calculate the entrainment.

$$\frac{L}{G}\left(\frac{\rho_G}{\rho_L}\right)^{0.5} = \left(\frac{15,300}{24,500}\right)\left(\frac{0.165}{50.4}\right)^{0.5} = 0.0357$$

For 70% approach to flooding, the rate of entrainment $\psi = 0.053$ mol per mol gross downflow. Since $\psi < 0.1$, it is acceptable.

(h) *Weeping and turndown ratio:* The design of the column has to be checked for the turndown ratio. This can be done by finding out the maximum vapour velocity at which the tray weeps. We shall first check the design for possible weeping using the Fair's weep point chart [Figure 5.12(g)].

Putting $\sigma = 20.5$ dyne/cm, $\rho_L = 50.4$ lb/ft^3, and $d_H = 3/8$ inch in Eq. (5.19), we have

$$h_\sigma = \frac{(0.04)(20.5)}{(50.04)(3/8)} = 0.043 \text{ inch liquid. Using other values already calculated,}$$

$$h_w + h_{ow} = 2 + 0.92 = 2.92 \text{ inches}; \qquad h_d + h_\sigma = 1.74 + 0.043 = 1.78 \text{ inches}$$

The point (2.92, 1.78) lies pretty much above the weep point curve in Figure 5.12(g) for $A_h/A_a = 0.1$. So weeping *will not* occur.

Now we calculate the vapour velocity at which the tray weeps. For $h_w + h_{ow} = 2 + 0.92 = 2.92$ inches, the ordinate of the weep point curve is $h_d + h_\sigma = 0.62$ inch liquid.

$\Rightarrow \quad h_d = 0.62 - h_\sigma = 0.62 - 0.043 = 0.58$ inch = dry tray pressure drop at weeping.

The corresponding vapour velocity at the hole at weeping can be obtained from Eq. (5.15a) as

$$h_d = 0.58 = \left(\frac{0.186}{(0.73)^2}\right)\left(\frac{0.165}{50.4}\right)u_h^2 \qquad \Rightarrow \qquad u_h = 22.5 \text{ ft/s}$$

The calculated weep point hole velocity is $22.5/39.1 \Rightarrow 57\%$ of the design hole velocity of 39.1 ft/s.

So the column turndown ratio is $1/0.57 = 1.75$ which is acceptable for a sieve tray.

The turndown ratio can be increased by using a smaller hole dia, say ¼ inch. However, this will increase the pressure drop across the tray and hence the total column pressure drop.

(i) *Total pressure drop:* The column has 30 trays. Pressure at the top = 18 psia = 120 kPa. The total pressure drop = (30)(7.3 inch liquid) = 18.25 ft liquid = 6.4 psi. Total pressure at the bottom = 18 + 6.4 = 24.4 psia.

(j) *Column height:* There are 29 tray spacings $\Rightarrow$ (29)(1.5 ft) = 43.5 ft.

Extra space at feed trays: Keep two extra feed nozzles at tray no. 12 and 14. Add 6 inches extra spacing for each of these three trays $\Rightarrow$ (3)(0.5) = 1.5 ft.

Extra space at trays with manholes: Keep the provision of two manholes, add 6 inches extra spacing for each tray having a manhole $\Rightarrow$ (3)(0.5) = 1.5 ft.

Bottom space: Provide 3 ft liquid depth at the bottom and 6 ft clear space above that $\Rightarrow$ 9 ft bottom space.

Top space: Provide 4 ft space to accommodate nozzles, demister, etc. above the top tray. Total column height = 43.5 + 1.5 + 1.5 + 9 + 4 = 59.5, say 60 ft.

The essential items of tray design are presented in the form of a 'tray data sheet'. A typical tray data sheet prepared on the basis of the above design example is shown in Table 5.4

Table 5.4 Sieve tray data sheet

Service: ABSORBER		Item Number: A-23-0047
Tray data	*All trays (1 to 30)*	
	Top	*Bottom*
Vessel ID, mm	1850	
Operating pressure, kPa (abs)	124	168
Operating temperature, °C	81	83
Structural design temperature, °C	150	
Fluid description	Hydrocarbon	
Foam deaeration factor		
Gas flow rate, kg/h	23,300	24,500
Density, kg/m^3	2.65 kg/m^3 (average)	
Liquid flow rate, kg/h	14,100	15,300
Density, kg/m^3	808	812
Viscosity, cP	1.3 (average)	
Surface tension, dyne/cm	20.5 (average)	
Tower height, mm	18290	
Manhole	460 (2 nos)	
(one each on the 7th and the 20th tray)		
For Sieve Tray		
Weir height, mm	50	
Downcomer clearance, mm	13	
Total number of holes	3025	
Hole diameter, mm	9.5	
Hole area/Bubbling area, A_h/A_a	0.101	
Tray spacing, S, mm	460	
Tray layout		
Number of passes	1	
A, mm	325	
B, mm	1200	
C, mm	325	

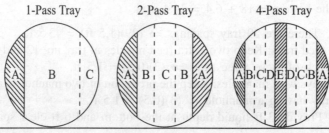

1-Pass Tray 2-Pass Tray 4-Pass Tray

Design of a valve tray

The methodology of design of a valve tray (or any other proprietary tray) is not readily available. Besides the basic physical properties and operating data, the manufacturer's technical data, the correlations and the design charts are required for the purpose. These are not available in the open literature. So far as a valve tray is concerned, the procedure for the pressure drop calculation has been described by Klein (1982). A typical valve tray pressure drop profile is shown in Figure 5.12(h). The pressure drop increases almost linearly till the valve starts opening (even when a valve is closed, some gas flow occurs through the narrow passages between the valve disk and the tray deck). Over the region AB, the valve opening increases with gas velocity but the pressure drop essentially remains constant. The point B corresponds to a 'fully open' valve beyond which the pressure drop again increases with the gas velocity.

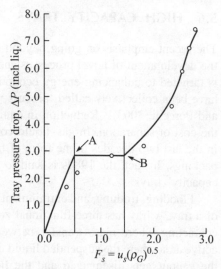

Figure 5.12(h) A typical valve tray pressure drop profile.

Klein (1982) suggested equations for the calculation of the pressure drop for gas flow through a valve in the region AB and also the pressure drop for flow through the aerated liquid. A chart similar to Figure 5.12(e) has also been given to calculate the 'aeration factor' and the 'relative froth density'. Klein's procedure has been reproduced by Kister (1992) and Ludwig (1997).

Common ranges of values of the more important parameters of a tray column are given in Table 5.5.

Table 5.5 Tray towers: a few important data and ranges of important parameters

Tower diameter	A tower less than 3 ft dia is rarely used (a tray cartridge is used in small dia columns)
Tray spacing	18 inches (if the diameter is not large; pressure ≥ 1 atm) to 30 inches (for vacuum service); a lesser tray spacing is used in certain multiple downcomer (MD) trays.
Downcomer area	5 to 15% of the tray area (on one side)
Liquid residence time in the downcomer	3 to 5 seconds
Clear liquid velocity in the downcomer	0.3 to 0.5 ft/s
Downcomer clearance	0.5 to 1 inch
Calming zone near the downcomer or the weir plate	3 to 4 inches
Tray support	Support rings fixed to the tower wall *plus* support beams below a tray
Hole size of a sieve tray	⅛ to ½ inch
Area of the holes of a sieve tray	6 to 10% of the active tray area
Weir length	60 to 80% of the tower diameter
Manhole diameter	16 to 24 inches; one manhole each for 10 to 15 trays
Hydraulic gradient	Preferably below ½ inch
Weep hole area	4 inches^2 per 100 ft^2 tray area
Weep hole size	⅛ to ⅝ inch diameter
Allowable entrainment	A few per cent (not more than 10% in any case)
Turndown ratio	About 2 for a sieve tray; about 4 for a valve tray
Common valve size	1.5 to 2 inches; 12 to 16 valves per ft^2
Tray leveling tolerance	About ±⅛ inch

5.6   HIGH CAPACITY TRAYS

The recent emphasis on going beyond the traditional practice of chemical engineering through the development of novel processes and equipment which are more efficient but smaller in size is targeted to enhancing energy economy and minimizing generation of waste. Such strategies have been collectively called 'process intensification' (Stankiewicz and Moulijn, 2000; Tsouris and Porcelli, 2003).[†] Reduction in equipment size and pressure drop are important in lowering the cost of separation. In gas–liquid contacting too, many new developments have taken place in the last two decades in the form of high capacity trays, divided-wall columns and structured packings. In fact, the 1980s is said to be a decade of structured packings, the 1990s of 'high capacity' trays.

Flooding, frothing, and entrainment are the three important phenomena that limit the capacity of a tray. A tray has three functional zones (Sloley, 1999): (i) the active area for vapour–liquid contacting where mass transfer between the phases occurs, (ii) the vapour space above the active area where the suspended liquid droplets separate out, and (iii) the downcomer area where the vapour gets disengaged and the liquid flows down to the lower tray. The capacity of a standard tray (e.g. bubble-cap, sieve or valve tray) can be enhanced by a few modifications of one or more of these functional zones, although any such modification may have the accompanying disadvantages as well.

(a) *Increasing the tray spacing:*   This allows more tolerance against entrainment since more space becomes available for the descent of the liquid droplets. A tray can be operated at a larger vapour throughput by this modification. But the disadvantage is that less number of trays can be accommodated in a tower of given height.

(b) *Increasing the open area of a tray:*   This can be done by punching bigger holes or more number of holes. The vapour velocity at the holes and the total tray pressure drop are reduced as a result. So, the tray can be operated at a higher capacity. But the tray efficiency and the turndown ratio are reduced.

(c) *Use of a sloped or stepped downcomer:*   This modification, which increases the active tray area, is in common use and does not cause any disadvantage on another count. More flow area for the froth is allowed in the upper part of the downcomer where most of the vapour bubbles get disengaged [see Figure 5.5(a)]; the flow area is reduced in the lower part where only the clear liquid flows into the lower tray. For a non-foaming system, the distance between the downcomer plate and the column wall at the lower region may be just half of that at the upper end of the downcomer.

In contrast to the above simple modifications, a few novel changes in the tray hardware have been put to practice since the 1990s. Such modified trays are called *high capacity trays* or *high performance trays* (Sloley, 1999; Bravo and Kusters, 2000; Porter, 2001). A high capacity tray attempts to improve upon the performance of a tray in relation to one of the following: (i) active area of gas–liquid contact, (ii) vapour space, and (iii) downcomer. Practical achievements in this direction are briefly described below.

---

† The first significant success of 'process intensification' in mass transfer operation was the development of ICI Higee technology in the early 1980s for liquid–liquid extraction.

(i) *Hanging downcomer:* Active tray area for vapour–liquid contacting has been increased in a high capacity tray by using 'hanging downcomer' [Figure 5.13(a)]. The area under a hanging downcomer has perforations or 'directional valves' to direct the momentum of the gas away from the downcomer [Figure 5.13(b)]. The *Max-frac* tray of Koch Engg. is based on this idea. This area is utilized for gas–liquid contacting as well as for receiving the liquid from the upper tray. The liquid head in the downcomer and the perforations at the bent downcomer bottom should be such that the liquid flows down to the tray below but no short-circuiting of the gas occurs. In some designs the downcomer weir is totally removed, providing only a 'dynamic seal' at the downcomer.

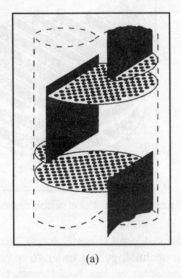

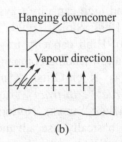

(a)   (b)

Figure 5.13(a) and (b) (a) A tray with hanging downcomers with restriction at the downcomer outlet and (b) the directional vapour flow below a hanging downcomer.

(ii) *Lengthening of the downcomer weir:* This is another simple technique to reduce liquid height over the downcomer [Figure 5.13(c)]. The liquid height over the weir can be calculated using Eq. (5.13). If the weir length is increased, the crest height at the weir as well as the clear liquid depth on the tray decreases. The tray pressure drop decreases as a result and the tray can be operated at a higher capacity.

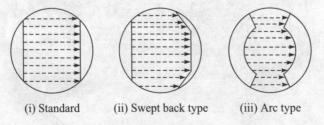

(i) Standard   (ii) Swept back type   (iii) Arc type

Figure 5.13(c) Lengthened downcomer weirs.

(iii) *Use of smaller deck devices:* By reducing the size of the perforations, the vapour handling capacity of a tray is improved simultaneously reducing the possibility of weeping. Perforations as low as ⅛ inch have been used instead of the common size of ½ inch. Smaller size valves also help to increase the tray capacity.

(iv) *Liquid de-entrainment devices:* Entrainment can be reduced and vapour throughput increased by fitting a baffle in the vapour space. However, this technique has not gained much popularity.

(v) *Use of multiple downcomers:* MD trays, as these are called, combine hanging downcomers and increased weir length [Figure 5.14(a)]. Such a tray has a high liquid handling capacity but the tray efficiency is a bit less because of shorter liquid flow paths. A smaller tray spacing (12 to 14 inches) can be used compensating for the reduced efficiency.

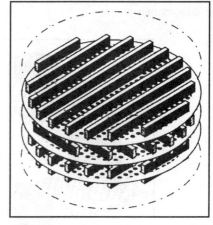

More detailed discussions on the ideas and concepts behind high capacity trays are available (Bravo, 1998; Sloley, 1999; Bravo and Kusters, 2000). High capacity trays are supplied by quite a few leading companies (Bravo, 1997) such as Koch-Glitsh (*Superfrac*™, *Nye*™, *MaxFrac*™, *Bi-frac*™ trays), Nutter

Figure 5.14(a) A stack of multiple downcomer (MD) trays.

Engineering (*MVG*™ trays), Norton Chemical Process Corp (*Triton*™ trays), etc. These high capacity trays basically use advanced downcomer technology (in order to avoid premature downcomer flooding) and enhance the active tray area for gas–liquid contact. A two-pass Superfrac tray is shown in Figure 5.14(b). Various valve designs are used in such a tray; two typical designs—'fixed minivalves' and 'floating minivalves'—are shown in Figure 5.14(c). The

Figure 5.14(b) A two-pass Superfrac tray (Courtesy: Koch–Glitsch).

operating regimes of the above Koch-Glitsch high capacity trays are shown in Figure 5.14(d). The Triton tray of Norton Company [Figure 5.14(e)] uses a hanging downcomer technology

Minivalve deck—fixed valve

Minivalve deck—floating valve

Figure 5.14(c)   Fixed and floating 'minivalves' of a Superfrac tray (Courtesy: Koch–Glitsch).

with a patented fixed valve. The MVG (Mini V-Grid) tray of Nutter Engineering also uses fixed valves [Figure 14.5(f)]. Sulzer Chemtech also supplies different high capacity trays. The Jaeger *Co-flo* tray is based on a novel idea. The vapour flows at a high velocity through the tray deck and carries the liquid as droplets (it is an extreme case of spray flow regime) to a 'coalescer', placed between two trays where the liquid droplets get separated. Since the vapour and the liquid (as droplets) flow in the same direction between the two trays, the device is called *Co-flo*. The vapour enters the upper tray and the liquid flows to the downcomer along an inclined path [Figure 5.14(g)]. The downcomer liquid *does not* have any entrained vapour bubbles, and the required downcomer area is small. The liquid–vapour contact is very efficient. The tray is claimed to have double the capacity of a sieve tray of the same diameter. It is expected to be very useful for retrofitting an existing column to increase its capacity. Besides larger capacities, the modern 'high capacity trays' have a few other advantages like low fouling tendency and lower entrainment. The major disadvantages are reduced flexibility, lower efficiency in

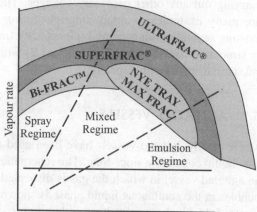

Figure 5.14(d)   Operating regimes of Koch–Glitsch high capacity trays.

Figure 5.14(e)   Norton Triton tray (Courtesy: Norton).

some cases (but lesser tray spacing to compensate for this limitation) and sensitivity to foaming.

High capacity trays are finding increasing popularity, particularly in 'revamping' or 'retrofitting' operations. If an existing column is required to operate at an enhanced capacity, the old trays can be replaced by high capacity trays keeping the shell and other accessories intact as far as possible. This is called *revamping*. The strategy of reusing the existing equipment more efficiently, with only minor changes if necessary, without installing the new equipment, with the objective of reducing energy consumption and increasing the throughputs is called *retrofitting* (Gadalia et al., 2003). Retrofitting of a distillation column generally involves changing the column internals with more efficient ones, modifying the heat exchanger and the liquid and gas flow line networks, and carrying out any other necessary changes. There are many examples of revamping/retrofitting of existing separation units using high capacity trays or structured packings (see Section 5.11.2) with a substantial increase in capacity.

Figure 5.14(f)   Nutter *V-Grid*.

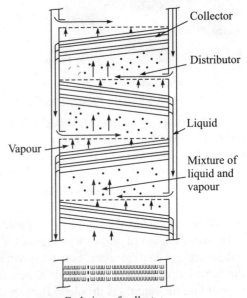

Figure 5.14(g)   The Jaeger 'Co-Flo' tray.

5.7   AGITATED VESSELS

Mechanically agitated vessels have been used for gas–liquid contacting since long. The schematic of an agitated vessel in which the gas is dispersed as bubbles in the continuous liquid phase is shown in Figure 5.15. Such a vessel is provided with (i) an agitator with a suitable impeller, (ii) inlet and outlet nozzles for the gas and the liquid, (iii) baffles, (iv) a drain and a vent, and (v) a manhole for the purpose of cleaning and maintenance. A stuffing box, or preferably a 'mechanical seal', is used to prevent the leakage of the gas at the top where the shaft enters the vessel (shaft seal). The shaft is held by bearings at the gear box and at the shaft seal. In a tall vessel, the shaft may also have to be supported by a bush near the bottom to check shaft vibration. The agitator motor may be supported on I-beams mounted on the vessel itself. Other kinds of motor support are also used. A gear box is used to maintain the required speed of the shaft. The vessel itself is sometimes supported by a few brackets that rest on and are bolted to the floor as per the plant layout.

An agitated vessel for gas absorption contains a few 'internals' such as the gas sparger, baffles, and an agitator shaft with impellers. The gas is sparged below the impeller midway between the centre and the periphery of the impeller. It is dispersed in the form of small bubbles by the shear stress created by impeller rotation. This greatly increases the gas–liquid interfacial area of contact and also the mass transfer coefficients. A variety of impeller designs are available. The turbine-, disk- and paddle-type impellers are more common. Four vertical baffles are used to prevent the formation of a vortex at the free liquid surface. The baffles also help to increase the turbulence in the tank. Thin metal plates having a width equal to 8 to 10% of the tank diameter, spot-welded to the tank, act as the baffles. The power input to the impeller depends upon a number of factors such as the impeller design and rpm, liquid properties, the gas rate, and the presence of suspended solids, etc. Empirical correlations for the calculation of power input are available.

The impeller is usually located at about one-third of the liquid depth from the bottom. The superficial gas velocity (it is the ratio of the volumetric gas flow rate and the area of cross-section of the vessel) is kept low—in the range of 0.1 to 0.25 ft/s. The impeller tip speed may be as high as 50 ft/s. The gas hold-up (it is the volume fraction of the gas in the gas–liquid dispersion)

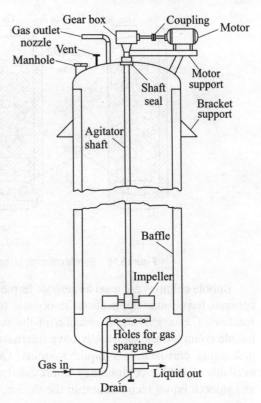

Figure 5.15 An agitated vessel for gas absorption.

usually remains within 0.4. The liquid-phase mass transfer coefficient k_L ranges from 0.008 to 0.05 cm/s, and the specific interfacial area $\bar{a}$, ranges from 1 to 2 cm^2/cm^3 for many commercial agitated contactors.

Agitated vessels are used when the dissolved gas undergoes a chemical reaction in the liquid. This vessel is not used for physical absorption since 'backmixing' in the liquid phase substantially reduces the mass transfer driving force. Hydrogenation of vegetable oils in the presence of suspended nickel catalyst, absorption of carbon dioxide in a lime slurry to make precipitated calcium carbonate, liquid-phase oxidation and chlorination in organic synthesis, etc. are a few common cases of application.

5.8 THE BUBBLE COLUMN

The bubble column is another important equipment used for carrying out gas–liquid reactions. Like an agitated vessel, it is not normally used for physical absorption. A bubble column consists of a tall tower fed with the gas at the bottom through a gas sparger (Figure 5.16). It has a simple construction and does not contain any moving parts but sometimes may have immersed cooling tubes or coils for removing the heat of absorption and reaction. The liquid may be fed batchwise or continuously. Both cocurrent (upflow of the liquid) and countercurrent (downflow of the liquid) operations of a continuous bubble column are possible. Multiple-orifice gas spargers made from pipes or tubes in the form of concentric rings are frequently used.

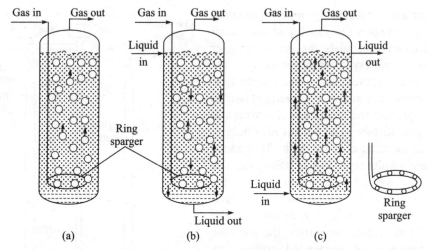

Figure 5.16   Bubble columns: (a) batch, (b) countercurrent, and (c) cocurrent.

Bubble columns are used as aerobic fermenters and also for aerobic waste treatment. Bubble columns have found applications in organic oxidation reactions, gas–liquid or gas–liquid–solid reactions (i.e. a gas–liquid reaction in the presence of suspended catalyst particles). Since a bubble column does not usually have internals and moving components, it is suitable for use in processing corrosive gas–liquid systems. Quite a few designs of the bubble columns are available. A bubble column may be provided with a 'draft tube' in order to create a much better and smooth liquid recirculation in the device.

5.9   THE SPRAY TOWER

The spray tower is another simple gas–liquid contactor (Rousseau, 1987). The common design consists of an empty cylindrical shell through which the gas flows upwards against a downflowing spray of the absorbing liquid. Here the gas is the continuous phase and the liquid is the dispersed phase. The liquid is dispersed in the form of fine droplets near the top by forcing it through spray nozzles. Spraying should be uniform over the cross-section of the vessel for the sake of better gas–liquid contact. The liquid droplets have a distribution of size. The contact time between the droplets and the gas has also a distribution. A fraction of the droplets unavoidably strike the wall of the tower and the liquid flows down as a film. 'Backmixing' of the gas remains small in a spray tower. The raining droplets collect at the bottom and the liquid leaves through a nozzle. A demister is invariably used to prevent entrainment of the droplets in the exit gas. A manifold of spray nozzles, sometimes installed at

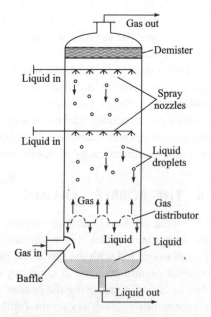

Figure 5.17   Schematic of a two-stage spray tower.

different levels in the tower, and a demister pad are the only tower internals used (Figure 5.17).

Cross-flow spray scrubbers with the gas flowing horizontally have been used in some cases (Brekelmans, 1998; Pedersen and Bhattacharjee, 1997).

The spray tower can handle a large volumetric gas flow rate at a low pressure drop. The 'height of a transfer unit' (HTU; this will be discussed later) is substantially large. Only one or two theoretical contact stages are realized in a normal spray tower. Pumping the liquid at a high pressure to the spray nozzles involves substantial power consumption.

The absence of any moving parts is also an advantage of the spray tower. The device is particularly suitable for (i) corrosive liquids and gases, (ii) liquids containing suspended solids, (iii) gas streams that may contain dust, soot or other suspended particles, and (iv) low gas pressure drop applications. As such the spray tower is very useful for scrubbing various waste gas streams. A spray tower also finds application in liquid–liquid extraction.

5.10 THE VENTURI SCRUBBER

As the name implies, the venturi scrubber has a converging and a diverging section. There are several designs available. One of the fluids enters the venturi at one end. The velocity of the fluid is maximum at the venturi throat where the pressure is minimum and the other fluid is sucked in leading to the formation of a gas–liquid dispersion. In the scrubbing of a dust-laden gas, the gas is the continuous phase and the liquid is injected as drops at the throat as shown in Figure 5.18(a). A venturi scrubber coupled to a gas–liquid separator vessel (cyclone separator type) and fitted with a mist eliminator and a partial liquid recycling pump is shown in Figure 5.18(b).

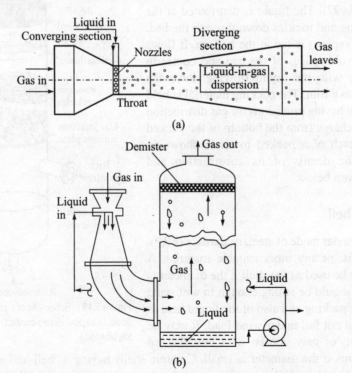

Figure 5.18   (a) A venturi scrubber, and (b) a venturi scrubber and gas–liquid separator vessel (cyclone).

The gas is accelerated to a very high speed of the order of 250 ft/s. The high speed gas atomizes the feed liquid causing 'impaction' of the dust particles with the suspended droplets. But in gas absorption applications, the liquid enters the venturi at the end and sucks the gas at the throat. A gas-in-liquid dispersion is formed. The foamy dispersion leaves the venturi at the other end and goes to a gas–liquid separator.

Venturi scrubbers are largely used for scrubbing of particulates (dust or suspended particles) and submicron fumes (Calvert, 1977a,b; Crawford, 1976). These are also suitable for corrosive gas–liquid systems because of absence of any moving parts or internals. A venturi scrubber has a simple construction too. Removal efficiency of a venturi scrubber has been studied recently by Ananthanarayanan and Viswanathan (1998).

5.11 THE PACKED TOWER

A packed tower is a continuous contact equipment widely used for gas absorption, distillation and liquid–liquid extraction. It consists of a cylindrical shell filled with a suitable packing material to provide a large interfacial area of contact between the phases. A set of 'tower internals' such as packing support, liquid and gas distributors and redistributors, demister, etc. are fitted into the tower (Zenz, 1972; Fadel, 1984; Kister, 1989; Ludwig, 1997). The liquid is distributed at the top of the packing and trickles down through the bed. The gas (or the vapour) is fed at the bottom. It flows up through the void spaces of the bed and comes in intimate contact with the liquid flowing down the packing surface as a film. The packing material is held on a support plate having provisions for gas distribution at and liquid discharge from the bottom of the packed section. The sketch of a packed tower is shown in Figure 5.19. The details of its construction and operation are given below.

5.11.1 The Shell

The shell is a cylinder made of steel, or plastics (FRP), ceramic materials, or any other suitable material. A pipe section may be used as the shell if the diameter is small. The shell should be strong enough to withstand the weight of the packing and also of the liquid held in the bed. It should not fail under wind load. It may be a single cylinder, or may consist of a few flanged cylindrical sections if the diameter is small. Ceramic shells having a 'bell-and-spigot' joint are used in highly corrosive services (for example, for concentration of HNO_3 by extractive distillation). A column is supported at the bottom over a skirt or on a suitable structure.

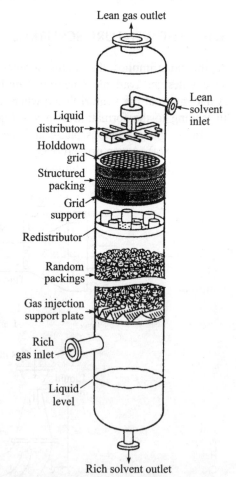

Figure 5.19 Schematic of a packed tower for gas–liquid or vapour–liquid contact. (The 'tray internals' are labelled.)

5.11.2 Packing

A variety of packings differing in shape, size and performance are available. These may be classified into three categories: (i) random or dumped packings, (ii) structured packings, and (iii) grid packings. Random packings are just dumped into the shell to give the packing pieces a random orientation. Structured packings are stacked in the shell to take the shape of a packed bed.

Characteristics of tower packings

Besides low cost, the desirable characteristics of packings are described below (Kister, 1992).

(a) *A large surface area:* Interfacial area of contact between the gas and the liquid is created in a packed bed by spreading of the liquid on the surface of the packing. Smaller packings offer a larger area per unit packed volume, but the pressure drop per unit bed height becomes more.

(b) *Uniform flow of the gas and the liquid:* The packed bed must have a uniform voidage so that a uniform flow of the gas and of the liquid occurs. The shape of the packing should be such that no stagnant pocket of liquid is created in the bed. A stagnant liquid pool is not effective for mass transfer.

(c) *Void volume:* A packed bed should have a high fractional voidage so as to keep the pressure drop low.

(d) *Mechanical strength:* The packing material should have sufficient mechanical strength so that it does not break or deform during filling or during operation under the weight of the bed.

(e) *Fouling resistance:* Fouling or deposition of solid or sediment within the bed is detrimental to good tower operation. Bigger packings are less susceptible to fouling. Also, the packings should not trap fine solid particles that may be present in the liquid.

Types of tower packings

Tower packings are made of ceramics, metals or plastics. Several innovations in the design of tower packings took place in the last quarter of the twentieth century and the process is continuing. Kister (1992) and Larson and Kister (1997) identified three *generations* of the evolutionary process (Table 5.6) of the *random packing*.

Table 5.6 Classifications of tower packings

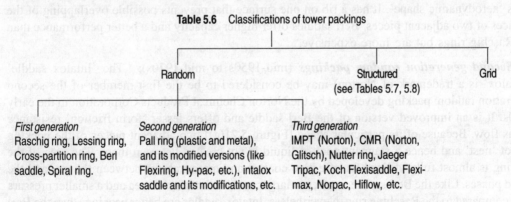

Random		Structured (see Tables 5.7, 5.8)	Grid
First generation Raschig ring, Lessing ring, Cross-partition ring, Berl saddle, Spiral ring.	*Second generation* Pall ring (plastic and metal), and its modified versions (like Flexiring, Hy-pac, etc.), intalox saddle and its modifications, etc.	*Third generation* IMPT (Norton), CMR (Norton), Glitsch), Nutter ring, Jaeger Tripac, Koch Flexisaddle, Fleximax, Norpac, Hiflow, etc.	

(a) *First generation random packings* (1907 to mid-1950s): These included three types of packings—Raschig rings, Lessing rings and other modifications of the Raschig ring and Berl saddles (Figure 5.20). These are mostly packed randomly; 'stacked' packings are used in only a few cases.

Raschig ring

Raschig ring: This is the oldest type of tower packing introduced by the German chemist F. Raschig in 1907. It is a hollow cylinder having a length equal to its outer diameter. The size of the Raschig ring ranges from ¼ inch to 4 inches. These rings are made of ceramic materials (unglazed porcelain), metals or plastics (e.g. high-density polyethylene, HDPE). Metal or plastic rings are made by cutting tubes of a suitable size. The Raschig ring is probably the most rugged packing and can be used even when a severe bumping or vibrating condition may occur. Other members of the Raschig ring family are: (i) 'Lessing ring', which is similar to the Raschig ring except that it has a partition along the axis of the ring. The partition increases the surface area but the advantage is rather small in practice. This packing has not been quite popular. (ii) The 'cross-partition ring' that has two partitions instead of one in a Lessing ring. (iii) The ceramic 'spiral ring' that has an internal helix which creates internal whirl of the gas and of the liquid and enhances the rate of mass transfer. The latter

Lessing ring   Cross-partition
                ring

Berl saddle

Figure 5.20   First generation random packings.

two types are sometimes stacked in one or two layers on the support grid of a randomly packed tower. Although Raschig rings are still in use, the other variations of them are rarely used.

Berl saddle: The Berl saddle (Figure 5.20) is the first modern packing developed in the late 1930s. It is so called because it has the shape of a saddle. A packed bed of Berl saddles has a larger specific surface area (i.e. surface area per unit packed volume) and a smaller voidage than the Raschig ring. Compared to the Raschig ring, the pressure drop is substantially less because of its 'aerodynamic shape'. It has a rib on one surface that prevents possible overlapping of the surfaces of two adjacent pieces. Berl saddles offer higher capacity and a better performance than the Raschig rings but are more expensive.

(b) *Second generation random packings* (mid-1950s to mid-1970s):   The 'Intalox saddle' ('Intalox' is a trademark of Norton) may be considered to be the first member of the second generation random packing developed by the Norton Chemical Products Corporation in the early 1950s. It is an improved version of the Berl saddle and offers lesser 'form friction' resistance to gas flow. Because of its particular shape [Figure 5.21(a)] two adjacent pieces of the packing do not 'nest' and hence a stagnant pool of liquid is not created between them. The area of the packing is almost fully utilized for effective contact and mass transfer between the gas and the liquid phases. Like the Berl saddle, it offers a larger specific interfacial area and a smaller pressure drop compared to the Rasching ring. Nevertheless, Intalox saddles are better packings than the Berl saddles. Koch-Glitsch[†] offers a similar ceramic packing under the trade name 'Flexisaddle'. The

---

[†] Koch Engineering Company and Glitsch, Inc., merged to form Koch-Glitsch in the late1990s.

Intalox saddle and its modified varieties (one important type from the erstwhile Norton Corp. is called 'Super Intalox saddle') are of ceramic or plastic make. The smooth edges of the Intalox saddle are scalloped and holes inserted to make the super Intalox. This design promotes quick drainage of the liquid, eliminates stagnant pockets and provides more open area, higher capacity and efficiency. 'Intalox snowflakes', introduced by the Norton Corp. in 1987, is a plastic packing of unique shape having a large number of liquid drip points, causing continuous renewal of the liquid surface and superior mass transfer performance.

Pall rings: The Pall ring and its modifications evolved from the Raschig ring. It is made by cutting windows on the wall of a metal Raschig ring and bending the window tongues inwards. While a bed of saddles offers reduced 'form friction' or drag because of the aerodynamic shape, Pall rings [Figure 5.21(b), (d), (e), (f)] do so by allowing 'through flow'

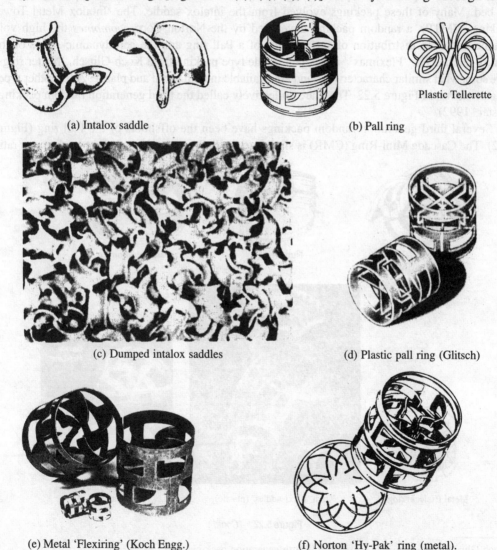

(a) Intalox saddle

(b) Pall ring

Plastic Tellerette

(c) Dumped intalox saddles

(d) Plastic pall ring (Glitsch)

(e) Metal 'Flexiring' (Koch Engg.)

(f) Norton 'Hy-Pak' ring (metal).

Figure 5.21 Second generation random packings.

of the gas, because direct passages on the wall are available. Since the interior surface is much more accessible to gas and liquid flow, the capacity and efficiency of the bed are enhanced. Similar packings are marketed by other companies under different trade names (for example, 'Flexiring' of Koch Engg.). Plastic Pall rings are also available (Norton Company, Koch-Glitsh, Jaeger Products, etc.). The metal 'Hy-Pak Tower Packing' of the Norton Corp. [Figure 5.21(f)], a slightly modified version of the Pall ring, has two bent tongues in each window and is claimed to have better efficiency. Ceramic Pall rings, which are Raschig rings with a few windows on the wall, have not been very popular.

(c) ***Third generation random packings*** (mid-1970s-):   A pretty large number of metal and plastic tower packings have been developed since mid-seventies that offer improved performance in terms of lower pressure drop, less weight, larger interfacial area and lesser liquid retention in the bed. Many of these packings evolved from the intalox saddle. The 'Intalox Metal Tower Packing' (IMTP), a random packing developed by the Norton Corp., *combines* the high void volume and even distribution of surface area of a Pall ring and the aerodynamic shape of the Intalox saddle. The 'Fleximax'[†] is an open saddle type packing from Koch-Glitsch. 'Nutter rings' have somewhat similar characteristics and are available in both metal and plastic. A few other types are also shown in Figure 5.22. These are collectively called the third generation random packings (Kister, 1992).

Several third generation random packings have been the offshoots of the Pall ring (Figure 5.22). The Cascade Mini-Ring (CMR) is similar to the Pall ring but has a height-to-diameter ratio

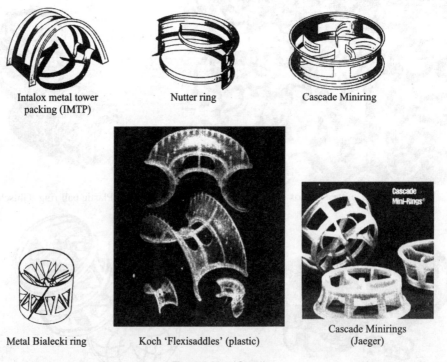

Intalox metal tower packing (IMTP)   Nutter ring   Cascade Miniring

Metal Bialecki ring   Koch 'Flexisaddles' (plastic)   Cascade Minirings (Jaeger)

Figure 5.22   *(Contd.)*

[†] Koch-Glitsch chooses to call *Fleximax* a 'fourth generation packing'.

Jaeger 'Tri-packs' high performance packing
made of corrosion-resistant plastic

Kock 'Fleximax' tower packing

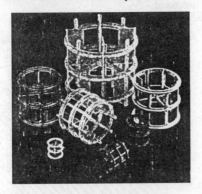

Hiflow ring (Rauschert Ind.)

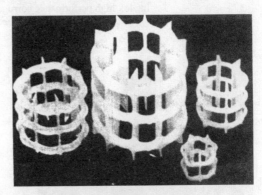

Nor-Pac, Plastic (NSW Corp.)

Figure 5.22 Several third generation random packings (IMTP: Norton Co; CMR: Norton Co, Glitsch).

(this is sometimes called the 'aspect ratio') of 1:3 compared to 1:1 of the latter. Because of low height, such a packing element has a lower centre of gravity and therefore tends to orient with the circular open end facing the vapour flow. This reduces friction and enhances the mass transfer coefficient and effective surface area. The 'Chempak' or 'Levapak' ring is made by cutting the Pall ring in two halves, exposing the tongues and promoting better performance. The Jaeger 'Tri-Packs' (metal or plastic) resembles the Pall ring but has a spherical shape (Figure 5.22). This packing offers more void volume and better distribution of surface area. It also prevents interlocking of the pieces in the bed. HcKp (from Koch), NOR PAC (from Nutter Engineering), LANPAC (from Lantec Products) are a few other third generation random packings.

Structured packings

Structured packings have emerged as the formidable competitor of random packings since the 1980s (Helling and DesJardin, 1994; Bennett and Kovac, 2000). These are made from woven wire mesh or corrugated metal or plastic sheet. Their major advantages are low gas pressure drop (because of 'through flow' of the gas) and improved capacity and efficiency. The first structured packing, called *Panapak*, made from thin metal strips to form a honeycomb-like structure did not gain much popularity because of severe maldistribution of liquid. Since the late 1970s and the early 1980s, Glitsch Inc., Sulzer and Nutter Engineering came up with acceptable high efficiency structured packings made of corrugated metal sheets or wire mesh (Figure 5.23).

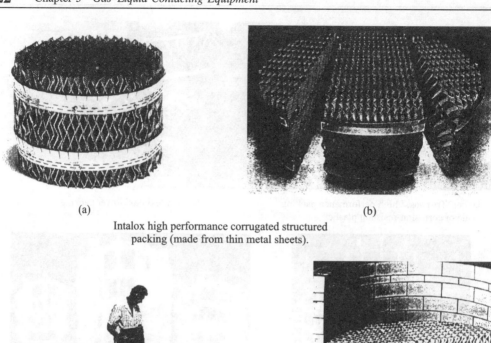

(a)   (b)

Intalox high performance corrugated structured
packing (made from thin metal sheets).

(c) The same as Figure 5.23(a) and (b).

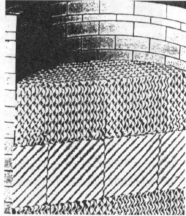

(d) 'Flexeramic' corrugated structured
packing (Koch Engg.).

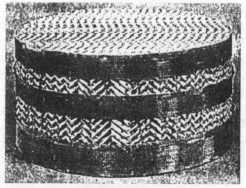

(e) 'Montz B1' Structured packing
(Nutter Engg. Corporation).

(f) Sulzer wire-gauge packing CY.

Figure 5.23   A few common high performance structured packings made from thin metal sheets or wire gauge.

Corrugated metal sheet structured packing: There are quite a few tower packings of this category. These are fabricated from thin corrugated (or crimped) metal sheets. The surface of a sheet is often made embossed, textured or grooved to promote mixing and turbulence in the falling liquid film and thereby to increase the mass transfer coefficient and efficiency.

The flow channel cross-section and flow channel arrangement in a common structured packing is shown in Figure 5.24. A bunch of corrugated sheets are arranged parallelly, keeping a suitable gap between the adjacent members to make a packing piece. A number of such pieces are arranged and stacked one after another. A piece of packing above is rotated at a certain angle relative to the piece immediately below it. The height of a piece is typically 8 to 12 inches. The corrugation angle of the sheets varies from 28° to 45° (Fair and Bravo, 1990; Olujic et al., 2001). Perforations are sometimes made on the sheets to provide channels of communication between the two surfaces of a corrugated sheet and to improve wetting of the surfaces. A larger corrugation angle increases the capacity in terms of the liquid load but reduces the mass transfer efficiency.

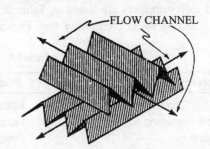

Figure 5.24 Flow channel arrangement in a corrugated structured packing (Fair and Bravo, 1990).

Wire mesh structured packings: Sulzer supply three types of such packing marked AX, BX and CY. The packing elements are made of corrugated layers of wire mesh. Sulzer packing type CY shown in Figure 5.23(f) has a surface area of about 200 ft^2/ft^3. Similar packings are marketed by Glitsch under the trade name *Gempak*, and by Norton Corp under the name 'Intalox High-Performance Wire Gauge Packing'. Glitsch also developed *Goodloe* for which the knitted wire-mesh is used. A cylindrical tube made by knitting multi-filament wires is flattened into a ribbon and then made into a packing by corrugation. It has a surface area above 550 ft^2/ft^3. *Montz A* packing (Nutter Engineering) is made from perforated wire mesh sheets with a specially contoured corrugation [Figure 5.23(e)]. The surface area is about 150 ft^2/ft^3. This packing is similar to the Sulzer wire mesh packing. The characteristics of a few structured packings are given in Table 5.7.

Table 5.7 Characteristics of a few structured packings

Structured packing	Material and surface	Crimp angle	Area
Mellapak	Metals, plastics; grooved and perforated	45° or 60°	About 250 m^2/m^3
Flexipak	Similar to Mellapak	–	
Gempak	Smooth or lanced	45°	
Montz	Metals, plastics; embossed	Sinusoidal	
MAX-PAC	Metals; smooth; W-shaped perforations	Sharp crimp angle	

Although developed in the late 1970s, the structured packings made visible inroads to separation technology in the late 1980s. The first major application was in air separation columns (Parkinson and Ondrey, 1997). The higher initial cost of such packings is amply compensated by the lesser operating costs because of lesser pressure drop across the bed. As a result, these packings have been very popular for use in vacuum distillation columns. The packings have high efficiency (low 'HETP') as well. Also, the well-defined geometric shape, particularly of those made from corrugated sheets, makes them amenable to theoretical analysis, modelling and scale-up (Fair and Sticklemayer, 1998). Now, the structured packings are being used for near-atmospheric services as well (Bravo, 1997).

Another class of packings, called 'grid packings', have been in use since long for high gas/vapour capacities at a low pressure drop. The more common structured and metal grid packings and their suppliers are listed in Table 5.8 (Bravo, 1997, 1998). Modern grid packings are also supplied by these companies (see Figure 5.25).

Table 5.8   Common structured packings

Supplier	Structured packing	Metal grid packing
Sulzer Chemtech	Mellapak series	Mellagrid series
Koch Engineering	Flexipak series	Flexigrid series
Glitsch Inc.	Gempak series	C-Grid and EF-25 Grid series
Nutter Engineering Co.	Montz series	Snap Grid series
Jaeger Products	MaxPak series	

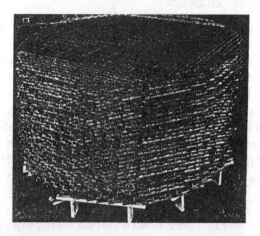

Figure 5.25   Glitsch EF-25A grid packing made of open area metal or plastic panels.

Materials for tower packings

Common materials for tower packings are ceramic, metals, and plastics. The selection of a material for fabrication of tower packings depends upon factors like ease of fabrication, mechanical strength, corrosion resistance, wetability, ease of cleaning, and cost. Ceramic packings declined in popularity since the advent of plastic packings. Ceramic packings are preferred for highly corrosive services (for example, the air-drying tower and SO_3 absorption tower in a H_2SO_4 plant) and also for operation at elevated temperatures. However, these have limited shapes (normally rings and saddles only), are prone to breakage, and require more 'downtime' for filling, removal and cleaning. Metal random packings offer higher capacity, efficiency and turndown ratio because of a smaller wall thickness and more open area. For example, 1 inch ceramic Raschig rings have a wall thickness of $\frac{1}{8}$ inch and a void volume of 74%, and weight 27 lb per ft^3 packed volume; the same size carbon steel packings have wall thickness of $\frac{1}{32}$ inch, voidage 92%, and weight 40 lb per ft^3. Metal packings are unbreakable and have higher compression resistance but have less wettability than that of ceramic rings. For corrosive services, a suitable type of stainless steel is used. Plastic packings are cheap, unbreakable, light, and corrosion-resistance. Common materials, are polyethylene, polypropylene, PVC, and poly-vinylidine fluoride. Plastic packings may be made into a large number of shapes. It is rather easy to fill them and clean them in situ by water or even steam, thus reducing the downtime to a tenth of that for ceramic packings. The disadvantages of plastics packings are: poor wettability, brittleness at low temperature or on aging, tendency to degrade in an oxidative environment or when exposed to UV. Plastic packings are more expensive than the ceramic packings.

5.11.3   The Packing Support and the Gas Distributor

The support plate or grid has three functions: (i) it supports the weight of the packing and the liquid held up in the packing during operation; (ii) it allows the gas to flow through it and to get distributed (uniform gas distribution at the support is extremely important for satisfactory performance of a packed bed); and (iii) it allows the liquid to leave the bed. There should also be an uninterrupted dripping of liquid through the support plate. Even small liquid pockets built up on the support plate badly affect the gas distribution and hence the tower performance.

The packing support ring is bolted or clamped to another ring which is welded to the wall. As such the support plate should be as open as possible. The open area should be above 70%, preferably above 85%. The gas pressure drop across the plate is small. A few types of support grids are described below. The selection of a support depends upon a number of factors including the tower diameter, the height of the packing, the packing type and size, and the mass flow rate (kg/h·m^2) of the gas and of the liquid stream.

The gas injection grid: This is a commonly used packing support [Figure 5.26(a)]. A gas injection grid allows the gas and the liquid to flow through separate openings—the liquid flows through the openings at the floor of the support, and the gas flows through the upper openings. It has an effective area of 80% to more than 100% of the tower cross-section. It is also known as multiple beam support.

The grid support: This type of design is shown in Figure 5.26(b). The structural elements of the grid remain on two different planes. A free area of 95% or more is attainable. Such support grids are suitable for reasonably clean liquids and can handle moderate-to-large vapour rates. Also, these are suitable for larger diameter columns.

The "Cap-type" support plate: Such a support is shown in Figure 5.26(c). This is a very good design but is more expensive. It is often used in small diameter columns.

A bad gas distributor creates channelling of the gas through the bed. Channelling means that the gas flows preferably through certain regions of the bed. This leads to uneven gas–liquid contact and unsatisfactory column performance. Channelling also occurs if the bed is not uniformly packed.

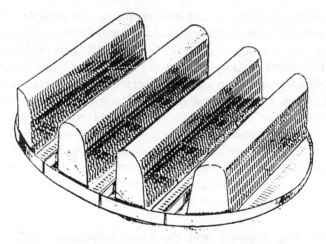

(a) Gas injection packing support plate (Koch Engineering).

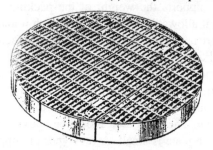

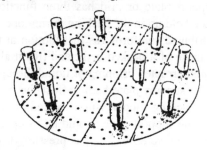

(b) Grid-type support plate (Koch).   (c) Orifice support plate-cum-liquid redistributor.

Figure 5.26   Packing support plate-cum-gas distributor.

5.11.4 Liquid Distribution and Redistribution

Proper distribution of the feed liquid over the bed is essential for satisfactory performance of a packed tower. Otherwise the bed will not be uniformly wetted and there will not be good gas–liquid contact. Ideally, the liquid should be distributed at an infinite number of points on the bed. In practice, a liquid distributor feeds the bed at a pretty large number of points (6–10 points/ft^2; Klemus and Bonilla, 1995) at equal rates. The more common liquid distributors are described below. The choice of a liquid distributor depends upon (i) the liquid flow rate, (ii) the plugging or fouling tendency, and (iii) the turndown ratio.

V-notched channel distributor: This type of distributor [Figure 5.27(a)] is widely used in columns of diameter 3 ft and above. The liquid is fed to a main trough provided with holes at the bottom or slots on the sides. It flows through the orifices or slots to a set of parallel troughs or channels below the main trough. V-notches on the sides of these lower troughs allow the liquid to flow into the packed bed. Levelling of the troughs is very important to ensure equal overflow through the weirs. This type of distributor offers a high turndown ratio because of the variable flow area available. It is also suitable for a liquid having a plugging tendency or having a little suspended solids.

Spray channel distributor: This is another commonly used liquid distributor [Figure 5.27(b)]. It has a simple construction. The feed liquid enters the distributor through a central pipe and comes out through a number of nozzles. This type of distributor can be plunged below a small depth of packing so that the thin layer of 'dry packing' above the distributor acts as a mist eliminator.

Orifice plate liquid distributor: In this type of distributor, the liquid is fed to a number of channels. The liquid flows down to the distribution plate [Figure 5.27(c)] having a large number of orifices. The gas flows up through a number of tubes without interfering with the liquid flow.

Liquid redistribution: A randomly packed bed is not truly random. Local non-homogeneities or variation in voidage and open area for gas flow occur. Although the overall direction of flow of the liquid is towards the bottom, local lateral flow occurs, depending upon the orientation of a piece of packing. But the liquid that reaches the wall of the tower rarely gets dispersed in the lateral direction again. Further, the liquid tends to flow along the wall because it is a continuous surface and because the voidage near the wall is always larger than that in the bulk. This is called *channelling of the liquid.* Such maldistribution is detrimental to a good gas–liquid contact. It is, therefore, necessary to collect the liquid from the wall region and to distribute it over the bed again. A liquid redistributor (Figure 5.28) does this job.

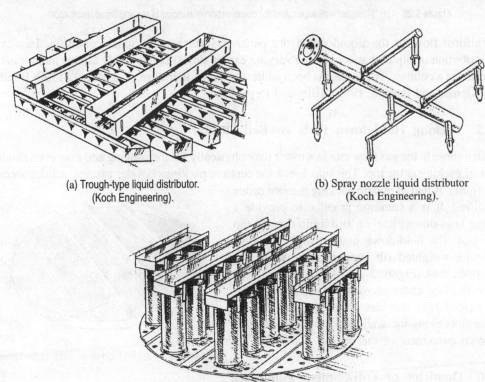

(a) Trough-type liquid distributor.
(Koch Engineering).

(b) Spray nozzle liquid distributor
(Koch Engineering).

(c) Orifice plate liquid distributor
(Koch Engineering).

Figure 5.27 A few types of liquid distributors in a packed tower.

For towers packed with Raschig rings, redistribution becomes necessary after a bed depth of 3 to 6 times the tower diameter; for a saddle-packed tower, it is 5 to 10 tower diameters. Also, the Raschig ring packing may have a depth of 10 to 15 ft per section. The depth may be 12 to 20 ft with saddle packing. This, however, depends upon the bed diameter.

For small towers of diameter 18 inches or less, a wall-wiper type distributor is popular [Figure 5.28(a)]. The wall wiper collects liquid near the wall and directs it to the central region. A packing support-cum-liquid redistributor is shown in Figure 5.28(b).

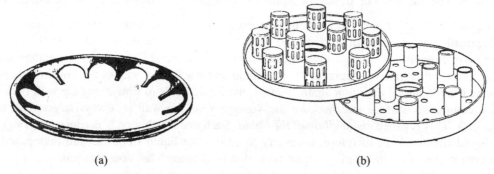

(a)   (b)

Figure 5.28   (a) "Rosette" wall wiper, and (b) combination of support plate and liquid distributor.

Uniform flow of the liquid down the packing surface is an ideal condition. However, maldistribution of liquid that occurs to a varying extent almost unavoidably affects mass transfer efficiency of a column. The issue has been addressed in the literature (Perry et al., 1990; Bonilla, 1993; Klemas and Bonilla, 1995; Killat and Rey, 1996).

5.11.5   Packing Hold-down Plate or Bed Limiter

A sudden surge in the gas flow rate in a tower may physically lift the packing and may even fluidize a layer of packing at the top. This may break the ceramic packings besides causing maldistribution of the fluids. A bed of plastic packing is more prone to be lifted. It is a common practice to provide a 'packing hold-down plate' or 'bed limiter' at the top of the bed. The hold-down plate is made of wire-mesh with weighted rib support and has nearly 100% open area (Figure 5.29). A hold-down plate may be in place under its own weight. It may also have welded lugs that can move through narrow guiding slots along the wall, thus allowing only up and down movement of the device.

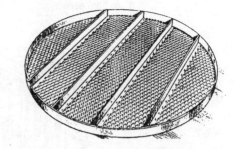

Figure 5.29   Packing 'hold-down plate' or 'bed limiter'.

5.11.6   Demister or Entrainment Eliminator

A 'demister', made of a wire-mesh or a thin metal sheet, is often placed below the gas exit nozzle to remove the entrained liquid droplets (Figure 5.30). Sometimes, a layer of packing is put above the liquid distributor. This layer, called 'dry packing', acts as an entrainment eliminator.

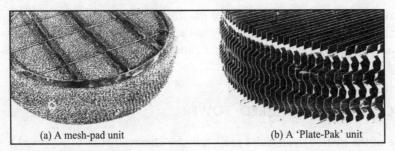

(a) A mesh-pad unit   (b) A 'Plate-Pak' unit

Figure 5.30 Two types of mist eliminators or demisters (*Courtesy*: ACS Industries).

5.11.7 Procedure of Packing a Tower

It is not advisable to pack a tower by dropping the packings into the tower from the top. Ceramic packing may break if dumped from above. Also the packings may not get spread uniformly; they may form a heap at the centre. A ring-type packing may roll down the heap and get a preferential horizontal orientation. There are a few common techniques (Figure 5.31) of installation of random packings. In the 'wet packing technique', popular with ceramic packings, the tower is filled with water or a suitable liquid and the packing is dumped into it. Plastic packings cannot be filled in this way because they will float in the liquid. 'Dry packing' may be done by lowering the packing in a wire bucket that is led into the column through a manhole (Figure 5.31). The chute-and-sock method is also used (this technique is very useful for loading a solid catalyst in a reactor).

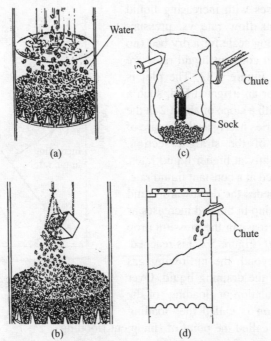

Figure 5.31 Techniques of filling a tower with random packings: (a) wet-packing by filling the tower with water, (b) dry-packing by lowering buckets filled with the packing, (c) the chute-and-sock method of packing, and (d) packing through a chute only (Chen, 1984).

On rare occasions, a random packing like the Raschig ring is stacked in a column in layers. The flow channels in such a bed are regular and the gas pressure drop becomes less as a result. Structured packings are made in pieces to fit a column of given diameter and are stacked in an appropriate way.

5.12   FLOODING IN A PACKED TOWER

A knowledge of the hydrodynamic and mass transfer characteristics of a packed tower such as the influence of the flow rate of the gas and of the liquid on pressure drop, liquid holdup and the gas- and the liquid-phase mass transfer coefficients in the bed is essential for the design of such a device for a given service. The more important hydrodynamic characteristics are discussed below.

5.12.1   Bed Pressure Drop and the Phenomena of Loading and Flooding

The liquid distributed on the top of a packed bed trickles down by gravity. Flow of the gas is pressure-driven and the pressure is generated by a blower or a compressor. The gas undergoes pressure drop as it flows through the bed because of (i) both skin friction[†] and form friction, (ii) frequent changes in the flow direction, and (iii) expansion and contraction. Maximum area for flow of the gas is available if the packing is dry, i.e. if there is *no* liquid throughput. But when a liquid flows through the bed, a part of the open space of the bed is occupied by the liquid (called 'liquid holdup' in the bed) and the area available for gas flow decreases. This is why the pressure

drop of the gas increases with increasing liquid throughput. Typical gas flow rate vs. pressure drop curves on the log-log scale for a dry bed (no liquid flow) and for two constant liquid rates are qualitatively shown in Figure 5.32. The plot is linear for a dry bed. For an irrigated bed, such a curve is nearly linear with a slope of about 2 in the lower region (i.e. ΔP varies nearly as the square of gas rate). The slope of the straight section, however, decreases slightly at higher liquid rates. If the gas rate is increased at a constant liquid rate, the drag of the gas impedes the downward liquid velocity. The liquid holdup in the bed increases as a result. This steady increase in the pressure drop continues till the point B (Figure 5.32) is reached. At the point B and beyond, the upflowing gas interferes strongly with the draining liquid. Over the region B–C, accumulation or 'loading' of the liquid starts. This region is called the 'loading region'. The point C is called the point of 'incipient flooding'.

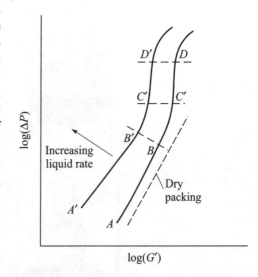

Figure 5.32   Typical pressure drop characteristics of a packed tower (qualitative).

[†] For flow past a piece of packing of 'aerodynamic design' such as saddles, the skin friction component prevails and hence the pressure drop remains low.

If the gas flow rate is further increased, the liquid accumulation rate increases very sharply. Liquid accumulates more in the upper region of the bed almost preventing the flow of gas. This phenomenon is called 'flooding'. The bed becomes 'flooded' (point *D*) when the voids in the bed become full of liquid and the liquid becomes the continuous phase — a case of 'phase inversion'. A number of definitions of flooding (more than ten!) have been put forward based on one or more of the phenomena that precede or follow flooding (Silvey and Keller, 1966; Kister, 1992; Piche et al., 2001). A widely accepted definition, suggested by Bravo and Fair (see Kister, 1992), runs as follows: "It is a region of rapidly increasing pressure drop with simultaneous loss of mass transfer efficiency." The visual and physical symptoms of flooding are: (i) accumulation of a layer of liquid at the top of the bed, (ii) a sharp rise in pressure drop, (iii) a sharp rise in liquid holdup in the bed, and (iv) a sharp fall in mass transfer efficiency (this will be discussed later).

While the operation of the column becomes very unstable over the region *CD* and the mass transfer efficiency drops significantly, some researchers have reported a reasonably stable operation beyond the point *D*. This is because beyond the point *D*, the column operates like a 'bubble column with gas–liquid upflow'.

5.12.2　Prediction of Pressure Drop and Flooding

Prediction of the flooding point and pressure drop is essential in connection with the design of packed towers. Charts, correlations and theoretical models have been proposed for this purpose. These have been thoroughly reviewed (Kister, 1992; Billet, 1995; Strigle, 1994; Piche et al., 2001). The initial significant attempt to correlate flooding data was made by Sherwood et al. (1938). Every packing has its own geometrical and surface characteristics. Pressure drop per unit bed height as well as the flooding characteristics are also different for individual packings even when all other parameters including 'nominal packing size' remain the same. However, it is not very realistic to work out separate correlations for pressure drop (and for mass transfer) for packings of different types and sizes. Instead efforts were made to develop a 'generalized pressure drop correlation' (GPDC) that would be applicable to all kinds of random packings. The idea of a GPDC was first introduced by Leva (1954). The major variables and parameters that determine the pressure drop and flooding characteristics are: (i) the properties (density, viscosity and surface tension) of the fluids and (ii) the packing type and its features (size, voidage and surface area and surface properties). A number of charts and correlations have been proposed by the US School (led by Leva, Eckert, Strigle, and Kister, to name a few; see Kister, 1992) during the last fifty years. A second group of charts and correlations have been proposed by the German School (led by Mersman, Stichlmair, Billet and others; see Billet, 1995). Some of the correlations have a semi-theoretical basis and include adjustable constants specific to a group of packing. Recently, Piche et al. (2001) reviewed all important correlations proposed for the flooding point coming from both US and German Schools. These researchers also proposed a new correlation developed by using artificial neural network (ANN) technique to 1019 data sets reported by different workers.

The GPDCs proposed by Eckert (1975 and before) of the erstwhile Norton Company[†] have been widely used for packed tower design. The 1970-version (Figure 5.33) gives a number of

---

[†] The Norton Corp. (formerly U.S. Stoneware) was acquired by Saint-Gobain in 1997 with the new name Saint-Gobain Norpro Corporation.

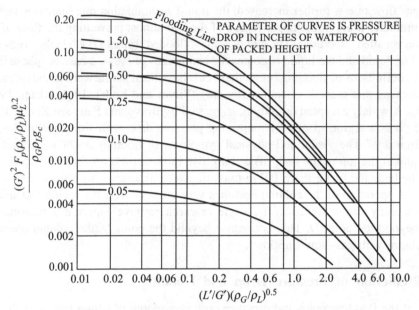

Figure 5.33 Generalized pressure drop correlation (GPDC) of Eckert (1970).

constant pressure drop curves and a flooding curve. The units of different quantities are given in Section 5.12.6. It works well with most first generation packings but not for several second generation packings and smaller modern packings. Eckert's 1975 version (not shown here) omitted the flooding curve because such a curve always has a doubtful accuracy. For first generation packings, the 'packing factor' is high (generally above 60 ft^{-1}, Section 5.12.3) and the pressure drop is $\Delta P/L \geq 2$ inches of water per foot packed height at 'incipient' flooding. Eckert's chart was further refined by Strigle (1994) using a data bank of 4500 pressure drop measurements on beds having different types and sizes of packings and using different liquids and gases. The Strigle's version[†] (Figure 5.34) is now most popular for packed tower design (Larson and Kister, 1997). The error in pressure drop prediction is claimed to be within ±11% for normal ranges of operation. It has a 'flow parameter' as the abscissa and a 'capacity parameter' as the ordinate.

$$\text{Flow parameter,} \qquad F_{lv} = (L'/G')(\rho_G/\rho_L)^{0.5} \qquad (5.20)$$

$$\text{Capacity parameter} \quad = C_s F_p^{0.5} v^{0.05}; \quad C_s = u_{sG}[\rho_G/(\rho_L - \rho_G)]^{1/2}, \text{ in ft/s} \qquad (5.21)$$

Interestingly, the abscissa and the ordinate of the Strigle's chart resemble the corresponding quantities of Fair's flooding chart for a tray tower [Figure 5.12(a)]. The flow parameter F_{lv}, represents the square root of the ratio of liquid and vapour kinetic energies. The ordinate describes a balance between forces due to vapour flow (that acts to entrain swarms of liquid droplets) and the gravity force that resists entrainment (Kister, 1992). Here F_p is a characteristic parameter of the packing, called the 'packing factor' (discussed in the next section). The quantity C_s, which is akin to the Souders–Brown constant [see Eq. (5.40], may be corrected for changes in interfacial tension and viscosity, if necessary.

$$(C_s)_{corr} = C_s(\sigma/20)^{0.16}(\mu/0.2)^{-0.11}; \qquad [\sigma \text{ in dyne/cm, } \mu \text{ in cP}] \qquad (5.22)$$

[†] The ordinate of Figure 5.34 has a linear scale and is more convenient to use than another version having a logarithmic ordinate (see Strigle, 1994).

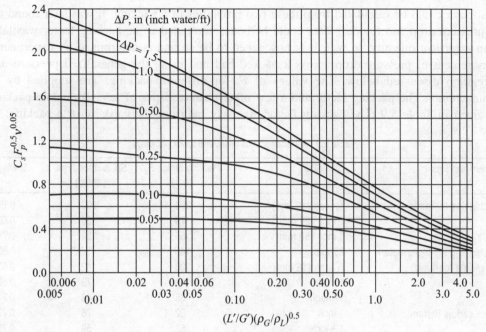

Figure 5.34 Strigle's GPDC (Strigle, 1994).

Strigle's chart also excluded the curve for pressure drop at flooding. However, the curve for $\Delta P/L = 1.5$ inches water per foot is considered to represent the 'incipient flooding' condition. Kister and Gill (1991) proposed the following correlation for flood point pressure drop in terms of the packing factor.

$$(\Delta P/L)_{fl} = 0.115 F_p^{0.7} \quad \text{(inch water/ft; } F_p \text{ in ft}^{-1}) \tag{5.23}$$

Robbin (1991) proposed another set of correlations for pressure drop prediction over a wide range of operating conditions. For dry bed pressure drop at nearly atmospheric pressure, he suggested the following equation.

$$(\Delta P/L)_d = 2.78 \times 10^{-10} F_{pd}(G'^2/\rho_G) \quad \text{(inch water/ft)} \tag{5.24}$$

Here G' is in lb/ft²·h, and ρ_G is in lb/ft³. The above equation has an important application. The dry bed packing factor F_{pd} of any packing, which is now considered an empirical quantity (see below), can be calculated from the above equation by measuring the pressure drop across an experimental packed bed. However, the packing factors for dry and irrigated beds are likely to be different. The dry bed pressure drop can also be calculated using the Ergun's equation.

5.12.3 Packing Factor

The Eckert chart (and a few similar charts) contains a parameter F_p that characterizes the packing and is called 'packing factor' (an alternative notation C_f has also been used to denote this quantity). Originally introduced by Lobo in 1945, the packing factor used to be taken as a_p/ε^3 (a_p = surface area of the packing per unit volume[†]; ε = void fraction of the packed bed).

[†] This is *not* the same as the specific interfacial area of contact between the gas and the liquid.

This factor could be calculated from these two properties of a packing. It was later found that the pressure drop and flooding data could be better correlated if the packing factor was taken as an *empirical* quantity. In fact, it is now taken to be so and is determined by experimental measurement of pressure drop across a packed bed and using the generalized pressure drop correlation discussed below. The values of F_p for different packings are supplied by the manufacturers. The packing factor and a few other characteristics of several random packings are given in Table 5.9. The packing factor inversely indicates the capacity of a packing; the

Table 5.9 Characteristics of several tower packings

Random packings	Size	Packing factor, F_p (ft^{-1})	Sp. surface area, a (ft^2/ft^3)	Voidage, ε
Raschig ring (ceramic)	⅝ inch (15 mm)	380	100	0.69 2
	1 inch (25 mm)	179	56	0.68
	2 inch (50 mm)	65	28	0.74
Raschig ring (¹⁄₁₆-inch, metal)	25 mm	145	56.7	0.85
Berl saddle (ceramic)	½ inch (13 mm)	380	142	0.63
	1 inch	110	79	0.68
	1½ inch	65	46	0.71
Intalox saddle (ceramic)	1 inch	92	78	0.73
	1½ inch	52	59	0.76
	2 inch	40	35	0.76
Intalox saddle (plastic)	2 inch	28	37.2	0.91
Pall ring (metal)	1 inch	56	68.1	0.954
	2 inch	27	34.3	0.951
Pall ring (plastic)	1 inch	55	68.6	0.89
	2 inch	26	34	0.92
IMTP (metal)*	# 25	41	74.7	0.967
	# 50	18	24.7	0.978
CMR	1 inch	40	70.8	0.971
	1½ inch (38 mm)	29	53.3	0.974
Nutter ring (metal)*	# 1	27	51	0.978
	# 2	17	29	0.98
Bialecki ring	1 inch		72.5	0.94
	2 inch		37	0.966
Nor-Pac ring (plastic)	1 inch	31	55	0.927
	2 inch	14	26.4	0.947
Hi-flow ring (ceramic)	2 inch	29	27.3	0.81
Hi-flow ring (plastic)	2 inch	20	35.6	0.924
Hi-flow ring (metal)	2 inch	16	28	0.977
Structured Packings				
Gempak 2A (Glitsch)			68	0.95
3A			120	0.96
Flexipac 2 (Koch)			68	0.95
3			41	0.96
Mellapak 250Y (Sulzer)			76	0.988
350Y			107	0.975

* IMTP and Nutter rings are denoted by a number rather than a nominal size.

specific surface area indicates its mass transfer efficiency. It is intriguing that the values of the packing factor of the same packing obtained from different sources are found to vary.

5.12.4 Liquid Holdup

There must be a reasonable liquid holdup in the bed in order to facilitate mass transfer. However, excessive holdup increases pressure drop over the bed and is also undesirable if the liquid is heat-sensitive. Normally it ranges from a few percent to about 15% of the bed volume. Two types of liquid holdup (expressed as volume of liquid per unit bed volume) have been defined.

Static holdup: It is the amount of liquid remaining in unit volume of the bed after the bed is drained for a reasonable time. It is pretty small compared to the total holdup.

Operating holdup (h_{Lo}): It is the difference between the total holdup and the static holdup when the bed is in operation. It is also called 'dynamic holdup'. Several correlations for estimation of the quantity are available (Kister, 1992). A recent correlation (Engel et al., 1997) for h_{Lo} (volume fraction of the bed) given below is claimed to have an error within 16% for most systems.

$$h_{Lo} = 0.93 \left(\frac{u_{Ls}^2 a_p}{g} \right)^{1/6} \left(\frac{\mu_L^2 a_p^3}{\rho_L^2 g} \right)^{1/10} \left(\frac{\sigma_L a_p^2}{\rho_L g} \right)^{1/8} \tag{5.25}$$

5.12.5 Minimum Wetting Rate (MWR)

It is the liquid throughput below which the film on the packing surface breaks up reducing the wetted area. A liquid rate below MWR is too small to wet all the packing surface. The effective interfacial area of the gas–liquid contact decreases and the efficiency of mass transfer decreases as a result. Among the many correlations available for its prediction, the one due to Schmidt (1979) has been found to work pretty well.

$$u_{sL} = 7.7 \times 10^{-6} \left(\frac{\rho_L \sigma_L^3}{\mu_L^4 g} \right)^{2/9} \left(\frac{g}{a_p} \right)^{1/2} \quad m^3/m^2 \cdot h \quad [g \text{ in } m/s^2; \ a_p \text{ in } m^{-1}] \tag{5.26}$$

Minimum liquid rate for random packings is reported to lie in the range 0.5–2 gpm/ft^2 (1.25–5 m^3/m^2·h); for structured packing it is 0.1–0.2 gpm/ft^2 (0.12–0.25m^3/m^2·h).

5.12.6 Determination of the Diameter of a Packed Tower and Packed Tower Design

The design of a packed tower for a particular service involves a number of things such as the selection of solvent, the selection of the type and size packing, the determination of column diameter and height of packing, and the design of column internals. Mass transfer phenomena in a packed tower and the determination of the height of packing for a given separation job will be taken up in Chapters 6 and 7. So far as column internals are concerned, there is no well-defined procedure. It may be done by using the limited information available in the open literature and the manufacturer's catalogue. In this section, we discuss one very important item of design, i.e. the determination of the diameter of a packed column.

There are broadly two approaches. One approach, based on the determination of the flooding[†] velocity by using the Eckert's GPDC chart (Figure 5.33), proceeds as follows. (i) From the total liquid and gas flow rates (either specified or calculated by material balance) the abscissa (i.e. the flow parameter, F_{lv}) is evaluated. (ii) The value of the ordinate is obtained from the flooding curve and the mass flow rate of the gas at flooding is calculated. (iii) The operating gas flow rate is *normally* taken as 70 to 80% of the flooding velocity to guard against inherent errors in the flooding curve and also to keep some flexibility in the design to take care of any sudden surge in the gas flow rate. Once the design gas flow rate is fixed, the tower diameter and the pressure drop across the bed may be estimated. The latter is obtained from the same chart, i.e. Figure 5.33. An algebraic correlation for the Eckert's flooding curve (and a dozen similar equations) has been given by Piche et al. (2001).

$$\log_{10}(Y)_{fl} = -0.296[\log(F_{lv})]^2 - 1.081\log(F_{lv}) - 1.668$$

$$(Y)_{fl} = \frac{(G')_{fl}^2 \, F_p \, (\rho_w/\rho_L)(\mu_L)^{0.2}}{\rho_G \, \rho_L \, g_c} \tag{5.27}$$

$[G'$ in lb/ft^2·h; F_p in ft^{-1}; ρ in lb/ft^3; μ in cP; g_c in ft.lb$_f$/lb$_m$·s$^2]$

The second approach does not use the flooding curve at all because of its limited accuracy and applicability. The allowable pressure drop in the bed is taken as a basis of design and the Strigle's GPDC chart is used directly. The value of the flow parameter is calculated and the capacity parameter corresponding to the allowable pressure drop is obtained from the chart. The column diameter is now easy to determine. The pressure drop at flooding for the particular packing can be calculated from the Kister and Gill equation [Eq. (5.23)]. The gas velocity at flooding can also be calculated from these results. A step-by-step procedure is outlined in Ludwig (1997). A few practical values of the allowable pressure drop, $\Delta P/L$ [(inch water)/(ft packing)], (Ludwig, 1997) are: low to medium pressure column operation: 0.4–0.6; absorption or similar systems: 0.25–0.4 for non-foaming systems, 0.1–0.25 for foaming systems;[††] atmospheric pressure distillation: 0.5 to 1.0 inch; vacuum distillation: 0.1–0.2. The recommended sizes of packing for different column diameters are: $D_c <$ 1ft, $d_p <$ 1 inch; $D_c =$ 1–3 ft, $d_p =$ 1–1½ inches; $D_c >$ 3 ft, $d_p =$ 2–3 inches. Normally, d_p/D_c ranges between 1/20 and 1/10. Limited data and information on pressure drop calculation for a bed of structured packings are available (Fair and Bravo, 1990; Strigle, 1994; Olujic et al., 2001).

For the first generation random packings, the flood point pressure drop is about 2–2.5 inch water per foot of packed bed; for Paul rings, it is 1.5 inch per foot. For most modern packings, it is 0.5–1.5 inch per foot. Manufacturers of packings generally supply the pressure drop and flooding characteristics of their products as plots of ΔP versus F_s [$= u_{sG}(\rho_G)^{0.5}$]. It may be noted that the quantity F_s is also taken as a measure of the 'capacity parameter' or 'factor' for flow through a packed tower at low-to-moderate pressure when $\rho_G \ll \rho_L$. If enough data are available in the company's catalogue, it is desirable that the flooding point or pressure drop is determined by interpolation of the available data.

[†] Flooding limits the liquid and vapour flow capacity of a column. The assessment of the capacity of an existing column has been discussed by Capps (1993).

[††] Anti-foaming agents are sometimes used to suppress foaming in an absorption column.

In order to maintain proper vapour distribution through the bed, the operating bed pressure drop should not be less than 0.1 inch water/ft. In a column operating near atmospheric pressure, the superficial gas velocity normally remains below 1 m/s; the liquid velocity remains around 1 cm/s. Common ranges of values of the more important packed-bed parameters are given in Table 5.10.

Table 5.10   Ranges of a few important packed-tower parameters

Random packing nominal size	$D_c/20$ to $D_c/10$, D_c = column diameter
Bed voidage	70 to 90% (more for structured packings)
Open area of packing support (for gas/liquid flow)	70 to 85% or more
Re-distribution of liquid	After 3 to 10 tower diameter (10 to 20 ft)
Gas pressure drop	Less than 0.5 inch water per foot bed depth
Operating velocity	70 to 80% of flooding velocity
Minimum wetting rate	0.5 to 2 gpm/ft² for random packings; 0.1 to 0.2 gpm/ft² for structured packings

EXAMPLE 5.2   A gas mixture containing 10% SO_2 and 90% inerts at 1 atm total pressure and 30°C is to be scrubbed with water to remove 97% of SO_2. The inerts have essentially the properties of air. The feed gas rate is 1500 kg/h and the water rate is 37,525 kg/h at the tower bottom. Estimate in each case the diameter of a packed tower for this service if either 1½ inch Raschig ring or 50 mm plastic Pall ring is used as the packing. Calculate the pressure drop across the tower for the second case and the blower horsepower required if the packed height is 5 m. The liquid properties are like those of water. Both gas and liquid flow rates are the maximum at the bottom and design calculations may be based on these values. The flow rates at the top can be easily calculated.

Solution

The tower diameter is to be calculated on the basis of the largest liquid and gas flow rates that occur at its bottom.

Given: Liquid rate, L = 37,525 kg/h; gas rate, G = 1500 kg/h at the bottom.

The pressure at the tower bottom will be above atmospheric. Since the pressure drop will not be large, we take the properties of air at 1 atm (1.013 bar) and 30°C (303 K).

Average molecular weight of the feed gas (90% air, 10% SO_2),

$$M = (0.9)(28.8) + (0.1)(64) = 32.3$$

Gas density, $\rho_G = \dfrac{P}{RT} M = \dfrac{(1.013)(32.3)}{(0.08317)(303)} = 1.298$ kg/m³ = 0.081 lb/ft³

Liquid viscosity (taken as that of water at 30°C),

$$\mu_L = 0.81 \text{ cP}; \quad \text{surface tension} = 70 \text{ dyne/cm}$$

$$\text{density, } \rho_L \approx 996 \text{ kg/m}^3 = 62 \text{ lb/ft}^3$$

Flow parameter, $F_{lv} = \dfrac{L'}{G'}\left(\dfrac{\rho_G}{\rho_L}\right)^{0.5} = \dfrac{L}{G}\left(\dfrac{\rho_G}{\rho_L}\right)^{0.5} = \left(\dfrac{37,525}{1500}\right)\left(\dfrac{1.298}{996}\right)^{0.5} = 0.903$

(a) *Calculation of column diameter—1½ inch Raschig ring packing (d_p = 1½ inch):* Use Eckert's GPDC chart (Figure 5.33) since it is good enough for a first generation packing. At flooding, for F_{lv} = 0.903, the capacity parameter is 0.021. The other parameters are:

$$\rho_w/\rho_L = 1; \qquad \mu_L = 0.81 \text{ cP}$$

Packing factor, $\qquad\qquad F_p = 94.5/\text{ft}; \qquad g_c = 4.18 \times 10^8 \text{ ft/h}^2$

i.e. $\quad \dfrac{(G')_{fl}^2 \, F_p (\rho_w/\rho_L)(\mu_L)^{0.2}}{\rho_G \, \rho_L \, g_c} = 0.021 \quad \Rightarrow \quad (G')_{fl}^2 = \dfrac{(0.021)(0.081)(62)(4.18 \times 10^8)}{(94.5)(1)(0.81)^{0.2}}$

$\Rightarrow \qquad\qquad\qquad (G')_{fl} = 697.5 \text{ lb/ft}^2\text{h}$

Take the operating gas flow rate as 70% of the flooding value.

$$\text{Operating } G' = (697.5)(0.7) = 488.3 \text{ lb/ft}^2\cdot\text{h} = 2384 \text{ kg/m}^2\cdot\text{h}$$

$$\text{Tower cross-section} = G/G' = 1500/2384 = 0.629 \text{ m}^2$$

$\Rightarrow \qquad\qquad \text{Tower diameter, } D_c = \boxed{0.90 \text{ m}} = 2.94 \text{ ft} \approx 3 \text{ ft}$

Now,

$$d_p/D_c = (1½ \text{ inch})/(36 \text{ inch}) = 1/24$$

This is acceptable. However, 2 inch rings could be used as well.
Let us calculate the *capacity parameter* at flooding for F_{lv} = 0.901 using Eq. (5.27).

$$\log_{10}(Y)_{fl} = -0.296[\log(0.903)]^2 - 1.081[\log(0.903)] - 1.668 = -1.665 \Rightarrow (Y)_{fl} = 0.0216$$

This appears to be close to the value (0.021) read directly from the chart.

(b) *Calculation of column diameter—50 mm Pall ring packing:* Use the Strigle version of the GPDC chart (Figure 5.34) since this is more appropriate for this packing.

Take the allowable pressure drop as 0.2 inch water per foot packing for this gas absorption operation.

For F_{lv} = 0.903 (calculated before) and $\Delta P/L$ = 0.2 inch water/ft, the capacity parameter = 0.52 is obtained by interpolation from the chart. Take F_p = 25 ft^{-1}; v = 0.81 centistoke.

$\Rightarrow \qquad\quad C_s (F_p)^{0.5} v^{0.05} = 0.52 \quad \Rightarrow \quad C_s (25)^{0.5}(0.81)^{0.05} = 0.52$

$\Rightarrow \qquad\qquad C_s = u_{sG} \left(\dfrac{\rho_G}{\rho_L - \rho_G} \right)^{0.5} = 0.105$

$\Rightarrow \qquad\qquad u_{sG} = (0.105) \left(\dfrac{996 - 1.298}{1.298} \right)^{0.5} = 2.91 \text{ ft/s}$

$$= 0.886 \text{ m/s} = \text{superficial gas velocity}$$

$$\text{Volumetric gas flow rate} = \dfrac{1500 \text{ kg/h}}{(1.298 \text{ kg/m}^3)(3600 \text{ s/h})} = 0.321 \text{ m}^3/\text{s}$$

$$\text{Tower cross-section} = (0.321 \text{ m}^3/\text{s})/0.886 \text{ m/s} = 0.362 \text{ m}^2$$

$\Rightarrow \quad \text{Tower diameter, } D_c = [(0.362)(4)/\pi]^{1/2} = \boxed{0.68 \text{ m}}$

[Compare this with D_c = 0.9 m in case (a)]

Thus, a substantially smaller diameter column is sufficient if the *second generation packing* is used.

Pressure drop at flooding for the Pall ring-packed column,

$$(\Delta P/L)_{fl} = 0.115(F_p)^{0.7}$$
$$= (0.115)(25)^{0.7}$$
$$= \boxed{1.09 \text{ inch water per foot packed height}}$$

Blower power requirement for feeding the gas: The tower is designed for $\Delta P/L = 0.2$ inch water per foot of packing.

Pressure drop across the bed of 5 m height, $\Delta P = (0.2)(5/0.3048) = 3.28$ inch water.

Add 10% to take into account contraction, expansion and other losses (nozzles, packing support, etc.)

$$\text{Operating pressure drop} = (3.28)(1.1) = 3.61 \text{ inch water} = (3.61)(0.0254)(996)(9.81)$$
$$= 895 \text{ N/m}^2$$

Gas flow rate, $G = 1500$ kg/h = 0.4167 kg/s

$$\text{Power requirement} = \left(\frac{\Delta P}{\rho}\right) G = \left(\frac{895 \text{ N/m}^2}{1.298 \text{ kg/m}^3}\right)(0.4167 \text{ kg/s})$$
$$= 287.5 \text{ N·m/s} = 287.5 \text{ W}$$

Take 65% overall efficiency of the motor-blower assembly.

$$\text{Actual power requirement} = 287.5/0.65 = 442 \text{ W} = \boxed{0.6 \text{ hp}}$$

A motor of this rating is not available, and a ¾ hp motor is uncommon. A blower of suitable design and powered by a 1 hp motor is recommended.

Calculation of operating liquid holdup: It is rather simple to calculate h_{Lo}, the operating liquid holdup, using Engel's equation, Eq. (5.25). The values of the different quantities are: for 2 inch Pall ring, $a_p = 102$ m^2/m^3; $\mu_L = 0.81$ cP = 8.1×10^{-4} kg/m.s; $\sigma_L = 70$ dyne/cm = 0.07 N/m; superficial liquid velocity, $u_{sL} = [(37,525/996) \text{ m}^3\text{/h}]/(0.362 \text{ m}^2) = 0.0289$ m/s.

Putting the values in Eq. (5.25), the volume fraction liquid holdup in the bed

$$h_{Lo} = (0.93)\left[\frac{(0.0289)^2 (102)}{9.81}\right]^{1/6} \left[\frac{(8.1 \times 10^{-4})^2 (102)^3}{(996)^2 (9.81)}\right]^{1/10} \left[\frac{(0.07)(102)^2}{(996)(9.81)}\right]^{1/8}$$

$$= 0.0588 \text{ m}^3 \text{ liquid per m}^3 \text{ bed volume}$$

A typical packed bed data-sheet incorporating the basic design information and parameters is given in Table 5.11. Since complete design of the bed has not been done here, only the approximate values of a few of the parameters have been given in the data sheet. The objective of inclusion of the data sheet is just to give an idea about what a design data sheet is.

Table 5.11 Packed bed data sheet

Service: ABSORBER		Item Number:	B-27-0103
Packed Bed Data			
	Top		*Bottom*
Vessel ID, mm		680	
Bed depth, mm		5000	
Random packing, mm		5000	
Packing type		50 mm Pall ring	
Fluid description		Water	
Hold down plate		KG- TP825	
Packing support plate		KG- TP814	
Liquid distributor		KG- TP916	
Structural design temperature, °C		150	
Liquid flow rate, kg/h	37,335		37,525
Density, kg/m³	995		996
Viscosity, cP		0.81 (average)	
Surface tension, dyne/cm		70 (average)	
Temperature, °C		30 (average)	
Pressure, kPa	101.3		102.1
Gas flow rate, kg/h	1210		1500
Density	1.16		1.298
Foam deaerating factor			0.75
Demister		Yes	

Note 1: The liquid distributor is to be placed 200 mm above the packing hold down plate.
Note 2: 'KG' refers to a Koch-Glitsch product of the given product number.

5.13 THEORETICAL MODELS OF FLOW THROUGH A PACKED TOWER

There have been a number of attempts to develop simplified models of two-phase (the gas and the liquid) flow through a packed bed for a better understanding of the flow phenomena as well as to theoretically determine the pressure drop and the flooding capacity. Any such model visualizes a simplified picture of the bed and of flow through it so as to make it amenable to theoretical analysis. Three models are cited here.

The particle model: In this model, the packed bed is visualized as consisting of a number of spheres of a size calculated on the basis of the void volume of the bed and the surface area of the packing (Figure 5.35). If the voidage is large (say over 0.4), the hypothetical spheres may not even touch each other (as if they remain 'suspended' but stationary). Pressure drop across the bed is a result of drag of the flowing gas on the spheres. With increasing liquid flow, the void volume in the bed decreases, the size of the hypothetical spheres increases and the pressure drop also increases. In fact, an early version of the model was used by Ergan back in 1952 to develop

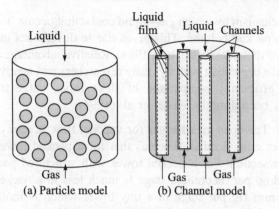

Figure 5.35   Models of a packed bed.

an equation for pressure drop across a packed bed of solid. Stichlmair et al. (1989) used this model to predict pressure drop and flooding for both random and structured packings.

The channel model: In this model, the packed bed is considered to act like a cylindrical block with a number of uniformly distributed vertical channels in it. The hypothetical channel diameter can be calculated from the voidage and specific area of the packings. The liquid flows as a film along the walls of the cylinders and is subject to shear force at the gas–liquid interface because of the upflowing gas. Billet (1995) used this model to develop equations for gas-phase pressure drop and the condition of beginning of loading of liquid in the bed. Loading starts when the shear force at the interface is large enough to reduce the liquid and vapour velocities at the interface to zero. The flooding conditions were also analytically laid down as

$$\frac{du_L}{dh_L} = 0 \quad \text{and} \quad \frac{du_G}{dh_L} = 0 \quad \text{for } u_L = u_{L,fl} \text{ and } u_G = u_{G,fl} \qquad (5.28)$$

Here u_L is the superficial liquid velocity and h_L is the liquid holdup in the bed. Billet (1995) and the German group used these criterion to determine the flooding capacity of the bed. The model has been criticized by some people because it visualizes the packing material to form a continuous medium. Nevertheless, it has been used by other people too (e.g. Rocha et al., 1993) to predict packed bed pressure drop.

Percolation model: This model (Hanley, 1994) assumes that a part of the liquid flowing through the bed gets accumulated in certain locations of the bed causing local blockage or 'localized flooding'. This creates the enhanced pressure drop. The number of flooded locations increases with the increasing liquid rate.

5.14   COMPARISON BETWEEN PACKED AND PLATE TOWERS

Tray columns and packed columns are the two most widely used devices for distillation, gas absorption and stripping, and, to some extent, for liquid–liquid extraction. Each class has characteristic but very different 'column internals' for achieving intimate contact between the two phases. But the mechanism by which gas–liquid contacting occurs in a tray column is totally different from that in a packed column. This gives rise to differences in the operating features as well as applications of these devices (Chen, 1984). Relative advantages and limitations of tray and packed columns have been dealt with by many researchers and neatly summarized by Kister (1992). Capacity and efficiency comparison of sieve trays, valve trays, and random and structured packings has been done by Kister et al. (1994).

(i) *Pressure drop:*   The open area for gas (or vapour) flow in a tray tower typically varies from 6 to 15% of tower cross-section, whereas that for a packed tower is often greater than 50% of the tower cross-section. For a packed tower with structured packings, it is more than 90%. So the pressure drop per theoretical stage is much less in a packed tower than in a tray tower. It is about 3–5 mm Hg per stage in a tray tower which is more than three times the pressure drop per HETP for a tower filled with random packings and more than ten times for that having structured packings. The gas compression energy required for a packed tower is significantly lower than that in a tray tower. This advantage becomes particularly important in vacuum applications where packed towers, particularly with structured packings, are the choice.

(ii) *Liquid holdup:*   For a tray tower, the liquid holdup remains within 8 to 12% of tower volume against 1 to 6% in case of a packed tower. So the packed tower offers a smaller liquid residence time and is more suitable for processing heat sensitive liquids.

(iii) *Corrosion:*   Ceramic and plastic packing materials are highly corrosion resistant. Even the shell of a packed tower may be made of a few smaller pieces of ceramic shell with bell and spigot joints[†] as stated before. The tray towers, on the other hand, are made of metals or alloys and possess more internals. So, a packed tower is the choice for a highly corrosive service. For example, a packed tower is used for absorption of SO_3 in a sulphuric acid plant, for nitric acid concentration by extractive distillation, and for drying of moist chlorine gas in a caustic-chlorine plant.

(iv) *Foaming liquids:*   It is difficult to process a foaming liquid in a tray tower since bubbling aggravates the problem of foaming and flooding. The problem is less severe in a packed tower.

(v) *Suspended solids:*   The packings are more prone to deposition and choking if the liquid has suspended solids in it. A tray tower can handle a dirty liquid or a slurry with relative ease. Also, it can be cleaned easily. Cleaning of packings, particularly the structured ones, is difficult.

(vi) *Heat removal:*   If there is an excessive heat generation (this may occur in case of 'reactive distillation' or for absorption with reaction) necessitating intermediate cooling of the liquid, a tray tower is convenient. A tray can be provided with a cooling coil without much difficulty. Alternatively, the liquid from a tray may be withdrawn, passed through an external cooler and fed to the next tray. However, liquid cooling cannot be done easily and efficiently in a packed tower.

There are a few other factors that affect selection between these two towers. A packed tower can be operated at a low gas rate, but a tray tower is prone to weeping and liquid dumping if the gas flow rate is insufficient. On the other hand, a tray tower with suitable tray design can handle a large liquid rate that a packed tower may not because of possible flooding. A tray tower

---

[†] This kind of joint is frequently used to join cast iron pipes.

can be made to function at a low liquid rate by using a reverse flow tray; a packed tower may not wet properly if the liquid rate is low. The liquid distributors of a packed tower may get clogged at a low liquid turndown. Also there is a greater uncertainty in predicting the performance of a packed tower. The hydrodynamics of two-phase flow in a packed bed is less well-understood. A tray tower can be equipped with multiple nozzles for intermediate feed supply or product withdrawal, but it is difficult to do it in a packed tower because a liquid collection and redistribution device has to be installed within the tower for each such nozzle. However, a packed tower is cheaper. A tray tower has many more internal components (a number of trays, supports, downcomers, weirs, etc.) than those a packed tower (a packing support and one liquid redistributor for about 15 ft of packing). Thus the former entails substantially more fabrication cost. A tray tower smaller than 3 ft in diameter becomes much more expensive to build (since a tray cartridge has to be used), and hence is not preferred.

NOTATIONS

$\bar{a}$	:	specific interfacial area of gas–liquid contact; ft^2/ft^3, m^2/m^3
a_p	:	specific surface area of the packing; ft^2/ft^3, m^2/m^3
A_a	:	active tray area (= cross-section – downcomer area); ft^2, m^2
A_d	:	downcomer area (one side only); ft^2, m^2
A_{da}	:	area for liquid flow below the downcomer apron; ft^2, m^2
A_h	:	total area of the holes on a sieve tray; ft^2, m^2
A_T	:	tray or column cross-section; ft^2, m^2
C_o	:	orifice discharge coefficient
C_s	:	the quantity defined in Eq. (5.21)
C_{SB}	:	Souders–Brown flooding constant, ft/s
d_H	:	sieve tray hole diameter; inch, mm or m
d_p	:	'nominal size' of a packing; inch, mm
f_a	:	fractional hole area, A_d/A_T
f_d	:	fractional downcomer area = $1 - 2A_d/A_T$
f_h	:	fractional hole area, A_h/A_a
F_{lv}	:	packed or tray tower flow parameter
F_p	:	packing shape factor, a_p/ε^3; ft^{-1}, m^{-1}
h_{ad}	:	head loss for liquid flow below the downcomer apron, inch liquid
h_c	:	'clear liquid height' on a tray, inch
h_d	:	dry tray pressure drop, inch liquid
h_{db}	:	downcomer backup, inch liquid
h_l	:	pressure drop for flow of the gas through the aerated liquid, inch liquid

h_{ow} : height of liquid over the weir (in terms of clear liquid), inch

h_t : total tray pressure drop, inch liquid

h_w : weir height, inch

h_σ : liquid head corresponding to surface tension force, Eq (5.19), inch liquid

G, L : gas or liquid flow rate; lb/h, kg/s

G', L' : gas or liquid mass flow rate; lb/ft^2·h, kg/m^2·s

Q_L : liquid flow rate over the weir, gpm per inch weir length

S : tray spacing; inch, m

u_h : gas velocity through the holes; ft/s, m/s

u_s : superficial fluid velocity (based on active tray area for a tray column, cross-section for a packed column (subscript L = liquid, G = gas or vapour); ft/s; m/s

$u_{s,fl}$: superficial flooding velocity of the gas; ft/s, m/s

$(Y)_{fl}$: ordinate of the GPDC flooding curve, Eq. (5.27)

β : aeration factor, Eq. (5.16)

Δ : hydraulic gradient, inch or mm liquid

μ_L : liquid viscosity; cP or kg/m.s

φ_d : relative dispersion density

ρ : density; lb/ft^3, kg/m^3 (subscript L = liquid, G = gas)

σ_L : surface tension; dyne/cm, N/m

MULTIPLE CHOICE QUESTIONS

1. Gas–liquid contacting may be broadly classified into the following three categories:
   (i)   gas dispersed in the liquid
   (ii)   liquid dispersed in the gas
   (iii)   both the gas and the liquid are continuous.

   Indicate the category to which each of the following devices belongs by putting the appropriate serial number within the brackets:
   Packed tower ( ); Tray tower ( ); Spray tower ( ); Falling film absorber ( ); Bubble column ( ); Agitated vessel ( ).

2. Specific interfacial area in a packed column is defined as
   (i)   the effective area of contact between the gas and the liquid per unit bed volume
   (ii)   the actual surface area of the packing per unit volume
   (iii)   the total wetted area of the packing in the bed.

3. The grid packing is suitable for gas absorption if
   (i)   a large liquid rate has to be handled

(ii) the feed gas has a high solute content

(iii) a large gas rate is to be handled at a low pressure drop.

4. Saddle packings offer less pressure drop than Raschig rings because of their
   (i) larger fractional voidage
   (ii) smooth surface finishing
   (iii) aerodynamic shape.

5. Which of the following three types of packing is most efficient?
   (i) Intalox saddle
   (ii) Berl saddle
   (iii) Cross partition ring

6. Which of the following three packings offers the lowest pressure drop?
   (i) Plastic Raschig ring
   (ii) Metal Paul ring
   (iii) Ceramic Intalox saddle

7. Dynamic liquid holdup in a packed tower is defined as
   (i) the volume of the packed section less the true volume of the packing
   (ii) the amount of liquid sticking to the packing and held up in the interstices after the tower operation is stopped
   (iii) the amount of liquid contained in the bed when the tower is in operation.

8. Which of the following sizes of saddles would you recommend for filling a column of 1.5 m diameter?
   (i) ½ inch   (ii) 1 inch   (iii) 3 inch

9. The open area of the packing support should be
   (i) more than 70%
   (ii) not more than 50%
   (iii) at least 90%.

10. Which of the following techniques is effective for reducing entrainment of liquid droplets in the gas leaving a packed bed?
    (i) Placing the liquid distribution points a little below the top of the packing
    (ii) By using large size packings
    (iii) By putting a layer of stacked cross partition rings above the randomly packed bed

11. What is the range of void volume of most structured packings?
    (i) 50–80%   (ii) 70–80%   (iii) 90–98%

12. A 3 ft diameter column should have a packed height of 40 ft. How many liquid redistributors would you recommend?
    (i) None   (ii) 2   (iii) 6

13. Which of the following is an acceptable tray spacing in a 2 m column operating at 10 kg/cm^2 pressure?
    (i) 15 cm   (ii) 0.7 m   (iii) 1 m

14. Which of the following is an acceptable tray spacing in a 2 m column operating at 2 kPa pressure?

    (i) 30 cm   (ii) 0.5 m   (iii) 0.9 m

15. For which of the following reasons it may be necessary to select a split flow for a 3 m diameter column?

    (i)   To increase the tray efficiency
    (ii) To protect against excessive hydraulic gradient
    (iii) To reduce entrainment

16. A sloped downcomer

    (i)   bends towards the column wall in the lower part
    (ii) has a right-angled bend at the bottom
    (iii) bends towards the column wall in its upper part.

17. The clearance below a downcomer for liquid flow is of the order of

    (i) 2 mm   (ii) 15 mm   (iii) 10 cm

18. Under a given set of conditions a tray is estimated to have a hydraulic gradient of 40 mm. It is expected that

    (i)   the tray will operate with a slightly reduced efficiency
    (ii) there will be a large downcomer backup
    (iii) maldistribution of gas and dumping of liquid will occur.

19. The downcomer weir is

    (i)   welded to the tray to get sufficient strength
    (ii) bolted to the tray with provision of adjustment of weir height
    (iii) rivetted to the tray to protect against vibration.

20. A 6 ft dia tray should be levelled to within

    (i) ±0.5 mm   (ii) ±3 mm   (iii) ±10 mm

21. A tray in a moderate size distillation column is

    (i)   made of a few pieces for easy installation and maintenance
    (ii) made of a single piece to get adequate strength
    (iii) always made of three pieces, one central and two downcomer pieces.

22. Which of the following three common trays (a) offers the lowest pressure drop, (b) offers the maximum turndown ratio, (c) enjoys the maxium share of the market?

    (i)   Bubble-cap tray
    (ii) Sieve tray
    (iii) Valve tray

23. Weep holes are provided on a tray for

    (i)   drainage of all the liquid from a tray during shutdown
    (ii) equalization of pressure on the trays
    (iii) drainage of some liquid to reduce hydraulic gradient.

24. The combined area of the inlet and exit downcomer of a tray may be about

    (i) 6%   (ii) 20%   (iii) 50% of the tower cross-section.

25. Trays are fixed to the column
    (i) by flanges
    (ii) by welding to the wall
    (iii) by bolting or clipping to the tray support ring.

26. Liquid residence time in the downcomer remains in the range
    (i) 3–5 s   (ii) 5–15 s   (iii) 20 s–1 min

27. In a tower of 2 m diameter, the area of each downcomer is 0.32 m^2. What is the active tray area?
    (i) 0.62 m^2 (ii) 2.5 m^2 (iii) 3.1 m^2

28. The following data for the gas–liquid dispersion on a tray are given. Tray inlet: average depth of gas–liquid dispersion = 16 cm, holdup fraction of gas = 50%; tray outlet: depth of dispersion = 14.5 cm; holdup fraction = 53%. Density of the liquid = 0.87 gm/cm^3, and of the vapour = 1.6 kg/m^3. What would be the hydraulic gradient on the tray?
    (i) 1.5 cm   (ii) 1.03 cm   (iii) 1.18 cm

29. The turndown ratio of a valve tray is about
    (i) 4   (ii) 2   (iii) 8

30. Maximum entrainment occurs in a column having
    (i) bubble-cap   (ii) sieve   (iii) valve tray.

31. If a tray has a large gas rate but a small liquid rate, which flow regime it is likely to be?
    (i) Spray   (ii) Emulsion   (iii) Froth

32. Which flow regime is more common to commercial columns?
    (i) Froth   (ii) Emulsion   (iii) Spray

33. Which of the following is an acceptable and reasonable velocity in the feed (liquid) nozzle?
    (i) 0.5 ft/s   (ii) 3 ft/s   (iii) 10 ft/s

34. Increasing the fractional hole area of a sieve tray enhances
    (i) the tray pressure drop
    (ii) the hydraulic gradient
    (iii) the weeping tendency.

35. What is an effective strategy of operating an existing sieve tray column at a high turndown ratio (i.e. at a gas or vapour rate less than the minimum operable rate) for a long period?
    (i) Alternate rows of holes may be blocked by blanking strips
    (ii) Increase the weir length
    (iii) Make the downcomer sloped

36. A designer selects a tray column for a separation job. Which of the following types of tray would be suitable if the column diameter is 0.8 m?
    (i) Cascade tray
    (ii) Two-pass tray
    (iii) Tray cartridge

37. For what type of packing, a bed-limiter *must* be used?
    (i)   Metal structured packings
    (ii) Ceramic Intalox saddles
    (iii) Plastic random packings

38. Which of the following problems is very likely to occur if the packings are not thoroughly cleaned before filling a tower?
    (i)   Flooding
    (ii) Channelling of liquid
    (iii) Foaming

39. Murphree efficiency of a sieve tray usually remains in the range
    (i) 20–50%   (ii) 50–90%   (iii) 90–95%

40. The total pressure drop in a distillation column should not exceed 30 mm Hg pressure. Which of the following packings should be the first choice?
    (i)   Plastic CMR
    (ii) IMTP
    (iii) Structured packings

41. A good liquid distributor in a packed bed should have drip points (per ft^2) in the range
    (i) 6–10   (ii) 1–50   (iii) any number.

42. Any local maldistribution of the liquid in a packed bed may be automatically corrected if transverse or lateral dispersion of the liquid occurs. Which of the following random packings has a reasonable lateral dispersion ability?
    (i)   Intalox saddle
    (ii) Paul ring
    (iii) Raschig ring

43. Weir-type liquid distributors are suitable for
    (i)   a tall column
    (ii) a column less than 1 m diameter
    (iii) columns larger than 4 ft diameter.

44. A packed tower should be operated
    (i)   above the loading point
    (ii) near the flooding point
    (iii) sufficiently below the loading point.

45. What is the aspect ratio of a Raschig ring?
    (i) 0.1   (ii) 1.0   (iii) 10.0

46. Dynamic liquid holdup in a packed tower is in the range
    (i) 2–10%   (ii) 5–25%   (iii) 20–40%

47. Liquid holdup on the trays in a tower is about
    (i)   1–4% of tower volume
    (ii) 8–12% of tower volume
    (iii) 20–30% of tower volume.

48. The design gas velocity is usually selected as
   (i) 30–40% of the flooding gas velocity
   (ii) 70–80% of the flooding gas velocity
   (iii) 90–100% of the flooding gas velocity.

49. By retrofitting a sieve tray distillation column by structural packings, the column capacity can be increased by
   (i) 80–90%   (ii) 20–30%   (iii) 5–10%

50. Pressure drop (per ft packing depth) in a randomly packed bed generally ranges from
   (i) 0.05–0.2 inch of water
   (ii) 0.2–0.8 inch of water
   (iii) 1–5 inches of water.

51. A packed bed handles a liquid that causes fouling by deposition in the bed with time. What kind of problem may occur if the bed is not cleaned from time to time?
   (i) Flooding
   (ii) Noise in the bed
   (iii) Degradation of the packing

52. An orifice-type liquid distributor in a packed bed has been installed tilted. Which of the following problems may occur as a result?
   (i) Blockage of gas flow through the bed
   (ii) Flooding of the bed
   (iii) Channelling of the liquid

53. Which of the following will offer the least gas-phase pressure drop per foot (all metal packings, 3 inch nominal size)?
   (i) Stacked Raschig rings
   (ii) Randomly packed Pall rings
   (iii) Randomly packed Raschig rings

54. Which of the following sizes of ceramic intalox saddles is expected to be the cheapest?
   (i) ½ inch   (ii) 2 inches   (iii) 3 inches

55. In some cases, a packed bed is operated in the cocurrent fashion with both gas and liquid flowing downwards (example: flow of oil and hydrogen through a packed bed of catalyst in 'hydrodesulphurization'). All other things remaining the same, how does the dynamic liquid holdup in the two beds compare?
   (i) $[h_{Lo}]_{cocurr} > [h_{Lo}]_{counter}$
   (ii) $[h_{Lo}]_{cocurr} = [h_{Lo}]_{counter}$
   (iii) $[h_{Lo}]_{cocurr} < [h_{Lo}]_{counter}$

56. In which of the following proprietary trays almost all the liquid entering a tray is carried by the vapour as droplets?
   (i) Jaeger *Co-flo* tray
   (ii) *MD* tray
   (iii) Koch-Glitsch *Superfrac* tray

57. In which of the following conditions does the pressure drop across a valve tray remain independent of the gas flow rate?
    (i)   When the valve opening gradually increases
    (ii) Before the valves start opening
    (iii) After the valves are fully open
    What is the explanation?

58. Which of the following packings is now commonly used in a liquid air distillation column?
    (i)   Third generation plastic packings
    (ii) Stacked metal packings
    (iii) Structured packings

59. Which of the following contacting devices is *not preferred* for gas absorption in a foaming liquid?
    (i)   Tray tower
    (ii) Packed tower
    (iii) Spray tower

60. If a calming zone is provided on a tray before the downcomer,
    (i)   the relative froth density in the downcomer increases
    (ii) downcomer flooding is more likely
    (iii) there will be more entrainment.

61. If substantial clogging of the holes of a sieve tray occurs, which of the following is likely to happen?
    (i)   Downcomer flooding
    (ii) Severe entrainment
    (iii) Foaming on the tray

62. Which of the following flow regimes is most likely to occur on a sieve tray if the holes are small?
    (i)   Spray regime
    (ii) Emulsion regime
    (iii) Froth regime

63. What is the maximum allowable fractional entrainment in a tray tower?
    (i) 0.03   (ii) 0.1   (iii) 0.3

64. One morning, an operator hears a noise coming from a sieve tray ethanol distillation column. Which of the following may be the cause?
    (i)   Tray vibration
    (ii) Tray fouling
    (iii) Tray weeping

65. Which of the following contact devices can accommodate the largest gas flow rate for the same column diameter?
    (i)   Spray tower

(ii) Tray tower

(iii) Agitated vessel

66. Which of the following is/are least prone to operational problems if the liquid contains suspended particles?
   (i) Packed tower
   (ii) Venturi scrubber
   (iii) Bubble-cap tray
   (iv) Spray tower

67. Which of the following tower internals is most difficult to clean?
   (i) Valves
   (ii) Random packings
   (iii) Structured packings

68. Which of the following has the largest packing factor?
   (i) 2 inch ceramic Berl saddles
   (ii) 2 inch ceramic intalox saddles
   (iii) 2 inch ceramic Raschig rings

69. For which of the following weir heights of a sieve tray, the spray flow regime is likely to occur? The liquid and gas flow rates are moderate.
   (i) 1 inch   (ii) 2.5 inches   (iii) 4 inches

70. Which of the following is the likely flow regime on a sieve tray if the liquid cross-flow velocity is low and the hole diameter is small?
   (i) Spray regime
   (ii) Emulsion regime
   (iii) Froth regime

71. How does the 'theoretical' packing factor change with increasing nominal size of a packing?
   (i) Decreases
   (ii) Increases
   (iii) Remains unchanged

SHORT QUESTIONS

1. Applying a layer of 'glaze' reduces fouling of the surface of a ceramic ware. Is it advisable to apply glaze to ceramic random packings to keep them clean?

2. How is a tall tower supported? What problems may occur if a tall tray or packed tower has tilted by 5 degrees, say?

3. What kind of arrangement is made for each of the following?
   (i) Entry of a feed which is a mixture of liquid and vapour
   (ii) Withdrawal of a part of the liquid from an intermediate tray

4. Explain how liquid maldistribution in a packed bed affects its performance. Can liquid maldistribution lead to maldistribution of the gas too?

5. What kinds of problems may occur if the liquid drawn by a pump from the bottom of a tower contains gas/vapour bubbles?

6. What are the effects of reducing perforation diameter on the performance and hydraulics of a sieve tray?

7. What is the common range of weir height? How is the column performance affected if the weir height is increased?

8. How are packings spread and levelled in a bed during filling?

9. Explain the fact that the vapour injection support [Figure 5.26(a)] may have more than 100% open area based on the tower cross-section?

10. Explain the terms: (i) revamping, and (ii) retrofitting of a distillation column.

11. It has been reported that other variables remaining the same, the pressure drop per foot decreases with decreasing column diameter. How do you explain it?

12. It is planned to retrofit a bubble column with Sulzer structured packing in order to increase its capacity. What changes need to be made within the column for this purpose?

13. Spraying the liquid on the top of a bed will ensure its uniform distribution. Is there any problem with it?

14. How does a hanging downcomer help to increase the capacity of a column?

15. Give the physical basis of the conditions $du_L/dh_L = 0$ [Eq. (5.28)] mentioned under the channel model.

16. What is 'balancing of liquid flow' on a multipass tray and why is it important? What are the common techniques of balancing?

17. On which part of a tray it is advisable to make weep holes and why?

18. Define/explain the terms: (i) downcomer seal, (ii) downcomer apron, (iii) weeping, (iv) dumping, (v) active tray area, (vi) seal pot, and (vii) downcomer backup.

19. Name a few commercial 'high capacity trays' and their manufacturers.

20. What are the common types of flooding of a tray tower? Explain the mechanism of each.

21. Qualitatively discuss the common models of a packed bed.

22. Why was the flooding line removed from the Strigle's GPDC chart?

23. Give an example each of the three generations of random packings.

24. Is it possible to attribute a physical significance to the flow parameter, F_{lv}, in Eq. (5.20)?

PROBLEMS

5.1 (*Design of a sieve tray*)[3]   Design a sieve tray, *given:* $L = 6000$ gal/h; $G = 30,000$ lb/h; $\rho_L = 56$ lb/ft^3; $\rho_G = 0.15$ lb/ft^3; $\mu_L = 0.3$ cP; and $\sigma_L = 21$ dyne/cm.

5.2 (*Design of a sieve tray*)[3]   Given below are the liquid and vapour flow rates and the properties at the top and at the bottom of a distillation column. Design a sieve tray for the service.

	L(lb/h)	G(lb/h)	M(mol wt)	ρ_L(lb/ft^3)	ρ_G(lb/ft^3)	μ_L(cP)	σ_L(dyne/cm)	T(°C)
Top	5240	9850	33.6	68.7	0.078	0.4	22	100
Bottom	22,220	6500	24.2	68.1	0.061	0.35	21	110

5.3 (*Suitability of an existing sieve tray*)[3]   A sieve tray has to operate with the following flow rates and gas and liquid properties.

	L(kg/h)	G(kg/h)	ρ_L(kg/m^3)	ρ_G(kg/m^3)	μ_L(cP)	σ_L(dyne/cm)
Top	2800	4400	815	2.85	0.35	14
Bottom	8240	3000	720	3.05	0.30	12

A column having sufficient number of sieve trays, 2.5 ft diameter, 12 inch tray spacing and 0.1 ft^2 downcomer area (one side), is available. Will this column be suitable? If not, suggest minor changes to make this column suitable for this service.

5.4 (*Diameter of a packed tower*)[2]   Cyclo-hexane is the starting material for the manufacture of two bulk organic intermediates—caprolactum and adipic acid. It is made by catalytic hydrogenation of benzene followed by separation by distillation. Calculate the diameter of a packed column for separation of a mixture of cyclo-hexane and benzene on the basis of the following data using (i) 1.5 inch ceramic intalox saddles and (ii) #50 IMTP. The column may operate at 70% of flooding velocity.

$L = 8500$ kg/h; $G = 6800$ kg/h; $\rho_L = 710$ kg/m^3; $\rho_G = 0.15$ lb/m^3; $\mu_L = 0.73$ cP; and $\sigma_L = 23$ dyne/cm. Calculate the pressure drop per metre of the bed and the operating liquid holdup in both cases.

5.5 (*Diameter of a packed tower*)[2]   A high pressure packed distillation column for separation of lower hydrocarbons is to handle a liquid load of 378,000 kg/day, a vapour load of 480,000 kg/day. The fluid properties are: $\rho_L = 470$ kg/m^3; $\rho_G = 0.40$ lb/ft^3; $\mu_L = 0.1$ cP; and $\sigma_L = 14$ dyne/cm. Calculate the tower diameter with the following being used as the tower packings: (i) #25 IMTP and (ii) 25 mm metal Pall ring.

5.6 (*Pressure drop for the channel model*)[3]   Following the 'channel model', a packed bed may be considered to consist of a number of cylindrical passages in an otherwise solid bed. While the length of a channel is the same as that of the bed, its diameter should be such that the voidage and the specific surface area should be the same as that of the packing. It is further assumed that the liquid flows at steady state as a laminar film of uniform thickness along the surface of the channels. Without neglecting the shear stress at the liquid surface, obtain expressions for the gas pressure drop and liquid holdup in a 'simulated' bed of length *l*.

5.7 (*Derivation*)[2]   Derive Eqs. (5.4) and (5.19) by appropriate force balances [on the liquid droplets for Eq. (5.4); liquid head and surface tension for Eq. (5.19)].

5.8 (*Suitability of an existing column*)[3]   It is planned to scrub ethanol vapour from the gases leaving a continuous ethanol fermenter by water. The total gas rate is 10 kg/s. It is essentially carbon dioxide containing 0.8 vol% ethanol vapour. A sieve tray column having 6 trays of the following brief specification is available: tower diameter = 2 m; weir length = 1.4 m; weir height = 0.1 m; hole diameter = 5 mm; hole pitch = 14 mm; and plate spacing = 0.6 m. The temperature is 40°C, and the column pressure may be taken to be atmospheric. Will the column operate properly if a water rate of 3.6 kg/s is used? Check for flooding and weeping.

REFERENCES

Ananthanarayanan, N.V., and S. Viswanathan, 'Estimating maximum removal efficiency in venturi scrubbers', *AIChE J.*, *44*(1998) 2549–2560.

Bennett, D.L. et al., 'New correlation for sieve tray point efficiency, entrainment and section efficiency', *AIChE. J.*, *43*(June 1997) 1.

Bennett, D.L., and K.W. Kovak, 'Optimize distillation columns', *Chem. Eng. Prog.*, May 2000, 19–34.

Biddulph, M.W. et al., 'Don't downplay downcomer design', *Chem. Eng. Progr.*, Dec. 1993, 56–60.

Billet, R., *Distillation Engineering*, Chemical Publ. Co., New York, 1979.

Billet, R., *Packed Towers in Processing and Environmental Technology*, VCH, Weinheim, 1995.

Bonilla, J.A., 'Don't neglect liquid distributors', *Chem. Eng., Progr.*, March 1993, 47–61.

Bravo, J.L., 'Select structured packings or trays?' *Chem. Eng. Prog.*, July 1997, 36–40.

Bravo, J.L., 'Column internals', *Chem Eng.*, Feb, 1998, 76–83.

Bravo, J.L., and M.A. Kusters, 'Tray technology for new millennium', *Chem. Eng. Progress*, Dec. 2000, 33–37.

Brekelmans, P.A., 'Analyze a spray column the easy way', *Chem. Eng.*, Feb. 1998, 141–144.

Capps, R.W., 'Consider the ultimate capacity of fractionation trays', *Chem. Eng. Progress*, March 1993, 37–42.

Calverts, S., 'How to choose particulate scrubbers', *Chem Eng.*, August 29, 1977*a*, 54–68.

Calverts, S., 'Get better performance from particulate scrubbers', *Chem Eng.*, Oct. 24, 1977*b*, 133–148

Chase, J.D., 'Sieve tray design', Parts 1 and 2, *Chem. Eng.*, July 31, 105–116; Aug. 28, 139–146, 1967.

Chen, G.K., 'Packed column internals', *Chem. Eng.*, March 5, 1984, 40–57.

Chopey, N., 'Distillation internal matters', *Chem. Eng.*, Nov. 1997, 34–36.

Crawford, M., *Air Pollution Control Theory*, McGraw-Hill, New York, 1976.

Eckert, J.S., 'Selecting the proper distillation column packing', *Chem. Eng. Progr.*, March 1970, 39–49.

Eckert, J.S., 'How tower packings behave?', *Chem. Eng.*, April 14, 1975, 70–76.

Engel, V. et al., 'A new model to predict liquid holdup in packed columns', *I. Ch. E. Symp. Ser.*, *142*(1997) 939–947.

Fadel, T.A., 'Selecting packed column auxiliaries', *Chem. Eng.*, January 23, 1984, 71–76.

Fair, J.R., 'How to predict sieve tray entrainment and flooding?', *Petro/Chem. Eng.*, *33*(10, 1961) 45–52.

Fair, J.R., and J.L. Bravo, 'Distillation columns containing structured packing', *Chem. Eng. Progr.*, Jan. 1990, 19–29.

Gadalia, M. et al., 'Increase capacity and decrease energy for existing refinery distillation columns', *Chem. Eng. Progr.*, April 2003, 44–50.

Helling, R.H., and M.A. DesJardin, 'Get the best performance from structured packing', *Chem. Eng. Progr.*, Oct. 1994, 62–66.

Killat, G.R., and T.D. Rey, 'Properly assess maldistribution in packed towers', *Chem. Eng. Progr.*, May 1996, 69–73.

Kister, H.Z., *Distillation Operation*, McGraw-Hill Book Co., New York, 1989.

Kister, H.Z., and I.R. Haas, *Chem. Eng. Progr.*, Sept. 1990, 63.

Kister, H.Z., and R.D. Gill, 'Predict flood point and pressure drop for modern random packings', *Chem. Eng. Progr.*, Feb. 1991, 32–42.

Kister, H.Z., *Distillation Design*, McGraw-Hill Book Co., New York, 1992.

Kister, H.Z., et al., 'How do trays and packings stack up?', *Chem. Eng. Progr.*, Feb. 1994, 23–32.

Klein, G.F., 'Simplified model calculates valve-tray pressure drop', *Chem. Eng.*, May 3, 1982, 81–85.

Klemas, L., and J.A. Bonilla, 'Accurately assess packed column efficiency', *Chem. Eng. Progr.*, July 1995, 27–44

Larson, K.F., and H.Z. Kister, 'Distillation Tray Design' in *Handbook of Separation Techniques for Chemical Engineers*, 3rd ed., P.A. Schweitzer (Ed.), McGraw-Hill, New York, 1997.

Leva, M., 'Flow through irrigated dumped packings—pressure drop, loading and flooding', *CEP Symp. Ser.*, *50*(1954) 51.

Lockett, M.J., *Distillation Tray Fundamentals*, Cambridge University Press, U.K., 1986.

Ludwig, E., *Applied Process Design for Chemical and Petrochemical Plants*, 3rd ed., Gulf Publ. Houston, 1997.

Moss, D., *Pressure Vessel Design Manual*, 3rd ed., Elsevier, 2004.

Olujic, Z. et al., 'Stretching the capacity of structured packings', *Ind. Eng. Chem. Res.*, *40*(2001) 6172–6180.

Parkinson, G., and G. Ondrey, 'Packing towers', *Chem Engg.*, Dec. 1999, 39–43.

Paul, E.L. et al., *Handbook of Industrial Mixing*, Wiley Interscience, 2004.

Pedersen, G.C., and P.K. Bhattacharjee, 'Scrubbers with a level head', *Chem. Eng.*, Nov. 1997, 130–134.

Perry, D., D.E. Nutter, and A. Hale, 'Liquid distribution for optimum packing performance', *Chem. Eng. Progr.*, Jan. 1990, 30–35.

Piche, S. et al., 'Flooding capacity in packed towers — database, correlations and analysis', *Ind. Eng. Chem. Res.*, *40*(2001) 476–487.

Pilling, M., 'Ensure proper design and operation of multi-pass trays', *Chem Eng. Prog.*, July 2005, 22–27.

Porter, K.E., 'Developments in distillation and separation technology', *A.I.Ch.E. J.*, *47*(May 2001) 1060–1066.

Rocha, J.A. et al., 'Distillation columns containing structured packings', *Ind. Eng. Chem. Res.*, *32*(1993) 641.

Robbins, L.A., 'Improve pressure drop prediction with a new correlation', *Chem. Eng. Progr.*, May 1991, 87–91.

Sands, R.R., 'Distillation: how to specify and install cartridge trays', *Chem. Engg.*, April 2006, 82–92.

Schmidt, R., 'The lower capacity limits of packed columns', *I. Ch. E. Symp. Ser.*, *56*(1979, V.2) 1–14.

Sherwood, T.K. et al., Flooding velocities in packed columns, *Ind. Eng. Chem.*, *30*(1938) 765–769.

Shiveler, G.H., 'Use heavy duty trays for severe services', *Chem. Eng. Progr.*, Aug. 1995, 72–81.

Silvey, F.C., and G.J. Keller, 'Testing on a commercial scale', *Chem. Eng. Progr.*, Jan. 1966, 68.

Sloley, A.W., 'Should you switch to high capacity trays?', *Chem. Eng. Progr.*, Jan. 1999, 23–35.

Souders, M., and G.G. Brown, 'Design of fractionating columns', *Ind. Eng. Chem.*, *26*(1934) 98.

Stankiewicz, A.I., and J.A. Moulijn, 'Process intensification—transforming chemical engineering', *Chem. Eng. Progr.*, Jan. 2000, 22–34.

Stichlmair, J.G., and J.R. Fair, *Distillation—Principles and Practice*, Wiley-VCH, New York, 1998.

Strigle, R.F., Jr., *Packed Tower Design and Applications*, 2nd ed., Gulf Publ. Co, Houston, 1994.

Tsouris, C., and J.V. Porcelli, 'Process intensification—has its time finally come?', *Chem. Eng. Progr.*, Oct. 2003, 50–55.

Winter, J.R., 'Avoid vibration damage to distillation trays', *Chem Eng. Prog.*, May 1993, 42–47.

Yanagi, T., 'Inside a trayed distillation column', *Chem. Eng.*, Nov. 1990, 120–129.

Yaws, C.L., *Chemical Properties Handbook*, McGraw-Hill, New York, 1999.

Zenz, F.A., 'Designing gas absorption towers', in Schweitzer, P.A., see under Larsen and Kister.

6 | Gas Absorption and Stripping

Gas absorption is a mass transfer operation in which one or more species (*solute*) is removed from a gaseous stream by dissolution in a liquid (*solvent*). The insoluble component(s) present in the gas which is not absorbed is called the *carrier gas*. For example, in the process of removal of H_2S from natural gas using a suitable solvent such as an aqueous solution of an alkanolamine, H_2S is the solute, natural gas is the carrier and aqueous alkanolamine is the solvent. An intimate contact between the gas and the liquid is achieved in a suitable equipment or device like a packed column, tray tower, spray tower, venturi scrubber, etc. The construction and operation of such equipment have been described in Chapter 5. Here we will discuss the basic principles of gas absorption and stripping and deal with the calculations for sizing and design of devices for gas absorption or stripping.

Gas absorption is an integral part of many chemical processes. Examples are numerous. Table 6.1 cites a few of them. Many industrial gas absorption and purification processes are described by Kohl and Nielsen (1997) and Strigle (1994)[†]. It is interesting to note that the phenomenon of gas absorption is not confined to the realm of the process industries only. Absorption of oxygen from air in the vast expanse of water on the surface of earth keeps the aquatic creatures alive. When we breathe, oxygen from air is absorbed in the blood. This is again a case of gas absorption. In many situations, the absorbed gas also undergoes a chemical reaction in the liquid phase. For example, in the case of *sweetening* of natural gas cited above, the solvent (alkanolamine) is chemically reactive to the absorbed H_2S. The rate of absorption of a gas is substantially enhanced if it is consumed by a chemical reaction in the liquid phase. The process is sometimes called 'chemical absorption' as distinguished from 'physical absorption'. The latter does not involve any chemical reaction.

The reverse of absorption is called 'desorption' or 'stripping'. This is nearly as important as absorption. Very often the loaded solvent (i.e. the solvent, with the solute dissolved in it, leaving the bottom of an absorber) is subjected to desorption. By desorption, we recover the dissolved gas from a solution for further use and to regenerate the solvent. The regenerated solvent is

---

[†] Both these books deal with real-life gas absorption systems. While Kohl and Nielsen give an exhaustive account of absorption processes, Strigle offers useful information and tips on process design.

Table 6.1 Examples of industrial gas absorption processes

Example	Industry/Purpose	Solvent
1. Absorption of SO_3	Production of sulphuric acid and oleum	98% H_2SO_4/Concentrated H_2SO_4
2. Absorption of H_2S	Treatment of sour natural gas	Mono- or diethanol amine
3. Drying of a gas	Air for sulphur burning	Concentrated H_2SO_4
	Drying of natural gas	Di- and tri-ethylene glycol
4. Absorption of ammonia	Ammoniation of brine in a soda ash plant	Brine
	Ammonia removal/recovery from the coke oven gas	Water or dilute H_2SO_4
5. Absorption of SO_2 from flue gases	Pollution abatement	Lime slurry
6. Absorption of NO_2	Nitric acid manufacture	Water
7. Absorption of acrylonitrile	Manufacture of acrylonitrile by ammoxidation of propylene	Water
8. Absorption of oxygen from air	Aerobic bioreactor	Fermentation broth, Waste water
9. Absorption of ethylene oxide	Ethylene oxide manufacture	Water
10. Absorption of HF	Pollution control in phosphoric acid and phosphatic fertilizer plants	Water, dilute alkali
11. Absorption of HCl gas	Hydrochloric acid production	Water
12. Absorption of CO_2	CO_2 removal from the synthesis gas in an ammonia plant	Aqueous alkanolamines, Sodium carbonate-bicarbonate buffer solution with a dissolved catalyst
13. Absorption of light hydrocarbons	Refineries	Absorption oil
14. Absorption of formaldehyde and methanol	Production of formaldehyde by air-oxidation of methanol	Water
15. Absorption of aromatics (benzene, naphthalene, etc.)	Recovery of the substances from raw coal gas	Absorption oil

recycled to the absorber. This point may be illustrated by a practical example. Absorption of carbon dioxide is an important operation in the production of synthesis gas in an ammonia plant (see Ullmann, 1985). An aqueous solution of an alkanolamine (methanolamine, ethanolamine, etc.) is commonly used. The CO_2-loaded amine solution leaving the absorption column is stripped of the dissolved CO_2 by using open steam in a 'stripping column'. The recovered CO_2 is sent to the urea plant. The regenerated or lean solvent (which may have traces of the solute, CO_2, left in it) is cooled in a heat exchanger and pumped to the amine storage tank for recycling. The arrangement is schematically shown in Figure 6.1.

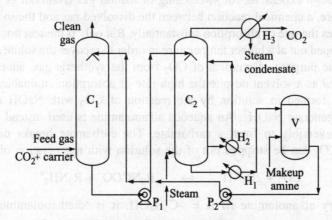

Figure 6.1 Schematic of a carbon dioxide absorption and solvent regeneration system; C_1: absorption column; C_2: regeneration column; P_1, P_2: pumps; H_1: cooler for the regenerated solvent; H_2: reboiler; H_3: condenser for steam from column C_2; V: amine storage vessel.

6.1 EQUILIBRIUM IN A GAS–LIQUID SYSTEM

A knowledge of the equilibrium distribution of a solute between two phases, i.e. the solubility of a species in a solvent, is very important in determining the driving force in any mass transfer operation. For an 'ideal' gas–liquid or vapour–liquid system, the solubility is given by Raoult's law; Henry's law is often applicable at low solute concentrations for a 'real' gas–liquid system. These laws have already been discussed in Section 4.2. The techniques of equilibrium calculation for a non-ideal solution will be discussed later.

The solubility of a gas in a liquid decreases with temperature almost as a rule. Absorption of a gas is done at a rather lower temperature so that there is a larger driving force for transfer of the solute from the gas phase to the solvent. Desorption or stripping, on the other hand, is carried out at an elevated temperature so that the direction of the driving force is reversed.

6.2 SELECTION OF SOLVENT AND STRIPPING MEDIUM

A brief but good account of the general criteria for the selection of a solvent for absorption is available in Treybal (1980). The more important criteria and considerations are described here.

(i) *Solubility:*   The right solvent is one in which the species to be absorbed (i.e. the solute) is highly soluble, but it should not dissolve the carrier gas. Sometimes there may be more than one solute of similar chemical nature, but it may be desirable to remove only one of them. In such a case, a solvent which is 'selective' for the particular solute is preferred. For example, natural gas contains both CO_2 and H_2S as undesirable constituents. While CO_2 need not be removed when the gas is used for certain purposes, H_2S has to be. A common solvent like aqueous ethanolamine absorbs both CO_2 and H_2S. But a solution of an *hindered* amine (for example, N-methyl diethanolamine) preferentially absorbs H_2S; only a little of CO_2 is absorbed. So it is the right solvent, although expensive, for sweetening of natural gas (Haimour et al., 1983).

As stated before, a chemical reaction between the dissolved gas and the solvent or a reagent added to it increases the rate of absorption substantially. But only if the reaction is reversible, the solute may be stripped out at a higher temperature in order to recover the solute and to regenerate the solvent. For the purpose of removal of CO_2 from the synthesis gas, aqueous caustic soda (NaOH) is *not used* as a solvent despite the high rate of absorption attainable. This is because Na_2CO_3 which is formed in solution by the reaction of CO_2 with NaOH cannot be easily decomposed to regenerate NaOH[†]. An aqueous alkanolamine is used instead since CO_2 reacts with the amine reversibly to form a carbamate. The carbamate breaks down at a higher temperature and CO_2 can be stripped out of the solution with regeneration of the solvent.

$$CO_2 + 2R_2NH \quad \leftrightarrow \quad R_2NCOO^- + R_2NH_2^+$$

R_2NH = secondary alkanolamine (if $R = -C_2H_4OH$, it is 'diethanolamine'); R_2NCOO^- = carbamate.

(ii) *Volatility:*   A good solvent should have a low volatility or vapour pressure so that the solvent loss with the carrier gas because of vaporization remains small. A higher rate of solvent loss can cause air pollution in the nearby area, besides financial loss.

(iii) *Viscosity:*   A solvent should have a low viscosity so that it flows easily. A viscous solvent used in a mechanically agitated absorber requires greater power consumption. In a packed tower, a viscous solvent causes flooding at lower liquid and gas flow rates.

(iv) *Corrosiveness:*   Use of a non-corrosive or less corrosive solvent reduces the material cost of the equipment as well as its maintenance cost.

(v) *Cost:*   A solvent should not be very expensive so that vaporization and other losses are not significant in terms of economy.

(vi) *Hazard and toxicity:*   A solvent should not be hazardous or toxic. It should preferably be non-inflammable.

[†] On the other hand, an aqueous K_2CO_3–$KHCO_3$ buffer solution with a dissolved arsenite catalyst (Benfield process) is a common solvent for CO_2 ($KHCO_3$ is preferred to $NaHCO_3$ since the former has a higher solubility and a concentrated solution can be used for the absorption). At a lower temperature, CO_2 reacts with $CO_3^=$ to form HCO_3^-. At an elevated temperature, HCO_3^- decomposes to release CO_2 when $CO_3^=$ is regenerated.

The preceding criteria are general and by no means exclusive or stringent. While selecting a solvent, one has to strike a balance between the properties and efficacy of the solvent on the one hand and its cost and convenience of use on the other.

For 'desorption' or 'stripping' of a solute from the loaded solvent, a carrier gas, which is the stripping medium, has to be brought in contact with the solution. Steam is a common stripping medium. Use of steam is very convenient because the stripped solute can be easily recovered by condensing the steam leaving the stripping tower. If the solute is not soluble in water (as in the case of stripping of a hydrocarbon from an absorption oil), it can be separated from the condensate by decantation. On the other hand, if the solute is soluble in water, it can be recovered from the condensate by distillation. An inert gas like N_2 is also sometimes used as a carrier for stripping.

6.3 MINIMUM LIQUID RATE FOR ABSORPTION

Refer to Figure 4.7 in relation to gas absorption. Let G refer to the gas and L to the liquid. These symbols also represent the local gas and the liquid flow rates respectively in the column; G_s and L_s are the constant rates of flow of the two streams on *solute-free* basis (i.e. G_s and L_s are the flow rates of the 'carrier' phases). In gas absorption calculations, the flow rate of the feed gas G_1, and its concentration y_1 are generally specified in a design problem. The exit gas concentration y_2 is also specified in many cases; y_2 indicates the extent of separation of the solute from the feed gas. A suitable solvent for absorption has to be selected and the equilibrium data at the chosen operating conditions (temperature and pressure) have to be obtained from the literature or from any other source.

Now the question is how to determine the required solvent flow rate for a given absorption problem. Recall the overall material balance equation (4.27) which is renumbered below.

$$G_s(Y_1 - Y_2) = L_s(X_1 - X_2) \qquad (6.1)^\dagger$$

If the concentration of the solute in the exit gas (Y_2, in mole ratio unit) and that in the solvent (X_2) supplied at the top of the column are known, there still remain two unknown quantities — L_s and X_1. If one of these quantities (say L_s) is fixed, the other (X_1) can be calculated from the material balance equation given above (and vice versa). The operating line can then be drawn by locating and joining the terminal points (X_1, Y_1) and (X_2, Y_2) on the X–Y plane. The slope of the operating line is L_s/G_s. Two types of equilibrium lines and a set of operating lines of different slopes are shown in Figures 6.2(a) and 6.2(b). If L_s is reduced (i.e. a lower liquid rate is used), the slope decreases and the operating line (PQ), having one fixed terminal at the point (X_2, Y_2), comes closer to the equilibrium line [see Figure 6.2(a)]. The driving force will decrease as a result, and a larger height of packing, or a larger number of plates (if a tray tower is used), has to be provided to achieve the desired degree of separation. But we cannot keep on reducing the liquid flow rate indefinitely. As the liquid rate is gradually reduced, the orientation of the operating

---

† The concentration of the solute in the solvent entering at the top is X_2 (or x_2 in the mole fraction unit). If the solvent is 'fresh', it does not contain any solute, i.e. $X_2 = 0$. However, very often the solvent is regenerated by stripping the rich solution from the absorber (see Figure 6.1) and is recycled back to the absorption tower. Traces of the solute may be left in the regenerated solvent. In such a case, $X_2 \neq 0$.

line will change and eventually a situation will arise when the operating line meets the equilibrium line at a certain point. The driving force at this point is zero. The corresponding liquid rate is the theoretical 'minimum liquid rate'. On further reduction of the liquid rate beyond the minimum, the operating line crosses the equilibrium line which means that absorption of the gas occurs in one section of the column and desorption in the other [see the line PQ''' in Figure 6.2(b)]. This is physically impossible. So a column cannot operate, even theoretically, at a liquid rate less than the minimum as defined above.

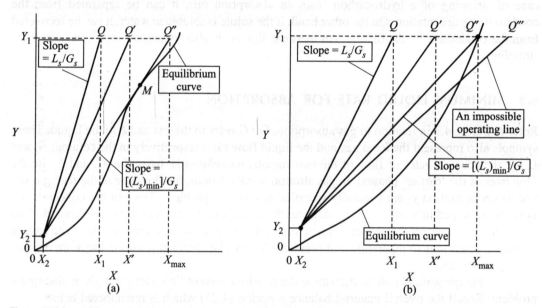

Figure 6.2(a) and (b)   (a) Graphical determination of the minimum liquid rate for gas absorption (the equilibrium line is convex upwards), and (b) graphical construction for the minimum liquid rate for gas absorption (the equilibrium line is convex downwards).

The determination of the minimum liquid rate is illustrated in Figures 6.2(a) and 6.2(b) for absorption and in Figure 6.3 for stripping. In Figure 6.2(a), the equilibrium line is convex upwards around the feed gas concentration of Y_1. The concentration pair (X, Y) at the tower bottom (for absorption) must lie on the horizontal line through Y_1, which is the given concentration of the feed gas. As the liquid rate is decreased, the operating line changes from PQ to PQ' to PQ'' with decreasing slope. The line PQ'' is tangent to the equilibrium curve [Figure 6.2(a)] and M is the point of tangency. So

$$\text{Slope of the line } PQ'' = \frac{(L_s)_{\min}}{G_s} \qquad (6.2)$$

Since G_s (the flow rate of the carrier gas) is known, $(L_s)_{\min}$ can be calculated from the slope of the line PQ''. The corresponding concentration of the exit liquid is $X_{\max}$, which is the maximum possible concentration of the liquid. The driving force is zero at the point M (i.e., the point of tangency for the particular shape of the equilibrium line) which is called the *pinch point*.

The graphical construction is shown in Figure 6.2(b) for a system having an equilibrium curve which is convex downwards. In this case it is not possible to draw an operating line that will pass through (X_2, Y_2) and touch the equilibrium line for $Y_1 > Y > Y_2$. So the minimum liquid rate is determined from the slope of the line PQ'', Q'' being the point where the horizontal line through Y_1 meets the equilibrium curve. The driving force is zero at the point Q'' which is the *pinch point* in this case. If the liquid rate is reduced still further, we get an 'operating line' like PQ''' which crosses the equilibrium curve. This is physically impossible; a line like PQ''' cannot be an operating line. So PQ'' is the operating line for the theoretical minimum liquid rate.

What result do we expect if we want to find out the number of ideal plates required for the desired separation using the minimum liquid rate? In order to address this question, we redraw the equilibrium line and the operating line PQ'' for the minimum liquid in Figure 6.2(c). To find out the number of 'ideal stages', we may construct steps between the equilib-

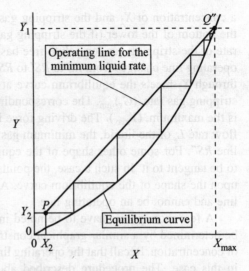

Figure 6.2(c) An infinite number of plates are required if the minimum liquid rate is used.

rium line and the operating line starting from either end. Let us start at the end P. As we approach Q'' (which is the pinch point), the driving force tends to zero and it becomes impossible to reach the point Q'' by drawing a finite number of steps. Theoretically speaking, it will need an *infinite number of plates* (or an infinite height of packing, if a packed tower is used) to achieve the desired separation using the minimum liquid rate.

In the case of stripping of a solute from a solution, the feed liquid concentration X_2 is known. So Y_2 will lie on the vertical line through X_2 (Figure 6.3). The lean liquid leaves the column at

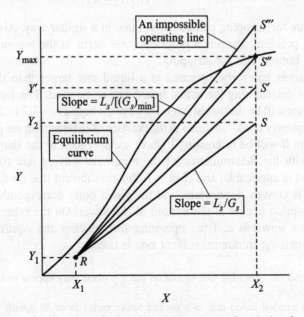

Figure 6.3 Graphical determination of the minimum gas rate for stripping of a solute.

a concentration of X_1 and the stripping gas concentration is Y_1. The point $R(X_1, Y_1)$ represents the bottom of the tower (if the stripping gas is free from the solute, $Y_1 = 0$). Let G_s be the flow rate of the stripping gas (on solute-free basis). If we keep on reducing G_s, the orientation of the operating line changes from RS to RS' to RS'' with a gradually increasing slope. The vertical line through X_2 meets the equilibrium curve at S'', and RS'' is the operating line for the minimum stripping gas rate, $(G_s)_{min}$. The corresponding solute concentration in the stripping gas at the exit is the maximum, (Y_{max}). The driving force is zero at S''; it is the 'pinch point'. From the known flow rate L_s of the liquid, the minimum gas rate, $(G_s)_{min}$, can be found out from the slope of the line RS''. For some other shape of the equilibrium curve, it could be possible for the line RS'' to be tangent to it. In such a case, the point of tangency would be the pinch point. It all depends upon the shape of the equilibrium curve. A line like RS''' in Figure 6.3 crosses the equilibrium line and cannot be an operating line.

A few more points have to be noted in this connection. The minimum liquid rate can also be determined by a similar graphical construction on the x–y plane using the mole fraction unit of concentration. Recall that the operating line will no longer be a straight line (see Section 4.5.1)[†] in this case. The procedure described above can be followed in principle to determine the minimum liquid rate for absorption (or the minimum gas rate for stripping). But we will have to deal with two curves in order to determine the point of tangency or the pinch point. This poses a practical difficulty. So, as a matter of convenience and practice, the minimum liquid rate is determined by graphical construction on the X–Y plane as illustrated in Example 6.1.

If the equilibrium relation, expressed in terms of mole ratio unit, is linear ($Y = \alpha X$), the minimum liquid rate can be determined algebraically by calculating $X_{max} = Y_1/\alpha$ and substituting it in the material balance Eq. (6.1). In this case, the coordinate of the pinch point is $(Y_1/\alpha, Y_1)$, and

$$[L_s]_{min} = G_s \frac{Y_1 - Y_2}{(Y_1/\alpha) - X_2} \tag{6.3}$$

The minimum gas rate for stripping can be determined in a similar way. Also, it has to be noted that in any practical problem, the pinch point *does not* occur at the top end of the column for absorption or at the bottom end for stripping.

An absorption tower has to be operated at a liquid rate larger than the minimum. There is no general rule for determining the actual liquid rate to be used. The factors that govern the choice of the liquid rate will be discussed later. However, a liquid rate 1.2 to 2 times the minimum (Branan, 1998) is frequently used[††]. Similar is the practice of determining the gas rate for stripping.

In this connection it will be interesting to have a closer look at the shape of an equilibrium line in connection with the determination of the minimum solvent rate for gas absorption. If Henry's law ($y = mx$) is applicable, and if $m > 1$, the equilibrium line on the X–Y plane (i.e. in the mole ratio unit) is convex downwards and the pinch point corresponding to the minimum solvent rate for absorption occurs at the bottom of the tower. On the other hand, if $m < 1$, the X–Y^* curve is convex upwards and the operating line touches the equilibrium line at some intermediate point when the minimum solvent rate is used.

[†] The equilibrium line and the operating line drawn on the x-y plane may appear to be straight lines at low concentrations of the solute.

[††] The maximum recommended liquid rate in a packed tower varies from 40 gpm/ft^2 for 1-inch packing to 125 gpm/ft^2 for 3½-inch packing (Strigle, 1994).

EXAMPLE 6.1 (*Calculation of the minimum solvent rate*) In a petrochemical plant, a gas containing 4% *cyclo*-hexane and 96% inerts has to be treated with a non-volatile absorption oil in a packed tower. It is required to remove 98% of the *cyclo*-hexane of the feed gas. The feed solvent is free from *cyclo*-hexane. If the feed gas rate is 80 kmol per hour, calculate the minimum solvent rate. The equilibrium relation is given as

$$Y = \frac{0.2 X}{1 + 0.8 X}$$

Solution

The following equilibrium data are calculated from the given equilibrium relation.

X	0	0.01	0.03	0.05	0.07	0.09	0.12
Y	0	0.00198	0.00586	0.0097	0.0113	0.0168	0.0219

Given: feed gas rate = 80 kmol/h; concentration of *cyclo*-hexane, $y_1 = 0.04$ (mole fraction).

Rate of input of the solute (*cyclo*-hexane) = $(80)(0.04) = 3.2$ kmol/h; carrier gas in, $G_s = 80 - 3.2 = 76.8$ kmol/h; 98% of the solute is absorbed, and 2% leaves the tower with the carrier gas.

$$Y_1 = \frac{y_1}{1 - y_1} = \frac{0.04}{1 - 0.04} = 0.0417$$

$$Y_2 = (0.02)Y_1 = 0.000834$$

Also $X_2 = 0$ (the feed solvent is solute-free). $(X_2, Y_2) \to (0, 0.000834)$

(i) Plot the equilibrium data calculated above on the X–Y plane; (ii) locate the point $Q(X_2, Y_2)$; (iii) draw the operating line through (X_2, Y_2) that touches the equilibrium line. The point of tangency P is the *pinch point*. This operating line QP corresponds to the *minimum liquid rate*; its slope is $(L_s/G_s)_{min} = 0.19$. The graphical construction is shown in Figure 6.4.

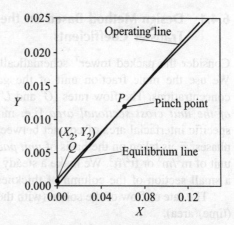

Given: $G_s = 76.8$ kmol/h; therefore, the minimum liquid rate, $(L_s)_{min} = (76.8)(0.19) = \boxed{14.6 \text{ kmol/h}}$

Figure 6.4 Determination of the minimum liquid rate.

(The slope of QP may be obtained from the coordinates of the points P and Q as well.)

6.4 DESIGN OF A PACKED TOWER

The constructional features of a packed column have already been described in the previous chapter. The packed tower and the plate tower are the two common choices for carrying out a gas absorption operation (there are other options like the venturi scrubber, the spray column, the agitated contactor, etc.). In a plate column, the gas and the liquid phases come in contact on discrete stages. So it is called 'stage-wise contact'; and the gas and liquid concentrations undergo step changes from one plate to the next. In a packed tower, on the other hand, the liquid flowing down through the packing remains in contact with the up-flowing gas at every point of the packed section. Also, the concentration of both phases change continuously. So, a packed column is called a 'continuous differential contact equipment'.

Sizing of a packed column basically includes the following steps: (i) selection of the solvent; (ii) selection of packing; (iii) determination of the minimum and the actual solvent rate; (iv) determination of the column diameter; (v) determination of the packed height; and (vi) design of the liquid distributor and redistributor (if necessary), packing support and the gas distributor, design of shell, nozzles, column support, etc. (including selection of the materials to be used for the tower internals and to build the tower).

The first four steps have already been discussed. In this section, we shall concentrate upon the determination of the height of packing required for a particular separation. The discussion will be confined to the case of transfer of a single solute. Separation of multicomponent mixtures will be treated later. The following items and variables should be known or available for design purpose:

(a) Equilibrium data
(b) Flow rates and terminal concentrations of the gas and liquid phases
(c) Individual or overall volumetric mass transfer coefficients, sometimes called 'capacity coefficients' ($k_y \bar{a}$, $k_x \bar{a}$, $K_G \bar{a}$, $K_L \bar{a}$, $K_y \bar{a}$, etc.).

6.4.1 Design Method Based on the Individual Mass Transfer Coefficients

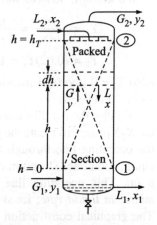

Figure 6.5 Differential section of a packed column for mass balance.

Consider the packed tower[†] schematically shown in Figure 6.5. We use the mole fraction unit of the gas and the liquid-phase concentrations. The flow rates (G' and L') are taken on the basis *of the unit cross-sectional area* [i.e. mol/(time)(area)] and the specific interfacial area of contact between the gas and the liquid phases, $\bar{a}$, is taken on the basis of *unit packed volume* and has the unit of m^2/m^3 or ft^2/ft^3. We make a steady state mass balance over a small section of the column of thickness dh.

The rate of flow of the solute (with the carrier gas) = $G'y$ mol/ (time)(area).

The change in the solute flow rate over the section = $d(G'y)$; this is intrinsically negative in the case of absorption.

Let N_A be the local flux and k_y be the individual gas-phase mass transfer coefficient. Then, the packed volume in the differential section for unit cross-sectional area of the bed = $(1)(dh)$

$$\text{Interfacial area of contact in the differential section} = (\bar{a})(1)(dh)$$
$$\text{Rate of mass transfer of the solute} = (\bar{a})(dh)(N_A)$$

A mass balance over the elementary section of the bed yields

$$(\bar{a})(dh)(N_A) = -d(G'y) = -G'dy - ydG' \tag{6.4}$$

Since the carrier gas is not soluble, the change in the total gas flow rate is also equal to the rate of mass transfer of the solute, i.e.

$$-dG' = (\bar{a})(dh)(N_A) \tag{6.5}$$

[†] As stated in Chapter 4, the bottom of the continuous contact tower is location '1', and the top, location '2'. The flow rates and concentrations bear the corresponding subscripts.

Substituting Eq. (6.5) in Eq. (6.4), rearranging and putting $N_A = k_y(y - y_i)$,

$$(\bar{a})(dh)N_A(1 - y) = -G'dy \tag{6.6}$$

$$\Rightarrow \qquad dh = \frac{-G'\,dy}{k_y\bar{a}(1 - y)(y - y_i)} \tag{6.7}$$

Integrating within the appropriate limits, we get

$$h_T = \int_0^{h_T} dh = -\int_{y_1}^{y_2} \frac{G'dy}{k_y\bar{a}(1 - y)(y - y_i)} = \int_{y_2}^{y_1} \frac{G'dy}{k_y\bar{a}(1 - y)(y - y_i)} \tag{6.8}$$

Evaluation of the above integral gives the height of the packing. The integration is not straightforward, since the interfacial concentration y_i is not explicitly known as a function of the variable y. The following steps should be followed in general (McNulty, 1994):

(a) Draw the equilibrium curve on the x-y plane for the particular gas–liquid system.

(b) Draw the operating line from the material balance equation, see Eq. (4.26).

$$G_s\left(\frac{y}{1 - y} - \frac{y_2}{1 - y_2}\right) = L_s\left(\frac{x}{1 - x} - \frac{x_2}{1 - x_2}\right); \qquad Y = \frac{y}{1 + y}, \; X = \frac{x}{1 - x} \tag{6.9}$$

If the liquid mass flow rate (i.e. the rate of flow per unit cross-sectional area) is given, L_s is known. Otherwise, the minimum liquid rate on solute-free basis $(L_s)_{min}$ is to be determined following the procedure detailed in Section 6.4. The actual liquid rate L_s is taken as a suitable multiple (commonly 1.2 to 2 times) of the minimum rate. The outlet liquid concentration x_1 is obtained from the overall material balance, Eq. (6.1).

(c) Take any point (x, y) on the operating line (see Figure 6.6). Using the known values of k_x and k_y (or $k_x\bar{a}$ and $k_y\bar{a}$), draw a line of slope $-k_x/k_y$ from the point $S(x, y)$ to meet the equilibrium curve at $R(x_i, y_i)$ (recall Section 4.3.3). So y_i is known for the particular value of y. The line SR is called a 'tie line'.

(d) Repeat step (c) for a number of other points on the operating line. If k_x and k_y or their ratio are constant, a set of lines parallel to the one drawn in step (c) may be constructed. [Note that very often the mass transfer coefficients combined with the specific interfacial area (i.e. $k_x\bar{a}$ and $k_y\bar{a}$), rather than k_x and k_y, are given or known.] Now we have a set of (y, y_i) pair for $y_2 \leq y \leq y_1$.

(e) Calculate $G = G_s(1 + y)$ at each point. Note that G_s can be calculated from the given feed gas flow rate[†].

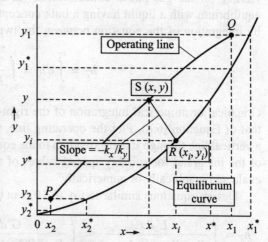

Figure 6.6 Concentration terms in the equations for packed tower design illustrated.

[†] Either the total flow rates (G, L, or G_s, L_s) or the mass flow rates (G', L') can be used to draw the operating line. However, for the calculation of the packed height, the mass flow rates (G', L') are used.

(f) Calculate the value of the integrand for a set of suitably spaced values of y. Evaluate the integral in Eq. (6.8) graphically or numerically. This procedure is illustrated in Example 6.2.

The height of the packing can also be determined using other types of individual mass transfer coefficients (k_x, k_G, k_L, K_y, K_x, etc.). The design equations given below can be derived following the above procedure.

$$h_T = \int_{x_2}^{x_1} \frac{L' dx}{k_x \bar{a}(1-x)(x_i - x)} = \int_{y_2}^{y_1} \frac{G' dy}{k_G \bar{a} P(1-y)(y-y_i)} = \int_{x_2}^{x_1} \frac{L' dx}{k_L \bar{a}(C)_{\text{av}}(1-x)(x_i - x)} \quad (6.10)$$

The height of the packing for a *stripping column* can be obtained in a similar way. But here $y_2 > y_1$ and the gas-phase driving force at any point is $y_i - y$. So the design equation corresponding to Eq. (6.8) becomes

$$h_T = \int_{y_1}^{y_2} \frac{G' dy}{k_y \bar{a}(1-y)(y_i - y)} \quad (6.11)$$

6.4.2 Design Method Based on the Overall Mass Transfer Coefficient

If we express N_A in terms of the overall mass transfer coefficient $[N_A = K_y(y - y^*)]$, Eq. (6.7) becomes

$$dh = \frac{-G' dy}{K_y \bar{a}(1-y)(y-y^*)} \quad (6.12)$$

Here y^* is the gas-phase concentration (in mole fraction) that is capable of remaining in equilibrium with a liquid having a bulk concentration x. The required packed height is obtained by integration of the equation between the two terminal concentrations.

$$h_T = \int_{0}^{h_T} dh = \int_{y_2}^{y_1} \frac{G' dy}{K_y \bar{a}(1-y)(y-y^*)} \quad (6.13)$$

Graphical or numerical integration of the right-hand side of the above equation is simpler than that of Equation (6.8). Plot the operating line, take any point (x, y) on the operating line, draw a vertical line through it and extend up to the equilibrium curve to reach the point y^*. If the values of the integrand for suitably spaced values of the variable y are calculated, the integral can be evaluated graphically or numerically.

Design equations similar to Eq. (6.10) can be obtained when the overall coefficient is given.

$$h_T = \int_{x_2}^{x_1} \frac{L' dx}{K_x \bar{a}(1-x)(x^* - x)} = \int_{y_2}^{y_1} \frac{G' dy}{K_G \bar{a} P(1-y)(y-y^*)} = \int_{x_2}^{x_1} \frac{L' dx}{K_L \bar{a}(C)_{\text{av}}(1-x)(x^* - x)} \quad (6.14)$$

The locations of x, y, y_i, y^*, x_i, x^* are schematically shown in Figure 6.6. Design equations based on the overall coefficients for a stripping operation can be easily derived from above.

6.4.3 Design Method Based on Height of a Transfer Unit

Let us recall Eq. (6.8) and write it in the following form

$$h_T = \int_{y_2}^{y_1} \frac{G' \, y_{iBM} \, dy}{k_y \, \bar{a} \, y_{iBM} (1 - y)(y - y_i)} = \int_{y_2}^{y_1} \frac{G' (1 - y)_{iM} \, dy}{k_y \, \bar{a} \, (1 - y)_{iM} (1 - y)(y - y_i)} \tag{6.15}$$

where y_{iBM} is the log mean value of y_B [$= (1 - y)$] defined as follows:

$$y_{iBM} = (1 - y)_{iM} = \frac{(1 - y_i) - (1 - y)}{\ln \dfrac{1 - y_i}{1 - y}} \tag{6.16}$$

[Note that we are dealing with a binary gas mixture in which B is the carrier gas (non-diffusing), and $y_B = (1 - y)$; the suffix M means 'log mean'.]

The gas-phase mass transfer coefficient often varies as $(G')^{0.8}$. Also, the 'Colburn-Drew mass transfer coefficient', $k_y' = k_y y_{iBM}$, remains independent of the prevailing driving force (but the coefficient k_y depends upon the concentration through y_{iBM}, see Section 3.2.2). As a result, the quantity $G'/k_y \bar{a} (1 - y)_{iM}$ remains fairly constant over the packed section of the bed although the total gas mass flow rate, G', varies. Chilton and Colburn (1935) called this quantity 'height of a transfer unit' based on the individual gas-phase coefficient or the 'height of an individual gas-phase transfer unit', denoted by H_{tG}. Taking this quantity out of the integral sign, we may rewrite Eq. (6.15) as

$$h_T = \frac{G'}{k_y a (1 - y)_{iM}} \int_{y_2}^{y_1} \frac{(1 - y)_{iM} \, dy}{(1 - y)(y - y_i)} = H_{tG} \int_{y_2}^{y_1} \frac{(1 - y)_{iM} \, dy}{(1 - y)(y - y_i)} \tag{6.17}$$

where

$$H_{tG} = \frac{G'}{k_y \, \bar{a} (1 - y)_{iM}} = \frac{G'}{k_y' \, \bar{a}} \tag{6.18}$$

The integral in Eq. (6.17) is called the 'number of individual gas-phase transfer units', designated as N_{tG} (sometimes abbreviated NTU_G). So the packed height is

$$h_T = H_{tG} \, N_{tG} \tag{6.19}$$

The height of a transfer unit and the number of transfer units can be defined similarly when any other kind of mass transfer coefficient is used. For example, if the rate of mass transfer is expressed in terms of the individual liquid-phase mass transfer coefficient, the height of the packing can be written as

$$h_T = H_{tL} N_{tL} \tag{6.20}$$

where

$$H_{tL} = \frac{L'}{k_x \, \bar{a} \, x_{iBM}} = \frac{L'}{k_x \bar{a} (1 - x)_{iM}} \, ; \qquad N_{tL} = \int_{x_2}^{x_1} \frac{(1 - x)_{iM} \, dx}{(1 - x)(x_i - x)}$$

and

$$(1 - x)_{iM} = \frac{(1 - x) - (1 - x_i)}{\ln \dfrac{1 - x}{1 - x_i}} \tag{6.21}$$

Here H_{tL} is the 'height of an individual liquid-phase transfer unit' and N_{tL} is the 'number of individual liquid-phase transfer units'.

If the overall gas-phase mass transfer coefficient is used to express the rate of mass transfer, the height of the packing can be obtained from the following equation:

$$h_T = \int_{y_2}^{y_1} \frac{G' \, y_{BM}^* \, dy}{K_y \, \bar{a} \, y_{BM}^* (1-y)(y-y^*)} = \frac{G'}{K_y \, \bar{a} \, y_{BM}^*} \int_{y_2}^{y_1} \frac{y_{BM}^* \, dy}{(1-y)(y-y^*)} = H_{tOG} \, N_{tOG} \qquad (6.22)$$

where

$$H_{tOG} = \text{height of an overall gas-phase transfer unit} = \frac{G'}{K_y \, \bar{a} \, y_{BM}^*}$$

$$N_{tOG} = \text{number of overall gas-phase transfer units} = \int_{y_2}^{y_1} \frac{y_{BM}^* \, dy}{(1-y)(y-y^*)}$$

and $\quad y_{BM}^* = (1-y)_M^* = \dfrac{(1-y^*)-(1-y)}{\ln[(1-y^*)/(1-y)]}$

Table 6.2 summarizes the expressions for the various forms of HTUs and NTUs.

Table 6.2   Expressions for HTUs and NTUs

Driving force	Height of a Transfer Unit (HTU)			Number of Transfer Units (NTU)	
	Symbol	DANB	ECD	Symbol	
$y - y_i$	H_{tG}	$\dfrac{G'}{k_y \, \bar{a}(1-y)_{iM}}$	$\dfrac{G'}{k_y' \, \bar{a}}$	N_{tG}	$\displaystyle\int_{y_2}^{y_1} \dfrac{(1-y)_{iM} \, dy}{(1-y)(y-y_i)}$
$y - y^*$	H_{tOG}	$\dfrac{G'}{K_y \, \bar{a}(1-y)_M^*}$	$\dfrac{G'}{K_y' \, \bar{a}}$	N_{tOG}	$\displaystyle\int_{y_2}^{y_1} \dfrac{(1-y)_M^* \, dy}{(1-y)(y-y^*)}$
$Y - Y^*$	H_{tOG}	$\dfrac{G_s'}{K_Y \, \bar{a}}$	$\dfrac{G_s'}{K_Y \, \bar{a}}$	N_{tOG}	$\displaystyle\int_{Y_2}^{Y_1} \dfrac{dY}{(Y-Y^*)}$
$x_i - x$	H_{tL}	$\dfrac{L'}{k_x \, \bar{a}(1-x)_{iM}}$	$\dfrac{L'}{k_x' \, \bar{a}}$	N_{tL}	$\displaystyle\int_{x_2}^{x_1} \dfrac{(1-x)_{iM} \, dx}{(1-x)(x_i-x)}$
$x^* - x$	H_{tOL}	$\dfrac{L'}{K_x \, \bar{a}(1-x)_M^*}$	$\dfrac{L'}{K_x' \, \bar{a}}$	N_{tOL}	$\displaystyle\int_{x_2}^{x_1} \dfrac{(1-x)_M^* \, dx}{(1-x)(x^*-x)}$
$X^* - X$	H_{tOL}	$\dfrac{L_s'}{K_X \, \bar{a}}$	$\dfrac{L_s'}{K_X \, \bar{a}}$	N_{tOL}	$\displaystyle\int_{X_2}^{X_1} \dfrac{dX}{(X^*-X)}$

$$(1-y)_{iM} = \frac{(1-y_i)-(1-y)}{\ln[(1-y_i)/(1-y)]}; \qquad (1-y)_M^* = \frac{(1-y^*)-(1-y)}{\ln[(1-y^*)/(1-y)]}$$

DANB: Diffusion of *A* through non-diffusing *B*; ECD: Equimolar counterdiffusion of *A* and *B*.

Packed bed mass transfer data for gas–liquid systems are often reported in terms of the height of a transfer unit. For a particular gas–liquid system, HTU depends upon the type of packing and the gas and the liquid flow rates. The HTU data on typical systems may be obtained from the manufacturer of a particular packing.

Some qualitative physical significances can be attributed to the HTU and the NTU. The HTU indicates *inversely* the relative ease with which a given packing can accomplish separation for a particular system. For a 'good packing' (especially the one that provides more specific interfacial area of contact), the value of HTU is less and the packed height required for a specified degree of separation is smaller. The number of transfer units (NTU), on the other hand, indicates the difficulty of separation. The greater the extent of separation desired, the less will be the driving force available (particularly near the top of the column in case of absorption and near the bottom of the column in case of stripping), and the larger will be the NTU. A quantitative significance can be attributed to NTU in certain limiting cases. For example, in the case of absorption of a dilute gas [when $(1 - y)^*_M/(1 - y) \approx 1$], if the operating and the equilibrium lines are nearly straight and parallel, $(y - y^*)$ is approximately constant. So

$$N_{tOG} = \int_{y_2}^{y_1} \frac{(1 - y^*)_M \, dy}{(1 - y)(y - y^*)} \approx \int_{y_2}^{y_1} \frac{dy}{(y - y^*)} \approx \frac{y_1 - y_2}{(y - y^*)_{av}} \tag{6.23}$$

If we consider one overall gas-phase transfer unit, i.e. if we put $N_{tOG} = 1$ in the above equation, $(y_1 - y_2) \approx (y - y^*)_{av}$. Thus, a single transfer unit corresponds to the height of packing over which the change in gas concentration is approximately equal to the average driving force.

If the equilibrium relation is linear with a slope m (i.e. $y^* = mx$ or $y = mx^*$) the heights of the individual and overall transfer units are related as follows (The derivation of these equations is left as an exercise).

$$H_{tOG} = \frac{y_{iBM}}{y^*_{BM}} H_{tG} + \frac{mG'}{L'} \frac{x_{iBM}}{y^*_{BM}} H_{tL} \tag{6.24a}$$

and

$$H_{tOL} = \frac{L'}{mG'} \frac{y_{iBM}}{x^*_{BM}} H_{tG} + \frac{x_{iBM}}{x^*_{BM}} H_{tL} \tag{6.24b}$$

The relations may be considerably simplified if the solute concentrations are low. For example, putting

$$y_{iM} \approx y^*_{iM} \quad \text{and} \quad x_{iM} \approx x^*_{iM},$$

we have

$$H_{tOG} = H_{tG} + (1/\overline{A}) H_{tL} = H_{tG} + (\overline{S}) H_{tL} \tag{6.24c}$$

where $\overline{A} = L'/mG' (= L/mG)$ is the absorption factor, and $\overline{S} = mG'/L' (= mG/L)$ is the stripping factor.

EXAMPLE 6.2 (*Packed tower design using individual coefficients*)   A gas mixture containing 10 mol% SO_2 and 90 mol% air at 1 atm total pressure and 30°C is to be scrubbed with water to remove 97% of the SO_2 in a tower packed with 25 mm ceramic Raschig rings. The feed gas rate is 1500 kg per hour. Calculate (a) the minimum liquid rate, (b) the tower diameter if the liquid rate is 1.25 times the minimum and the tower operates at 70% of the flooding velocity, and (c) the packed height.

For the calculation of the tower diameter, the liquid may be assumed to have properties like water. Equilibrium data for SO_2–water system at 30°C may be taken from Perry's Handbook. The Colburn-Drew *volumetric mass transfer coefficients* at the given conditions are:

$$k_x' \bar{a} = 1.25 \ \text{kmol/(m}^3)(\text{s})(\Delta x) \qquad \text{and} \qquad k_y' \bar{a} = 0.075 \ \text{kmol/(m}^3)(\text{s})(\Delta y).$$

Solution

See Figure 6.5 for the notations of flow rates and concentrations.

Average molecular weight of the feed gas (10% SO_2, 90% air) = $(0.10)(64) + (0.90)(28.8)$
$$= 32.3$$

Total feed gas rate = 1500 kg/h = 1500/32.3 = 46.41 kmol/h = G_1

Feed concentration, $y_1 = 0.1$ (mole fraction); $Y_1 = 0.1/0.9 = 0.111$ (in mole ratio unit)

Feed gas rate on solute-free basis = $G_s = G_1(1 - y_1) = (46.41)(1 - 0.10) = 41.77$ kmol/h

SO_2 entering = $G_1 y_1 = (46.41)(0.10) = 4.641$ kmol/h; 97% of this SO_2 is absorbed.

Therefore, SO_2 absorbed = $(4.641)(0.97) = 4.502$ kmol/h; SO_2 leaving = 0.14 kmol/h;

Concentration: $Y_2 = 0.14/G_s = 0.14/41.77 = 0.00335$

$$y_2 = Y_2/(1 + Y_2) = 0.00335/1.00335 \approx 0.00335$$

The calculated equilibrium data in mole fraction unit (30°C, 1 atm total pressure) are given below:

$10^4 x$	0	0.562	1.403	2.8	4.22	8.42	14.03	19.65	27.9
$10^3 y$	0	0.790	2.23	6.19	10.65	25.9	47.3	68.5	104

(a) *Determination of the minimum liquid rate*

The equilibrium (x, y) data are converted to mole ratio units (X, Y) and plotted on the $X–Y$ plane (not shown here; this part is left as an exercise). The curve is slightly convex downwards. So the operating line corresponding to the minimum liquid rate *will not touch* the equilibrium line. It will rather meet the equilibrium line at the point having an ordinate $Y_1(0.111)$. This is the pinch point having the abscissa = $(X_1)_{max} = 0.00272$. The feed water is SO_2-free. Therefore, $X_2 = 0$.

By an overall material balance,

$$G_s(Y_1 - Y_2) = (L_s)_{min}(X_{1,max} - X_2)$$

$\Rightarrow$ $(41.77)(0.111 - 0.00335) = (L_s)_{min}(0.00272 - 0), \text{ i.e. } (L_s)_{min} = \boxed{1655 \ \text{mol/h}}$

(b) *Determination of the tower diameter*

The molecular weight of the solvent (water) = 18; $(L_s)_{min} = (1655)(18) = 29{,}790$ kg/h. Take the actual liquid rate as 1.25 times the minimum. The feed liquid is *solute-free*. The actual feed liquid rate (1.25 times the minimum),

$$L_s = (1655)(1.25) = 2069 \ \text{kmol/h} \ (= 37{,}237 \ \text{kg/h})$$

The liquid rate at the bottom of the tower,

$$L_1 = L_s + SO_2 \text{ absorbed} = 37{,}237 + (4.502)(64) = 37{,}525 \ \text{kg/h}$$

The flooding velocity should be calculated at a point of the tower where the liquid and the gas flow rates are maximum. In an absorption tower, it occurs at the bottom; in a stripping tower, it occurs at the top. In the given case, the flow rates at the bottom of the tower are taken.

Total pressure in the tower = 1 atm (the pressure drop across the tower is neglected); temperature = 303 K

Following the procedure of Example 5.2, the tower diameter can be calculated. At 70% of the flooding velocity, tower cross-section = 0.781 m^2; diameter = 1 m; and gas mass flow rate, G' = 1921 kg/m$^2 \cdot$h. Determination of these values is left as an exercise.

(c) *Determination of the packed height*

Overall material balance, $G_s \left(\dfrac{y_1}{1-y_1} - \dfrac{y_2}{1-y_2} \right) = L_s \left(\dfrac{x_1}{1-x_1} - \dfrac{x_2}{1-x_2} \right)$

G_s = 41.77 kmol/h; L_s = 2069 kmol/h; y_1 = 0.10; y_2 = 0.00335; x_2 = 0

$\Rightarrow$ x_1 = 0.00217 = concentration of SO$_2$ in the exit solution

$$X_1 = \frac{x_1}{1-x_1} = 0.002175$$

Individual gas- and liquid-phase mass transfer coefficients are given. The following equations are to be used to determine the packed height.

$$h = H_{tG} N_{tG}; \quad H_{tG} = \frac{G'}{k'_y \bar{a}} \quad \text{and} \quad N_{tG} = \int_{y_2}^{y_1} \frac{(1-y)_{iM}}{(1-y)(y-y_i)}\, dy = \int_{y_2}^{y_1} f(y)\, dy \qquad \text{(i)}$$

In order to evaluate the integral (graphically or numerically), it is required to determine the interfacial concentration on the gas-side, i.e. y_i. We follow the procedure described in Section 6.4.1.

The equilibrium data are plotted on the x–y plane. The operating line as given below is also plotted on the same graph [Figure 6.7(a)].

$$G_s \left(\frac{y_1}{1-y_1} - \frac{y}{1-y} \right) = L_s \left(\frac{x_1}{1-x_1} - \frac{x}{1-x} \right)$$

G_s = 41.77, L_s = 2069, y_1 = 0.1, x_1 = 0.00217

In order to determine the interfacial gas-phase concentration y_i at a particular section of the column where the bulk concentrations are (x, y), we proceed as follows:

(i) Locate any point $P(x, y)$ on the operating line; (ii) draw a line of slope $-k'_x \bar{a}/k'_y \bar{a}$ $(= -1.25/0.075 = -16.67)$ from (x, y) to meet the equilibrium line at the point M_1 which gives the

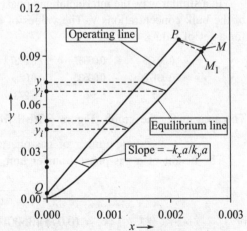

Figure 6.7(a)   Determination of interfacial concentrations.

first approximation of the interfacial concentrations (x_i, y_i). Because in the given system, mass transfer occurs by *diffusion of A through non-diffusing B*, the true value of (x_i, y_i) can be obtained by drawing a line of slope $k_x\bar{a}/k_y\bar{a}$ from the point (x, y) on the operating line to meet the equilibrium line at M_1. Now

$$-\frac{k_x\bar{a}}{k_y\bar{a}} = -\frac{(k_x'\bar{a}/(1-x)_{iM})}{(k_y'\bar{a}/(1-y)_{iM})} = -\left(\frac{1.25}{0.075}\right)\left(\frac{(1-y)_{iM}}{(1-x)_{iM}}\right) = -16.67\left(\frac{(1-y)_{iM}}{(1-x)_{iM}}\right)$$

Using the values of interfacial concentrations at the point M_1, the log-mean concentrations $(1 - x)_{iM}$ and $(1 - y)_{iM}$ can be calculated. From this we get a better estimate of $-k_x\bar{a}/k_y\bar{a}$. A line having this recalculated slope drawn from the point P meets the equilibrium line at M that gives a better estimate of (x_i, y_i). Since we have chosen the upper terminal point $P(0.00217, 0.1)$ on the operating line and drawn a line of slope -16.67, we reach the point $M_1(0.00255, 0.0937)$ on the equilibrium line. We have

$$(1 - y)_{iM} = \frac{(1-0.0937)-(1-0.1)}{\ln\dfrac{1-0.0937}{1-0.1}} = 0.903$$

$$(1 - x)_{iM} = \frac{(1-0.00217)-(1-0.00255)}{\ln\dfrac{1-0.00217}{1-0.00255}} = 0.9976$$

$$\Rightarrow \quad -\frac{k_x\bar{a}}{k_y\bar{a}} = -(16.67)(0.903/0.9976) = -15.1$$

Draw a line of slope -15.1 through P to reach M $(0.00256,$ $0.0947)$ on the equilibrium line [see Figure 6.7(a)]. The point M gives a fairly accurate estimate of the interfacial concentration (x_i, y_i). No further trial is necessary.

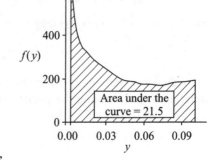

Figure 6.7(b)   Graphical integration to determine N_{tG}.

In a similar way, the interfacial gas-phase concentrations y_i are determined for a set of values of the bulk concentrations y. The values of the integrand, $f(y)$, are now calculated and plotted for a set of values of y.

y	0.00335	0.00887	0.0237	0.0427	0.0569	0.0734	0.1
y_i	0.00178	0.00633	0.02	0.0376	0.0513	0.068	0.047
$f(y)$	640	395	273	198	180	170	190

The area under the graph [Figure 6.7(b)] from $y_2 = 0.00335$ to $y_1 = 0.1$ is 21.5. Therefore,

Number of gas-phase transfer units, $N_{tG} = 21.5$

The height of a gas-phase transfer unit,

$$H_{tG} = \frac{G'}{k_y\,\bar{a}(1-y)_{LM}} = \frac{G'}{k_y'\bar{a}}$$

or
$$k_y' = (0.075)(3600) = 270 \text{ kmol/(h)(m}^2)(\Delta y)$$

Use the average gas flow rate to calculate H_{tG}.

Tower cross-section $= 0.781$ m^2

$$G_1' = G_1/0.781 = 46.41/0.781 = 59.42 \text{ kmol/h·m}^2$$

$$G'_2 = G_s/(1 - y_2)(0.781) = 53.66 \text{ kmol/h} \cdot \text{m}^2$$

$$G' = (G'_1 + G'_2)/2 = (59.42 + 53.66)/2 = 56.54 \text{ kmol/h} \cdot \text{m}^2$$

$$H_{tG} = 44.3/(270)(0.7823) = 0.21 \text{ m}$$

$$\text{Packed height} = H_{tG}N_{tG} = (0.21)(21.5) = \boxed{4.52 \text{ m}}$$

Note: It is easy to check that except for highly concentrated gases (> 25% of solute), it is safe

to assume that $\dfrac{(1-y)_{iM}}{1-y} \approx 1$, and the simplified expression for N_{tG} becomes $N_{tG} = \displaystyle\int_{y_2}^{y_1} \dfrac{dy}{y - y_i}$.

6.4.4 A Simplified Design Procedure for Dilute Gases

Making the approximation $y^*_{BM} \approx (1 - y) \approx 1$ for a dilute gas, Eq. (6.22) is reduced to

$$N_{tOG} \approx \int_{y_2}^{y_1} \frac{dy}{y - y^*} \tag{6.25}$$

If the equilibrium relation is linear, it is possible to evaluate the above integral analytically assuming that the gas and the liquid rates remain reasonably constant over the height of the packing. If L' and G' remain nearly constant (which is true for dilute gases), the equation of the operating line becomes

$$G'(y - y_2) = L'(x - x_2) \quad \Rightarrow \quad x = (G'/L')(y - y_2) + x_2 \tag{6.26}$$

Since $y^* = mx$ (y^* is the mole fraction of the solute in the gas phase that can remain in equilibrium with a solution having a bulk concentration x of the solute), the overall local driving force becomes

$$y - y^* = y - mx = y - [m(G'/L')(y - y_2) + mx_2] = y(1 - \bar{S}) + \bar{S}y_2 - mx_2$$

where $\bar{S} = mG'/L'$.

$$\Rightarrow N_{tOG} = \int_{y_2}^{y_1} \frac{dy}{y - y^*} = \int_{y_2}^{y_1} \frac{dy}{y(1 - \bar{S}) + \bar{S}y_2 - mx_2} = \frac{1}{(1 - \bar{S})} \ln \frac{y_1(1 - \bar{S}) + \bar{S}y_2 - mx_2}{y_2(1 - \bar{S}) + \bar{S}y_2 - mx_2} \tag{6.27a}$$

The above equation is similar to Eq. (6.26) of McNulty (1994). It may be put in a more compact form by using the overall material balance

$$G'(y_1 - y_2) = L'(x_1 - x_2) = (L'/m)(mx_1 - mx_2) = (L'/m)(y^*_1 - y^*_2)$$

i.e. $$\bar{S} = \frac{mG'}{L'} = \frac{y^*_1 - y^*_2}{y_1 - y_2} \Rightarrow 1 - \bar{S} = 1 - \frac{y^*_1 - y^*_2}{y_1 - y_2} = \frac{(y_1 - y^*_1) - (y_2 - y^*_2)}{y_1 - y_2}$$

Now, $$\frac{y_1(1 - \bar{S}) + \bar{S}y_2 - mx_2}{y_2(1 - \bar{S}) + \bar{S}y_2 - mx_2} = \frac{y_1 - m[(G'/L')(y_1 - y_2) + x_2]}{y_2 - mx_2} = \frac{y_1 - mx_1}{y_2 - mx_2} = \frac{y_1 - y^*_1}{y_2 - y^*_2}$$

$$\Rightarrow \qquad N_{tOG} = \frac{y_1 - y_2}{(y_1 - y_1^*) - (y_2 - y_2^*)} \ln \frac{y_1 - y_1^*}{y_2 - y_2^*} = \frac{y_1 - y_2}{\dfrac{(y_1 - y_1^*) - (y_2 - y_2^*)}{\ln \dfrac{y_1 - y_1^*}{y_2 - y_2^*}}} = \frac{y_1 - y_2}{(y - y^*)_M} \quad (6.27b)$$

Here $(y - y^*)_M$ is the log mean of the driving forces at the top and the bottom terminals. This is similar to 'log mean temperature difference' (LMTD) in heat transfer. (Note that $G'/L' = G/L$.)

EXAMPLE 6.3 (*Tower design for scrubbing a lean gas*)   A stream of waste gas containing 0.6 vol% ammonia in air is to be cleaned by removing 99.5% of the ammonia before it can be discharged in the atmosphere. Because of the low concentration of the gas and the very high degree of removal desired, a dilute mineral acid is a good solvent. Dilute sulphuric acid is selected as the absorbent because of its low cost and negligible vapour pressure of the acid.

Removal of ammonia is to be done in a packed tower, 1 m^2 in cross-section, in which the feed gas rate is 2000 kg/h·m^2 and the liquid (20% H$_2$SO$_4$) is supplied at a rate of 2200 kg/h·m^2. The absorption is *gas-film resistance controlled* and the overall volumetric mass transfer coefficient of NH$_3$ on the gas-phase basis is $K_G \bar{a}$ = 1350 kg/(h)(m^3)(Δp, bar). Although absorption of ammonia in a dilute acid is considerably exothermic, the temperature is assumed to be constant at 28°C because of the low concentration of ammonia. The total pressure in the column is 101.3 kPa. The process starts with 1000 kg of the 20% acid solution in the storage tank for the scrubbing liquid, and the liquid is recirculated through the column continuously. The concentration of the acid in the liquid gradually decreases as a result.

(a) How long will it take before the acid concentration falls to half of the original (in wt%)?
(b) What total packed height is required to accomplish the separation if 0.3 m dry packing is provided above the liquid distributor in order to prevent entrainment of the liquid?
(c) Recalculate the packed height if only 95% of the ammonia in the feed gas is removed.
(d) What would be the value of the individual gas-phase mass transfer coefficient, k_c (kmol/ (s)(m^2)(ΔC)], if the effective specific interfacial area of the gas–liquid contact in the tower is estimated to be 60 m^2 per cubic metre of the packed volume?
(e) Estimate the thickness of the gas-film if the diffusivity of ammonia in the carrier gas is 0.0756 m^2/h.

Solution

Average molecular weight of the gas (0.6% NH$_3$ and 99.5% air),

$$= (0.995)(28.8) + (0.006)(17) = 28.73$$

Cross-section of the tower = 1 m^2

Mass flow rate of the feed gas = 2000 kg/h·m^2 = 2000/28.73 = 69.61 kmol/h·m^2

NH$_3$ entering with the feed = (69.61)(0.006) = 0.4177 kmol/h·m^2

NH$_3$ absorbed = (69.61)(0.006)(0.995) = 0.4156 kmol/h·m^2; NH$_3$ leaving = 0.00213 kmol/h·m^2

Total gas leaving = 69.61 – 0.4156 = 69.19 kmol/h·m^2

Mole fraction of NH$_3$ in the exit gas, y_2 = 0.00213/69.19 = 0.0000308; in the feed, y_1 = 0.006

(a) Amount of H_2SO_4 in the liquid at the beginning $= (1000)(0.20) = 200\,kg = 200/98 = 2.041\,kmol$

$$2NH_3 + H_2SO_4 = (NH_4)_2SO_4$$

Acid consumed per hour $=$ (moles of NH_3 absorbed)$/2 = 0.4156/2 = 0.2078\,kmol$

$$\text{Time of consumption of 50\% of the acid} = \frac{(2.041)(0.5)}{0.2078} = \boxed{4.91\,h}$$

(b) Assume that the operation continues till the solution remains *sufficiently acidic*. After this the solution is replaced by a fresh batch of the acid.

As the feed gas concentration is pretty low, we may take $y_{BM}^* \approx 1$; gas rate $G \approx$ constant

$$H_{tOG} = \frac{G'}{K_y\,\bar{a}\,y_{BM}^*} \approx \frac{G'}{K_G\,\bar{a}\,P} = \frac{69.61\,kmol/h \cdot m^2}{\left(\dfrac{1350}{17}\right)\dfrac{kmol}{(h)(m^3)(bar)}(1.013)\,bar} = 0.865\,m$$

Again we can take $y_{BM}^*/(1-y) \approx 1$ and $y^* = 0$ (NH_3 absorbed reacts instantaneously to form $(NH_4)_2SO_4$ in solution; the vapour pressure of NH_3 over the solution is zero). The number of transfer units is

$$N_{tOG} = \int_{y_2}^{y_1} \frac{y_{BM}^*\,dy}{(1-y)(y-y^*)} = \int_{y_2}^{y_1} \frac{dy}{y} = \ln\frac{y_1}{y_2} = \ln\frac{0.006}{0.0000308} = \ln 195 = 5.27$$

Height of packing required $= H_{tOG}N_{tOG} = (0.865)(5.27) = 4.56\,m$

Add 0.3 m dry packing above the distributor. Total packed height $= 4.56 + 0.3 = \boxed{4.86\,m}$

[If the packed height is about 20 ft or more, intermediate redistribution is necessary, and the packed height should be reasonably increased in order to accommodate the redistributor(s).]

(c) $H_{tOG} = 0.865\,m$. 95% of the NH_3 is absorbed

$$\Rightarrow \qquad N_{tOG} = \ln\frac{y_1}{y_2} = \ln\frac{0.006}{(0.006)(1-0.95)} = 3$$

Adding 0.3 m dry packing, the packed height required

$$= (H_{tOG})(N_{tOG}) + 0.3 = (0.865)(3) + 0.3 = \boxed{2.9\,m}$$

This shows that the required packed height increases by over 50% when the percentage removal of ammonia changes from 95% to 99.5%.

(d) As the absorption of NH_3 in an acid solution is gas-film diffusion controlled, the overall gas-phase mass transfer coefficient is virtually the same as the individual gas-film coefficient.

$$\Rightarrow \qquad k_G\,\bar{a} = K_G\,\bar{a} = 1350\,kg/(h)(m^3)(\Delta p,\,bar)$$

Specific interfacial area, $\qquad \bar{a} = 60\,m^2/m^3; \qquad$ mol. wt. of $NH_3 = 17$

$$k_G = 1350/60 = 22.5 \text{ kg/(m}^2)(\text{h})(\Delta p, \text{bar}) = 22.5/17 = \boxed{1.324 \text{ kmol/(h)(m}^2)(\Delta p, \text{bar})}$$

The individual gas-phase mass transfer coefficient, k_c (see Table 3.1),

$$k_c = RTk_G = (0.08317)(301)(1.324) = \boxed{33.14 \text{ kmol/(h)(m}^2)(\text{kmol/m}^3)}$$

(e) Transport of NH_3 through the gas-film occurs by 'diffusion of A through non-diffusing B (air)'.

$$\Rightarrow \qquad k_G = \frac{D_{AB}\,P}{RT\,p_{BM}\,\delta}; \qquad \delta = \text{film thickness}; \qquad P/p_{BM} \approx 1.$$

Take $D_{AB} = 0.0756$ m^2/h, as given.

$$\Rightarrow \qquad \delta = \frac{D_{AB}}{RT\,k_G} = \frac{D_{AB}}{k_c} = \frac{0.0756 \text{ m}^2/\text{h}}{33.14 \text{ (m/h)}} = 0.0023 \text{ m} = \boxed{2.3 \text{ mm}}$$

6.4.5 An Approximate Design Equation for Concentrated Gases

For a 'concentrated gas', a simplified form of Eq. (6.22) can be obtained by approximating the log mean quantity y^*_{BM} by the 'arithmetic mean'.

$$y^*_{BM} = (1 - y)^*_M \approx \frac{(1 - y^*) + (1 - y)}{2}$$

$$\Rightarrow \qquad N_{tOG} = \int_{y_2}^{y_1} \frac{[(1 - y^*) + (1 - y)]dy}{2\,(1 - y)(y - y^*)} = \int_{y_2}^{y_1} \frac{[2\,(1 - y) + (y - y^*)]dy}{2\,(1 - y)(y - y^*)}$$

$$= \int_{y_2}^{y_1} \frac{dy}{y - y^*} + \frac{1}{2}\int_{y_2}^{y_1} \frac{dy}{1 - y} = \int_{y_2}^{y_1} \frac{dy}{y - y^*} + \frac{1}{2}\ln\frac{1 - y_2}{1 - y_1} \qquad (6.28)$$

The integral on the right-hand side is to be evaluated graphically or numerically. However, at the top of the column, both y and y^* are very small and the integrand will be very large. This may make the integration cumbersome. Numerical integration becomes more convenient if the integral is expressed in the form

$$\int_{y_2}^{y_1} \frac{dy}{y - y^*} = \int_{y_2}^{y_1} \frac{y}{y - y^*}\frac{dy}{y} = \int_{y_2}^{y_1} \frac{y}{y - y^*}\,d(\ln y) \qquad (6.29)$$

EXAMPLE 6.4 (*Packed tower design using the overall gas-phase coefficient*)   Ammonia is to be scrubbed from a stream of air containing 16 mole% of the solute by water at 25°C and 1 atm total pressure. The feed gas rate is 60 kmol/h·m^2 and the water rate is 70 kmol/h·m^2. It is required to remove 99% of the ammonia in the feed. If the overall gas-phase volumetric mass transfer coefficient is $K'_y\bar{a} = 100$ kmol/(h)(m^3)(Δy), determine the HTU, NTU and the height of the packing required.

Equilibrium data: $\log \dfrac{P(1-x)\,y^*}{55.5\,x} = 4.699 - \dfrac{1922}{T}$; P = total pressure (atm) less vapour pressure of water at the given temperature; x = mole fractions of the solute in the liquid, and y^* = equilibrium mole fraction of NH_3 in air.

Solution

The design problem involves absorption of a solute from a concentrated gas. The following calculation is based on 1 m^2 of tower cross-section and 1 hour of operation.

Molecular weight of the feed gas (16% NH_3, 84% air) = $(0.16)(17) + (0.84)(28.8) = 26.9$

Feed gas: Feed gas rate, $G_1' = 60$ kmol/h·m^2; mole fraction ammonia, $x_1 = 0.16$; moles ammonia input = $(60)(0.16) = 9.6$ kmoles; moles air input = $(60)(0.84) = 50.4$ kmol ($= G_s'$); ammonia removed = 99%; moles ammonia out = $(9.6)(0.01) = 0.096$ kmol; $G_2' = 50.4 + 0.096 = 50.496$ kmol/m^2·h.

$$\text{Concentration of ammonia in the outlet gas, } y_2 = \frac{0.096}{50.4 + 0.096} = 0.002$$

Equilibrium relation: The vapour pressure of water at 25°C = 0.4574 psi; $P = 14.7 - 0.4574 = 14.24$ psi = 0.969 atm. Putting $P = 0.969$ and $T = 298$, the given equilibrium relation becomes

$$y^* = 1.017\,\frac{x}{1-x} \tag{i}$$

The liquid phase: Water rate = 70 kmol/h ($= L_s'$); NH_3 absorbed = $(9.6)(0.99) = 9.504$ kmol/h

Liquid concentrations: $x_1 = \dfrac{9.504}{70 + 9.504} = 0.1195$; $x_2 = 0$ (since the inlet water is NH_3-free).

Equation of the operating line:

$$G_s'\left(\frac{y_1}{1-y_1} - \frac{y}{1-y}\right) = L_s'\left(\frac{x_1}{1-x_1} - \frac{x}{1-x}\right)$$

$$\Rightarrow \qquad (50.4)\left(\frac{0.16}{1-0.16} - \frac{y}{1-y}\right) = (70)\left(\frac{0.1195}{1-0.1195} - \frac{x}{1-x}\right)$$

$$\Rightarrow \qquad \left(\frac{y}{1-y}\right) = 1.3889\left(\frac{x}{1-x}\right) + 0.02 \tag{ii}$$

We have to evaluate the integral given in Eq. (6.28) or (6.29) to determine the number of overall gas-phase transfer units. For this purpose, we have to obtain a set of values of y and y^* along the packed bed. We select a value of y ($0.002 \geq x \geq 0.16$), calculate the corresponding bulk liquid concentration x from the operating line equation (ii), and the corresponding equilibrium concentration in the gas phase using the given equation for the equilibrium relation (i) above. The following tabulated data are used for the graphical evaluation of the integral given in the alternative form, Eq. (6.29).

y	0.002	0.01578	0.02945	0.04302	0.06985	0.1093	0.1352	0.16
y^*	0.0	0.0103	0.02075	0.03145	0.0535	0.08843	0.113	0.1381

$y/(y - y^*)$	1.0	3.522	3.385	3.72	4.272	5.24	6.09	7.3
$\ln y$	−6.215	−4.15	−3.525	−3.146	−2.66	−2.214	−2.0	−1.83

The area under the plot of $y/(y - y^*)$ vs. $\ln y$ is 14.7 (see Figure 6.8).

$$\Rightarrow \qquad N_{tOG} = 14.7 + \frac{1}{2} \ln \frac{1 - 0.002}{1 - 0.16}$$

$$= 14.7 + 0.086 = \boxed{14.8}$$

(Note that the contribution of the second term is pretty small.)

Given: $K_y' \, \bar{a} = 100$ kmol/(h)(m^2)(Δy). Average gas flow rate, $G' = (G_1' + G_2')/2 = 55.25$ kmol/h·m^2

$$\Rightarrow \qquad H_{tOG} = \frac{G'}{K_y \bar{a} \, y_{BM}^*} = \frac{G'}{K_y' \bar{a}}$$

$$= \frac{55.25}{100} = \boxed{0.552 \text{ m}}$$

Packed height = $(14.8)(0.552) = \boxed{8.2 \text{ m}}$

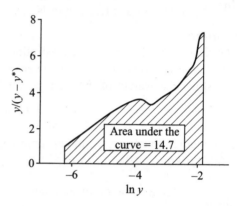

Figure 6.8   Graphical integration for the determination of N_{tOG}.

6.4.6   Analytical Determination of Number of Overall Transfer Units

If the gas and the liquid streams are 'dilute' and the Henry's law ($y^* = mx$) is applicable, Eq. (6.25) can be integrated to have an algebraic equation for N_{tOG}. Substituting $x = y^*/m$ in Eq. (6.25), we get an expression for y^* in terms of y. This is substituted in Eq. (6.25) followed by integration when the following expression for N_{tOG} is obtained.

$$N_{tOG} = \frac{\ln \left[\left(\frac{y_1 - mx_2}{y_2 - mx_2} \right)(1 - \bar{S}) + \bar{S} \right]}{1 - \bar{S}}; \quad \bar{S} = 1/\bar{A} = mG/L \qquad (6.30)$$

The above equation, suggested by Colburn in 1939, looks somewhat similar to Eq. (4.41) for calculation of the number of ideal stages. But N_{tOG} should not be confused with the number of ideal stages, although the quantities become equal if the absorption factor is unity (i.e. $\bar{A} = 1 = \bar{S}$).

6.4.7   Design Equations with Concentrations Expressed in the Mole Ratio Units

In this case the differential mass balance equation over a thin section of the bed becomes

$$G_s' \, dY = \bar{a} \, (dh)(N_A) = \bar{a} \, (dh) \, k_Y(Y - Y_i) = \bar{a} \, (dh) K_Y(Y - Y^*) \qquad (6.31)$$

where k_Y is the individual gas-phase coefficient and K_Y is the overall gas-phase coefficient, and the concentrations are expressed in the mole ratio units. The height of the packing is given by

$$h_T = \int\limits_{Y_2}^{Y_1} \frac{G_s' \, dY}{k_Y \, \bar{a}(Y - Y_i)} = \int\limits_{Y_2}^{Y_1} \frac{G_s' \, dY}{K_Y \, \bar{a}(Y - Y^*)} \qquad (6.32)$$

The gas flow rate on solute-free basis, G_s', remains constant over the height of the packing. If the mass transfer coefficients also remain reasonably constant, the above equation can be written as

$$h_T = \frac{G_s'}{k_Y \, \bar{a}} \int\limits_{Y_2}^{Y_1} \frac{dY}{Y - Y_i} = \frac{G_s'}{K_Y \, \bar{a}} \int\limits_{Y_2}^{Y_1} \frac{dY}{Y - Y^*} \qquad (6.33)$$

The design equations based on the liquid-phase mass transfer coefficients can be written following a similar procedure.

6.5   CORRELATIONS FOR MASS TRANSFER COEFFICIENTS IN PACKED TOWERS

The data on mass transfer coefficients in a packed tower are generally expressed in terms of the Sherwood number (Sh), the Colburn factor (j_D), the height of a transfer unit (H_{tG} or H_{tL}), or in the form of a direct correlation. The mass transfer coefficients (k_G, k_L, etc.) primarily depend upon (i) the type and size of the packing; (ii) the gas and the liquid flow rates; (iii) fluid properties and the transport coefficients like density, viscosity, molecular diffusivity, etc. The HTUs also depend upon these variables and parameters. The data on H_{tG} and H_{tL} for absorption of CO_2 in water (or dilute NaOH) or of NH_3 in water in a packed tower are normally available from the vendor of a packing. The former system is liquid-phase resistance controlled and is used for experimental determination of $K_L\bar{a}$ or H_{tL}; the latter system, being gas-phase resistance controlled, is convenient for determining $K_G\bar{a}$ or H_{tG}. Typical values of the overall mass transfer coefficients in industrial columns (Strigle, 1994; Ludwig, 1997) are given in Table 6.3. Cornell et al. (1960) and Bolles and Fair (1982) reviewed and suggested correlations for the heights of gas-phase and liquid-phase transfer units for the first and second generation packings. Major correlations for HTUs and mass transfer coefficients are listed in the Perry's Handbook (7th ed., 1997, Ch. 5). Mass transfer characteristics of structured packings have been discussed by Fair and Bravo (1990), Kister (1992), Strigle (1994), Billet (1995), and others.

Table 6.3   Typical values[†] of overall mass transfer coefficients in packed towers

Packing	System	$K_G\bar{a}$ lbmol/(h)(ft³)(atm)	System	$K_L\bar{a}$ lbmol/(h)(ft³)(lb mol/ft³)
#25 IMTP			CO_2/dilute NaOH	3.42
# 50 IMTP			CO_2/dilute NaOH	2.44
1-inch Pall Ring (M)			CO_2/dilute NaOH	3.10
#2 Superintalox (P)	NH_3/dilute acid	13	CO_2/dilute NaOH	1.5
#2 Superintalox (P)	Hydrogen chloride/Water	14	H_2S/dilute NaOH	4.4
1-inch Intalox saddle (C)	CO_2/dilute NaOH	2.82		
Intalox Structured (M) Packing (2T)	CO_2/dilute NaOH	3.80		

[†] Strigle, 1994; M: Metal; P: Plastic; C: Ceramic; 1 lbmol/(h)(ft³)(atm) = 16 kmol/(h)(m³)(atm)

A few simple correlations are cited below.

For gas-phase mass transfer in a bed with Raschig rings or Berl saddles packing, Shulman et al. (1955) suggested the following correlation.

$$j_D = 1.195 Re^{-0.36}; \qquad Re_G = \frac{G'd}{(1-\varepsilon)\mu_G} \qquad (6.34)$$

where G' = gas mass flow rate, μ_G = gas viscosity, ε = bed porosity, d = diameter of a sphere having the same surface area as a piece of packing.

For absorption of SO_2 in water in a packed bed with 1 inch Raschig ring packing, the following correlations for H_{tG} and H_{tL} are available.

$$H_{tG} = 1.24(G')^{0.3}/(L')^{0.25} \text{ ft} \qquad (6.35)$$

$$H_{tL} = 0.37/(L')^{0.18} \text{ ft} \qquad (6.36)$$

where L', G' = liquid and gas mass flow rates, in $lb/ft^2 \cdot h$. If the values of H_{tG} and H_{tL} are available for any system (e.g. SO_2–water system), their values for any other system can be calculated by applying the following "correction" (McNulty, 1994), provided the packing size, the packing type and the phase flow rates remain the same.

$$[H_{tG}]_1 = [H_{tG}]_2 \left[\frac{(Sc)_1}{(Sc)_2}\right]^{0.5}; \qquad [H_{tL}]_1 = [H_{tL}]_2 \left[\frac{(Sc)_1}{(Sc)_2}\right]^{0.5} \qquad (6.37)$$

where the suffixes 1 and 2 refer to the two systems concerned for the respective phases.

A few correlations for gas- and liquid-phase mass transfer coefficients in packed towers have been listed by Wagner et al. (1997). The correlations suggested by Onda et al. (1968) and by Billet and his group (1995) are frequently cited. Onda et al. used experimental data to develop empirical correlations for the mass transfer parameters as given below:

$$\frac{\bar{a}_{eff}}{a_p} = 1 - \exp[-1.45(\sigma_c/\sigma)^{0.75}(Re_L)^{0.1}(Fr_L)^{-0.05}(We)^{0.2}] \qquad (6.38a)$$

$$k_L\left(\frac{\rho_L}{\mu_L g}\right)^{1/3} = 0.0051(Re_L)^{2/3}\left(\frac{a_p}{a_{eff}}\right)^{2/3}(Sc_L)^{-1/2}(a_p d_p)^{0.4} \qquad (6.38b)$$

$$k_c/(a_p D_G) = C(Re_G)^{0.7}(Sc_G)^{1/3}(a_p d_p)^{-2.0} \qquad (6.38c)$$

Here C = 2.0 for $d_p <$ 15 mm, and C = 5.23 for $d_p >$ 15 mm; d_p = 'nominal packing size'; σ_c = 'critical surface tension' at the packing surface in dyne/cm (ceramics—61, polyethylene—33, glass—73, and metal—75[†]).

The correlations for k_L, k_c, the effective gas–liquid specific interfacial area of contact ($\bar{a}_{eff}$) and the dynamic liquid holdup (h_L) suggested by Billet and cited below are semi-empirical and are based on the 'channel model of a packed tower' (see Section 5.13) as well as on the experimental data. Billet assumed that the liquid flows as a film on the packing surface and liquid-phase mass transfer occurs according to the penetration theory over a path length l_τ (see below) with intermittent mixing of the liquid flowing down the bed.

Liquid-phase coefficient: $\qquad k_L = (12)^{1/6} C_L \left(\frac{u_L D_L}{h_L l_\tau}\right)^{1/2} \text{ m/s} \qquad (6.39a)$

[†] The Onda et al. correlations were reassessed by Dvorak et al. (1996) for towers packed with large random packings.

Gas-phase coefficient:
$$k_c = C_G \left(\frac{a_p}{l_\tau}\right)^{1/2} \frac{D_G}{(\varepsilon - h_L)^{1/2}} (\text{Re}_G)^{3/4} (\text{Sc}_G)^{1/3} \text{ m/s} \qquad (6.39b)$$

Specific interfacial area:
$$\frac{\bar{a}_{eff}}{a_p} = 3(\varepsilon)^{0.5} (\text{Re}_L)^{-0.2} (\text{Fr}_L)^{-0.45} (\text{We}_L)^{0.75} \qquad (6.39c)$$

$$\text{Re}_G = \frac{u_G \rho_G}{a_p \mu_G}; \quad \text{Sc}_G = \frac{\mu_G}{\rho_G D_G}; \quad \text{Re}_L = \frac{u_L \rho_L}{a_p \mu_L} \qquad (6.40a)$$

$$\text{Fr}_L = \frac{u_L^2 a_p}{g}; \quad \text{We}_L = \frac{u_L^2 \rho_L}{\sigma_L a_p}; \quad h_L = \left(\frac{12\,\text{Fr}_L}{\text{Re}_L}\right)^{1/3} \qquad (6.40b)$$

Here, Re = Reynolds numbers; Sc = Schmidt number; Fr = Froude number; We = Weber number; h_L = dynamic liquid holdup in the bed (volume fraction); a_p = specific surface area of the dry packing, in m^2/m^3; l = hydraulic diameter of the packing = $4\varepsilon/a_p$; ε = fractional bed voidage; D = diffusivity, in m^2/s; u = superficial fluid velocity, in m/s; subscripts L = liquid; G = gas; SI units are to be used in Eqs. 6.39(a) and 6.39(b). The constants C_L and C_G are specific to a packing. Their values for a few packings are given in Table 6.4 (for other packings, see Billet, 1995).

Table 6.4 Values* of C_L and C_G for a few random packings for use in Eqs. 6.39(a) and 6.39(b)

Packing	Material	Size	C_L	C_G
Raschig Ring	Ceramic	25 mm	1.361	0.412
Berl Saddle	Ceramic	25 mm	1.246	0.387
Pall Ring	Plastic	25 mm	0.905	0.446
Pall Ring	Metal	25 mm	1.44	0.336
Pall Ring	Metal	50 mm	1.192	0.410
NORPAC Ring	Plastic	50 mm	1.080	0.322
HiFlow Ring	Metal	50 mm	1.641	0.402

* From Billet (1995).

Recently, Piche et al. (2001) developed correlations[†] for gas- and liquid-phase mass transfer coefficients (in terms of Sherwood number) for random packings using the artificial neural network (ANN) technique[††]. The average error in prediction is claimed to remain within 22%.

The mass transfer efficiency of a tower packing is also expressed frequently in terms of the height equivalent to a theoretical plate or stage (HETP or HETS). This is discussed in Section 6.7.

[†] The authors claim these as "confident correlations".
[††] Work of these authors on pressure drop in a packed bed has been referred to in Chapter 5.

EXAMPLE 6.5 It is required to design a packed tower for absorption of ethylene oxide (1.5 mol%) from a gas stream at a total pressure of 10 atm and 25°C. The feed gas rate is 15,000 kg/h and the solute concentration in the exit gas must not exceed 0.01 mol%. The solvent is 'pure' water. The carrier gas has properties like air and has negligible solubility in water. If 50 mm metal Pall ring is used as the tower packing, calculate the height of an overall gas-phase transfer unit using the Billet's correlations. The solubility of ethylene oxide in water at such low concentration can be described by the Henry's law [see Bonilla and Baron, *AIChE J.*, *1*(1955) 49–54], $y = 1.07x$, at the given pressure and temperature.

The following data, information and simplifications may be used: average molecular weight of feed gas = 29.1; the operating line on the x–y plane is straight at such low concentrations; for 50 mm metal Pall ring: $\varepsilon = 0.95$, $a_p = 100$ m^2/m^3, packing factor, $F_p = 88.6$ m^{-1} (= 27 ft^2/ft^3), $C_G = 0.41$, $C_L = 1.192$; $\mu_G = 1.8 \times 10^{-5}$ kg/m.s; $\mu_L = 0.86$ cP = 8.6×10^{-4} kg/m.s; $\sigma_L = 72$ dyne/cm (= 0.072 kg/s^2); $\rho_G = 11.81$ kg/m^3 (this value is calculated by assuming the gas to be ideal); $\rho_L = 997$ kg/m^3; diffusivities: $D_G = 1.587 \times 10^{-6}$ m^2/s, $D_L = 1.553 \times 10^{-9}$ m^2/s; the liquid rate is 1.3 times the minimum.

Solution

Only an outline of the solution is given here. The complete solution is left as an exercise.

Calculation of the water rate: Feed gas rate, $G_1 = 15,000/29.1 = 515$ kmol; feed gas concentration, $y_1 = 0.015$; moles solute (ethylene oxide) in the feed = $(515)(0.015) = 7.8$ kmol; moles carrier gas = $515 - 7.8 = 507.2$ kmol $\approx$ moles exit gas (since the exit gas concentration is very small). Moles solute absorbed = 7.749 kmol.

Material balance to calculate the minimum liquid rate,
$$G_1 y_1 - G_2 y_2 = L_1 x_1^* - L_2 x_2$$
At the pinch point that occurs at the bottom,
$$x_1^* = y_1/1.07 = 0.015/1.07 = 0.01402; \qquad y_2 \approx 0; \qquad x_2 = 0.$$
Total liquid rate at the bottom = $(515)(1.07) = 551$ kmol

Min. water rate = $551(1 - x_1^*) = 543.3$ kmol

Actual water rate = 1.3 times the minimum = $(543.3)(1.3) = 706.3$ kmol

Total liquid rate at the bottom = $706.3 + 7.749$ kmol, i.e. 13,050 kg

Use this liquid rate to calculate the tower diameter.

Tower diameter: Flow parameter, $F_{lv} = (L/G)(\rho_G/\rho_L)^{0.5} = 0.0947$; taking $\Delta P/L = 0.25$ inch water/ft packed height, we get from Strigle's GPDC chart (Figure 5.34),
$$\text{Ordinate} = 0.92 = C_s(F_p)^{0.5}(v_L)^{0.05}$$
Put $F_p = 27$ ft^{-1}, $v_L = 0.86$ centistoke $\Rightarrow$ capacity parameter, $C_s = (u_G)[\rho_G/(\rho_L - \rho_G)]^{0.5} = 0.178$ $\Rightarrow u_G = 1.626$ ft/s. Density of the feed gas = 11.81 kg/m^3 = 0.734 lb/ft^3; gas flow rate = 15,000 kg/h = 9.186 lb/s

$\Rightarrow$ $\qquad$ tower cross-section = $(9.186)/(0.734)(1.626) = 7.693$ ft^2

$\Rightarrow$ $\qquad$ tower diameter = 3.13 ft = $\boxed{0.95 \text{ m}}$

If the pressure drop at flooding is calculated by using the Kister's Eq. (5.23), we have $(\Delta P/L)_{\text{flood}}$ = 1.15 inch water/ft. For this pressure drop and $F_{lv} = 0.0947$, the ordinate of the GPDC chart

$= 1.5 \Rightarrow (u_G)_{flood} = 2.63$ ft/s. This means that the column is designed at 1.626/2.63, i.e. at 62% of the flooding velocity, which is acceptable.

Calculation of mass transfer coefficients: The relevant quantities (in SI units) are: superficial velocities, $u_G = 1.626$ ft/s = 0.496 m/s; $u_L = 5.087 \times 10^{-3}$ m/s (this can be calculated from the liquid rate and the tower cross-section); $l_\tau = 4\varepsilon/a_p = (4)(0.95)/100 = 0.038$; calculate $Re_G = 3254$, $Re_L = 59$, $Sc_G = 0.9604$, $Fr_L = 2.638 \times 10^{-4}$, $We_L = 3.583 \times 10^{-3}$. Putting these values in Eqs. 6.39(a), (b) and (c)

$$h_L = 0.0377 \text{ (volume fraction)}; \qquad k_L = 1.34 \times 10^{-4} \text{ m/s}$$

$$k_c = 1.485 \times 10^{-2} \text{ m/s}; \qquad \bar{a}_{eff} = 77.25 \text{ m}^2/\text{m}^3$$

$$\Rightarrow \quad k_x = (k_L \text{ m/s})(C \text{ kmol/m}^3) = (1.34 \times 10^{-4})(55.4) = 7.424 \times 10^{-3} \text{ kmol/(m}^2)(s)(\Delta x)$$

and $k_y = (k_c)(P/RT) = (1.485 \times 10^{-2})[(10)/(0.0821)(298)] = 6.07 \times 10^{-3} \text{ kmol/(m}^2)(s)(\Delta y)$

Heights of transfer units:

$$H_{tG} = (G')/(k'_y \bar{a}_{eff}) \approx (G')/(k_y \bar{a}_{eff}) = \boxed{0.43 \text{ m}}$$

$$H_{tL} = \boxed{0.495 \text{ m}}$$

Stripping factor, $\bar{S} = mG/L = (1.07)(15,000/28.9)/(13,054/18) = \boxed{0.766}$

From Eq. 6.24(c),

Height of an overall gas-phase transfer unit,

$$H_{tOG} = H_{tG} + \bar{S} H_{tL} = 0.43 + (0.766)(0.495) = \boxed{0.809 \text{ m}}$$

It is to be noted that the gas-phase and the liquid-phase resistances are comparable for this system.

6.6 DETERMINATION OF THE NUMBER OF STAGES IN A TRAY TOWER

The determination of the number of ideal stages is a major step in the design of a tray tower. In the case of absorption of a gas, the rate at which the feed enters the tower and the terminal concentrations (i.e. the concentrations of the gas at the inlet and at the exit) are specified. The minimum liquid rate is determined by following the procedure laid down in Section 6.3. The actual liquid rate L_s is usually taken as 1.2 to 2 times the minimum liquid rate. The equilibrium curve is drawn using the tabulated data or equation available and the operating line of slope L_s/G_s is drawn. The number of ideal trays is determined by drawing steps between the equilibrium curve and the operating line following the procedure given in Section 4.6.3. If the equilibrium curve is reasonably straight and has an average slope m, the number of trays can be determined algebraically using the Kremser equation, i.e. Eq. (4.41). The absorption factor, $\bar{A} = L/mG$ has been used in that equation. Similar is the procedure of graphical construction of the number of ideal stages for a stripping column. Also, the number of ideal stages for stripping can be determined algebraically from Eq. (4.44) if the equilibrium line is linear $(Y = \alpha X)^\dagger$.

Sometimes an absorption tower is required to treat two or more feed gas streams of two different concentrations of the solute. It is *not* advisable to mix up the streams and then feed the

---

† Note that if the gas is dilute, Kremser equation [Eqs. (4.41) and (4.44)] can be used for systems having linear equilibrium relations in the form $y = mx$. The geometric value of the absorption factor should be used.

mixture to the column as this will necessitate a larger number of trays to carry out the desired separation. The feed gas streams are rather supplied to the column at different locations. For example, in gas absorption, the richest gas is fed at the bottom and the less concentrated gas stream is fed to the column at appropriate locations where the concentration of such a feed stream matches the concentration of the upcoming gas from below. Thus, if there are two feed gas streams, there will effectively be two sections of the column having two different gas flow rates, and there will be two operating lines as a result. The operating lines can be drawn using the material balance equations of the two sections separately. To determine the number of ideal trays, steps are drawn between the equilibrium curve and the two operating lines shifting from one operating line to the other as their point of intersection is crossed. This is illustrated in Example 6.7 for stripping two feed streams containing the same components, albeit at different concentrations. The procedure is also illustrated under 'Distillation' (Chapter 7).

6.7   HEIGHT EQUIVALENT TO A THEORETICAL PLATE (HETP)

The packed tower and the plate tower are the two common devices for the absorption of a solute gas from a mixture. If the former device is selected, the packed height is to be determined; in the case of a plate tower, the number of plates is to be found out for a given separation job. The ratio is the HETP [HETP = h_T/N_T; h_T = height of packing, and N_T = number of ideal trays required to do the same separation]. Here we develop a simple expression for the HETP of a packed bed in terms of H_{tG} and H_{tL} which represent mass transfer efficiency of a packed bed.

Let us refer to Figure 6.9 in which the operating line, the equilibrium curve and the two trays (the nth and the $(n+1)$th, represented by the two steps) are shown. Consider the $(n+1)$th plate. The gas enters this tray at a concentration (in mole fraction) of y_{n+2} and leaves at y_{n+1}, while the liquid enters at a concentration x_n and leaves at x_{n+1}. If G' and L' are the gas and liquid flow rates per unit area at these plates (assumed to remain reasonably constant), the rate of mass transfer on the nth tray is

$$\text{Rate of mass transfer} = G'(y_{n+2} - y_{n+1}) = L'(x_{n+1} - x_n) \qquad (6.41)$$

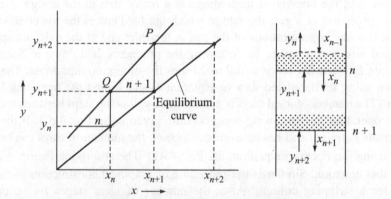

Figure 6.9   Illustration of the concept of HETP.

The rate of mass transfer over a height h of a packed section may be written as

$$\text{Rate of mass transfer} = K_G \bar{a} P h(y - y^*)_{av} \qquad (6.42)$$

where $(y - y^*)$ is the average driving force over the packed height h. If the rate of mass transfer on a tray [given in Eq. (6.41)] is the same as that achieved over a height h of a packed tower [given by Eq. (6.42)] are equal (i.e. h = HETP),

$$K_G \bar{a} Ph(y - y^*)_{av} = G'(y_{n+2} - y_{n+1})$$

i.e.

$$h = \frac{G'(y_{n+2} - y_{n+1})}{K_G \bar{a}P(y - y^*)_{av}} \qquad (6.43)$$

It is reasonable to take $(y - y^*)_{av}$ as the log-mean of the overall gas-phase driving forces at the points P and Q (see Figure 6.9). Therefore,

$$(y - y^*)_{av} = \frac{(y - y^*)_P - (y - y^*)_Q}{\ln\left[\dfrac{(y - y^*)_P}{(y - y^*)_Q}\right]} = \frac{(y_{n+2} - y_{n+1}) - (y_{n+1} - y_n)}{\ln\left[\dfrac{y_{n+2} - y_{n+1}}{y_{n+1} - y_n}\right]} \qquad (6.44)$$

We see from Figure 6.9,

$$\frac{y_{n+1} - y_n}{y_{n+2} - y_{n+1}} = \frac{(y_{n+1} - y_n)/(x_{n+1} - x_n)}{(y_{n+2} - y_{n+1})/(x_{n+1} - x_n)} = \frac{\text{slope of the equilibrium line}}{\text{slope of the operating line}} = \frac{m}{L'/G'} \qquad (6.45)$$

$$\Rightarrow \qquad \frac{mG'}{L'} - 1 = \frac{y_{n+1} - y_n}{y_{n+2} - y_{n+1}} - 1 = \frac{(y_{n+1} - y_n) - (y_{n+2} - y_{n+1})}{y_{n+2} - y_{n+1}} \qquad (6.46)$$

Comparing Eqs. (6.44), (6.45) and (6.46),

$$(y - y^*)_{av} = \frac{\left(\dfrac{mG'}{L'} - 1\right)(y_{n+2} - y_{n+1})}{\ln\left(\dfrac{mG'}{L'}\right)} \qquad (6.47)$$

Substituting for $(y - y^*)_{av}$ from Eq. (6.47) in Eq. (6.43),

$$h = \frac{G'}{K_G \bar{a} P} \frac{\ln(mG'/L')}{(mG'/L') - 1} = H_{tOG} \frac{\ln(mG'/L')}{(mG'/L') - 1} \qquad (6.48)$$

But, h = the packed height required to achieve the same separation as on the nth tray = HETP.

$$\Rightarrow \qquad \text{HETP} = H_{tOG} \frac{\ln(mG'/L')}{(mG'/L') - 1} = H_{tOG} \frac{\ln(\bar{S})}{\bar{S} - 1} \qquad (6.49)$$

Thus, if the slope of the equilibrium line and H_{tOG} of the packing for a particular gas–liquid system are known, the HETP can be calculated. The above equation is not valid for $mG = L$.

The quantity HETP is often used to characterize the performance of a packing. A good packing has a small HETP. The concept of HETP is more widely used in packed tower distillation calculations. Its value usually ranges between 1 and 3 ft. Like HTUs, the HETP values of a packing for the separation of typical mixtures are often available from the vendor of the packing. The HETP of a packing depends upon quite a few factors (compare with HTUs) like: (i) the type and size of the packing, (ii) the gas and liquid flow rates, (iii) the physical and transport properties as well as the equilibrium relation, and (iv) the uniformity of liquid and gas distribution.

Limited data and correlations for HETP of different types of packings are available in the open literature (see, for example, Kister, 1992; Strigle, 1994; Billet, 1995; Ludwig, 1997; Perry's Handbook, 7th ed., 1997). In fact, Kister reported HETP values and charts for many of the three generations of random packings and also for structured packings. Wagner et al. (1997) reported a correlation for HETP for modern random packings. It is interesting to note that the classical data on mass transfer in a round 'wetted-wall column' reported long ago by Gilliland and Sherwood (1934) agree well with the results obtained in a bed of structured packing since mass transfer occurs in a falling film in both cases. Besides direct charts and correlations, the HETP of a packing can be calculated from the mass transfer correlations by first obtaining the HTU and then using Eq. (6.48). A few thumb rules for the estimation of HETP have been suggested by Strigle (1994).

EXAMPLE 6.6 (*Tower design for scrubbing a lean gas—number of ideal stages and HETP*) Emission of toxic and hazardous volatile compounds is a challenging pollution control problem. Volatile organic compounds (VOCs) constitute the largest class of volatile emissions. An effective strategy is to construct a 'permanent total enclosure' (PTE) around the source of emission. An exhaust fan pulls out the emitted gases from the enclosure. The waste gas containing the volatiles may be cleaned by absorption using a suitable solvent or by adsorption in a solid adsorbent. The function of a PTE is to collect the emission in a rather concentrated form and to prevent its free mixing with the ambient air (mixing with air causes dilution and makes recovery almost impossible).

Carbon disulphide is a volatile hazardous substance emitted from the acid bath of a viscose plant. In a particular plant, it is planned to build a permanent total enclosure covering the acid baths. It is estimated that the exhaust gas from the PTE would leave at a rate of 12,000 Nm^3 per hour containing 2% CS_2 in air. The gas has to be treated in a tower packed with 2-inch intalox saddles using an absorption oil (37 API; mol. wt. = 220; density = 840 kg/m^3; viscosity = 4.7 cP at 25°C) in order to remove 98% of the CS_2. The liquid rate to be used is 1.35 times the minimum. If the overall gas-phase mass transfer coefficient is $K_G \bar{a}$ = 102 kmol/(h)(m³)(bar), calculate the diameter and height of the tower. The solution is ideal and the vapour pressure of CS_2 at 25°C is 359 mm Hg. The oil (loaded with CS_2) leaving the absorption tower is pumped to the top of a steam-stripping tower for recovery of the solute and regeneration of the solvent oil. The stripped oil having 50 ppm CS_2 is cooled and fed back to the absorption tower. The tower operates at 25°C and 1.1 bar total pressure.

Also, determine the number of ideal trays required for this separation. Note that the values of the absorption factor at the top and at the bottom of the tower differ only slightly.

Solution

The solution is ideal. Equilibrium relation,

$$y = (P^v/P)x \quad \text{where } P^v = 359 \text{ mm Hg and } P = 1.1 \text{ bar} = 827 \text{ mm Hg}$$

$$\Rightarrow \quad y = 0.434x; \text{ in mole ratio unit, } Y = \frac{0.434\,X}{1 + 0.566\,X} \approx 0.434X \text{ (at low concentrations)} \quad \text{(i)}$$

Gas flow rate and concentrations: Molecular weight of the feed (98% air, 2% CS_2)

$$= (0.98)(28.8) + (0.02)(76) = 29.7$$

Feed gas rate

$$= 12,000 \text{ m}^3/\text{h at NTP} = 12,000/22.414 = 535.4 \text{ kmol/h} = (535.4)(29.7) = 15,901 \text{ kg/h} = G_1$$

Feed gas concentration,

$$y_1 = 0.02; \qquad Y_1 = 0.02/0.98 = 0.0204$$

CS_2 entering $= (535.4)(0.02) = 10.7$ kmol/h; air entering $= (535.4)(0.98) = 524.7$ kmol/h $(= G_s)$

CS_2 absorbed $= (10.7)(0.98) = 10.5$ kmol/h; $\qquad CS_2$ leaving $= 0.2$ kmol/h.

Total gas out $= 524.7 + 0.2 = 524.9$ kmol/h $= G_2$; concentration $= Y_2 = 0.2/524.7 = 0.00038$

Calculation of the minimum liquid rate: At low concentrations of the streams, the equilibrium relation in mole ratio unit can also be taken to be $Y = 0.434X$.

At the pinch point (it occurs at the bottom of the tower in this case),

$$X_1^* = Y_1/0.434 = 0.0204/0.434 = 0.047 \qquad \text{[using Eq. (i)]}$$

Concentration of CS_2 in the feed solvent $= 50$ ppm $= 50$ kg CS_2 in 10^6 kg solvent

i.e. $$X_2 \approx \frac{50/76}{10^6/220} = 0.000145$$

Material balance: $G_s(Y_1 - Y_2) = [L_s]_{min}(X_1^* - X_2)$

$$[L_s]_{min} = \frac{(524.7)(0.0204 - 0.00038)}{0.047 - 0.000145} = 225.3 \text{ kmol/h}$$

Actual liquid rate (solute-free basis),

$$L_s = (1.35)[L_s]_{min} = (1.35)(225.3) = 304.2 \text{ kmol/h}$$

Material balance: $G_s(Y_1 - Y_2) = L_s(X_1 - X_2)$

$$\Rightarrow \qquad (524.7)(0.0204 - 0.00038) = (304.2)(X_1 - 0.000145)$$

$$\Rightarrow \qquad X_1 = 0.0347 \qquad \text{and} \qquad x_1 = 0.0347/1.0347 = 0.0335$$

Calculation of the number of overall gas-phase transfer units:

Use the simplified equation for a dilute gas,

$$N_{tOG} = \int_{y_2}^{y_1} \frac{dy}{y - y^*} = \frac{y_1 - y_2}{(y - y^*)_M} \qquad \text{[Eq. (6.27(b)]}$$

$$y_1 = 0.02; \qquad y_2 \approx 0.00038; \qquad x_1 = 0.0335; \qquad x_2 \approx 0.000145$$

$$y_1 - y_1^* = y_1 - mx_1 = 0.02 - (0.434)(0.0335) = 0.00546 \qquad \text{[using Eq. (i)]}$$

$$y_2 - y_2^* = y_2 - mx_2 = 0.00038 - (0.434)(0.000145) = 0.000317$$

$$(y - y^*)_M = \frac{(y_1 - y_1^*) - (y_2 - y_2^*)}{\ln[(y_1 - y_1^*)/(y_2 - y_2^*)]} = \frac{0.00546 - 0.000317}{\ln(0.00546/0.000317)} = 0.001807$$

$$N_{tOG} = \frac{0.02 - 0.00038}{0.001807} = \boxed{10.8}$$

Tower diameter: Tower diameter $= 3.35$ m (taking the gas velocity as 65% of the flooding velocity); tower cross-section $= 8.78$ m^2. (Calculations are not shown here; follow Example 6.2)

Calculation of the height of a transfer unit:

Gas flow rate at the bottom, G_1 = 535.4 kmol/h; gas flow rate at the top, G_2 = 524.9 kmol/h

Average flow rate, G_{av} = (535.4 + 524.9)/2 = 530.1 kmol/h

Gas mass flow rate, G' = (530.1 kmol/h)/(8.78 m^2) = 60.4 kmol/h·m^2

$$H_{tOG} = \frac{G'}{K_y \bar{a}} = \frac{G'}{K_G \bar{a} P} = \frac{60.4}{(102)(1.1)} = 0.538 \text{ m}$$

Packed height = $(N_{tOG}) \times (H_{tOG})$

= (10.8)(0.538) = $\boxed{5.8 \text{ m}}$

Number of ideal stages required: As the gas and the liquid concentrations are both low (below 5%), the equilibrium and the operating lines are practically straight. The Kremser equation can be used to determine the number of ideal stages (use the notations conforming to Figure 4.11). The average value of the absorption factor will be used.

Top of the column:

G_1 = 524.9   and L_0 = (304.2)(1 + X_0) = (304.2)(1 + 1.000145) ≈ 304.2 kmol/h

$$\bar{A}_1 = L_0/mG_1 = (304.2)/(0.434)(524.9) = \boxed{1.335}$$

Bottom of the column: G_{N+1} = 535.4; L_N = 304.2 + 10.5 = 314.7 kmol/h

$\bar{A}_N = L_N/mG_{N+1} = (314.7)/(0.434)(535.4) = \boxed{1.355}$. Average value, $\bar{A}$ = $\boxed{1.345}$

The number of ideal stages is [use Eq. (4.41) and mole fraction unit (at low concentration)]

$$N = \frac{\log\left[\left(\dfrac{y_{N+1} - mx_0}{y_1 - mx_0}\right)\left(1 - \dfrac{1}{\bar{A}}\right) + \dfrac{1}{\bar{A}}\right]}{\log \bar{A}}$$

$$= \frac{\log\left[\left(\dfrac{0.02 - (0.434)(0.000145)}{0.00038 - (0.434)(0.000145)}\right)\left(1 - \dfrac{1}{1.345}\right) + \dfrac{1}{1.345}\right]}{\log (1.345)} = \boxed{9.5}$$

HETP = 5.8 m/9.5 = $\boxed{0.61 \text{ m}}$

The absorption factor at the bottom is about 1.5% less than the value at the top. The HETP can also be calculated using Eq. (6.49) for a dilute gas–liquid system.

$$mG/L = \bar{S} = 1/1.345 = 0.7435; \quad H_{tOG} = 0.538 \text{ m (calculated above)}$$

$$\text{HETP} = \frac{mG}{L} \frac{\ln(mG/L)}{(mG/L) - 1} = 0.538\frac{\ln(0.7435)}{0.7435 - 1} = \boxed{0.62 \text{ m}}$$

This is practically the same as calculated above by dividing the height of packing by the number of ideal stages.

EXAMPLE 6.7 (*Design of a stripping tower with two feeds*)   It is required to design a stripping tower to remove *cyclo*-hexane from a non-volatile oil (molecular weight = 240). Two feed streams are available — 40 kmol/h, 10 mole% *cyclo*-hexane, and 55 kmol/h, 5.5 mole% *cyclo*-hexane. The lean oil leaving the bottom of the tower must not contain more than 0.5 mole% of the solute. The stripping column should operate at 105°C and essentially 1 atm pressure with superheated steam as the stripping medium. The steam rate is 1.2 times the minimum steam rate. Calculate the minimum steam rate and the number of ideal stages required. A solution of *cyclo*-hexane in the oil is almost ideal and Raoult's law can be used to determine the equilibrium in this system. The vapour pressure of *cyclo*-hexane can be calculated using the Antoine equation: $\ln P^v = 10.776 - (3807/T)$; P^v in bar and T in K.

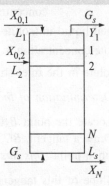

Figure 610(a)   A stripping column with two feeds.

Solution
The stripping column has two feeds. The more concentrated feed should enter at the top and the other feed should enter at a suitable intermediate tray of the column [Figure 6.10(a)]. The stripping steam enters the tower at the bottom. Thus the tower has two sections—the liquid rate is smaller in the upper section. But the steam rate (on solute-free basis) is constant. There will be two operating lines—the upper operating line will have a smaller slope.

Using the given equation, vapour pressure of *cyclo*-hexane at 105°C (= 378 K), $P^v = 2.023$ bar

Equilibrium relation (Raoult's law): $Py = xP^v$, P = total pressure = 1.013 bar $\Rightarrow y = 2x$

Equilibrium relation in the mole ratio unit: $Y = \dfrac{y}{1-y} = \dfrac{2x}{1-2x} = \dfrac{2(X/1+X)}{1-2(X/1+X)} = \dfrac{2X}{1-X}$

The equilibrium line given by the above equation is plotted on the X–Y plane, Figure 6.10(b).

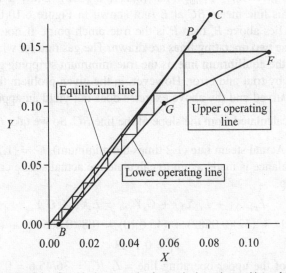

Figure 6.10(b)   Graphical construction for a stripping column with two feeds.

Feed flow rates and concentrations:

Feed-1 (higher conc., to be fed at the top of the stripping tower), 40 kmol/h, 10 mole% solute.

$L_{s1} = (40)(1 - 0.1) = 36$ kmol/h; concentration (mole ratio), $X_{0,1} = 0.1/0.9 = 0.111$

Feed-2 (lower conc., to be fed at an intermediate position in the tower), 55 kmol/h, 5.5 mole% solute

$$L_{s2} = (55)(1 - 0.055) = 52 \text{ kmol/h}$$

concentration (mole ratio), $X_{0,2} = 0.055/(1 - 0.055) = 0.0582$

Total liquid in (solute-free basis), $L_s = L_{s1} + L_{s2} = 36 + 52 = 88$ kmol/h

Solute concentration in the exit liquid = 0.5 mole% $\Rightarrow X_N = 0.005/(1 - 0.005) = 0.00502$

No solute in the inlet stripping gas (superheated steam) $\Rightarrow Y_{N+1} = 0$.

Determination of the minimum steam rate, $G_{s,\min}$:

Locate the point $B(0.00502, 0)$ on the X–Y plane [see Figure 6.10(b)].

Draw a tangent, BC, to the equilibrium line from the point B. The point of tangency, P, is the pinch point (*this has to be checked, however*).

Slope of this tangent = $2.316 = L_s/(G_{s,\min}) \Rightarrow G_{s,\min} = 88/2.316 = \boxed{38 \text{ kmol/h}}$

Now we make a material balance over the column for this minimum steam rate, $G_{s,\min}$.

$$L_{s1}X_{0,1} + L_{s2}X_{0,2} + G_{s,\min}Y_{N+1} = L_s X_N + G_{s,\min}Y_{1,\max}$$
$$\Rightarrow \quad (36)(0.111) + (52)(0.0582) + (38)(0) = (88)(0.00502) + (38)Y_{1,\max}$$
$$\Rightarrow \quad Y_{1,\max} = 0.1732$$

Slope of the operating line of the upper section for this steam rate = $L_{s1}/G_{s,\min} = 36/38 = 0.9474$. In order to check if the point P is the *true* pinch point, the following steps are to be followed.

(i) Locate the point $D(X_{0,1}, Y_{1,\max})$, i.e. $(0.111, 0.1732)$. Draw a line of slope 0.9474 through D. This line meets BC at E [not shown in Figure 6.10(b)].

(ii) If the point E lies above P, then P is the true pinch point. If not, a smaller gas rate is selected and the two operating lines are drawn. The gas rate for which the two operating lines meet on the equilibrium line, is the true minimum stripping gas rate. This gas rate is to be found by trial-and-error. However, in the given problem the equilibrium line is only slightly curved and the above exercise does not yield an appreciably different gas rate than that calculated from the slope of the line BC. So we take $G_{s,\min} = \boxed{38 \text{ kmol/h}}$.

The operating lines: Actual steam rate (1.2 times the minimum), $G_s = (1.2)(38) = 45.6$ kmol/h. The overall material balance is made again to calculate the actual solute concentration Y_1 in the steam leaving at the top.

$$L_{s1}X_{0,1} + L_{s2}X_{0,2} + G_s Y_{N+1} = L_s X_N + G_s Y_1$$
$$\Rightarrow \quad (36)(0.111) + (52)(0.0582) + (45.6)(0) = (88)(0.00502) + (45.6)Y_1$$
$$\Rightarrow \quad Y_1 = 0.1443$$

Slope of the upper operating line = $L_{s1}/G_s = 36/45.6 = 0.7895$

Slope of the lower operating line = $L_s/G_s = 88/45.6 = 1.93$

Draw the lower operating line, *BG*, through the point *B* having the slope 1.93. Locate the point *F* (0.111, 0.1443) corresponding to the top of the column, draw the upper operating line, *FG*, through *F* having the slope 0.7895. The two operating lines meet at the point *G* [Figure 6.10(b)].

Number of ideal stages: The number of ideal stages can be determined by drawing steps between the operating lines and the equilibrium line. We start from the point *F*, draw steps changing from the upper to the lower operating line as the common point *G* is crossed. A total of 9.4 ideal plates are required. The second feed enters the tower at the second plate from the top where we move from the upper to the lower operating line during construction of steps.

(*Note:* Construction of steps may start from the lower point *B* as well.)

6.8 TRAY EFFICIENCY

In Chapter 5, we introduced the concept of an ideal stage. An *ideal stage* provides quite an efficient contact between the phases so that they attain equilibrium. Or, in other words, the phases leaving an ideal stage are at equilibrium irrespective of the inlet concentrations. However, the performance of a *real stage* will expectedly be different from that of an ideal stage. The *tray efficiency* is an indicator of how closely the performance of a real tray approaches that of an ideal tray.

6.8.1 Point Efficiency

The contact between the phases on a tray is not uniformly good at all locations, i.e. the tray efficiency is likely to vary from one location to another on a tray. However, if we assume that (i) the liquid is 'vertically well-mixed' (i.e. the liquid concentration is uniform in the vertical direction at any point on the tray and (ii) the gas-phase is in plug flow (i.e. the gas concentration changes along the depth), we can define a 'point efficiency' based on the gas-phase concentration. In the following analysis, we consider gas–liquid contact on a tray, but the results are applicable to other types of systems as well. The point efficiency is defined as

$$E_{OG} = \frac{y_{n,\,local} - y_{n+1,\,local}}{y_{n,\,local}^* - y_{n+1,\,local}} \tag{6.50}$$

The notations used in Eq. (6.50) are illustrated in Figure 6.11. The local concentration (i.e. the concentration at any point or location on the tray) of the gas leaving the $(n+1)$th tray is $y_{n+1,local}$. This is also the concentration of the gas entering the nth tray. Similarly, $y_{n,local}$ is the local concentration of the gas leaving the nth tray. The local concentration of the liquid is $x_{n,local}$ (note that this concentration is the same at all depths at a given location on the tray since the liquid is assumed to be 'vertically well-mixed'), and the concentration of the solute in the gas phase that can remain in equilibrium with a liquid of this concentration is $y_{n,local}^*$. So E_{OG} is the ratio of actual enrichment of the gas (as it bubbles through the liquid on the tray) to the maximum enrichment that could have been achieved if the exiting gas had reached equilibrium with the local liquid.

Tray efficiency depends upon the rate of interphase mass transfer in the dispersion on a tray. If the rate of mass transfer is very high, the efficiency will be close to 100%. However, at a high rate of mass transfer, the phases will approach equilibrium and the mass transfer driving force will be rather small. Therefore, a large mass transfer coefficient and a large interfacial area are required in order to achieve a high tray efficiency. We shall show below how the point efficiency is related to these quantities.

Let us refer to Figure 6.11(b) in which a small area dS of the tray and the gas–liquid dispersion over it are shown. Let G' be the molar gas flow rate (on unit area basis) which is assumed to remain constant. We write the steady-state mass balance over a small thickness dz of the dispersion.

$$\text{The rate of mass transfer to the gas phase} = G'dS\ dy \tag{6.51}$$

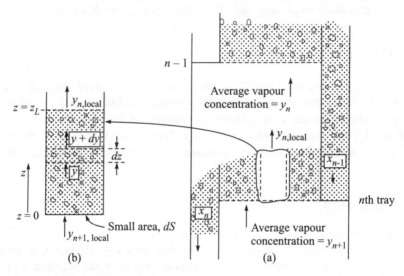

Figure 6.11 (a) Point efficiency illustrated; (b) local differential mass balance over a small element of the gas–liquid dispersion.

The rate of mass transfer (it is assumed that mass transfer occurs from the liquid to the gas phase)

$$= K_y(\bar{a}\ dS\ dz)(y^*_{n,\text{local}} - y) \tag{6.52}$$

where

K_y = overall gas-phase mass transfer coefficient
$\bar{a}$ = specific interfacial area (say square metre of gas–liquid contact area per cubic metre volume of the dispersion)
$dS.dz$ = small volume of the dispersion
$\bar{a}\,dSdz$ = gas–liquid contact area in the small volume of the dispersion
$(y^*_{n,\text{local}} - y)$ = local mass transfer driving force at a height z from the tray floor.

Equating the right-hand sides of Eqs. (6.51) and (6.52),

$$G'dS\ dy = K_y(\bar{a}\ dS\,dz)(y^*_{n,\text{local}} - y)$$

Integrating over the height z_L of the dispersion [see Figure 6.11(b)],

$$\int_{y_{n+1,\text{local}}}^{y_{n,\text{local}}} \frac{dy}{(y^*_{n,\text{local}} - y)} = \int_0^{z_L} K_y\,\bar{a}\,\frac{dz}{G'} \tag{6.53}$$

Since the local liquid is vertically well-mixed, x_{local} is uniform over the depth z_L of the dispersion. So the corresponding equilibrium gas-phase concentration, $y^*_{n,local}$ is also constant. So we have from Eq. (6.53),

$$-\ln \frac{y^*_{n,local} - y_{n,\,local}}{y^*_{n,local} - y_{n+1,\,local}} = \frac{K_y \bar{a} z_L}{G'} = N_{tOG} \tag{6.54}$$

$$\Rightarrow \qquad -\ln \left[1 - \frac{y_{n,\,local} - y_{n+1,\,local}}{y^*_{n,local} - y_{n+1,\,local}} \right] = -\ln(1 - E_{OG}) = N_{tOG}$$

$$\Rightarrow \qquad E_{OG} = 1 - e^{-N_{tOG}} \tag{6.55}$$

Here N_{tOG} is the number of overall gas-phase transfer units. A similar expression based on liquid-phase mass transfer can be easily derived. If the number of transfer units is high (which is possible if $K_y \bar{a}$ is high), then E_{OG} approaches unity, i.e. the tray approaches ideal performance.

EXAMPLE 6.8 (*Point efficiency on a tray*)   For a particular tray in a gas absorption column, the following data are available: superficial gas flow rate (taken on the basis of 'active tray area'), $G' = 198$ kmol/m^2·h; overall gas-phase volumetric mass transfer coefficient, $K_c \bar{a} = 2.1$ kmol/(m^3)(s)(kmol/m^3); depth of the froth on the tray, $z_L = 0.25$ m; total pressure, $P = 1.2$ bar; temperature, $T = 35°C$. Calculate the point efficiency.

Solution

Calculate the overall mass transfer coefficient, $K_y \bar{a}$. Given, $T = 308$ K.

$$K_y \bar{a} = K_c \bar{a} (P/RT) = (2.1)[(1.2)/(0.08317)(308)] = 0.0984 \text{ kmol/(s)(m}^3)(\Delta y)$$

From Eq. (6.54),

$$N_{tOG} = \frac{K_y \bar{a} z_L}{G'} = \frac{(0.0984)(0.25)}{(198/3600)} = 0.447$$

Point efficiency [Eq. (6.55)],

$$E_{OG} = 1 - e^{-N_{tOG}} = 1 - e^{-0.447} = 1 - 0.64 = \boxed{0.36}$$

6.8.2 Murphree Efficiency

It is quite reasonable to assume that the gases leaving the dispersion at different locations of a tray get mixed up before entering the upper tray. The concentration of the liquid on a tray changes as it flows over the tray. Let x_n be the concentration of the liquid leaving the nth tray and y^*_n be the corresponding equilibrium concentration of the gas phase. On the basis of these concentrations, Murphree (1925) defined a tray efficiency as given below.

$$E_{MG} = \frac{y_n - y_{n+1}}{y^*_n - y_{n+1}} \tag{6.56}$$

Here y_n and y_{n+1} are the average concentrations of gases leaving the nth and the $(n+1)$th tray respectively [see Figure 6.11(a)].

The Murphree tray efficiency can be related to the 'point efficiency' depending upon the extent of mixing of the liquid as it flows across a tray as well as of the vapour between two consecutive trays. The following limiting cases may be identified.

(a) If the liquid phase is assumed to be 'well-mixed' over a tray, the liquid composition remains uniform at x_n. Then

$$E_{MG} = E_{OG} \tag{6.57}$$

The above assumption is good for a tower of small diameter. In such a tower, the liquid moves through a rather small distance on a tray to reach the downcomer. The gas bubbling through the liquid creates enough turbulence to ensure almost uniform concentration of the liquid over the tray. However, in a tower of larger diameter, the liquid has to travel through a longer distance to reach the downcomer and its concentration varies substantially from one end of the tray to the other (i.e. along its flow path). The extent of 'backmixing' on a tray is generally taken into account by introducing an 'axial dispersion coefficient' (see the Appendix).

(b) The other limiting case arises if the liquid is in 'plug flow' and no axial mixing at all occurs in the liquid. In such a case, the following relation between the Murphree efficiency and the 'point efficiency' can be developed (this is called 'Lewis case 1').

$$E_{MG} = \frac{L'}{mG'}\left[\exp\left(\frac{mG'E_{OG}}{L'} \right) - 1 \right] \tag{6.58}$$

Here L' = liquid mass flow rate in mole/(area)(time) and m = Henry's Law constant [$y_n^* = mx_n$].

EXAMPLE 6.9 (*Murphree tray efficiency*)   The following data were collected by analyzing the gas and liquid samples to and from a particular tray (call it the nth tray) in an experiment on plate efficiency in an absorption column.

$$G_s = 90 \text{ kmol/h}; \quad L_s = 100 \text{ kmol/h}; \quad y_{n+1} = 0.12; \quad x_n = 0.078; \quad x_{n-1} = 0.06$$

The equilibrium relation is linear in the form, $y = 1.01x$. If the liquid on the tray is 'well mixed', calculate the Murphree tray efficiency.

Solution

First we calculate y_n from the material balance equation.

$X_n = x_n/(1 - x_n) = 0.078/0.922 = 0.0846$. Similarly, $X_{n-1} = 0.06383$; $Y_{n+1} = 0.1364$.

$G_s(Y_{n+1} - Y_n) = L_s(X_n - X_{n-1}) \Rightarrow (90)(0.1364 - Y_n) = (100)(0.0846 - 0.06383)$

$\Rightarrow$ $Y_n = 0.1133$

$$y_n = Y_n/(1 + Y_n) = 0.1133/1.1133 = 0.1018$$

$$y_n^* = mx_n = (1.01)(0.078) = 0.0788$$

Murphree efficiency, $E_{MG} = \dfrac{y_{n+1} - y_n}{y_{n+1} - y_n^*} = \dfrac{0.12 - 0.1018}{0.12 - 0.0788} = 0.442$, i.e. $\boxed{44.2\%}$

EXAMPLE 6.10 (*Murphree efficiency when the liquid is in plug flow*).   If, in Example 6.8, the liquid is in 'plug flow' and its flow rate L' is 240 kmol/m^2·h, the equilibrium relation is $y = 1.01x$, calculate the Murphree efficiency.

Solution
The absorption factor,
$$\bar{A} = L'/mG' = (240)/(1.01)(198) = 1.2$$
Using Eq. (6.58),

Murphree efficiency, $E_{MG} = \bar{A}\,[\exp(E_{OG}/\bar{A}) - 1] = 1.2[\exp(0.36/1.2) - 1] = 0.42$, i.e. $\boxed{42\%}$

6.8.3   Effect of Liquid Entrainment on Tray Efficiency

Entrainment of liquid droplets in the up-flowing gas considerably affects the efficiency. If E is the fractional entrainment (moles of liquid entrained per mole of liquid entering a tray), the Murphree efficiency, corrected for the entrainment, is given by

$$E_{MGE} = \frac{E_{MG}}{1 + E_{MG}\,[E/(1 - E)]} \tag{6.59}$$

6.8.4   Overall Tray Efficiency

An *overall tray efficiency* (or overall column efficiency in a section of the column) is sometimes used to determine the number of real trays. It is defined as

$$E_O = \frac{\text{number of ideal trays}}{\text{number of real trays}} \tag{6.60}$$

The overall tray efficiency E_O is sometimes obtained from plant data. If (i) the gas and liquid flow rates (G', L')) and the equilibrium parameter m remain constant over a section of the column, and (ii) the Murphree efficiency remains the same for all the trays, the following relation between the overall column efficiency and the Murphree efficiency can be derived.

$$E_O = \frac{\ln\left[1 + E_{MG}\left(\dfrac{mG'}{L'} - 1\right)\right]}{\ln\left(\dfrac{mG'}{L'}\right)} \tag{6.61}$$

If $\dfrac{mG'}{L'} \sim 1$, E_O and E_{MG} become nearly equal.

EXAMPLE 6.11 (*Determination of the number of real trays if the Murphree efficiency is known*)   A gas absorption column is to receive 130 kmol/h of feed gas containing 12 mole% of a solute. It is required to remove 93% of the solute using 150 kmol/h of a solvent. The feed solvent has 0.4 mol% of residual solute in it. The Murphree tray efficiency is known to be 0.45. Determine the number of ideal trays as well as the number of real trays required for the separation. The equilibrium data for the system are given as:

x	0.0133	0.0333	0.0493	0.064	0.0747	0.0933	0.1053
y	0.01	0.0266	0.0433	0.06	0.0733	0.1	0.12

Solution

Flow rates:

$$G_s = (130)(1 - 0.12) = 114.4; \qquad L_s = (150)(1 - 0.004) = 149.4 \text{ kmol/h}$$

Concentrations: feed liquid: $x_0 = 0.004$, $X_0 = 0.004/0.996 = 0.00402$; feed gas: $y_{N+1} = 0.12$, $Y_{N+1} = 0.12/0.88 = 0.1364$; exit gas (93% of the solute is removed): $Y_1 = (0.1364)(1 - 0.93) = 0.00945$.

Material balance: $G_s(Y_{N+1} - Y_1) = L_s(X_N - X_0) \Rightarrow 114.4(0.1364 - 0.00945) = 149.4(X_N - 0.00402)$

i.e. $\qquad\qquad X_N = 0.1012 \qquad$ and $\qquad x_N = 0.1012/(1 + 0.1012) = 0.092$

   Terminal concentrations: top, $(x_0, y_1) \rightarrow (0.004, 0.00945)$; bottom, $(x_N, y_{N+1}) \rightarrow (0.092, 0.12)$

Operating line: $\qquad G_s\left(\dfrac{y}{1-y} - Y_1\right) = L_s\left(\dfrac{x}{1-x} - X_0\right)$

$$\Rightarrow \qquad\qquad \frac{y}{1-y} = 1.306\left(\frac{x}{1-x} - 0.00402\right) + 0.00945 \qquad\qquad \text{(i)}$$

Determination of the number of trays: The given equilibrium data and the operating line given by Eq. (i) are plotted on the x–y plane (Figure 6.12). By constructing steps between these lines (*OA* and *BC*), we get the number of $\boxed{\text{ideal trays 5.5}}$.

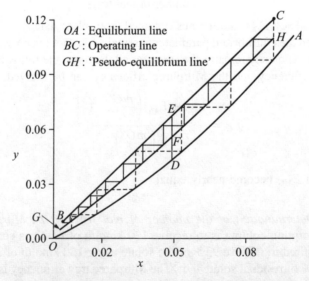

Figure 6.12   Construction of real plates, Murphree efficiency given.

To determine the *number of real trays*, we have to plot a 'pseudo-equilibrium line' using the given value of the Murphree efficiency. Take any vertical distance *DE* between *OA* and *BC*. Divide *DE* by the point *F* such that *FE* = 0.45*DE*. The locus of the point *F* is the 'pseudo-equilibrium line' (*GH*). Steps are now drawn between the operating line (*BC*) and the pseudo-equilibrium line (*GH*). The number of | real stages = 12. |

6.8.5 Prediction of Tray Efficiency

Prediction of tray efficiency has received a lot of attention. Besides the types of efficiency described before, a few other types were proposed by Hausen, Standart and Holland (see Lockett, 1986) although those have not been of much practical use. An excellent review of the important literature till the early 1980s has been made by Lockett. There are three methods of determination or estimation of tray efficiency: (i) totally empirical, (ii) direct scale-up from laboratory data, and (iii) semi-theoretical or theoretical models for mass transfer on a tray.

As the name suggests, the empirical method attempts to correlate the experimental tray efficiency data collected by bench scale, pilot plant, or plant data with the relevant properties and parameters of the gas–liquid systems. A chart (Figure 6.13) for 'overall tray efficiency' was given by O'Connell (1946) long ago and is still used. It was prepared by plotting the experimental efficiency data (collected by absorption/stripping of solutes in a number of aqueous and non-aqueous systems in columns of different diameters up to 9 ft) versus the group $mM_L\mu_L/\rho_L$. The efficiency decreases with increasing viscosity of the liquid since increasing viscosity reduces mixing and the mass transfer rate. The dependence of E_O on M_L can be explained in a similar way, but the cause of dependence on m is not very apparent. The following correlation for E_O prepared from the plot shown in Figure 6.13 is more convenient to use.

$$E_O = 1.597 - 0.199 \log(mM_L\mu_L/\rho_L) - 0.0896[\log(mM_L\mu_L/\rho_L)]^2 \qquad (6.62)$$

Here μ_L is in cP and ρ_L in lb/ft^3.

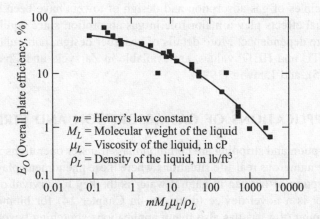

Figure 6.13 O'Connell's chart for tray efficiency of an absorption/stripping column.

Experimental data for a system collected by using a small model column (the Oldershaw coulmn, for example) can be scaled up to predict the efficiency in an industrial column. This technique has been used in quite a few cases.

Semi-theoretical or theoretical models for tray efficiency attempt to calculate the point efficiency E_{OG}, using equations or correlations for mass transfer coefficients or HTUs. A number of correlations for H_{tG} and H_{tL} (and also for k_G and k_L) are available in the literature (Lockett, 1986; Perry's Handbook, 7th ed., 1997, Ch. 14) may be used for this purpose. The calculated point efficiency is converted to the Murphree efficiency and then to the overall plate efficiency [$E_{OG} \rightarrow E_{MG} \rightarrow E_O$; Eq. (6.55) $\rightarrow$ (6.57) $\rightarrow$ (6.61)]. The assumption that the liquid is in plug flow is again an approximation. Partial 'backmixing' of the liquid on a tray, only partial mixing of the gas between adjacent trays, or existence of partially stagnant pools of liquid near the tower wall (the 'stagnant region model') occur frequently (Stichlmair and Fair, 1998) on real trays. These phenomena have to be taken into account in a model for tray efficiency. A relation between E_{OG} and E_{MG} where the gas is well mixed but the liquid is partially backmixed was reported in the AIChE Bubble Tray Design Manual of 1958. Recently Bennett et al. (1997) proposed the following correlation for the estimation of point efficiency of a sieve tray on the basis of their 'two-zone model'. They assumed a liquid-continuous zone near the tray deck, and a vapour-continuous zone above it. Mass transfer in both the zones is estimated using suitable correlations to obtain the correlation for E_{OG}.

$$E_{OG} = 1 - \exp\left[\frac{-0.0029}{1 + m\left(\dfrac{\rho_{mG}}{\rho_{mL}}\right)\left(\dfrac{D_G}{D_L}\dfrac{1-\varphi_e}{A_h/A_a}\right)^{0.5}} \left[\frac{\rho_G u_h h_{Fe}}{\mu_L}\right]^{0.4136} \left(\frac{h_L}{d_H}\right)^{0.6074} \left(\frac{A_h}{A_a}\right)^{-0.3195} \right] \quad (6.63)$$

Here m = slope of the equilibrium line ($y = mx$); ρ = density; ρ_m = molar density; D = diffusivities; A_h = area of the holes; A_a = active tray area; φ_e = effective relative froth density (= h_L/h_{Fe}); h_L = clear liquid height on the tray; h_{Fe} = effective froth height; u_h = hole velocity of the gas; d_H = hole diameter.

The basic principles of gas absorption and design of towers have been briefly discussed in this chapter. Thermal effects play a major role in gas absorption since equilibrium relation has a strong temperature dependence. More details of absorber design, particularly design data and information like HTU and HETP values, are available in Zarzycki and Chacuk (1993), Strigle (1994), Billet (1995), and Ludwig (1997).

6.9   OTHER APPLICATIONS OF GAS ABSORPTION AND STRIPPING

Although gas absorption and stripping are common mass transfer operations in chemical process industries, there are numerous real-life situations where these phenomena play an important role. For example, absorption of oxygen in natural water is the key to survival of aquatic creatures. A blood oxygenator is a novel device (discussed in Chapter 14) for biomedical applications. Desorption or stripping of a gas has also many applications stretching beyond the boundary of process industries. Example 6.12 deals with such an application.

EXAMPLE 6.12 (*VOC stripping in a shower*) Exposure to volatile organic compounds has been a major human health concern in recent years. On the basis of experimental evidences, several researchers argued that important sources of exposure to VOCs occur indoor rather than the outdoor environment. One such potential source is contaminated tap water used for bathing or even washing [see Moya et al., *Environ. Sci. Technol.*, *33*(1999) 1341–1349; 2321–2327. They reported experimental investigations on volatilization of contaminants in showers and dishwashers.]. A simple model of stripping and resulting accumulation of a contaminant in a shower was proposed by Little [*Environ. Sci. Technol.*, 26(1992) 1341–1349]. Let us use the following notations for the relevant parameters to make a simplified analysis of the phenomenon (see Figure 6.14): Q_L(m³/s) = rate of water discharge and V_L(m³) = volume of water present ('water holdup') in the shower chamber at any time; Q_G = the rate of air exhaust through the shower; V_s = 'volume of the shower' which is taken as the volume of air in it; K_L(m/s) = overall desorption mass transfer coefficient; a' = total air–water contact area in the shower; C_G, C_L = concentrations (kg/m³) of the VOC in the air and in the water in the chamber respectively at any time t; $\hat{H}$ = Henry's law constant for equilibrium distribution of the VOC in air and water ($C_G = \hat{H} C_L^*$). Assuming that the shower air is 'well-mixed', determine the time rate of change of VOC concentration in the shower. Also, determine the 'steady state' concentration of VOC in the shower.

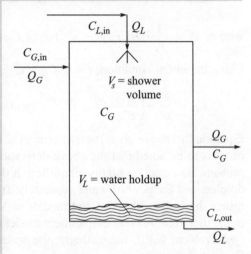

Figure 6.14 Schematic of a shower.

Solution

We first determine the VOC concentration in the shower water as a function of time, using a 'pseudo-steady state approximation'. Since C_G is the gas-phase VOC concentration, the corresponding equilibrium water-phase concentration is $C_L^* = C_G/\hat{H}$. The overall liquid-phase driving force for desorption is $\Delta C_L = C_L - C_L^* = C_L - C_G/\hat{H}$. The following differential mass balance for the liquid-phase concentration can be written.

$$- V_L \frac{dC_L}{dt} = K_L a'(C_L - C_L^*) = K_L a'(C_L - C_G/\hat{H})$$

We integrate the above equation from $t = 0$, $C_L = C_{L,\text{in}}$ to $t = \tau$, $C_L = C_{L,\text{out}}$. Here τ is the 'average residence time' of water in the shower, $\tau = V_L/Q_L$.

$$\ln \frac{C_{L,\text{out}} - C_G/\hat{H}}{C_{L,\text{in}} - C_G/\hat{H}} = - \frac{K_L a'}{V_L} \tau = - \frac{K_L a'}{V_L} \cdot \frac{V_L}{Q_L} = - \frac{K_L a'}{Q_L} = - \beta \text{ (dimensionless)}$$

$$\Rightarrow \qquad C_{L,\text{out}} = (C_{L,\text{in}} - C_G/\hat{H})e^{-\beta} + C_G/\hat{H}$$

$$\Rightarrow \qquad C_{L,\text{in}} - C_{L,\text{out}} = C_{L,\text{in}}(1 - e^{-\beta}) - (C_G/\hat{H})(1 - e^{-\beta}) \qquad \text{(i)}$$

Now, a differential mass balance equation for the VOC accumulation in the shower air may be written taking into account the rate of desorption of VOC from water and that carried away by the exhaust air.

$$V_s \frac{dC_G}{dt} = Q_L(C_{L,\text{in}} - C_{L,\text{out}}) - Q_G(C_G - C_{G,\text{in}}); \quad C_{G,\text{in}} = \text{inlet VOC concentration in air}$$

Substitute for $C_{L,\text{in}} - C_{L,\text{out}}$ from Eq. (i) to get

$$V_s \frac{dC_G}{dt} = Q_L \left[C_{L,\text{in}}(1 - e^{-\beta}) - \frac{C_G}{\hat{H}}(1 - e^{-\beta}) \right] - Q_G(C_G - C_{G,\text{in}}) \Rightarrow \frac{dC_G}{dt} = A' - B'C_G \quad \text{(ii)}$$

where, $A' = \dfrac{1}{V_s}[Q_L C_{L,\text{in}}(1 - e^{-\beta}) + Q_G C_{G,\text{in}}]$ and $B' = \dfrac{1}{V_s}\left[Q_G + \dfrac{Q_L}{\hat{H}}(1 - e^{-\beta}) \right]$

Using the initial condition, $t = 0$, $C_G = C_{G,\text{in}}$, and integrating,

$$C_G = \frac{A'}{B'} - \left(\frac{A'}{B'} - C_{G,\text{in}} \right) e^{-B't} \quad \text{and} \quad C_G = A'/B' \text{ at steady state (i.e. at } t = \infty) \quad \text{(iii)}$$

Equation (iii) above gives the transient VOC concentration in the shower air after the tap is turned on. It is to be noted that the above derivation based on Little's model (see the ref. given in the problem statement) is highly simplified. It does not take into account desorption from the water droplets and the pool of water separately. It considers the air to be well-mixed which does not reflect the reality. More refined models of VOC accumulation in a shower have been proposed in the literature. A two-compartment model of the shower takes care of partial mixing of the air (see Problem 6.30). Interestingly, the water 'holdup' in the shower, V_L, does not appear in Eq. (iii) above.

NOTATIONS

$\bar{a}$	: specific interfacial area of contact, m^2/m^3 packed volume
$\bar{A}$	: absorption factor, L/mG (= L'/mG')
E	: fractional entrainment of liquid (see Section 6.8.3)
E_{OG}, E_{MG}, E_O	: point, Murphree, overall plate efficiency
C, $[(C)_{\text{av}}]$	: solute concentration [average total molar concentration] in the liquid, $kmol/m^3$
G (G_s)	: flow rate of the gas (flow rate on solute-free basis), $kmol/h$ or kg/h
G', L'	: gas and liquid flow rates per unit area basis, $kmol/h \cdot m^2$
h_T	: packed height, m
H_{tG}, H_{tOG}	: height of individual and overall gas-phase mass transfer unit respectively, m
k_x, k_y	: individual mass transfer coefficients, $kmol/(h)(m^2)(\Delta x)$, $kmol/(h)(m^2)(\Delta y)$
k'_x, k'_y	: Colburn-Drew mass transfer coefficients (see Chapter 4)
K_G, K_L	: overall gas-phase mass transfer coefficients, $kmol/(h)(m^2)(\Delta p$ or $\Delta C)$

K_x, K_y	: overall mass transfer coefficients
K_X, K_Y	: overall mass transfer coefficients, $kmol/(h)(m^2)(\Delta X$ or $\Delta Y)$
$L\ (L_s)$	: liquid flow rate (solvent flow rate, solute-free basis), kmol/h or kg/h
m, α	: Henry's law constant (in the form $y = mx$, or $Y = \alpha X$)
N_{tG}, N_{tOG}	: number of individual and overall gas-phase mass transfer unit respectively
P	: total pressure, atm, bar, mm Hg
$\overline{S}$	: stripping factor, $mG/L\ (= mG'/L') = 1/\overline{A}$
Sc	: Schmidt number
x	: solute concentration in the liquid, mol fraction
X, Y	: solute concentration in the liquid or in the gas, mol solute per mol solute-free medium
y	: solute concentration in the gas, mol fraction
y_{iBM}	: log mean concentration of the carrier (B), Eq. (6.16)
y^*	: solute concentration in the gas in equilibrium with bulk liquid of concentration x, mol fraction

SHORT AND MULTIPLE CHOICE QUESTIONS

1. The point P represents the partial pressure of a solute in the bulk gas (p_{Ab}) and the molar concentration in the bulk liquid (C_{Ab}) at a section of a column; the point M represents the interfacial composition (see Figure 6.15). The other relevant quantities and the equilibrium line are also shown. What is the slope of the line PM?

    (i) $-k_x/k_y$ (ii) $-k_L/k_G$ (iii) $-k_c/k_L$

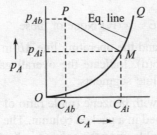

Figure 6.15

2. Equilibrium and operating lines (OP and AB) for four gas–liquid contacting operations are shown in Figure 6.16(a)–(d). (a) Identify the figures as cases of cocurrent/counter-current absorption/stripping. (b) Which of the figures represents an equilibrium co-current unit (i.e. having 100% stage efficiency)? Which one does not?

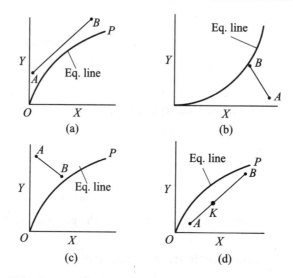

Figure 6.16 (a)–(d) A few sets of equilibrium and operating lines.

3. The equilibrium line for a gas–liquid system is shown in Figure 6.17 (admittedly it is of an unrealistic shape). The solute A is to be scrubbed in a packed tower. The top compositions (represented by the point B on the $X–Y$ plane) are $(0, Y_2)$ and the feed gas concentration is Y_1 (in mole ratio unit, as the notation indicates). In order to determine the minimum liquid rate, a student drew a horizontal line through $Y = Y_1$ that met the equilibrium line at C. He joined BC and was wondering which one of the points C, D, and E was the pinch point. What is your answer?

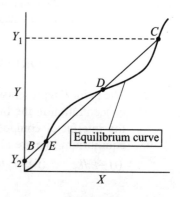

Figure 6.17

(i) C (ii) D (iii) E (iv) None of these

4. The equilibrium line OP and the operating line AB in a gas–liquid contacting operation are shown in Figure 6.16(d). Indicate the overall gas-phase and liquid-phase driving forces at the point K by line segments.

5. An absorption oil loaded with benzene (mole ratio of benzene $= X_1$) is to be steam-stripped in a packed column. The benzene concentration in the lean oil leaving the column is X_2. (a) If the steam rate is increased (for a fixed liquid rate and for constant values of X_1 and X_2), the terminal point P (Figure 6.18) of the operating line will shift towards the point

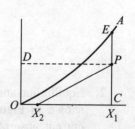

Figure 6.18

(i) C (ii) D (iii) E.

(b) For the given shape of the equilibrium line, where shall the *pinch point* for minimum steam rate for stripping lie?

(i) at the top of the packed section

(ii) at the bottom

(iii) somewhere midway in the packed section.

6. A student has calculated the number of theoretical plates required for a particular gas absorption operation by using the Kremser equation. He ignored the fact that although the equilibrium line is nearly straight over the lower 60% of the concentration range involved, it is appreciably convex upwards over the upper 40% of the concentration range (Figure 6.19). In fact, he used the slope of the lower part of the equilibrium line and got N number of plates. If N' is the number of plates obtained by using a more precise method, then

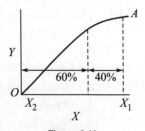

Figure 6.19

(i) $N' = N$ (ii) $N' > N$ (iii) $N > N'$.

7. A dissolved solute is to be removed from a solution by stripping with a gas in a packed tower. The height of the packing (Raschig rings) is estimated to be h under a given set of temperature conditions. Which of the following changes in the operating conditions may be done in order to reduce the packed height without reducing the degree of separation?

(i)   Increase the operating pressure

(ii)   Decrease the operating temperature and the rate of flow of the stripping gas

(iii)   Increase the temperature or decrease the pressure

(iv)   Use saddle packings rather than rings

(v)   Increase the stripping gas rate

(vi)   Add a suitable reagent to the solvent that reacts with the dissolved solute

8. How does the number of ideal trays required for *stripping* of a solute from a solution vary with the absorption factor $\bar{A} = L/mG$? With increasing $\bar{A}$, the number of ideal trays required to achieve a specified degree of separation will

(i) increase   (ii) decrease   (iii) remain unchanged.

9. A gas is to be absorbed in a liquid of low volatility in a tray tower. Both the gas and the liquid streams are available at room temperature. The number N of real plates required has been calculated by assuming isothermal operation. But the absorption process releases considerable amount of heat and the number of ideal plates for adiabatic absorption will be greater than N. The main reason for this is:

(i)   A small amount of solvent that may vaporize will increase the gas flow rate, thereby reducing the mole fraction of the solute in the gas. This will, in turn, reduce the driving force for absorption.

(ii)   In the case of adiabatic absorption, the equilibrium line becomes steeper, and the driving force (i.e. the vertical distance between the equilibrium and the operating lines) is thus reduced.

(iii)   In adiabatic absorption, the physical properties of the phases change appreciably along the column and the number of plates required becomes more.

10. The adiabatic absorption referred to in Question 6.9 is proposed to be carried out in an existing unused column having N trays. The diameter of the column is also suitable to accommodate the given flow rates. The heat of absorption is not very high. Which of the following strategies seems attractive?

    (i) Cool down the solvent adequately before feeding it into the column.

    (ii) Properly cool the feed gas stream.

    (iii) Take out a liquid stream from one (or more) intermediate tray, cool it in a heat exchanger and feed the liquid back into the tray, thus removing the heat of absorption.

11. What is the physical significance of HTU?

    (i) It indicates inversely the ease with which a column performs separation.

    (ii) It is the height of packing required to achieve unit change in the concentration of the solute gas.

    (iii) It gives a measure of the interfacial area of contact in a packed column.

12. Which one of the following appears to be a representative value of the specific interfacial area of contact in an industrial scale packed tower?

    (i) 0.5 cm^{-1} (ii) 0.5 ft^{-1} (iii) 0.5 m^{-1}

13. What is the physical significance of NTU?

    (i) It indicates the ease of separation of a mixture.

    (ii) It indicates the difficulty of separation of a mixture.

    (iii) It indicates the efficiency of a particular packing for mass transfer.

14. The number of transfer units for absorption of three gases A, B and C in water are 10, 4 and 15 m respectively. The inlet and exit concentrations (mole fraction) of the gas-phase and of the liquid-phase have the same values in all the cases. For which system is the average driving force for mass transfer minimum?

15. How does the height of a transfer unit (HTU) depend on the gas and liquid flow rates (G and L)?

    (i) It increases slowly with increasing G.

    (ii) It increases with increasing L.

    (iii) It is independent of G but increases with L.

    (iv) It is independent of both G and L.

    (More than one answer may be correct.)

16. A gas is being absorbed in a pure liquid and in this particular case, the liquid-side interfacial concentration is negligibly small. What fraction of the inlet gas is expected to be absorbed in one transfer unit?

    (i) 50%   (ii) 23.6%   (iii) 63.2%

17. Which of the following is a probable value of the HTU of a 3 ft diameter column packed with #25 IMTP?

    (i) 2.7 m   (ii) 1.3 ft   (iii) 105 mm

18. Which of the following quantities is appreciably dependent on the solubility of a gas in the solvent?

    (i) HTU   (ii) NTU   (iii) $\bar{a}$ (specific interfacial area)

19. For absorption of a lean gas in a packed column, the absorption factor turns out to be very high. Which of the following statements is correct for this system?

    (i) The height of the overall gas-phase transfer unit is close to that of the individual gas-phase transfer units.

    (ii) The height of the overall gas-phase transfer unit is very small.

    (iii) The height of the gas-phase transfer unit will definitely be smaller than that of the liquid-phase transfer unit.

20. In a small section of a packed tower, the fraction of the solute absorbed corresponds to one transfer unit. The overall gas-phase driving forces (in mole fraction) at the two ends of this section are 0.014 and 0.0098 respectively. The slope of the equilibrium line is 1.1 and the absorption factor is 0.99. What is the change in the gas-phase concentration over this transfer unit?

    (i) 0.02   (ii) 0.0106   (iii) 0.012

21. Under which of the following conditions the gas-phase driving force will be constant along the column?

    (i) $L/G = 1$ (ii) $L > G$ and $m = 1$ (iii) $L/G = m$

22. In which of the following cases the number of the overall gas-phase transfer units will be equal to the number of ideal plates for the same degree of separation?

    (i) The equilibrium line and the operating line are nearly straight.

    (ii) The equilibrium line and the operating line are straight and parallel.

    (iii) The slope of the operating line is unity.

23. A dissolved gas is being stripped out from a dilute solution in a packed tower using steam. Concentration of the solute in the inlet liquid is 0.06 (mole fraction) and that in the lean solution at the bottom must not exceed 0.002. The equilibrium and the operating lines are nearly straight. The overall liquid-phase driving forces at the top and at the bottom of the column are found to be 0.00472 and 0.00102 respectively. What is the number of overall liquid-phase transfer units?

    (i) 24   (ii) 14   (iii) 21

24. For the absorption of a *dilute* gas in a packed tower, the heights of the individual transfer units are $H_{tG} = 1.2$ ft and $H_{tL} = 0.9$ ft. The average gas flow rate is 50 kmol/h and the water rate is 1800 kg/h. The equilibrium relation is $y = 1.5x$. What is the height of an overall liquid-phase transfer unit?

    (i) 3.5 ft   (ii) 1.6 ft   (iii) 0.3 ft

25. What is the physical significance of the *absorption factor A*?

    (i) It is the ratio of the slopes of the equilibrium line and the operating line.

    (ii) It is ratio of the individual gas-phase and liquid-phase mass transfer coefficients.

    (iii) It is fractional absorption of the feed gas.

26. A larger absorption factor means

(i) an increased driving force for absorption

(ii) an increased rate of flow of the liquid

(iii) an increased packed height for the same degree of separation.

27. The optimum ratio of the actual liquid rate to the minimum liquid rate for gas absorption *generally* lies between

(i) 0 and 1   (ii) 0.5 and 1.5   (iii) 1.2 and 2.0

28. In the design of a packed tower based on individual gas-phase and liquid-phase coefficients, the *tie lines* are found to be nearly parallel. This may occur because

(i) the log mean mole fraction of the carrier is nearly unity

(ii) the absorption is gas-film resistance controlled

(iii) the feed gas is concentrated.

29. In a packed column the height of an overall gas-phase transfer unit is 1.2 ft. The absorption factor is 1.6. What is the value of HETP?

(i) 1.2 ft   (ii) 1.5 ft   (iii) 2.8 ft

30. Which of the following is a practical range of the 'absorption factor' in gas absorption?
(i) 1 to 10   (ii) 0.5 to 1.5   (iii) 1.25 to 2.0

31. In a gas absorption column the absorption factor $\bar{A} = L/mG = 1$ and the Murphree tray efficiency is 0.60. What is the overall column efficiency?

32. A particular tray in an absorption column is equivalent to 0.8 overall gas-phase transfer units. The local absorption factor is $L/mG = 1.5$. What is the Murphree efficiency of the tray?

(i) 0.456   (ii) 0.62   (iii) 0.664

33. The equilibrium in a gas–liquid system follows the Henry's law, $y = mx$. Give the range of values of the Henry's law coefficient m, for which the equilibrium data plotted in mole ratio units $[Y = f(X)]$ is

(i) convex downwards   (ii) convex upwards.

34. The equilibrium line for a gas–liquid system is given by $Y = 2.5X$. Fresh liquid enters the top of a counter-current packed bed and the gas leaves at a concentration, $Y_2 = 0.001$. The overall gas-phase driving force is $\Delta Y = 0.004$ at a section where the bulk gas concentration is $Y = 0.035$. What is the overall liquid-phase driving force (ΔX) at a section where the bulk gas concentration is $Y = 0.04$?

35. Analysis of samples drawn from the fifth tray from the top in an absorption column shows that its Murphree efficiency is 0.55. The tower diameter is not large, and the liquid-phase at a tray may be considered to be *well-mixed*. What is the number of overall gas-phase transfer units equivalent to this tray?

36. Explain how Eq. 6.24(b) can be simplified for a dilute gas–liquid system.

37. Derive Eqs. 6.24(b), (6.58), and (6.61).

38. Many random packings have multiple drip points at which the liquid film terminates to form drops. Explain qualitatively how this feature improves the mass transfer efficiency of a packing.

39. What are the physical significances of the absorption factor and the stripping factor?

40. Which of the following is a probable value of dynamic liquid holdup (volume fraction) in a packed bed?

    (i) 0.5   (ii) 0.35   (iii) 0.035

41. Which of the following is a probable value of $K_G\bar{a}$ [kmol/(h)(m^3)(atm)] for absorption of NH_3 in an acidic solution in a 1 m diameter column packed with 2-inch Koch Flexiring?

    (i) 10   (ii) 200   (iii) 2000

42. If the liquid on a tray is well-mixed and the gas also gets well-mixed in the space between two consecutive trays, then

    (i) $E_{OG} = E_{MG}$ (ii) $E_{OG} > E_{MG}$ (iii) $E_{OG} < E_{MG}$

43. With increasing viscosity of the liquid, the tray efficiency generally

    (i) increases   (ii) decreases   (iii) remains unchanged.

44. Discuss the reasoning behind considering the quantity $G'/k_y\bar{a}(1-y)_{iM}$ nearly constant and calling it 'height of a gas-phase transfer unit'.

45. The individual mass transfer coefficient k_y is associated with a gas-film thickness δ. How can the concept be extended to the overall coefficient K_y? Is it possible to extend the concept to define an 'effective film thickness' corresponding to K_y in terms of the individual gas-film and liquid-film thicknesses?

46. What are the factors that influence H_{tOG} and N_{tOG} of a packed tower?

47. How can the H_{tG} and H_{tL} values of a packing available for one gas–liquid pair be modified for use in the design of another gas–liquid system?

48. Do mass transfer data collected in a wetted-wall column have relevance to mass transfer in a packed tower?

49. Comment on the assumptions made to develop Eq. (6.55) for the 'point efficiency'. How is tray efficiency affected by liquid entrainment?

50. From Eq. (6.49) obtain the following relation between the number of transfer units and the number of ideal trays $N.$: $N_{tOG} = N\cdot(\ln\bar{S})/(\bar{S}-1)$. Under what condition is N_{tOG} larger (or smaller) than the number of ideal trays?

51. Which solvent/liquid would you recommend for the following gas absorption processes?

    (i) Drying of air in a H_2SO_4 plant

    (ii) Separation of acrylonitrile from the reaction products of ammoxidation of propylene

    (iii) Drying of natural gas

    (iv) Drying of chlorine prior to liquefaction

    (v) Separation of H_2S from natural gas

(vi)   Recovery of ammonia from the 'bleed stream' from an ammonia reactor

(vii) Separation of CO_2 from the ammonia synthesis gas

(viii) Recovery of light hydrocarbons from a refinery vent stream.

52. Is there a value of the absorption factor, $\overline{A} = L/mG'$, for which the Murphree efficiency (for the liquid in plug flow) is the same as the point efficiency?

PROBLEMS

6.1 (*Minimum liquid rate for absorption*)[1]   A packed tower is to be designed for the absorption of 98% of the ammonia(*A*) from an air–ammonia mixture containing 4% ammonia at a rate of 4200 Nm^3 (normal cubic metre) per hour using water as the solvent. The tower operates at 105.1 kPa and 303 K. The equilibrium data for NH_3–water system at 303 K [Sherwood, T.K., *Ind. Eng. Chem.*, *17*(1925) 745] are given below:

Partial pressure of NH_3 (mm Hg)	19.3	29.6	40.1	51.0	79.5	110
kg NH_3 per 100 kg water	2	3	4	5	7.5	10

(a) Calculate and plot the equilibrium data as x_A vs. p_A, x_A vs. y_A and X_A vs. Y_A . Up to what value of p_{NH3} can the Henry's law be used to describe the equilibrium?

(b) Calculate the minimum liquid rate for the absorption (the inlet water is NH_3-free).

6.2 (*Flooding velocity*; *number of trays*)[2]   A stream of nitrogen gas containing 9.5% benzene by volume is to be scrubbed in a packed tower with an absorption oil in order to reduce the benzene content to 0.5% by volume before the gas can be recycled. The feed gas rate is 1550 Nm^3/h; it enters the column at 308 K. The column operates at 308 K and 1.07 bar pressure. Benzene-free oil is fed to the column at a rate of 4600 kg/h. The equilibrium distribution of benzene between the gas and the oil is given below.

$$Y = \frac{0.19X}{1+0.81X}$$

where X = moles of benzene per mole of benzene-free oil, and Y = moles of benzene per mole of nitrogen. The properties of the oil are: density = 840 kg/m^3, viscosity = 4.5 cP, and mol. wt. = 230.

(a) Do you think that the system is ideal (i.e. obeys the Raoult's law) in respect of equilibrium? Justify your answer by calculations. Can you calculate the vapour pressure of benzene at the given temperature?

(b) Calculate the mole fraction of benzene in the oil at the bottom of the tower.

(c) Calculate the diameter of the tower if the superficial gas velocity is 0.32 m/s. If the tower is packed with 1½ inch ceramic Raschig ring, calculate the ratio of the actual gas rate to that at flooding.

(d) If the separation is done in a plate column and the overall tray efficiency is 35%, determine the number of real trays required. [*Note:* Tray efficiency for absorption is often found to be substantially lower than for distillation.]

6.3 (*Number of trays in a stripping tower*)[2] The absorption oil loaded with CS_2 leaving the tower described in Example 6.6 is to be subjected to steam stripping in a tray tower. The pressure in the column is 1.12 bar and the temperature is 105°C. The steam is essentially saturated. Vapour pressure of CS_2 at this temperature is 4.7373 bar. Calculate the number of ideal trays required if the stripped oil leaving the bottom of the tower does not have more than 50 ppm of CS_2. The steam rate used is 1.3 times the minimum. The Raoult's law is applicable. Note that the bottom liquid has a very low concentration of the solute and graphical construction may be difficult in this low concentration region.

6.4 (*Calculation of N_{tOG} and packed height*)[2] Sulphur dioxide is to be scrubbed from an air stream in a small packed tower by contacting it with an organic amine. The feed gas 3% SO_2 by volume, and 95% of it is to be absorbed. The total gas rate is 150 m^3/h at 20°C and 1.1 bar absolute pressure. The liquid enters the column at a rate of 1.40 kmol/ h. *Given:* the overall mass transfer coefficient, $K_G = 3.2 \times 10^{-4}$ kmol/$(m^2)(s)(\Delta p$, bar); the effective gas–liquid contact area = 105 m^2 per m^3 of packed volume; slope of the equilibrium line, $m = 0.17$. Determine the number of overall gas-phase mass transfer units and the packed height if the column is 1 ft in diameter.

6.5 (*Use of Kremser equation*)[2] Groundwater contaminated with 1,1,1-trichloroethane (TCA)[#] is to be air-stripped at 25°C and 1.1 bar pressure at a rate of 9000 kg/h. The feed water has 600 ppm of the VOC. A stripping column of suitable diameter with eight trays having 40% overall efficiency is available. The exit stripping air must not contain more than 2.5% TCA by volume. The equilibrium distribution of TCA between water and air has been reported by Turner et. al. [*AIChE J*, *42*(1996) 1772–1788].

$$K' = 0.204 + 0.0182\theta + 0.000173\theta^2 \ \frac{mg/lit, \ air}{mg/lit, \ water}; \qquad \theta \ in \ °C.$$

Calculate (a) the Henry's law constant (i.e. 'm' in $y = mx$) for TCA at 25°C and (b) the percentage removal of TCA achievable in the column.

6.6 (*Use of Colburn-Drew coefficients*)[2] A packed column receives 10 kmol/h·m^2 of feed gas (8 mol% solute, 92% carrier) and 30 kmol/h·m^2 of fresh solvent. It is required to remove 97% of the solute. The equilibrium relation for the gas–liquid system is $y = 2.5x + 4.5x^2$, $x \leq 0.08$. Is the solvent rate more than the minimum? Calculate the value of the absorption factor at a section of the column where the bulk liquid concentration is $x = 0.02$? If the individual 'Colburn-Drew mass transfer coefficients' are $k'_x = 1.2$ kmol/$(m^2)(s)(\Delta x)$ and $k'_y = 0.15$ kmol/$(m^2)(s)(\Delta y)$, calculate the interfacial concentrations and the individual gas-phase driving force.

6.7 (*Effect of column pressure on the extent of separation*)[3] An absorption column is to be designed for reducing the concentration of a toxic vapour in an air emission from 1% to 0.02 mole%. The column will operate at 20°C and 0.5 bar gauge pressure. The scrubbing liquor flow rate is 1.3 times the minimum. The gas–liquid equilibrium relation $(p = Hx)$ is linear and the Henry's law constant is 10 bar. (a) How many trays are required

[#]Chlorinated hydrocarbons such as trichloroethane and trichloroethylene were used in large quantities in the past for cleaning of metal parts and sometimes for dry cleaning of garments. Spills and leakages of such compounds have been a cause of contamination of groundwater at some places of a few countries like the US.

to achieve this separation if the overall tray efficiency is 40%? (b) After the column is designed, it becomes necessary to reduce the concentration of the toxic vapour in the vent air to 0.01% in order to meet a modified pollution control regulation. Is it possible to achieve this goal by operating the column at the same temperature but at an enhanced pressure? If so, at what pressure should the column be operated?

6.8 (*Packed tower calculations*)[2] Formaldehyde present in an effluent air stream is to be absorbed into an effectively non-volatile solvent at 1 atm total pressure and 30°C. The inlet and outlet concentrations of the organic in the air stream are 4.25% and 0.08 mole% respectively. The solvent entering the column has only traces of formaldehyde. The ratio of molar rates of liquid and gas inputs is 2.9 and the equilibrium relation is $y = 2.5x$. Determine: (a) the equation of the operating line, (b) the number of overall gas-phase transfer units, and (c) the maximum admissible ratio of the gas and liquid rates for this separation.

6.9 (*Use of Murphree effieciency*)[3] Benzene from a stream of N_2 is to be and separated in an absorption column followed by steam stripping to recover the hydrocarbon. The feed (100 kmol/h) enters the absorption column at 25°C and is 90% saturated with benzene. Not more than 2.5% of the feed benzene should leave the column. The feed solvent has 0.007 mole benzene per mole of 'pure' solvent (mol. wt. = 240). The loaded solvent leaving the absorber has 0.3 mole benzene per mole of pure solvent. The solution is heated and fed to the stripping tower to reduce the benzene content to 0.007 mole ratio so that the lean liquid can be cooled and recycled to the absorption. The steam rate used is 1.5 times the minimum. Both the towers operate at atmospheric pressure. The absorption tower operates at 25°C and the stripping tower at 110°C. The equilibrium data at 25°C are given below.

X	0.04	0.08	0.12	0.16	0.20	0.24
Y	0.011	0.0215	0.032	0.040	0.051	0.060

The Raoult's law may be used to determine the equilibrium relationship at the stripping temperature of 110°C. Vapour pressure of benzene can be calculated from the Antoine equation,

$\ln P^v = 17.5818 - (3867/T)$; P^v = vapour pressure in mm Hg; T = temperature, K.

(a) Calculate the liquid rate to the absorber. (b) Determine the number of ideal trays required for absorption. (c) What is the minimum possible steam rate? (d) Determine the number of ideal trays in the stripping column. (e) How many real trays are required for stripping if the Murphree plate efficiency is 50%?

6.10 (*Effect of pressure; packing size*)[3] A gaseous effluent stream containing 2 mole% ammonia is scrubbed with water at 30°C and 1.2 bar total pressure to remove 99% of the solute in a tower packed with 1-inch intalox saddle. The feed water may have 0.00008 mole fraction of ammonia in it. The gas rate is 1200 normal cubic metre (Nm^3) per hour and the equilibrium relation is $p = x$ (p in bar). (a) If 52 kmol/h·m^2 water is used, calculate the concentration of NH_3 in the water leaving the tower in kmol/m^3 (the density of the liquid is the same as that of water). (b) What is the Henry's law constant for the given form of the equilibrium line? (c) Determine the mass transfer driving force (gas-phase basis) at a section of the column where 50% of the inlet gas has been absorbed. (d) What will be the effect of: (i) doubling the operating pressure, and (ii) using the ½-inch size saddles as packing on the fractional removal of the solute?

6.11 (*Calculation of liquid rate in an existing tower*)[2]   A solute is removed from a gas stream by using an existing absorption tower filled to 8.6 m by IMTP. The tower diameter is considered suitable for the required service, but the water rate has to be calculated. The feed gas has 3.5 mole% of the solute and the exit gas may have 0.05 mole% of it. The solubility of the solute is given by Henry's law: $y = 2.53x$. Following data are available: superficial gas velocity at the top of the column = 0.8 m/s; total pressure = 1 atm; temperature = 26°C; overall gas-phase mass transfer coefficient, $K_G\bar{a}$ = 7050 kg/ (h)(m^3)(Δp, bar); molecular weight of the solute = 30. Determine the liquid flow rate and HETP of the packing.

6.12 (*A simple design problem*)[3]   It is required to design a packed tower to treat 40,000 ft^3/h of an air stream containing 20 mole% of SO$_2$ at 70°C and 1 atm total pressure. It is necessary to recover 96% of the SO$_2$ using water at a rate 30% more than the minimum. The column may be packed with 1½-inch Raschig rings and may be operated at 60% of the flooding velocity. The individual mass transfer coefficients are: $k_G a = 0.028(G)^{0.7}(L')^{0.25}$ and $k_L a = 0.044(L')^{0.82}$ where G' and L' are the gas and liquid mass flow rates, in lb/h·ft^2. Design the tower.

6.13 (*A simple case of solvent selection*)[3]   It is required to absorb 97% of the solute from a feed gas of concentration 8% by volume. The gas enters the column at a rate of 100 kmol/h. A column of suitable diameter with ten ideal trays is available. It is necessary to select one of two solvents otherwise suitable. The following data are supplied. Solvent 1: molecular weight = 200; equilibrium relation, $Y = 2.5X$; cost, Rs 50 per kg. Solvent 2: molecular weight = 130; equilibrium relation, $Y = 1.5X$; cost, Rs 30 per kg. Pumping and spillage loss is estimated to be 0.001% of the circulation rate for both the solvents. But solvent 2, though cheaper, is volatile and 0.004% of it is lost in the stripping column. Which solvent will you recommend considering the above costs only?

6.14 (*Packed tower calculations*)[2]   Hydrogen sulphide has to be removed from a light refinery hydrocarbon stream before the gas is subjected to further processing. The feed gas contains 0.035 mole fraction of H$_2$S, 99% of which has to be removed by scrubbing with an aqueous weakly basic solution. The 1.5 m diameter absorption column operates at 25°C and 101.3 kPa total pressure. The feed gas rate is 45 kmol/h·m^2 and the concentration of the solute(H$_2$S) in the absorbent solution leaving the tower is 0.015 mole H$_2$S per mole of the H$_2$S-free liquid. The equilibrium relation is linear and is given by $y = 1.95x$ and the overall gas-phase film coefficient is $K_y\bar{a}$ = 130 kmol/ (m^3)(h)(Δy). Calculate (a) the rate of solvent flow, (b) the slope of the operating line in small concentration range if mole fraction units are used in the calculations, (c) the overall driving forces at the top and at the bottom of the tower on (i) gas phase basis and (ii) liquid phase basis, (d) the number of transfer units, and (e) the packed height.

6.15 (*Design of a column receiving two feeds*)[3]   A tray tower is to be designed for processing two feed streams having the same solute and carrier gases but at different concentrations. Feed 1 enters at a rate of 90 kmol/h with 10 mol% of the solute.

Feed 2 has a flow rate of 60 kmol/h with 5 mol% solute. The equilibrium relation is linear, $Y = 1.2X$. It is required to absorb 95% of the total solute. What is the minimum liquid rate for the separation? If 1.25 times the minimum liquid rate is used, determine the number of ideal trays.

6.16 (*Packed tower calculations*)[2]   A binary gas mixture containing 7.5% of a solute A has to be scrubbed with the solvent B in a packed tower. Based on the flooding calculations, a tower diameter of 1.2 m has been selected. The total gas rate at the bottom is 60 kmol/h. The exit gas must not contain more than 0.2% of the solute. Solute-free liquid entering the column at the rate of 40 kmol/h is used. The gas-phase and the liquid-phase mass transfer coefficients (based on the mole ratio unit of concentration) are $k_X = 2.05$ kmol/$(m^2)(h)(\Delta X)$, and $k_Y = 1.75$ kmol/$(m^2)(h)(\Delta Y)$. The equilibrium line is linear, $Y = 0.63X$. The specific interfacial area of gas–liquid contact is 71 m^2/m^3. Calculate the height of packing necessary for the separation. By what per cent must the packed height be increased in order to remove 99.5% of the solute? Determine the slope of the operating line in each case.

6.17 (*A column having trays above the packing*)[3]   A mixture containing 10% of the solute A is to be scrubbed with a solvent in order to remove 98% of it. The absorption column has three ideal trays at the top below which there is a packed section The gas flow rate at the bottom is 70 kmol/m^2·h, and the liquid leaving the column has 8.2 mol% solute in it. The equilibrium relation is given by $y = 1.05x + 0.32x^2$, $x \le 0.1$. If the overall volumetric mass transfer coefficient is $K_y\bar{a} = 95$ kmol/$(h)(m^3)(\Delta y)$, calculate the height of the packed section.

6.18 (*Calculation of packed height and HETP*)[3]   Benzene is absorbed from a stream of air into a non-volatile oil in a countercurrent packed tower at 299 K and 105 kPa. The equilibrium is approximately linear, $y = 0.19x$. The solvent (mol. wt. = 240) enters the column at a rate of 8500 kg/h·m^2. Terminal concentrations of benzene in the liquid and the gas phases are: $x = 0.0008$, $y = 0.0005$ at the top, and $x = 0.152$, $y = 0.038$ at the bottom. The heights of individual gas and liquid phase transfer units are $H_{tG} = 0.33$ m and $H_{tL} = 0.43$ m. Calculate (a) the heights of overall gas-phase and the overall liquid-phase transfer units, and (b) the HETP of the packing. Equations 6.24(c) and (6.49) may be used.

6.19 (*Use of Billet's correlations for tower design*)[3]   A stream of air having 3% acetone vapour is to be scrubbed with water at a rate of 6000 m^3/h at 27°C and essentially atmospheric pressure in a packed tower of 1 m^2 cross-section in order to remove 98% of acetone. The tower should use 2-inch metal Pall ring packing. Water is supplied at a rate 1.3 times the minimum. A linear equilibrium relation, $y = 2.31x$, is applicable. The mass transfer coefficients (k_L and k_c) can be calculated using the Billet's correlations, Eqs. (6.39) and (6.40). The parameters of the packing are given in Tables 5.9 and 6.4. Following physical property data may be used. Gas: $\mu_G = 1.813 \times 10^{-5}$ kg/m.s; $D_G = 1.08 \times 10^{-5}$ m^2/s; liquid: $\mu_L = 8.57 \times 10^{-4}$ kg/m.s; $D_L = 1.18 \times 10^{-9}$ m^2/s; $\rho_L = 997$ kg/m^3; $\sigma_L = 0.072$ kg/s^2. Calculate the required height of packing.

6.20 (*How N_{tOG} increases with the degree of removal of the solute*)[2]   A stream of air containing 5% by volume of ammonia is to be scrubbed with dilute H_2SO_4 in a packed tower. The gas and the liquid rates are the same, 1200 lb/h·ft². The overall gas-phase mass transfer coefficient is 18 lbmol/(ft³)(h)(atm). Prepare a plot of N_{tOG} versus the fractional removal of ammonia from the gas (starting with 93% removal).

6.21 (*Calculations for a particular tray*)[2] Following data on concentration of the gas and the liquid streams entering the *p*th tray of a gas absorption column are available: $y_{p+1} = 0.08$, $x_{p-1} = 0.044$. The equilibrium relation is $y^* = 1.8x^{1.2}$. The ratio of liquid and gas flow rates on solute free basis (L_s/G_s) in the column is 1.3. If the *p*th tray has a Murphree efficiency of 0.55 [expressed in terms of mole fraction unit, see Eq. (6.56)], calculate the concentrations of the streams leaving the tray.

6.22 (*Calculation of point efficiency*)[2] The gas flow rate to the *p*th tray of an absorption tower is 120 kmol/h·m². The froth depth is 0.28 m and it is equivalent to 0.4 transfer units. Calculate the overall volumetric gas-phase mass transfer coefficient and the point efficiency. The equilibrium relation is given by $y = 2.3x$.

6.23 (*Tray tower calculations*)[3] A solute is to be steam-stripped from a solution containing 0.08 mole fraction of *A* in order to remove 98% of the solute. At the temperature and pressure of the column the equilibrium relation is $Y = 2.08X$. (a) Determine the terminal points of the operating line on the *X–Y* line for minimum steam rate. (b) If 1.3 times the minimum liquid rate is used, determine the equation of the operating line and the number of ideal trays required for removal of 98% of the solute. (c) Calculate the change in concentration of the stripping gas (steam) in mole fraction as it passes through the fifth tray from the top. Calculate algebraically; do not use a graph paper.

6.24 (*Calculation of HETP*)[2] A packed absorption tower operates at an average absorption factor of 1.35. The liquid flow rate is 65 kmol/h·m² and the equilibrium relation is $y = 1.5x$. The overall gas-phase mass transfer coefficient is $K_G\bar{a} = 0.0113$ kmol/(s)(m³) (Δp, bar) and the total pressure is 1.05 bar. Calculate the HETP of the packing if the feed gas is 'dilute'.

6.25 (*Stripping of VOC*)[3] A column provided with a 3-m packed bed is being used to air strip trichloroethylene (TCE) in contaminated water (400 ppm) in order to reduce the concentration to 3 ppm. The air rate is twice the minimum. Is it possible to strip TCE from contaminated water having 600 ppm of the VOC down to 0.1 ppm in the same column with an enhanced packed height, keeping the water and air rates unchanged? What packed height do you suggest? The equilibrium relation is $y = 661.1x$ (Yaws et al., *Chem. Eng. Progr.*, Feb 2005, 50–56).

6.26 (*Efficiency calculation*)[3] Following data are available for a particular tray in a gas absorption column: $G' = 160$ kmol/m²·h; $k_G = 4.7$ kmol/(m²)(h)(atm); $k_L = 5.56$ m/h; total pressure, $P = 1.3$ atm; froth height, $z_L = 0.2$ m; absorption factor, $\bar{A} = 1.2$; specific interfacial area, $\bar{a} = 100$ m²/m³; and the equilibrium relation, $p = H'C$ [$H' = 0.3$ atm/(kmol/m³)]. Calculate (a) the point efficiency; (b) the Murphree efficiency if the liquid is in plug flow over the tray with (i) no entrainment, and (ii) for an entrainment rate of $E = 0.06$; (c) the overall column efficiency if the liquid is in plug flow on the tray and there is no entrainment.

6.27 (*Number of ideal stages given; calculate the liquid rate*)[3]   A feed having 12 mol% solute is to be scrubbed at a rate of 8000 m³/h (27°C; 1 atm) with a 'pure' solvent. The targeted removal of the solute is 96%. An existing tower with an equivalent of ten ideal trays is available for the purpose. Calculate the liquid rate required as well as the exit liquid concentration. The equilibrium relation is $y = 0.5x$.

6.28 (*Number of trays given; side stream withdrawal*)[3]   Three hundred kilomole per hour of a gas mixture is to be scrubbed in an existing column. The feed contains 10 mol% of a solute, 95% of which is to be absorbed. A side stream of the liquid having 10 mol% of the solute is to be withdrawn. The column has a total of ten ideal trays. There is a nozzle at the sixth ideal tray from the top which is to be used for side-stream withdrawal. The equilibrium relation is $y^* = 0.5x$. Determine the required liquid rate to the column, and the total moles of side stream that may be withdrawn per hour.

6.29 (*A case of side stream withdrawal*)[3]   An absorption column receives 225 kmol of feed gas having 10 mole% of a solute and it is desired to remove 98% of it. A solvent rate of 280 kmol/h is suggested. The feed solvent is solute-free. A side stream having 4 mol% of the solute is to be withdrawn from an appropriate plate at a rate of 75 kmol/h for use in another processing unit in the plant. Determine the total number of ideal trays required and the tray from which the side stream should be withdrawn. The equilibrium relation for the system is $Y = 1.1X$.

6.30 (*A two-compartment model of a shower*)[3]   To develop a seemingly more realistic model of accumulation of a contaminant in a shower, assume that the shower stall is separated from the rest of the bathroom by a partition that ends a little below the ceiling of the room. While the net rate of exhaust of air from the bathroom remains at Q_G m³/s, an exchange of air between the two compartments occurrs at a rate of Q_{Ge} m³/s. The arrangement is schematically shown in Figure 6.20.

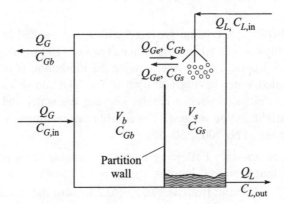

Figure 6.20   Schematic of the two-compartment model.

Develop an expression for the transient VOC concentration in the shower based on the above model. Following data are given: $V_s = 2.8$ m³; $V_b = 8.1$ m³; $Q_L = 0.0137$ m³/min; $Q_{Ge} = 0.11$ m³/min; $Q_G = 0.0378$ m³/min; $K_L a' = 0.029$ m³/min; $C_{L,in} = 3.4$ µg/litre; $C_{G,in} = 0.0014$ µg/litre; equilibrium relation, $C_G = \hat{H} C_L^*$; $\hat{H} = 0.57$.

6.31 (*A cell model for the point efficiency*)[3] In the derivation of Eq. (6.55) for the point efficiency, it has been tacitly assumed that the liquid is *vertically well-mixed* at any location on a tray but the gas is in *plug flow*. However, expectedly there will be some backmixing in the gas phase. So it may be a more realistic approach to consider that the depth of the dispersion (h) is divided into j-number of cells and the gas is *well-mixed* in each of the cells. In effect, the gas concentration changes in steps, not continuously. The liquid is considered vertically well-mixed as before. Show that the modified model leads to the following expression for the point efficiency [Kunesh et al., *Ind. Eng. Chem. Res.*, *35*(1996) 2660–2671].

$$E_{OG} = 1 - \left(1 + \frac{N_{tOG}}{j}\right)^j$$

It may be noted that if the number of cells is large ($j \to \infty$), the gas phase is virtually in plug flow and the above equation reduces to Eq. (6.55).

6.32 (*Murphree liquid tray efficiency and the number of real trays*)[3] For liquid-phase mass transfer controlled systems, the Murphree liquid tray efficiency is sometimes preferred. For a stripping column, we define it as

$$E_{ML} = \frac{x_n - x_{n+1}}{x_n^* - x_{n+1}}; \qquad y_n = m x_n^*$$

If we assume that: (i) the gas and the liquid flow rates do not change substantially, (ii) $\bar{A} = L/mG$ is small, (iii) the stripping gas is solute-free $y_{N+1} = 0$, and (iv) the concentration of the solute in the lean solution is small ($x_n << x_0$), show that the number of 'real trays' required for the separation is given by (see Kunesh et al., in Problem 6.31)

$$N = \frac{\ln(x_N/x_0)}{\ln(1 - E_{ML})}$$

6.33 (*Absorption of a dilute gas in an existing tower*)[2] A waste gas stream containing 2 mole% ammonia is to be scrubbed in a packed tower using dilute sulphuric acid. The gas rate is 92 kmol/h and 2.2 mole of the scrubbing liquid is to be used per mole of the gas. A packed tower of 1 m diameter having 3 m bed of a 25 mm size proprietary plastic packing is available. The height of an overall gas phase transfer unit is given as $H_{tOG} = 0.0484(G')^{0.15}(L')^{-0.2}$ [H_{tOG} in metre; G' and L' in kmol/m^2·h]. It is required to reduce the ammonia concentration to 10 ppm. Will the tower be suitable for the purpose? An average gas rate and the feed liquid rate can be used for H_{tOG} calculation.

REFERENCES

Bennett, D.L. et al., 'New correlation for sieve-tray point efficiency, entrainment and section efficiency', *AIChE J.*, *43*(June 1997) 1611–1626

Billet, R., *Packed Towers in Processing and Environmental Technology*, VCH, New York, 1995.

Bolles, W.L., and J.R. Fair, 'Improved mass transfer model enhances packed column design', *Chem Eng.*, July 12, 1982, 109–116.

Branan, G., *Rules of Thumb for Chemical Engineers*, Gulf Publishing, Houston, TX, 1998.

Chilton, T.H., and A.P. Colburn, *Ind. Eng. Chem.*, 27(1935) 255, 904.

Cornell, D. et al., *Chem., Eng. Progr.*, July 1960, 68–74; Aug. 1960, 48–53.

Dvorak, B.I. et al., 'Evaluation of the Onda correlations for mass transfer with large power packings', *Environ. Sci. Technol., 30*(1996) 945–953.

Fair, J.R., and J.L. Bravo, 'Distillation columns containing structured packings', *Chem. Eng. Progr.*, Jan. 1990, 19–29.

Gilliland, E.R., and T.K. Sherwood: *Ind. Eng. Chem.*, 26(1934) 516.

Haimour, N. et al., 'Simultaneous absorption of H_2S and CO_2 into aqueous methyl-diethyl-amine,' *Sep. Sci. Tech.*, 22(1983) 921–947.

Kister, H.Z., *Distillation Design*, McGraw-Hill, New York, 1992.

Kohl, A.L., and R.B. Nielsen, *Gas Purification*, 5th ed., Gulf Publishing, Houston, 1997.

Lockette, M.J., *Distillation Tray Fundamentals*, Cambridge University Press, Cambridge, 1986.

McNulty, K.J., 'Effective design for absorption and stripping', *Chem. Engg.*, Nov. 1994, 92–100.

Murphree, E.V., *Ind. Eng. Chem.*, 17(1925) 747.

O'Connell, H.E. et al., 'Plate efficiency of fractionating columns and absorbers', *Trans. AIChE J., 42*(1946) 741.

Onda, K. et al., 'Mass transfer coefficients between gas and liquid phases in packed columns', *J. Chem. Eng. Japan, 1*(1968) 56–62.

Perry's *Chemical Engineers' Handbook*, 7th ed., McGraw-Hill, 1997.

Piche, S. et al., 'Interfacial mass transfer in randomly packed towers — a confident correlation for environmental applications', *Env. Sci. Technol., 35*(2001) 4817–4822.

Shulman, H.J. et al. 'Wetted and effective interfacial area, gas and liquid phase mass transfer rates,' *AIChE J., 1*(1955) 253–258.

Stichlmair, J., and J.R. Fair, *Distillation – Principles and Applications*, Wiley VCH, New York, 1998.

Strigle, R.F., *Packed Tower Design and Applications*, 2nd ed., Gulf Publishing, Houston, 1994.

Treybal, R.E., *Mass Transfer Operations*, 3rd ed, McGraw-Hill, New York, 1980.

Wagner, I. et al., 'Mass transfer in beds of modern high efficiency random packings', *Ind. Eng. Chem. Res.*, 36(1997) 227–237.

Ullmann's *Encyclopedia of Industrial Chemistry*, VCH, 1985.

Zarzycki, R., and A. Chacuk, *Absorption—Fundamentals and Applications*, Pergamon Press, Oxford, 1993.

Zenz, F.A., 'Design of gas absorption towers', in *Handbook of Separation Process Techniques for Chemical Engineers*, 2nd ed., P. A. Schweitzer (Ed.), McGraw-Hill, 1997.

7 Distillation

Distillation is the technique of preferential separation of the more volatile component(s) from the less volatile ones in a feed solution by partial vaporization of the feed followed by condensation. The vapor produced is richer in the more volatile component(s). The distribution of the components in the two phases is governed by the vapour–liquid equilibrium relationship. Only partial separation of the components can be achieved in this way. In order to have a larger degree of separation, multistage contact between the vapour and the liquid phases is arranged in a suitable device called a 'distillation column' (for example, a tray column or tower described in Chapters 1 and 5). The most important parts of a distillation unit as illustrated in Figure 7.1 are: (a) a column having trays or a packing and suitable internals (discussed in Chapter 5), (b) a reboiler, and (c) a condenser. The feed enters at a suitable point of the tower. The reboiler, normally heated by steam, partially vaporizes the liquid received from the bottom of the column. The vapour flows up through the trays or through the packing in the column, leaves at the top and enters into an overhead condenser. A part of the condensate is withdrawn as the *top product* and the rest is fed back into the column as *reflux* which flows down the trays or the packing. An intimate contact between the downflowing liquid and the upflowing vapour occurs on the trays or on the packing surface. Exchange of mass takes place between the liquid and the vapour phases. The more volatile components move from the liquid to the vapour phase and the less volatiles move in the reverse direction—from the vapour to the liquid phase. As a result, the concentrations of the more volatiles gradually increase in the vapour as it goes up, and the concentrations of the less volatiles increase in the liquid phase as it flows down the column. In this way, a higher degree of separation of the more volatiles from the less volatiles is achieved. The top product drawn from the condenser is rich in the more volatiles. The bottom product has a high concentration of the less volatiles and only a small amount of the more volatiles. The more the number of trays (or the depth of packing) and the more the *reflux ratio* (it is defined in Figure 7.1), the better is the separation. A distillation column described above performs the job of 'fractional distillation', i.e. separation of a feed into two or more products differing in boiling points or boiling ranges. Distillation is the most mature, albeit energy-intensive, technique of separation of liquid mixtures in small to large capacities. Columns as big as 10 m in diameter and having 150 or more trays have been reported to be in operation.

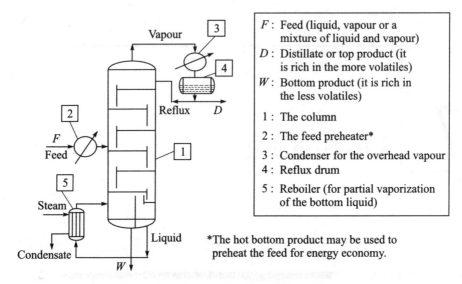

Figure 7.1 Schematic of a typical distillation column.

Distillation, which is one of the oldest mass transfer operations, is reported to have been invented in Alexandria (Egypt) in the first century AD. The early use was in the production of alcoholic beverages. The history of distillation has been described by Forbes (1948).

It will be useful to distinguish between distillation and evaporation since in the latter operation also, the components in solution are separated by volatilizing some of them. The major difference is that in evaporation a solution containing a volatile solvent and a non-volatile solute (or a solute having a very low volatility) is separated by vaporizing out a part or whole of the solvent. Examples are: evaporation of a sugar solution (sugar: a non-volatile solute; water: a volatile solvent), evaporation of a glycerol solution (glycerol: a solute having negligible volatility; water: a volatile solvent). But in distillation, the components (at least two of them) have reasonable volatility. Example: distillation of aqueous ethanol (both ethanol and water are volatile, but ethanol is more volatile).

Distillation is the most common mass transfer operation in the process industries, particularly the organic process industries. The function of distillation may be separation of products from a mixture (example: separation of aniline and nitrobenzene in the process of manufacture of aniline), recovery of a product (example: recovery of ethanol from its solution in water in the process of manufacture of alcohol), or increasing the purity of a product (example: drying of commercial benzene for the removal of traces of water present in it). Distillation is again the most important operation in a petroleum refinery. A petrochemical complex also uses a large number of distillation columns. Sometimes, distillation may be used in conjunction with a few other mass transfer operations (Stichlmair and Fair, 1998). For example, in an acrylonitrile plant, the product is separated from the reaction mixture by absorption in water. The aqueous solution of acrylonitrile leaving the absorption tower is separated in a distillation column to produce acrylonitrile of desired purity. Similarly, the extract and raffinate streams from an extraction column (discussed in Chapter 8) may be further separated in a distillation column depending upon the difference in volatility of the components (example: an aromatics extraction unit in a petroleum refinery). Because of its importance and wide use in separation of mixtures, distillation is called 'the workhorse of chemical industries'. Despite the advent of newer and advanced separation processes, distillation still remains the most widely used separation technique of liquid mixtures and solutions (Fair, 1988; Kunesh et al., 1995). The estimated cost of annual worldwide throughput of distillation columns was 524 billion dollars about ten years ago as reported by Porter (1995). A few common examples of applications of fractional distillation are cited in Table 7.1. Here we shall briefly discuss the basic principles of distillation calculations and design. There are a few excellent books that deal with the topic elaborately (Billet, 1985, 1995; Kister, 1989, 1992; Stichlmair and Fair, 1998).

Table 7.1   A few examples of separation of liquid mixtures by distillation

Feed/Components	Industry/Plant	Product
Crude petroleum	Refinery	Various petroleum products
Ethylene oxide/Water	Petrochemical	Ethylene oxide
Acrylonitrile/Water	—do—	Acrylonitrile
Styrene/Ethylbenzene	—do—	Styrene
Benzene/Ethyl benzene/others	—do—	Ethylbenzene
Propylene/Propane	—do—	Propylene
Ethanol/Water	Fermentation/Distillery	Ethanol
Acetic acid/Acetic anhydride	Acetic anhydride plant	Acetic anhydride
Air	Air separation plant	Nitrogen, Oxygen, Argon
Aniline/Nitrobenzene	Aniline plant	Aniline

7.1   VAPOUR–LIQUID EQUILIBRIUM

Separation of a mixture by distillation is based on equilibrium distribution of the components between the liquid and the vapour phases. A knowledge of vapour–liquid equilibrium is therefore essential for understanding the principles of distillation. Consider an aqueous solution of ethanol taken in a closed vessel like the one shown in Figure 4.1. The solution is boiled for some time and the vapour along with air in the space above the liquid is expelled through a valve so that the vessel now contains molecules of ethanol and water only. The valve is now closed and the vessel is put in a constant temperature bath. What do we expect to happen? Given sufficient time, the system reaches equilibrium and the liquid and the vapour compositions as well as the total pressure in the vapour space (i.e. the total pressure exerted by the solution) attain unique values. Now the vessel is taken out of the bath, some amount of ethanol (or water) is pushed into it and the vessel is again maintained at the same temperature in the bath. The system will attain a new equilibrium state, i.e. it will have a different set of liquid and vapour concentrations and a new total pressure in the vapour space. Under a *given set of conditions*, the equilibrium vapour composition is related to the liquid composition, This is what is called the *vapour–liquid equilibrium* (VLE).

But what is meant by 'a given set of conditions'? The answer is given by Gibb's phase rule (discussed before in Chapter 4) expressed as

$$\overline{F} = \overline{C} - \overline{P} + 2 \tag{7.1}$$

In the above example of equilibrium in the ethanol–water system, the number of components, $\overline{C} = 2$; the number of phases, $\overline{P} = 2$ (the vapour and the liquid phase). So $\overline{F} = 2$ and the system has two degrees of freedom. The total number of parameters and variables is four—temperature, total pressure, liquid composition and vapour composition. Since the number of degrees of freedom ($\overline{F}$) is 2, two of these four quantities need to be fixed to define the system in equilibrium. Thus if temperature and pressure are fixed, the liquid and the vapour compositions will be automatically fixed (i.e. there can be only one set of liquid and vapour compositions for which the total pressure exerted in the vapour space is equal to the given pressure at the given temperature). Similarly, if the temperature and the liquid composition are fixed, the total pressure and the vapour compositions will be automatically fixed if the system is in equilibrium. Extension to a multicomponent system is not difficult.

Vapour–liquid equilibria constitute the physical basis of separation of a mixture by distillation. The higher concentration of the more volatile component(s) in the vapour phase compared to the liquid phase makes separation by distillation possible (see the *x–y* data for the methanol–water system given in Example 7.15). Accurate VLE data are essential for reliable design of a distillation column. If the experimental data are not available (this happens frequently for multicomponent systems), a suitable predictive method (e.g. UNIFAC method) can be adopted for computation of equilibrium data. Now we shall describe a simple experimental setup for the determination of vapour–liquid equilibrium in the laboratory. This will be followed by a description of common types of equilibrium relationships exhibited by various liquid mixtures.

7.1.1 Experimental Determination of Vapour–Liquid Equilibrium (VLE)

Different types of experimental setup have been devised for the measurement of composition and temperature/pressure of liquid and vapour phases in equilibrium. The basic functions of an equilibrium still are to continuously vaporize a liquid mixture, condense all the vapour in a condenser (using a suitable coolant) and recycle the condensate to the still or the boiling flask. This kind of apparatus is called a 'liquid-recirculation still'. After equilibrium is reached, a sample of the liquid is drawn from the still and analyzed to determine the liquid composition (*x*, mole fraction). A sample of the condensate (which has the same composition as that of the vapour) is analyzed to get the composition of the vapour at equilibrium[†] (*y**, mole fraction). Experiments are repeated with liquid mixtures of different compositions to generate the vapour–liquid equilibrium data (*x–y** data) covering the entire range of composition of the binary ($0 \leq x \leq 1$).

An early version of the device used for this purpose is the 'Othmer still' devised by D.F. Othmer as early as in 1928. Various modifications of this apparatus have been suggested from time to time—for example, Colburn still, Gillespie still, Scheeline and Gilliland still, etc. Two common sources of error in the experiments are: (i) superheating of the liquid (the thermocouple/ thermometer indicates a wrong boiling temperature of the liquid mixture as a result); (ii) heat loss from the still or the boiling flask causing partial condensation of the vapour before it leaves the boiling flask. A modified version of the Gillespie still (Yuan and Lu, 1963) which is free from these problems is described in Figure 7.2.

A liquid mixture is taken in the boiling flask (B) which is provided with an internal electric heating coil (H) within a glass sheath (G). The liquid–vapour mixture flows through the vertical tube P (sometimes called 'Cottrell pump') and enters the equilibriation chamber (E) in which the vapour and the liquid phases get separated and reach equilibrium. The liquid flows to the liquid

---

[†] A star (*) is often used to indicate the equilibrium value; *x* and *y* refer to the more volatile in a binary.

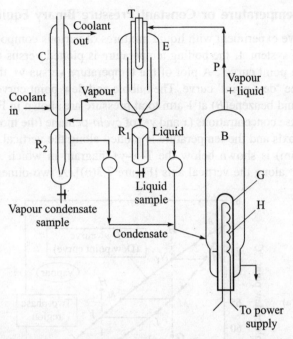

Figure 7.2 Schematic of a modified Gillespie still. B: boiling flask or 'still'; H: internal electric heater; G: glass sheath of the heater; P: Cottrell pump; E: equilibration chamber; R_1: liquid receiver; C: total condenser of a vapour; R_2: condensate receiver; T: thermometer or thermocouple.

receiver (R_1) and the vapour flows to the condenser (C). The condensate is collected in another receiver (R_2). Since all the vapour flowing into the condenser is condensed (it is a 'total condenser'), the composition of the vapour and that of the condensate are equal. The boiling flask (B), the equilibrium chamber (E) and the liquid receiver (R_1) are well-insulated. (If the insulation is not good, condensation of a little vapour may occur in E and R_1 causing 'rectification' of the vapour. As a result, the vapour will be more enriched in the more volatiles than it should be at 'equilibrium'). The liquid from R_1 and the condensate from R_2 continuously overflow and get recycled back to the boiling flask through the connecting tubes as shown in Figure 7.2. The still is operated for a sufficiently long time to reach equilibrium. Samples of the liquid and of the vapour (condensed in the receiver R_2) are collected by opening the stop cocks and then analyzed to find out the equilibrium compositions of the phases. The temperature in the equilibrium chamber is measured by inserting a thermocouple or a thermometer in the thermowell, T. The temperature indicated at equilibrium is equal to the bubble point of the liquid and also equal to the dew point of the equilibrium vapour. (It is to be noted that if the boiling temperature is measured by inserting a thermometer in a thermowell in the boiling flask, there may be an error because of the superheat of the liquid.) A suitable arrangement for maintaining the pressure in the still is made if it is operated at a pressure different from the ambient pressure.

The apparatus described above is useful to measure the 'constant pressure' equilibrium data. With some modifications, it can be used to measure 'constant temperature' equilibrium—when the total pressure, in addition to the equilibrium liquid and vapour concentrations, is measured at a given constant temperature.

7.1.2 Constant Temperature or Constant Pressure Binary Equilibria

By repeating the above experiment with liquid mixtures of various compositions, we can collect the T–x–$y*$ data for a system. If the boiling temperature is plotted versus the liquid composition x, we get the 'bubble point curve'. A plot of the temperature versus $y*$, the equilibrium vapour composition, gives the 'dew point' curve. The bubble and dew point curves for binary mixtures of *cyclo*-pentane(A) and benzene(B) at 1 atm total pressure are shown in Figure 7.3(a). Both the liquid and vapour phase concentrations (x and $y*$) of *cyclo*-pentane (the more volatile) are plotted along the horizontal axis and the temperature is plotted along the vertical axis. The equilibrium diagram (x–$y*$ diagram) is shown below the T–x–$y*$ diagram in which x is plotted along the horizontal axis and $y*$ along the vertical axis [Figure 7.3(b)]. A two-dimensional representation

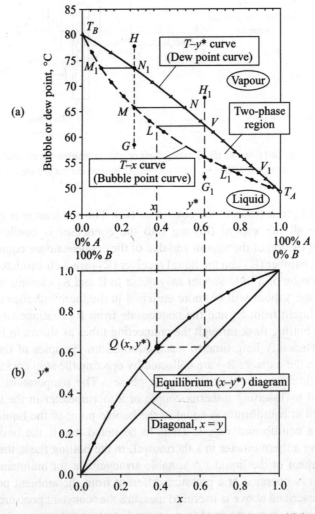

Figure 7.3 (a) Bubble and dew point curves, and (b) equilibrium diagram of *cyclo*-pentane (1)–benzene (2) system at 1 atm. [Myers, *Ind. Eng. Chem.*, **48**(1956) 1104.]

of T–x–y or x–y data is possible only for binary mixtures. For a three-component system, such data may be represented by surfaces in a three-dimensional space or in the tabular form.

On a horizontal line segment, say LV in Figure 7.3(a), the abscissa of the point L gives the concentration of A in the saturated[†] liquid phase (x), and that of the the point V gives its equilibrium vapour-phase concentration $(y*)$; LV is called a 'tie line'. The lines LV, MN, M_1N_1, and L_1V_1 in the figure are also tie lines.

Let us imagine that a small amount of a liquid mixture having a mole fraction x (a subscript is not generally used to denote the concentration of the more volatile in a binary mixture) of *cyclo*-pentane and the rest benzene is taken at a constant pressure of 1 atm in a vessel fitted with a 'frictionless piston' and heated gradually. The temperature and composition of the liquid are given by the point G in Figure 7.3(a). When its temperature reaches the point M, it starts boiling and the composition of the initial vapour is given by the abscissa of the point N, which is the other end of the tie line through M. It is seen that $y* > x$; i.e. the vapour is richer in A, the more volatile species in the mixture. As heating proceeds, more and more vapour is generated (we assume that all the vapour generated remains in the vapour space above the liquid at a constant pressure). The mole fraction of the more volatile component A in the residual liquid decreases and the boiling point of the liquid continues to increase along the T–x curve. The last droplet of liquid to vaporize has a composition and boiling point given by the point M_1. When all the liquid is vaporized, the accumulated vapour must have a composition equal to that of the initial liquid. No further heating is done and the final state of the vapour (as given by its temperature and composition) is given by the point N_1 on the vertical line through G. However, if further heating of this vapour (which is now saturated) is done, its temperature will only rise along the vertical line GH (this is superheating of the vapour). The line T_B–M_1–L–L_1–T_A is the bubble point curve; T_B–N_1–N–V–V_1–T_A is the dew point curve. The bubble and the dew point curves meet at the points T_B (the boiling point of pure B at the given pressure) and at T_A (the boiling point of pure A).

Similarly, if some amount of superheated vapour, whose state is represented by the point H_1 is taken in a vessel fitted with a frictionless piston and is gradually cooled while maintaining a constant pressure of 1 atm, condensation starts when the vapour temperature drops to the point V. The composition of the first droplet of liquid formed is given by the point L (the other end of the tie line through V). As condensation proceeds, the vapour composition changes along VV_1 and the composition of the condensate follows LL_1. When the entire vapour is condensed and the liquid is cooled, we reach a point G_1 vertically below H_1 in the subcooled liquid domain. The boiling point of pure B lies vertically above the point $x = 0$ ($x = 0$ means pure B). Similarly, T_A occurs vertically above $x = 1$.

The region below the bubble point curve T_B–M_1–M–L–L_1–T_A represents a single liquid phase; the region above T_B–N_1–N–V–V_1–T_A represents a single vapour phase. A point in the region enclosed by these curves represents a mixture of liquid and vapour. Any such mixture (given by the point F in Figure 7.5(a), for example) splits into a liquid and a vapour phase in equilibrium given by the ends of the tie line LV through the point F.

Let the amount of the two-phase mixture taken be also denoted by F kmol[††] at a concentration z_F. It splits into a liquid phase of amount L kmol (concentration $= x$) and an

---

[†] A liquid at its bubble point is called a 'saturated liquid'; a vapour at its dew point is a 'saturated vapour'.

[††] This practice of representing a stream and its flow rate or amount by the same notation is pretty common in the study of mass transfer operations.

equilibrium vapour phase of amount V kmol (concentration $= y*$). Now we may write the following mass balance equations [refer to Figure 7.5(a)].

Overall mass balance: $\quad F = L + V$ (7.2)

Component A balance: $\quad Fz_F = Lx + Vy*$ (7.3)

Eliminating F from Eqs. (7.2) and (7.3), we get

$$(L + V)z_F = Lx + Vy*$$

$$\Rightarrow \qquad \frac{L}{V} = \frac{y* - z_F}{z_F - x} = \frac{\text{length of the section } FV}{\text{length of the section } LF}$$ (7.4)

Thus, the amounts of liquid and vapour produced after phase separation of the mixture F can be calculated using Eq. (7.4). This equation is sometimes called the *Lever-arm Rule*. It is useful in the calculation of flash vaporization, calculations involving liquid–liquid and solid–liquid extraction, etc.

Figure 7.3(b) shows the equilibrium diagram on the x–y plane. It can be obtained directly by plotting the experimental x–$y*$ data (note that both x and $y*$ vary from 0 to 1). It can also be drawn from the bubble point and dew point curves, following the procedure indicated in the figure. The point Q on the x–$y*$ curve corresponds to the tie line LV on the T–x–y diagram. Because $y* > x$, the equilibrium line lies above the diagonal (at any point on the diagonal, $x = y$). The kind of data given in Figure 7.3 represent the equilibrium data collected at *constant pressure*.

Equilibrium data can also be collected at constant temperature. If so, the total vapour pressure P exerted by the solution at equilibrium depends upon its composition. At a lower concentration of A (i.e. at a higher concentration of the less volatile species B), the mixture will exert a lower total vapour pressure. Typical plots of such data, x–P and $y*$–P, are shown in Figure 7.4(a). A horizontal line such as LV is a *tie line*. The terminals (the points L and V) indicate the liquid and vapour phase concentrations of A under equilibrium. The liquid, the vapour and the two-phase regions are demarcated in the

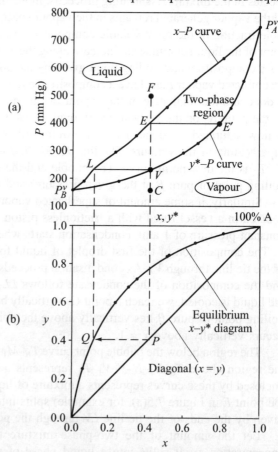

Figure 7.4 (a) Bubble point pressure (x–P and $y*$–P), and (b) equilibrium (x–$y*$) diagrams for dichloromethane-1, 2-dichloroethane system at 40°C. [Davies et al. *J. Soc. Chem. Ind.* (Lond), *68*(1949) 26.]

figure. The region below the curve P_B^v–V–E'–P_A^v represents the 'superheated' vapour; the region above P_B^v–L–E–P_A^v represents the 'subcooled' liquid (P_A^v and P_B^v are the vapour pressures of the pure liquids at the given temperature). If an amount of superheated vapour at the state given by the point C is compressed isothermally, it starts condensing as it reaches the point V and the first droplet of liquid formed has a composition given by the point L. On further compression, more vapour condenses and the composition of the accumulated condensate liquid changes along LE and the composition of the vapour changes along VE'. At a pressure corresponding to the point E, the vapour condenses completely. Now the liquid composition is the same as the composition of the original vapour. If the pressure is raised further, the liquid may be considered 'subcooled'. The equilibrium compositions corresponding to the tie line LV is represented by the point QP on the x–y diagram in Figure 7.4(b). The two-phase region on a T–x–y or P–x–y plot narrows down with increasing tepmerature and pressure and eventually disappears at the critical point. The details of these phenomena are available in standard texts on thermodynamics.

7.1.3 The Raoult's Law

Raoult's law which describes the vapour–liquid equilibria of *ideal solutions*, has been discussed in Section 4.3.1. Equation (4.1), which is the expression for Raoult's law, is written below [Eq. (7.5)] for both the components A and B to give the equilibrium partial pressures of the components in a binary liquid mixture. If x is the mole fraction of A in the binary solution, that of B is $(1 - x)$.

$$p_A^* = xP_A^v \quad \text{and} \quad p_B^* = (1 - x)P_B^v \tag{7.5}$$

The total pressure:
$$P = p_A^* + p_B^* = xP_A^v + (1 - x)P_B^v \tag{7.6}$$

Here p_A^* and p_B^* are the equilibrium partial pressures of A and B in the vapour; P_A^v and P_B^v are the vapour pressures of A and B at the given temperature. The mole fraction of A in the vapour is given by

$$y_A^* = p_A^*/P = (xP_A^v)/P \tag{7.7}$$

Equation (7.7) can be used to calculate the vapour–liquid equilibrium data (x–$y*$) for an ideal binary mixture. The procedure to calculate the equilibrium concentrations as well as the bubble point and the dew point *at a constant total pressure P*, is described below.

(a) Find the vapour pressures (P_A^v and P_B^v) of A and B at a temperature T ($T_A < T < T_B$).
(b) The total pressure P being known, calculate x from Eq. (7.6).
(c) Calculate $y*$ from Eq. (7.7).

The procedure is illustrated in Example 7.1. The constants of the Antoine equation for vapour pressure of some selected liquids are given in Table 7.2.

Table 7.2 Constants of the vapour pressure relation (Antoine equation)

Compound	BP (°C)	A′	B′	C′
Acetaldehyde	20.5	16.6006	2532.41	234
Acetic acid	118	18.47233	4457.83	258.46

(Contd.)

Table 7.2 Constants of the vapour pressure relation (Antoine equation) (*Contd.*)

Compound	BP (°C)	A'	B'	C'
Acetone	56.2	16.39112	2787.5	229.67
Acetonitrile	81.5	16.90395	3413.1	250.48
Acrylonitrile	77.5	15.92847	2782.21	222
Ammonia	−33.4	17.51202	2363.24	250.54
Aniline	184.5	16.67784	3858.22	200
Benzaldehyde	179	6.73163	1369.460	177.081
Benzene	80	15.9037	2789.01	220.79
n-Butane	−0.5	15.68151	2154.9	238.74
n-Butanol	117.6	17.62995	3367.12	188.7
iso-Butane	−11.7	15.77506	2133.24	245
iso-Butanol	108	18.02933	3413.34	199.97
Butyl acetate	126	16.4145	3293.66	210.75
Carbon disulphide	46	15.77889	2585.12	236.46
Carbon tetrachloride	76.5	15.8434	2790.78	226.46
Chlorobenzene	131.5	16.4	3485.35	224.87
Chloroform	61.2	16.017	2696.25	226.24
Cyclohexane	80.5	15.7794	2778	223.14
Cyclohexanol	161	19.23534	5200.53	251.7
Cyclohexanone	155.5	16.40517	3677.63	212.7
Cyclopentane	49.2	15.8602	2589.2	231.36
1-4-Dioxane	101.5	17.1151	3579.78	240.35
Dichloromethane	40	17.0635	3053.08	252.6
Diethyl ether	34.5	16.5414	2847.72	253
Diethylamine	55.5	15.73382	2434.73	212
Ethanol	78.3	18.68233	3667.70	226.1
Ethyl acetate	77	16.35578	2866.6	217.9
Ethyl benzene	136	16.04305	3291.66	213.8
Ethylamine	16.5	7.3862	1137.300	235.85
Formic acid	100.5	15.9938	2982.45	218
Furfural	162	15.14517	2760.09	162.8
n-Hexane	69	15.9155	2738.42	226.2
n-Heptane	98.5	15.877	2911.32	226.65
Methanol	64.5	18.61042	3392.57	230
Methyl acetate	57	16.58646	2839.21	228
Nitrobenzene	131.5	16.42172	3485.35	224.84
Nitrogen	−195.8	15.3673	648.59	270.02
n-Octane	126	15.9635	3128.75	209.85
Oxygen	−183	15.06244	674.59	263.07
1-Octanol	195	7.18653	1515.427	156.767
n-Pentane	36	15.8365	2477.07	233.21
Phenol	180	15.9614	3183.67	159.5

(*Contd.*)

Table 7.2 Constants of the vapour pressure relation (Antoine equation) (*Contd.*)

Compound	BP (°C)	A′	B′	C′
n-Propanol	97.2	17.8349	3310.4	198.5
iso-Propanol	82.2	20.4463	4628.95	252.64
Propane	−42	15.7277	1872.82	250
Pyridine	115	16.1520	3124.45	212.66
Styrene	135	15.94618	3270.26	206
Tetrahydrofuran	66	16.11023	2768.37	226.3
Toluene	110.6	16.00531	3090.78	219.14
Trichloroethylene	87	15.01158	2345.48	192.73
Triethylamine	89	15.7212	2674.7	205
o-Xylene	134.5	7.00154	1476.393	213.872
p-Xylene	129.2	6.99052	1453.430	215.307
Water	100	18.5882	3984.92	233.43

Antoine equation: $\ln P_A^v = A' - \dfrac{B'}{C' + \theta}$; P_A^v in mm Hg, θ in °C

EXAMPLE 7.1 (*Calculation of bubble point, dew point and equilibrium data for an ideal binary mixture*) *Cyclo*-pentane(A) and benzene(B) form nearly ideal solutions.

(a) Using the vapour pressure equation given in Table 7.2 (and assuming ideal behaviour), prepare the bubble point, the dew point and the vapour–liquid equilibrium curves for this binary at 1 atm total pressure.

(b) If one kilomole of a two-phase mixture having 42 mole% A at 68°C is allowed and 1 atm total pressure is allowed to separate into a liquid and a vapour phase at 1 atm total pressure, calculate the amounts and compositions of the two phases.

(c) Consider an equimolar mixture of A and B at 600 mm total pressure. (i) What is the bubble point of the mixture and the composition of the initial vapour? (ii) If a small quantity of the mixture is slowly vaporized in a closed vessel and *the vapour remains in contact and in equilibrium with the liquid*, calculate the composition of the last drop of the liquid.

(d) If an equimolar mixture of the compounds has a bubble point of 100°C, calculate the total pressure exerted at that temperature at equilibrium.

Solution

(a) The bubble and dew points of mixtures of different compositions remain within 49.2°C (boiling point of pure *cyclo*-pentane at 1 atm) and 80°C (boiling point of pure benzene at 1 atm). The total pressure remains constant at 1 atm (= 760 mm Hg). The vapour pressure of a component is *explicitly* given as a function of temperature. In order to compute the $T–x–y$ data, it is convenient to begin with a temperature and to calculate the corresponding liquid and vapour compositions at equilibrium. A sample calculation is shown below.

Take $T = 70°C$. $\ln P_A^v = 15.8602 - 2589.2/(231.36 + 70) \Rightarrow P_A^v = 1434$ mm Hg

$\ln P_B^v = 15.9037 - 2789.01/(220.79 + 70) \Rightarrow P_B^v = 551$ mm Hg

Using Eq. (7.6), total pressure, $P = 760$ mm Hg $= x(1434) + (1 - x)(551) \Rightarrow x = 0.237$

Therefore, at $T = 70°C$ and $P = 760$ mm Hg, the mole fraction of A in liquid at equilibrium is $x = 0.237$.

Mole fraction of A in the equilibrium vapour, $y* = x(P_A^v/P) = (0.237)(1434)/760 = 0.447$

So the bubble point of a solution having 0.237 mole fraction of A at 1 atm total pressure is 70°C. This is also the dew point of a vapour having 0.447 mole fraction of A.

The bubble and dew points of liquids and vapours of other compositions are similarly calculated and plotted in Figure 7.5(a). The calculated $x–y*$ data are plotted in Figure 7.5(b). The experimental $x–y*$ data are also shown on the same figure. It is seen that the deviation from ideal behaviour is small. The system is nearly ideal.

(b) The state of the feed (68°C; 1 atm; $z_F = 0.42$) is represented by the point F that lies in the two-phase region in Figure 7.5(a). Now the mixture is allowed to separate into a liquid and a vapour phase at equilibrium. Draw a horizontal line through F that meets the bubble point curve at L and the dew point curve at V. The abscissa of the point $L(x)$ gives the composition of the liquid; that of the point $V (y*)$ gives the composition of the equilibrium vapour. From Figure 7.5(a), we get $x = 0.294$, $y* = 0.521$.

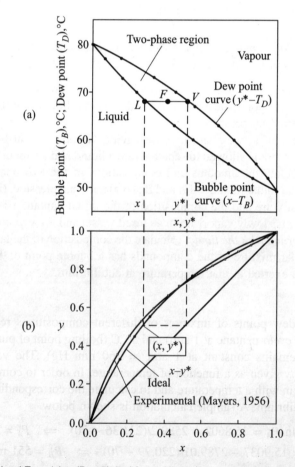

Figure 7.5 (a) The calculated $T–x–y*$ data (Raoult's law) for *cyclo*-pentane-benzene mixtures, and (b) the experimental $x–y*$ data from Mayers, *Ind. Eng. Chem.* **48**(1956) 1104.

To calculate the amounts of the liquid and vapour phases produced on phase separation, use the following material balance equations. Total amount of the mixture is $F = 1$ kilomole.

$$F = L + V \implies 1 = L + V \quad \text{and} \quad Fz_F = Lx + Vy^* \implies (1)(0.42) = L(0.294) + V(0.521)$$

Solving the preceding material balance equations,

Moles of liquid, $L = \boxed{0.555 \text{ kmol}}$ and moles of vapour, $V = \boxed{0.445}$

(c) Consider an equimolar mixture of the components (i.e. $x = 0.5$) at 600 mm Hg total pressure.

(i) If the bubble point is θ, using Eq. (7.6) and the given vapour pressure equations, we can write

$$P = x_A P_A^v + (1 - x_A)P_B^v \implies 600 = (0.5)10^{\left(15.8602 - \frac{2589.2}{231.36+\theta}\right)} + (1 - 0.5)10^{\left(15.9037 - \frac{2789.01}{220.79+\theta}\right)}$$

Solving this equation, the bubble point of the equimolar mixture at 600 mm Hg pressure is

$$\theta = \boxed{54°C}$$

At 54°C, the vapour pressures of the individual compounds are:

$$P_A^v = 885.7 \text{ mm Hg}; \qquad P_B^v = 315.3 \text{ mm Hg}$$

From Eq. (7.7), the composition of the *initial vapour*,

$$y^* = P_A^v x/P = (885.7)(0.5)/600 = \boxed{0.738 \text{ mole fraction}}$$

(ii) *Composition of the last drop of liquid remaining:* When all the liquid is vaporized except a tiny drop of it, the vapour composition is virtually the same as that of the initial liquid, i.e. $y_A = 0.5$, $y_B = 0.5$. In other words, the equimolar vapour containing A and B is at its dew point. Let us first calculate this dew-point temperature.

If x is the mole fraction of A in the last drop of the liquid (which is in equilibrium with the vapour of $y = 0.5$), then

Partial pressure of A in the vapour $= Py_A = P_A^v x_A \implies (600)(0.5) = 300 = P_A^v x_A$

Similarly, the partial pressure of B in the vapour, $300 = P_B^v x_B = P_B^v(1 - x_A)$

Eliminating x_A from the above two equations, $(300/P_A^v) + (300/P_B^v) = 1$. Putting the expressions for P_A^v and P_B^v (the vapour pressure equations) and solving for θ, we have $\theta = 61.4°C$.

At $\theta = 61.4°C$, $P_A^v = 1114$ mm Hg and $P_B^v = 411.3$ mm Hg.

Then the liquid composition, $x_A = Py_A/P_A^v = (600)(0.5)/(1114) = 0.27$

The last drop of liquid contains $\boxed{27 \text{ mole% of } cyclo\text{-pentane}(A)}$.

(d) Vapour pressures of the components at 100°C are:

$$P_A^v = 3120.2 \text{ mm Hg}; \qquad P_B^v = 1350.5 \text{ mm Hg}$$

The equilibrium total pressure exerted above an equimolar mixture at 100°C is given by

$$P = P_A^v x_A + P_B^v(1 - x_B) = (0.5)(3120.2) + (1350.5)(1 - 0.5) = \boxed{2235.3 \text{ mm Hg}}$$

[*Note:* The problem can also be solved using the K-values of the components; see Section 7.1.6]

7.1.4 Deviation from Ideality and Formation of Azeotropes

Qualitative criteria of ideal behaviour of a solution have been listed in Section 4.3.1. As a matter of fact, most solutions *do not* exhibit ideal behaviour. In other words, they show deviations from ideality. Deviations may be of two types—*positive deviation* and *negative deviation*. A liquid mixture exerting an equilibrium total vapour pressure more than that calculated by Eq. (7.6) is said to exhibit a 'positive deviation from ideality'. If the total vapour pressure is less than that calculated from Eq. (7.6), the deviation is called a 'negative deviation'.

Two extreme cases of deviation from ideal behaviour lead to what are called *azeotropes*. If there is a large positive deviation from ideality and the vapour pressures of the components *A* and *B* are not much different, the total pressure curve may pass through a maximum at a certain liquid concentration. A liquid mixture of such character and composition is a 'constant boiling mixture'[†] and is called a minimum boiling azeotrope. The *x*–*P* and *y**–*P* curves touch at the azeotropic composition (at the azeotropic point $x = y*$); the *x*–*T* and *y**–*T* curves pass through a common minimum. This is why such an azeotrope is called *minimum boiling*. The equilibrium curve (*x*–*y**) crosses the diagonal line at the azetropic composition. The equilibrium in a minimum boiling binary azeotropic system is shown in Figure 7.6.

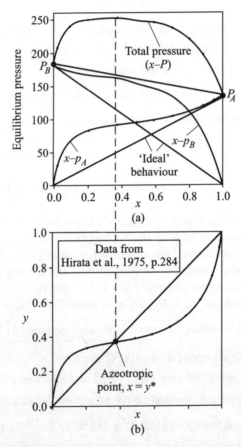

Figure 7.6   Isothermal vapour–liquid equilibrium diagram of a minimum-boiling azeotrope (ethanol–benzene, 40°C): (a) bubble point pressure, and (b) equilibrium diagrams.

[†] A 'constant boiling mixture' generates vapour of a composition equal to that of the liquid. So the liquid composition and the boiling temperature remain the same even if a part of the liquid is boiled out. Such a mixture cannot be separated by ordinary distillation.

Similarly, if the deviation from the ideal behaviour is negative and large, the partial pressures of the individual coefficients are less than the ideal values. The plots of the total pressure against the liquid and the vapour compositions at a constant temperature pass through a common minimum at the azeotropic point [Figure 7.7(a)]. The corresponding x–$y*$ diagram is shown in Figure 7.7(b). An azeotrope exhibiting such behaviour is called *maximum boiling* because the boiling temperature at the azeotropic point is maximum if the total pressure is held constant.

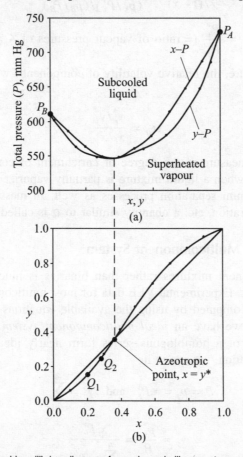

Figure 7.7   Isothermal vapour–liquid equilibrium diagram of a maximum-boiling azeotrope, acetone (A)–chloroform (B) at 55°C.

7.1.5   Relative Volatility

Relative volatility of a component A in a mixture indicates the ease of its separation from another component B. It is defined as the concentration ratio of A to B in the vapour *divided by* the same ratio in the liquid phase. It is usually denoted by α. For a binary mixture,

$$\alpha \text{ (or } \alpha_{AB}) = \frac{y*/(1 - y*)}{x/(1 - x)} = \frac{(1 - x)\,y*}{(1 - y*)\,x} \tag{7.8a}$$

$$\Rightarrow \qquad\qquad y* = \frac{\alpha\, x}{1 + (\alpha - 1)\, x} \tag{7.8b}$$

If A is the more volatile component in the mixture, α is larger than 1 (this is *not true* over the entire range of concentration if the system is azeotropic). Using Eqs. (7.5) and (7.7), the relative volatility $\alpha \ (= \alpha_{AB})$ in an ideal binary solution can be expressed in terms of the vapour pressures of the components, i.e.

$$\alpha = \frac{y*/(1-y*)}{x/(1-x)} = \frac{(p_A^*/P)/(p_B^*/P)}{(p_A^*/P_A^v)/(p_B^*/P_B^v)}$$

$$= \frac{P_A^v}{P_B^v} \ (= \text{ratio of vapour pressures of } A \text{ and } B) \tag{7.9}$$

In a multicomponent mixture, the relative volatility of component i with respect to component j is given by

$$\alpha_{ij} = \frac{y_i^*/y_j^*}{x_i/x_j} \tag{7.10}$$

The quantity α_{ij} gives a measure of the degree of enrichment of component i in the vapour compared to component j when a liquid mixture is partially vaporized. Its definition has been extended to other equilibrium separation processes as well. In mass transfer operations like extraction, membrane separation, etc. a quantity similar to α is called the *separation factor*.

7.1.6 Equilibrium in a Multicomponent System

Separation of multicomponent mixtures rather than binaries is much more common in the chemical process industries. Experimental VLE data for most multicomponent mixtures are not available and have to be computed by using the available equations or correlations. The job becomes pretty simple if we have an *ideal multicomponent system* so that Raoult's law is applicable. Hydrocarbons of a homologous series form nearly ideal solutions. For the *i*th component in an ideal solution, we can write

$$y_j^* P = p_j^* = x_j P_j^v \quad \text{and} \quad P = \sum_{i=1}^{n} p_i^* \tag{7.11}$$

$$\Rightarrow \qquad y_j^* = \frac{p_j^*}{P} = \frac{x_j P_j^v}{\sum\limits_{i=1}^{n} x_i P_i^v} \tag{7.12}$$

where, P_j^v = vapour pressure of component j at the given temperature

At a given temperature, the vapour pressures of the components, P_i^v's are known. Therefore, for a particular liquid composition (i.e. given for given values of $x_1, x_2, \ldots, x_n$), the vapour compositions $(y_1^*, y_2^*, \ldots, y_n^*)$ can be calculated. Noting that $\alpha_{ij} = P_i^v/P_j^v$, Eq. (7.12) can be rewritten as

$$y_j^* = \frac{x_j}{(1/P_j^v) \sum\limits_{i=1}^{n} x_i P_i^v} = \frac{x_j}{\sum\limits_{i=1}^{n} \alpha_{ij} x_i} = \frac{\alpha_{ji} x_j}{\sum\limits_{k=1}^{n} \alpha_{ki} x_k} \tag{7.13}$$

Once the equilibrium vapour phase mole fractions are known, the partial pressures and the total pressure can be calculated from Eq. (7.11).

For hydrocarbon mixtures, a quantity called *equilibrium vaporization ratio* (denoted by K_i for the ith component) is extensively used for VLE computation. It is defined as

$$K_i = \frac{y_i}{x_i} = \frac{P_i^v}{P} \tag{7.14a}$$

Distillation calculations, including the bubble and dew point calculations, can be done using the K-values, if available. The DePriester chart [Figures 7.8(a) and (b)] may be conveniently used to obtain K-values for lower hydrocarbons at different temperatures and pressures.

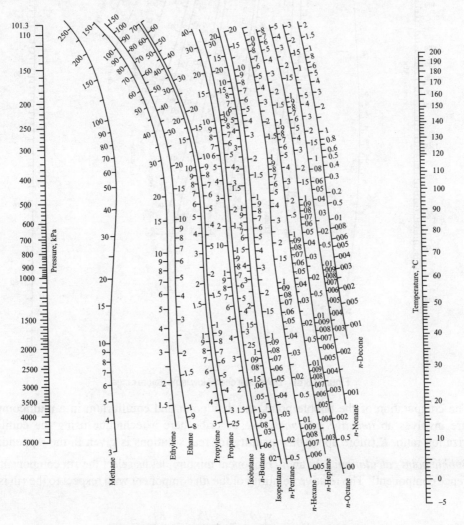

Figure 7.8(a) DePriester chart—high temperature range.

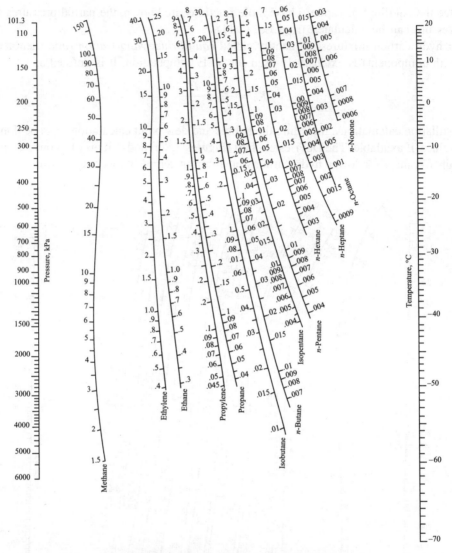

Figure 7.8(b)   DePriester chart—low temperature range.

The computation of the bubble point, the dew point and equilibrium in a multicomponent mixture involves an *iterative approach*. We describe here a technique using the equilibrium vaporization ratio, K (more about this quantity for real solutions is given in the Appendix).

Bubble point calculation: In an n-component mixture, let us select the rth component as the 'reference component'. The relative volatility of the ith component with respect to the rth is given as

$$\alpha_{ir} = \frac{y_i / y_r}{x_i / x_r} = \frac{y_i / x_i}{y_r / x_r} = \frac{K_i}{K_r}$$

Therefore, $K_i = K_r \alpha_{ir} \Rightarrow y_i = K_i x_i = K_r \alpha_{ir} x_i \Rightarrow \sum_{i=1}^{n} y_i = K_r \sum_{i=1}^{n} \alpha_{ir} x_i$ (7.14b)

In a bubble point calculation problem, the liquid composition is known and the total pressure is given. We start with an assumed temperature and calculate the vapour pressures or K-values of all the components. Then we can calculate the values of $y_i = K_i x_i (= x_i P_i^y/P$ if the solution is ideal). At the bubble point, the sum of the y_i's should be unity, i.e.

$$\sum_{i=1}^{n} y_i = \sum_{i=1}^{n} K_i x_i = 1 \tag{7.15a}$$

The boiling point of the reference substance may be taken as the *initial guess*. The values of K_i ($i = 1, 2,..., r, ..., n$) and α_{ir} are calculated at this temperature and put in Eq. [7.14(b)] to get a revised value of K_r. We use this revised value of K_r to determine the *second approximation* to the bubble point. Computation is repeated till Eq. [7.14(b)] is satisfied to the desired degree of accuracy. The computational procedure is illustrated in Example 7.2.

EXAMPLE 7.2 (*Calculation of the bubble point of an ideal multicomponent mixture*)   Calculate the bubble point of an *ideal solution* containing 20 mole% n-pentane(1) and 40 mole% each of n-hexane(2) and n-heptane(3) at 1.5 bar total pressure. Use the vapour pressure equation given in Table 7.2.

Solution

Step 1:   Calculate the average molecular weight of the mixture.

Since $M_1 = 72$, $M_2 = 86$, and $M_3 = 100$, $M_{av} = (0.2)(72) + (0.4)(86) + (0.4)(100) = 88.8$.

This is close to the molecular weight of n-hexane. We select n-hexane as the *reference component*.

Step 2:   Calculate the boiling point of the reference component (i.e. n-hexane) at the given pressure (1.5 bar = 1125 mm Hg). From the Antoine equation,

$$\ln(1125) = 15.9155 - 2738.42/(\theta + 226.2) \Rightarrow \theta = 82°C \Rightarrow T = 355 \text{ K}$$

Take this temperature as the *first approximation* of the bubble point of the mixture. Calculate the relative volatility of the other components — n-pentane (1) and n-heptane (3) — with respect to the reference component, i.e. n-hexane(2).

At 355 K, vapour pressure of n-pentane,

$$\ln P_1^y = 15.8365 - 2477.07/(82 + 233.21) \Rightarrow P_1^y = 3.8604 \text{ bar}$$

Vapour pressure of n-heptane,

$$\ln P_3^y = 15.877 - 2911.32/(82 + 226.65) \Rightarrow P_3^y = 0.6066 \text{ bar}$$

Since the solution is *ideal*, $\alpha_{12} = P_1^y/P_2^y = 3.8604/1.5 = 2.5736$; $\alpha_{32} = 0.6066/1.5 = 0.4044$

Now use Eq. [7.14(b)].

$$K_r \sum_{i=1}^{3} \alpha_{i2}x_i = 1 \Rightarrow K_r[2.5736)(0.2) + (1)(0.4) + (0.4044)(0.4)] = 1 \Rightarrow K_r = 0.9289$$

Step 3:   We have to recalculate the whole thing taking the above 'revised value' of K_r.

$$K_r = P_2^v/P; \ P = 1.5 \text{ bar; i.e. } 0.9289 = P_2^v/P = P_2^v/1.5$$

$\Rightarrow$ $P_2^v = (0.9289)(1.5) = 1.3934 \text{ bar} = 1045.4 \text{ mm Hg}$

Recalculate the boiling point of the reference component, *n*-hexane (2), at 1.3934 bar pressure

$$\ln(1045.4) = 15.9155 - 2738.42/(\theta + 226.2) \Rightarrow = 79.5°C \Rightarrow T = 352.5 \text{ K}$$

Vapour pressures of the other two components at this temperature (352.5 K) are:

n-pentane: $P_1^v = 3.625$ bar;   *n*-heptane: $P_3^v = 0.5586$ bar

K-values are: $K_1 = 3.625/1.5 = 2.4167$; $K_2 = K_r = 0.9289$; $K_3 = 0.5586/1.5 = 0.3724$

Step 4:   Check if the recalculated *K*-values satisfy Eq. [7.15(a)].

$$\sum_{i=1}^{3} K_i x_i = (2.4167)(0.2) + (0.9289)(0.4) + (0.3724)(0.4) = 1.004 \approx 1$$

This is good enough. Another cycle of calculation may be done if still better accuracy is desired.

Dew point calculation: For the calculation of the dew point of a vapour of known composition, i.e. known y_i's, we may start with an assumed value of the dew point, and obtain the vapour pressures (or *K*-values) of all the components at this temperature. Since the total pressure is given, we can calculate the mole fractions of the components in the liquid phase, $x_i = y_i/K_i$. ($= y_i P/P_i^v$, if the solution is ideal). If the assumed temperature is the correct dew point, the sum of x_i's must be unity. The following equations may be used for an efficient iterative computation.

$$\sum_{i=1}^{n} x_i = \sum_{i=1}^{n} \frac{y_i}{K_i} = \sum \frac{y_i}{K_r \alpha_{ir}} = \frac{1}{K_r} \sum \frac{y_i}{\alpha_{ir}} = 1 \qquad (7.15b)$$

One of the components is selected as the *reference component* and the boiling point of the reference component is taken as the *initial guess* of the dew point of the vapour mixture. The vapour pressures and the values of α_{ir} of all the components are calculated at this assumed temperature and substituted in Eq. [7.15(b)]. A revised value of K_r and the corresponding temperature are then obtained. This is the *second approximation* to the dew point. The computation is repeated till the desired accuracy is achieved. The procedure is illustrated in Example 7.3.

EXAMPLE 7.3 (*Calculation of the dew point of an ideal vapour mixture*)   Calculate the dew point of a vapour containing 15 mol% *n*-butane(1), 15 mol% *n*-pentane(2), 20 mol% *cyclo*-hexane(3), 20 mol% *n*-hexane(4) and 30 mol% *n*-heptane(5) at 1.5 bar total pressure. Raoult's law applies. Use Table 7.2 to calculate vapour pressures of the components.

Solution

Step 1:   Calculate the average molecular weight of the vapour mixture. The molecular weights of the individual components are: $M_1 = 58$, $M_2 = 72$, $M_3 = 84$, $M_4 = 86$, and $M_5 = 100$. Average molecular weight,

$$M_{av} = (0.15)(58) + (0.15)(72) + (0.20)(84) + (0.20)(86) + (0.30)(100) = 83.6$$

This is close to the molecular weight of *cyclo*-hexane(3). Take this as the reference component.

Calculate the boiling point of *cyclo*-hexane(3) at 1.5 bar pressure (= 1125 mm Hg = given total pressure) using the vapour pressure equation,

$$\ln(1125) = 15.7794 + 2778/(\theta + 223.14) \Rightarrow T = 367.5 \text{ K}$$

Take 367.5 K (94.3°C) as the first approximation of the dew point of the mixture.

Step 2: Calculate the vapour pressures of the other components at the *assumed* bubble point, 367.5 K.

n-Butane: $\ln P^v(1) = 15.68151 - 2154.9/(94.3 + 238.74) \Rightarrow P^v(1) = 9985.8$ mm Hg = 13.31 bar

Similarly, $P^v(2) = 5.211$ bar; $P^v(4) = 2.122$ bar; $P^v(5) = 0.8978$ bar

The relative volatilities (with respect to the reference component, *cyclo*-hexane) are:

$$\alpha_{13} = P^v(1)/P^v(3) = 13.31/1.5 = 8.873; \quad \alpha_{23} = P^v(2)/P^v(3) = 5.211/1.5 = 3.474;$$

$$\alpha_{43} = P^v(4)/P^v(3) = 2.122/1.5 = 1.415; \quad \alpha_{53} = P^v(5)/P^v(3) = 0.8978/1.5 = 0.5985$$

From Eq. (7.17), $\dfrac{1}{K_3} \displaystyle\sum_{i=1}^{5} \dfrac{y_i}{\alpha_{i3}} = 1$

$$\Rightarrow \quad \frac{1}{K_3}\left(\frac{0.15}{8.873} + \frac{0.15}{3.474} + \frac{0.20}{1.0} + \frac{0.20}{1.415} + \frac{0.30}{0.5985} \right) = 1 \quad \Rightarrow \quad K_3 = 0.9027$$

Now $\qquad\qquad\qquad\qquad K_3 = P^v(3)/P \Rightarrow 0.9027 = P^v(3)/1.5$

$$\Rightarrow \qquad\qquad\qquad P^v(3) = (0.9027)(1.5) = 1.354 \text{ bar } (= 1016 \text{ mm Hg})$$

From Antoine Eq. for *cyclo*-hexane (3),

$$\ln(1016) = 15.7794 - 2778/(\theta + 223.14) \Rightarrow T = 363.8 \text{ K}$$

Step 3: Take $T = 363.8$ K (= 90.6°C) as the second approximation to the dew point of vapour mixture. Calculate the vapour pressures of the other components at this temperature.

n-butane: $\ln P^v(1) = 15.68151 - 2154.9/(90.6 + 238.74) \Rightarrow P^v(1) = 12.3772$ bar

Similarly, at $T = 363.8$ K, $P^v(2) = 4.7802$ bar; $P^v(4) = 1.417$ bar; $P^v(5) = 0.5924$ bar.

Now calculate the K-values of all the components at $T = 363.8$ K.

$$K_1 = P^v(1)/P = 12.3772/1.5 = 8.2514$$

$$K_2 = P^v(2)/P = 4.7802/1.5 = 3.187$$

$$K_3 = P^v(3)/P = 1.354/1.5 = 0.9027$$

$$K_4 = P^v(4)/P = 1.9188/1.5 = 1.279$$

$$K_5 = P^v(5)/P = 0.8021/1.5 = 0.5347$$

Step 4: Use these K-values to check if Eq. 7.15(b) is satisfied.

$$\sum_{i=1}^{5} \frac{y_i}{K_i} = \frac{0.15}{8.2514} + \frac{0.15}{3.187} + \frac{0.20}{0.9027} + \frac{0.20}{1.279} + \frac{0.30}{0.5347} = 1.004$$

So Eq. 7.15(b) is satisfied. The bubble point is $\boxed{363.8 \text{ K}}$. Another iteration may be done if further accuracy is desired.

7.1.7   Equilibrium in a Nonideal System

Equilibrium in a real system cannot generally be represented by Raoult's law or the Henry's law[#]. At equilibrium, the fugacities of the component i in the vapour and in the liquid phase are equal, i.e.

$$f_i^v = f_i^l \tag{7.16a}$$

The two fugacities are given by

$$f_i^v = \varphi_i^v y_i P \tag{7.16b}$$

$$f_i^l = x_i \varphi_i^l P = x_i \gamma_i f_i^0 \tag{7.16c}$$

where

φ_i^v = the fugacity coefficient
γ_i = the activity coefficient of component i in solution
f_i^0 = fugacity of component i at standard state.

For low-to-moderate pressures, the fugacity at standard state can be approximately taken as the vapour pressure of a component at the prevailing temperature, i.e.

$$f_i^l = x_i \gamma_i P_i^v \tag{7.16d}$$

Thus at a equilibrium

$$\varphi_i^v y_i P = x_i \gamma_i P_i^v \tag{7.17}$$

Here P_i^v is the vapour pressure of component i at the given temperature. For a known liquid composition (i.e. known x_i), the activity coefficient γ_i can be calculated using a suitable equation (for example, the Wilson equation) or technique (e.g. UNIFAC). If the pressure is 'low', the vapour phase may be considered 'ideal' ($\varphi_i^v = 1$) and the corresponding vapour phase composition can be calculated directly from Eq. (17.17). If the pressure is above moderate, non-ideality of the vapour-phase has to be taken into account and the fugacity coefficient φ_i^v of the component has to be calculated using a suitable equation of state. Since φ_i^v depends upon the vapour composition (i.e. y_i) an iterative approach is necessary. This is illustrated in the Appendix.

In the following discussion we shall explain and illustrate the principles of distillation either *assuming* a solution to be *ideal* or using experimental vapour–liquid equilibrium data. This will be done in order to make the presentation simple and easily understandable. However, for problems involving non-ideal solutions, either experimental equilibrium data or that calculated using fugacity and activity coefficients of the components should be used. For obvious reasons, experimental multicomponent equilibrium data available in the literature are scanty and calculated equilibrium data are almost invariably used in process design.

7.2   ENTHALPY–CONCENTRATION DIAGRAM

A change in the composition of a phase during distillation is accompanied by a change in its enthalpy. Enthalpy–concentration diagrams of liquid and vapour phases in equilibrium are useful in distillation calculation. For a given temperature T and concentration x of a liquid, the molar enthalpy H_L can be calculated using the following equation[†].

$$H_L = c_{ps} M_{av}(T - T_0) + \Delta H_s \tag{7.18}$$

[#] Henry's law describes a real system only at low concentrations. In a sense, this law is also a kind of idealization.
[†] We take the following steps to get a solution of specified composition. The components are mixed at the reference temperature. The enthalpies of the pure components are zero at the reference temperature. The only heat effect occurs due to the release of the heat of solution. The mixture is then heated to the required temperature.

where

H_L = molar enthalpy of the solution at temperature T, in kJ/kmol

c_{ps} = specific heat of the solution, in kJ/kg·K

M_{av} = average molecular weight of the solution

T_0 = reference temperature

ΔH_s = heat of solution at the reference temperature T_0, in kJ/kmol.

Since the heat of mixing of the vapour is negligible, we can use the following equation[††] to calculate the molar enthalpy of the saturated vapour H_V at a given temperature T and concentration $y*$.

$$H_V = y*M_A[c_{pA}(T - T_0) + \lambda_A] + (1 - y*)M_B[c_{pB}(T - T_0) + \lambda_B] \qquad (7.19)$$

where

c_{pA}, c_{pB} = specific heats of the pure liquids A and B, in kJ/kg·K

λ_A, λ_B = heats of vaporization of A and B at temperature T, in kJ/kg.

The calculation of enthalpies of solutions and vapours is illustrated in Example 7.4.

EXAMPLE 7.4 (*Calculation of enthalpy–concentration data*)   Enthalpy–concentration data have to be calculated for acetone(A)–water(B) system at 1 atm total pressure. The integral heat of solution (at 15°C) at different concentrations, the specific heats of solutions and the x–$y*$ data are given below (x, $y*$ = mole fractions of acetone in solution and in the equilibrium vapour respectively).

Temperature, θ (°C)	x	$y*$	ΔH_s (kcal/kmol)	c_{ps} (kcal/kg·K)
56.5	1.0	1.0	0	0.54
57	0.95	0.963	0	0.56
57.5	0.90	0.935	−10.55	0.56
58.2	0.80	0.898	−23.88	0.61
58.9	0.70	0.874	−41.11	0.66
59.5	0.60	0.859	−60.3	0.70
60	0.50	0.849	−83.56	0.75
60.4	0.40	0.839	−121.5	0.80
61	0.30	0.83	−171.7	0.85
62.2	0.20	0.815	−187.7	0.91
66.6	0.1	0.755	−159.7	0.96
75.7	0.05	0.624	−106.8	0.98
91.7	0.01	0.253	−22.2	1.0
100	0.0	0.0	0	1.0

The other relevant data: average specific heat of liquid acetone, $c_{pA} = 0.57$ kcal/kg·K; average specific heat of water, $c_{pB} = 1.0$ kcal/kg·K; heat of vaporization of acetone, $\lambda_A = 125.8 - 0.252(\theta - 50)$ kcal/kg; θ = temperature in °C; average heat of vaporization of water, $\lambda_B = 550$ kcal/kg.

Solution

The enthalpy–concentration data can be calculated by using Eq. (7.18) for a solution and Eq. (7.19) for a vapour. We select a reference temperature, $T_0 = 15$°C (at which the integral heats of solution are given). Sample calculations for a solution and for the equilibrium vapour are shown.

[††] It is assumed that the individual components are heated to the temperature T from the reference temperature T_0, followed by vaporization and mixing of the vapours.

Consider a solution having 20 mole% acetone ($T = 62.2°C$), i.e. $x_A = 0.20$. Molecular weights: acetone–58; water–18. Average molecular weight of the solution, $M_{av} = (0.20)(58) + (0.80)(18) = 26$. From Eq. (7.18),

$$H_L = c_{ps}M_{av}(T - T_0) + \Delta H_s = (0.91)(26)(62.2 - 15) - 187.2 = \boxed{929 \text{ kcal/kmol solution}}.$$

Calculate H_V from Eq. (7.19) at 62.2°C (composition of the equilibrium vapour: $y_A^* = 0.815$, given)

$$H_V = y_A^* M_A[c_{pA}(T - T_0) + \lambda_A] + (1 - y_A^*)M_B[c_{pB}(T - T_0) + \lambda_B]$$

$$= (0.815)(58)[(0.57)(62.2 - 15) + \{125.8 - (0.252)(62.2 - 50)\}]$$

$$+ (1 - 0.815)(18)[(1)(62.2 - 15) + 550]$$

$$= \boxed{9056 \text{ kcal/kmol vapour}}.$$

The enthalpy values at other concentrations have been calculated. Some of the values are given below. The enthalpy values have been plotted in Figure 7.9(a)

x	1.0	0.90	0.80	0.60	0.20	0.10	0.05	0.01	0.0
y^*	1.0	0.935	0.898	0.859	0.815	0.755	0.625	0.253	0.0
H_L (kcal/kmol)	1300	1297	1294	1248	929	930	1083	1390	1530
H_V (kcal/kmol)	8500	8722	8812	8916	9056	9259	9659	10,754	11,250

The typical x–H_L and y^*–H_V curves (system: methanol–water) are also shown in Figure 7.9. A point in the region below the x–H_L curve represents a liquid (a point on the x–H_L curve represents a saturated liquid, i.e. a liquid at its bubble point). A point in the region above the y^*–H_V curve represents a vapour (a saturated vapour if the point is on the y^*–H_V curve). A point, say F, in the region between the two curves represents a two-phase vapour–liquid mixture. The mixture tends to separate into a liquid and a vapour phase at equilibrium represented by the points W and D on the 'tie line' through the point F [comparable to the tie line LV in Figure 7.3(a)]. The amounts of the liquid and vapour phases can be determined by the Lever-arm Rule, Eq. (7.4). The line IJ is another tie line. The point R on the $(x$–$y^*)$ diagram [Figure 7.9(b)] drawn below the H–x–y^* diagram corresponds to the tie line WD; the point Q on the equilibrium diagram corresponds to the tie line IJ on the enthalpy diagram.

Similarly, let us take two solutions whose *states* (given by the enthalpies and compositions) and amounts are both represented by M and N. The solutions are mixed to produce another solution having its state and composition represented by the point P [Figure 7.9(a); here the point P represents a stream by composition as well as by flow rate and should not be confused with total pressure]. Following the nomenclature used before, we may write the material and enthalpy balance equations as given below.

Total material balance:	$M + N = P$	(7.20)
Component A balance:	$Mz_M + Nz_N = Pz_P$	(7.21)
Enthalpy balance:	$MH_M + NH_N = PH_P$	(7.22)

Here z stands for the concentration of the species A in a phase and H is its molar enthalpy (the notation z, instead of x, has been used because the phases represented by the points M and N may be two-phase mixtures in the general case).

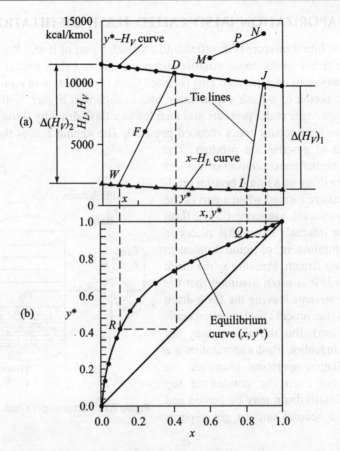

Figure 7.9 (a) Enthalpy–concentration (x–y^*–H), and (b) equilibrium diagrams for the methanol (1)–water (2) system [Henley and Seader, 1982]. ▲ enthalpy of liquid; ● enthalpy of vapour.

Eliminating P from Eqs. (7.20) and (7.21),

$$\frac{M}{N} = \frac{z_N - z_P}{z_P - z_M} \tag{7.23}$$

Similarly, eliminating P from Eqs. (7.20) and (7.22),

$$\frac{M}{N} = \frac{H_N - H_P}{H_P - H_M} \tag{7.24}$$

$$\Rightarrow \qquad \frac{H_N - H_P}{z_N - z_P} = \frac{H_P - H_M}{z_P - z_M} \tag{7.25}$$

The left-side of Eq. (7.25) gives the slope of the section NP and its right-side gives that of MP [Figure 7.9(a)]. So the points M, N and P are collinear. The relation among the points M, N and P may be viewed in another way as well. If we have a mixture represented by the point P (in respect of both state and amount), and we remove a part of it represented by the point M (again in respect of both state and quantity), the part of P left behind should have enthalpy and composition represented by the point N.

After this brief introduction to the relevant physico-chemical principles, we shall now discuss the principles of the more important distillation operations.

7.3 FLASH VAPORIZATION (ALSO CALLED FLASH DISTILLATION)

If a sufficiently hot liquid mixture is throttled into a vessel, a part of it will vaporize. The vapour produced will be richer in the more volatile component(s) and thus partial separation of the desired component(s) will be achieved. This is called *flash vaporization* or *equilibrium vaporization*. A schematic sketch of a flash vaporization unit is shown in Figure 7.10. The feed is first heated in a heat exchanger under pressure and then led to a flash drum by throttling where partial vaporization of the feed occurs under reduced pressure. The vapour leaves the drum at the top and is condensed to get the top product. The fraction having a higher concentration of the less volatiles leaves the drum as a liquid bottom product. Liquid droplets are formed when a part of the liquid flashes into a vapour vigorously. The flash drum should have internals like baffle plates in order to reduce 'entrainment' of liquid droplets in the outgoing vapour stream. Pressure in the drum is suitably adjusted. It is often assumed that the liquid and vapour streams leaving the flash drum are in equilibrium (the process is also called *equilibrium vaporization*). But the phases may not reach equilibrium in reality. Flash vaporization is a single-stage distillation operation. However, the bottom product (or even the condensed top product) from the flash drum may be heated and flashed again in a second unit to get a purer product.

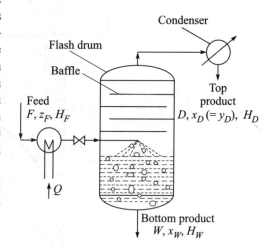

Figure 7.10 Schematic of a flash distillation unit.

7.3.1 Flash Vaporization of a Binary Mixture

We start with a binary mixture of the components A and B. If the flow rate, the composition, and enthalpy of the feed, the condensed top product (or *distillate*) and the bottom liquid product are denoted as (F, z_F, H_F), $(D, x_D{}^\dagger, H_D)$, and (W, x_W, H_W), respectively, and Q is the rate of supply of heat to the heat exchanger, we may write the following material and energy balance equations for a steady-state equilibrium vaporization unit.

Total material balance: $\qquad\qquad F = D + W$ (7.26)

Component A balance: $\qquad\qquad F z_F = D x_D + W x_W$ (7.27)

$\Rightarrow \qquad\qquad\qquad (D + W) z_F = D x_D + W x_W$ (7.28)

Enthalpy balance: $\qquad\qquad F H_F + Q = D H_D + W H_W$ (7.29)

Eliminating F from Eqs. (7.26) and (7.29) and using Eq. (7.28), we have

$$-\frac{W}{D} = \frac{x_D - z_F}{x_W - z_F} = \frac{H_D - (H_F + Q/F)}{H_W - (H_F + Q/F)}$$ (7.30)

$\dagger$ The vapour leaving the flash chamber is condensed into a liquid. So its composition is denoted by x_D. The subscript 'D' stands for the distillate.

Binary flash vaporization problems can be solved by graphical construction and the above equation is extremely useful for this purpose. Vapour–liquid equilibrium data and also the enthalpy–concentration data are required for the graphical construction and calculations. The *cold feed* (if the feed is below its bubble point under the given pressure, it is called *cold feed*) is represented by the point F_1 on Figure 7.11(a) under Example 7.6. The feed passes through the heat exchanger and receives an amount of heat energy Q. The state of the hot feed is represented by the point F that lies in the two-phase region of the H–x–y diagram. It flashes into a vapour and a liquid phase upon throttling into the flash drum. The enthalpy and the composition (in terms of mole fraction of A) of the vapour and the liquid streams, denoted by the points D and W, are obtained by drawing the tie line through F. The point $F'(z_F, z_F)$ is located on the diagonal on the x–y plot [see Figure 7.11(b) under Example 7.6], and the point P is located on the equilibrium curve such that the slope of the line $F'P$ is $-W/D$ by virtue of Eq. (7.30). The line $F'P$ is, in fact, the 'operating line' for the single-stage flash vaporization process.

By using the enthalpy and equilibrium curves, the amounts and the compositions of the two products can be calculated for a given feed for the given rate of heat supply, Q. Alternatively, if the fraction of feed to be vaporized is specified, the required rate of heat supply Q can be calculated. In the above analysis, we have tacitly assumed that the flash vaporization represents an ideal stage. The analysis can be easily extended to the case of a real stage of given stage efficiency. The stage efficiency typically ranges between 0.8 and 1.0.

Single-stage flash calculations are illustrated in Examples 7.5 and 7.6.

EXAMPLE 7.5 (*Binary flash distillation*)   A mixture of 40 mol% benzene and 60 mol% toluene is being flash-distilled at a rate of 10 kmol/h at 1 atm total pressure. The liquid product should not contain more than 30 mol% benzene. Calculate the amounts and the compositions of the top and the bottom products. The relative volatility of benzene in the mixture is 2.5. Solve analytically as well as graphically.

Solution
Refer to Figure 7.10.

Algebraic solution

Total material balance: $F = D + W$;   given: $F = 10$, $z_F = 0.4 \Rightarrow 10 = D + W$ (i)
Benzene balance: $Fz_F = Dx_D + Wx_W$

Given: x_W = mole fraction of benzene in the bottom product = 0.3

$\Rightarrow$ $(10)(0.4) = Dx_D + W(0.3)$ i.e. $4 = Dx_D + (0.3)W$ (ii)

In equilibrium flash distillation, the distillate (vapour) and the bottom products (liquid) are in equilibrium, i.e. x_D and x_W are in equilibrium, and are related through the relative volatility as follows:

$$\frac{x_D/(1-x_D)}{x_W/(1-x_W)} = 2.5$$ (iii)

Equations (i), (ii) and (iii) can be solved for the three unknowns to get:

$$D = \boxed{4.61}; \qquad W = \boxed{5.39 \text{ mol/h}}; \qquad x_D = \boxed{0.517}.$$

Graphical solution

The equilibrium line is plotted using the given value of the relative volatility [see Eq. 7.8(b)].

$$y = \frac{\alpha x}{1 + (\alpha - 1)x} \quad \text{i.e.} \quad y = \frac{2.5x}{1 + 1.5x}$$

The point $F(z_F, z_F)$, i.e. (0.4, 0.4) is located on the diagonal, and the vertical line through $x_W = 0.3$ meets the equilibrium line at $P(0.3, 0.52)$. The slope of the line FP equals $(-W/D)$. Calculations are left as a small exercise problem.

EXAMPLE 7.6 (*Calculation of the energy requirement in binary flash vaporization*)   Fifty kmol of 35 mole% aqueous solution of acetone at 25°C is heated and flashed in a drum at 1 atm pressure when 35% of the liquid is vaporized. Using the enthalpy–concentration data of Example 7.4, calculate (a) the amounts and the concentrations of the vapour and liquid products, and (b) the heat supplied to the feed.

Solution

(a) Let F (= 50 kmoles; $z_F = 0.35$) be the moles of feed, and W and D be the moles of liquid and vapour products. Fraction of liquid vaporized = 0.35. Therefore,

$$D/F = D/(W + D) = 0.35 \Rightarrow W/D = 1.86$$

(i) Locate the point $F'(z_F, z_F)$ on the x–y diagram drawn below the enthalpy–concentration diagram in Figure 7.11(b) and draw a line $F'P$ of slope $-W/D = -1.86$ through the point F' which meets the equilibrium curve at P.

Concentration of acetone in the liquid product, $x_W = \boxed{0.105}$; that in the (condensed) vapour product, $x_D = \boxed{0.765}$.

We have $W + D = 50$ and $W(0.105) + D(0.765) = (50)(0.35)$

$\Rightarrow$ $W = \boxed{31.44 \text{ kmol}}$ $D = \boxed{18.56 \text{ kmol}}$

(b) Draw the tie line WD on the enthalpy–concentration diagram corresponding to the point P. A vertical line through F' meets WD at the point F [see Figure 7.11(b)]. The coordinates of the point F are $(z_F, H_F + Q/F)$.

From Figure 7.11(b), $H_F + Q/F = 4000$ kcal/kmol

Average molecular weight of the feed is 32. The integral heat of solution is taken as $\Delta H_s = -145$ kcal/kmol and $c_{ps} = 0.825$ kcal/kg·K (*interpolated* from the data of Example 7.4). Taking a reference temperature of 15°C, the enthalpy of the feed ($x_A = 0.35$; temp., $T = 25$°C) is

$$H_F = (0.825)(32)(25 - 15) - 145 = 119 \text{ kcal/kmol}$$

$\Rightarrow$ $119 + Q/50 = 4000 \Rightarrow Q = \boxed{1.94 \times 10^5 \text{ kcal} = \text{required heat input}}$.

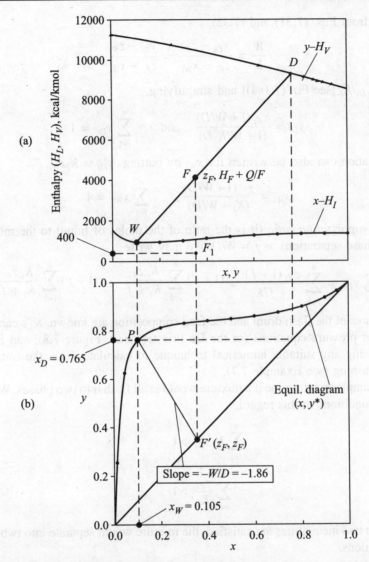

Figure 7.11 (a) Enthalpy–concentration, and (b) equilibrium diagram of acetone–water system at 1 atm pressure.

7.3.2 Multicomponent Flash Distillation

We shall now analyze flash vaporization of an n-component mixture. For simplicity, we assume that vapour–liquid equilibrium of the multicomponent mixture can be quantitatively described by K-values (see Section 7.1.6). The material balance equations for the component i are given below (the notations are the same as in the previous section; an additional subscript i is used to denote the ith component).

Total material balance: $\qquad\qquad F = D + W$ (7.31)

Component i balance: $\qquad F z_{Fi} = D x_{Di} + W x_{Wi}$ (7.32)

Eliminating F from Eqs. (7.31) and (7.32),

$$\frac{W}{D} = \frac{x_{Di} - z_{Fi}}{z_{Fi} - x_{Wi}} = \frac{y_{Di} - z_{Fi}}{z_{Fi} - x_{Wi}} \tag{7.33}^{\#}$$

Putting $x_{Wi} = y_{Di}/K_i$ [see Eq. (7.14a)] and simplifying,

$$\Rightarrow \qquad y_{Di} = \frac{z_{Fi}(1 + W/D)}{(1 + W/K_i D)} \quad \text{and} \quad \sum_{i=1}^{n} y_{Di} = 1 \tag{7.34}$$

The above equation can also be written for x_{Wi} by putting $y_{Di} = K_i x_{Wi}$.

$$x_{Wi} = \frac{z_{Fi}(1 + W/D)}{(K_i + W/D)}; \qquad \sum_{i=1}^{n} x_{Wi} = 1 \tag{7.35}$$

If we define a *vaporization ratio* (it is the ratio of the moles of liquid to the moles of vapour produced on phase separation) as $f = W/D$, we may write

$$1 = \sum_{i=1}^{n} y_{Di} = \sum_{i=1}^{n} \frac{z_{Fi}(1 + f)}{1 + f/K_i} = (1 + f) \sum_{i=1}^{n} \frac{K_i z_{Fi}}{K_i + f} \Rightarrow (1 + f) \sum_{i=1}^{n} \frac{K_i z_{Fi}}{K_i + f} = 1 \tag{7.36}$$

If the temperatures of the flash drum and the feed composition are known, K_i's can be calculated from the vapour pressure equations (or the De Priester chart, Figure 7.8), and Eq. (7.36) can be solved by using any suitable numerical technique to calculate f, i.e. the fraction of liquid vaporized on flashing (see Example 7.7).

It is rather simple to determine if a mixture would at all flash into two phases. We may specify the following conditions in this regard.

$$\sum_{i=1}^{n} K_i z_{Fi} > 1 \tag{7.37}$$

$$\sum_{i=1}^{n} \frac{z_{Fi}}{K_i} > 1 \tag{7.38}$$

If the above two inequalities are satisfied, the mixture would separate into two phases under the given conditions.

EXAMPLE 7.7 (*Multicomponent flash distillation*)   We have a mixture of 25 mol% n-hexane(1), 40 mol% n-heptane(2) and 35 mol% n-octane(3) at 400 K and 2 bar total pressure. Will the mixture separate into two phases? If so, calculate the amounts and the compositions of the liquid and the vapour products. Assume the solution to be ideal. See Table 7.2 for the Antoine constants.

Solution
Vapour pressure of n-hexane(1) at 400 K (= 127°C):

$$\ln P^v(1) = 15.9155 - 2738.42/(127 + 226.2) = 3490 \text{ mm Hg} = 4.652 \text{ bar}$$

[#] Since the vapour generated on flashing is completely condensed, the composition of the condensate is the same as that of the vapour ($x_{Di} = y_{Di}$).

Vapour pressures of the other two components are: $P^v(2) = 2.177$ bar and $P^v(3) = 1.05$ bar. If we assume ideal behaviour, the vaporization equilibrium constants are:

$K_1 = P^v(1)/P = 4.652/2.0 = 2.326$

$K_2 = 1.0885$; $K_3 = 0.525$ [The K-values can also be obtained from Figure 7.8.]

Composition of the mixture: $z_1 = 0.25$; $z_2 = 0.4$; $z_3 = 0.35$.

Now,

$$\sum_{i=1}^{3} z_{Fi} K_i = (0.25)(2.326) + (0.40)(1.0885) + (0.35)(0.525) = 1.2006 > 1$$

$$\sum_{i=1}^{3} \frac{z_{Fi}}{K_i} = \frac{0.25}{2.326} + \frac{0.40}{1.0885} + \frac{0.35}{0.525} = 1.1416 > 1$$

Since the conditions of existence of two phases [Eqs. (7.37) and (7.38)] are satisfied, the mixture will split into two phases. The fraction of vapour is to be calculated by solving Eq. (7.36), i.e.

$$\frac{K_1 z_{F1}}{K_1 + f} + \frac{K_2 z_{F2}}{K_2 + f} + \frac{K_3 z_{F3}}{K_3 + f} = \frac{1}{1+f}$$

$$\Rightarrow \qquad \frac{(2.326)(0.25)}{2.326 + f} + \frac{(1.0885)(0.40)}{1.0885 + f} + \frac{(0.525)(0.35)}{0.525 + f} = \frac{1}{1+f}$$

The solution of the above equation gives the vaporization ratio, $f = 0.812$.

Taking $F = 1$ kmol $= D + W$ and $f = W/D = 0.812$, W and D can be easily calculated. The compositions of the liquid and vapour products can be obtained from Eqs. (7.34) and (7.35).

A simpler technique of flash calculations was suggested by Eubank et al. (2000). If ζ is the fraction of the feed vaporized in the flash chamber,

$$\zeta = \frac{D}{W + D} = \frac{1}{1 + W/D} = \frac{1}{1 + f} \qquad (7.39)$$

From Eqs. (7.35), (7.36) and (7.39),

$$1 = \sum_{i=1}^{n} x_{Wi} = \sum_{i=1}^{n} y_{Di} \Rightarrow \sum_{i=1}^{n} \frac{z_{Fi}}{1 + \zeta(K_i - 1)} = \sum_{i=1}^{n} \frac{K_i z_{Fi}}{1 + \zeta(K_i - 1)}$$

$$\Rightarrow \qquad \sum_{1}^{n} \frac{K_i z_{Fi}}{1 + \zeta(K_i - 1)} - \sum_{1}^{n} \frac{z_{Fi}}{1 + \zeta(K_i - 1)} = 0$$

$$\Rightarrow \qquad \psi(z_{Fi}, \zeta) = \sum \frac{z_{Fi}(K_i - 1)}{1 + \zeta(K_i - 1)} = 0 \qquad (7.40)$$

It is easy to establish that $\partial \psi / \partial \zeta < 0$ for positive values of ζ (in fact, ζ lies between 0 and 1). So Eq. (7.40) has a unique solution within $0 < \zeta < 1$. The root of Eq. (7.40) can be obtained by a numerical technique like the Newton–Raphson[#] method. It is interesting to note that for a

---

[#] See the Appendix for more about the solution of Eq. (7.40).

ternary mixture, Eq. (7.40) reduces to a quadratic algebraic equation. If we put the data of Example 7.7 in Eq. (7.40), we get

$$\frac{(0.25)(2.326-1)}{1+(2.326-1)\zeta} + \frac{(0.4)(1.0885-1)}{1+(1.0885-1)\zeta} + \frac{(0.35)(0.525-1)}{1+(0.525-1)\zeta} = 0 \Rightarrow \zeta = 0.552$$

The vaporization ratio, $f = (1 - \zeta)/\zeta = (1 - 0.552)/0.552 = 0.812$.

7.4 STEAM DISTILLATION

When a solution boils, the mole fraction of a component A in the vapour ($y*$) depends upon its mole fraction in the liquid (x). If the solution is an ideal binary, the vapour phase mole fraction of A is given by Eq. (7.7). However, if the components A and B are not miscible, their mixture exerts a total vapour pressure which is equal to the sum of the vapour pressures of the individual liquids at the given temperature. So the bubble temperature of such a mixture is lower than the boiling point of either A or B. This property of an immiscible liquid mixture forms the basis of steam distillation.

Steam distillation is a separation process in which live steam is blown through a liquid containing a component A (usually having a low volatility and low solubility in water) when A vaporizes slowly (depending upon its vapour pressure at the operating temperature) and leaves with the steam. The compound A is the target compound which we want to recover in a reasonably pure state. The mixture to be separated may contain traces of a non-volatile impurity or it may be a mixture of A and another compound C which is essentially non-volatile. In some cases steam distillation is similar to steam stripping. The schematic of a steam distillation unit is shown in Figure 7.12. The feed is taken in the distillation vessel or still through which live steam is sparged at the bottom. The vapour containing the vaporized product A as well as steam is led to a condenser. If A has only little miscibility

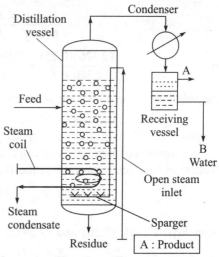

Figure 7.12 Schematic of a steam distillation unit.

with water, the condensate forms two layers (a layer of the target material A and another of water) and can be easily separated to recover the product. Some loss of heat occurs from the distillation unit. Energy is also required for heating the feed to its bubble point and for vaporization of A. A steam coil may be provided in the still to make up such energy requirements and to avoid condensation of the live steam. Steam distillation may be conveniently used in the following cases:

- Separation of a high boiling material from a solution. Examples: decolourization/deodorization of vegetable oils, recovery and purification of essential oils
- Separation and purification of hazardous and inflammable substances like turpentine
- Separation of a thermally unstable substance from a mixture

- Separation of volatile impurities from waste water. Examples: removal of ammonia, volatile organic compounds (VOCs) like halogenated hydrocarbons from waste water.

We consider the following two important cases of calculation of steam requirement for a steam distillation process. Case 2 is discussed after Example 7.8.

Case 1: *The substance A is immiscible with water. The feed contains A and traces of non-volatile impurities.*

Let P_A^v be the vapour pressure of A at the operating temperature, P_B^v be the vapour pressure of water (B = water), and P be the total pressure. Since A (the target compound) and B (water) are essentially immiscible, the total pressure is the sum of the individual vapour pressures (here the partial pressure of a substance is the same as its vapour pressure).

$$P = P_A^v + P_B^v \quad \Rightarrow \quad P_B^v = P - P_A^v$$

If m_A moles of the substance is volatilized out by putting in m_B moles of steam, and if the system operates at equilibrium, we may write

$$\frac{m_A}{m_B} = \frac{P_A^v}{P_B^v} = \frac{P_A^v}{P - P_A^v} \quad \Rightarrow \quad m_A = m_B \frac{P_A^v}{P - P_A^v} \tag{7.41}$$

However, if the system does not operate at equilibrium, the partial pressure of A will be less than its vapour pressure. To take into account such a deviation, we define a factor called *vaporizing efficiency E* of the product such that the partial pressure of A in the steam phase is $p_A = EP_A^v$. Equation (7.41) then becomes

$$m_A = m_B \frac{EP_A^v}{P - EP_A^v} \tag{7.42}$$

The vaporization efficiency usually ranges between 0.6 and 0.9. Equation (7.42) can be used to calculate the steam requirement for a desired separation.

EXAMPLE 7.8 (*Simple steam distillation*)   Geraniol ($C_{10}H_{18}O$) is an essential oil of commercial value. It is conventionally purified by steam distillation. A pilot scale unit is charged with 0.5 kg of crude geraniol containing a small amount of non-volatile impurities. Live saturated steam at 105°C is passed through the still at a rate of 20 kg/h. Calculate the distillation time assuming that geraniol is immiscible with water. Neglect condensation of steam. The vaporization efficiency is 0.8. Vapour pressure of water at 105°C is 1.211 bar and that of geraniol(A) is given by

$$\ln P_A^v = 21.1 - 7217/T; \qquad P_A^v \text{ is in mm Hg and } T \text{ in K.}$$

Solution

From the given equation, vapour pressure of geraniol at 105°C, $P_A^v = 7.48$ mm Hg.
Vapour pressure of water at 105°C (given),

$$P_B^v = 1.211 \text{ bar} = (1.211/1.013)(760) = 908.7 \text{ mm Hg}$$

Molecular weight of geraniol, $M_A = 154.1$; moles of geraniol in the feed, $m_A = 0.5/154.1 = 3.244 \times 10^{-3}$ kmol.

Use Eq. (7.42) to calculate the moles of steam required,

$$m_B = m_A \frac{P_B^v}{E P_A^v} = (3.244 \times 10^{-3}) \frac{908.7}{(0.8)(7.48)}$$

$$= 0.493 \text{ kmol} = (0.493)(18) = 8.874 \text{ kg steam}$$

Steam rate = 20 kg/h.   Time required = 8.874/20 h = $\boxed{26.6 \text{ min}}$

Case 2: *The feed is a mixture of A and C; C is an essentially non-volatile substance. A and C form an ideal solution and are immiscible with water.*

Let us start with a feed containing m_{Ai} moles of A [here the subscript i means initial, and f means final] and m_C moles of C. At the operating temperature, the vapour pressure of A is P_A^v and that of steam is P_B^v. Since C is non-volatile, m_C remains constant. We need to calculate the amount of steam required to reduce the number of moles of A from m_{Ai} to m_{Af}. The vaporization efficiency is E.

If the moles of A in the still at any time t is m_A, its mole fraction in C is

$$x_A = \frac{m_A}{m_A + m_C} \tag{7.43}$$

Partial pressure of A in the vapour is: $p_A = E x_A P_A^v$

$$\text{Moles of A per mole of steam} = \frac{p_A}{P_B^v} = \frac{E x_A P_A^v}{P - E x_A P_A^v}$$

If $\dot{m}_B$ is the rate of supply of steam, the rate of volatilization of A may be written as

$$-\frac{dm_A}{dt} = \dot{m}_B \frac{p_A}{P_B^v} = \dot{m}_B \frac{E x_A P_A^v}{P - E x_A P_A^v} \tag{7.44}$$

Substituting for x_A from Eq. (7.43) in Eq. (7.44), rearranging and integrating from $t = 0$, $m_A = m_{Ai}$ to $t = t$, $m_A = m_{Af}$,

$$-\int_{m_{Ai}}^{m_{Af}} \left[P\left(1 + \frac{m_C}{m_A}\right) - E P_A^v \right] dm_A = E \dot{m}_B P_A^v \int_{t=0}^{t} dt$$

$$\Rightarrow \quad \left(\frac{P}{E P_A^v} - 1\right)(m_{Ai} - m_{Af}) + \frac{P m_C}{E P_A^v} \ln \frac{m_{Ai}}{m_{Af}} = \dot{m}_B t = \text{total steam required} \tag{7.45}$$

Example 7.9 illustrates the theoretical principles discussed above.

EXAMPLE 7.9 (*Steam distillation of a substance from a mixture*) Thirty kilograms of crude citranellol ($C_{10}H_{20}O$), an essential oil, is to be purified by steam distillation. The material contains 20 mass% of the essential oil and the rest constitute non-volatile impurities of average molecular weight 260. Assuming Raoult's law to apply, calculate the rate of steam supply for the recovery of 90% of the oil if the batch time is 2 hours. It is estimated that 2% of the inlet steam condenses to make up the heat losses from the still and also to supply sensible and latent heat to the oil. The operating temperature is 105°C and the vaporization efficiency is 75%. Vapour pressure of citranellol(A) can be calculated from the equation: $\ln P_A^v$(mm Hg) = 21.33 − 7241/T.

Solution

Use Eq. (7.45). Vapour pressure of citranellol at 105°C (calculated from the above equation), $P_A^v = 8.8$ mm Hg. Total mass of the crude product = 30 kg with 20% of the oil. Mol. wt. of the oil = 156.1.

Mass of oil = (30)(0.20) = 6 kg = 6/156.1 kmol = 0.03842 kmol = m_{Ai}

Mass of non-volatile impurities = 24 kg = 24/260 kmol = 0.0923 kmol = m_C

90% of the oil is to be recovered.

Moles of the oil left, $\qquad m_{Af} = (0.03842)(0.10) = 0.003842$ kmol

Vapour pressure of water(B), $\quad P_B^v = 908.7$ mm Hg

Vaporization efficiency, $\qquad E = 0.75$

Total pressure, $\qquad\qquad\quad P = 908.7 + 8.8 = 917.5$ mm Hg

Putting the values of different quantities in Eq. (7.45),

$$\dot{m}_B t = \left[\frac{917.5}{(0.75)(8.8)} - 1\right](0.03842 - 0.003842) + \frac{(917.5)(0.0923)}{(0.75)(8.8)} \ln\frac{0.03842}{0.003842} = 34.32 \text{ kmol}$$

Heat loss = 2% $\Rightarrow$ Actual steam requirement = 34.32/0.98 = 35 kmol = 630 kg

The batch time, $t = 2$ h. Steam rate, $\dot{m}_B = 35/2 = 17.5$ kmol/h = $\boxed{315 \text{ kg/h}}$

7.5 BATCH DISTILLATION (ALSO CALLED DIFFERENTIAL DISTILLATION OR RAYLEIGH DISTILLATION)

In batch distillation, the feed is charged to the stillpot to which heat is supplied continuously through a steam jacket or a steam coil. As the mixture boils, it generates a vapour richer in the more volatiles. But as boiling continues, concentrations of more volatiles in the liquid decrease. It is generally assumed that equilibrium vaporization occurs in the still. The vapour is led to a condenser and the condensate or top product is collected in a receiver. At the beginning, the condensate will be pretty rich in the more volatiles, but the concentrations of the more volatiles in it will decrease as the condensate keeps on accumulating in the receiver. The condensate is usually withdrawn intermittently having products or *cuts* of different concentrations. Batch distillation is used when the feed rate is not large enough to justify installation of a continuous distillation unit. It may also be used when the constituents greatly differ in volatility. Two cases of batch distillation are discussed below. Batch

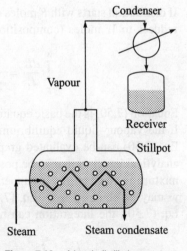

Figure 7.13 A batch distillation setup.

distillation with reflux will be dealt with in Section 7.7. The schematic of a batch distillation setup is shown in Figure 7.13.

7.5.1   Batch Distillation of a Binary Mixture

Theoretical analysis of batch distillation is based on a 'differential mass balance' because the liquid and the vapour phase concentrations of the components change continuously as distillation proceeds. Let, at any moment, the number of moles of liquid in the still be L having a mole fraction x of the more volatile component (i.e. A) and let the moles of *accumulated* condensate be D. Concentration of the equilibrium vapour is $y*$. Over a small time, the change in the amount of liquid in the still is dL and the amount of vapour withdrawn is dD. The following differential mass balance equations may be written:

Total material balance: $$-dL = dD \qquad (7.46)$$

Component A balance: $$-d(Lx) = y*dD \qquad (7.47)$$

$\Rightarrow$ $$-Ldx = y*dD + xdL = y*dD - xdD = (y* - x)dD \qquad (7.48)$$

Equation (7.46) means that the total amount of vapour generated must be equal to the decrease in the total amount of liquid (note that dL is inherently negative and a negative sign is used in this equation so that it is consistent with respect to sign). Similarly, Eq. (7.47) means that loss in the number of moles of A from the still because of vaporization is the same as the amount of A in the small amount of vapour generated.

Putting $dD = - dL$ in Eq. (7.48) and rearranging,

$$\frac{dL}{L} = \frac{dx}{y* - x} \qquad (7.49)$$

If distillation starts with F moles of feed of concentration x_F and continues till the amount of liquid reduces to W moles (composition $= x_W$), the above equation can be integrated to give

$$\int_F^W \frac{dL}{L} = \int_{x_F}^{x_W} \frac{dx}{y* - x} \quad \Rightarrow \quad \ln\frac{F}{W} = \int_{x_W}^{x_F} \frac{dx}{y* - x} \qquad (7.50)$$

Equation (7.50) is the basic equation of batch data distillation and is called the 'Rayleigh equation'. If the vapour–liquid equilibrium data (x–$y*$) are available in a tabular form, the right side of Eq. (7.50) can be evaluated graphically. If an algebraic relation between x and $y*$ is available, analytical integration may be possible. For example, if the relative volatility α of A in the binary mixture is constant (as it happens in the case of an ideal solution), the relation between x and $y*$ may be obtained from Eq. [7.8(b)]. Substituting for $y*$ from Eq. [7.8(b)] in the right-side of Eq. (7.50), the integration can be performed to have

$$\ln\frac{F}{W} = \int_{x_W}^{x_F} \frac{dx}{\dfrac{\alpha x}{1+(\alpha-1)x} - x} = \frac{1}{(\alpha-1)}\ln\frac{x_F(1-x_W)}{x_W(1-x_F)} + \ln\frac{1-x_W}{1-x_F} \qquad (7.51a)$$

The integral can be expressed in an alternative, and sometimes more convenient form

$$\ln \frac{F x_F}{W x_W} = \alpha \ln \frac{F(1 - x_F)}{W(1 - x_W)} \tag{7.51b}$$

Equation (7.51) involves four quantities—F, W, x_F, and x_W. If any three of these are known, the remaining one can be calculated. The average composition ($y_{D,av}$) of the accumulated distillate (D) can be obtained by a simple material balance.

$$F x_F = D y_{D,av} + W x_W \quad \text{and} \quad F = D + W \tag{7.52}$$

EXAMPLE 7.10 (*Simple batch distillation*) A charge of 50 kmol of a mixture of benzene and chlorobenzene having 55 mol% of the less volatile is to be batch-distilled. (a) If 25 moles of the solution is vaporized and condensed as the distillate, calculate the concentration of the accumulated distillate. (b) If the concentration of the accumulated product is found to be 72 mol% benzene, calculate its amount. The relative volatility of benzene in the mixture is 4.15.

Solution

Use Eq. [7.51(b)]. *Given:* moles of feed, $F = 50$ kmol; feed concentration, $x_F = 1 - 0.55 = 0.45$.

(a) Distillate, $D = 25$ kmol, and $W = 25$ kmol; $y_{D,av}$ ($= x_D$) = ? Putting the values in Eq. [7.51(b)],

$$\ln \left[\left(\frac{50}{25} \right) \left(\frac{0.45}{x_W} \right) \right] = (4.15) \ln \left[\left(\frac{50}{25} \right) \left(\frac{1 - 0.45}{1 - x_W} \right) \right]; \quad \text{solving, we get } x_W = 0.218$$

Material balance: $F x_F = W x_W + D y_{D,av} \Rightarrow (50)(0.45) = (25)(0.218) + (25) y_{D,av}$

$\Rightarrow$ $\qquad\qquad\qquad\qquad\qquad\qquad y_{D,av} = 0.682$

Composition of the distillate collected, $x_D = y_{D,av} = \boxed{0.682}$

(b) *Given:* $y_{D,av} = x_D = 0.72$; $D = $?

Total material balance, $50 = D + W$; benzene balance, $(50)(0.45) = W x_W + D(0.72)$

From the above two equations, $\qquad W = \dfrac{13.5}{0.72 - x_W}$

Substituting in Eq. [7.51(b)],

$$\ln \left[\left(\frac{50}{13.5/(0.72 - x_W)} \right) \left(\frac{0.45}{x_W} \right) \right] = (4.15) \ln \left[\left(\frac{50}{13.5/(0.72 - x_W)} \right) \left(\frac{1 - 0.45}{1 - x_W} \right) \right]$$

Solving, $\qquad x_W = 0.309$; $\qquad W = (13.5)/(0.72 - 0.309) = 32.85$

Amount of distillate, $\qquad D = F - W = 50 - 32.85 = \boxed{17.15 \text{ kmol}}$

EXAMPLE 7.11 (*Batch distillation with gradual addition of the feed*) Sixty kilomoles of a mixture of benzene and toluene containing 60 mol% benzene is to be separated by batch distillation. A still that can hold 20 kmol of the mixture is available. It is planned to start distillation with a charge of 20 kmol and to add the rest (i.e. 40 kmol) to the still continuously over a period of one hour. It is possible to maintain a constant rate of heat supply to the still by steam coils so that the rate of vaporization becomes the same as the rate of addition of the feed mixture to the still. Calculate the amount and concentration of the composited distillate that would be obtained at the end of an hour. Relative volatility of benzene in the mixture is 2.51.

Hints: Let F = kmol feed initially charged with a benzene concentration, x_F; F' = the hourly rate of addition of the mixture to the still; x = mole fraction of benzene in the liquid in the still and $y*$ = mole fraction of benzene in the vapour generated at any time t. Since the rates of addition and vaporization are the same, moles of liquid in the still remain constant at F. An instantaneous material balance gives

$$\frac{d}{dt}(Fx) = F'x_F - F'y* = F\frac{dx}{dt}$$

The above equation means that the rate of accumulation of benzene in the still is the difference between the rate of its addition with the incoming feed and the rate of removal with the vapour.

Rearranging and integrating the above equation,

$$\frac{F'}{F}\int_0^t dt = -\int_{x_F}^x \frac{dx}{y* - x_F} = \int_x^{x_F} \frac{dx}{\frac{\alpha x}{1+(\alpha-1)x} - x_F} = \int_x^{x_F} \frac{[1+(\alpha-1)x]dx}{x[\alpha-(\alpha-1)x_F]-x_F}$$

The integral is of the form:

$$I = \int \frac{(1+ax)dx}{bx-c} = \frac{a}{b}\int \frac{(bx-c)+(c+b/a)}{bx-c}dx = \frac{a}{b}x+\left(\frac{a}{b}\right)\left(c+\frac{b}{a}\right)\left(\frac{1}{b}\right)\ln(bx-c)$$

Putting the values of the different quantities in the integrated equation, we have

$$2t = -0.4254 - 0.9414x - 0.9756 \ln(1.604x - 0.6); \; t = 1 \text{ hour} \Rightarrow x = \boxed{0.49}$$

The concentration of the composited distillate can be found by material balance, $x_D = \boxed{0.695}$

We may consider a situation that a large quantity of feed is available and the distillation can be continued for a long time, i.e.

$$\text{At } t = \infty, \; \ln(1.604x - 0.6) \to -\infty \Rightarrow 1.604x - 0.6 = 0 \Rightarrow x = \boxed{0.374}$$

This is the concentration of the liquid in the still at a large time. The corresponding vapour phase concentration of benzene is 0.6. This indicates that at large time steady state is attained and the vapour leaves at the rate and concentration as that of the feed entering the still.

7.5.2 Batch Distillation of a Multicomponent Mixture

Consider L moles of a solution containing components 1, 2, ..., n at mole fractions $x_1, x_2, ..., x_n$. So the number of moles of the individual components in the solution are:

$$L_1 = Lx_1; \quad L_2 = Lx_2; \quad \dots \quad L_n = Lx_n \tag{7.53}$$

For simplicity we assume the solution to be ideal. The relative volatility α_{ij} of the component i with respect to another component j is taken as a constant. Further, we shall take component j as the base or 'reference component' with respect to which the relative volatility of any other component in the mixture is defined. The differential mass balance equations for components i and j become

For the component i:
$$-dL_i = -y_{Di}^* \, dL \qquad (7.54)$$

For the component j:
$$-dL_j = -y_{Dj}^* \, dL \qquad (7.55)$$

$$\Rightarrow \qquad \frac{dL_i}{dL_j} = \frac{y_{Di}^*}{y_{Dj}^*} = \alpha_{ij} \frac{x_i}{x_j} = \alpha_{ij} \frac{L_i}{L_j} \qquad \text{[from Eqs. (7.53) to (7.55)]}$$

Integrating from the initial to the final state,

$$\ln \frac{(L_i)_{\text{initial}}}{(L_i)_{\text{final}}} = \alpha_{ij} \ln \frac{(L_j)_{\text{initial}}}{(L_j)_{\text{final}}} \qquad (7.56)$$

This equation can be written for all possible pairs with the component j as common to get

$$\left[\frac{(L_i)_{\text{initial}}}{(L_i)_{\text{final}}} \right]^{\alpha_{ji}} = \left[\frac{(L_j)_{\text{initial}}}{(L_j)_{\text{final}}} \right] = \cdots = \left[\frac{(L_n)_{\text{initial}}}{(L_n)_{\text{final}}} \right]^{\alpha_{jn}} \qquad \text{[Since } \alpha_{ij} = 1/\alpha_{ji}] \qquad (7.57)$$

Equation (7.57) together with the condition $x_1 + x_2 + x_3 + \cdots + x_n = 1$, can be used to solve a multicomponent batch distillation problem.

EXAMPLE 7.12 (*Multicomponent batch distillation*)   A mixture of 0.3 kmol *n*-pentane (1), 0.3 kmol *n*-hexane (2) and 0.4 kmol *n*-octane (3) is batch distilled at 1 atm pressure to remove 90% of *n*-pentane. Calculate the amount and composition of the distillate. Take the *K*-values from the DePriester chart, Figure 7.8(b).

Solution
The initial number of moles of the components are: $(L_1)_{\text{in}} = 0.3$, $(L_2)_{\text{in}} = 0.3$, and $(L_3)_{\text{in}} = 0.4$. These are also the mole fractions of the components at the beginning. ('in' = initial; 'fi' = final). Initial bubble point temperature of the mixture is 64°C (the calculations are not shown here; this may be obtained by following the procedure of Example 7.2 and using the *K*-values given in Figure 7.8).

   Amount of *n*-pentane removed = 90% of 0.3 kmol = 0.27 kmol. Pentane remaining = 0.03 kmol = $(L_1)_{\text{fi}}$. Taking *n*-hexane as the reference component, the working equation [Eq. (7.57)] can be written as

$$\frac{(L_2)_{\text{in}}}{(L_2)_{\text{fi}}} = \left[\frac{(L_1)_{\text{in}}}{(L_1)_{\text{fi}}} \right]^{\alpha_{21}} = \left[\frac{(L_3)_{\text{in}}}{(L_3)_{\text{fi}}} \right]^{\alpha_{23}} \Rightarrow \frac{0.3}{(L_2)_{\text{fi}}} = \left[\frac{0.3}{(0.03)_{\text{fi}}} \right]^{\alpha_{21}} = \left[\frac{0.4}{(L_3)_{\text{fi}}} \right]^{\alpha_{23}} \qquad (i)$$

   If α_{21} and α_{23} are known, the final amounts of components 2 and 3 in the mixture can be easily calculated. The values of α at the beginning can be obtained at 101.3 kPa and 64°C (the initial bubble point) using the *K*-values from Figure 7.8(b). However, as boiling continues, the more volatile components are preferentially removed and the bubble point of the liquid gradually increases. The *K*-values and relative volatilities also change as a result.

An approximate method of calculation uses the average values of α over the boiling point range. For this purpose, the final boiling temperature is *guessed* and the relative volatilities (α_{21} and α_{23}) at this temperature are found out. The steps are given below.

(i)   The initial bubble point temperature, the K-values and the α-values are determined.

(ii) The final temperature is guessed. The K-values and α-values are determined at this temperature.

(iii) The arithmetic mean values of α are determined. The final number of moles of the components are calculated from Eq. (7.57) or Eq. (i).

(iv) The final bubble point is now calculated. The values of α at this temperature are determined. The mean α-values and the number of moles (L_i's) are recalculated from Eq. (i). The procedure can be repeated for better accuracy, if necessary.

At 101.3 kPa (1 atm) and 64°C, $K_1 = 2.3$, $K_2 = 0.87$, $K_3 = 0.144$ [from Figure 7.8(b)]

$$\alpha_{21} = K_2/K_1 = 0.87/2.3 = 0.378; \quad \alpha_{23} = K_2/K_3 = 0.87/0.144 = 6.04$$

Assume a final boiling temperature (when 90% of n-pentane is removed) of 95°C. At this temperature,

$$K_1 = 4.65, \ K_2 = 2.03 \text{ and } K_3 = 0.45 \Rightarrow \alpha_{21} = 2.03/4.65 = 0.437 \text{ and } \alpha_{23} = 4.51$$

Average values of α:

$$\alpha_{21} = (0.378 + 0.437)/2 = 0.407 \quad \text{and} \quad \alpha_{23} = (6.04 + 4.51)/2 = 5.27$$

Putting these values of α in Eq. (i),

$$(L_2)_{\text{fi}} = (L_2)_{\text{in}}/(10)^{(1/0.407)} = \boxed{0.1175 \text{ kmol}}; \quad (L_3)_{\text{fi}} = \boxed{0.335 \text{ kmol}}.$$

Check for the assumed final temperature of 95°C:

Total number of moles at the end $= 0.03 + 0.1175 + 0.335 = 0.482$

Liquid composition:

$$x_1 = 0.03/0.482 = 0.0623; \quad x_2 = 0.1175/0.482 = 0.245; \quad x_3 = 0.3337/0.482 = 0.6927$$

$$\sum_{i=1}^{3} K_i x_i = (4.65)(0.0623) + (2.03)(0.245) + (0.45)(0.6927) = 1.0987 > 1$$

So the assumed final temperature of 95°C is *a bit too high.* Because the component 2 (n-hexane) is the reference component, its revised K-value is taken as

$$K_2 = (K_{295°C})/1.0987 = 2.03/1.0987 = 1.85$$

The corresponding temperature [from Figure 7.8(b)] is 91°C. The K-values for components 1 and 3 at this temperature are:

$$K_1 = 4.4, \ K_3 = 0.39; \quad \alpha_{21} = 1.85/4.4 = 0.42, \ \alpha_{23} = 1.85/0.39 = 4.74$$

Average α-values are:

$$\alpha_{21} = (0.378 + 0.42)/2 = 0.4; \quad \alpha_{23} = (6.04 + 4.74)/2 = 5.4$$

The values of $(L_i)_{fi}$ are recalculated.

$$(L_2)_{fi} = (L_2)_{in}/(10)^{(0.4)} = 0.1194 \text{ kmol}; \quad (L_3)_{fi} = 0.3373 \text{ kmol}$$

These values are pretty close to the previous estimates. The total moles of the final liquid are:

$$0.03 + 0.1194 + 0.3373 = 0.4867$$

Mole fractions:
$$x_1 = 0.03/0.4867 = 0.0616$$
$$x_2 = 0.12/0.4867 = 0.2466$$
$$x_3 = 0.692$$

$$\sum_{i=1}^{3} K_i x_i = (4.4)(0.0616) + (1.85)(0.2466) + (0.39)(0.692) = 0.9971 \approx 1.0$$

So the estimate of the final temperature (91°C) is good enough.

Number of moles of distillate = $1.0 - 0.4867 = \boxed{0.5133 \text{ kmol}}$

Composition:
$$(x_1)_D = (0.3 - 0.03)/0.5133 = \boxed{0.526}$$
$$(x_2)_D = (0.3 - 0.12)/0.5133 = \boxed{0.351}$$
$$(x_3)_D = \boxed{0.123}$$

7.6 CONTINUOUS MULTISTAGE FRACTIONATION OF BINARY MIXTURES

Separation of a volatile liquid mixture to relatively pure products is very often done in a continuous fractionating column. A packed or a tray tower can be used, the choice depending upon several factors. Understandably, a continuous column is much more effective than multistage flash distillation or batch distillation. In this section we shall discuss the basic design principles of a continuous tray tower for the distillation of a binary mixture.

A tray column and the flow rates and the concentrations of the vapour and the liquid phases at different trays are schematically shown in Figure 7.14(a). For the sake of simplicity, we discuss here the basic principles of fractionation of a binary liquid mixture. The feed (it may be a liquid, a vapour or a two-phase mixture containing components A and B; A is the more volatile component) enters the column at a suitable location. The liquid stream flows down the column from one tray to the next lower tray; the vapour stream flows up bubbling through the liquid on the trays. The vapour from the top tray is condensed and the condensate is collected in a *reflux drum*. A part of this liquid is drawn as the *top product* and the other part is fed back to the top tray (the top tray is marked tray no. 1) as *reflux*. The top product contains the more volatile component A and a little of the less volatile B. The liquid from the bottom tray goes to a *reboiler* where it is partly vaporized, the vapour is fed back to the tower and the liquid part is continuously withdrawn as the *bottom product*. The bottom product is rich in the less volatile component B and has only a small amount of A in it. An intimate contact between the liquid and the vapour phases occurs on a tray, facilitating rapid exchange of mass between them. Transport of the more volatile component A occurs from the liquid to the vapour phase, while transport of the less volatile B occurs from the vapour to the liquid phase. Thus, a distillation column involves counter-diffusion of the components (*not necessarily equimolar*). As the vapour flows up, it becomes progressively richer in A. Similarly, the liquid becomes richer in the less volatile B as it flows down the column.

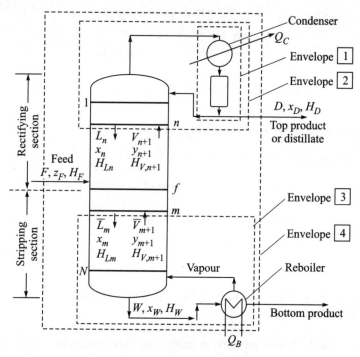

Figure 7.14(a)   Material and energy balance envelopes in continuous distillation.

In the section of the column above the feed point, the concentration of the more volatile is larger than that in the feed. This means that the vapour is enriched or 'purified' by discarding the less volatile component B into the downflowing liquid. So the section of the column above the feed tray is called the *rectifying* or *enriching section*. In the section of the column below the feed tray, the more volatile component is removed or *stripped* out of the liquid (by the process of counterdiffusion, of course) to get a relatively pure B at the bottom. So this section is called the *stripping section*.

Now we shall deal with the basic principles of design of a trayed distillation tower. We shall first describe the more important variables, parameters and factors involved in the design.

- *The flow rate, composition and state of the feed.*   The state of the feed may be described by its temperature, pressure, phase, etc. The feed may be a liquid, a vapour, or a mixture of liquid and vapour (i.e. a two-phase mixture).

- *The required degree of separation.*   The degree of separation is mainly determined by the requirement of quality or purity of the products drawn from the column. Example: Oxygen (bottom product) and nitrogen (top product) are the product streams from a liquid air distillation column. Nitrogen must be of very high purity (~99.99%) if it is to be used for creating an inert atmosphere (*blanketing*), for example, for a special welding job. A high purity oxygen is required for steel making (> 99%) or for the partial oxidation of naphtha (> 98%) in a fertilizer plant. But oxygen of lesser purity (about 90%) is good enough for medical purposes. The higher the required degree of separation, the more is the number of trays and the more expensive will be the tower.

- *The reflux ratio and the condition of the reflux.* The ratio of the reflux fed back to the top tray and the top product withdrawn is called the *reflux ratio* (L_0/D). This is an important design parameter. A specified degree of separation can be achieved with a lesser number of trays if the reflux ratio is increased. The condition of reflux means whether the reflux is a saturated liquid or a subcooled liquid.

- *The operating pressure and the allowable pressure drop across the column.* The operating pressure also determines the temperature of the column. The pressure drop for the vapour flow depends upon the type, the number and the hydraulic design of the trays. Pressure drop becomes a more important factor if a column is run at a low pressure.

- *Tray type and column internals.* The efficiency of separation (given by the *tray efficiency*) is largely determined by these factors.

In a column design problem for continuous multistage distillation, the rate, the composition and the state of the feed are given. The design engineer has to select the operating conditions (these may be sometimes specified in the problem also), the reflux ratio, the tray type and the column internals, and has to determine the number of trays. He has also to design the column, the tray, the column internals (see Chapter 5) and the auxiliaries like the reboiler and the condenser. It must be kept in mind that the design variables and parameters are interrelated. If a few of them are given or selected, the rest can be determined. Sometimes the number of trays may be known and the engineer has to check if it is suitable for achieving a desired degree of separation of a mixture. For example, we may have a problem of determining if an existing column containing a fixed number of trays of a particular design can be used for the separation of a given feed at a given rate. In this case the reflux ratio and the operating conditions are the important quantities to be calculated in order to ascertain if the existing column is at all suitable for the purpose.

Counter-transport of the components *A* and *B* takes place on each tray of a fractionating column. The molecules of the more volatile component leaving the liquid phase absorb latent heat of vaporization. Also, transport of the less volatile component from the vapour to the liquid phase causes its condensation accompanied by release of latent heat. So the mass transfer of the components between the vapour and the liquid has associated thermal effects (this has been indicated before in a simple problem on non-equimolar counterdiffusion, Example 2.5). The solution of a distillation problem involves the solution of mass and energy balance equations over the trays and over the column. We develop here the relevant equations over three sections of a column and also over the whole device.

Pictures of a few distillation columns in one of the major petrochemical complexes in India are shown in Figure 7.14(b).

Figure 7.14 (b)   A few distillation columns in Haldia Petrochemicals Limited (India).

7.6.1   Material and Energy Balance Equations

The determination of the number of trays is based on steady-state material and energy balance equations over the envelopes shown in Figure 7.14(a). A subscript is used with the flow rate, enthalpy and concentration terms to indicate the tray from which it originates. The notations L and V denote the liquid and the vapour flow rates above the feed tray; $\overline{L}$ and $\overline{V}$ denote the same quantities below the feed tray. Thus V_n is the molar flow rate of vapour leaving the nth tray; $H_{L,n}$ is the molar enthalpy of the liquid leaving the nth tray. The rate of reflux to the top tray is L_0; the suffix '0' signifies that the stream is as if coming from the 'hypothetical' 0th plate above the top tray (the top tray is tray no. 1). The rate at which heat is removed from the overhead condenser (the *condenser heat load*) is Q_C. The rate of heat supply to the reboiler (*the reboiler heat load*) for vaporizing a part of the liquid leaving the bottom tray is Q_B. The feed rate to the column is F having a mole fraction z_F of the more volatile. The distillate (x_D = mole fraction of A, the more volatile, in the distillate) is removed from the reflux drum at a rate of D mole/h;

the bottom product leaves the reboiler at a rate W and the mole fraction of A in it is x_W. We define a reflux ratio (also called the *external reflux ratio*) as

$$\frac{L_0}{D} = R = \text{reflux ratio} \; (\Rightarrow L_0 = RD) \tag{7.58}$$

Consider envelope $\boxed{1}$ (enclosing the *condenser* and the *reflux drum*) in Figure 7.14(a).

Total material balance: $\quad\quad V_1 = L_0 + D = RD + D = D(R + 1) \tag{7.59}$
$\quad\quad\quad\quad\quad\quad\quad\quad\quad$ total input $\quad$ total output

Component A balance: $\quad\quad\quad V_1 y_1 = L_0 x_0 + D x_D \tag{7.60}$
$\quad\quad\quad\quad\quad\quad\quad\quad\quad\quad$ input of A $\quad$ output of A

Energy balance: $\quad\quad\quad\quad V_1 H_{V1} = L_0 H_{L0} + D H_D + Q_C \tag{7.61}$
$\quad\quad\quad\quad\quad\quad\quad\quad\quad\quad$ input $\quad\quad\quad$ output

From Eqs. (7.59) and (7.61),

$$D(R + 1)H_{V1} = L_0 H_{L0} + D H_D + Q_C$$
$$\Rightarrow \quad\quad Q_C = D[(R + 1)H_{V1} - R H_{L0} - H_D] \tag{7.62}$$

The condenser heat load Q_C can be calculated from the above equation.

Now we consider envelope $\boxed{2}$ (enclosing a part of the *rectifying section* and the *condenser* in Figure 7.14(a)).

Total material balance: $\quad\quad\quad V_{n+1} = L_n + D \tag{7.63}$
Component A balance: $\quad\quad\quad V_{n+1} y_{n+1} = L_n x_n + D x_D \tag{7.64}$
Energy balance: $\quad\quad\quad\quad V_{n+1} H_{V,n+1} = L_n H_{L,n} + D H_D + Q_C \tag{7.65}$

Considering envelope $\boxed{3}$ (enclosing a part of the *stripping section* and the *reboiler*),

Total material balance: $\quad\quad\quad \overline{L}_m = \overline{V}_{m+1} + W \tag{7.66}$

Component A balance: $\quad\quad\quad \overline{L}_m x_m = \overline{V}_{m+1} y_{m+1} + W x_W \tag{7.67}$

Energy balance: $\quad\quad\quad \overline{L}_m H_{L,m} + Q_B = \overline{V}_{m+1} H_{V,m+1} + W H_W \tag{7.68}$

Envelope $\boxed{4}$ (enclosing the *entire column*, the *condenser* and the *reboiler*) gives
Total material balance: $\quad\quad\quad\quad F = D + W \tag{7.69}$
Component A balance: $\quad\quad\quad\quad F z_F = D x_D + W x_W \tag{7.70}$
Energy balance: $\quad\quad\quad\quad F H_F + Q_B = D H_D + W H_W + Q_C \tag{7.71}$

A material balance and an energy balance equation are also to be written over the feed tray. All the above equations together with the vapour–liquid equilibrium relationship can be solved *algebraically* to determine the number of ideal trays required to achieve a specified degree of separation of the feed. The oldest method of calculation that uses a tray-by-tray approach is called the Sorel method (Sorel, 1893). Many computational methods and strategies have been devised over the years for multicomponent distillation problems. However, a graphical procedure can be conveniently used to determine the number of trays required for the separation of a *binary* mixture.

7.6.2   Determination of the Number of Trays—the McCabe–Thiele Method

The McCabe–Thiele method developed in 1925 involves a graphical solution of the material balance equations described in Section 7.61 together with the equilibrium relation or the equilibrium data.

Assumptions

The most important assumption underlying the McCabe–Thiele method is that the molar rate of overflow of the liquid from one tray to another is constant over any section of the column. Thus, $L_0 = L_1 = L_2 = \cdots = L_n = L =$ constant in the 'rectifying section', and $\bar{L}_m = \bar{L}_{m+1} = \cdots = \bar{L}_N = \bar{L} =$ constant in the 'stripping section'. The constant flow rates of the liquid (or vapour) in the two sections differ by the rate of input of liquid (or vapour) feed to the column at the feed tray. By virtue of the material and energy balance Eqs. (7.63) and (7.66), the molar vapour rates in the respective sections also remain invariant. This assumption is called the *constant molar overflow* (CMO). The assumption is obviously true when the molar heat of vaporization of the mixture does not depend upon the composition or the temperature in the column (example: a mixture of hydrocarbons not differing much in the molecular weight); for many liquid mixtures the assumption is a good approximation. Lewis (1922) showed that the use of the constant molar overflow assumption greatly simplifies the tray-by-tray calculation by the Sorel method. If constant molar overflow occurs, the mass exchange between the phases occurs in the *equimolar counterdiffusion* mode. Tray-by-tray calculation for a ternary mixture is illustrated in Example 15.3.

Another assumption made in the following analysis is that heat loss from the column is negligible. Let L and $\bar{L}$ represent the constant liquid flow rates, and V and $\bar{V}$ the constant vapour flow rates in the rectifying and the stripping sections. Since the flow rates are constant, the suffixes indicating the trays from which they come out have been dropped. It is to be noted that if there is heat loss or gain, there will be accompanying condensation or vaporization within the column, and the flow rates will vary along the column as a result. The major steps of the graphical construction in the McCabe–Thiele method are to draw: (i) the equilibrium curve using the available data, (ii) the operating lines for the rectifying and the stripping sections, and (iii) the steps between the equilibrium and the operating lines to find out the number of ideal trays.

The rectifying section

Equation (7.63) that represents the material balance of component A over *envelope* $\boxed{2}$ is rewritten below. The reflux is assumed to be at its bubble point.

$$V y_{n+1} = L x_n + D x_D \tag{7.72}$$

From Eq. (7.58), $R = L_0/D = L/D$; from Eq. (7.59), $R + 1 = V/D$

$$\Rightarrow \qquad y_{n+1} = \frac{L}{V} x_n + \frac{D}{V} x_D = \frac{L/D}{V/D} x_n + \frac{x_D}{V/D} \Rightarrow y_{n+1} = \frac{R}{R+1} x_n + \frac{x_D}{R+1} \tag{7.73}$$

This is the equation of a straight line on the x–y plane with a slope $R/(R + 1)$ and an intercept $x_D/(R + 1)$ on the y-axis. Also the equation is satisfied by the point $x_n = x_D$, $y_{n+1} = x_D$. So the straight line passes through the point (x_D, x_D) which is a point (say D) on the diagonal (see Figure 7.15). Equation (7.68) is called the equation of the operating line of the rectifying section. It is called an *operating line* because it relates the concentrations of the liquid and the vapour phases leaving or entering a section. Usually the reflux ratio R and the distillate composition x_D are the known quantities (if the reflux ratio is not given, the designer has to select a suitable value), and the operating line can be drawn. It is, however, easier to draw this line through (x_D, x_D) with an intercept of $x_D/(R + 1)$ on the y-axis [rather than using the slope, $R/(R + 1)$]. This is illustrated in Example 7.13 and Figure 7.15. A vertical length segment between operating line and the equilibrium line effectively stands for the overall vapour phase driving force at the particular location in a column.

The stripping section

With the constant molar overflow assumption, the material balance for component A over *envelope* $\boxed{3}$ given by Eq. (7.67) can be rewritten as

$$\bar{L} x_m = \bar{V} y_{m+1} + W x_W \tag{7.74}$$

Putting $\bar{V} = \bar{L} - W$ [from Eq. (7.66)],

$$y_{m+1} = \frac{\bar{L}}{\bar{V}} x_m - \frac{W}{\bar{V}} x_W = \frac{\bar{L}}{\bar{L} - W} x_m - \frac{W}{\bar{L} - W} x_W \tag{7.75}$$

This is the equation of the operating line for the stripping section. It has a slope of $\bar{L}/(\bar{L} - W)$ and passes through the point (x_W, x_W) which lies on the diagonal. This line is also shown in Figure 7.15.

Similar to the reflux ratio defined for the rectified section, we may define a quantity called the *boil-up ratio*, R_v, for the stripping section.

$$R_v = \frac{\bar{V}}{W} = \frac{\text{moles of vapour leaving the reboiler per hour}}{\text{moles of liquid drawn as the bottom product per hour}} \tag{7.76}$$

EXAMPLE 7.13 (*Drawing the operating lines*)   A mixture of benzene and toluene containing 40 mole% benzene is to be separated continuously in a tray tower at a rate of 200 kmol/h. The top product should have 95 mole% of benzene and the bottom must not contain more than 4 mole% of it. The reflux is a saturated liquid and a reflux ratio of 2.0 is maintained. The feed is a saturated liquid (i.e. it is at its bubble point). Obtain and plot the operating lines for the rectifying and the stripping sections on the x–y plane. What is the boil-up ratio? The vapour–liquid equilibrium data at the operating pressure of 101.3 kPa are given below.

x	0	0.1	0.2	0.3	0.4	0.5	0.6	0.7	0.8	0.9	1.0
y	0	0.21	0.38	0.511	0.627	0.719	0.79	0.853	0.91	0.961	1.0

Solution

Assume 'constant molar overflow'. *Given:* feed rate, $F = 200$ kmol/h; feed composition, $z_F = 0.4$ mole fraction; top product composition, $x_D = 0.95$; bottom product composition, $x_W = 0.04$; reflux ratio, $R = 2.0$.

Total material balance [Eq. (7.69)]:

$$F = D + W \quad \Rightarrow \quad 200 = D + W$$

Total benzene balance [Eq. (7.70)]:

$$Fz_F = Dx_D + Wx_W \quad \Rightarrow \quad (200)(0.4) = D(0.95) + W(0.04)$$

Solving the above equations, we get $D = 79.1$ kmol/h and $W = 120.9$ kmol/h

$$R = L_0/D \Rightarrow 2.0 = L_0/79.1$$

$$\Rightarrow \qquad L_0 = 158.2; \quad V_1 = D(R + 1) = (79.1)(2 + 1) = 237.3, \text{ from Eq. (7.59)}.$$

Since the feed is a liquid, the vapour rate remains constant at $V = V_1 = 237.3$ kmol/h in the rectifying section.

Flow rates in the stripping section: Since the feed is a saturated liquid, the liquid rate increases by 200 kmol/h below the feed plate. However, the vapour rate remains constant all through.

Liquid flow rate, $\bar{L} = L + 200 = 158.2 + 200 = 358.2$; vapour rate, $\bar{V} = V = 237.3$

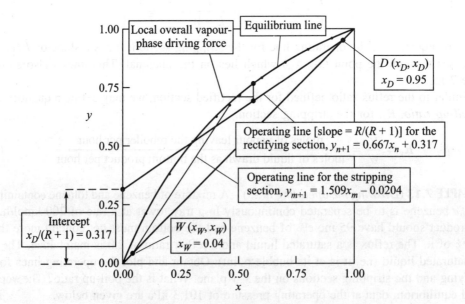

Figure 7.15 The operating lines on the *x–y* plane.

Operating lines: rectifying section, Eq. (7.73): $y_{n+1} = \dfrac{R}{R+1} x_n + \dfrac{x_D}{R+1}$

$$\Rightarrow \qquad\qquad y_{n+1} = \frac{2}{2+1}x_n + \frac{0.95}{2+1}$$

$$\Rightarrow \qquad\qquad y_{n+1} = 0.667x_n + 0.317 \qquad\qquad\qquad (i)$$

Stripping section, Eq. (7.75), $\quad y_{m+1} = \dfrac{\overline{L}}{\overline{L} - W}x_m - \dfrac{W}{\overline{L} - W}x_W$

$$\Rightarrow \qquad\qquad y_{m+1} = \frac{358.2}{358.2 - 120.9}x_m - \frac{(120.9)(0.04)}{358.2 - 120.9}$$

$$\Rightarrow \qquad\qquad y_{m+1} = 1.509x_m - 0.0204 \qquad\qquad\qquad (ii)$$

Equations (i) and (ii) are the rectifying and stripping section operating lines respectively.

The equilibrium line is plotted on the x–y plane (Figure 7.15). The operating line (i) for the rectifying section passes through the point $D(x_D, x_D)$, i.e. (0.95, 0.95) and has an intercept of 0.317. The line is shown in Figure 7.15. The stripping section operating line (ii) passes through the point $W(x_W, x_W)$, i.e. (0.04, 0.04) and has a slope of 1.509. This line is also shown in the figure.

The boil-up ratio, $\qquad\qquad R_v = \dfrac{\overline{V}}{W} = \dfrac{237.3}{120.9} = \boxed{1.963}$

The feed line

As the feed enters the column, the liquid and vapour flow rates undergo step changes depending upon the state of the feed (i.e. upon how much liquid and vapour it has). We shall now write the material and energy balance equations over the plate to which the feed is introduced. Let us designate this plate by the suffix 'f'. The feed plate along with related flow, composition and enthalpy terms are shown in Figure 7.16.

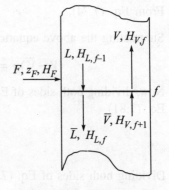

Figure 7.16 The feed plate.

Total material balance:

$$F + L + \overline{V} = \overline{L} + V \qquad\qquad (7.77)$$

Energy balance:

$$FH_F + LH_{L,f-1} + \overline{V}H_{V,f+1} = \overline{L}H_{L,f} + VH_{V,f} \qquad\qquad (7.78)$$

If we assume that the change in the enthalpy of a phase as it passes through the feed plate is small, we can write (omitting the subscript f),

$$H_{L,f-1} \approx H_{L,f} \approx H_L$$

and
$$H_{V,f+1} \approx H_{V,f} \approx H_V \qquad\qquad (7.79)$$

Substituting the relations (7.79) in Eq. (7.78),

$$FH_F + LH_L + \overline{V}H_V = \overline{L}H_L + VH_V$$

i.e.
$$(\overline{L} - L)H_L = (\overline{V} - V)H_V + FH_F \qquad\qquad (7.80)$$

From Eqs. (7.77) and (7.80),

$$(\bar{L} - L)H_L = (\bar{L} - L - F)H_V + FH_F = (\bar{L} - L)H_V + F(H_F - H_V)$$

$$\Rightarrow \qquad\qquad (\bar{L} - L)(H_L - H_V) = F(H_F - H_V)$$

$$\Rightarrow \qquad\qquad \frac{\bar{L} - L}{F} = \frac{H_F - H_V}{H_L - H_V} = \frac{H_V - H_F}{H_V - H_L} = q \text{ (say)} \qquad (7.81)$$

But $\bar{L} - L$ = increase in the liquid flow rate across the feed tray as a result of introduction of the feed = rate of input of liquid with the feed. So q is the fraction of liquid in the feed.

On the basis of Eq. (7.81), the quantity q may also be attributed another physical significance.

$$q = \frac{\text{heat required to convert 1 mole feed to saturated vapour}}{\text{molar heat of vaporization of the saturated liquid}} \qquad (7.82)$$

If the feed is a liquid at its bubble point (saturated liquid), $q = 1$; if it is a vapour at dew point (saturated vapour), $q = 0$. If the feed is a two-phase mixture of liquid and vapour, q represents the fraction of liquid in it. So $(1 - q)$ gives a measure of the 'quality' of the feed.

The point of intersection of the two operating lines, rectifying section and stripping section, must satisfy Eqs. (7.72) and (7.74). If the point of intersection is (x, y),

From Eq. (7.72), $\qquad\qquad\qquad\qquad Vy = Lx + Dx_D$

From Eq. (7.74), $\qquad\qquad\qquad\qquad \bar{V}y = \bar{L}x - Wx_W$

Subtracting the above equations and using Eq. (7.70),

$$(V - \bar{V})y = (L - \bar{L})x + (Dx_D + Wx_W) = (L - \bar{L})x + Fz_F \qquad (7.83)$$

Now, dividing both sides of Eq. (7.77) by F, simplifying, and using the definition of q given by Eq. (7.81),

$$\frac{\bar{V} - V}{F} + 1 = \frac{\bar{L} - L}{F} = q \qquad (7.84)$$

Dividing both sides of Eq. (7.83) by F and using the above result,

$$-(q - 1)y = -qx + z_F \qquad \Rightarrow \qquad y = \frac{q}{q - 1}x - \frac{z_F}{q - 1} \qquad (7.85)$$

The above equation represents a straight line passing through (i) the point (z_F, z_F) on the diagonal (recall that z_F is the overall mole fraction of A in the feed) and (ii) the point of intersection of the operating lines. The line has a slope $q/(q - 1)$, where q is the quality of the feed as stated before [Eq. (7.82)]. Since the line given by Eq. (7.85) is completely described by the state (quality) and concentration of the feed, it is called the *feed line*.

The stripping section operating line can be drawn by taking the help of the feed line. The upper operating line and the feed line are drawn on the x–y plane and their point of intersection is located. The line joining this point of intersection and the point (x_W, x_W) is the stripping section operating line. The following characteristics of the feed line may be noted (also see Example 7.14).

(a) If the feed is a saturated liquid, $q = 1$; and the slope of the feed line is infinite. So the feed line is a vertical line through (z_F, z_F).

(b) If the feed is a saturated vapour, $q = 0$; and the slope of the feed line is zero. So the feed line is a horizontal line through (z_F, z_F).

(c) If the feed is a mixture of liquid and vapour or a superheated vapour or a subcooled liquid, the slope of the feed line can be calculated from the enthalpy data and Eq. (7.81).

Drawing of feed lines under different thermal conditions of the feed is illustrated in Example 7.14.

EXAMPLE 7.14 (*Drawing the feed line for different feed conditions*)   A mixture of benzene and toluene containing 58 mole% benzene is to be separated in a continuous column operating at 1 atm total pressure. Draw the feed line for the following feed conditions: (a) saturated liquid, (b) saturated vapour, (c) 65 mass% vapour, (d) vapour at 120°C, and (e) liquid at 50°C.

The other relevant data are given as follows: Benzene: average specific heat of liquid = 146.5 kJ/kmol·K, of vapour = 97.6 kJ/kmol·K; heat of vaporization = 30,770 kJ/kmol. Toluene: average specific heat of liquid = 170 kJ/kmol·K, of vapour = 124.3 kJ/kmol·K; heat of vaporization = 32,120 kJ/kmol.

Solution

The feed line is given by Eq. (7.85). To draw the line, we need to know the value of q. The feed line must pass through the point $F(z_F, z_F)$, i.e. (0.58, 0.58) which lies on the diagonal on the x–y plane. We consider the cases given.

(a) The feed is a *saturated liquid*. So, q = the fraction of liquid in the feed = 1.

Therefore, the slope of the feed line = $q/(q - 1) = 1/0 = \infty$. The feed line is a vertical line through the point F. This is line I on Figure 7.17.

(b) The feed is a saturated vapour, i.e. $q = 0$ and the slope of the feed line is zero. The feed line is a horizontal line through the point F (line II).

(c) The feed is 65 mass% vapour. So on the average, the feed contains 35 mole% liquid (in this case mass% and mole% can be used interchangeably). So $q = 0.35$ and the slope of the feed line = $0.35/(0.35 - 1) = -0.538$ and its intercept on the y-axis = $-z_F/(q - 1) = -(0.58)/(0.35 - 1) = 0.892$. The line is drawn through the point (0.58, 0.58) on the x–y plane and is marked III on Figure 7.17.

(d) The feed is a superheated vapour at 120°C. In this case the value of q has to be calculated from Eq. (7.81). The values of the enthalpy terms H_F, H_V and H_L are required. In order to calculate the enthalpies, a reference state is to be selected. Using the Antoine constants given in Table 7.2, the bubble point of a solution having 58% benzene can be calculated (assuming that the solution is ideal). The bubble point is 90°C (the calculation of the bubble point is left as an exercise). We take pure liquids at 90°C as the reference state for convenience. The *heat of solution* (ΔH_s) is assumed to be *zero*.

Enthalpy of the liquid: For the solution at its bubble point ($T = 90°C$), put $T_0 = 90$ and $\Delta H_s = 0$ in Eq. (7.18) $\Rightarrow H_L = 0$.

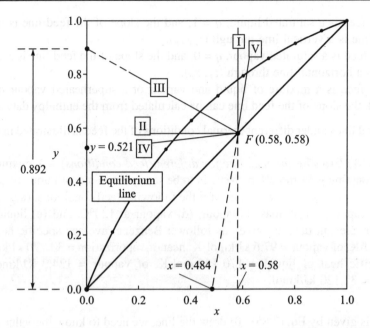

Figure 7.17 Feed lines for different conditions of the feed: (I) saturated liquid, (II) saturated vapour, (III) two-phase mixture, (IV) superheated vapour, and (V) subcooled liquid.

Enthalpy of the vapour: The mole fraction of benzene in the saturated vapour in equilibrium with a liquid with $x = 0.58$ is $y* = 0.78$. Putting $y* = 0.78$, T (vapour temp.) = 90°C, T_0 (ref. temp.) = 90°C, $M_A \lambda_A = 30{,}770$ kJ/kmol, and $M_B \lambda_B = 32{,}120$ kJ/kmol in Eq. (7.19), the enthalpy of the saturated vapour is

$$H_V = (0.78)(30{,}770) + (1 - 0.78)(32{,}120) = 31{,}067 \text{ kJ/kmol}$$

Enthalpy of the feed: We imagine that 0.58 kmol of benzene and 0.42 kmol of toluene are vaporized separately at 90°C, the vapours are heated to 120°C and then mixed to get one kmole of the feed.

$$H_F = \underbrace{[(0.58)(30{,}770)}_{\text{latent heat}} + \underbrace{(0.58)(97.6)(120 - 90)]}_{\text{sensible heat}}$$

$$+ \underbrace{[(0.42)(32{,}120)}_{\text{latent heat}} + \underbrace{(0.42)(124.3)(120 - 90)]}_{\text{sensible heat}} = 34{,}601$$

Then, $\qquad q = \dfrac{H_V - H_F}{H_V - H_L} = \dfrac{31{,}067 - 34{,}601}{31{,}067 - 0} = -0.114$

To draw the feed line in this case, it will be more convenient to use the intercept on the y-axis, i.e.

$$-z_F/(q - 1) = -0.58/(-0.114 - 1) = 0.521$$

The feed line is marked IV on Figure 7.17.

(e) The feed is a subcooled liquid at 50°C. We imagine that 0.58 kmol of benzene and 0.42 kmol of toluene are separately cooled from the reference temperature ($T_0 = 90°C$) to $T = 50°C$ and then mixed to get one mole of the subcooled feed.

The enthalpy of the feed,

$H_F = (0.58)(146.5)(50 - 90) + (0.42)(170)(50 - 90) = - 6240$ kJ/kmol (the heat of mixing is neglected).

$$q = \frac{H_V - H_F}{H_V - H_L} = \frac{31,067 - (-6240)}{31,067 - 0} = 1.2$$

From Eq. (7.85), the intercept on the x-axis = $z_F/q = 0.58/1.2 = 0.58/1.2 = 0.484$.

The feed line is drawn through (0.58, 0.58) with this intercept on the x-axis. It is marked V on Figure 7.17.

Feed tray location and the number of ideal trays

The next step of graphical construction is to determine the number of equilibrium trays (or ideal trays) required for a specified degree of separation (i.e. for specified values of x_D and x_W) and to locate the feed tray. This is illustrated in Example 7.15 and Figure 7.18(a). The rectifying section operating line DE is drawn through the point D (x_D, x_D) with an intercept $x_D/(R + 1)$ on the y-axis. If the feed is a saturated liquid, the feed line FN is a vertical line through the point F (z_F, z_F). The feed line FN intersects the rectifying section operating line DE at M. The point W (x_W, x_W) is located on the diagonal. WM is joined to give the stripping section operating line. The line WM, when extended, intersects the equilibrium curve at S'', and the line DE, when extended, intersects the equilibrium curve at S'.

The number of equilibrium trays is determined by step or staircase construction between the equilibrium curve and the operating lines (see Example 7.15). The basis of such construction has been described in Section 4.6.2. The point (x_n, y_n) lies on the equilibrium curve whereas the point (x_n, y_{n+1}) lies on the operating line. Construction may start from either end, i.e. from D (the top tray) or W (the bottom tray). When the feed line is crossed in course of construction, a changeover from one operating line to the other is necessary. This means a transition from the rectifying to the stripping section (or vice versa). For example, starting the stage construction from the point D in Figure 7.18(a), we should make a changeover from the upper operating line to the lower after tray number 5 from the top. The step construction should thereafter proceed along the lower operating line MW. In this way we take the advantage of maximum possible change in the concentration in each tray. So the sixth tray from the top is the *optimum feed tray*. The stage construction (solid line) shows that the number of ideal stages required is 7.8. If the graphical construction does not give an integral number of trays (in fact, it rarely does), it is customary to report the number of ideal trays as a mixed fraction. The idea behind this is that the integral number of real trays is determined after considering tray efficiency. Usually, the reboiler partly vaporizes the liquid from the lowest tray. Because equilibrium vaporization in the reboiler is quite a reasonable assumption, the reboiler also acts as a tray. So the number of ideal trays in the construction shown in Figure 7.18(a) is 7.8 *including the reboiler*; i.e. 6.8 number of trays and a reboiler are required for the desired separation.

The above discussion does not mean that the feed has to be introduced always on the 'optimum feed tray'. Consider the staircase construction on Figure 7.18(b). The feed is deliberately introduced on the fifth tray from the top. So a changeover to the lower operating line has been made at the fifth tray from the top, and construction has thereafter been done along *WMS"*, the stripping section operating line. The number of equilbrium trays required to reach the point *W* is 8, which is 0.2 ideal trays more than the previous case. This is expected because full advantage of the driving force has not been exploited on a few trays.

However, a changeover from one operating line to the other is possible only in the section *S'S"*. When a new column is designed, the optimum feed tray location is used. But if an existing column with a feed nozzle at a particular tray has to be considered for possible use to separate a mixture, a changeover from one operating line to the other during staircase construction should be done at the tray which is provided with a feed nozzle [see Example 7.15, part (d)]. Complete construction of the steps will tell whether the existing column is suitable for a particular service. If not, further calculations may be done with a different reflux ratio before discarding the possibility of use of the available column.

It is to be noted that a liquid feed is introduced just above the feed tray, but a vapour feed is introduced just below it. If the feed is a mixture of liquid and vapour, it is desirable that it is separated into the vapour and the liquid phases first. The liquid part should enter the column just above the feed tray and the vapour part just below it. However, this is not always done in practice, and a mixed feed is often introduced as a whole over the feed tray.

If a high purity product is required, the graphical constructon of the trays may pose a problem. The operating and the equilibrium lines may be too close at the top and the bottom region to allow graphical construction. One way is to draw steps for these regions on separate graphs drawn using expanded scales. Alternatively, the Kremser equation may be used assuming the equilibrium line to be linear at low concentrations. Another technique of plotting the equilibrium and the operating line for McCabe–Thiele construction has been suggested by Ryan (2001).

EXAMPLE 7.15 (*Determination of the number of ideal trays*)   A stream of aqueous methanol having 45 mol% CH_3OH is to be separated into a top product having 96 mole% methanol and a bottom liquid with 4% methanol. The feed is at its bubble point and the operating pressure is 101.3 kPa. A reflux ratio of 1.5 is suggested. (a) Determine the number of ideal trays. (b) Find the number of real trays if the 'overall tray efficiency' is 40%. On which real tray should the feed be introduced? (c) Plot the temperature profile along the column. (d) A column having twenty-two trays with a feed nozzle at tray number 13 from the top is available in the plant. The trays are presumed to be 40% efficient on the average. Is this column suitable for the above separation?

The equilibrium and bubble point data for the methanol–water system at 101.3 kPa are given below.

x	0	0.02	0.04	0.06	0.08	0.10	0.20	0.30	0.40	0.50	0.60	0.70	0.80	0.90	0.95	1.0
y	0	0.134	0.23	0.304	0.365	0.418	0.579	0.665	0.729	0.779	0.825	0.87	0.915	0.958	0.979	1.0
Temp.	100	96.4	93.5	91.2	89.3	87.7	84.4	78.0	75.3	73.1	71.2	69.3	67.6	66	65	64.5

Solution
The equilibrium data are plotted, the diagonal is drawn. *Given:* $x_D = 0.96$; $x_W = 0.04$ and $z_F = 0.45$. The points *D*(0.96, 0.96), *W*(0.04, 0.04) and *F*(0.45, 0.45) are located on the *x–y* plane.

(a) *Number of ideal trays:* The reflux ratio is $R = 1.5$. The intercept of the rectifying section operating line on the y-axis is $x_D/(R + 1) = 0.96/(1.5 + 1) = 0.384$.

The upper operating line is drawn through the point $D(0.96, 0.96)$ with an intercept of 0.384 on the vertical axis [Figure 7.18(a)]. The extended operated line meets the y-axis at E (intercept $= 0.384$). The feed is a saturated liquid and the feed line is a vertical line through F. The upper operating line meets the feed line at the point M. The points M and W are joined to get the lower or stripping section operating line WM. Now the number of ideal trays is determined by drawing steps between the equilibrium line and the operating lines DM and WM, changing from the upper to the lower operating line as the feed line is crossed. The number of ideal trays is 7.8. It is to be noted that the feed is to be introduced on the 6th ideal tray.

(b) *Number of real trays:* The number of real trays is obtained by dividing the number of ideal trays by the fractional overall tray efficiency(the given value is 0.4). The number of real trays is $6.8/0.4 = 17$ real trays *plus* the reboiler which is assumed to act like an ideal stage.

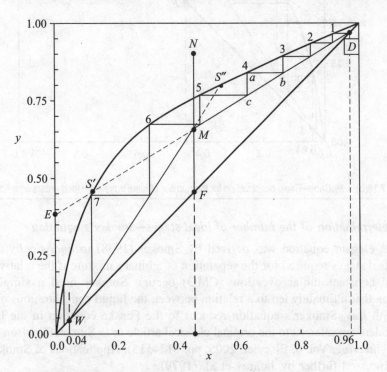

Figure 7.18(a) McCabe–Thiele construction for the number of ideal trays.

(c) The temperature on the nth tray can be obtained from the values x_n, y_n and the given bubble point data. The temperatures on the different ideal trays are given below.

n	1	2	3	4	5	6	7	8
x_n	0.913	0.853	0.773	0.667	0.575	0.35	0.15	0.0405
Temp.	66	66.9	68	70	72.8	76.5	85	94

(d) This part is left as an exercise. Note that now the feed is introduced on the fifth ideal tray from the top [see Figure 7.18(b)].

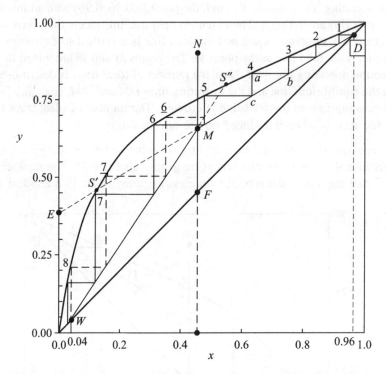

Figure 7.18(b) McCabe–Thiele construction for the number of ideal trays—the feed enters a particular tray.

Analytical determination of the number of ideal stages—Smoker's equation

A simple but elegant equation was derived by Smoker (1938) to *analytically* determine the number of ideal stages required for the separation of a binary mixture if the relative volatility is constant and constant molar overflow (CMO) occurs. Smoker used a simple coordinate transformation that ultimately led to a relation between the liquid concentrations on the top tray and on the nth tray. Smoker's equation reduces to the Fenske equation in the limit $R \to \infty$. Interested readers are referred to the original classical article or to Sinnott (Coulson–Richardson's *Chemical Engineering*, Vol. 6, Elsevier, 2005, pp. 512–515). Applications of Smoker's equation have been discussed further by Jafarey et al. (1979).

Total reflux

If the liquid from the overhead condenser is totally recycled to the column, i.e. no distillate is removed from the reflux drum ($D = 0$), the column is said to run at 'total reflux'. The reflux ratio becomes $R = L_0/D = L_0/0 = $ infinity. No product is drawn from the reboiler either. All the liquid flowing to the reboiler is vaporized and fed back to the column. So, in a column operating at total reflux under steady-state conditions, there should not be any flow of feed into it.

At total reflux, the slope of the rectifying section operating line is $[R/(R + 1)]$ for $R \to \infty$, i.e. the slope of the line is unity and it passes through the point (x_D, x_D) on the diagonal. Therefore, the operating line coincides with the diagonal. So does the stripping section operating line. The number of ideal stages is obtained by staircase construction between the equilibrium line and the diagonal. This gives the *theoretical minimum* number of stages to achieve a given separation. The construction is illustrated in Figure 7.19. Total reflux is very often used during the startup of a column till the steady-state condition is reached. After this, continuous feed flow and product withdrawal are started.

Fenske's equation

This equation can be used to theoretically calculate the minimum number of trays if the relative volatility remains reasonably constant. Let N_m be the minimum number of trays in the column. Besides, there is a *total reboiler*. If α_W is the relative volatility of A at the reboiler temperature and pressure, and x_W and y_W are the equilibrium liquid and vapour concentrations in the reboiler, then by definition,

$$\frac{y_W}{1-y_W} = \alpha_W \frac{x_W}{1-x_W} \tag{7.86}$$

The vapour leaving the reboiler and entering the lowest tray (tray number N_m in this case) has a mole fraction y_W of the component A. The liquid leaving this tray has a composition x_{Nm}. So the point (x_{Nm}, y_W) lies on the operating line. Because the operating line coincides with the diagonal at total reflux, $x_{Nm} = y_W$. Putting this result in Eq. (7.86),

$$\frac{x_{Nm}}{1-x_{Nm}} = \alpha_W \frac{x_W}{1-x_W} \tag{7.87}$$

Applying the same procedure to the case of tray number N_m,

$$\frac{y_{Nm}}{1-y_{Nm}} = \alpha_{Nm} \frac{x_{Nm}}{1-x_{Nm}} = \alpha_{Nm} \cdot \alpha_W \cdot \frac{x_W}{1-x_W}$$

Similarly for tray number $N_m - 1$,

$$\frac{y_{(Nm-1)}}{1-y_{(Nm-1)}} = \alpha_{(Nm-1)} \frac{x_{(Nm-1)}}{1-x_{(Nm-1)}} = \alpha_{(Nm-1)} \cdot \alpha_{Nm} \cdot \alpha_W \cdot \frac{x_W}{1-x_W}$$

[Note that the point (x_{Nm-1}, y_{Nm}) lies on the operating line which coincides with the diagonal; therefore, $x_{Nm-1} = y_{Nm}$]

Continuing the procedure up to the top tray (where $y_1 = x_D$),

$$\frac{x_D}{1-x_D} = \frac{y_1}{1-y_1} = \alpha_1 \alpha_2 \ldots \alpha_{Nm} \cdot \alpha_W \cdot \frac{x_W}{1-x_W}$$

$$\Rightarrow \qquad \frac{x_D}{1-x_D} = (\alpha_{av})^{Nm+1} \cdot \frac{x_W}{1-x_W}$$

i.e. $$\qquad N_m + 1 = \frac{\log \dfrac{x_D(1-x_W)}{x_W(1-x_D)}}{\log \alpha_{av}} \tag{7.88}$$

Here α_{av} is the average relative volatility of the more volatile component. The above equation is called *Fenske's equation*, which is useful for the calculation of the minimum number of trays.

EXAMPLE 7.16 (*Number of theoretical plates at total reflux*)   A mixture of benzene and toluene having 40% benzene is to be separated at a rate of 200 kmol/h into a top product containing 95% benzene and a bottom product with 4% of it. It is a common practice to run a column at total reflux for some time for the purpose of stabilization during startup. Determine the number of ideal trays required for this separation if the column is operated at total reflux (no feed input at this time). Also calculate the same using the Fenske equation if the average relative volatility of benzene in the mixture is 2.5. Vapour–liquid equilibrium data for this system at the operating pressure of 1 atm are also given in Example 7.13.

Solution

At total reflux, the reflux ratio is infinite ($R = \infty$) and the slope of the rectifying section operating line is $R/(R + 1) = 1$. So both the operating lines should coincide with the 45° line (i.e. the diagonal). *Given:* top product composition, $x_D = 0.95$; bottom liquid composition, $x_W = 0.04$.

The equilibrium data are plotted on the x–y plane in Figure 7.19. The points $D(0.95, 0.95)$ and $W(0.04, 0.04)$ are located on the diagonal. The number of ideal trays is obtained by construction of steps between the equilibrium line and the diagonal, starting at one end (say at D) and terminating at the other. The number of trays is 7.

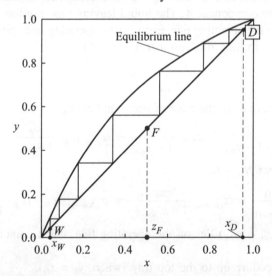

Figure 7.19   Number of plates for operation at total reflux (the minimum number of plates).

Use of the Fenske equation: Put the values of x_D, x_W and α_{av} ($= 2.5$) in Eq. (7.88). The total number of trays is

$$N_m + 1 = \frac{\log \dfrac{x_D(1 - x_W)}{x_W(1 - x_D)}}{\log \alpha_{av}} = \frac{\log \dfrac{(0.95)(1 - 0.04)}{(0.04)(1 - 0.95)}}{\log 2.5} = 6.7$$

This is very close to the number of ideal trays determined graphically. One of the reasons of the small difference is the assumption of an average value of the relative volatility.

Note: For operation at total reflux, sufficient amount of feed is charged into the reboiler and flow of steam (to the reboiler) and of cooling water (to the condenser) are started. The entire condensate is fed back as reflux. The rate, the concentration and the thermal state of the feed are not relevant for a column operated at total reflux since there is no feed input at all.

Minimum reflux ratio

In Section 6.4, we discussed the method of determination of the minimum liquid rate for gas absorption by identifying the pinch point for a given system. The determination of the minimum reflux ratio for distillation is also based on identifying the pinch point. Let us refer to Figure 7.20 in which the equilibrium curve and the feed line are shown; $D(x_D, x_D)$ and $W(x_W, x_W)$ are the terminal points of the operating lines. For a particular reflux ratio (R_1, say), DE_1 is the enriching section operating line having a slope $R_1/(R_1 + 1)$. It intersects the feed line at the point M_1; WM_1 is the stripping section operating line. The ordinate of the point E_1 gives the intercept of the upper operating line on the y-axis. The number of theoretical trays required is obviously finite. As the reflux ratio R_1 decreases to R_2, the slope of the upper operating line decreases, but the intercept increases, i.e. the point E_1 moves to E_2 (say). The upper operating line is DM_2; the stripping section operating line is WM_2; and they intersect at M_2 on the feed line. Now the driving force is less at all the points and the number of theoretical trays will be more. If the reflux ratio is gradually reduced, a situation will appear when the upper operating line DE_3 intersects the feed line at the point M_3 that lies on the equilibrium curve. The driving force is zero at the point M_3. It is the *pinch point*. The number of theoretical trays required to achieve the given separation becomes infinite. This operating line DM_3 corresponds to the minimum reflux ratio, bacause if the reflux ratio is further reduced, the operating line will intersect the feed line at a point M_4 above the equilibrium curve. This is impossible. To determine the minimum reflux ratio R_m, for the kind of equilibrium line shown in Figure 7.20, the steps given below should be followed.

(a) Locate the points $D(x_D, x_D)$ and $F(z_F, z_F)$ on the diagonal on the x–y plane.
(b) Draw the feed line through F from the known feed composition z_F, and the feed quality (given by q); locate the point M_3.
(c) Join DM_3 and extend to intersect the y-axis at E_3. Find out the ordinate of E_3 and equate it to $x_D/(R_{m+1})$. Calculate the minimum reflux ratio, R_m.

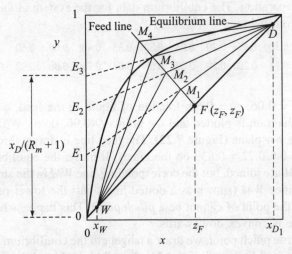

Figure 7.20 Operating lines for changing reflux ratios and for the minimum reflux (R_m).

The above strategy fails for some other shapes of the equilibrium curve. Examples are shown in Figure 7.21 and Figure 7.22. Because of the typical curvature, the pinch point does not occur at the intersection of the feed line and the equilibrium curve. As the reflux ratio is reduced, at a certain value of it the pinch point K occurs at the point of tangency of the rectifying section operating line (Figure 7.21) or the stripping section operating line (Figure 7.22) and the equilibrium line. The location of the point of tangency depends upon the shape of the equilibrium line. This type of pinch point and the minimum reflux ratio can be determined only graphically. Example 7.17 illustrates the procedure.

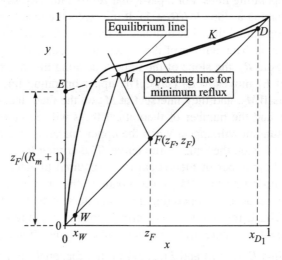

Figure 7.21   A pinch point (K) on the operating line for the rectifying section.

EXAMPLE 7.17   (*Determination of the minimum reflux ratio*)   A binary solution of 60 mol% A and 40 mol% B is to be separated into a top product having 96 mol% A and a bottom product with 6 mol% A. The feed is a two-phase mixture containing 72% liquid. Determine the minimum reflux ratio for this separation. The equilibrium data for the system at the operating condition of the column are given below.

x	0	0.05	0.07	0.10	0.15	0.20	0.25	0.30	0.35	0.40	0.50	0.60	0.70	0.80	0.90	1.0
y	0	0.07	0.10	0.14	0.205	0.29	0.39	0.55	0.67	0.75	0.86	0.93	0. 96	0.98	0.99	1.0

Solution

Given: $x_D = 0.96$; $x_W = 0.06$; $z_F = 0.60$; fraction of liquid in the feed, $q = 0.72$.

The equilibrium diagram is plotted and the points $D(0.96, 0.96)$, $W(0.06, 0.06)$ and $F(0.6, 0.6)$ are located on the x–y plane (Figure 7.22). The feed line is drawn through the point F with an intercept of $z_F/q = 0.6/0.72 = 0.833$ on the x-axis. It meets the equilibrium line at the point M. The points W and M are joined, but the corresponding line WM in the stripping section cannot be an operating line since WM (shown as a dotted line) cuts the lower part of the equilibrium line at two points. So the point M cannot be a *pinch point*. This happens because the lower part of the equilibrium line is convex downwards.

To determine the true pinch point, we draw a tangent to the equilibrium line through the point W. This line meets the feed line at the point M_1. Join DM_1 and produce it to meet the y-axis at

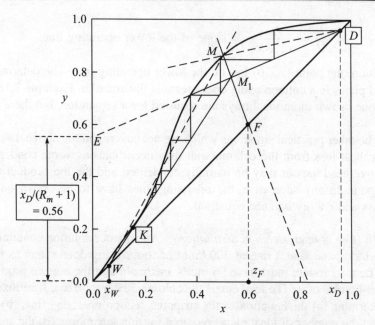

Figure 7.22 A pinch point on the operating line for the stripping section.

E. The point of tangency is *K*. If we make step construction starting at *D*, it is seen that as we approach the pinch point *K*, the step size becomes progressively smaller, and it is not possible to reach *K* by drawing a finite number of plates. The situation corresponds to the minimum reflux and *DE* is the rectifying section operating line for minimum reflux. If R_m is the minimum reflux, the ordinate of the point *E* is

$$0.56 = x_D/(R_m + 1) = 0.96/(R_m + 1) \quad \Rightarrow \quad R_m = (0.96/0.56) - 1 = \boxed{0.174}$$

Open steam

While separating an aqueous solution, if the residue or bottom product consists of water and traces of the solute, sometimes it may be convenient to feed live steam at the bottom of the tower. No reboiler is necessary. The arrangement is shown in Figure 7.23.

The operating line equation for the rectifying section remains the same as Eq. (7.73), but that for the stripping section is obviously different. The material balance of component *A* over the envelope shown in Figure 7.23 is [assume that the inlet steam is saturated]

$$\bar{L} x_m + \bar{V} \cdot (0) = \bar{V} y_{m+1} + W x_W \tag{7.89}$$

Since there is no reboiler, $\bar{L} = W$. Therefore,

$$\bar{L} x_m = \bar{V} y_{m+1} + \bar{L} x_W$$

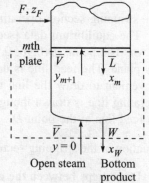

Figure 7.23 A distillation column using open steam.

$$\Rightarrow \qquad \frac{\overline{L}}{\overline{V}} = \frac{y_{m+1}}{x_m - x_W} = \text{slope of the lower operating line} \qquad (7.90)$$

Also, by definition, the point $(x_W, 0)$ lies on the lower operating line. The determination of the number of ideal plates in a column using open steam is illustrated in Example 7.18. When open steam is used, one or two more ideal trays are required for a separation, but there is no reboiler cost.

There may be other practical situations which are not covered in the above discussion. Cases may arise when heat loss from the column wall may occur causing some condensation of the vapour, or the overhead vapour may be partially condensed and the top product may be withdrawn as a vapour. In any such case, the operating lines have to be drawn on the basis of appropriate mass and energy balance equations.

EXAMPLE 7.18 (*Use of open steam in distillation*)   An aqueous solution containing 40 mol% methanol is to be separated at a rate of 300 kmol per hour using open steam as the source of heat energy. The top product must have 96 mol% methanol and the bottom product must not have more than 4 mol% of it. The feed enters the column 50% vaporized. A reflux ratio of 2.25 is suitable. Determine (a) the equation of the stripping section operating line, (b) the slope of the feed line, (c) the number of ideal plates required for this separation, (d) the steam rate, and (e) the condenser heat load. The following enthalpy data for 96 mol% methanol solution at 1 atm are available: saturated vapour, $H_V = 9725$ kcal/kmol; saturated liquid, $H_L = 1260$ kcal/kmol (reference state: pure liquids at 15°C; see Example 7.4).

Hints: *Given:* reflux ratio, $R = 2.25$; Top product concentration, $x_D = 0.96$.
Operating line for the rectifying section: intercept on the y-axis $= x_D/(R + 1) = 0.96/3.25 = 0.295$

    Feed line: q = fraction of liquid in the vapour–liquid mixture = 0.5; feed concentration, $z_F = 0.4$.

$$\text{Slope of the feed line} = q/(q - 1) = 0.5/(0.5 - 1) = \boxed{-1}$$

$$\text{[this is the answer to part (b) of the problem]}$$

$$\text{Intercept of the feed line on the } x\text{-axis} = -z_F/(q - 1) = -0.4/(0.5 - 1) = 0.8$$

The stripping section operating line passes through W (0.04, 0).

    The equilibrium data [see Example 7.15] are plotted on the x–y plane and the diagonal is drawn. The points $D(0.96, 0.96)$, $W(0.04, 0)$ and the feed point $F(0.4, 0.4)$ are located on the x–y plane. The feed line is drawn through F with an intercept of 0.8 on the x-axis (it is more convenient to draw the line using this intercept rather than the slope). The rectifying section operating line is drawn though D with an intercept of 0.295 on the y-axis. This line intersects the feed line at the point D_1. Join WD_1 which is the stripping section operating line.

Equation of the stripping section operating line, WD_1: $\boxed{y = 1.944x - 0.078}$ [answer to part (a)].

    Draw steps between the equilibrium line and the operating lines (we start from the end D) changing from the upper to the lower operating line as the feed line is crossed. The number of ideal stages is $\boxed{7}$ [answer to part (c)]. *The graphical construction is left as an exercise.*

In order to calculate the steam rate we have to use the following material balance equations.

Total material balance: $\qquad F + \bar{V} = D + W \Rightarrow 300 + \bar{V} = D + W$ $\qquad$ (i)

Methanol balance: $\quad F z_F + \bar{V}(0) = D x_D + W x_W \Rightarrow (300)(0.4) = D(0.96) + W(0.04)$ $\quad$ (ii)

Liquid flow rate in the stripping section, $\bar{L} = W$ (because there is no reboiler).

Slope of the operating line of this section $= \bar{L}/\bar{V} = W/\bar{V} = 1.944 \Rightarrow \bar{V} = 0.514W$ $\qquad$ (iii)
Solving Eqs. (i), (ii) and (iii),

$$D = 108.6 \text{ kmol}, \quad W = 394.3 \text{ and } \bar{V} = 202.9 \text{ kmol/h} = \boxed{3652 \text{ kg steam per hour}}$$

[Answer to part (d)];

The condenser heat load [part (e)]: The vapour (96 mol% methanol) leaving the top tray is condensed to the saturated liquid. Condenser heat load

$$= V_1(H_V - H_L) = D(R + 1)(H_V - H_L)$$

$$= 108.6(2.25 + 1)(9725 - 1260) = \boxed{2.987 \times 10^6 \text{ kcal/h}}$$

Use of reflux below its bubble point

The vapour from the top tray may sometimes be condensed and then cooled below its bubble point (*subcooled*) in the condenser. This is 'cold reflux'. On entering the top tray, the 'cold reflux' reaches its bubble point very quickly. The required energy is supplied by condensation of some of the vapour on the top tray. Thus, the vapour flow rate V_1 from the top tray will be less than that at the lower trays, and the liquid flow rate L in the rectifying section (Figure 7.24) will be larger than the reflux L_0 fed to the column from the condenser. As a result, the 'internal reflux ratio', $R' (= L/D)$, will be greater than the 'external reflux ratio', $R (= L_0/D)$. In order to calculate the internal reflux ratio R', we need to know the liquid flow rate L.

If θ_r is the temperature of the *cold reflux*, and θ_{rb} is its bubble point, energy required for heating the reflux,

$$Q = L_0 c_{pr} M_r (\theta_{rb} - \theta_r); \quad \text{vapour condensed} = \frac{Q}{M_r \lambda} = \frac{L_0 c_{pr} M_r (\theta_{rb} - \theta_r)}{M_r \lambda}$$

where
$\quad c_{pr}$ = specific heat of the reflux (kJ/kg·°C)
$\quad M_r$ = its average molecular weight (this is the same as that of the vapour from the top tray)
$\quad \lambda$ = latent heat of condensation of the vapour (kJ/kg). Then the internal liquid flow rate,

$$L = L_0 + \frac{L_0(c_{pr} M_r)(\theta_{rb} - \theta_r)}{M_r \lambda}; \qquad R' = L/D \qquad (7.91)$$

The equation of the rectifying section operating line: $y_{n+1} = \dfrac{R'}{R'+1} x_n + \dfrac{x_D}{R'+1}$ $\qquad$ (7.92)

The rest of the graphical construction is pretty much the same as described before. This is illustrated in Example 7.19.

Use of murphree efficiency in graphical construction of stages

One more case deserves attention. Trays are never ideal. As discussed in Chapter 6, tray efficiency is an indicator of how good the mass transfer performance of a tray is. If an overall fractional tray efficiency is given, the number of real trays is calculated by simply dividing the number of ideal trays by the fractional tray efficiency. The Murphree tray efficiency E_M is given as

$$E_M = \frac{y_n - y_{n+1}}{y_n^* - y_{n+1}} \qquad (7.93)$$

Note that the actual enrichment of the vapour over the nth tray is $(y_n - y_{n+1}) = E_M(y_n^* - y_{n+1})$; the theoretically possible enrichment is $(y_n^* - y_{n+1})$, which is the vertical distance between the operating line and the equilibrium line. A *pseudo-equilibrium line* is drawn (see also Section 6.8.2) such that its vertical distance from the operating line is E_M-times the distance between the operating line and the equilibrium curve. Staircase construction between the pseudo-equilibrium curve and the operating lines gives the number of real plates. This is illustrated in Example 7.19.

EXAMPLE 7.19 (*Number of real trays—cold reflux; the Murphree efficiency is given*) An aqueous methanol having 45 mol% of the alcohol at 40°C is to be separated into a top product with 96 mol% methanol and a bottom stream with not more than 4% of methanol. The vapour leaving the tower is condensed and cooled. The reflux is returned to the column at 50°C and the external reflux ratio is 2.25. It is required to determine (a) the number of real trays for this separation if the Murphree efficiency is 60%, and (b) the heat duty of the reboiler and of the condenser.

The following data are supplied: Enthalpy values (reference states—pure liquids at 0°C): saturated feed (45 mol% methanol, 74°C): 1390 kcal/kmol; saturated reflux (96 mol% methanol, 66°C): 1253 kcal/kmol; saturated 'vaporized' feed (45 mol% methanol): 10,630 kcal/kmol; heat of vaporization of the top product (96% methanol): 8470 kcal/kmol; c_p of water: 18 kcal/kmol·°C, c_p of methanol: 19.4 kcal/kmol·°C (average values over the temperature range).

Solution

Enthalpy values of the 'cold' feed at 40°C and of the 'cold reflux' at 50°C are required for the calculations. These can be obtained from the given enthalpies of the streams at the 'saturated' condition. For this purpose we need the heat capacities of these solutions. We assume that the heat capacity of a solution is a linear function of its concentration.

Heat capacity of the feed (45 mol% methanol),

$$c_{pf} = (0.45)(19.4) + (0.55)(18) = 18.62 \text{ kcal/kmol·°C}$$

Heat capacity of the reflux (96 mol% methanol),

$$c_{pf} = (0.96)(19.4) + (0.04)(18) = 19.3 \text{ kcal/kmol·°C}$$

The feed line: Enthalpy of the feed is 1390 kcal/kmol, if saturated (74°C). Its value at 40°C, $H_F = 1390 - (18.62)(74 - 40) = 757$ kcal/kmol.

Similarly, the enthalpy of the 'cold reflux' (50°C),

$$H_r = 1253 - (19.3)(66 - 50) = 944.2 \text{ kcal/kmol}$$

$$\Rightarrow \qquad q = \frac{H_V - H_F}{H_V - H_L} = \frac{10,630 - 757}{10,630 - 1390} = 1.068$$

The intercept of the feed line on the x-axis = z_F/q = 0.45/1.068 = 0.421. The feed line can be drawn.

Internal reflux ratio: This can be calculated from Eq. (7.91). The external reflux ratio, $R = L_0/D$ = 2.25.

$$R' = \frac{L}{D} = \frac{L_0}{D}\left[1 + \frac{c_{pr}M_r(\theta_{rb} - \theta_r)}{M_r\lambda}\right] = (2.25)\left[1 + \frac{19.3(66 - 50)}{8470}\right] = 2.33$$

The intercept of the rectifying section operating line on the y-axis = $x_D/(R' + 1)$ = (0.96/3.33) = 0.284.

Determination of the number of trays: Given: x_D = 0.96, x_W = 0.04, z_F = 0.45. The equilibrium data are plotted on the x–y plane and the diagonal line is drawn. The points D(0.96, 0.96), W(0.04, 0.04), and F(0.45, 0.45) are located. The feed line is drawn through F with an intercept of 0.421 on the x-axis. The operating line for the rectifying section is drawn through the point D with an intercept of 0.284. The feed line and the upper operating line meet at the point E_1. The points W and E_1 are joined to get the lower operating line. The graphical construction is shown in Figure 7.24.

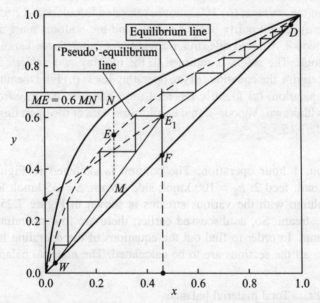

Figure 7.24   McCabe–Thiele construction of real trays for a given Murphree tray efficiency.

The Murphree efficiency is given as 60%. We draw the 'pseudo-equilibrium line' which is the locus of a point E located at 60% of the height of a vertical line segment MN between the operating line and the equilibrium line. Now steps are constructed between the operating line and the pseudo-equilibrium line (we started from the end D). The total number of real stages = $\boxed{11}$.

Multiple feed or product withdrawal

If two feeds of different compositions are to be treated in a column, each should normally be introduced on the tray of matching composition. Similarly, a product stream of any intermediate composition may be withdrawn from the appropriate tray. Withdrawal of side streams is done frequently in refinery columns. Developing the equations of the operating lines and the determination of the number of plates in such a column is discussed in Example 7.20.

A column with two feeds and one side stream is shown in Figure 7.25(a). We may consider the column as consisting of four sections on the basis of the flow rates of the liquid and the vapour phases. (As stated before, a section means a part of the column between two input or output points.) The number of such sections in a column is one less than the total number of input and output streams. The liquid and vapour flow rates vary from one section to another. The operating line for each section has a different slope. So, there will be as many operating lines as the number of sections.

Determination of the minimum reflux ratio for such a column is a bit tricky. The pinch point may occur at the intersection of a feed line, or a side stream line, and the equilibrium curve. If the equilibrium curve has any unusual curvature, a pinch point may have to be found out by drawing an operating line that touches the equilibrium curve.

EXAMPLE 7.20 (*McCabe–Thiele construction—multiple feed and product withdrawal*) A distillation column receives two feeds: (i) 200 kmol/h, 80% liquid and 20% vapour, with 42.86 mole% methanol on the average; (ii) 100 kmol/h, saturated liquid, with 17.65 mole% methanol. The top product must have a purity of 96.1 mole% and the bottoms must not have more than 3.1 mole% of the alcohol. A liquid side stream having 66.67 mole% methanol is to be withdrawn at a rate of 35 kmol/h. The reflux is returned to the top tray as a saturated liquid at a reflux ratio of 2.0. (a) Determine the equations of the operating lines. (b) Find the number of ideal trays required for the separation. (c) Identify the feed trays and also the tray from which the side stream should be withdrawn. Vapour–liquid equilibrium data at the operating pressure of 1 atm is given in Example 7.15.

Solution

Basis of calculation: 1 hour operation. The column is sketched in Figure 7.25(a). *Given:* Feed 1: $F_1 = 200$ kmol; feed 2: $F_2 = 100$ kmol; side stream, $S = 35$ kmol. Reflux ratio, $R = 2$. A sketch of the column with the various streams is shown in Figure 7.25(a). There are two feeds and one side stream. So, as discussed earlier, there are four operating lines of the four sections of the column. In order to find out the equations of the operating lines, the liquid and vapour flow rates in all the sections are to be calculated. The material balance calculations are done first.

Material balance: Total material balance:

$$F_1 + F_2 = D + S + W \Rightarrow 200 + 100 = D + 35 + W \qquad \text{(i)}$$

Methanol balance: $\qquad F_1 z_{F1} + F_2 z_{F2} = D x_D + S x_S + W x_W$

$$\Rightarrow \qquad (200)(0.4286) + (100)(0.1765) = (0.961) x_D + (35)(0.6667) + (0.031) x_W$$

$$\Rightarrow \qquad\qquad\qquad (0.961) x_D + (0.031) x_W = 84.3 \qquad \text{(ii)}$$

Solving Eqs. (i) and (ii), $D = 77.25$ kmol/h; $W = 187.75$ kmol/h.

The equilibrium diagram and the diagonal are drawn in Figure 7.25(b). The points $D(x_D, x_D)$, $W(x_W, x_W)$, $S(x_S, x_S)$, $F_1(z_{F1}, z_{F1})$ and $F_2(z_{F2}, z_{F2})$ are located on the x–y plane.

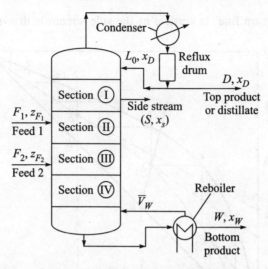

Figure 7.25(a) A distillation column with two feeds and one side stream withdrawal.

Operating lines: The liquid flow rate of Section I decreases by an amount of $S = 35$ kmol as the liquid enters Section II (because of side stream withdrawal). Because of addition of the feed 1 (which is 80% liquid and 20% vapour), the liquid flow rate increases by $(0.8)(2000) =$ 160 kmol/h in Section III, and again by 100 kmol/h in Section IV (because the second feed is a saturated liquid).

The liquid rate in Section I, $L_0 = RD = (2)(77.25) = 154.5$.

(a) Vapour rate, $V_1 = V = (R + 1)D = (2 + 1)(77.25) = 231.75$. This value remains constant in Section I.

The flow rates of the streams in different sections and the equations of the operating lines are given below.

Section	Liquid rate	Vapour rate	Slope of the operating line	Equation of the operating line
I	$L(I) = L_0 = 154.5$	$V = 231.75$	$L_0/V = 0.6667$	$y = 0.6667x + 0.3203$
II	$L(II) = L(I) - S = 119.5$	$V = 231.75$	$L(II)/V = 0.5156$	$y = 0.5156x + 0.421$
III	$L(III) = L(II) + 0.8F_1$	$V = 231.75 - 0.2F_1$	$L(III)/V = 1.4576$	$y = 1.4576x + 0.06176$
	$= 119.5 + (0.8)(200) = 279.5$	$= 231.75 - 40$	$L(IV)/V = 1.9791$	$y = 1.9791x - 0.03028$
		$= 191.75$		
IV	$L(IV) = L(III) + F_2$	$V = 191.75$		
	$= 279.5 + 100 = 379.5$			

Some details of the calculations are given here. Operating line I starts at $D(x_D, x_D)$, i.e. (0.961, 0.961) and has an intercept $= x_D/(R + 1) = 0.961/(2 + 1) = 0.3203$. Its equation is $y = 0.6667x + 0.3203$.

Operating line II starts at the point E_1 [see Figure 7.25(b)] having coordinates (0.6667, 0.7647) which is the point of intersection of the vertical 'side stream line', $x = 0.6667$ and $y = 0.6667x + 0.3203$. Also the operating line II has a slope 0.5156. Its equation is $y = 0.5156x + 0.421$.

(*Note:* The 'side stream line' is vertical as the side stream is drawn as a saturated liquid.)

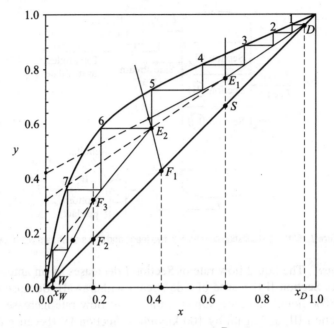

Figure 7.25(b) McCabe–Thiele construction of the number of ideal trays for multiple feed and product withdrawal.

Feed-1 has 80% liquid in it, i.e. $q = 0.8$. Feed line-1 has a slope of $q/(q-1) = -4$. It passes through (z_{F1}, z_{F1}), i.e. (0.4286, 0.4286) on the diagonal. Its equation is $y = -4x + 2.143$. The point of intersection of the feed line-1 and the operating line II is E_2(0.3813, 0.6176).

The operating line III starts at E_2(0.3813, 0.6176) and has a slope of 1.4576. Its equation is $y = 1.4576x + 0.0618$. This line meets the feed line-2 (it is a vertical line since this feed is a saturated liquid) at E_3. Join E_3W to get the operating line IV.

(b) The operating lines are drawn and the steps are constructed between the equilibrium line and the four operating lines as shown in Figure 7.25(b). The number of ideal trays is $\boxed{7.8}$.

(c) From Figure 7.25(b), the side stream is drawn from tray no. 4, the feed-1 enters the tray no. 5 and the other feed enters the tray no. 7.

7.7 MULTISTAGE BATCH DISTILLATION WITH REFLUX

In single-stage batch distillation (Rayleigh distillation), the purity of the product is practically governed by the concentration of the feed and the fraction distilled out. However, if a batch of liquid is distilled in a multistage column with reflux, a significantly higher product purity as well as higher fractional recovery of the product can be achieved. A schematic of a multistage batch distillation unit is shown in Figure 7.26.

In the theoretical analysis given below we assume that: (a) constant molar overflow occurs, i.e. the vapour rate V and the liquid rate L remain constant in the column; (b) liquid holdup on the plates is negligible; (c) although batch distillation is an unsteady state process, we assume that pseudo-steady state condition prevails; this means that the liquid and the vapour concentration profiles in the column at any moment are the same as the steady-state profiles achievable under identical conditions.

It is easy to understand that if the reflux ratio is held constant, the distillate concentration will decrease as the distillation proceeds. So the column may be operated till the distillate quality remains within the acceptable limit. This is called the *constant reflux operation*. Alternatively, the reflux ratio is continuously increased so that the product concentration remains constant for some time. This is called the *variable reflux operation*. In practice, the constant reflux operation is more common.

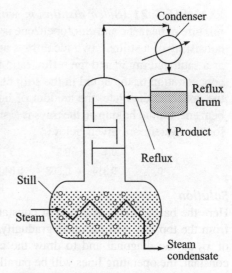

Figure 7.26 Schematic of a multistage batch distillation setup.

7.7.1 Constant Reflux Operation

Let the amount of liquid in the stillpot of the multistage unit at any moment be W mole at a concentration x_W. Over a small time, dD mole of distillate is withdrawn and the amount of liquid in the stillpot decreases by dW mole. Following Eq. (7.47),

$$- d(Wx_W) = x_D dD \quad \Rightarrow \quad - W dx_W - x_W dW = - x_D dW \quad \text{(since } dD = - dW\text{)} \tag{7.94}$$

$$\Rightarrow \qquad \frac{dW}{W} = \frac{dx_W}{x_D - x_W} \tag{7.95}$$

If W_i and W_f are the initial and final amounts of liquid in the stillpot, then on integration,

$$\ln \frac{W_i}{W_f} = \int_{x_{Wf}}^{x_{Wi}} \frac{dx_W}{x_D - x_W} \tag{7.96}$$

As distillation proceeds, x_D and x_W both keep on changing. This is shown in Figure 7.27(a) for a batch column having two ideal trays and a stillpot (equilibrium vaporization occurs in the stillpot). An operating line of slope $= R/(R + 1)$, for the constant reflux ratio R, is drawn. Three stages are constructed starting from (x_D, x_D) on the diagonal. A value of x_W ($x_{Wf} \leq x_W \leq x_{Wi}$) is reached at the end of three stages. A set of such operating lines are drawn to yield a set of (x_D, x_W) values. The integral in Eq. (7.96) can now be evaluated graphically. Of the four quantities—W_i, W_f, x_{Wi}, x_{Wf}—any one can be calculated by this way if the others are known. The accumulated distillate composition can be found out by material balance.

$$x_{D,\text{av}} = \frac{W_i x_{Wi} - W_f x_{Wf}}{W_i - W_f} \tag{7.97}$$

EXAMPLE 7.21 (*Batch distillation with constant reflux*) Forty kilomoles of an equimolar mixture of benzene and chlorobenzene is to be batch-distilled at 1 atm total pressure in a column consisting of a stillpot, two ideal trays and a total condenser. Reflux is returned to the top tray as a saturated liquid and the reflux ratio is 1.0. Distillation is to be continued until the benzene concentration of the liquid in the stillpot becomes 6 mol%. Calculate the amount and purity of the collected distillate, the amount of liquid left in the stillpot, and the fractional recovery of benzene. Liquid holdup on the trays is assumed to be rather small. Vapour–liquid equilibrium data for the system are given below.

x	0	0.1	0.2	0.3	0.4	0.5	0.6	0.7	0.8	1.0
y	0	0.314	0.508	0.640	0.734	0.806	0.862	0.905	0.943	1.0

Solution
Here the batch still is operated at constant reflux. As a result, the concentration of the vapour from the top tray will decrease gradually. Our procedure will be: (i) select a number of values of x_D on the diagonal and to draw the corresponding operating lines (since the reflux rate is constant, the operating lines will be parallel); (ii) for each value of x_D, determine the value of x_W by drawing three stages (two trays and the stillpot) between the operating line and the equilibrium line. Thus, we shall have a set of values of x_D and x_W within the concentration range $x_{Wi} = 0.5$ (initial) and $x_{Wf} = 0.06$ (final). The integral in Eq. (7.96) can then be evaluated graphically.

Reflux ratio, $R = 1.0$; constant slope of the operating lines $= R/(R + 1) = 0.5$

The equilibrium line, the two operating lines and the graphical construction are shown in Figure 7.27(a). The values of x_D, x_W and $(x_D - x_W)^{-1}$ obtained from the graph are as follows:

x_D	0.95	0.90	0.85	0.80	0.75	0.70	0.65	0.60	0.50	0.40	0.30
x_W	0.50	0.35	0.28	0.245	0.205	0.175	0.15	0.135	0.105	0.090	0.056
$(x_D - x_W)^{-1}$	2.222	1.818	1.754	1.802	1.835	1.905	2.0	2.151	2.532	3.226	4.10

$(x_D - x_W)^{-1}$ is plotted versus x_W in Figure 7.27(b) and the area under the curve from $x_{Wf} = 0.06$ to $x_{Wi} = 0.50$ is 0.9065.

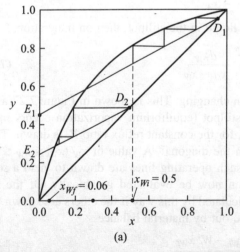 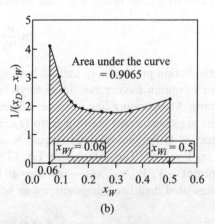

(a) (b)

Figure 7.27 (a) Parallel operating lines and three ideal stages for constant reflux batch distillation, and (b) graphical evaluation of the integral in Eq. (7.96).

Also the initial amount of liquid, $W_i = 40$ kmol. From Eq. (7.96),

$$\ln \frac{W_i}{W_f} = \int_{x_{Wf}}^{x_{Wi}} \frac{dx_W}{x_D - x_W} \Rightarrow \ln(40/W_f) = 0.9065$$

$\Rightarrow \qquad W_f = 16.16$ kmol $\qquad$ and $\qquad D = W_i - W_f = 23.84$ kmol

By benzene balance, we get the concentration of the accumulated distillate, $(x_D)_{av}$. Use Eq. (7.97) to get

$$(x_D)_{av} = \frac{(40)(0.5) - (16.16)(0.06)}{23.84} = 0.8$$

Amount of distillate collected = $\boxed{23.84 \text{ kmol}}$, its purity = $\boxed{80 \text{ mol\% benzene}}$;

liquid left = $\boxed{16.16 \text{ kmol}}$.

Fractional recovery of benzene = $(23.84)(0.8)/(40)(0.5) = \boxed{0.954}$.

EXAMPLE 7.22 (*Simple batch distillation, graphical/numerical evaluation of the integral*) Consider that the separation of the mixture in Example 7.21 (40 moles feed with 50 mol% benzene) is to be done in a simple batch distillation unit in which the vapour from the stillpot is condensed to get the distillate (see Figure 7.13). If the amount of accumulated distillate is the same as in Example 7.21, calculate the composition of the distillate and the fractional recovery of benzene. Also, approximately calculate the ratio of the energy requirements in the two cases.

Solution
The working equation is Eq. (7.50) which may be written in the form

$$\ln \frac{W_i}{W_f} = \int_{x_f}^{x_i} \frac{dx}{y^* - x}$$

Given: $W_i = 40$ kmol; $D = 23.84$ (as calculated in Example 7.21); $W_f = 40 - 23.84 = 16.16$; $x_i = 0.5$; $\ln(W_i/W_f) = \ln(40/16.16) = 0.9065$; $x_f = ?$

A set of values of x is selected starting from $x = 0.5$. The equilibrium vapour composition y^* is obtained from the plot of the equilibrium data. A plot of $1/(y^* - x)$ versus x is prepared. The value of x_f is obtained from the plot such that the area under the curve is 0.9036. The tabulated values are given below and the plot is shown in Figure 7.28.

x	0.50	0.45	0.40	0.35	0.30	0.25	0.20	0.15	0.10
y^*	0.81	0.773	0.734	0.69	0.64	0.581	0.508	0.415	0.314
$1/(y^* - x)$	3.226	3.096	2.994	2.941	2.941	3.021	3.247	3.773	4.673

From Figure 7.28, $x_f = 0.21 =$ concentration of the liquid left in the stillpot. The product composition is obtained by material balance.

$$(40)(0.5) = (16.16)(0.21) + (23.84)(x_D)_{av} \Rightarrow (x_D)_{av} = \boxed{0.696}$$

Fractional recovery of benzene = (23.84)(0.696)/(40)(0.5) = $\boxed{0.83}$. (Compare with the value of 0.954 obtained in Example 7.21.)

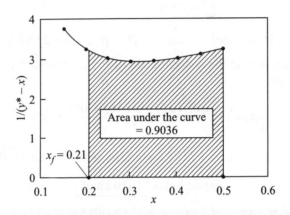

Figure 7.28   Graphical integration.

In Example 7.21, the reflux ratio was $R = 1.0$. The total amount of vapour generated, $V = (R + 1)(23.84) = (2)(23.84) = 47.68$, which is double the amount of vapour generated in simple batch distillation. So the energy consumption is about twice the value of that in Example 7.21.

7.7.2   Variable Reflux Operation

In a variable reflux operation, the reflux ratio is continuously increased in such a manner that the distillate concentration remains unchanged despite the fall in concentration of the more volatile in the stillpot. If dV, dL and dD are the changes in the rates of vapour flow, liquid flow and distillate withdrawal,

$$dV = dL + dD \tag{7.98}$$

$$\Rightarrow \qquad dD = [1 - (dL/dV)]dV \tag{7.99}$$

By material balance,

$$Wx_W = W_i x_{Wi} - (W_i - W)x_D \quad [x_D = \text{constant}] \quad \Rightarrow \quad W = W_i\left(\frac{x_{Wi} - x_D}{x_W - x_D}\right) \tag{7.100}$$

Substituting for dD and W from Eqs. (7.99) and (7.100), in the material balance Eq. (7.98) and noting that $dD = -dW$,

$$dV = \frac{W_i(x_{Wi} - x_D)\,dx_W}{(x_D - x_W)^2\,(1 - dL/dV)}$$

Total amount of vapour generated,

$$V = \int_{x_{Wi}}^{x_{Wf}} \frac{W_i(x_{Wi} - x_D)\,dx_W}{(x_D - x_W)^2\,(1 - dL/dV)} = W_i\,(x_D - x_{Wi}) \int_{x_{Wf}}^{x_{Wi}} \frac{dx_W}{(x_D - x_W)^2\,(1 - dL/dV)} \tag{7.101}$$

For a given number of ideal trays, a bunch of operating lines of different slopes ($dL/dV = L/V$ = slope of the operating line) can be drawn, and the plates can be constructed to get the x_W value. This allows graphical integration of Eq. (7.101) and calculation of any relevant quantity. Example 7.23 illustrates a practical batch distillation problem with variable reflux.

EXAMPLE 7.23 (*Batch distillation with variable reflux*) Ten kilomoles of acetone has been pumped by mistake into a storage vessel of ethanol containing 10 kilomoles of ethanol. It is decided to separate the mixture by batch distillation. Ten mole% of alcohol in the top product and 12 mole% acetone in the bottom product are acceptable. A column having six theoretical plates, a reboiler and a condenser is available. The operation is to be carried out at essentially atmospheric pressure and the reflux is to be returned at its bubble point.

(a) Calculate the amounts of top and bottom products. (b) What initial and final reflux ratios should be used? (c) Determine the total moles of vapour to be generated to achieve the separation. (d) If steam is supplied to the coils in the still at such a rate that 6 kmol of vapour is generated per hour, calculate the time required for distillation. The vapour–liquid equilibrium data for the acetone–ethanol system are given below.

x	0.05	0.10	0.20	0.30	0.40	0.50	0.60	0.70	0.80	0.90	1.00
y	0.16	0.25	0.42	0.51	0.60	0.67	0.72	0.79	0.87	0.93	1.00

Solution

(a)   The quantities of the top and the bottom products can be calculated from material balances.
Total material balance:

$$F = D + W \Rightarrow 20 = D + W ; \qquad D = \text{moles distillate}; \; W = \text{moles residue}.$$

Acetone balance:

$$Fx_F = Dx_D + Wx_W \Rightarrow (20)(0.50) = D(0.9) + W(0.12)$$

$$\Rightarrow \qquad\qquad D = \boxed{9.74}; \quad W = \boxed{10.26}$$

(b) and (c)   This is a case of operating a batch still with variable reflux. The concentration of the more volatile (acetone) in the still decreases gradually. But the reflux ratio has to be increased continuously until the bottom liquid concentration (x_{Wf}) drops down to 12 mol% acetone while *seven* ideal trays (*six* plates and a reboiler) are fitted between the operating line and the equilibrium line. The overhead vapour concentration should always be 90 mol% acetone. The steps are:

(i)   Draw the equilibrium line on the x–y plane.
(ii)   Locate the point (x_D, x_D) where $x_D = 0.90$.
(iii)   Draw a bunch of operating lines emanating from (0.9, 0.9) and having varying slopes.
(iv)   In each case, fit seven ideal stages between the operating line and the equilibrium line and determine the bottom concentration, x_W.
(v)   Using the (x_D, x_W) data as well as the slopes of the bunch of operating lines drawn, evaluate the integral in Eq. (7.101) numerically to get the total moles of vapour generated during distillation.

The equilibrium line and only two operating lines (DE_1 at the beginning of the operation, and DE_2 at the end; a few other operating lines were drawn for calculations but are not shown) are shown in Figure 7.29(a). The graphical construction of seven ideal stages is also shown. The calculated data for graphical evaluation of the integral in Eq. (7.101) are given below. Graphical integration is shown in Figure 7.29(b).

$dL/dV = (L/V)$	0.733	0.787	0.838	0.905	0.919
x_W	0.5	0.335	0.21	0.13	0.12
$\dfrac{1}{(x_D - x_W)^2 (1 - L/V)}$	23.4	14.7	12.96	17.75	20.3

The initial reflux ratio is $R_i = \boxed{0.733}$ and the end reflux ratio is $R_f = \boxed{0.919}$.

The area under the curve in Figure 7.29(b) is 6.04.

Total quantity of vapour generated [Eq. (7.101)],

$$V_{tot} = W_i(x_D - x_{Wi})I = (20)(0.9 - 0.5)(6.04) = \boxed{48.32 \text{ kmol}}$$

(d) Rate of vapour generation = 6 kmol/h. Time of distillation = 48.32/6 = $\boxed{8.05 \text{ h}}$

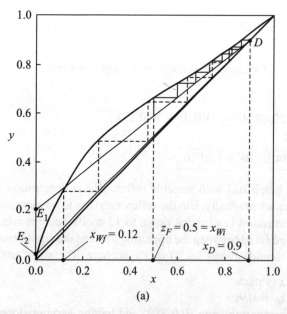

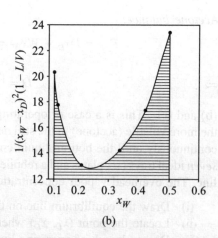

(a)

(b)

Figure 7.29   (a) Graphical construction of stages for variable reflux batch distillation (the two extreme operating lines only are shown), and (b) graphical integration.

Another strategy of operation of a multistage batch distillation column, called the 'optimal reflux' operation has been described by Divekar (1995).

7.8 THE PONCHON–SAVARIT METHOD

This method was developed by Ponchon and Savarit independently in 1921–22. It is a more rigorous method and is free from the assumption of 'constant molar overflow'. So the use of this method is suggested if the enthalpy of a stream appreciably depends upon its composition. The Ponchon–Savarit method is also a graphical method of solution of the material and energy balance equations as well as the equilibrium relation taken together.

The rectifying section: Refer to Figure 7.14(a). Consider the material and energy balance Eqs. (7.64) and (7.65) taken over envelope $\boxed{2}$:

$$V_{n+1}y_{n+1} = L_n x_n + (V_{n+1} - L_n)z_D \quad \Rightarrow \quad \frac{L_n}{V_{n+1}} = \frac{z_D - y_{n+1}}{z_D - x_n} \tag{7.102}$$

[*Note:* Here we assume that the reflux may be a sub-cooled liquid (i.e. below its bubble point) in general and z_D is the mole fraction of the more volatile in it.]

The energy balance Equation (7.65) is rewritten as

$$V_{n+1}H_{V,n+1} = L_n H_{Ln} + D\left(H_D + \frac{Q_C}{D}\right) = L_n H_{Ln} + DQ'_d \tag{7.103}$$

Here $Q'_d = H_D + Q_C/D$ = thermal energy removed from the top section of the column per mole of distillate. Putting $D = V_{n+1} - L_n$ [see Eq. (7.63)] in the above equation,

$$V_{n+1}H_{V,n+1} = L_n H_{Ln} + (V_{n+1} - L_n)Q'_d \quad \Rightarrow \quad \frac{L_n}{V_{n+1}} = \frac{Q'_d - H_{V,n+1}}{Q'_d - H_{Ln}} \tag{7.104}$$

[The quantity L_n/V_{n+1} is the *internal reflux ratio*.]

From Eqs. (7.102) and (7.104),

$$\frac{z_D - y_{n+1}}{z_D - x_n} = \frac{Q'_d - H_{V,n+1}}{Q'_d - H_{Ln}} \quad \Rightarrow \quad \frac{Q'_d - H_{Ln}}{z_D - x_n} = \frac{Q'_d - H_{V,n+1}}{z_D - y_{n+1}} \tag{7.105}$$

Refer to Figure 7.30 on which the liquid and vapour enthalpy–concentration curves (x–H_L and y–H_V) are plotted. A point on this diagram represents the composition and enthalpy of a phase (liquid, vapour or mixed), and we denote this point by a term that also represents the flow rate of the particular phase (this convention has been used before). Thus, the point L_n represents the liquid phase leaving the nth plate (and entering the $(n+1)$th plate) at a rate L_n mole/h with enthalpy H_{Ln} and concentration x_n.

The right side of Eq. (7.105) is the slope of a line through the points $(y_{n+1}, H_{V,n+1})$ and (z_D, Q'_d), and the left side is the slope of a line through the points (x_n, H_{Ln}) and (z_D, Q'_d) on the concentration–enthalpy plane. So the points (x_n, H_{Ln}), $(y_{n+1}, H_{V,n+1})$ and (z_D, Q'_d) are collinear. The point (z_D, Q'_d) can be viewed as a phase obtained by subtracting L_n from V_{n+1} (see the discussion in the last para of Section 7.2). We represent this point by D' in Figure 7.30. The flow rate of the phase D' is also denoted by $D' = V_{n+1} - L_n$. However, none of the phases can have the concentration z_D and enthalpy $Q'_d = H_D + Q_C/D$. So this stream D' is a "fictitious stream" defined solely for the purpose of graphical construction.

The point $D(z_D, H_D)$ and $D'(z_D, Q'_d)$ are located on the enthalpy–concentration diagram, D' lying vertically above D (because they have the same abscissa, z_D). In Figure 7.30, the point D

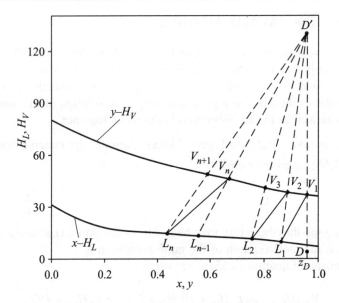

Figure 7.30 Ponchon–Savarit construction for the rectifying section of a distillation column.

lies below the x–H_L curve. So, the reflux is a sub-cooled liquid here. If we put $n = 0$ in Eq. (7.105), it appears that the vertical line joining the points D and D' should intersect the y–H_V curve at (y_1, H_{V1}) because these points are collinear. The point (y_1, H_{V1}) is denoted by V_1 according to our convention. The point $L_1(x_1, H_{L1})$ is now located by drawing a tie line through V_1, because x_1 and y_1 are in equilibrium for an ideal tray. Next, L_1D' is joined to get the point V_2. The graphical construction now proceeds from one tray to the next.

Now we consider Eq. (7.104), again. Inverting both sides and putting $n = 0$,

$$\frac{V_1}{L_0} = \frac{Q'_d - H_{L0}}{Q'_d - H_{V1}}; \qquad \text{we note that } H_{L0} = H_D; \ V_1 = L_0 + D$$

$$\Rightarrow \quad \frac{V_1}{L_0} = \frac{L_0 + D}{L_0} = 1 + \frac{D}{L_0} = \frac{Q'_d - H_D}{Q'_d - H_{V1}}$$

$$\Rightarrow \quad R = \frac{L_0}{D} = \frac{Q'_d - H_{V1}}{H_{V1} - H_D} = \frac{\text{vertical distance } V_1D'}{\text{vertical distance } DV_1} \tag{7.106}$$

If the reflux ratio is given, Eq. (7.106) can be used directly to locate the point D'. First the point $D(z_D, H_D)$ is located from the known state (concentration z_D, and enthalpy H_D). A vertical line through z_D intersects the y–H_V curve at V_1. Then obtain D' so that Eq. (7.106) is satisfied.

The stripping section: The material and energy balance equations for the stripping section (envelope ⬚3, Figure 7.14(a) are given by Eqs. (7.66) through (7.68). Putting $W = \bar{L}_m - \bar{V}_{m+1}$ from Eq. (7.66) in Eq. (7.67),

$$\bar{L}_m x_m = \bar{V}_{m+1} y_{m+1} + (\bar{L}_m - \bar{V}_{m+1}) x_W \tag{7.107}$$

$$\Rightarrow \quad \frac{\bar{L}_m}{\bar{V}_{m+1}} = \frac{y_{m+1} - x_W}{x_m - x_W} \tag{7.108}$$

We may write the energy balance Equation (7.68) as

$$\bar{L}_m H_{Lm} - \bar{V}_{m+1} H_{V,m+1} = W H_W - Q_B = W(H_W - Q_B/W)$$

$$\Rightarrow \qquad \bar{L}_m H_{Lm} - \bar{V}_{m+1} H_{V,m+1} = W Q'_W; \quad Q'_W = H_W - Q_B/W \qquad (7.109)$$

Putting $W = \bar{L}_m - \bar{V}_{m+1}$,

$$\bar{L}_m H_{Lm} - \bar{V}_{m+1} H_{V,m+1} = (\bar{L}_m - \bar{V}_{m+1}) Q'_W \quad \Rightarrow \quad \frac{\bar{L}_m}{\bar{V}_{m+1}} = \frac{H_{V,m+1} - Q'_W}{H_{Lm} - Q'_W} \qquad (7.110)$$

From Eqs. (7.108) and (7.110), $\dfrac{H_{V,m+1} - Q'_W}{y_{m+1} - x_W} = \dfrac{H_{Lm} - Q'_W}{x_m - x_W}$ $\qquad (7.111)$

Extending the arguments put forward in the analysis of the rectifying section, we can say:

(a) The points $\bar{V}_{m+1}(y_{m+1}, H_{V,m+1})$, $\bar{L}_m(x_m, H_{Lm})$, and $W'(x_W, Q'_W)$, are collinear

(b) The point W' denotes a "fictitious stream" of concentration x_W, enthalpy $Q'_W = H_W - Q_B/W$ (= the rate of enthalpy removal at the bottom, per mole of the bottom product), and flow rate $W' = \bar{L}_m - \bar{V}_{m+1}$.

Now, let us see how to proceed with the graphical construction of stages for the stripping section (Figure 7.31). The points $W(x_W, H_W)$ and $W'(x_W, Q'_W)$, are located on the enthalpy–concentration plane. The output stream or the bottom product, W, leaving the partial reboiler is in equilibrium with the vapour generated in the reboiler and entering the bottom tray. If there is a total of N trays in the column, we may call the reboiler the $(N + 1)$th tray. So the flow rate as well as the state

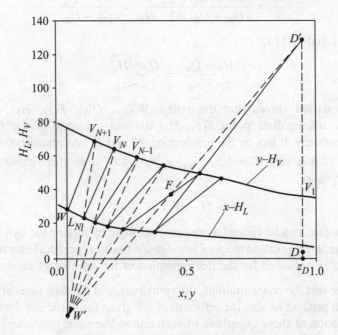

Figure 7.31 Ponchon–Savarit construction for the stripping section of a distillation column.

of the vapour from the reboiler is denoted by $\overline{V}_{N+1}$; $\overline{V}_{N+1}$ should lie on the y–H_V curve at the end of the tie line through W. The line connecting $\overline{V}_{N+1}$ and W' intersects the x–H_L curve at $\overline{L}_N$ by virtue of the collinearity condition given by Eq. (7.111). The tie line through $\overline{L}_N$ identifies $\overline{V}_N$ on y–H_V curve and thus the construction for trays in the stripping proceeds.

The feed line: The procedures of graphical construction of ideal trays for the rectifying and for the stripping sections have been discussed above. However, a changeover from one section to the other is necessary at the feed tray and for this purpose we have to draw the 'feed line'. Consider the material and energy balance equations over envelope $\boxed{4}$ of the column in Figure 7.14(a) as given by Eqs. (7.69) through (7.71). Substituting for F from Eq. (7.69) in Eq. (7.70),

$$(D + W)z_F = Dz_D + Wx_W \tag{7.112}$$

[*Note:* We use z_D to denote the reflux or distillate concentration because these may be subcooled liquids; the notation x_D may be used if the streams are at bubble point.]

$$\Rightarrow \qquad \frac{D}{W} = \frac{z_F - x_W}{z_D - z_F} \tag{7.113}$$

Similarly, from Eqs. (7.69) and (7.71),

$$(D + W)H_F + Q_B = DH_D + WH_W + Q_C$$

$$\Rightarrow \qquad DH_F + WH_F = D(H_D + Q_C/D) + W(H_W - Q_B/W)$$

$$\Rightarrow \qquad \frac{D}{W} = \frac{H_F - (H_D + Q_C/D)}{(H_W - Q_B/W) - H_F} = \frac{H_F - Q'_W}{Q'_d - H_F} \tag{7.114}$$

From Eqs. (7.113) and (7.114),

$$\frac{H_F - Q'_W}{z_F - x_W} = \frac{Q'_d - H_F}{z_D - z_F} \tag{7.115}$$

The above equation shows that the points $W'(x_W, Q'_W)$, $F(z_F, H_F)$, and $D'(z_D, Q'_d)$ are collinear. The intermediate point $F(z_F, H_F)$ denotes the state of the feed in terms of composition and enthalpy. It lies on the line joining W' and D'. As stated before, W' represents a fictitious stream of flow rate $W' = \overline{L}_m - \overline{V}_{m+1} = W$, and D' is another fictitious stream of flow rate $D' = \overline{V}_{n+1} - \overline{L}_n = D$.

$$\Rightarrow \qquad F = D + W = D' + W' \tag{7.116}$$

So, F, a real stream, can be viewed as a stream obtained by mixing the two fictitious streams W' and D'. The line $W'D'$ is called the *feed line*. On the basis of graphical construction described above, the steps to be followed for the determination of the number of ideal stages are:

(a)   We assume that the concentrations, the enthalpies, and the flow rates of the distillate and the bottom product as also the reflux ratio are given (or sufficient data are supplied for the calculation of these quantities by material and/or energy balance). Then the points D and D' are located on the H–x,y diagram.

(b) The feed point $F(z_F, H_F)$ is located.

(c) $D'F$ is joined and extended to meet the vertical line through $W(x_W, H_W)$ at the point W'.

(d) Construction of stages may proceed either from D' or from W'. A changeover has to be done after the feed line is crossed. The tray at which the changeover is made is the feed tray. Construction proceeds till the other point is reached.

It is possible (and perhaps more convenient) to construct the stages on the x–y plane rather than on the H–x,y plane. The steps of such construction are given below.

(a) Draw the equilibrium curve using separate axes below the H–x–y curves with matching scales.

(b) Locate (z_D, z_D) and (x_W, x_W) on the diagonal.

(c) It is obvious from Eq. (7.105) that any line emanating from D' (or W') intersects the H–x and H–y curves at x_n and y_{n+1} respectively. The point (x_n, y_{n+1}) is a point on the operating line in the lower diagram (see Figure 7.32). Several lines are now drawn from D' and W' and for each such line, the point (x_n, y_{n+1}) is located on the x–y plane. All such points are joined by two continuous curves. These two curves are the two operating lines. Because the flow rates in any of the sections are not constant (since constant molar overflow is not applicable), the operating lines are not straight. Staircase construction between the equilibrium line and the operating lines gives the number of ideal stages. The procedure is illustrated in Example 7.24.

Minimum reflux ratio (R_m)

If the reflux ratio is minimum, there must be a pinch point on the diagram. If a line through D' or W' coincides with a tie line, the corresponding (x, y) values give the pinch point. The expression for the reflux ratio given by Eq. (7.106) indicates that the smaller the distance V_1D' (or the nearer the point D' is to the concentration axis), the smaller is the reflux ratio. For many liquid mixtures this happens when the line $D'W'$ coincides with the tie line through the feed point (compare with Figure 7.20). But for some highly non-ideal mixtures, it so happens that a tie line through a point other than F intersects the vertical line through z_D at the smallest distance. This gives the true pinch point. The minimum reflux ratio is calculated by Eq. (7.106) once the point $(D')_{min}$ is identified.

EXAMPLE 7.24 (*Determination of the number of ideal trays using the Ponchon–Savarit method*) An aqueous solution of ethanol (30 mass% ethanol) is to be enriched into a top product having 88 mass% alcohol. The bottom product must not contain more than 4 mass% alcohol. The feed enters the column at 40°C at a rate of 5000 kg per hour. The reflux is at its bubble point and the reflux ratio is 1.0. Determine (a) the number of ideal trays required using the Ponchon–Savarit method and (b) the heat duty of the condenser and of the reboiler. The enthalpy–concentration (kJ/kmol; reference states: pure liquids at 0°C) and the vapour–liquid equilibrium data at the operating pressure of 1 atm are given below.

x, y	0	0.0417	0.0891	0.1436	0.207	0.281	0.37	0.477	0.61	0.779	1.0
H_L	7540	7125	6880	6915	7097	7397	7750	8105	8471	8945	9523
H_V	48150	48250	48300	48328	48436	48450	48450	48631	48694	48950	

x	0	0.00792	0.016	0.0202	0.0417	0.0891	0.1436	0.281	0.37	0.477
y	0	0.0850	0.1585	0.191	0.304	0.427	0.493	0.568	0.603	0.644
x	0.61	0.641	0.706	0.779	0.86	0.904	0.95	1.0		
y	0.703	0.72	0.756	0.802	0.864	0.902	0.9456	1.0		

Given: enthalpy of the feed = 4790 kJ/kmol.

Solution

Molecular weights: ethanol = 46; water = 18. The concentrations of the feed z_F, the top and the bottom products (x_D and x_W) in mole fraction units and mol. wt. of the feed M_F are given by

$$z_F = \frac{30/46}{(30/46) + (70/18)} = 0.1436; \quad x_D = 0.7416; \quad x_W = 0.01604$$

$$M_F = \frac{100}{(30/46) + (70/18)} = 22.02$$

Feed rate, $F = 5000/22.02 = 227$ kmol/h

Total material balance equation: $F = D + W \Rightarrow 227 = D + W$ \hfill (i)

Ethanol balance: $Fz_F = Dx_D + Wx_W \Rightarrow (227)(0.1436) = D(0.7416) + W(0.01604)$ \hfill (ii)

Solving Eqs. (i) and (ii), $D = 39.9$ kmol/h; $W = 187.1$ kmol/h

Enthalpy values of the feed (H_F), *the top and the bottom products* (H_D and H_W):

Enthalpy of the feed at 40°C, $H_F = 4790$ kJ/kmol (given).

The other enthalpy values can be obtained by interpolation of the given data.

Enthalpy of the top vapour ($y_1 = 0.7416$), $H_{V1} = 48,680$ kJ/kmol; enthalpy of the distillate ($x_D = 0.7416$), $H_D = 8850$ kJ/kmol; enthalpy of the bottom product, $H_W = 7380$ kJ/kmol.

(a) *Graphical construction of the number of ideal trays*

   (i)   The given enthalpy–concentration data are plotted in Figure 7.32(a).
   (ii) The points $F(z_F, H_F) \rightarrow (0.1436, 4790)$, $D(x_D, H_D) \rightarrow (0.7416, 8850)$, and $W(x_W, H_W) \rightarrow (0.01604, 7380)$ are located on the enthalpy–concentration plane.
   (iii) Next the difference point, $\Delta D'(x_D, Q'_d)$, is to be located; Q'_d is related to the reflux ratio as given in Eq. (7.106). The reflux ratio is $R = 1.0$ (given).

$$R = \frac{Q'_d - H_{V1}}{H_{V1} - H_D} \Rightarrow 1 = \frac{Q'_d - 48,680}{48,680 - 8850}$$

$$\Rightarrow \qquad Q'_d = 88,510 \text{ kJ/kmol}; \ \Delta D' \rightarrow (0.7416, 88,510)$$

   (iv) A vertical line is drawn through the point W; $\Delta D'F$ is joined and extended to meet this vertical line through W at $\Delta W'$ [$\Delta D'$ and $\Delta W'$ are the same as D' and W' in Figures 7.30 and 7.31].
   (v)   The number of ideal trays or stages can be determined by drawing tie lines and operating lines (through $\Delta D'$) as described in Section 7.8. However, it is more convenient to adopt the following procedure.

Draw a number of lines from the point $\Delta D'$ on the right side of the feed point F [Figure 7.32(a)]. Consider one such line $\Delta D'MM_1$ (M is on the saturated vapour line and M_1 is on the saturated liquid line). The abscissa of the point M_1 (i.e. the liquid composition x) and the abscissa of the point M (i.e. the vapour composition y) give the coordinates of the point P on the x–y diagram drawn below the enthalpy–concentration diagram [Figure 7.32(b)]. A set of such points on the x–y plane are joined to get the operating line for the rectifying section.

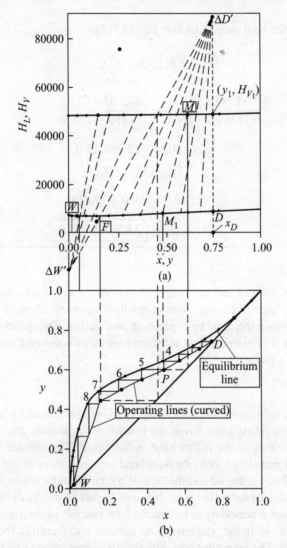

Figure 7.32   Construction of plates using the Ponchon–Savarit method: (a) enthalpy–conc. diagram, and (b) plate.

Similarly, a set of lines are drawn from the point $\Delta W'$ on the left side of the feed point F. The points of intersection of such lines and the enthalpy–concentration curves are used to draw the operating line for the stripping section on the x–y plane. Now steps are drawn between the operating lines and the equilibrium curve on the x–y plane starting from the top or the bottom end. The number of ideal trays is found to be $\boxed{10}$. The intersection of the operating lines is crossed at tray number 7 from the top. So the 7th tray is the optimum feed tray.

(b) *Calculation of heat duties of the reboiler and condenser:* To calculate the condenser heat duty, use the following equation:

$$Q'_d = H_D + Q_C/D \quad \Rightarrow \quad 88{,}510 = 8850 + Q_C/39.9 \Rightarrow Q_C = \boxed{3.16 \times 10^6 \text{ kJ/h}}$$

To calculate the reboiler heat duty, first use Eq. (7.115).

$$\frac{H_F - Q'_W}{z_F - x_W} = \frac{Q'_d - H_F}{z_D - z_F}$$

$$\Rightarrow \qquad \frac{4790 - Q'_W}{0.1436 - 0.01604} = \frac{88{,}510 - 4790}{0.7416 - 0.1436}$$

$$\Rightarrow \qquad Q'_W = -13.068 \text{ kJ/h}$$

Now use Eq. (7.109). $\qquad Q'_W = H_W - Q_B/W$

$$\Rightarrow \qquad -13{,}068 = 7380 - Q_B/187.1$$

$$\Rightarrow \qquad Q_B = \boxed{3.826 \times 10^6 \text{ kJ/h}}$$

Total reflux

Here the reflux ratio is infinite and the points D' and W' lie at infinity. So all the lines through D' and W' are vertical lines. The construction involves drawing alternate tie lines and vertical lines starting at V_1 to obtain the number of plates at total reflux. This gives the minimum number of plates too. However, it is easier to find it by drawing steps between the equilibrium curve and the diagonal on the *x–y* plane.

Optimum reflux ratio

While designing a new column (or even for using an existing column) for a given separation, the designer has to choose a reflux ratio. From the foregoing discussion, it is clear that the number of plates required decreases as the reflux ratio is increased. The column height decreases as a result. However, at a higher reflux, both the liquid and vapour flow rates are higher. This increases the column diameter. But, on the whole, the cost of the column decreases with increasing reflux ratio. On the other hand, a larger reflux ratio demands higher heat duty of both the reboiler (more heat supply to the reboiler is necessary to maintain a larger supply of the vapour) and the condenser (more heat is to be removed in the condenser). So the size, and therefore the capital cost, of these equipment will be more. The operating cost will also be higher because of larger heat duty of the reboiler and the condenser. So there are a number of opposing factors that govern the different types of cost. A simplified approach to determine the optimum reflux ratio is to plot the fixed cost of the equipment taken together and also the operating cost versus the reflux ratio as shown in Figure 7.33. The plot of the total cost shows a minimum which gives the optimum reflux ratio.

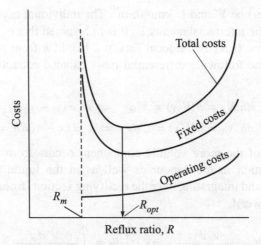

Figure 7.33 Optimum reflux ratio in distillation.

An important point needs attention in this context. The fixed cost has the unit of rupees, dollars, etc. but the operating cost is based on unit time (rupee/year, dollar/year, etc.). How to calculate the total cost, then? Without going into details, we can divide the fixed cost by the estimated "life" of the equipment and then estimate the 'total annual cost'. A more realistic calculation should take into account the interest rate on various cost items, if necessary. In actual practice, a reflux ratio of 1.2 to 1.5 times the minimum is common.

7.9 DISTILLATION IN A PACKED TOWER

Distillation of a liquid mixture in a packed tower is preferred in the following cases: (a) vacuum or low pressure operation, (b) low capacity or feed rate, (c) small allowable pressure drop, and (d) corrosive service. A packed tower for distillation is essentially similar to the one used for gas absorption. However, the tower should be provided with a distributor for the feed at an appropriate location (this is in addition to the distributor of the reflux at the top), besides a condenser, a reflux drum and a reboiler.

There are two methods for the determination of the height of packing: (a) from the height and number of transfer units (H_G and N_G) and (b) from the HETP. To derive the design equations for the calculation of the packed height based on H_G and N_G, refer to Figure 7.34. Let us consider the rectifying section first. Constant molar overflow is assumed. The vapour and liquid flow rates remain constant over a section. Let the flow rates (based on unit

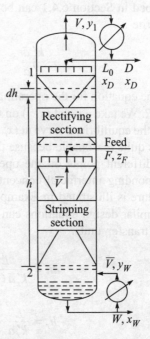

Figure 7.34 Schematic of a packed distillation tower.

cross-section of the tower) be V' and L' kmol/h·m^2. The individual mass transfer coefficient are k'_x and k'_y, and the specific interfacial area is $\bar{a}$. It is to be noted that equimolar counterdiffusion of the components occurs. If N_A is the local flux at a height h from the bottom of the packed section, we may write the following differential mass balance equations for the more volatile component.

Vapour phase: $\qquad \bar{a}.dh.N_A = d(V'y) = V'dy \implies k'_y\bar{a}(y_i - y)dh = V'dy$ (7.117)

Liquid phase: $\qquad \bar{a}.dh.N_A = d(L'x) = L'dx \implies k'_x\bar{a}(x - x_i)dh = L'dx$ (7.118)

Note that transport of the more volatile component occurs from the liquid to the vapour phase and its concentration in the vapour as well as in the liquid phase increases with h. Rearranging Eq. (7.117) and integrating over the rectifying section [from $y = y_F$ (at the feed point) to $y = y_1$ (top of the tower)],

$$dh = \frac{V'dy}{k'_y\bar{a}(y_i - y)} \implies \int_0^{h_r} dh = \int_{y_F}^{y_1} \frac{V'dy}{k'_y\bar{a}(y_i - y)}$$

$$\implies \qquad h_r = \frac{V'}{k'_y\bar{a}} \int_{y_F}^{y_1} \frac{dy}{y_i - y} \implies h_r = H_G N_G \qquad (7.119)$$

Here h_r is the packed height of the rectifying section. The value of H_G can be calculated if the individual volumetric mass transfer coefficient, $k'_y\bar{a}$, is known; N_G can be obtained by numerical or graphical evaluation of the integral in Eq. (7.119). The interfacial vapour concentrations, y_i, for a set of values of y ($y_F < y < y_1$) are required for the numerical integration. The procedure described in Section 6.4.1 can be followed for this purpose. From Eqs. (7.117) and (7.118), we can write

$$-\frac{k'_x\bar{a}}{k'_y\bar{a}} = \frac{y - y_i}{x - x_i} \qquad \text{[Compare with Eq. (4.10)]} \qquad (7.120)$$

The equation for the operating line for the rectifying section can be written for a given reflux ratio, R. We take a point (x, y) on the operating line and draw a line of slope $-k'_x\bar{a}/k'_y\bar{a}$; this line meets the equilibrium curve at (x_i, y_i). If the individual coefficients remain constant over a section (this is quite reasonable because the flow rates do not vary over a section), such lines emanating from different points on the operating line are parallel. Thus, for a set of points (x, y), the corresponding interfacial concentrations (x_i, y_i) required for integration can be obtained. The procedure is illustrated in Example 7.25.

Similar design equations can be written for the height and the number of individual liquid phase transfer units.

$$dh = \frac{L'dx}{k'_x\bar{a}(x - x_i)} \implies \int_0^{h_r} dh = \int_{x_F}^{x_1} \frac{L'dx}{k'_x\bar{a}(x - x_i)}$$

$$\implies \qquad h_r = \frac{L'}{k'_x\bar{a}} \int_{x_F}^{x_1} \frac{dy}{x - x_i} \implies h_r = H_L N_L \qquad (7.121)$$

The packed height can also be determined using the overall coefficients ($K_y'\,\bar{a}$ and $K_x'\,\bar{a}$). The design equations can be obtained by putting $N_A = K_y'(y^* - y)$ in Eq. (7.117) or $N_A = K_x'(x - x^*)$ in Eq. (7.118).

$$h = H_{OG} \int_{y_F}^{y_1} \frac{dy}{y^* - y} = H_{OL} \int_{x_F}^{x_1} \frac{dx}{x - x^*} ;$$

$$H_{OG} = \frac{V'}{K_y'\bar{a}} \quad \text{and} \quad H_{OL} = \frac{L'}{K_x'\bar{a}} \tag{7.122}$$

We assume that the heights of overall transfer units, H_{OG} and H_{OL}, remain reasonably constant over the section. The number of overall gas-phase or liquid-phase transfer units are to be determined by graphical integration. Corresponding to a point (x, y) on the operating line, y^* is the ordinate of the point vertically above it on the equilibrium curve; x^* is the abscissa of a point on the equilibrium line horizontally left to (x, y). Thus the values of y^* for a set of values of y ($y_F < y < y_1$) can be obtained and N_{OG} can be evaluated graphically or numerically.

Mass exchange between the vapour and the liquid phases in distillation is mostly controlled by the vapour phase resistance. Thus, for the sake of accuracy, it is advisable to calculate the packed height using the 'gas-phase coefficient'.

Following the procedure described in Section 6.4.3, it is possible to combine the heights of individual transfer units to obtain the height of an overall transfer unit. Thus,

$$H_{OG} = H_G + \lambda H_L; \qquad \lambda = mV'/L', \qquad (m = \text{slope of the equilibrium line}) \tag{7.123}$$

It is obvious that the slope of the equilibrium line varies with composition. Even if H_G and H_L remain constant over a section, H_{OG} and H_{OL} are liable to variation. However, an average value can be used. A similar procedure is used to determine the packed height for the stripping section.

EXAMPLE 7.25 (*Determination of packed height of a distillation column*) A mixture of diethylamine (1) and triethylamine (2) containing 40 mol% of the higher amine is to be separated in a packed distillation column (dia = 0.75 m) at a rate of 2000 kg/h and at a total pressure of 113.3 kPa. The top product should have 97 mol% of diethylamine and the bottom product, 96 mol% triethylamine. The feed is at its bubble point and the reflux ratio used is twice the minimum. The individual volumetric mass transfer coefficients are:

Rectifying section: $\quad k_x'\bar{a} = 600 \quad$ and $\quad k_y'\bar{a} = 170$ kmol/h·m^3

Stripping section: $\quad\ \ k_x'\bar{a} = 750 \quad$ and $\quad k_y'\bar{a} = 200$ kmol/h·m^3

The equilibrium data for the system at the given pressure are available [Bittrich, H.J., and E. Kruer: *Z. Physik. Chem.* (Leipzig), 219 (3/4), 1962, p. 224].

x	0	0.02	0.104	0.227	0.342	0.424	0.522	0.79	0.923	0.969	1.0
y	0	0.052	0.231	0.451	0.60	0.674	0.755	0.91	0.978	0.988	1.0

Solution

Molecular weights: $M_1 = 73.09$; $M_2 = 101.1$

Average mol. wt. = $(0.6)(73.09) + (0.4)(101.1) = 84.3$

Molar feed rate, $F = 2000/84.3 = 23.72$ kmol/h

Total material balance: $F = D + W \Rightarrow 23.72 = D + W$

Component 1 balance: $Fz_F = Dx_D + Wx_W \Rightarrow (23.72)(0.6) = D(0.97) + W(0.04)$

Solving, $D = 14.3$ kmol/h; $W = 9.42$ kmol/h

The minimum reflux ratio, $R_m = 0.796$ [this can be obtained by the usual procedure].

Actual reflux ratio (2 times the minimum), $R = (2)(0.796) = 1.592$; vapour rate at the top tray, $V = D(R + 1) = (14.3)(1.592 + 1) = 37.06$ kmol/h ; reflux rate, $L_0 = DR = (14.3)(1.592) = 22.76$ kmol/h.

The feed is a saturated liquid. Vapour rate in the stripping section, $\overline{V} = V = 37.06$; liquid rate in the stripping section, $\overline{L} = L + F = 22.76 + 23.72 = 46.48$ kmol/h.

Rectifying section operating line:

$$y = \frac{R}{R+1}x + \frac{x_D}{R+1} \Rightarrow y = \frac{1.592}{1+1.592}x + \frac{0.97}{1+1.592} = 0.614x + 0.374$$

Stripping section operating line: It passes through $W(0.04, 0.04)$ and the intersection of the feed line ($x = 0.6$) and the rectifying section operating line $\Rightarrow y = 1.255x - 0.01$

The number of gas-phase transfer units N_G can be obtained by evaluation of the integral in Eq. (7.119). A set of values of $(y_i - y)$ is required for this purpose.

A set of lines of slope $-k'_x\overline{a}/k'_y\overline{a} = -600/170 = -3.75$ are drawn between the operating line and the equilibrium lines for the rectifying section to get a set of values of y and y_i and hence of $y_i - y$. Similarly, another set of lines of slope $-k'_x\overline{a}/k'_y\overline{a} = -750/200 = -3.53$ are drawn between the operating line and the equilibrium line for the stripping section. A few such lines are shown in Figure 7.35(a) and several values of $y_i - y$ are given below.

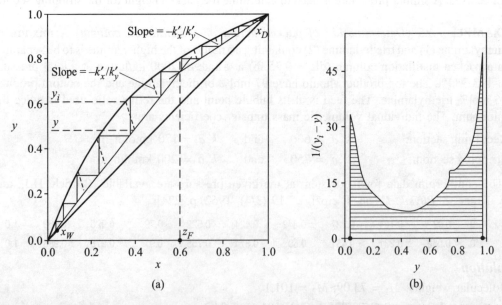

Figure 7.35 (a) Determination of the interfacial concentrations y_i in a packed distillation column. A set of (dotted) lines of slope k'_x/k'_y is shown. Step construction for ideal trays is also shown. (b) Graphical integration.

y	0.97	0.95	0.895	0.835	0.77	0.725	0.615	0.49	0.365	0.168	0.04
y_i	0.99	0.977	0.935	0.885	0.828	0.792	0.713	0.625	0.495	0.263	0.07
$1/(y_i - y)$	50	37.04	25	20.83	18.2	14.3	10.2	7.41	7.7	13.2	33.3

The integral for N_G is obtained by graphical integration as shown in Figure 7.35(b). The areas under the curves are:

Rectifying section: $N_G = 5.02$ units; stripping section: $N_G = 8.7$ units

The values of H_G for both the sections are required in order to find out the column height. It is to be noted that the vapour flow rates are the same in both the sections, but the volumetric vapour phase mass transfer coefficients vary. The column dia is 0.75 m; its cross-section is 0.442 m^2.

Vapour flow rate = $V' = 37.06/0.442 = 83.85$ kmol/h·m$^2 = \overline{V}'$ (for the stripping section)

$(H_G)_{\text{recti}} = V'/k'_y\overline{a} = 83.85/170 = \boxed{0.49 \text{ m}}$; $(H_G)_{\text{strip}} = \overline{V}'/k'_y\overline{a} = 83.85/200 = \boxed{0.42 \text{ m}}$

Total packed height of the two sections = (0.49 m)(5.02) + (0.42 m)(8.7) = $\boxed{6.1 \text{ m}}$

Eleven theoretical plates are required for the separation as shown in Figure 7.35(a). The average height of a theoretical plate (HETP) for the packing under the given conditions is

$$\text{HETP} = 6.1/11 = 0.55 \text{ m}$$

The concept of HETP (see also Chapter 6) is widely used in packed tower design. Experimental data on the performance of a particular packing are sometimes expressed in terms of HETP rather than the volumetric mass transfer coefficients. If the HETP value is known, the packed height can be determined from the calculated number of theoretical trays required for the separation. The diameter of a packed column is calculated from flooding considerations as usual. As the flow rates differ in the two sections, it is advisable to estimate the diameter based on the larger flow rates for a safer design.

NOTATIONS

c_{pA}	: specific heat of component A (liquid)
D	: rate of withdrawal of the distillate at the top of a column, kmol/h
E_M	: Murphree efficiency, Eq. (7.93)
F	: feed rate, kmol/h
H_G	: height of a vapour-phase mass transfer unit, m
H_L	: height of a liquid-phase mass transfer unit, m
H_L	: enthalpy of liquid, kcal/kmol
H_V	: enthalpy of vapour, kcal/kmol
H_s	: heat of solution, kcal/kmol

K_i	: equilibrium vaporization ratio of component i in a mixture, Eq. (7.14)
L	: liquid flow rate, kmol/h (in the rectifying section of a continuous column)
$\bar{L}$	: liquid flow rate in the stripping section of a column, kmol/h
M_A	: molecular weight of component A
N_m	: minimum number of trays (at total reflux)
p_A	: partial pressure of A in a vapour mixture, kPa/bar/atm
P	: total pressure, kPa/bar/atm
P_A^v	: vapour pressure of pure component A
q	: a parameter indicating the quality of the feed, Eq. (7.82)
Q	: rate of heat input to the column/chamber, kcal/h
Q_B	: heat load of the reboiler, kcal/h
Q_C	: heat load of the condenser, kcal/h
R	: reflux ratio ($= L_0/V$)
T_A	: boiling point of pure component A
T_B	: boiling point of pure B; bubble point of a mixture
V	: vapour flow rate, kmol/h (in the rectifying section of a continuous column)
$\bar{V}$	: vapour flow rate in the stripping section of a column, kmol/h
W	: rate of withdrawal of bottom product from a column, kmol/h
x	: liquid-phase mole fraction of a component (the more volatile component in a binary) in a mixture
x_D	: mole fraction of the more volatile in the distillate
x_n	: mole fraction of the more volatile of a binary in the liquid leaving the nth plate
x_W	: mole fraction of the more volatile in the bottom product
y	: vapour-phase mole fraction of a component (the more volatile component in a binary) in a mixture
$y*$	: vapour-phase mole fraction of a component in equilibrium with the liquid at mole fraction x
y_n	: mole fraction of the more volatile of a binary in the vapour leaving the nth plate
z_F	: mole fraction of the more volatile in a binary feed mixture
z_i, z_{Fi}	: mole fraction of component i in the feed
α	: relative volatility, Eqs. [7.8(a)] and (7.10)
λ_A	: heat of vaporization of pure component A, kcal/kmol

SHORT AND MULTIPLE CHOICE QUESTIONS

1. The relative volatility of A in a mixture with B is $\alpha_{AB} = 2.0$. The equilibrium vaporization ratio of B is $K_B = 0.7$. (a) What is the value of α_{BA}?

    (i) 2.0   (ii) 0.5   (iii) 1.0

    (b) What is the value of K_A?

    (i) 1.4   (ii) 0.35   (iii) 2.7

2. Consider equilibrium in the ternary system of benzene (1), toluene (2) and *o*-xylene (3). *Given:* $T = 393$ K, $P = 1.2$ bar and $x_3 = 0.2$. Is the system completely defined?

3. What are the major sources of error in the experimental determination of vapour–liquid equilibrium using a liquid recirculation type still?

4. (a) The overall mole fraction of benzene in a mixture of benzene and toluene is $z_F = 0.3$ at 1 atm total pressure and 95°C. Then the mixture is

    (i) a liquid

    (ii) a vapour

    (iii) a two-phase mixture.

    (b) What is the minimum temperature at which a vapour of this composition can exist at 1 atm total pressure?

    (i) 370 K   (ii) 376.8 K   (iii) 382.7 K

    [Ideal solution; vapour pressure equation in Table 7.2]

5. Water (1) and formic acid (2) form a higher-boiling azeotrope. At 1 atm total pressure, the azeotropic composition is $x = 0.409$. Then which of the following is correct?

    (i) $\alpha_{12} = 1$,   at $x = 0.409$
    (ii) $\alpha_{12} > 1$,   at $x = 0.617$
    (iii) $\alpha_{12} < 1$,   at $x = 0.803$
    (iv) $\alpha_{12} < 1$ at $x = 0.205$.

6. The relative volatility of A in a mixture of A and B is $\alpha_{AB} = 1.5$. What is the mole fraction of B in the first droplet of liquid condensed from an equimolar saturated vapour mixture of A and B?

    (i) 0.5   (ii) 0.6   (iii) 0.4

7. A binary totally miscible mixture forms a maximum boiling azeotrope at $x = x_a$. Two sets of equilibrium data points for the system are (x_1, y_1^*) and (x_2, y_2^*). If $x_1 < x_a < x_2$, identify the correct inequalities.

    (i) $x_1 < y_1^*$ (ii) $x_2 < y_2^*$ (iii) $y_1^* > y_2^*$

8. A given mixture of *n*-pentane and *n*-octane is heated and flashed when one mole liquid having a mole fraction $x = 0.15$ of *n*-pentane and two moles of vapour are generated. At the temperature of the flash drum, the relative volatility of *n*-octane with respect to *n*-pentane is 0.216. The solution is ideal. Calculate the composition of the original mixture.

9. A mixture of compounds A and B forms a higher-boiling azeotrope at $x = 0.75$ at 1 atm

total pressure. A solution of this composition has a bubble point T_b and a vapour of the same composition has a dew point T_d. Then:

(i) $T_b > T_d$ (ii) $T_b = T_d$ (iii) $T_b < T_d$

10. Consider a mixture of 40 mole% benzene (1), 40% toluene (2) and 20% p-xylene (3). The solution is approximately ideal. The following relative volatility values are known at 1 atm total pressure: $\alpha_{12} = 2.4$ and $\alpha_{32} = 0.43$. Then (a) the value of α_{31} is

(i) 0.18   (ii) 1.03   (iii) 5.58

(b) And the mole fraction of toluene in the equilibrium vapour at 100°C is

(i) 0.688   (ii) 0.277   (iii) 0.743

(c) Given the values $K_1 = 1.67$ and $K_2 = 0.688$, the value of K_3 is

(i) 1.15   (ii) 2.43   (iii) 0.296

11. One mole of a solution of A and B (enthalpy = 900 kcal/kmol; $x = 0.4$) is mixed with two moles of another solution of the components (enthalpy = 1200 kcal/kmol, $x = 0.8$). Calculate the enthalpy and composition of the mixture.

12. A ternary solution of n-hexane (20 mole%), n-heptane (40 mole%) and n-octane may be considered to be ideal. The equilibrium vaporization ratios are: $K_1 = 2.25$, $K_2 = 1.02$, and $K_3 = 0.6$ at 1 atm total pressure. The solution is

(i) below its bubble point
(ii) saturated
(iii) above its bubble point.   •

13. A student was asked to do flash calculation of an ideal mixture of four components having an overall composition (in mole fraction) of $w_1 = 0.2$, $w_2 = 0.15$, and $w_3 = 0.40$. At the condition of the flash drum, the equilibrium vaporization ratios were: $K_1 = 2.1$, $K_2 = 1.02$, $K_3 = 0.6$, and $K_4 = 0.2$. The student reported that 38 mole% of the feed vaporized on flashing. (a) Was the calculation reasonably correct? (b) What was the value of relative volatility α_{43}?

(i) 0.33   (ii) 3.1   (iii) 0.4

14. An essential oil, virtually immiscible with water, is steam-distilled by passing live steam at 107°C through a mixture of the oil and water (one mol of the oil per 200 mol water). The vapour pressure of water at 107°C is 1.3 bar and that of the essential oil is 6.55 mm Hg. How much steam is necessary to recover 80% of the essential oil? Neglect condensation of steam.

15. What are the important factors that determine the selection of a batch distillation column for the separation of a liquid mixture?

16. A mixture of benzene and p-xylene is batch distilled at atmospheric pressure. The rate of heat input to the still is 4000 kcal/h. Individual heats of vaporization are: benzene = 100 kcal/kg, p-xylene = 85 kcal/kg, and the relative volatility of benzene in the mixture is 5.6. Calculate the instantaneous rate of vaporization of p-xylene when the liquid in the still has 40 mole% benzene in it.

17. One thousand kilograms of an equimolar mixture of benzene and nitro-benzene is being separated by batch distillation. After an hour of operation, 500 kg of the mixture remains

in the still. The operator takes a sample of the accumulated condensate and reports that it has 70 mole% benzene in it. The relative volatility of benzene in the mixture can be taken as 7. Is the reported concentration of the distillate reasonably accurate?

18. A quaternary solution is being distilled in a batch still. Over a period of time, 30 mol% of component 1 is distilled out. The following relative volatility values are given: $\alpha_{31} = 0.2$; $\alpha_{23} = 1.8$; $\alpha_{43} = 0.7$. What fraction of component 3 is distilled out over this period?

19. Given: $x_D = 0.95$, $x_W = 0.05$, $\alpha = 2$, $z_F = 0.5$ and the feed is saturated. Algebraically, calculate the theoretical minimum slope of the rectifying section operating line for distillation of the binary mixture. Does it differ from the theoretical minimum slope of the stripping section operating line?

20. At a particular section of a packed distillation column, the bulk liquid concentration in a binary mixture is $x = 0.7$. *Given:* internal reflux ratio = 0.9, $\alpha = 2.5$, $H_G = 0.42$ m, $H_L = 0.15$ m. What is the height of an overall vapour phase transfer unit, H_{OG}?

    (i) 0.52   (ii) 0.38   (iii) 0.65

21. The stripping section operating line for a binary distillation problem is $y = 1.4x - 0.02$. The relative volatility is $\alpha = 2.6$. On a particular tray the liquid composition is $x = 0.2$. What is the composition of the vapour leaving the tray if the Murphree tray efficiency is 0.7?

    (i) 0.32   (ii) 0.354   (iii) 0.26

22. What happens if a column heated by open steam is operated at total reflux for a long time?

23. The stripping section operating line of a distillation column receiving saturated open steam for the separation of an aqueous solution is $y = 1.1x - 0.022$.

    (a) If $\alpha = 2.7$, what is the bottom product composition?

    (i) 0.22   (ii) 0.022   (iii) 0.02

    (b) What is the enrichment of the vapour across the bottom tray?

    (i) 0.052   (ii) 0.022   (iii) 0.011

24. A column receives saturated steam at the bottom for heat supply. If the feed ($z_F = 0.5$) is a mixture of 40 mole% liquid and 60 mole% vapour, calculate the slope of the stripping section operating line corresponding to the minimum reflux. *Given:* $\alpha = 2.6$, and $x_W = 0.03$ mole fraction.

25. A column has to separate a mixture of A and B to yield a top product of $x_D = 0.97$ and a bottom product of $x_W = 0.04$. Calculate the minimum number of ideal trays required to achieve this separation, *Given:* $\alpha_{AB} = 1.8$ at the bottom condition and $\alpha_{AB} = 2.0$ at the top condition.

26. The following concentrations of the vapour at two consecutive trays in the rectifying section of a column have been measured: $y_3 = 0.94$ and $y_4 = 0.925$. The equation of the operating line is $y = 0.6667x + 0.32$. The relative volatility at the liquid composition on the third tray is $\alpha = 1.85$. Calculate the Murphree efficiency of the tray.

27. A column receives a 'cold reflux', and the 'external reflux ratio' is 2.0. For each mole

of the cold reflux, 0.05 mole of the vapour condenses at the top tray. What is the true slope of the rectifying section operating line?

(i) 0.677   (ii) 0.5   (iii) 1.0

28. A saturated equimolar mixture of vapours of A and B enters a partial condenser at a rate of 1 kmol/h. The vapour leaves the condenser at a rate of 0.6 kmol/h. If the relative volatility of B with respect to A is 0.3, calculate the composition of the vapour and the liquid leaving the partial condenser.

29. A mixture (40 mole% vapour, the rest liquid) of aniline and nitrobenzene (80 mole% aniline) is separated into a distillate having 98 mole% aniline and a bottom product with 3 mole% aniline. The reflux ratio used is 2.2. (a) Determine the equations of the operating lines and of the feed line. (b) Write down the same equations if the column operates at total reflux.

30. A column is designed to operate at a reflux ratio of 1.3 (saturated reflux). In actual operation the reflux is well below its bubble point. What reflux ratio would you suggest *qualitatively*?

(i) $R > 1.3$ (ii) $R < 1.3$ (iii) $R = 1.3$

31. The equation of the rectifying section operating line for distillation of a mixture of A and B in a packed column is $y = 0.6x + 0.376$. The relative volatility of A with respect to B is $\alpha_{AB} = 2.0$. At a point in the rectifying section, $x = 0.8$. *Given:* $k'_x \bar{a} = 400$ kmol/$(m^3)(h)(\Delta x)$, and $k'_y \bar{a} = 170$ kmol/$(m^3)(h)(\Delta y)$.

(a) What is the reflux ratio?

(i) 0.5   (ii) 1.0   (iii) 1.5

(b) What is the top product mole fraction?

(i) 0.49   (ii) 0.94   (iii) 0.98

(c) What are the concentrations of the more volatile at the vapour–liquid interface?

32. A column for distillation of a mixture of A and B operates at total reflux. The liquid concentration of the fifth tray from the top is $x = 0.4$. If the relative voltality is $\alpha_{AB} = 1.8$, what are the concentrations of vapour streams (i) entering the tray and (ii) leaving the tray?

33. In order to reduce energy supply to a tray column for the separation of a binary mixture of A and B, it is planned to retrofit it with the Intalox high performance structured packing. The column receives a saturated liquid feed having 60 mol% A. The top product purity is 98 mol% A and the relative volatility is $\alpha_{AB} = 2.0$. The plant engineer suggests reduction of the reflux ratio from the present value of 1.8 to 1.5. Is the suggestion practicable?

34. If the relative volatility of A in a binary mixture of A and B is constant, show that the product of the terminal slopes of the equilibrium curve (i.e. $[dy/dx]_{x=0} \cdot [dy/dx]_{x=1}$) is unity.

35. The relative volatility of A with respect to B is $\alpha_{AB} = 2$. At what concentration of a mixture of A and B is the slope of the equilibrium line unity?

36. For distillation of an equimolar binary mixture of A and B, the equations of the operating lines are:

Rectifying section: $y = 0.663x + 0.32$

Stripping section: $y = 1.329x - 0.01317$

What is the condition of the feed?

37. A binary distillation column separating A and B is being operated at total reflux in the startup period. The relative volatility of A with respect to B is $\alpha_{AB} = 2.0$. If the vapour entering the top tray has 95 mole% A, what is the mole fraction of A in the liquid leaving the tray?

(i) 0.95   (ii) 0.5   (iii) 0.475

38. Write down the equations of the operating lines of the column (that runs under total reflux) described in Problem 37.

39. Prepare sketches of typical energy–concentration diagram of binary liquid and vapour mixtures of A and B if constant molar overflow (i) occurs and (ii) does not occur in the distillation column. Explain the sketches.

40. An aqueous solution of ethanol [30 mole% ethanol (1) and 70 mole% water (2)] at 75°C exerts an equilibrium total pressure of 592 mm Hg. Given $P_1^v = 661$ mm Hg, $P_2^v = 289.5$ mm Hg, $\gamma_1 = 1.765$, and $\gamma_2 = 1.195$, calculate the equilibrium vaporization ratios K_1 and K_2.

PROBLEMS

[Note: To calculate vapour pressures, use the Antoine equation constants given in Table 7.2.]

7.1 (*Equilibrium in a binary mixture*)[1] Mixtures of n-hexane and n-octane form essentially ideal solutions. (a) Prepare the bubble point, dew point and equilibrium curves (T–x–y and x–y plots) at 1 atm total pressure. (b) Calculate the values of the relative volatility of n-hexane and n-octane in mixtures containing 10 mole% and 90 mole% hexane using vapour pressure equations given in Table 7.2. Do these values suggest that the solutions may be ideal? (c) A solution of concentration $x = 0.2$ is slowly heated. What is the composition of the initial vapour formed if the total pressure is (i) 1 atm, (ii) 2 atm? (d) If a vapour of composition as in part (c) (ii) above is cooled at 2 atm total pressure and a differential amount of vapour is formed from the condensate, calculate its composition. How can the quantities be calculated using the T–x–y and x–y data?

7.2 (*Bubble point/dew point calculation, ternary mixture*)[3] Calculate the bubble point of a mixture of 30% methanol, 30% ethanol and 40% n-propanol (all in mole%) at 1 atm total pressure. Also calculate the dew point of a vapour of the above composition at 1.5 atm total pressure. Assume ideal behaviour of the solution.

7.3 (*Equilibrium in a multicomponent heterogeneous system*)[3] A heterogeneous mixture containing benzene (0.025 gmol), toluene (0.025 gmol) and water (0.05 gmol) is heated slowly at 1 atm total pressure. The vapour generated remains in equilibrium with the liquid. Calculate (a) the temperature at which boiling starts, (b) the composition of the initial vapour, and (c) the temperature at which vaporization is complete.

7.4 (*Binary flash distillation—yield* vs *composition*)[1] Ethanol forms a nearly ideal solution with *iso*-butanol and has a relative volatility 2.2. A heated feed containing 40 mole% ethanol and 60 mole% *iso*-butanol enters a flash drum at a rate of 50 kmol/h. Prepare a plot of the fractional yield of the distillate versus its composition. What fraction of the feed should be vaporized in order to have a bottom product containing not more than 10% ethanol?

7.5 (*Two-stage flash distillation*)[2] Consider Problem 7.4 again. Now there is a second flash drum that receives the bottom product from the first drum. If 60% of the feed is vaporized in each drum, find the vapour and the liquid flow rates from each chamber as well as their composition.

7.6 (*Two-stage flash distillation*)[3] A mixture of acetone and phenol (40 mass% acetone) is flashed consecutively in a cascade consisting two flash drums at 1 atm. The feed enters at a rate of 3000 kg/h and half of it is flashed in the first flash drum. The liquid from the first drum is heated and flashed again in the second drum. What fraction of the feed entering the second drum should be vaporized so that the residue contains not more than 1 mass % acetone? The vapour–liquid equilibrium data of the acetone–phenol system are given below.

x	0.01	0.04	0.10	0.20	0.30	0.40	0.50	0.60	0.70	0.80	0.90	0.96	0.99
y	0.67	0.776	0.852	0.91	0.94	0.962	0.98	0.99	0.991	0.994	0.997	0.999	0.9996

7.7 (*Heat requirement for a simple flash distillation*)[2] Components A and B form approximately ideal solutions and the relative volatility is $\alpha_{AB} = 3.0$. One kilomol of a mixture ($x = 0.5$) at 40°C is passed through a heat exchanger and then flashed to get equal amounts of liquid and vapour products. The temperature in the flash drum is 80°C. The molar specific heats are $c_{pA} = 20$ kcal/kmol, $c_{pB} = 30$ kcal/kmol. The molar heats of vaporization are $\lambda_A = 1250$ kcal/kmol, $\lambda_B = 1700$ kcal/kmol. Calculate the heat absorbed by the liquid in the heat exchanger.

7.8 (*Use of enthalpy–concentration relations*)[1] The molar enthalpies of saturated liquid and vapour mixtures of A and B at 1 atm total pressure (reference temp. = 5°C) may be expressed as: $H_L = 9000 + 1000x$ kJ/kmol; $H_V = 35,000 + 8000y$ kJ/kmol. The relative volatility is $\alpha_{AB} = 1.8$. (a) Calculate the molar heats of condensation of saturated pure vapours of compounds A and B at 1 atm. (b) We have one kmol of a liquid ($x = 0.3$, $H_L = 8500$ kJ/kmol), and one kmol of a vapour ($y = 0.5$, $H_V = 40,000$ kJ/kmol). What is the condition of the liquid (subcooled, saturated or superheated) and the condition of the vapour (saturated or superheated)?

7.9 (*Ternary flash distillation*)[2] A mixture of 38 mol% propane, 22.5 mol% *iso*-butane, and 39.5 mol% *n*-butane is flashed in a drum. If 50 mol% of the feed vaporizes, estimate the compositions of the liquid and the vapour phases. The K-values at the given conditions are as follows: Propane—1.42; *iso*-butane—0.86 and *n*-butane—0.72.

7.10 (*Bubble point of a heterogeneous mixture*)[2] Liquids A and B are miscible in all proportions and $P_A^v = 1.75 P_B^v$ at all temperatures. The vapour pressure of B is given by

$\ln P_B^v$ (mm Hg) = 14.243 − 2570/(θ, °C + 232.5). At what temperature does an equimolar mixture of A and B boil if the total pressure is 1.5 bar? Write down the Antoine equation for A.

Neither A or B is miscible with water. If some water is added to the mixture, at what temperature should it boil if the total pressure remains unchanged? The vapour pressure relation for water is given in Table 7.2.

7.11 (***Binary batch distillation***)[1] Ten kmol of a feed having 65 mole% benzene and 35 mole% toluene is batch distilled at 1 atm pressure. Calculate the moles of distillate produced and the composition of the bottom product if distillation is done until (a) 75 mole% of the feed benzene leaves with the vapour; (b) the stillpot contains 35 mol% benzene; (c) 50 mole% of the feed is vaporized; (d) the accumulated distillate contains 75 mole% of benzene. Take α = 2.51.

7.12 (***Partial condensation of a vapour***)[2] The vapour (containing 85 mole% methanol and 15 mole% water) from the top tray of a methanol distillation column enters a partial condenser at a rate of 70 kmol/h at 1 atm pressure. (a) If 70 mole% of the vapour is condensed, calculate the composition of the uncondensed vapour. (b) If the uncondensed vapour leaving the condenser has 91.5 mole% methanol in it, how much condensate leaves the condenser per hour? The vapour–liquid equilibrium data are given in Example 7.15.

7.13 (***Steam distillation***)[1] Two kg charge of geraniol (mol. wt. = 154.1) is to be steam-distilled at a temperature of 108°C. The steam is saturated and it is passed at a rate of 50 kg/h. Calculate the time for distillation of 95% of the material. The vaporization efficiency is 0.90. Vapour pressure at 108°C: water—1.34 bar; geraniol—8.65 mm Hg.

7.14 (***Steam distillation in presence of an impurity***)[2] Twenty kg charge containing 40 mass% of an essential oil (mol. wt. = 170) and the rest a non-volatile impurity (mol. wt. = 282) having complete mutual miscibility but both immiscible with water, is being steam-distilled. The steam supplied is saturated at 108°C. Calculate the rate of volatilization of the oil when 50% of it has been removed. The vaporization efficiency is 0.85. The vapour pressure of the substance at the given temperature is 6.5 mm Hg.

7.15 (***McCabe–Thiele construction for ideal trays***)[1] A feed mixture of A and B (45 mole% A and 55 mole% B) is to be separated into a top product containing 96 mole% A and a bottom product having 95 mole% B. The feed is 50% vapour and the reflux ratio is 1.5 times the minimum. What is the equation of the feed line? Determine the number of ideal trays required and the location of the feed tray. *Given:* α_{AB} = 2.8.

7.16 (***Use of the McCabe–Thiele method***)[1] A mixture of di- and tri-ethylamines containing 55 mole% of the former is fed to a distillation column at a rate of 40 kmol/h. The feed is at its bubble point. The column is to operate at atmospheric pressure and the top product should not have more than 2.5 mol% of the less volatile. Also, not more than 2% of the diethylamine in the feed should be allowed to leave at the bottom. The reflux to the column is a saturated liquid. Determine (a) the minimum reflux ratio, (b) the number of theoretical plates if the actual reflux ratio is 1.4 times the minimum, (c) the slopes of the two operating lines, and (d) the number of theoretical plates if the reflux is a subcooled liquid at such a temperature that one mole of vapour is condensed for twenty moles of reflux. The equilibrium data in terms of the more volatile are:

| x | 0.02 | 0.039 | 0.052 | 0.065 | 0.09 | 0.092 | 0.14 | 0.215 | 0.43 | 0.601 | 0.782 | 0.853 | 0.932 | 0.985 |
| y | 0.042 | 0.085 | 0.124 | 0.153 | 0.225 | 0.243 | 0.316 | 0.449 | 0.678 | 0.802 | 0.910 | 0.948 | 0.970 | 0.993 |

7.17 (*Use of the McCabe–Thiele method*)[2]   Styrene, a tonnage organic chemical used in the production of moulding resins and rubbers, is produced by catalytic dehydrogenation of ethylbenzene followed by separation of the product by distillation. A fractionating column receives an equimolar mixture of styrene and ethylbenzene at a rate of 120 kmol/h. The purity of the top product (ethylbenzene) and that of the bottom product (styrene) must not be less than 98% and 99.5% respectively. Determine (a) the minimum external reflux ratio, (b) the minimum number of ideal trays required for the above separation, (c) the number of ideal trays and the feed-tray location if the actual reflux ratio is twice the minimum and the feed is a saturated liquid, and (d) the vapour load in the condenser. It will be convenient to use the Kremser equation to determine the number ideal trays near the top and bottom ends. The column operates at 20 mm pressure and the equilibrium data at this pressure are given below (x, y are for ethylbenzene).

| x | 0.0 | 0.0555 | 0.0782 | 0.115 | 0.139 | 0.2405 | 0.2715 | 0.335 | 0.460 | 0.545 | 0.755 | 0.874 | 0.965 | 1.0 |
| y | 0.0 | 0.090 | 0.120 | 0.162 | 0.201 | 0.318 | 0.355 | 0.4055 | 0.535 | 0.630 | 0.825 | 0.910 | 0.975 | 1.0 |

In industrial practice too, styrene is purified by distillation under vacuum. How are the column parameters (diameter, tray spacing, number of trays) affected if a mixture is distilled under vacuum rather than at atmospheric pressure?

7.18 (*Calculation of the minimum reflux*)[2]   A saturated vapour feed containing benzene (30 mole%) and chlorobenzene is to be separated into a top product having 98 mol% benzene and a bottom product having 99 mol% chlorobenzene. Calculate the minimum reflux ratio algebraically. What is the corresponding boil-up ratio? The relative volatility of benzene in the mixture is 4.12.

7.19 (*Effects of operating parameters on column performance*)[3]   A distillation column provided with a partial reboiler and a total condenser separates a mixture of A and B to yield products of compositions x_D (top) and x_W (bottom). (a) How can the purity of the distillate be increased without changing its quantity and without the addition of extra trays? How is the purity of the bottom product affected as a result? (b) If the rate of withdrawal of distillate is increased (without making any changes in the reboiler heat input), identify the consequent changes. (c) If the pressure of the saturated steam fed to the reboiler undergoes a step change and no other change occurs to the parameters, how is the performance of the column affected?

7.20 (*Algebraic calculations for a tray column*)[2]   A mixture of 60 mole% A and 40 mole% B is separated in a column to yield 96 mole% A as the top product. Also, 97% of A entering the tower must be recovered in the distillate. The feed is a saturated vapour. The following concentrations have been measured by analyzing the liquid and vapour samples around the 6th tray: $x_6 = 0.55$, $y_6 = 0.72$, $y_7 = 0.63$. (a) What is the local value of the relative volatility of A with respect to B? (b) How many ideal trays does the column have? Assume that the relative volatility remains constant.

7.21 (*A stripping column having a given number of trays*)[3] A saturated liquid mixture of benzene and toluene having 70 mole% benzene is fed continuously at a rate of 40 kmol/h to the top tray of a column having six theoretical trays. There is no reflux at the top. The rate of vapour generation in the reboiler is 30 kmol/h. Determine the equation of the operating line and the rates and compositions of the product. (*Note:* This column may be called a 'stripping column'.)

7.22 (*Algebraic calculation of the vapour/liquid concentrations in a tray column*)[3] A distillation column separates a saturated feed containing 25 mole% A and 75 mole% B. The relative volatility is $\alpha_{AB} = 2.51$. The liquid concentration on the 5th tray is $x_5 = 0.54$. The distillate has 98 mole% A and the reflux ratio is 3.0. (a) Determine the concentration of the vapour (i) entering the 5th tray from the top, and (ii) leaving the 5th tray. (b) Which section of the column (rectifying or stripping) does the 5th tray belong to? (c) Calculate the enrichment of the vapour across the 4th tray. (d) If 97% of A present in the feed goes to the top product, calculate the moles of liquid vaporized in the reboiler per mole of distillate and also the boil-up ratio. Assume that the trays are ideal. Solve the problem algebraically (i.e. without any graphical construction).

7.23 (*High purity product*; *use of Kremser equation*)[3] An equimolar mixture of A and B is to be separated in a tray tower. A top product having 95 mol% A is acceptable. However, a very pure bottom product having not more than 0.1 mol% A is required. The feed is liquid at its bubble point. A reflux ratio of 2.0 is suggested. The relative volatility of A with respect to B is $\alpha_{AB} = 2.2$. Determine the number of ideal stages.

The graphical construction of stages is difficult at low concentration and an algebraic method is convenient. Use the McCabe–Thiele method to make stage construction up to about 5 mol% of A. Then use the Kremser equation to determine the number of trays required to reach the stipulated value of 0.1 mol% A in the bottom product.

7.24 (*A stripping column with a given number of trays*)[3] The vapour phase alkylation of phenol is carried out by a selective zeolite catalyst to yield a mixture of 35 mole% *p*-cresol and the rest phenol. The mixture which is at its bubble point is to be separated at 1 atm pressure in a stripping column having nine ideal trays and a partial reboiler at a rate of 50 kmol/h to yield 95% *p*-cresol as the bottom product. The relative volatility of phenol in the mixture is 1.76. Calculate (a) the composition of the top product and (b) the boil-up rate, $\bar{V}/W$, where $\bar{V}$ is the vapour rate and W is the rate removal of the bottom product.

7.25 (*Performance of a column with an additional number of trays*)[3] A column having 16 trays of 25% overall efficiency separates a mixture of 60 mole% benzene and 40 mole% toluene available as a saturated vapour. The overhead product is 85 mole% benzene and the bottom product is 20 mole% benzene. It is possible to add a section having eight trays of the same efficiency to the column. If all process conditions remain unchanged, calculate the percentage saving in steam fed to the reboiler that can be achieved by this increase in the number of trays. On which tray of the modified column should the feed be introduced? Equilibrium data for the system is given under Example 7.13.

7.26 (*Given the number of trays and efficiency, to determine the product composition*)[3] A distillation column has five plates that are 60% efficient. The heat input to the stillpot is

100,800 kcal/h and the condenser load is 280,000 kcal/h. The reflux is at 37°C below the boiling point. A feed, an equimolar mixture of benzene and toluene, enters the column at a rate of 50 kmol/h. Also the feed is 55% vapour. Latent heat of vaporization of the liquid can be taken as 7000 kmol/kmol irrespective of the composition. The specific heat of liquid is 38 Btu/(lb)(mol)(°F). Find the compositions of the top and the bottom products.

7.27 (*McCabe–Thiele construction—feed is not supplied at the optimum location*)[3] A distillation column receives an equimolar saturated liquid mixture of benzene and toluene ($\alpha = 2.51$). The top product has 95 mol% benzene, the bottom product contains 95 mol% toluene, and the reflux ratio is 2.0. (a) Determine the feed tray and the number of ideal trays if the feed is supplied to the optimum location. (b) How many more trays would be required for this separation if the feed is supplied at the ninth ideal tray from the top? (c) Determine the number of real trays if the Murphree efficiency is 60% and the feed enters the optimum position in the column.

7.28 (*McCabe–Thiele method, number of trays given, Murphree efficiency given*)[2] A distillation column which separates pinene and limonene consists of a reboiler, 15 theoretical plates and a total condenser. The feed is at its bubble point and has 72% pinene in it. The overhead product contains 95 mole% pinene and the bottom product has 94% limonene. Determine (a) the reflux ratio to be maintained, (b) the location of the feed plate, (c) the number of ideal stages required for the above separation for total reflux. *Given:* $\alpha = 1.71$.

7.29 (*A column receiving two feeds*)[3] A distillation column for separation of methanol from water receives two feeds—100 kmol/h saturated liquid having 30 mol% methanol, and 100 kmol/h 20% vaporized feed having 60 mol% methanol. The top product should have 96 mol% methanol, and the bottom must not contain more than 3 mol% of it. If an external reflux ratio of 1.45 is used, calculate the amounts of the top and bottom products, and determine the number of ideal trays required for the separation. The vapour–liquid equilibrium data are given in Example 7.15.

7.30 (*Withdrawal of a side stream from a distillation column*)[2] A saturated liquid feed having 45 mole% methanol is distilled at a rate of 200 kmol/h in a column to yield a top product, 96% methanol, a bottom product, 97% water, and a liquid side stream, 20 kmol/h, having 70 mole% methanol, from the appropriate tray. Determine the number of ideal trays required. From which tray should the side stream be withdrawn? A reflux ratio of 1.5 may be used.

7.31 (*A column with an arrangement for heat supply to a particular tray*)[3] A distillation column separates an equimolar mixture of methanol and water at its bubble point to a top product having 95% methanol and a bottom product with 95% water.

(a) How many trays should be used to achieve this separation if the column is operated at total reflux?

(b) Determine the number of theoretical trays required and the location of the feed tray if a reflux ratio of 1.5 is used.

(c) It is planned to instal a heading coil on the third tray from the top so as to vaporize 10% of the liquid it receives. What will be the number of trays for this arrangement?

7.32 (*A column receiving two feeds; feeds supplied to the wrong plates*)[3] A column receives two feeds—20 kmol/h, 40 mole% benzene, and 40 kmol/h, 60 mole% benzene, both liquid at the respective bubble points. The top product rate is 30 kmol/h with 94% benzene, and the reflux ratio is 1.5. After an annual shutdown, the feed pipe connections got interchanged inadvertently. Can you predict the top product composition at this condition? The reflux ratio remains unchanged.

7.33 (*Side stream withdrawal from a column—algebraic calculations*)[3] A continuous distillation column receives a saturated liquid feed ($z_F = 0.45$). It produces a distillate of $x_D = 0.98$ and a bottom product of $x_W = 0.015$. A side stream amounting to 25% of the downflowing liquid ($x_S = 0.75$) is withdrawn as a saturated liquid from the appropriate tray. The rectifying section operating line for the part of the column above the point of side stream withdrawal is $y = 0.821x + 0.175$. Determine the equations of the operating lines for the middle and the last sections of the column. What fraction of the feed is drawn as the bottom product?

7.34 (*Binary batch distillation*)[1] A charge of 15 kmol of an equimolar mixture of methanol and water is batch-distilled to recover 85% of the alcohol. Calculate the amount of distillate and its composition. Equilibrium data are available under Example 7.15.

7.35 (*Multicomponent batch distillation*)[2] A mixture containing 2 kmol each of *n*-hexane, *n*-heptane and *n*-octane is batch-distilled at 1 atm pressure to remove 80% of hexane. Taking *K*-values from Figure 7.8, calculate the amount and composition of the distillate. What fraction of heptane remains in the still?

7.36 (*Batch distillation with constant reflux*)[3] A batch distillation column having a stillpot and one ideal tray separates a mixture of benzene and toluene. At the beginning there is 10 kmol of liquid in the still with 40 mole% benzene. The rate of vapour generation is 15 kmol/h and a reflux ratio of 3.0 is used. Determine the concentration of the overhead vapour and the instantaneous rate of removal of benzene. The relative volatility of benzene is 2.51.

7.37 (*Batch distillation with variable reflux*)[3] Fifty kilomols of aqueous methanol (60 mole% methanol) is charged into a batch still having a reboiler and five ideal trays. The reflux ratio is continuously increased so that the distillate always contains 90 mol% methanol. If distillation is stopped after the reflux ratio required to maintain the stipulated top product concentration exceeds 8.0, calculate the fractional recovery of methanol.

7.38 (*Batch distillation*)[3] Twenty kilomoles of a mixture of *A* and *B* ($x_F = 0.45$) is charged in the stillpot of a batch distillation unit. A constant vaporization rate of 5.0 kmol/h is maintained and there is a total condenser. (a) What is the concentration of the distillate after one hour? (b) At the end of one hour, it is planned to start withdrawal of the condensate from the receiver at a rate equal to that of the rate of vaporization. Thus the amount of condensate in the receiver remains constant (it is also assumed to be well-mixed all the time). Calculate the concentration of the distillate in the receiver at the end of two hours of operation. The equilibrium vaporization constants at the operating condition are: $K_A = 2.6$, and $K_B = 0.9$.

7.39 (*Batch distillation in a unit having a partial condenser*)[2] The vapour from a batch still flows to a partial condenser in which 50 mole% of the vapour is condensed. The condensate is fed back to the still and the uncondensed part flows to a second total condenser and gets accumulated in a receiver vessel (Figure 7.36). The still is charged with 10 kmol of a mixture of A and B and batch distillation continues. What is the composition of the accumulated distillate after 5 kmols of the charge is distilled out? The relative voltality is $\alpha_{AB} = 2.8$.

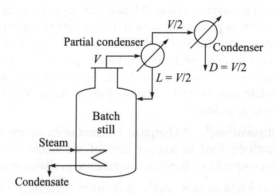

Figure 7.36   A batch still with a partial condenser.

7.40 (*Continuous distillation using open steam*)[2] An aqueous solution of ethanol with 25 mole% of the alcohol is to be distilled in a tray column at a rate of 200 kmol/h to get a distillate with 80 mol% ethanol. The feed is at its bubble point. If 95% recovery of the alcohol in the distillate is required, and saturated *open steam* at 1 atm is fed to the bottom of the column, calculate the number of ideal trays required for the separation. A reflux ratio of 2.2 is suggested. Constant molar overflow may be assumed. (The VLE data is given under Example 7.24.)

7.41 (*Use of the Ponchon–Savarit method*)[3] A dilute aqueous solution of ethanol is to be concentrated from 20 mass% to 85 mass% alcohol in a tray tower at 1 atm pressure. The feed rate is 8000 kg/h at its bubble point. The bottom product must not contain more than 3.5 mass% ethanol. Determine (a) the minimum reflux ratio, (b) the number of ideal trays, and (c) the reboiler and condenser heat duties. The enthalpy–concentration and the equilibrium data are given under Example 7.24.

7.42 (*Use of the Ponchon–Savarit method*)[3] An aqueous solution of ammonia is continuously generated in the absorption column for its recovery from the ammonia reactor bleed stream. Ammonia is separated from this aqueous solution by distillation at around 20 atm pressure. A distillation unit is to be designed for treating 5000 kg/h of a solution containing 25 mass% ammonia. The top product should have 97 mass% ammonia and the bottom must not have more than 1.5% of it. A reflux ratio of 1.6 may be used.

   If the feed is at its bubble point, determine (a) the number of ideal trays, (b) the location of the feed tray, and (c) the number of ideal trays if constant molar overflow is assumed.

x or y	0	0.1053	0.2094	0.312	0.414	0.514	0.614	0.712	0.809	0.905
H_L, kcal/kmol	0	−500	−970	−1310	−1540	−1650	−1580	−1400	−960	−520
H_V, kcal/kmol	8430	7955	7660	7495	7210	6920	6620	6300	5980	5470
x or y	0.923	0.942	0.962	0.981	1.00					
H_L, kcal/kmol	−430	−310	−210	−110	0.0					
H_V, kcal/kmol	5350	5240	5050	4870	4250					

[Reference states: pure liquids at their boiling points at 20 atm pressure]

7.43 (*Calculation of the packed height*)[2] A saturated aqueous feed (20 mole% ethanol; 50 kmol/h) is to be distilled in a packed tower filled with 1-inch metal Pall ring. The top product should have 80 mole% ethanol and the bottom not more than 2 mole% of it. A reflux ratio of $R = 1.7$ may be used. (a) If a vapour flow rate of 70% of flooding velocity is maintained, determine the tower diameter. (b) Given the following values of heights of individual transfer units—$H_{tG} = 0.4$ m and $H_{tL} = 0.25$ for the enriching section; $H_{tG} = 0.28$ m and $H_{tL} = 0.11$ for the enriching section—calculate the packed height required.

7.44 (*Packed height and HETP*)[2] An aqueous solution of methanol (30 mol% methanol; 2000 kg/h) is to be separated in a 0.7 m diameter packed tower to yield a distillate having 97% methanol and a bottom product having 4% methanol. The following values of the volumetric mass transfer coefficients are supplied.

$$\text{Rectifying section} \qquad\qquad\qquad \text{Stripping section}$$
$$k'_x\bar{a} = 800 \quad k'_y\bar{a} = 170 \qquad k'_x\bar{a} = 1250 \quad k'_y\bar{a} = 255 \text{ kmol/(m}^3\text{)(h)}(\Delta x \text{ or } \Delta y)$$

A reflux ratio of 1.4 times the minimum may be used. Calculate the height of the packed section. Also determine the HEPT of the packing.

7.45 (*Relation between the reflux ratio and the boil-up ratio*)[1] If the relative volatility remains constant, show that the reflux ratio R and the boil-up ratio R_v, are related as follows (Stichlmair and Fair, 1998) for distillation of a binary mixture.

$$R_v = \frac{(D/F)(R+1) - (1-q)}{(1-D/F)}$$

7.46 (*The minimum reflux ratio if the relative volatility is constant*)[1] If the relative volatility is constant and the feed is a saturated liquid, show that the minimum reflux ratio is given by the following expression.

$$R_m = \frac{1}{\alpha - 1}\left(\frac{x_D}{z_F} - \alpha \frac{1 - x_D}{1 - z_F}\right)$$

7.47 (*A column receiving cold reflux*)[2] A saturated liquid feed containing 50 mol% *A* and 50 mol% *B* enters a distillation column at a rate of 100 kmol/h. The top product must have 95 mol% *A*, and 4% of *A* should leave at the bottom. An external reflux ratio of $R = 2$ is maintained. However, the reflux is subcooled having an enthalpy of 4,000 kJ/ kmol of reflux. Given the following relations for enthalpies (kJ/kmol) of saturated liquid and vapour, calculate (a) the equations of the top and the bottom operating lines, and (b) the boil-up ratio.

$$\text{Saturated liquid:} \quad H_L = 9000 - 3000x$$
$$\text{Saturated vapour:} \quad H_L = 40,000 - 3000y$$

7.48 (*A column receiving open steam*)[3] An equimolar mixture of methanol and water is to be separated at a rate of 200 kmol/h in a tray tower to yield a top product having 96 mol% methanol. At least 97% of the total methanol is to be recovered. A small reboiler that can generate 150 kmol/h vapour hour is available and will be used. Any additional heat supply necessary will be met by injecting live steam at the bottom If a reflux ratio of 2.0 is used, determine the amount of live steam to be supplied per hour and the number of ideal trays required. The column operates at essentially atmospheric pressure.

7.49 (*A leaking batch still*)[2] Forty kilomols of a mixture of methanol and water (40 mol% methanol) was charged in a still for batch distillation to yield 15 kmol of distillate over a period of 1 hour. Immediately after distillation started, the drainage valve at the bottom of the still was found leaking. The liquid that had leaked out over the period of 1 hour is found to be 5 kmol. Both the rate of distillation and the leakage at the valve occurred at uniform rates. If the relative volatility of methanol is approximately taken as 3.0, calculate the distillate composition and the amount of methanol that had leaked out.

7.50 (*The minimum reflux ratio for multistage batch distillation*)[2] An equimolar mixture of A and B having 50 mol% A is to be batch-distilled in a multistage column maintaining a constant reflux ratio. It is desired that the initial distillate should have 90 mol% of A. If the relative volatility of A with respect to B is 3.0, what is the minimum reflux ratio required?

7.51 (*A packed column operated at total reflux*)[2] A packed distillation column for separation of benzene and toluene is operated at total reflux. The benzene concentration in the distillate is 97 mol% and that in the bottoms is 2 mol%. If the relative volatility of benzene in the mixture is $\alpha = 2.51$, calculate the number of *overall gas-phase transfer units*.

7.52 (*A multistage batch distillation unit having a large number of trays*)[3] It is an interesting exercise to theoretically calculate the separation capability of a multistage batch column having an *infinite number of trays* (see Bauerle and Sandall, *AIChE J.,* June 1987, 1034–1036). An equimolar mixture of A and B ($\alpha_{AB} = 3.5$) is to be batch distilled in a column having a very large number of trays at a constant reflux ratio of 2.5. If one-third of the liquid is distilled out, calculate the composition of the accumulated distillate.

7.53 (*Number of trays given, get the reflux ratio*)[3] An equimolar mixture of *iso*-pentane and benzene is to be separated into a top product having 96 mole% iso-pentane and a bottom product with 95% benzene. The feed rate is 100 kmol/h, saturated vapour. A column of suitable diameter having twenty trays of 40% efficiency and a partial reboiler is available. If saturated liquid reflux is fed back to the column, what reflux ratio should be used to get the desired separation in the column. The average relative volatility is 2.5. (The problem can be solved algebraically as well as by *tray-by-tray* calculation.)

7.54 (*Stripping of an aqueous solution using open steam*)[2] Ethanol is to be steam-stripped from a dilute aqueous waste stream in a tray tower using open steam. The feed that has 2.5 mass% ethanol in it is heated to its bubble point before it enters into the column. The steam rate is 0.25 mole per mole of the feed. At this low concentration, the equilibrium relation is approximately linear, $y = 8.5x$. Determine the number of ideal trays required if 95% of the ethanol is to be removed.

7.55 (*A column with side streams*)[3]   A distillation column should separate 200 kmol/h of a saturated liquid feed containing 45 mole% methanol and 55 mole%. The top product should have 97 mole% methanol and the bottom, 96 mole% water. The reflux is saturated liquid and a reflux ratio of 2.0 is suggested. A vapour side stream containing 80 mole% methanol is to be withdrawn at a rate of 50 kmol/h from the appropriate tray and condensed in a heat exchanger. Half of it should be taken as an intermediate product and the rest returned into the column as an additional reflux stream. Determine (a) the number of ideal stages required, (b) the feed tray, (c) the tray from which the side stream should be withdrawn, and (d) the tray that should receive the additional reflux.

REFERENCES

Billet, R., *Distillation Engineering*, Chemical Publishing, 1979.

Billet, R., *Packed Towers in Processing and Environmental Engineering*, VCH, 1995.

Divekar, U.M., *Batch Distillation*, Taylor and Francis, 1995.

Eubank, P.T. et al., 'Simplify flash calculations', *Chem. Eng.*, Nov. 2000, 125–130.

Fair, J.R., 'Distillation, whither, not whether', *Chem. Eng. Res. & Des.*, 66(July 1988) 363–370.

Forbes, R.J., *Short History of the Art of Distillation*, E.J. Brill, Leiden, 1948.

Hala, M. et al., *Computer-aided Data Book of Vapor-Liquid Equilibria*, Kodansa, Tokyo, 1975.

Jafarey, A., J.M. Douglas, and T.J. McAvoy, 'Shortcut techniques for distillation column design and control column design', *Ind Eng. Chem. Proc. Des. Dev.*, 18(1979) 197–202.

Kister, H.Z., *Distillation Operation*, McGraw-Hill, New York, 1989.

Kister, H.Z., *Distillation Design*, McGraw-Hill, New York, 1992.

Kunesh, J.G. et al., 'Distillation: still towering over other options', *Chem. Eng. Progr.*, Oct. 1995, 43–54.

Lewis, W.K., 'The efficiency and design of rectifying columns for binary mixtures,' *Ind. Eng. Chem.*, 14(1922) 492.

Porter, K.E., 'Why research is needed in distillation', *Trans. Inst. Chem. Engrs.*, 73 (Part A), May 1995, 357–362.

Ryan, J.M., 'Replotting the McCabe-Thiele diagram', *Chem. Eng.*, May 2001, 109–113.

Smoker, E.H., 'Analytic determination of plates in fractionating columns', *Trans. AIChE*, 34(1938) 165–172.

Sorel, E., *La Rectification de l'Alcohol*, Gauthiers Villars, Paris, 1893.

Stichlmair, J.G., and J.R. Fair, *Distillation—Principles and Practice*, Wiley-VCH, New York, 1998.

Yuan, K.S., and B.C.-Y. Lu, 'Vapour-liquid equilibria,' *J. Chem. Eng. Data*, 8(Oct. 1963) 549.

8 | Liquid–Liquid Extraction

Liquid–liquid extraction (sometimes abbreviated LLX) is a mass transfer operation in which a solution (called the *feed* which is a mixture of a solute and a carrier liquid) is brought into intimate contact with a second immiscible or slightly miscible liquid (called the *solvent*) in order to achieve transfer of the solute(s) from the feed to the solvent. The two liquid phases that have different densities are then separated. The solute-rich phase (this is the solvent stream, now enriched with the solute) is called the *extract*; the residual feed stream that may have a little of the solute left in it is called the *raffinate*. If the carrier in the feed and the solvent are partly miscible, the raffinate will also have a little solvent dissolved in it, and the extract phase will contain a little dissolved carrier. The solute is separated from the extract phase in an acceptably pure form, and the solvent dissolved in the raffinate is recovered. An extraction process generally involves four major steps.

(a) Bringing the feed and the solvent into intimate contact by dispersing one phase into the other as droplets.
(b) Separation of the extract and the raffinate phases that have different densities.
(c) Removal and recovery of the solute from the extract phase in a relatively pure form (by distillation, evaporation, crystallization, etc.).
(d) Removal and recovery of the solvent from each phase, usually by distillation.

Separation of a liquid mixture or solution by distillation is operationally simpler than extraction. For example, a binary liquid mixture having components of different volatilities can, in principle, be separated into two relatively pure products (a 'distillate' and a 'residue') in a single column. But separation of the same mixture by extraction requires *at least* one distillation column in addition to the extractor. Very often more than one distillation column is used for the recovery of the solvent from the raffinate (called *raffinate clean-up*) and for separation of the carrier liquid from the extract phase (Figure 8.1). Phase separation of the extract and the raffinate may not be rapid if the difference in their densities is small and the interfacial tension is low. Loss of solvent may also occur in some cases. In its totality, solvent extraction is a more elaborate technique than distillation. In a typical liquid–liquid extraction process, only about 15% of the capital cost goes towards the extractor and the remaining 85% goes towards the distillation

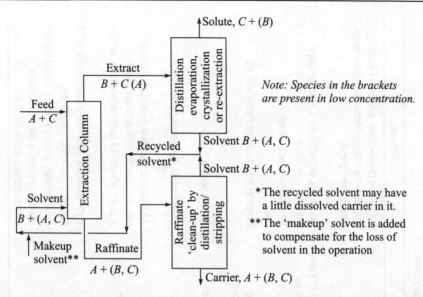

Figure 8.1   Schematic of an extraction unit with product recovery and raffinate clean-up arrangements; *A*: carrier, *B*: solvent, *C*: solute.

columns and other equipment for solvent recovery and product purification. Also, only about 5% of the operating cost of the unit is required for the extractor and the remaining 95% goes towards solvent recovery. Despite these limitations, there are situations when the technique of distillation either fails or becomes uneconomic. A few such cases, where solvent extraction is an attractive separation technique, are described below.

(a)   The components to be separated have close boiling points. For example, aromatics are extracted from paraffinic feedstocks in the refineries by using a solvent like sulphur dioxide, *n*-methyl pyrolidone, sulpholane, etc. The number of distillation trays becomes prohibitively large if the relative volatility is close to unity (say less than 1.2), and solvent extraction, therefore, may be an attractive alternative for such a mixture.

(b)   Separation of heat-sensitive materials such as antibiotics, vitamins, etc. Penicillin is recovered from the fermentation broth by using a suitable solvent such as butyl acetate.

(c)   Recovery of non-volatile solutes, usually from aqueous solutions, in hydro-metallurgy.

(d)   Recovery of a solute from a very dilute solution—for example, bioseparation (proteins, antibiotics, high-value bioproducts).

(e)   Removal of organics from aqueous streams—for example, removal of phenol from aqueous wastes.

8.1   A FEW EXAMPLES OF SOLVENT EXTRACTION

Liquid–liquid extraction is also called 'solvent extraction'. A number of common industrial extraction processes are listed in Table 8.1 (also see Cusack and Glatz, 1996). A few such representative processes are briefly described below.

Table 8.1 Some commercially important extraction processes

Extraction process	Feed	Solvent
1. Separation of BTX (benzene, toluene and xylenes) from petroleum fractions. (BTX is used as a feed-stock for the preparation of petrochemicals).	Petroleum fractions containing aromatics	Sulpholane (tetrahydrothiophene, 1-1-dioxide), furfural, N-methylpyrrolidone, diethylene glycol, tetraethylene glycol.
2. Lube oil extraction	Hydrocarbons including *n*-paraffins, *iso*-paraffins, naphthenes, aromatics and mixed aliphatic-aromatic ring structures	Liquid SO_2, phenol, furfural, liquid propane, N-methyl-pyrrolidone
3. Separation of aromatic hydrocarbons from petroleum fractions	Petroleum fractions containing aromatics	Tetraethylene glycol–water
4. Extraction of caprolactum from 'lactum oil'	'Lactum oil', aqueous $(NH_4)_2SO_4$–liquor containing caprolactum (such liquids are obtained in the process of caprolactum manufacture)	Benzene, toluene, trichloroethylene, etc.
5. Extraction of phenolics from coal tar and liquors	Light liquor containing phenolics (obtained in a coal carbonization plant)	Isobutyl acetate
6. Extraction of phenol from aqueous wastes	Aqueous waste streams, coal carbonization plants, phenolic resin plants	Butyl acetate, di-isopropyl ether, MIBK
7. Extraction of citral (a flavouring substance used in food and some other industries)	Lemon grass and orange oil	An alcohol and a lower hydrocarbon(solvent pair; for example, methanol and pentane)
8. Refining of oils and fats (mono- and diglycerides removed from tri-glycerides)	Oil and fat products	A polar solvent like acetone or a lower alcohol
9. Extraction of copper	Dilute Cu-ion bearing acidic leach liquor	Hydroxylamine, proprietary solvents like LIX-63, LIX-64N, LIX-65N, LIX-70, etc.
10. Extraction of penicillin	Penicillin fermentation broth	*n*-Amylacetate (most common), *n*-butyl acetate
11. Removal of H_2S	Liquefied natural gas (LNG)	Monoethanolamine (MEA), methanol-diethanolamine amine (MDEA).

8.1.1 Extraction of Aromatics

Solvent extraction is an important separation technique in petroleum refineries, particularly for lube oil production. The viscosity index (V.I.) is an important parameter for a lubricating oil. Many undesirable compounds, especially aromatics that reduce the V.I., have to be removed from the lube oil feed stock to ensure the required viscosity index. Aromatics (benzene, toluene and xylenes, BTX) must also be removed from kerosene and jet fuels. This can be done conveniently by using a solvent selective for aromatics, sulphur, nitrogen, and oxygenated compounds. Important solvents are furfural, sulpholane (tetrahydrothiophene-1,1-dioxide), N-methyl pyrrolidone (NMP), diethylene glycol, tetraethylene glycol, methyl-ethyl-ketone (MEK), and methyl-isobutyl-ketone (MIBK) which selectively remove aromatics and weakly polar compounds (Lucan, 2000). Phenol and sulphur dioxide are no longer used because of their toxicity and other problems. The process involves extraction followed by distillation-stripping of both the raffinate (that contains the purified lube and some solvent) and the extract (containing the aromatics and the solvent). A very simple flow diagram of the sulpholane process is shown in Figure 8.2(a). A rotating disk contactor (RDC, see Section 8.5.4) is commonly used for this purpose. The separated aromatics are further fractionated in pure form for use as feedstocks for the petrochemical industry.

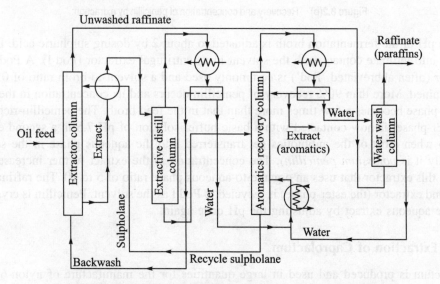

Figure 8.2(a)   Separation of aromatics from a feedstock—the sulpholane process.

8.1.2 Recovery and Concentration of Antibiotics by Solvent Extraction

Penicillin, a major antibiotic, is produced by fermentation. The concentration of the substance in the fermentation broth is small (typically 20–35 gram penicillin per litre broth). Recovery and concentration of penicillin from the broth is done by extraction (Hatton, 1985) using a solvent such as amyl acetate, butyl acetate, or methyl-isobutyl-ketone (MIBK). At a pH of about 2, penicillin remains in the acid form and has a low solubility in water. But at this pH, it is favourably transported to an organic solvent (mentioned earlier) from the aqueous fermentation broth because of a high distribution coefficient. However, a reversal of the distribution coefficient occurs at a pH above 7. This pH-dependent distribution of penicillin in the water-ester pair is made use of to recover, purify and simultaneously concentrate the antibiotic from the broth. The extraction process, which is carried out at about 4°C, is schematically shown in Figure 8.2(b).

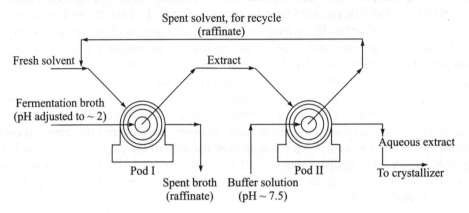

Figure 8.2(b)   Recovery and concentration of penicillin by extraction.

The pH of the fermentation broth is adjusted to about 2 by dosing sulphuric acid. It is then brought into intimate contact with the solvent in a centrifugal extractor (Pod I). A Podbielniak extractor (often abbreviated 'Pod') is commonly used and a solvent-to-broth ratio of 0.1 to 0.2 is maintained. More than 90% recovery of penicillin occurs and its concentration in the solvent or ester-phase becomes a few times more than that in the feed broth. The penicillin-rich extract (the ester-phase) is now contacted with a basic buffer solution of pH 7.5 in a second extractor (Pod II) when most of the antibiotics get transferred into the aqueous phase in the salt form (generally it is *potassium penicillin*). The concentration in the extract further increases a few times in this extractor that uses an organic-to-aqueous phase ratio of 5 to 10. The raffinate from the second extractor (the ester-phase) is recycled to Pod I as the solvent. Penicillin is crystallized from the aqueous extract by adjusting the pH once again.

8.1.3   Extraction of Caprolactum

Caprolactum is produced and used in large quantities for the manufacture of nylon-6, a bulk polymer. It is synthesized from cyclohexane (cyclohexane → cyclohexanol → cyclohexanone → cyclohexanone oxime → caprolactum). The last step of the process involves reaction of the oxime with sulphuric acid when caprolactum and ammonium sulphate are formed. The aqueous reaction mixture separates into an organic-rich phase ('lactum oil' containing 65–70% caprolactum) and a water-rich phase having ammonium sulphate and 2–3% caprolactum. The two phases are fed at appropriate locations of a rotating disk contactor [Figure 8.2(c)]. Toluene, benzene and trichloroethylene are good solvents (the last two are carcinogens and are not used any more). Caprolactum goes to the extract, and ammonium sulphate remains in the raffinate. The two streams are further treated to get caprolactum in a pure form and to recover the solvent and ammonium sulphate.

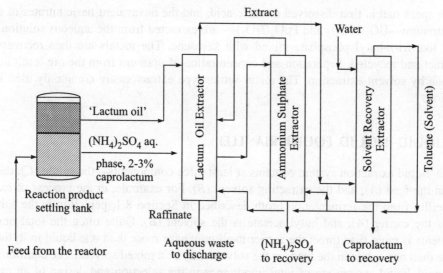

Figure 8.2(c) Recovery of caprolactum by solvent extraction.

8.1.4 A Few Other Applications

Solvent extraction has many other uses in food, pharmaceutical, metallurgical, environmental, and organic and inorganic chemical industries. It is used for purification of wet-process phosphoric acid to prepare the food-grade material. Recovery of acetic acid from a dilute aqueous solution has been practised since long because separation by distillation is very energy-intensive. Ethyl acetate and di-iso-propyl ether are the preferred solvents. Extraction of protein from ground fish or refining of fats by using propane as the purifying solvent (Solexol process) are typical applications in the food industry. Natural vitamins A and D are extracted from fish liver oil using liquid propane. Solvent extraction has proved to be effective in wastewater treatment. A typical application is separation and recovery of toxic organics like phenol. With the rapid growth in biotechnology, separation of high value bioproducts from dilute aqueous solutions (often called *bioseparation*) has assumed great importance. Solvent extraction is an effective and widely used technique for this purpose. One novel application is separation and concentration of proteins and other biomolecules by 'aqueous two-phase extraction' (Rao et al., 1998). The carrier and the solvent phases are aqueous solutions of two mutually incompatible polymers. The most common two polymers used for this purpose are polyethylene glycol (PEG) and dextran. Two major disadvantages of the technique occur due to small density difference and low interfacial tension of such two 'immiscible' aqueous phases.

Solvent extraction is an important technique of recovery of some metals. Extraction of copper from the ore leach liquor is a very important process. It can recover copper from very dilute solutions. A chelating extractant derived from hydroxyoximes or quinolinol in kerosene solution is largely used. Applications to nickel and cobalt extraction are also well known. Solvent extraction is an important separation step in 'nuclear fuel reprocessing'. Spent fuel from a nuclear reactor contains ^{238}U, ^{235}U, ^{239}Pu, ^{239}Th, and a few other fission products. Reprocessing consists of a number of steps for the separation of plutonium and residual uranium from the rest with a view to reusing them by mixing with fresh nuclear fuel. Alternatively, these materials may be disposed of safely.

The spent fuel is first dissolved in nitric acid, and the hexavalent basic nitrates of uranium and plutonium—$UO_2(NO_3)_2$ and $PuO_2(NO_3)_2$—are extracted from the aqueous solution using a solvent like tri-*n*-butyl phosphate mixed with kerosene. The metals are then recovered from the extract and recycled. Separation and concentration of uranium from the ore leach liquor are also done by solvent extraction. The mixer-settler type extractors are commonly used in metal extraction.

8.2 LIQUID–LIQUID EQUILIBRIA (LLE)

A liquid–liquid extraction system contains at least three components—the solute (*C*), the carrier liquid in the feed (*A*), and the extracting solvent (*B*). For example, in the process of extraction of penicillin from the fermentation broth described in Section 8.1, penicillin is the solute (*C*), water is the carrier (*A*), and butyl acetate is the solvent (*B*). Quite often the total number of components is more than three; the carrier itself may have more than one liquid in it, there may be more than one solute in the feed, or the solvent may be a mixed solvent. The equilibrium data for a liquid–liquid system are of vital importance in the selection and design of an extraction equipment.

8.2.1 Classification of Ternary Systems

Here we shall confine our discussion only to ternary systems comprising a carrier (*A*), a solvent (*B*), and a solute (*C*). Three binary mixtures can be formed out of these components: *A–B*, *B–C* and *C–A*. The mutual miscibility behaviour of the components in each of these binaries determines the nature of the equilibrium diagram for the ternary system. Most of the ternary systems fall in one of the following categories.

(a) The carrier (*A*) and the solvent (*B*) are practically immiscible. The equilibrium in such a system may be represented in the form of a '*x–y*' plot as in the case of distribution of a solute between a carrier gas and a solvent. If the solute concentration is small, a Henry's law-type linear distribution law applies.

(b) The solute is miscible with the carrier and with the solvent in all proportions, but the carrier and the solvent are only partially miscible (*A–C* and *B–C* are miscible pairs; the pair *A–B* is partially miscible). Such a system is called a Type-I ternary system. About 75% of ternary liquid systems fall in this category.

(c) The solute is completely miscible with the carrier; but both the solute and the carrier have limited miscibility with the solvent (the binary *A–C* is miscible in all proportions; the pairs *B–C* and *A–B* are only partially miscible). A ternary mixture of this type is called a Type II system.

8.2.2 Experimental Determination of Liquid–liquid Equilibrium Data

As in the case of determination of gas–liquid or vapour–liquid equilibria, liquid–liquid equilibrium data are obtained by measuring the concentrations of the three components in the two liquid phases in equilibrium at a given temperature. The following steps are followed: (a) Suitable quantities of purified *A, B*, and *C* are taken in an equilibrium cell maintained at a constant temperature. The content is mixed vigorously for a sufficient time to ensure attainment of equilibrium. (b) The content is allowed to separate into two phases. (c) Samples are drawn from the two phases and analyzed for the concentrations (expressed as mass fractions or mole fractions) of *A, B*, and *C*. A set of such experiments conducted with varying amounts of the three components at a constant temperature yields the data for the construction of a liquid–liquid equilibrium diagram. The liquid phase rich in the solvent (*B*) is called the *extract*, and the other phase which is rich in the 'carrier' is called the *raffinate*.

8.2.3   Graphical Representation of Liquid–liquid Equilibrium Data

For any of the two liquid phases in equilibrium in a ternary system, there are three concentration terms of the three components. If concentrations are expressed in mole fraction or in mass fraction, the sum of the three concentrations is unity. It is not possible to describe a phase or the equilibrium of two phases in contact in terms of the three concentrations using the normal rectangular coordinate system. But this can be done conveniently on an 'equilateral triangular graph'. Also there are two other techniques of representation of ternary equilibrium data using the rectangular coordinate system: (a) a 'right-angled triangular diagram' in which only two concentrations are plotted, and (b) using rectangular coordinates and plotting the mass fractions (or mole fractions) of the solute and of the solvent in the two phases on 'solvent-free basis'.

The equilateral triangular diagram

The basis of the technique of presentation of equilibrium data on an equilateral triangular graph paper is that the sum of the distances of a point within an equilateral triangle from the three sides is equal to the height of the triangle. On the equilateral triangle *ABC* in Figure 8.3(a), the vertices *A, B* and *C* represent the 'pure components' *A, B* and *C* respectively; the sides *AB, BC* and *CA*

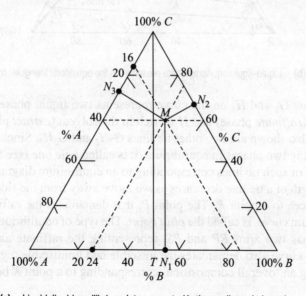

Figure 8.3(a)   Liquid–liquid equilibrium data presented in the equilateral triangular coordinates.

represent mixtures of *A* and *B, B* and *C,* and *C* and *A* respectively. A point within the $\triangle ABC$ represents a mixture of the components *A, B* and *C.* Consider the point *M,* for example. The sum of its distances from the three sides is $MN_1 + MN_2 + MN_3 = CT$, which is equal to the altitude of the triangle. From Figure 8.3(a) it is found that the point *M* lies on the dotted line representing 60% *C* ($MN_1 = 0.6CT$, *CT* being the altitude). Also, the point *M* lies on the dotted lines representing 16% *A* and 24% *B* respectively. So a mixture of *A, B* and *C* having 16% *A,* 24% *B,* and 60% *C* is represented by the point *M* on the triangular diagram. The LLE diagram of a ternary system is depicted in Figure 8.3(b). Here the solute *C* is miscible with the carrier *A* and with the solvent *B* in all proportions, but the carrier and the solvent are only partially miscible (Type I system). The curve *RPS* is the equilibrium diagram in the equilateral triangular coordinate system. It is obtained by plotting the data points representing the two liquid phases in equilibrium. The point *R* on the line *AB* represents the solubility of the solvent *B* in the carrier *A;* the point *S* represents that of the carrier *A* in the solvent *B* if there is no solute.

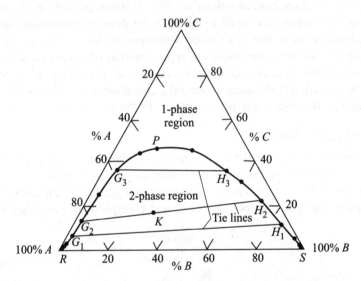

Figure 8.3(b) Liquid–liquid equilibrium data presented in the equilateral triangular coordinates.

The pair of points G_1 and H_1 on the curve represents two liquid phases in equilibrium; G_1 is rich in the carrier (*raffinate* phase) and H_1 is rich in the solvent (*extract* phase). The line $G_1 H_1$ is called a *tie line.* Also shown are two other tie lines $G_2 H_2$ and $G_3 H_3$. Since such a line connects two points representing two phases in equilibrium, it is called a *tie line* (see Section 7.1.2). There is an infinite number of such tie lines corresponding to an equilibrium diagram. Usually, these are not parallel. The length of a tie line decreases as we move away from the side *AB,* and eventually the last tie line reduces to a point *P.* The point *P,* that demarcates the raffinate and the extract sides of the equilibrium curve, is called the *plait point.* The type of equilibrium curve *RPS* is called *binodal* because it has two arms *RP* and *PS,* representing the raffinate and the extract sides.

The equilibrium curve also demarcates the miscible and immiscible regions on the graph. A liquid mixture having an 'overall composition' corresponding to a point *K* below the equilibrium curve *RPS* is a two-phase mixture. Such a mixture, when left undisturbed, separates into two phases at equilibrium. The compositions of these two phases are given by the terminals (G_2 and H_2) of the tie line passing through the point K; their amounts are given by the 'Lever Arm Rule' [see Eq. (7.4)].

The equilibrium curve is different for a Type II system; Figure 8.3(c) shows a representative equilibrium diagram. The raffinate and the extract arms of the equilibrium diagram do not meet. So there is *no plait point*. A few tie lines are shown in the figure.

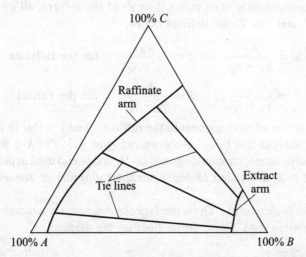

Figure 8.3(c)   Liquid–liquid equilibrium for a type II system (*A–B* and *B–C* partially miscible).

The right-angled triangular diagram

The rectangular coordinate system is used to prepare such a plot. Mass fractions of the solute in the two phases (the raffinate and the extract phases) at equilibrium are plotted against the corresponding mass fractions of the solvent [Figure 8.4(a)]. Concentrations of the extract phase (usually in mass fraction) are denoted by y_A, y_B, and y_C; those of the raffinate are x_A, x_B, and x_C. The raffinate arm *PQ* is obtained by plotting the set of points (x_B, x_C); the extract arm *PR* is

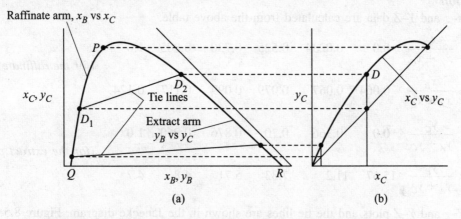

Figure 8.4   (a) Equilibrium plot on the right triangular coordinate, and (b) the *x–y* plot.

obtained by plotting the set of points (y_B, y_C). The point P is the plait point. The point D_1 on the raffinate arm and D_2 on the extract arm represent compositions at equilibrium. If they are joined, we get the tie line D_1D_2. The equilibrium diagram can also be drawn on the x_C–y_C plane [Figure 8.4(b)]. The tie line D_1D_2 corresponds to the point D on that plane.

Equilibrium plot on solvent-free basis

In this presentation of LLE data, the mass ratios of the solute (X and Y) in the two phases are plotted versus the corresponding mass ratios (z or Z) of the solvent, all on 'solvent-free basis'. The quantities (X, Y, and z or Z) are defined below.

$$X = \frac{x_C}{x_A + x_C}, \qquad z = \frac{x_B}{x_A + x_C} \qquad \text{for the raffinate}$$

$$Y = \frac{y_C}{y_A + y_C}, \qquad Z = \frac{y_B}{y_A + y_C} \qquad \text{for the extract}$$

Here x is the mass fraction of a component in the raffinate, and y is that in the extract. A typical equilibrium plot on "solvent-free basis" is shown in Figure 8.5. The X–z and Y–Z plots of LLE are similar to the enthalpy–concentration diagrams (x–H_L and y–H_V) used in distillation calculations. Such plots (X–z and Y–Z) are called *Maloney-Schubert diagram* or *Janecke diagram*.

EXAMPLE 8.1 (*Janecke diagram*)   Draw the Janecke diagram for a liquid–liquid system using the following equilibrium data. Show the tie lines on the diagram.

	Raffinate phase			Extract phase	
x_A	x_B	x_C	y_A	y_B	y_C
0.939	0.0601	0.0	0.06	0.94	0.0
0.7327	0.0654	0.0219	0.0520	0.918	0.03
0.4402	0.0732	0.4866	0.036	0.88	0.084
0.246	0.090	0.664	0.0185	0.851	0.1305
0.103	0.1047	0.7923	0.0069	0.8276	0.1655
0.0	0.1103	0.8897	0.0	0.8246	0.1754

Solution

The X–z and Y–Z data are calculated from the above table.

$$X = \frac{x_C}{x_A + x_C} \qquad 0.0 \quad 0.0234 \quad 0.525 \quad 0.730 \quad 0.885 \quad 1.0$$

(*for the raffinate phase*)

$$z = \frac{x_B}{x_A + x_C} \qquad 0.064 \quad 0.067 \quad 0.079 \quad 0.099 \quad 0.117 \quad 0.124$$

$$Y = \frac{y_C}{y_A + y_C} \qquad 0.0 \quad 0.366 \quad 0.70 \quad 0.876 \quad 0.960 \quad 1.0$$

(*for the extract phase*)

$$Z = \frac{y_B}{y_A + y_C} \qquad 15.67 \quad 11.2 \quad 7.33 \quad 5.71 \quad 4.8 \quad 4.7$$

The X–z and Y–Z plots and the tie lines are shown in the Janecke diagram, Figure 8.5.

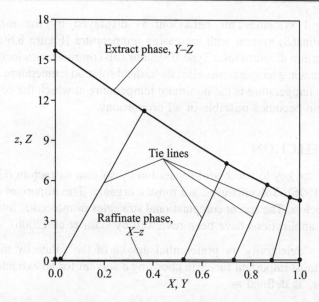

Figure 8.5   Janecke plot of liquid–liquid equilibrium data. (A few tie lines are also shown.)

8.2.4   Effect of Temperature on Liquid–Liquid Equilibria

The effect of temperature on liquid–liquid equilibria shown in Figure 8.6 is pretty strong. Miscibility of a liquid pair generally increases with temperature. With increasing temperature, the miscibility of the *B–C* pair (the solvent and the solute) in a Type II system increases more quickly than that of the *A–B* pair. At the critical solution temperature of the *B–C* pair, a Type II system

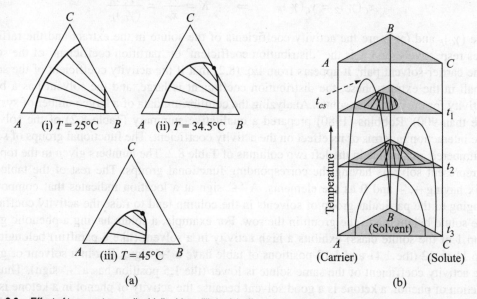

Figure 8.6   Effect of temperature on liquid–liquid equilibria: (a) effect of temperature on solubility for the system *n*-hexane (*A*)–methyl-cyclohexane (*C*)–aniline (*B*), and (b) temperature effect illustrated by a three-dimensional sketch.

turns into a Type I system. This behaviour is displayed by the *n*-hexane(*A*)–methyl-cyclohexane(*C*)–aniline(*B*) system with increasing temperature [Figure 8.6(a)]. The two-phase region of the equilibrium diagram for a Type II system still contracts with increasing temperature and eventually vanishes at a temperature called its 'critical solution temperature', t_{cs} [Figure 8.6(b)]. The critical solution temperature is the minimum temperature at which the components *A*, *B* and *C* of a Type I system becomes miscible in all proportions.

8.3 SOLVENT SELECTION

The right solvent is the key to successful separation by solvent extraction (Cusack et al., 1991; Cusack and Glatz, 1996). Solvents used are mostly organic. The important criteria for solvent selection are given below. The recent computational strategies of molecular interaction for solvent selection in diverse applications have been reviewed by Gani et al. (2006).

(a) *Selectivity:* 'Selectivity' or preferential uptake of the solute by the solvent over the carrier is the single most important factor in choosing a solvent for an extraction job. Selectivity or 'separation factor' is defined as

$$\beta_{C,A} = \frac{y_C/y_A}{x_C/x_A} \tag{8.1}$$

Selectivity of the solute varies with the compositions of the two phases in equilibrium and depends on temperature. It is unity at the plait point because the compositions of the two phases become the same. A theoretical approach to selection of a solvent for a particular type or class of solute was proposed by Robbins (see Cusack et al., 1991). The basis of the approach is the following simple equality of the activities of the solute in the two phases at equilibrium.

$$x_C(\gamma_C)_R = y_C(\gamma_C)_E \quad \Rightarrow \quad K = \frac{y_C}{x_C} = \frac{(\gamma_C)_R}{(\gamma_C)_E} \tag{8.2}$$

where $(\gamma_C)_E$ and $(\gamma_C)_R$ are the activity coefficients of the solute in the extract and the raffinate phases respectively, and *K* is the 'distribution coefficient' or 'partition coefficient' of the solute for the carrier-solvent pair. It appears from Eq. (8.2) that if the activity coefficient of the solute is small in the extract phase, the distribution coefficient is large, and the solvent has a better selectivity for the particular solute. Analyzing the equilibrium data of a large number of systems (more than 900), Robbins (1980) prepared a qualitative summary (Table 8.2) of the solvent-solute interaction in terms of its effect on the activity coefficient. The functional groups of solute are numbered and named in the left two columns of Table 8.2. The numbers given in the top row also represent solvents having the corresponding functional groups. The rest of the table is a matrix having +, – and 0 as the elements. A '+' sign at a location indicates that compounds belonging to the particular group of solvents in the column tend to raise the activity coefficient of the solute belonging to the group in the row. For example, a solute having a phenolic group (group 1 of the solute class) exhibits a high activity in a solvent (like a paraffin) belonging to group 11 or 12 (the 1,11 and 1,12 positions of table have a '+' sign). But in a solvent of group 5, the activity coefficient of the same solute is lower (the 1,5 position has a '–' sign). Thus for extraction of phenol, a ketone is a good solvent because the activity of phenol in a ketone is low and the distribution coefficient is predicted to be large. Table 8.2 classifies solvents primarily on the basis of hydrogen bonding and electron donor–acceptor interaction with solutes.

Table 8.2 Solute–solvent group interactions—preliminary guide to solvent selection[#]

Solute class	Group	Solvent class											
		1	2	3	4	5	6	7	8	9	10	11	12
1.	Phenol	0	0	–	0	0	–	–	–	–	–	–	–
2.	Acid, thiol	0	0	–	0	–	–	0	0	0	0	+	+
3.	Alcohol, water	–	–	0	+	+	0	–	–	+	+	+	+
4.	Active-H on multihalo paraffin	0	0	+	0	–	–	–	–	–	–	0	+
	H-acceptor												
5.	Ketone, amide with no H on N, sulphone, phosphine oxide	–	–	+	–	0	+	+	+	+	+	+	+
6.	Tertiary amine	–	–	0	–	+	0	+	+	0	+	0	0
7.	Secondary amine	–	0	–	–	+	+	0	0	0	0	0	+
8.	Primary amine, ammonia, amide with 2H on N	–	0	–	–	+	+	0	0	+	+	+	+
9.	Ether, oxide, sulphoxide	–	0	+	–	+	0	–	0	+	0	+	+
10.	Ester, aldehyde, carbonate phosphate, nitrate, nitrite nitrile, intramolecular bonding (for example, *o*-nitro phenol)	–	0	+	–	+	+	0	+	+	0	+	+
11.	Aromatic, olefin, halogen aromatic multi-halo-paraffin without active H, mono-halo-paraffin	+	+	+	0	+	0	0	+	0	+	0	0
	Non-H-bonding												
12.	Paraffin, carbon disulphide	+	+	+	+	+	0	+	+	+	+	0	0

Key: Deviation from normality for mixtures (+) = positive; (–) = negative; (0) = neutral

[#]*Source:* Robbins, L.A., *Chem. Eng. Prog.*, 76, October 1980, pp. 58–61.

(b) *Carrier-solvent immiscibility:* If the mutual solubility of the carrier and the solvent is low, they can be satisfactorily separated in the settler. Only a small quantity of the solvent will be retained in the raffinate and a small quantity of the carrier will remain dissolved in the solvent. So the cost of further separation of the phases by distillation or otherwise will be small.

(c) *Interfacial tension:* Interfacial tension between the carrier and the solvent has two opposing effects. A low interfacial tension favours fine dispersion of one liquid in the other, thereby increasing the specific interfacial area of mass transfer. The power consumption for dispersing one liquid into the other is also lower. On the other hand, coalescence of droplets leading to the separation of the raffinate and the extract phases does not occur readily if the interfacial tension is low. It is desirable to strike a balance between these opposing effects while selecting a solvent.

(d) *Density:* The driving force for phase separation in a settler is the difference in the densities of the two phases. The density of the lighter phase should generally be at least 5% less than that of the heavier phase in order to ensure smooth phase separation.

(e) *Viscosity:*   The solvent viscosity should be low. This reduces power consumption for mixing the phases.

(f) *Other factors:*   The solvent should preferably be less expensive, non-toxic, and non-corrosive. It should have a low flamability and volatility. Another very important phenomenon is accumulation of impurities in the solvent. If the solvent is of low volatility, it leaves the solvent clean-up tower at the bottom (Figure 8.1) and is recycled. There is a strong probability of accumulation of impurities and surface active agents. This causes lowering of interfacial tension and surface resistance to mass transfer between the two phases. The performance of an extractor may be greatly reduced by such phenomena. It has been estimated (see *Chem. Engg. Progress*, June 2002, p. 74) that the presence of impurities can reduce the capacity of a column by 20% or more and its efficiency by as much as 60%.

Hardly any solvent will satisfactorily meet all the above criteria. Choosing a solvent is again a matter of striking a balance between the properties and cost of the solvent on the one hand, and the equipment and operating costs and ease of operation on the other.

8.4   DESIGN CALCULATIONS FOR STAGE-WISE EXTRACTION

While dealing with the problem of separation of a liquid mixture, a decision has to be taken first about the separation process (such as distillation, extraction, crystallization, etc.) to be adopted. If liquid–liquid extraction appears to be the choice, the next job is to select the solvent to be used. The design of extractors is far less standardized than that of absorption or distillation columns. Pilot plant tests may have to be done if reliable design data collected from operating units handling a similar mixture are not available (Cusack and Glatz, 1998).

Like other mass transfer operations, solvent extraction can be carried out in a staged or in a continuous contact equipment (see Section 8.6). The important stage-wise pieces of contact equipment are (i) mixer-settler, (ii) sieve tray column, and (iii) Schiebel column. Continuous contact takes place in an equipment like (i) the rotating disk contactor (RDC), (ii) Graesser raining bucket contactor, (iii) Podbielniak extractor, (iv) the packed column, and (v) the spray column, etc. In this section, we will discuss the methods of determination of the number of ideal stages required for solvent extraction in a stage-wise contact equipment. The methods to be described here are based on graphical construction of ideal stages for partially miscible ternary systems. Determination of the number of ideal stages for extraction systems in which the solvent and the carrier (the *A–B* pair) are practically immiscible can be done by following the procedures already described in Chapter 4.

8.4.1   Single-Stage Operation

A single-stage equilibrium contact device is shown in Figure 8.7(a). The feed enters the mixer at a rate F having a solute concentration x_F (the solute concentration in the raffinate is denoted by x and that in the extract by y, both in mass%). The solvent is supplied at a rate of S; it has a solute concentration $y_S{}^\oplus$. The liquid–liquid dispersion attains equilibrium and leaves the mixer at a rate M with an overall solute concentration x_M. The raffinate (flow rate = R, solute

---

$\oplus$ The solute is separated from the extract (solvent) phase (as shown in Figure 8.1) and the solvent is recycled. So the feed solvent is likely to have a little solute left in it.

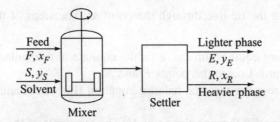

Figure 8.7(a) Schematic of a single-stage extraction unit.

concentration = x_R) and the extract (flow rate = E, solute concentration = y_E) phases leave the settler after phase separation. The following material balance equations may be written.

Total material balance:
$$F + S = M = E + R \qquad (8.3)$$

Solute balance:
$$Fx_F + Sy_S = Mx_M = Ey_E + Rx_R \qquad (8.4)$$

$$\Rightarrow \qquad x_M = \frac{Fx_F + Sy_S}{F + S} \qquad (8.5)$$

Combining the above two equations, we may write

$$Fx_F + Sy_S = (F + S)x_M$$

$$\Rightarrow \qquad \frac{F}{S} = \frac{x_M - y_S}{x_F - x_M} \qquad (8.6)$$

The ternary equilibrium data are plotted on a suitable diagram. Let us select the equilateral triangular diagram [Figure 8.7(b)]. The compositions of the feed and the solvent streams are located at points F and S on the diagram[†]. By virtue of the Lever Arm Rule (Section 7.4), we may conclude that the mixture of mass M and solute concentration x_M can be represented by a point M on the line joining F and S. From Eqs. (8.3) and (8.4), we may also write

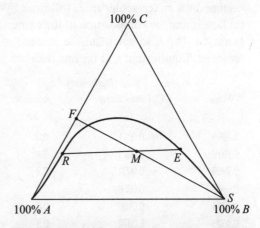

Figure 8.7(b) Single-stage liquid extraction calculation using the equilibrium plot on the right triangular coordinate.

$$Rx_R + Ey_E = (R + E)x_M \quad \Rightarrow \quad \frac{E}{R} = \frac{x_M - x_R}{y_E - x_M} \qquad (8.7)$$

The above equation indicates that the point M also lies on the line joining the points E and R. Since the mixer acts as a 'theoretical' or 'equilibrium stage', the phases E and R are at equilibrium and must lie on the terminals of the tie line through the point M on the equilateral triangular diagram. Thus the solute concentrations in the extract and the raffinate phases (y_E and x_R) can

---

[†] By convention the symbols F and S represent the flow rates and locations of the two points representing their compositions. Similar convention has been used in Section 7.2.

be obtained by drawing the tie line through the point *M*. The steps of the graphical procedure are given below.

(a)   Draw the ternary equilibrium curve on the equilateral triangular diagram (or any other suitable diagram). Locate the points *F* and *S*.

(b)   Calculate x_M from the material balance equation [Eq. (8.5)] and locate the point *M* on the line *FS*.

(c)   Draw the tie line *ER* through the point *M*. The terminals of the tie line give the extract and raffinate concentrations, y_E and x_R. The amount of the extract and raffinate phases (*E* and *R*) and the percentage of the solute separated from the feed can now be calculated from Eqs. (8.3) and (8.4) or Eq. (8.7).

If a required percentage separation of the solute is specified, the necessary solvent rate can be calculated. However, this will involve a trial-and-error procedure. This is illustrated in Example 8.2 using the right triangular coordinate.

EXAMPLE 8.2 (*Single-stage extraction*)   One thousand kilograms of an aqueous solution containing 50% acetone is contacted with 800 kg of chlorobenzene containing 0.5 mass% acetone in a mixer-settler unit, followed by separation of the extract and the raffinate phases. (a) Determine the composition of the extract and the raffinate phases and the fraction of acetone extracted. (b) Also calculate the amount of solvent required if 90% of the acetone is to be removed. Equilibrium and tie line data are given below.

Aqueous phase (*Raffinate*)			Organic phase (*Extract*)		
Water	Chlorobenzene	Acetone	Water	Chlorobenzene	Acetone
x_A	x_B	x_C	y_A	y_B	y_C
0.9989	0.0011	0.0	0.0018	0.9982	0.0
0.8979	0.0021	0.1	0.0049	0.8872	0.1079
0.7969	0.0031	0.2	0.0079	0.7698	0.2223
0.6942	0.0058	0.3	0.0172	0.608	0.3748
0.5864	0.0136	0.4	0.0305	0.4751	0.4944
0.4628	0.0372	0.5	0.0724	0.3357	0.5919
0.2741	0.1259	0.6	0.2285	0.1508	0.6107
0.2566	0.1376	0.6058	0.2566	0.1376	0.6058

Solution

Given: mass of the feed, *F* = 1000 kg; mass fraction acetone (*C*) in the feed, $x_{C,F} = 0.5$; and the mass fraction of chlorobenzene in the feed, $x_{B,F} = 0$.

(a)   Solvent: mass, *S* = 800 kg; $y_{C,S} = 0.005$; $y_{B,S} = 0.995$
From Eqs. (8.3) and (8.5),

$$M = F + S = 1800; \qquad x_{M,C} = \frac{F\,x_{C,F} + S\,y_{C,S}}{M} = \frac{(1000)(0.5) + (800)(0.005)}{1800} = 0.28$$

The equilibrium data are plotted using the right triangular coordinates [Figure 8.8(a)]. The points *F* and *S* are plotted on the diagram; the point *M* is located on the line *FS* (for $x_{M,C} = 0.28$). The tie line *RE* through *M* is determined by trial taking help of the x_C–y_C curve [Figure 8.8(b)] drawn alongside on the same scale. It is to be noted that a point on the x_C–y_C curve gives the equilibrium concentrations of the solute (C) in the two phases. The point P on the x_C–y_C diagram corresponds to the tie line RE.

From Figure 8.8(a) or 8.8(b), the solute concentrations in the raffinate (R) and the extract (E) phases are:

$$x_{C,R} = 0.236 \quad \text{and} \quad y_{C,E} = 0.302$$

From Eqs. (8.3) and (8.7),

$$E + R = 1800 \quad \text{and} \quad \frac{E}{R} = \frac{0.28 - 0.236}{0.302 - 0.28} \quad \Rightarrow \quad E = \boxed{1200 \text{ kg}} \quad R = \boxed{600 \text{ kg}}$$

Mass of acetone leaving with the raffinate = $(R)(x_{C,R})$ = $(1200)(0.302)$ = $\boxed{362.4 \text{ kg}}$

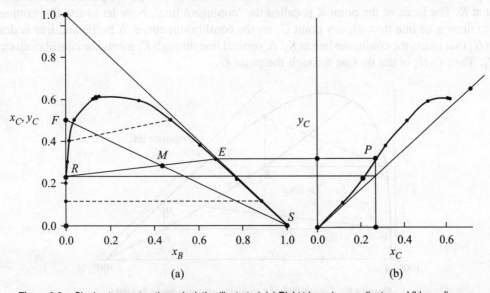

(a)   (b)

Figure 8.8 Single-stage extraction calculation illustrated: (a) Right triangular coordinate, and (b) x–y diagram.

Mass of acetone in the feed = $(1000)(0.5)$ = 500 kg

Acetone entering with the solvent = $(800)(0.005)$ = 4 kg

Net amount of acetone transported to the extract stream = $362.4 - 4$ = 358.4 kg

Fraction of acetone removed by extraction = $\dfrac{358.4}{500}$ i.e. $\boxed{71.7\%}$

(b) If 90% of the acetone is removed,

acetone remaining in the aqueous phase = $(500)(0.1)$ = 50 kg

It is to be noted that at this low concentration of the solute, the mutual solubility of water and chlorobenzene is negligible. Therefore, the raffinate may be assumed to be virtually free from chlorobenzene. Then the concentration of acetone in the raffinate is $50/550 = 0.0909$.

At $x_{C,R} = 0.0909$, we have $y_{C,E} = 0.105$ (from the equilibrium curve).

Also, the mass of the raffinate, R = 550 kg

If S is the mass of the solvent required, we can write the following material balance for the solute.

$$(1000)(0.5) + (S)(0.005) = (S + 450)(0.105) + (550)(0.0909) \Rightarrow S = \boxed{4027 \text{ kg}}$$

8.4.2 Determination of the Tie Line Through a Point on the Equilibrium Line

Only a few experimental tie line data for a ternary system are generally available. There are two 'interpolation' techniques of drawing a tie line through any point on the equilibrium curve. Both the techniques use the available tie line data and a 'conjugate line' (Sherwood and Pigford, 1952; Seader and Henley, 1998). One technique is illustrated in Figure 8.9. A horizontal line is drawn through the end G of the tie line GH. A vertical line is drawn through the point H. The two lines meet at K. The locus of the point K is called the 'conjugate line'. Now let us use this conjugate line to draw a tie line through any point G_1 on the equilibrium curve. A horizontal line is drawn from G_1 that meets the conjugate line at K_1. A vertical line through K_1 meets the equilibrium curve at H_1. Then G_1H_1 is the tie line through the point G_1.

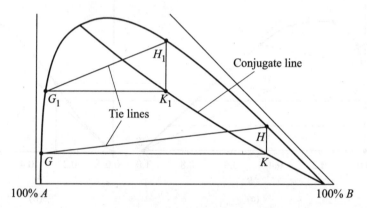

Figure 8.9 Construction of a conjugate line using the tie-line data.

8.4.3 Multistage Cross-current Extraction

A multistage cross-current cascade is schematically shown in Figure 8.10. The solvent is fed to the stages separately and the amounts need not be equal. The feed is supplied to the stage at one

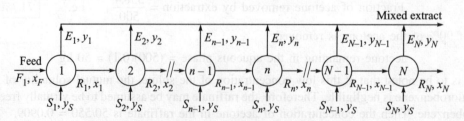

Figure 8.10 Schematic of a cross-current extraction cascade.

end of the cascade (let us call it stage 1). It moves from one stage to the next in succession with gradually decreasing solute concentration. If the solvent and the carrier liquid have negligible miscibility, extraction calculations can be done following the procedure described in Section 4.6.4. Here we shall deal with ternary systems in which the carrier and the solute have limited solubility.

The graphical method of calculation is convenient. Any of the three types of equilibrium diagrams (drawn using equilateral triangular, right triangular or 'solvent-free' coordinates) may be used. But the calculation procedures are similar.

Let there be N number of stages in the cross-current extraction cascade. The flow rates and concentrations of all the input and output streams are shown in Figure 8.10. We may write the following mass balance equations for the nth stage.

Total mass balance $\quad : \quad R_{n-1} + S_n = M_n = E_n + R_n$ (8.8)

Mass balance of the solute $C \quad : \quad R_{n-1}x_{n-1} + S_n y_S = M_n x_{M,n} = E_n y_n + R_n x_n$ (8.9)

The principle of multistage extraction calculation is similar to that of a single-stage extraction unit. From Eq. (8.8), we see that if the flow rates and concentrations of the streams R_{n-1} and S_n are known, the point M_n can be located on the line joining R_{n-1} and S_n. Again, if the tie line through the point M_n is drawn, its terminals give the points R_n and E_n. A step-by-step procedure is given below.

(a) Stage 1 receives the fresh feed which does not generally contain any solvent. Putting $n = 1$, in Eq. (8.8), we get the material balance equation for stage 1.

$$F + S_1 = M_1 = E_1 + R_1 \qquad (8.10)$$

The point F is located on the x–y plane. The point S_1 is also located. The point M_1 is located on the line joining F and S_1 by using the Lever Arm Rule or by calculating the value of x_{M1} from Eq. (8.9). The tie line through the point M_1 is drawn and the points E_1 and R_1 are located at its terminals.

(b) For stage 2, the solvent rate is S_2 and the rate of input of feed is R_1(which is nothing but the 'first-stage raffinate'). The point S_2 is located on the graph; the other point R_1 is known. These two points are joined and the mixture of the phases M_2 is located on the line joining these points R_1 and S_2. Again the terminals of the tie line through M_2 give the points E_2 and R_2.

(c) The procedure is repeated for the remaining stages. In the above analysis, we have tacitly assumed that the rates of solvent input to the stages and its concentrations are known. The flow rates and concentrations of the 'raffinates' and 'extracts' from all the stages can be found out by following the above steps. In practical problems, the solute concentrations, if any, in the feed solvent streams to the different stages remain the same. The procedure is illustrated in Example 8.3.

There may be other versions of the design problem. For example: the feed rate and composition, the solvent composition and the maximum allowable concentration of the solute in the final raffinate are given; the same amount of solvent is fed to the stages; it is required to determine the solvent rate if the extraction is to be done in a specified number of stages. This and other versions of the design problem may be solved using the principles discussed above. But trial-and-error calculations may sometimes be necessary depending upon the nature of the problem.

EXAMPLE 8.3 (*Cross-current extraction calculation*)   One thousand kilograms of an aqueous solution containing 35 mass% trimethyl amine (TMA) and 65% water is to be extracted using benzene as the solvent. A three-stage cross-current extraction scheme is suggested. The amounts of solvent (98% benzene, 2% TMA) to be used in successive stages are 815 kg, 950 kg and 2625 kg. Determine the fraction of the solute removed if the stages are ideal. The compositions of the raffinate and the extract (two phases) as well as the tie-line data are given below (water: *A*; benzene: *B*; TMA: *C*).

Water-rich phase:	x_B	0.004	0.006	0.01	0.02	0.03	0.036	0.07	0.13
	x_C	0.05	0.10	0.15	0.20	0.35	0.30	0.35	0.40
Benzene-rich phase:	y_B	0.95	0.90	0.84	0.78	9.71	0.63	0.50	0.26
	y_C	0.05	0.10	0.15	0.20	0.25	0.30	0.35	0.40
Tie-line data:	x_C	0.04	0.083	0.13	0.215	0.395			
	y_C	0.035	0.068	0.09	0.145	0.31			

Solution

The problem is solved using the right triangular coordinate.

Feed, F = 1000 kg. Feed composition: 35% TMA ($x_{C,F}$ = 0.35); 65% water ($x_{A,F}$ = 0.65).

The equilibrium data are plotted and the tie lines are drawn (dotted lines) in Figure 8.11.

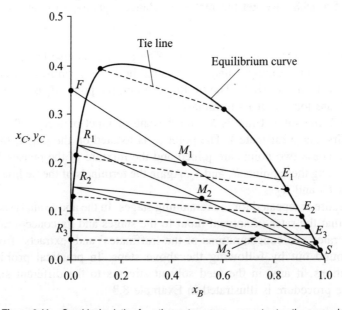

Figure 8.11   Graphical solution for a three-stage cross-current extraction cascade.

Stage 1:   The solvent rate, S_1 = 815 kg; $y_{B,S}$ = 0.98, $y_{C,S}$ = 0.02 (2% TMA, rest benzene).

M_1 = 1000 + 815 = 1815 kg; $x_{C,M1}$ = [(1000)(0.35) + (815)(0.02)]/1815 = 0.202

The points F ($x_{B,F}$ = 0, $x_{C,F}$ = 0.35), S ($y_{B,S}$ = 0.98, $y_{C,S}$ = 0.02) are located on the diagram. The point M_1 is located on the line FS ($x_{C,M1}$ = 0.202). The tie line R_1E_1 is drawn; the extremities of the tie line give the compositions of the raffinate and extract phases leaving stage 1 in equilibrium.

From the figure, $x_{C,R1} = 0.24$; $y_{C,E1} = 0.166$

Total material balance: Eq. (8.3), $M_1 = R_1 + E_1 = 1815$ (i)

Solute balance: $(M_1)(x_{C,M1}) = (R_1)(x_{C,R1}) + (E_1)(y_{C,R1})$

$\Rightarrow$ $(1815)(0.202) = (R_1)(0.24) + (E_1)(0.166)$ (ii)

Solving the material balance equations (i) and (ii), $R_1 = \boxed{882 \text{ kg}}$; $E_1 = \boxed{933 \text{ kg}}$

Stage 2: The raffinate from stage 1 (R_1) is the feed to stage 2. Solvent added, $S_2 = 950$ kg; $y_{C,S2} = 0.02$.

$M_2 = R_1 + S_2 = 882 + 950 = 1832$ kg; solute balance: $M_2 x_{C,M2} = (R_1)(x_{C,R1}) + (S_2)(y_{C,S2})$

Putting the values of different quantities, $x_{C,M2} = 0.126$.

The composition of the solvent to the second stage being the same as that to the first, it is represented by the same point S. The line $R_1 S$ is joined and the point M_2 ($x_{C,M2} = 0.126$) is located on this line as shown in Figure 8.11. The tie line $R_2 E_2$ is drawn through the point M_2.

The compositions of the raffinate and the extract phases from stage 2 are obtained from the figure as: $x_{C,R2} = 0.15$ and $y_{C,E2} = 0.105$

Material balance equations similar to Eqs. (i) and (ii) are written. Solving these equations, we get

$$R_2 = \boxed{854.3 \text{ kg}} \qquad E_2 = \boxed{977.7 \text{ kg}}$$

Stage 3: Similarly, the third stage receives $R_2 = 854.3$ kg 'feed' and $S_3 = 2625$ kg of the solvent. Proceeding in the same way we can locate the point M_3 ($x_{C,M3} = 0.052$) on the line $R_2 S$ and draw the tie line through M_3 to meet the equilibrium curve at the points R_3 ($x_{C,R3} = 0.0596$) and E_3 ($y_{C,E3} = 0.0506$). The amounts of the phases can be obtained from material balance as before:

$$R_3 = \boxed{540.8 \text{ kg}} \qquad \text{and} \qquad E_3 = \boxed{2938.5 \text{ kg}}$$

Total amount of TMA leaving the stages

$= (E_1)(y_{C,E1}) + (E_2)(y_{C,E2}) + (E_3)(y_{C,E3})$

$= (933)(0.166) + (977.7)(0.105) + (2938.5)(0.0506) = 406.2$ kg

Total amount of TMA entering the three stages with the solvent

$= (S_1 + S_2 + S_3)(y_{C,S}) = (815 + 950 + 2625)(0.02) = 87.8$ kg

Net amount of TMA removed = $406.2 - 87.8 = 318.4$ kg

Total amount of solute in the feed = $(1000)(0.35) = 350$ kg

Fraction of TMA removed = $(318.4/350)(100) = \boxed{91\%}$

8.4.4 Countercurrent Extraction—Determination of the Number of Ideal Stages

A countercurrent extraction cascade, along with the flow rates and concentrations of the input and output streams at the stages, is shown in Figure 8.12. The concentrations and flow rates of the feed and the solvent are usually given. If the solvent rate is not specified, it can be taken as a suitable multiple of the 'minimum solvent rate'. We have to determine the number of ideal contact stages required if the maximum permissible concentration of the solute in the raffinate is given. We may write the following material balance equations.

Total material balance over the entire unit (over envelope I): $F + S = E_1 + R_N = M$ (8.11)

Solute balance over envelope I: $Fx_F + Sy_S = E_1y_1 + R_Nx_N = Mx_M$ (8.12)

Total material balance over envelope II: $R_{n-1} + S = E_n + R_N$ (8.13)

Solute balance over envelope II: $R_{n-1}x_{n-1} + Sy_S = E_ny_n + R_Nx_N$ (8.14)

The equilibrium curve is drawn using a suitable coordinate system. From the known compositions of the feed, the solvent and the raffinate, the points F, S and R_N, can be located on the diagram. The point M representing the mixture of F and S is also located on the line FS. Equation (8.11) says that the point M lies also on the line joining the points R_N and E_1 (the point E_1 represents the extract phase leaving stage 1; see Figure 8.12). Therefore, the line R_NM when extended meets the equilibrium curve at the point E_1.

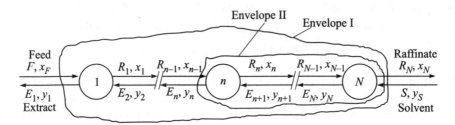

Figure 8.12   Schematic of a countercurrent extraction cascade.

Now we rewrite Eq. (8.11) in the following form:

$$E_1 - F = S - R_N = \Delta \qquad (8.15)$$

Also from Eqs. (8.13) and (8.15),

$$E_n - R_{n-1} = S - R_n = \Delta \qquad (8.16)$$

Here Δ may be considered to be a fictitious stream obtained by 'removing' a mass F of the feed from the first stage extract E_1, or by 'removing' a mass R_N of the 'last stage raffinate' from the solvent S. It represents a 'difference point' (similar to that identified in Section 7.8) lying on the line FE_1 extended and also on R_NS extended. In other words, it is the point of intersection of FE_1 and R_NS. Also, it follows from Eq. (8.16) that if the line $R_{n-1}E_n$ is extended, it has to pass through the difference point Δ. These results can be directly used to determine the number of ideal contact stages required to achieve the given degree of separation.

Since the stages are ideal, the streams E_n and R_n leaving the nth stage are at equilibrium. Thus the tie line through the point E_1 meets the equilibrium curve at R_1. Equation (8.16) says that for $n = 2$, the line joining R_1 and Δ meets the equilibrium curve at E_2. The tie line through E_2 meets the equilibrium curve at the point R_2. The procedure is repeated till the point R_N representing the raffinate is reached. The number of tie lines drawn in the process to reach the point R_N is the number of ideal stages. The procedure is illustrated in Example 8.4.

EXAMPLE 8.4 (*Multistage countercurrent extraction*) It is planned to extract diphenyl hexane (DPH) from a solution in docosane (*A*) using 'pure' furfural (*B*) as the solvent. The feed enters the extractor cascade at a rate of 2000 kg/h with 45% DPH (*C*) that has to be reduced to 4% in the final raffinate. The solvent rate is 2500 kg/h. Determine the number of theoretical stages required. Extraction is to be carried out at 45°C. Several compositions on the extract and the raffinate arms and the tie-line data in mass% of the components at 45°C are given below.

Equilibrium data

A:	96.0	84.0	67.0	52.5	32.6	21.3	13.2	7.7	4.4	2.6	1.5	1.0	0.7
B:	4.0	5.0	7.0	10.0	20.0	30.0	40.0	50.0	60.0	70.0	80.0	90.0	99.3
C:	0	11.0	26.0	37.5	47.4	48.7	46.8	42.3	35.6	27.4	18.5	9.0	0.0

Tie-line data

Raffinate (Docosane) phase, mass%			Extract (Furfural) phase, mass%		
A	*B*	*C*	*A*	*B*	*C*
85.2	4.8	10.0	1.1	89.1	9.8
69.0	6.5	24.5	2.2	73.6	24.2
43.9	13.3	42.6	6.8	52.3	40.9

Solution

Given: $F = 2000$; $x_{C,F} = 0.45$; $x_{C,N} = 0.04$; $S = 2500$; $x_{C,S} = 0.0$

By Eq. (8.5), $$x_{C,M} = \frac{F x_{C,F} + S y_{C,S}}{F + S} = \frac{(0.45)(2000) + (0)(2500)}{2000 + 2500} = 0.2$$

The raffinate (i.e. the stream R_N) has 4% DPH in it. So mass fraction of DPH in it is $x_C = 0.04$.

The equilibrium data are plotted using the right triangular coordinate in Figure 8.13(a); the tie lines are shown by light dotted lines. The points $F(0, 0.45)$, $S(1.0, 0)$, M (on the line *FS* at $x_{C,M} = 0.2$), R_N (at $x_C = 0.04$ on the equilibrium curve) are located. R_N and M are joined and the line is extended to meet the equilibrium curve at E_1. The lines FE_1 and $R_N S$, when extended, meet at the 'difference point', Δ.

The stages being ideal, the tie line through E_1 meets the equilibrium curve at the point R_1, the raffinate phase leaving the first stage. Also, putting $n = 2$, it is evident from Eq. (8.16) that E_2 lies on the point of intersection of the line $R_1 \Delta$ and the equilibrium curve. In fact, $R_1 E_2$ is the 'operating line' for the second stage of the cascade. The tie line through the point E_2 meets the equilibrium curve at R_2. Proceeding in the same way, we can draw successive stages till the point R_N is reached.

From Figure 8.13(a), the number of ideal stages required for the separation is 4.

An alternative technique can be more conveniently used for graphical construction of stages. A line emanating from the difference point, Δ, intersects the extract arm of the LLE curve at a point E_{n+1} [corresponding solute concentration is $y_C = (y_C)_{n+1}$] and the raffinate arm at a point R_n [where $x_C = (x_C)_n$]. A few such lines (drawn as broken lines) are shown in Figure 8.13(b). The 'locus' of the point $[(x_C)_n, (y_C)_{n+1}]$ is the operating line on the x_C–y_C plane [see

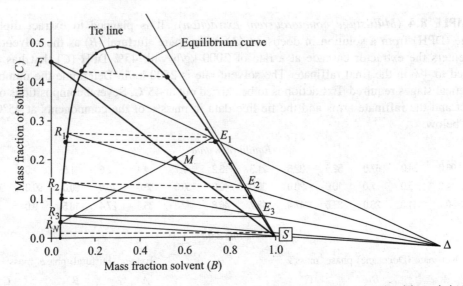

Figure 8.13(a)   Graphical construction of ideal stages for countercurrent extraction using the right-angled triangular coordinate system.

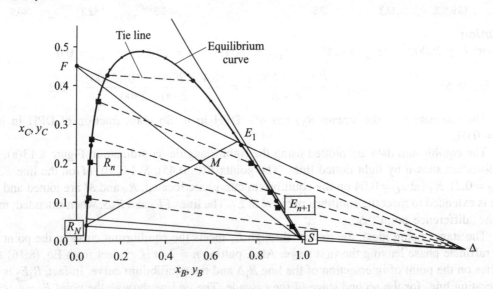

Figure 8.13 (b)   Graphical construction for obtaining points on the operating line.

Figure 8.13(c)]. The set of (x_C, y_C) values derived from Figure 8.13(b) and used to draw the operating line on Figure 8.13(c) is given below.

x_C	0.04	0.1	0.14	0.17	0.22	0.26	0.30	0.33	0.38	0.415
y_C	0.03	0.051	0.018	0.09	0.125	0.15	0.178	0.20	0.252	0.280

The equilibrium line is drawn in Figure 8.13(c) using the given 'tie line' data. The operating line is also drawn by plotting the above x_C–y_C data. Stages are now constructed by drawing stages

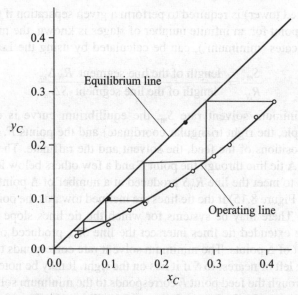

Figure 8.13(c) Construction of stages on the x_C–y_C plane.

between the equilibrium line and the operating line. The number of ideal stages is 4.8 [compared to 4 obtained from Figure 8.13(a); the difference probably occurs because of the error in drawing the tie lines].

This technique of construction is simpler and gives a more accurate estimate of the number of stages and is recommended for use.

8.4.5 Stage-wise Extraction with Reflux

The solute concentration in the extract leaving a countercurrent cascade can at best be nearly at equilibrium with the feed stream. It is possible to have a richer extract by use of *reflux* at the product end of the cascade. This works like adding reflux to the rectifying section of a distillation column. An arrangement of countercurrent multistage extraction with reflux is schematically shown in Figure 8.14.

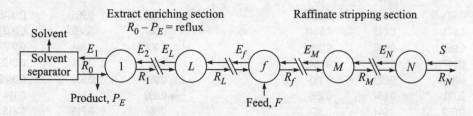

Figure 8.14 Countercurrent multistage extraction with reflux.

8.4.6 The Minimum Solvent Rate

This is an important quantity often determined in connection with the design of an extraction equipment. An infinite number of contact stages (or an infinite height of a continuous contact device such as a packed tower) is required to perform a given separation if the minimum solvent rate is used. If the Δ point for an infinite number of stages is known, the minimum solvent rate, S_m (the suffix m indicates 'minimum'), can be calculated by using the Lever Arm Rule.

$$\frac{S_m}{R_N} = \frac{\text{length of the line segment } R_N\Delta_m}{\text{length of the line segment } S\Delta_m} \tag{8.17}$$

To determine the minimum solvent rate S_m, the equilibrium curve is drawn on a suitable coordinate (for example, the right triangular coordinate) and the points F, S and R_N are located from the given compositions of the feed, the solvent and the raffinate. The points R_N and S are joined and produced. A tie line through the point F and a few others below it are drawn. All these tie lines are extended to meet the line $R_N S$ produced at a number of Δ points. The meeting point *closest* to S is Δ_m (see Figure 8.15) if the tie lines are inclined towards the point S for the particular liquid–liquid system. There may be systems for which the tie lines slope away from the point S. In such a case, the extended tie lines intersect the line SR_N produced on the left side of the diagram yielding a set of Δ points. The minimum solvent rate corresponds to the Δ point *farthest* from S if it lies on the left or nearest to S if it lies on the right. It may be noted that in many cases, the tie line passing through the feed point F corresponds to the minimum solvent rate. This means that the pinch point lies on the feed end of the cascade. Determination of the minimum solvent rate is illustrated in Example 8.5.

Once the minimum solvent rate is found, the actual solvent rate is chosen on the basis of economic considerations. A higher solvent rate will no doubt reduce the fixed costs because less number of stages are required, but the operating cost will be higher primarily because of (i) handling a larger quantity of liquids, (ii) larger equipment size, and (iii) higher cost of separation of the solvent.

EXAMPLE 8.5 (*Minimum solvent rate calculation*)   Acetic acid (*C*) is to be extracted from a 45% aqueous solution using isopropyl ether (*B*) as the solvent at 20°C. The feed rate is 1500 kg/h and the raffinate must not contain more than 2.5% acid. If the solvent supplied to the extractor has 0.5% acetic acid in it, calculate the minimum solvent rate. The liquid–liquid equilibrium data at 20°C are given below.

Water layer (*raffinate*), mass%				Ether layer (*extract*), mass%		
A	*B*	*C*		*A*	*B*	*C*
0.981	0.012	0.0069		0.005	0.993	0.0018
0.971	0.015	0.0141		0.007	0.989	0.0037
0.955	0.016	0.0289		0.008	0.984	0.0079
0.917	0.019	0.0642		0.01	0.971	0.0193
0.844	0.023	0.133		0.019	0.933	0.0482
0.711	0.034	0.255		0.039	0.847	0.114
0.589	0.044	0.367		0.069	0.715	0.216
0.451	0.106	0.443		0.108	0.581	0.311
0.371	0.165	0.464		0.151	0.487	0.362

Solution

The equilibrium data are plotted on the right triangular coordinate to get the equilibrium curve (Figure 8.15). A set of tie lines are also drawn (these are the dotted lines in Figure 8.15). The

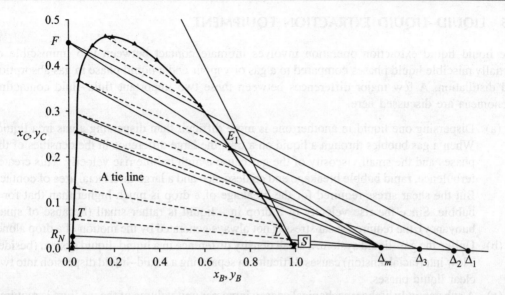

Figure 8.15 Graphical determination of the minimum solvent rate (Δ_m is the difference point corresponding to the minimum solvent rate).

point F (feed $F = 1500$ kg/h; $x_{B,F} = 0$, $x_{C,F} = 0.45$) and the point S (solvent; $y_{B,S} = 0.995$, $y_{C,S} = 0.005$) are located on the diagram. The raffinate has 2.5 mass% acid in it. The point R_N, representing the raffinate, is located on the equilibrium curve corresponding to $x_{C,RN} = 0.025$. The points R_N and S are joined and the line $R_N S$ is extended.

A set of tie lines are drawn including one which, when extended, passes through the feed point F. The tie lines are found to slope towards the point S, and meet the extension of the line $R_N S$ at a number of Δ points. The Δ point (Δ_m) nearest to S corresponds to the minimum solvent rate, S_m. Here it happens for the tie line TL. We use Eq. (8.17) and material balances to calculate S_m.

The length segments $R_N \Delta_m$ ($= 4.13$ units) and $S\Delta_m$ ($= 1.17$ units) are measured from the diagram.

Then
$$S_m/R_N = R_N\Delta_m/S\Delta_m = 4.13/1.17 = 3.53 \qquad \text{(i)}$$

But R_N is not known, and S_m cannot be obtained from the above equation alone. It is necessary to obtain the concentration of the extract stream E_1, corresponding to the minimum solvent rate. The line $F\Delta_m$ intersects the extract arm of the equilibrium curve at E_1 and the concentration of the solute in it is found to be $y_1 = 0.232$. Now we can write down two more equations—the total material balance and the solute balance.

Total material balance: $\quad F + S_m = R_N + E_1 \quad \Rightarrow \quad 1500 + S_m = R_N + E_1 \qquad \text{(ii)}$

Solute balance: $\qquad\qquad F(0.45) + S_m(0.005) = R_N(0.025) + E_1(0.232) \qquad \text{(iii)}$

Solving the above Eqs. (i), (ii) and (iii) we get, $S_m = \boxed{1942.4 \text{ kg}}$ = minimum solvent rate.

8.5   LIQUID–LIQUID EXTRACTION EQUIPMENT

The liquid–liquid extraction operation involves intimate contact between two immiscible or partially miscible liquid phases compared to a gas or vapour and a liquid phase in gas absorption and distillation. A few major differences between these two important fluid–fluid contacting phenomena are discussed here.

(a)   Dispersing one liquid in another one is more difficult than dispersing a gas in a liquid. When a gas bubbles through a liquid on a tray, the large difference in the densities of the phases and the small viscosity of the gas cause a high bubble rise velocity. This creates turbulence, rapid bubble breakage and coalescence and a large interfacial area of contact. But the shear stress required for the breakage of a drop is much higher than that for a bubble. Since the rise velocity of a drop in a liquid is rather small (because of small buoyancy), the required shear stress is not always generated by the motion of a drop alone.

(b)   Unlike the gas–liquid system, a small density difference in a liquid–liquid system (besides a low interfacial tension) causes difficulty in separating a liquid–liquid dispersion into two clear liquid phases.

(c)   A substantially higher mechanical energy input per unit volume of the medium is required for creating a liquid–liquid dispersion compared to that of a gas–liquid dispersion in a stirred vessel.

For the reasons mentioned above, the solvent extractors mostly have design and construction features much different from those of absorption and distillation columns. A classification of the more common extractors is given in Figure 8.16 (Reissinger and Schroter, 1978; Lo et al., 1983). Their construction and operation are briefly described below. Table 8.3 shows some important characteristics of common extractors.

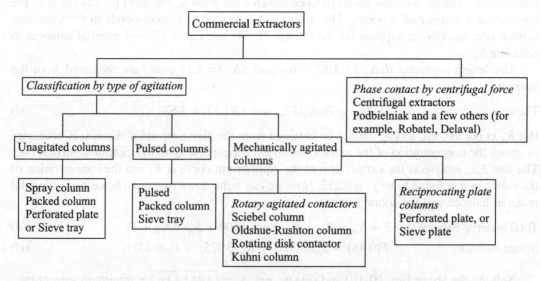

Figure 8.16   Classification of commercial extractors.

Table 8.3   Characteristics of the common extractors (Wankat, 1988)

Extractor class	Extractor type	Important characteristics
Mixer-settlers	Agitated vessel Static mixers	High stage efficiency, handles wide phase ratios and liquids with high viscosity, flexibility, reliable scale-up, not suitable for large number of theoretical stages.
Unagitated columns	Plate, packed and spray columns	Low capital cost, low operating/maintenance cost, simple construction, handles corrosive materials.
Pulsed columns	Perforated plate Packed columns	Low HETS, high mass transfer coefficient, no internal moving parts.
Rotary agitated columns	RDC, Oldshue-Rushton, Scheibel, Kuhni extractor	Moderate to high capacity, reasonable HETS, accommodates many theoretical stages, moderate cost, low cost of operation and maintenance.
Reciprocating plate	Karr column	High loading, low HETS, high versatility and flexibility, simple construction, handles liquids with suspended solids.
Centrifugal	Podbielniak	Short contact time, suitable for unstable materials, small size (limited space requirement), handles easily emulsifiable and small $\Delta\rho$ systems.

8.5.1   The Mixer-settler

This is the simplest and oldest type of extraction equipment. A stage of a mixer-settler cascade [Figure 8.7(a)] consists of a 'mixer' and a 'settler'.

Mixer

A common mixer is a vertical vessel in which one liquid phase is finely dispersed into the other by an agitator. The vessel is generally provided with four baffles to prevent the formation of vortex and also to create intense turbulence. The two liquid streams enter the mixer near the bottom. Sufficient time of contact is allowed for mass transfer from one phase to the other. This is the 'holding time'. The dispersion leaves the mixer at an upper level. A liquid–liquid mixing vessel is broadly similar to the one shown in Figure 5.15 except that it should be provided with two liquid inlets and one outlet for the dispersion.

A variety of impeller designs are available, for example, propeller, turbine, paddle, etc. A few common impeller types are shown in Figure 8.17. An impeller is usually positioned halfway the liquid depth. Power consumption or the rate of mechanical energy input depends upon a number of factors—the dimensions of the tank, the volume of dispersion, the impeller size and the design, the physical properties of the liquids (density, viscosity, interfacial tension), the ratio of the masses of the liquids in the tank ('phase ratio'), the degree of dispersion required, etc. Another important factor is, which phase is dispersed in the two-phase dispersion. If we start with pure *A* (the carrier) and go on adding *B* (the solvent) to it, we see that up to a certain mass per cent of *A*, it (i.e. the phase *A*) remains the continuous phase and *B* remains in it in the form of droplets. But after a threshold phase ratio, *phase inversion* occurs when *B* becomes the continuous phase while *A* remains dispersed in it. The power consumption, hydrodynamics and mass transfer characteristics of a liquid–liquid dispersion greatly change when the inversion point is crossed.

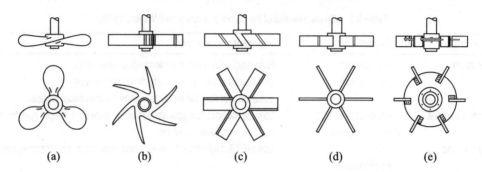

Figure 8.17   A few common impeller types: (a) marine-type propeller, (b) centrifugal turbine, (c) pitched-blade turbine, (d) flat-blade paddle, and (e) flat-blade turbine (Treybal, *Mass Transfer Operations*, 1980).

As an alternative to mechanical agitation, dispersion of the phases in the mixing vessel may be achieved by pump circulation, inline non-mechanical mixing by using a jet or nozzle, a static mixer or even by air agitation. It is understandable that an intense agitation or mixing will produce very small droplets and will provide a high rate of mass transfer because of enhanced interfacial area and mass transfer coefficient. Even a stage-efficiency of nearly 100% may be achieved. But this benefit is partially overshadowed by the accompanying problem of separation of the dispersion in distinct phases in the settler. So, a balance between the two—namely creating a very fine dispersion to achieve a high stage-efficiency and the time and efficiency of settling—has to be reached. Drop-size in dispersions typically ranges between 0.1 and 1 mm.

Settler

A dispersion leaves the mixer almost as an emulsion. This emulsion separates into two phases in the settler by coalescence of the fine droplets. A higher interfacial tension between the liquids enhances the coalescence rate; a lower value tends to produce a relatively stable emulsion that is difficult to separate into two phases. This factor also governs the selection of a solvent in liquid extraction. Phase separation becomes faster if the drop-size is larger, both the interfacial tension and the density difference between the liquids are higher, and the viscosity of the continuous phase is low. It may be noted that the drops are not of uniform size. There is always a 'distribution' of drop-size and 'drop-size' generally means the average size of the drops.

In order to improve the separation efficiency and to reduce the holding time and the volume of the settler, settling aids may be used. Tower packings, wire-mesh packings or oblique plate nests are effective settling aids. The surface of the settling aid is better wetted by the droplets or the dispersed phase. So, the impinging drops stick to the settling aid and then coalesce to form bigger drops that separate out of the dispersion.

A settling tank is a horizontal vessel provided with horizontal baffles (Figure 8.18). Typically, it has a length up to four times the diameter. For a system having $\Delta\rho \geq 0.1$ g/cm^3, a settler can separate about 300 gal/h of dispersion for 1 ft^2 of phase disengagement area (it is taken as LD_t, L = vessel length, D_t = diameter).

It will be pertinent to identify the advantages and disadvantages of the mixer–settler device. The *advantages* are: (a) high-stage efficiency (90% or more); (b) operational flexibility—a mixer-settler can handle difficult-to-disperse systems, like those having a large interfacial tension and/or

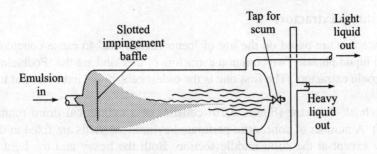

Figure 8.18 Horizontal gravity-settling vessel for phase separation of liquid–liquid dispersion (Treybal, 1963).

large density difference; it can also operate with varying flow rates and phase ratios; (c) scale-up design of mixer-settlers can be done more reliably from laboratory test data; (d) it can handle high viscous liquids and also liquids having suspended solids. The *disadvantages* are: (a) considerable pump and piping cost (for this reason, the use of mixer-settlers is often limited to separation jobs requiring less than five theoretical stages); (b) a larger floor area is required; (c) more solvent cost, because a large volume of solvent is always retained in the settling vessels.

Mixer-settlers are widely used in wet metallurgical processes.

Tower extractor

The tower extractor, developed by Lurgi Co., accommodates the mixers and settlers into a compact continuously operated unit as shown in Figure 8.19. The mixers of the cascade are placed outside the tower which has compartments for separating the phases. A drop coalescence zone is provided between a mixer and the corresponding settler.

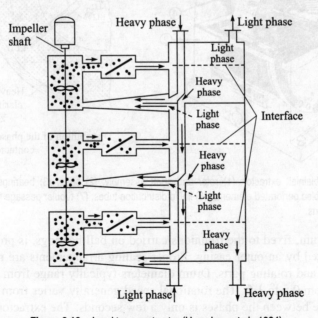

Figure 8.19 Lurgi tower extractor (Humphrey et al., 1984).

8.5.2   Centrifugal Extractors

Centrifugal extractors are based on the use of 'centrifugal force' to cause countercurrent radial flow of the two liquid phases. Two common extractors of this kind are the 'Podbielniak extractor' and the 'Quadronic extractor'. The first one is the oldest centrifugal extractor put to commercial use.

The Podbielniak extractor (Figure 8.20) consists of a cylindrical drum rotating around a horizontal shaft. A number of concentric perforated cylindrical shells are fixed to the drum. The shaft is hollow except at the solid middle section. Both the heavy and the light phases enter through the shaft but from opposite directions. The heavy liquid is let out near the centre of the drum. The light liquid is channelled to the inner periphery of the rotating drum. Because of the density difference of the liquids, the heavy phase flows radially outwards and displaces the light liquid phase that flows radially inwards (i.e. in the opposite direction). The heavy liquid that reaches the periphery returns through the channels and leaves the unit through an annular region around the shaft. The light liquid collects near the centre and also leaves through an annular passage around the shaft. The Podbielniak extractor is *functionally* similar to a sieve tray column in which the trays, as if, form concentric perforated shells and countercurrent radial flow of the phases occurs.

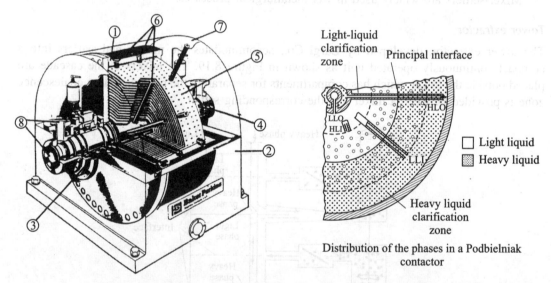

Distribution of the phases in a Podbielniak contactor

Figure 8.20   The Podbielniak extractor: (1) rotor and shaft assembly, (2) base, (3) bearings, (4) multi-V-belt drive, (5) concentrically assembled perforated elements, (6) liquid distribution tubes, (7) tubular passage for cleaning and flushing, and (8) inlet and outlet ports.

The rotating drum, fixed to the trunnions carried on ball bearings, is provided with a drive pulley and is covered by an outer casing. Proper sealing arrangements are made at the contact between stationary and rotating parts. Drum diameters typically range from 1.5 to 3 ft, and the length may vary from 0.5 to 1 ft. The rotational speed generally varies from 2000 to 5000 rpm, and the contact time between the phases is only a few seconds. The extractor typically provides about 3 to 5 theoretical stages of contact and is suitable when the liquid density difference is $\Delta\rho \geq 0.05$ g/cm^3. The advantages of the Podbielniak extractor are: (a) very short contact time between the phases (this makes the equipment suitable for unstable and sensitive materials like pharmaceuticals), (b) low space requirement, and (c) can handle liquids having a small difference in densities. The disadvantages are: (a) high capital cost, and (b) high maintenance cost.

8.5.3 Unagitated Extraction Columns

An extractor belonging to this category has a cylindrical shell with internals. The heavy liquid enters at the top and the light at the bottom through a distributor. One of the liquids remains dispersed in the other. Countercurrent flow of the liquids is driven by gravity and bouyancy forces. Drop breakage and coalescence occur all along the column and new interfacial area is created or the interfacial area is 'renewed'. The drop breakage and coalescence phenomena are enhanced in column extractors in which there is mechanical energy input by the motion of the internals (for example, a rotor) in the column.

Because the drops move under the effect of buoyancy only, the maximum allowable flow rates of the phases in a given column get limited by *flooding* of the tower. The mechanism of flooding is the same as that in a gas–liquid contactor. However, a small difference in the densities of the phases makes the flooding phenomenon more sensitive towards changes in flow rates.

Axial mixing of the phases occurs to some extent in the column. This reduces the theoretical rate of mass transfer in a countercurrent equipment. This phenomenon will be discussed later.

Spray towers

The spray tower is the simplest type of column extractor. It consists of a vertical cylinder with no internals, except spray nozzles at the top for the heavy liquid [Figure 8.21(a)]. Droplets of the dispersed phase form at the nozzles and move downwards through the light continuous phase. The 'throughputs' (i.e. the flow rates of the two phases through the column) greatly depend upon the density difference and viscosities of the phases. Alternatively, the heavy liquid

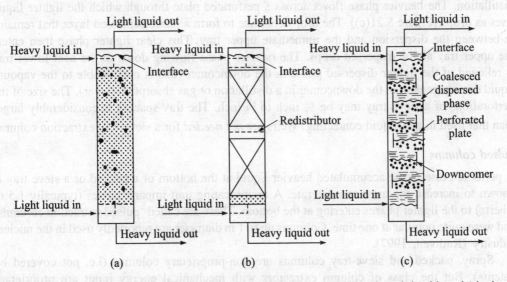

Figure 8.21   Unagitated column extractors: (a) spray column, (b) packed column, and (c) perforated-plate (sieve-plate) column.

may be continuous and the light solvent may be distributed at the bottom through a perforated pipe to form droplets that will rise upwards. In this case, the drops finally separate out from the dispersion and coalesce into a clear liquid phase at the top above the level of inlet of the heavy phase from the bottom. Considerable 'axial mixing' (also called *backmixing*) occurs in the continuous phase, lowering the available driving force for mass transfer. The small rate of drop breakage and coalescence in the dispersion is also responsible for the low mass transfer rate. As a result, the spray tower does not normally give more than one to two theoretical stages.

Because of the simple construction and operation, spray columns are used for simpler operations like nutralization, washing, etc. But these are pretty common in 'direct contact' heating or cooling of liquids.

Packed extraction columns

These are more efficient than the spray tower because the packing in the tower reduces backmixing and enhances drop breakage and coalescence (with frequent distortion) of the drops, thus providing a higher rate of mass transfer. The tower construction [Figure 8.21(b)] is similar to the packed gas absorber; it is provided with the packing support, the liquid distributor and redistributor, nozzles, etc. Similar packing materials are used (rings, saddles, modern high performance packings and structured packings). However, sufficient space must be provided above and below the liquid inlet nozzles for phase separation of the liquids. The separation efficiency of a packed column is strongly influenced by the wettability of the packing. If the packing is wetted by the dispersed phase, there will be more coalescence of the drops and hence the separation efficiency will be reduced. The 'height of a theoretical stage' (HETS) typically ranges between 0.6 and 1.6 m.

Sieve-tray columns

The construction of a sieve-tray extraction column is similar to the one for gas absorption or distillation. The heavier phase flows across a perforated plate through which the lighter liquid rises as drops [Figure 8.21(c)]. The drops coalesce to form a phase-separated layer that remains in-between the dispersion and the immediate upper tray. This clear lighter phase then enters the upper tray as the dispersed drops. The heavier phase flowing down to the next lower tray is relieved of the lighter dispersed phase in the downcomer (this is comparable to the vapour–liquid disengagement in the downcomer in a distillation or gas absorption tower). The size of the perforations of a sieve tray may be ⅛ inch to ¼ inch. The tray spacing is considerably larger than that used in gas–liquid contacting. Weirs are *not needed* for a sieve tray extraction column.

Pulsed columns

A periodic pulse to the accumulated heavier liquid at the bottom of a packed or a sieve tray is known to increase the mass transfer rate. A reciprocating unit imparts pulses (typically 1.5 to 4 hertz) to the lighter phases entering at the bottom. These are called 'pulsed extraction columns' and were quite popular at one time. Columns up to 1 m diameter are reportedly used in the nuclear industry (Ruthven, 1997).

Spray, packed and sieve-tray columns are non-proprietary columns (i.e. not covered by patents). But the class of column extractors with mechanical energy input are proprietary (patented) columns. The more important ones are described in the following section.

8.5.4 Rotary Agitated Extraction Columns

An extractor of this kind consists of a tall column having a long rotating shaft fitted with a set of impellers. The column is divided into a number of compartments by a set of fixed partition plates (annular, in most cases). These extractors provide a pretty large number of theoretical plates in a single unit (as many as 30 in some designs), and have a low HETS. A few such devices (Figure 8.22) are described below.

Scheibel column

This is the oldest column extractor with mechanical agitation. There are at least three designs. The one shown schematically in Figure 8.22(a)(i) consists of a vertical shell divided into a number of compartments by annular partition disks. A central agitator shaft has a set of double-bladed paddle or turbine impellers, one for each compartment. Dispersion is created by the agitator. In an older version, a wire mesh packing filled a part of a compartment. The packing helps in drop coalescence but makes the column prone to fouling.

Oldshue–Rushton column

It is an offshoot of the Scheibel column in which the wire-mesh packing is avoided. Annular partition disks (also called compartment baffles) are used as before but these are now perforated and have smaller inner diameter [Figure 8.22(a)(ii)]. Vertical baffles are placed along the column wall. Each compartment is agitated. This column was developed in the 1950s. Pretty large diameter units are now used.

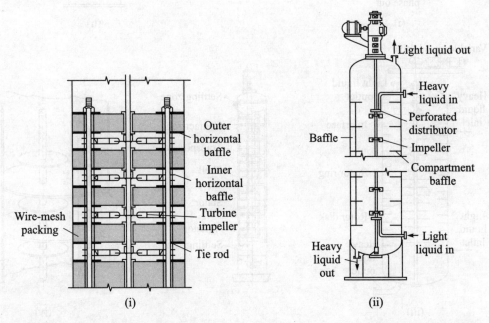

Figure 8.22(a)   Schematics of agitated extraction columns: (i) Schiebel column, and (ii) Oldshue–Rushton column.

Kuhni extractor

This is also similar to the Scheibel column, but does not contain any packing. A baffled turbine impeller agitates the contents in each compartment. Stators of the shape of perforated plates

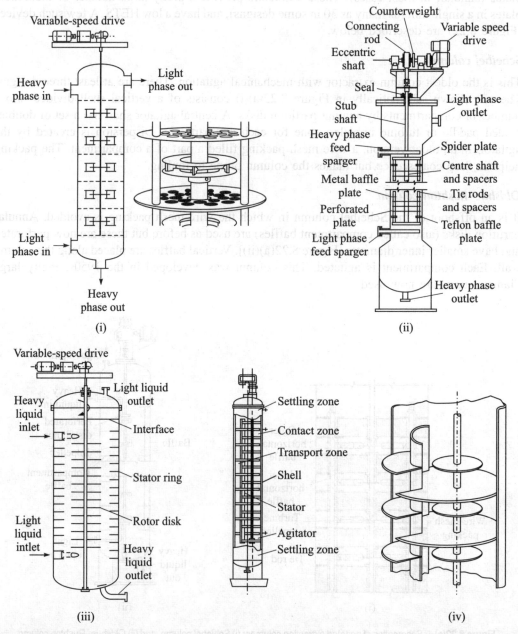

Figure 8.22(b)   (i) Kuhni extractor, (ii) Karr column, (iii) rotating disk contactor (RDC), and (iv) asymmetric rotating disk contactor (ARDC) [Seader and Henley, 1998].

separate the compartments. The column offers up to ten theoretical stages per metre. A schematic of this extractor is shown in Figure 8.22(b)(i).

Karr column

The Karr column [Figure 8.22(b)(ii)] is a descendant of the pulsed sieve-tray column. It has a reciprocating shaft with perforated plates mounted on it. The plates typically have 50–60% free area. The extractor is suitable for systems having intermediate to low interfacial tension.

Rotating disk contactor (RDC)

This extractor, developed in the 1950s by the Shell Company in the Netherlands, has been widely used in the chemical and petroleum industries. Nowadays, this is the best known agitated column extractor. Horizontal disks mounted on a central shaft in a vertical cylinder act as the agitating elements [Figure 8.22(b)(iii)]. A set of annular disks, having inner diameter slightly bigger than the rotating disks, is also mounted on the shaft. The rotor disks break the drops by shear force. The column has considerable flexibility of operation. It can be run at up to 50% of the rated capacity. It can also handle liquids having suspended solids. But it is not suitable for highly viscous liquids. Typical throughputs range between 1500 and 6000 gal/h, but capacities higher than these can also be built.

Considerable backmixing occurs in the RDC. A maximum of 0.5 to 1 theoretical stages can be achieved per metre of height. It is very convenient to handle large throughputs. RDC units up to several metres in diameter are in use. A recent modification of RDC is the asymmetric rotating disk contactor (ARDC) shown in Figure 8.22(b)(iv). In this equipment the shaft with its agitating disks is placed asymmetrically (i.e. away from the centre-line) in the column.

The details of extraction equipment are available in Lo et al. (1983). A good brief overview of extraction equipment is also available in Ruthven (1997).

8.6 SELECTION OF EXTRACTORS

The more important factors that govern the selection of an extractor are: (a) fluid properties, (b) throughputs and phase ratio, (c) settling characteristics of the liquid–liquid dispersion, (d) residence time in the extractor, (e) the number of theoretical stages required, (f) presence of suspended solids, (g) available space (floor area and height), and above all (h) the cost and maintenance of the equipment. A simple chart for preliminary selection of an extractor (Reissinger and Schroter, 1978) is shown in Figure 8.23. More detailed guidelines for extractor selection are given by Lo et al. (1983).

A few extractors based on novel ideas have been developed in the recent years. One is the membrane extractor in which mass transfer between the two liquid phases occurs through a porous 'hollow-fibre' membrane that keeps them separated (see Chapter 14). Application of an electric field has proved to be effective in producing very small droplets of a polar liquid like water or an aqueous solution to create a better dispersion. A lot of work has been done on it as well as on mass transfer and drop coalescence in an electric field (Godfrey and Slater, 1994), although the commercial applications have been only a few as yet.

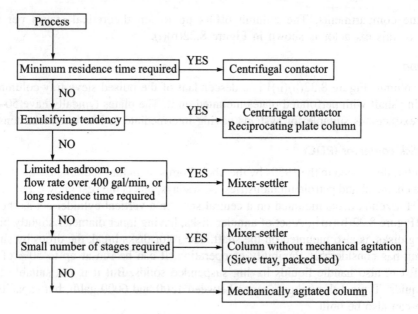

Figure 8.23   Simple guidelines for extractor selection.

8.7   HYDRODYNAMICS AND MASS TRANSFER IN A STIRRED LIQUID–LIQUID DISPERSION

Despite a large number of bench scale and pilot plant experimental studies (Godfrey and Slater, 1994), there is a dearth of generalized correlations for the design of commercial scale extraction equipment. Also the available correlations are hardly suitable beyond the systems and range of parameters for which these have been developed. Here we cite a few correlations available for mixer-type extractor calculation. These are generally applicable for mixing with four to six flat-blade turbine type impeller.

Drop-size, minimum impeller speed and power requirement

The drops in a liquid–liquid dispersion have a wide range of size distribution and several statistical distribution functions have been used to describe drop-size distribution (Godfrey and Slater, 1994). The physical process involves breakage and coalescence of drops in an agitated liquid mixture. Several mean values of drop-size have also been defined, the most widely used one is the volume-to-surface diameter d_{32}, called the *Sauter mean diameter*.

$$d_{32} = \frac{\sum\limits_{i=1}^{k} d_i^3}{\sum\limits_{i=1}^{k} d_i^2} \tag{8.18}$$

The more important properties and parameters that determine the drop-size and its distribution, impeller power requirement, rate and efficiency of mass transfer are: tank diameter (D_t), impeller type and diameter (D_i), volume fraction of the dispersed phase (φ), the impeller rpm (N_i), the densities, viscosities of the two liquid phases and of the mixture $(\rho_c, \rho_d, \rho_m; \mu_c, \mu_d, \mu_m)$, and the interfacial tension (σ). The interfacial area of liquid–liquid contact per unit volume of the dispersion $(\bar{a})$ can be expressed in terms of the Sauter mean drop diameter as

$$\bar{a} = \frac{6\varphi}{d_{32}} \tag{8.19}$$

Sauter mean drop-size

Here are two correlations for the Sauter mean drop-size in a stirred dispersion.

Gnansundram et al. (1979) *correlation:*

$$\frac{d_{32}}{D_i} = 0.052\,(\text{We})^{-0.6}\,\exp(4\varphi), \qquad \text{We} < 10{,}000 \tag{8.20a}$$

$$= 0.39(\text{We})^{0.6}, \qquad \text{We} > 10{,}000 \tag{8.20b}$$

Calabrese et al. (1984) *correlation:*

$$\frac{d_{32}}{D_i} = 0.053(1 + 4.42V_i)^{0.6}(\text{We})^{-0.6} \tag{8.21a}$$

$$V_i = \left(\frac{\mu_d N_i D_i}{\sigma}\right)\left(\frac{\rho_c}{\rho_d}\right)^{1/2}\left(\frac{d_{32}}{D_i}\right)^{1/3} \tag{8.21b}$$

Minimum impeller speed

Depending upon the liquid properties and the fractional dispersed phase holdup, a minimum impeller speed N_{im} is required to maintain a stable dispersion. The following correlation (Skelland and Ramsey, 1987) is useful to calculate this speed.

$$(\text{Fr}_m)_{\min} = 1.03\left(\frac{D_t}{D_i}\right)^{2.76}(\varphi)^{0.106}\,(\text{Ga}\,\text{Bo})^{-0.084} \tag{8.22}$$

Power consumption

The power input to the impeller under a given set of conditions can be expressed in terms of a dimensionless group called the *power number* (Po) as a function of the impeller Reynolds number (Re_i). If the impeller (*turbine* type) Reynolds number in a baffled vessel is above 10,000, the power number asymptotically attains a value of 5.7 (Godfrey and Slater, 1994). This relation is useful to estimate the impeller power requirement in many situations.

$$\text{Po} = 5.7 \qquad \text{for Re}_i > 10{,}000 \tag{8.23}$$

The dimensionless groups used in LLX and their physical significances are described below.

$$\text{We} = \text{Weber number} = \frac{D_i^3 N_i^2 \rho_c}{\sigma} = \frac{\text{inertial force}}{\text{force due to interfacial tension}} \tag{8.24a}$$

$$\mathrm{Fr}_c = \text{Froude number for the continuous phase} = \frac{D_i N_i^2}{g} = \frac{\text{inertia force}}{\text{gravity force}} \qquad (8.24\mathrm{b})$$

$$\mathrm{Fr}_m = \text{Froude number for the mixture} = \frac{D_i N_i^2 \rho_m}{g\,\Delta\rho} = \frac{\text{inertia force}}{\text{gravity force}} \qquad (8.24\mathrm{c})$$

$$\mathrm{Ga} = \text{Galileo number} = \frac{D_i^3 \rho_m g \Delta\rho}{\mu_m^2} = \frac{\text{buoyancy force}}{\text{viscous force}} \qquad (8.24\mathrm{d})$$

$$\mathrm{Bo} = \text{Bodenstein number} = \frac{D_i^2 g \Delta\rho}{\sigma} = \frac{\text{buoyancy force}}{\text{force due to interfacial tension}} \qquad (8.24\mathrm{e})$$

$$\mathrm{Re}_i = \text{Impeller Reynolds number} = \frac{D_i^2 N_i \rho_m}{\mu_m} \qquad (8.24\mathrm{f})$$

$$\mathrm{Po} = \text{Power number} = \frac{P}{N_i^3 D_i^5 \rho_m} \qquad (8.24\mathrm{g})$$

$$\mathrm{Eo} = \text{Eotvos number} = \frac{\rho_d d_{32}^2 g}{\sigma} = \frac{\text{gravity force}}{\text{interfacial tension force}} \qquad (8.24\mathrm{h})$$

The density and viscosity of the two-phase dispersion are expressed as (Godfrey and Slater, 1994)

$$\rho_m = \varphi\rho_d + (1-\varphi)\rho_c \qquad \text{and} \qquad \mu_m = \frac{\mu_c}{1-\varphi}\left(1 + \frac{1.5\,\mu_d\,\varphi}{\mu_c + \mu_d}\right) \qquad (8.25)$$

respectively.

EXAMPLE 8.6 (*Mixer-type extractor calculation: minimum impeller speed, power and interfacial area*)   Acetic acid is to be extracted from a dilute aqueous solution having 3% acid with di-iso-propyl ether as the solvent in a mixer–settler device. The impeller is of four flat-bladed turbine type, and the mixing vessel has four vertical baffles. The aqueous feed is the dispersed phase.

The following data and information are given: feed rate = 1200 kg (3% acid); solvent rate = 4500 kg ether, practically free from the acid; $\rho_c = 730$ kg/m³; $\rho_d = 1010$ kg/m³; interfacial tension, $\sigma = 13.5$ dyne/cm; $\mu_c = 2.5$ cP; $\mu_d = 0.9$ cP.

Calculate (a) the height and diameter of the tank (take $H/D_t = 1.1$), (b) the minimum impeller speed to maintain a stable dispersion, (c) the impeller power input if the impeller speed is maintained 20% above the minimum value, and (d) the Sauter drop diameter d_{32} and the specific interfacial area.

Solution
We perform calculations on the basis of the following configuration of the mixer[†]: impeller-flat-blade turbine (4 blades); height/diameter ratio, $H/D_t = 1.1$; number of vertical baffles = 4; baffle width, $w = D_t/12$.

[†] The common practice of mixer vessel design is: $H/D_t \approx 1$; $D_i/D_t \approx \frac{1}{2}$; number of baffles = 4 to 6; baffle width, $w = D_i/12$ to $D_i/10$; baffle height = at least $2D_i$, symmetrically placed; gap between a baffle and the tank bottom $\approx D_i/2$; gap between the edge of a baffle and the vessel wall (called 'offset') = $w/6$.

(a) *Volumes of the phases:* dispersed, $V_d = 1200/1010 = 1.188$ m³; ether, $V_c = 4500/730 = 6.164$ m³. Total volume of liquid in the vessel $= 1.188 + 6.164 = 7.352$ m³; $\varphi = 1.188/7.352 = 0.1616$.

Keep 20% of the vessel volume free $\Rightarrow$ Vessel volume $= 7.352/0.8 = 9.19$ m³

Take $H = 1.1D_t \Rightarrow$ volume $= (\pi/4)(D_t)^2(1.1D_t) = 9.19$ m³ $\Rightarrow D_t = \boxed{2.2 \text{ m}}$; $H = \boxed{2.42 \text{ m}}$

(b) Density of the dispersion,

$$\rho_m = \rho_d\varphi + \rho_c(1 - \varphi) = (1010)(0.1616) + (730)(1 - 0.1616) = 775.2 \text{ kg/m}^3$$

Viscosity of the dispersion [Eq. (8.25)],

$$\mu_m = \frac{2.5}{1 - 0.1616}\left(1 + \frac{(1.5)(0.9)(0.1616)}{0.9 + 2.5}\right) = 3.17 \text{ cP} = 3.17 \times 10^{-3} \text{ kg/m·s}$$

Interfacial tension, $\sigma = 13.5$ dyne/cm $= 0.0135$ N/m

Take impeller diameter, $D_i = 0.5D_t \Rightarrow D_i = (0.5)(2.2) = 1.1$ m

Galileo number, $\text{Ga} = \dfrac{D_i^3 \rho_m g \Delta\rho}{\mu_m^2} = \dfrac{(1.1)^3(775.2)(9.81)(1010 - 730)}{(3.17 \times 10^{-3})^2} = 2.82 \times 10^{11}$

Bodenstein number, $\text{Bo} = \dfrac{D_i^2 g \Delta\rho}{\sigma} = \dfrac{(1.1)^2(9.81)(1010 - 730)}{1.35 \times 10^{-3}} = 2.462 \times 10^5$

Minimum impeller speed for maintaining the dispersion is given by Eq. (8.22), i.e.

$$(\text{Fr}_m)_{\min} = 1.03\left(\frac{2.2}{1.1}\right)^{2.76}(0.1616)^{0.106}(2.82 \times 10^{11} \times 2.462 \times 10^5)^{-0.084} = 0.2213$$

$\Rightarrow \dfrac{(1.1)(N_{im}^2)(775.2)}{(9.81)(1010 - 730)} = 0.2213 \Rightarrow N_{im} = 0.844$ rps, i.e. $\boxed{50.6 \text{ rpm}}$

(c) Use an impeller speed 20% excess of the minimum speed, i.e.
$$N_i = (0.844)(1.2) = 1.013 \text{ rps} = 60.8 \text{ rpm}$$

Impeller Reynolds number, $\text{Re}_i = \dfrac{D_i^2 N_i \rho_m}{\mu_m} = \dfrac{(1.1)^2(1.013)(775.2)}{3.17 \times 10^{-3}} = 3 \times 10^5$

Since the impeller Reynolds number is larger than 10,000, we use the asymptotic relation, Eq. (8.23).

Power number, $\text{Po} = \dfrac{P}{N_i^3 D_i^5 \rho_m} = \dfrac{P}{(1.013)^3(1.1)^5(775.2)} = 5.7$

$\Rightarrow$ Power input, $P = 7.4$ kW(9.92 hp)

Power density $= (7.4 \text{ kW})/(7.352 \text{ m}^3 \text{ dispersion}) = \boxed{1 \text{ kW/m}^3}$

(d) Use the Gnansundram et al. (1979) correlation, Eq. (8.20).

Weber number, $\text{We} = \dfrac{D_i^3 N_i^2 \rho_c}{\sigma} = \dfrac{(1.1)^3(1.013)^2(730)}{0.0135} = 73,850$

$$\frac{d_{32}}{D_i} = (0.39)(We)^{-0.6} = (0.39)(73850)^{-0.6} = 4.68 \times 10^{-4}$$

$$\Rightarrow \qquad d_{32} = (4.68 \times 10^{-4})(1.1) \text{ m} = \boxed{0.5 \text{ mm}}$$

Let us also calculate the Sauter mean drop diameter using the Calabrese et al. correlation, Eq. (8.21).

$$V_i = \left(\frac{\mu_d N_i D_i}{\sigma}\right)\left(\frac{\rho_c}{\rho_d}\right)^{1/2}\left(\frac{d_{32}}{D_i}\right)^{1/3} = \left[\frac{(9 \times 10^{-4})(1.013)(1.1)}{0.0135}\right]\left(\frac{730}{1030}\right)^{1/2}\left(\frac{d_{32}}{D_i}\right)^{1/3}$$

$$= 0.0631\left(\frac{d_{32}}{D_i}\right)^{1/3}$$

$$\frac{d_{32}}{D_i} = 0.053(1 + 4.42V_i)^{0.6}(We)^{-0.6} = (0.053)\left[1 + (4.42)(0.0631)\left(\frac{d_{32}}{D_i}\right)^{1/3}\right](73850)^{-0.6}$$

$$\Rightarrow \qquad \frac{d_{32}}{D_i} = 6.5 \times 10^{-5}$$

$$\Rightarrow \qquad d_{32} = 7.15 \times 10^{-5} \text{ m} = 0.0715 \text{ mm}$$

The second correlation gives a much smaller value of the Sauter mean drop diameter.

$$\Rightarrow \qquad \text{Interfacial area of contact: } \bar{a} = \frac{6\varphi}{d_{32}} = \frac{(6)(0.1616)}{5 \times 10^{-4}} = \boxed{1.94 \times 10^3 \text{ m}^2/\text{m}^3}$$

Correlations for mass transfer coefficients

The dispersed phase mass transfer coefficient can be approximately calculated from the following relation (Treybal, 1963) assuming the drops to be rigid. A drop can generally be considered 'rigid' if it is smaller than about 1 mm and the interfacial tension is more than 15 dyne/cm.

$$(Sh_d) = \frac{k_d d_{32}}{D_d} = 6.6 \tag{8.26}$$

where (Sh_d) is the dispersed phase Sherwood number, k_d is the dispersed phase mass transfer coefficient, and D_d is the diffusivity of the solute in the dispersed liquid. More correlations for the dispersed phase mass transfer coefficient in an agitated liquid–liquid dispersion have been suggested by Skelland and Xien (1990).

The continuous phase mass transfer coefficient can be calculated from the Skelland and Moeti (1990) correlation.

$$(Sh_c) = \frac{k_c d_{32}}{D_c} = 1.237 \times 10^{-5}(Sc)^{1/3}(Fr_c)^{5/12}(Eo)^{5/4}(\varphi)^{-1/2}(Re)^{2/3}\left(\frac{D_i}{d_{32}}\right)^2\left(\frac{d_{32}}{D_t}\right)^{1/2} \tag{8.27}$$

If the distribution of the solute in the two phases follows a linear relation, $x = m'y*$, the overall mass transfer coefficient based on the dispersed force concentration difference is given by

$$\frac{1}{K_{Od}} = \frac{1}{k_d} + \frac{m'}{k_c} \tag{8.28}$$

The phenomenon of mass transfer between a drop (or a bubble) and a surrounding liquid depends upon a number of physical factors, the two important factors being *internal circulation* and *Marangoni effect*. Relative motion between a drop (or a bubble) and the continuous phase creates shear stress at the fluid–fluid interface which, in turn, gives rise to a circulating motion within the drop. This is called *internal circulation* (Figure 8.24). This phenomenon, which becomes more prominent in a large drop, greatly increases the drop-side mass transfer coefficient. However, the

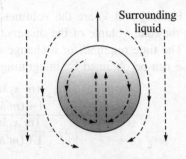

Figure 8.24   Internal circulation in a moving drop.

interfacial shear may not be sufficient to create internal circulation in a small drop. A small drop behaves more like a 'rigid sphere' and mass transfer within it occurs essentially by molecular diffusion.

Interfacial tension between two fluids is influenced by the presence of a dissolved solute. The solute concentration gradient near the interface that occurs during mass transfer creates a gradient of interfacial tension along the surface of a drop or bubble. This causes interfacial motion and even interfacial turbulence, influencing the rate of mass transfer as well as drop coalescence. The phenomenon is called *Marangoni effect* which has been discussed at length in the available literature (see, for example, Godfrey and Slater, 1994; Thorton, 1992).

Mass transfer in a batch agitated vessel

Let us consider a batch agitated vessel having a mass M_d of the dispersed and M_c of the continuous phase (assumed immiscible). The initial mass fraction of the solute in the dispersed phase is x_1 and the solvent is 'pure'. Transfer of the solute occurs from the dispersed to the continuous phase. The equilibrium relation is linear, $x = m'y*$, where $y* =$ mass fraction solute in the continuous phase in equilibrium with a mass fraction of x in the dispersed phase. It is further assumed that the solute concentration is low and the amounts of the individual phases remain practically constant. If the overall volumetric mass transfer coefficient is known, it is possible to calculate the mass transfer efficiency of the vessel.

The solute concentrations in the phases (x and y) at any time are related by the mass balance equation,

$$M_d x_1 = M_d x + M_c y \quad \Rightarrow \quad y = (x_1 - x)\frac{M_d}{M_c} \tag{8.29}$$

The flux of the solute (kg/m^2·s) is given by

$$N'_c = K_{Od}\rho_d(x - x^*); \quad \text{where} \quad x^* = m'y = m'(x_1 - x)(M_d/M_c) \tag{8.30}$$

The instantaneous rate of transport of the solute from the dispersed phase is

$$-\frac{d}{dt}(M_d x) = \overline{a}\, V N'_c = \overline{a}\, V K_{Od}\rho_d(x - x^*) = \overline{a}\, V K_{Od}\rho_d[x - m'(x_1 - x)(M_d/M_c)]$$

$$\Rightarrow \qquad -\frac{dx}{dt} = \frac{\overline{a}\, V K_{Od}\rho_d}{M_d}\left(x - m'(x_1 - x)\frac{M_d}{M_c}\right) \tag{8.31}$$

where $V = V_d + V_c =$ volume of dispersion, and $\varphi = V_d/V$

Here V_d and V_c are the volumes of the dispersed and the continuous phases respectively; V is the total volume of the dispersion; and φ is the volume fraction of the dispersed phase.

The time required for a change of the solute concentration from x_1 to x_2 in the dispersed phase can be obtained by integrating Eq. (8.31).

$$\ln \left[\frac{x_1 - \dfrac{(m'x_1 M_d/M_c)}{1+(m'M_d/M_c)}}{x_2 - \dfrac{(m'x_1 M_d/M_c)}{1+(m'M_d/M_c)}} \right] = \frac{\bar{a}\, V K_{Od}\rho_d}{M_d}\left[1 + \frac{m'M_d}{M_c} \right] t \qquad (8.32)$$

EXAMPLE 8.7 (*Calculation of the mass transfer coefficient and the batch contact time*)   Consider Example 8.6. If the distribution coefficient is $m' = 3.77$, calculate (a) the dispersed and the continuous phase mass transfer coefficients, and (b) the contact time required to attain 95% of the ultimate concentration of the solute in the dispersed phase.

Solution

(a)   We shall first obtain the diffusivities of acetic acid in water and in the ether.
Diffusivity in water (dispersed phase),

$$D_d = 1.2 \times 10^{-9} \text{ m}^2/\text{s (literature value)}$$

Let us use the Wilke–Chang equation, Eq. (2.66), to estimate the diffusivity of acetic acid in the solvent.

The following values are used: molar volume of the solute, $v = 0.0641$ m^3/kmol; mol. wt. of the solvent = 102; viscosity of the solvent, $\mu = 2.5 \times 10^{-3}$ kg/m.s, $T = 298$ K; association factor = 1.0 for the ether.

Putting the values in the Wilke–Chang equation, diffusivity of the solute in the continuous phase,

$$D_c = 7.34 \times 10^{-10} \text{ m}^2/\text{s}$$

Average drop-size, $d_{32} = 5 \times 10^{-4}$ m (see Example 8.6)
Dispersed phase mass transfer coefficient from Eq. (8.26):

$$(Sh_d) = \frac{k_d d_{32}}{D_d} = 6.6 \quad \Rightarrow \quad k_d = \frac{(6.6)(1.2 \times 10^{-9})}{5 \times 10^{-4}} = \boxed{1.584 \times 10^{-5} \text{ m/s}}$$

The following values of the different dimensionless groups are calculated for estimation of the continuous phase mass transfer coefficient from Eq. (8.27). Take impeller speed, $N_i = 1.013$ rps; other parameters as in Example 8.6.

$$Sc = 4.66 \times 10^3; \qquad (Fr_c) = 0.11; \qquad Eo = 0.183; \qquad (Re_c) = 3.58 \times 10^5$$

$$(Sh_c) = (1.237 \times 10^{-5})(4.66 \times 10^3)^{1/3}(0.115)^{5/12}(0.183)^{5/4}(0.1616)^{-1/2}$$

$$\times (3.58 \times 10^5)^{2/3}\left(\frac{1.1}{5 \times 10^{-4}}\right)^2 \left(\frac{5 \times 10^{-4}}{2.2}\right)^{1/2} = 2545 = \frac{k_c d_{32}}{D_c}$$

$$\Rightarrow \qquad k_c = \boxed{1.35 \times 10^{-2} \text{ m/s}}$$

Overall coefficient, dispersed phase basis

$$\frac{1}{K_{Od}} = \frac{1}{k_d} + \frac{m'}{k_c} = \frac{1}{1.584 \times 10^{-5}} + \frac{3.77}{0.0135} \quad \Rightarrow \quad K_{Od} = \boxed{1.577 \times 10^{-5} \text{ m/s}}$$

(b) At equilibrium, the material balance equation, Eq. (8.29), becomes

$$M_d x_1 = M_d x_{eq} + M_c y_{eq} \quad \text{where } x_{eq} = m' y_{eq}$$

Given: M_d = 1200 kg; M_c = 4500 kg (both are assumed to remain constant since the concentrations are low); x_1 = 0.03; m' = 3.77. From Eq. (8.29) at equilibrium,

$$\Rightarrow \quad (1200)(0.03) = (1200)(x_{eq}) + (4500)(x_{eq}/3.77) \quad \Rightarrow \quad x_{eq} = 0.01504$$

Final concentration of the solute in the dispersed phase

$$x_2 = x_{eq} + (x_1 - x_{eq})(1 - 0.95) = 0.01504 + (0.03 - 0.01504)(1 - 0.95) = 0.01579$$

Putting the values of the different quantities (V = 7.352 m^3, $\bar{a}$ = 1940 m^2/m^3) in Eq. (8.32),

$$\ln \frac{0.03 - \dfrac{(3.77)(0.03)(1200/4500)}{1 + (3.77)(1200/4500)}}{0.01579 - \dfrac{(3.77)(0.03)(1200/4500)}{1 + (3.77)(1200/4500)}}$$

$$= \left[\frac{(1940)(7.352)(1.577 \times 10^{-5})(1010)}{1200} \right] \left[1 + \frac{(3.77)(1200)}{4500} \right] t$$

$$\Rightarrow \quad t = \boxed{8 \text{ s}}$$

It appears that the mass transfer process in an agitated contactor is very fast. However, the actual time required for achieving a given fractional transport of the solute will definitely be larger than the theoretically calculated value because of many reasons including interfacial resistance to mass transfer.

8.8 EXTRACTION EQUIPMENT DESIGN

The design of an extractor primarily involves the determination of its physical dimensions (diameter and height) as well as the dimensions and size of the internals (e.g. agitator size and rpm, packing size, size and rpm of the rotor, etc. depending upon the type of the extractor). The height of a continuous contact equipment like a packed or spray tower is expressed as the product of NTU and HTU. That of a perforated tray column, an RDC, a Scheibel extractor or one of this type is expressed as the product of HETS[†] (height equivalent to a theoretical stage) or HETP and the number of theoretical stages.

It is not difficult to determine the number of theoretical stages required to achieve a specified degree of separation of a liquid mixture by solvent extraction. The examples solved in this chapter illustrate the procedures. However, there is no well-defined procedure in open literature for the determination of the height of a theoretical stage. A large number of correlations have been

---

[†] The term HETS (rather than HETP) is more frequently used to indicate the mass transfer efficiency of an extractor unit, although both have the same meaning.

suggested covering different aspects of drop-size distribution, drop breakage and coalescence, impeller power consumption, mass transfer coefficient, effect of axial dispersion, etc. (Treybal, 1963; Laddha and Degaleesan, 1978; Lo et al., 1983; Thornton, 1992; Godfrey and Slater, 1994). These correlations and theoretical analyses help a lot for better understanding of the phenomenon of liquid extraction but are only of limited utility so far as the design of a real-life equipment is concerned. Workable design of extraction equipment is still largely based on pilot plant tests and use of tested scale-up rules (Schweitzer, 1997). Pilot tests are carried out in columns of a few inches diameter. A useful guide to evaluation of the performance and efficiency of extraction columns has been suggested recently by Glatz and Parker (2004).

Unagitated columns like the spray tower, packed tower or the sieve tray column accommodate only a few theoretical stages. Spray towers are suitable for applications such as washing or neutralization of a liquid stream. Considerable 'backmixing' occurs in a spray tower. The diameter of an extractor is determined from flooding considerations. Both random and structured packings are used in a packed extraction tower as for gas absorption or distillation. The continuous phase should preferably wet the packing. The HETS varies from 2 to 7 ft for a random packing, and 1 to 5 ft for structured packings. Ranges of diameter, throughputs and HETS of a few commercial extractors are given in Table 8.4.

Table 8.4   Maximum throughput and size of different extractors (Reissinger and Schroter, 1978)[†]

Type	Maximum load, $m^3/m^2 \cdot h$	Maximum column dia, m	Maximum throughput, m^3/h	HETS m
Scheibel extractor	< 10	1.5	25	0.1–0.25
RDC	40	8.0	2000	0.3–0.70
ARDC	20	4.0	250	
Lurgi tower	30	8.0	1500	
Kuhni extractor	50	3.0	350	0.1–0.25
Karr extractor	80–100	1.5	< 180	0.15–0.3

[†] The above data apply for the following ranges of the physical properties of the liquids: interfacial tension: 30–40 dyne/cm; viscosity: near that of water; phase input ratio: 1:1, v/v; density difference: 0.06 g/cm^3.

NOTATIONS

A, B, C	: carrier, solvent, and solute respectively.
$\bar{a}$	: specific interfacial area of contact, m^2/m^3
d_{32}	: 'volume surface mean' or 'Sauter mean' drop diameter, m
D_t, D_i	: diameter (t = tank, i = impeller), m
F, E, R, S	: quantity (or flow rate) of feed, extract, raffinate and solvent respectively, kg or kg/h
HETS	: height equivalent to a theoretical stage
k_c, k_d	: individual mass transfer coefficient (c = continuous, d = dispersed), m/s
K_{Od}	: overall mass transfer coefficient, dispersed phase basis, m/s
m'	: solute partition coefficient given by $x = m'y*$

M_d, M_c, M	: amount of dispersed phase, continuous phase, or mixture of two phases, kg or kg/h
N_i	: impeller speed, rpm or rps
P	: power input, kW/m^3
S_m	: minimum solvent rate, kg/h
x, y	: mass fractions of a component in the raffinate phase and the extract phase respectively
X, Y	: mass fractions of the solute on solvent-free basis, see Section 8.2.3
z, Z	: mass fractions of the solvent on 'solvent-free' basis, see Section 8.2.3
$\beta_{C,A}$	: separation factor of C, Eq. (8.1)
μ_d, μ_c, μ_m	: viscosity of the dispersed and continuous phases, and of the mixture respectively, kg/m.s
ρ_d, ρ_c, ρ_m	: density of the dispersed and continuous phases and of the mixture respectively, kg/m^3
φ	: fractional holdup of the dispersed phase, V_d/V = dispersed phase volume/dispersion volume
Δ	: a fictitious stream and its mass, Eq. (8.15)

SHORT AND MULTIPLE CHOICE QUESTIONS

1. Consider distribution of the solute C in two partially miscible solvents A (carrier) and B (solvent). What is the selectivity of separation at the plait point?
   (i) 1.0 (ii) very large (iii) zero

2. One hundred kilograms of a 50% solution of C in A (carrier) is equilibriated with 70 kg of solvent B containing 2% of C. At equilibrium, the raffinate phase has a mass of 80 kg and has 52% A and 8% B in it. What is the selectivity or separation factor of C?
   (i) 0.15 (ii) 3.0 (iii) 10.2

3. Which of the following is a realistic value of the stage efficiency of a mixer of good design?
   (i) 100% (ii) 10% (iii) 85%

4. Three solvents have been identified for the extraction of a solute from an aqueous solution. The interfacial tension values in N/m corresponding to the three solvents are:
   (i) $\sigma_1 = 0.003$ (ii) $\sigma_2 = 0.01$ (iii) $\sigma_3 = 0.05$
   Which solvent appears to be suitable?

5. If the interfacial tension of a carrier-solvent pair is very small, which of the following problems may appear?
   (i) Dispersion of the solvent in the carrier becomes more power-consuming.
   (ii) Phase separation of the liquid–liquid dispersion becomes difficult.
   (iii) Interfacial mass transfer resistance becomes large.

6. Which of the following changes causes a Type-II liquid–liquid system to become a Type-I system?
   (i) An increase in temperature
   (ii) An increase in pressure
   (iii) Temperature increased to the critical solution temperature of the solvent-solute pair.

7. While finding out the minimum solvent rate S_m for a countercurrent extraction cascade without reflux it was found that the line $R_N S$ and the tie line through the feed point F were parallel (so that the point Δ_m lies at infinity). If it is so, which of the following relations is correct?
   (i) $S_m = R_N$ (ii) $(x_C)_F = (y_C)E_1$ (iii) $x_F/x_N = y_S/y_1$ (iv) $x_S - y_1 = x_F - x_N$
   (v) $F = E_1$

8. The coefficient of distribution of the solute C between two mutually immiscible liquids A (carrier) and B (solvent) is $K = y_C/x_C = 0.75$. Draw the equilibrium curve using the right triangular coordinates.

9. For the above case, what is the slope of the tie line if the mass fraction of the solute in the solvent phase is $y_C = 0.1$?
   (i) 0   (ii) 0.0984   (iii) 0.037

10. An ideal countercurrent mixer–settler cascade containing six stages removes 95% of the solute from the feed. One of the mixers has developed a mechanical problem and is bypassed. For the same percentage removal of the solute from the feed, the solvent rate should be
    (i) increased   (ii) decreased   (iii) may be kept unchanged.

11. Equilibrium data for the water(A)–acetone(C)–chloroform(B) system are given in Problem 8.2. How much chloroform should be added to 1 kg of an aqueous solution containing 20% acetone so that after equilibration, the acetone concentration in the non-aqueous phase becomes 10%?
    (i) 0.829   (ii) 0.95   (iii) 1.171

12. If extraction of the solute C in the ternary system $A–B–C$ is conducted at a considerably elevated temperature, the rate of mass transfer will definitely increase. The power consumption is also less because the viscosities of the liquids decrease at an increased temperature. In this context, is it advisable to carry out extraction at an elevated temperature? Discuss.

13. The following mass and solute concentrations are given for an ideal single-stage extraction system: $F = 500$ kg; $x_F = 0.4$; $S = 400$ kg; $x_S = 0$. The amount and concentration of the extract are $E = 550$ kg, and $y_E = 0.33$. What is the distribution coefficient K of the solute at the condition of the mixer–settler?
    (i) 0.523   (ii) 2.15   (iii) 6.23

14. What kind of solvent is suitable for the following separations? Answer using Table 8.2. Extraction of:
    (i) pyridine/ethyl alcohol/propionic acid from an aqueous solution
    (ii) BTX from reformer products

(iii) *o*-nitrophenol from a dilute aqueous solution

(iv) phosphoric acid from the crude acid obtained by the 'wet process'.

15. For what kind of liquid–liquid system is the use of extract reflux more convenient?

   (i) Type I system   (ii) Type II   (iii) Both of these

16. What should generally be the minimum fractional density difference between the carrier (*A*) and the solvent (*B*) so that phase separation may not be very difficult?

   (i) 20%   (ii) 5%   (iii) 1%

17. Can two tie lines intersect within the two-phase region of an LLE diagram? Explain qualitatively.

18. The solvent (*B*) in liquid extraction has the following as its analogue in distillation.

   (i) Enthalpy

   (ii) The more volatile component

   (iii) The reflux stream

19. In liquid–liquid equilibrium studies, a system is called Type-II if

   (i) the *A–C* pair is immiscible

   (ii) the *B–C* and *A–B* pairs are partly miscible

   (iii) the *B–C* pair is completely miscible.

20. What would be the effects of the following factors on flooding of an RDC?

   (i) The increased flow rate of the lighter continuous phase

   (ii) The larger density difference of the phases

   (iii) The larger interfacial tension between the phases

   (iv) The higher rotor speed

21. Which of the following factors favour formation of a stable and more effective dispersion?

   (i) Low interfacial tension

   (ii) Large density difference of the phases

   (iii) Low viscosity of the dispersed phase

   (iv) Higher impeller rpm

22. What is Marangoni effect? Does its effectiveness depend upon the direction of mass transfer?

23. Develop Eq. (8.19).

24. In which of the following cases is the separation of the solute (*C*) from the carrier (*A*) using solvent (*B*) impossible?

   (i) *A, B,* and *C* are completely miscible

   (ii) *A–C* and *B–C* pairs are completely miscible

   (iii) *A–B* is partly miscible

25. In a liquid–liquid dispersion, the volume fraction of the continuous phase is 0.7. The Sauter mean drop diameter is 500 μm. What is the specific interfacial area of contact in m^2/m^3?

   (i) 3600   (ii) 1250   (iii) 10

26. The diameter of an extractor column for pilot test is generally taken in the range:

    (i) 1–6 mm   (ii) 3–15 cm   (iii) 0.3–1.0 m

27. Which of the following is a likely value of the HETS of an RDC?

    (i) 2 m   (ii) 0.4 m   (iii) 0.1 m

28. Give a few examples of applications/potential applications of solvent extraction for wastewater treatment.

29. An unstable product is to be recovered by extraction, and the contact time in the extractor should not be more than 30 s. The interfacial tension for the system is low. What kind of extractor appears to be suitable?

    (i) Karr extractor   (ii) Scheibel column   (iii) Podbielniak extractor

PROBLEMS

8.1 (*Extraction in an immiscible system*)[1] A stream of wastewater containing 2% benzoic acid is to be extracted with benzene at a rate of 2000 kg/h in order to remove 98% of the solute. If water and benzene are assumed to be mutually immiscible and the distribution coefficient is $K = w_w/w_b = 1.707$ at the given temperature (where w_w and w_b are the mass fractions of the solute in water and benzene phases respectively), calculate the following:

(a) The minimum rate of benzene required for countercurrent separation of the mixture.

(b) The number of stages required if 1.3 times the minimum solvent is used.

(c) The fraction of the solute removed if the same amount of solvent is used for the separation using a four-stage countercurrent cascade.

(d) The amount of solvent required if the separation of 98% is done in a five-stage countercurrent unit.

(e) The total amount of solvent required for the separation in a four-stage cross-current device if the same amount of solvent is fed to each stage.

8.2 (*Single stage extraction*)[3] Five hundred kilograms of an aqueous feed containing 50 mass% acetone is contacted with a solvent containing 98% chloroform and 2% acetone. The mass ratio of the feed to the solvent is 1.1. Calculate the mass and composition of the extract and also the fraction of acetone in the feed extracted. The operation is carried out at 25°C and the equilibrium and tie line data are given below (Wankat, 1988).

Aqueous phase (mass fraction)			Chloroform phase (mass fraction)		
Water	Chloroform	Acetone	Water	Chloroform	Acetone
x_A	x_B	x_C	y_A	y_B	y_C
0.8297	0.0123	0.158	0.013	0.70	0.287
0.7311	0.0129	0.256	0.022	0.557	0.421
0.6229	0.0171	0.36	0.044	0.429	0.527
0.456	0.051	0.493	0.103	0.284	0.613
0.345	0.098	0.557	0.186	0.204	0.61

8.3 (*Cross-curremt extraction, partially miscible system, equal amount of solvent to each stage*)[2] Acetone is to be extracted from an aqueous solution (500 kg/h, 50 mass% acetone) using TCA (trichloroethane, it is carcinogenic!) in a three-stage cross-current cascade. Two hundred kilograms of solvent (98% TCA, 2% acetone) is added to each stage. Given the following LLE data, calculate the flow rate of the raffinate and the fraction of feed acetone removed in each stage.

Extract arm (mass fraction)			Raffinate arm (mass fraction)		
y_C	y_A	y_B	x_C	x_A	x_B
0.60	0.13	0.27	0.55	0.35	0.10
0.50	0.04	0.46	0.50	0.43	0.07
0.40	0.03	0.57	0.40	0.57	0.03
0.30	0.02	0.68	0.30	0.68	0.02
0.20	0.015	0.785	0.20	0.79	0.01
0.10	0.01	0.89	0.10	0.895	0.005

Tie-line data

Extract (mass fraction acetone)	Raffinate (mass fraction acetone)
0.18	0.12
0.40	0.29
0.56	0.44

8.4 (*Cross-curremt extraction, partially miscible system, equal amount of solvent to each stage*)[3] As an alternative strategy of removing acetone from the feed in Problem 8.3 supplied at the rate of 1000 kg/h, it was decided to use a four-stage cross-current cascade with different amounts of the solvent (TCA)—250, 300, 350 and 400 kg—in the successive stages. Since the first stage received the fresh feed, less solvent was supplied to it. Calculate the total amount of the solute removed from the feed. The equilibrium data given in Problem 8.3 are applicable. Assume that there is no acetone in the solvent supplied. (*Courtesy*: Dr. Basab Chaudhuri)

8.5 (*Optimum solvent rate for an N-stage cross-current extractor*)[3] Consider an N-stage cross-current extraction unit shown in Figure 8.10. A solution of C in the carrier liquid A (X_0 kg solute per kg A) is to be treated at a rate of F kg/h. Pure solvent B is supplied to the stages at a rate S_n kg/h to the nth stage. Extract from the nth stage leaves at a concentration of Y_n kg C per kg B. The equilibrium relation is linear [$Y_i = \psi(X_i) = \alpha X_i$]. The carrier liquid ($A$) and the solvent ($B$) are virtually immiscible and the stages are ideal. If c_1 (Rs per kg) is the price of the recovered solute and c_2 is the processing cost (Rs per kg solvent), it is required to determine the optimum rate of solvent flow to the nth stage and the maximum profit. For the sake of simplicity, work it out for a four-stage cascade. (Note that here X and Y have meanings as defined in this particular problem and should not be confused with the meanings of these notations used for partially miscible systems.)

8.6 (*Countercurrent extraction, minimum solvent rate, number of stages*)[2] An aqueous solution of acetic acid (35% acid, rest water) is to be extracted with 'pure' di-*iso*-propyl ether in a countercurrent cascade at a rate of 2000 kg/h. A solvent rate of 2970 kg/h is suggested. The raffinate stream must not contain more than 10% of acid in it. The ternary phase equilibrium data are available under Example 8.5. Determine the number of ideal stages required. Also determine the minimum solvent rate for the job.

8.7 (*Number of stages; minimum solvent rate*)[3]   An aqueous solution of acetic acid (35% acid; 1000 kg/h) is to be extracted with 'pure' MIBK (*B*) at 25°C supplied at a rate of 1300 kg/h. The raffinate may contain 3% acid (*C*). Determine the number of ideal stages and also the minimum solvent rate required to perform the separation in a countercurrent cascade. The LLE data at 25°C are given below.

Raffinate (Aqueous phase)			Extract (MIBK phase)		
x_A	x_B	x_C	y_A	y_B	y_C
0.9845	0.0155	0.0	0.0212	0.9788	0.0
0.9545	0.017	0.0285	0.028	0.9533	0.0187
0.858	0.025	0.117	0.054	0.857	0.089
0.757	0.038	0.205	0.092	0.735	0.173
0.678	0.06	0.262	0.145	0.609	0.246
0.550	0.122	0.328	0.220	0.472	0.308
0.429	0.225	0.346	0.310	0.354	0.336

8.8 (*Multistage countercurrent extraction*)[3]   A feed of one thousand kilograms aqueous solution of pyridine per hour (50% by mass) is to be extracted with pure benzene to reduce the solute content in the raffinate to 2%. Determine the number of ideal stages required if the solvent rate is 1.3 times the minimum.

Equilibrium data

Water layer		Benzene layer	
Pyridine, mass%	Benzene, mass%	Pyridine, mass%	Benzene, mass%
1.17	0.0	3.28	94.54
3.55	0.0	9.75	87.46
7.39	0.0	18.35	79.49
13.46	0.15	26.99	71.31
22.78	0.25	31.42	66.46
32.15	0.44	34.32	64.48
42.47	2.38	36.85	59.35
48.87	3.99	39.45	56.43
49.82	4.28	39.27	55.72
56.05	19.56	48.39	40.05

8.9 (*Janecke diagram*)[3]   The mutual solubility and the tie-line data for the MEK(*A*)–ethylene glycol(*C*)–water(*B*) system at 30°C are given below:

Extract (MEK phase)			Raffinate (water)		
y_A	y_B	y_C	x_A	x_B	x_C
0.884	0.111	0.005	0.208	0.697	0.095
0.871	0.112	0.017	0.21	0.656	0.134
0.849	0.113	0.038	0.221	0.583	0.196
0.827	0.116	0.057	0.236	0.524	0.240
0.806	0.118	0.076	0.261	0.461	0.278
0.50	0.205	0.295		Plait point	

(a) Prepare the maloney-Schubert (or Janecke) diagram for the above system. Show the tie lines. (b) A solution of ethylene glycol in water (30% glycol, 70% water) is extracted with MEK at a rate of 500 kg/h. The MEK flow rate is also 500 kg/h. Determine the flow rates and compositions of the raffinate and the extract phases using the Janecke diagram.

8.10 (*Time of contact in a stirred liquid–liquid extractor*)[3] For the stirred liquid–liquid contacting described in Example 8.7, calculate the time required for achieving 99% of the equilibrium transfer of acetic acid from the dispersed aqueous phase. All other parameters remain the same.

8.11 (*Minimum impeller speed and power in an agitated extractor*)[3] Benzoic acid is to be extracted from an aqueous solution using toluene as the solvent. A batch extractor is charged with 1000 kg of the feed containing 3.5% benzoic acid and 2500 kg toluene. The mixing vessel has a four-blade turbine impeller and four vertical baffles. Assuming the phases to be virtually immiscible, calculate (a) the minimum impeller speed to have a stable dispersion, (b) the impeller power if its speed is 25% above the minimum, (c) the Sauter mean drop size, and (d) the contact time required to attain 98% of the equilibrium concentration in the continuous phase.

The following data and information are given: $\rho_d = 998$ kg/m^3; $\rho_c = 870$ kg/m^3; $\mu_d = 0.9$ cP; $\mu_c = 0.6$ cP; $\sigma = 25$ dyne/cm; distribution coefficient, $m' = 10.1$ m^3 raffinate/m^3 extract. The organic phase is continuous.

8.12 (*Murphree efficiency of a stirred extractor*)[3] A continuously operated agitated mixing vessel of total liquid volume V_t receives a feed (dispersed phase) at a rate of Q_d m^3/s. If the overall volumetric mass transfer coefficient based on the dispersed phase concentration is $K_{Od}\bar{a}$, show that the Murphree dispersed phase efficiency of the mixer is given by

$$E_{MD} = \frac{N_{tOd}}{1 + N_{tOd}} = \frac{K_{od}\bar{a}\,(V_t/Q_d)}{1 + K_{od}\bar{a}\,(V_t/Q_d)}$$

where N_{tOd} = number of overall dispersed phase transfer units = $\int_{C_{d,out}}^{C_{d,in}} \dfrac{dC_d}{C_d - C_d^*}$;

C_d = dispersed phase concentration.

REFERENCES

Cusack, R.W., P. Fremeaux, and D.J. Glatz, 'A fresh look at liquid-liquid extraction', *Chem. Eng.*, Feb. 1991, 66–76; March 1991, 132–138; April 1991, 112–120.

Cusack, R.W., and D.J. Glatz, 'Apply liquid-liquid extraction to today's problems', *Chem. Eng.*, July 1996, 91–100.

Cusack, R.W., 'Designing a separation process', *Chem. Eng.*, May 1998, 128–136.

Cusack, R.W., 'Pilot plants confirm process validity', *Chem Eng.*, June 1998, 102–109.

Gani, R. et al., 'A modern approach to solvent selection', *Chem. Eng.*, March 2006, 30–42.

Glatz, D. J., and W. Parker, 'Enriching liquid-liquid extraction', *Chem. Eng. Progr.*, Nov 2004, 44–48.

Godfrey, J.C., and M.J. Slater, *Liquid-liquid Extraction Equipment*, John Wiley, New York, 1994.

Hatton, T.A., 'Liquid-liquid extraction of antibiotics', in *Comprehensive Biotechnology*, Vol. 2, M. Moo-Young (Ed.), Pergamon Press, 1985.

Hauer, E., and R. Marr, 'Liquid extraction in biotechnology', *Chem. Eng. Tech.*, *63*(1994) 809–816.

Humphrey, J.L., J.A. Rocha, and J.R. Fair, 'The essentials of extraction', *Chem Eng.*, Sept. 1984, 76–95.

Laddha, G.S., and T.E. Degaleesan, *Transport Phenomena in Liquid Extraction*, Tata McGraw-Hill, New Delhi, 1978.

Lo, T.C., M.H.I. Baird, and C. Hansen (Eds.), *Handbook of Solvent Extraction*, John Wiley, New York, 1983.

Lucan, A.D. (Ed.), *Modern Petroleum Technology*, John Wiley, New York, 2000.

Rao, K.S.M.S., M.R. Guin, and P. Todd, 'Recent developments in aqueous two-phase extraction in bioprocessing', *Sep. Pur. Methods*, *27*(1998) 1–49.

Reissinger, K.H., and J. Schroter, 'Selection criteria for liquid-liquid extraction', *Chem Eng.*, *6*(1978) 109–118.

Ruthven, R.D., *Encyclopedia of Separation Technology*, John Wiley, New York, 1997.

Schweitzer, P.A., *Handbook of Separation Techniques for Chemical Engineers*, McGraw-Hill, New York, 1997.

Seader, J.D., and E.J. Henley, *Separation Process Principles*, John Wiley, New York, 1998.

Sherwood, T.K., and R.L. Pigford, *Absorption and Extraction*, McGraw-Hill, New York, 1952, 402–419.

Skelland, A.H.P., and Hu Xien, 'Dispersed-phase mass transfer in agitated liquid-liquid systems', *Ind. Eng. Chem. Res.*, *29*(1990) 415–420.

Skelland, A.H.P., and L.T. Moeti, 'Mechanism of continuous-phase mass transfer in agitated liquid-liquid systems', *Ind. Eng. Chem. Res.*, *29*(1990) 2258–2267.

Thornton, J.D., *Science and Practice of Liquid-liquid Extraction*, Claredon Press, Oxford, 1992.

Todd, D.B., 'Improving performance of centrifugal extractors', *Chem. Eng.*, July 1972, 152–158.

Treybal, R.E., *Liquid Extraction*, 2nd ed., McGraw-Hill, New York, 1963.

Wankat, P.C., *Equilibrium Staged Separations,* Elsevier, New York, 1988.

9 Solid–Liquid Extraction

Solid–liquid extraction is the process of separation of soluble constituents of a solid material using a suitable solvent. Usually the soluble material is the target product, and the 'inert' solid residue is a by-product or just a solid waste (for example, in extraction of oil from oil seeds, the oil is the product, and the solid residue or cake is a by-product). In some cases, the undesirable soluble materials are removed from the solid by using a solvent and the extracted solid is the product (for example, extraction of de-fatted soy flour using aqueous ethanol as the solvent for removing sugars and some non-protein solids; the solid residue called 'soy protein concentrate' is the product; the solutes extracted may be recovered as by-products). The overall process of liquid–solid extraction basically involves four steps: (i) intimate contact between the solid feed with the solvent; (ii) separation of the solution (or *extract*) from the exhausted solid; (iii) separation of the solvent (and the entrained solid, if any) from the extract followed by purification of the product; (iv) recovery of the solvent from the moist solid (by squeezing/pressing and drying to get a dry cake). Solid–liquid extraction is also called 'leaching', although here we shall use the term leaching in a slightly restrictive sense. This operation is different from 'dissolution' in the sense that in dissolution almost the entire solid gets into solution leaving very little or no 'inerts' behind. But in solid–liquid extraction or in 'leaching', a substantial part of the solid does not dissolve and the soluble matters diffuse out through the solid during solid–liquid contact.

There are many examples of solid–liquid extraction in chemical and allied industries. Vegetable oils are frequently extracted from oil seeds by a suitable solvent. Sometimes a part of the oil is removed from the seeds by pressing, and the residual oil in the 'cake' is recovered by extraction. Hexane is the most popular solvent for oil extraction because (i) it can be easily removed from the extract by 'flashing', (ii) it is non-toxic, (iii) it is reasonably cheap, and (iv) it is miscible with vegetable oils in all proportions. Use of chlorinated solvents (e.g. trichloroethylene) has been discontinued mainly because these are toxic and carcinogenic. The solvent hexane is separated from the extract and the oil is subjected to the refining process. The process of 'solvent extraction' of oil seeds is schematically shown in Figure 9.1. Solid–liquid extraction is widely used in the food industries and a detailed account of it has been given by Schwartzberg (1980).

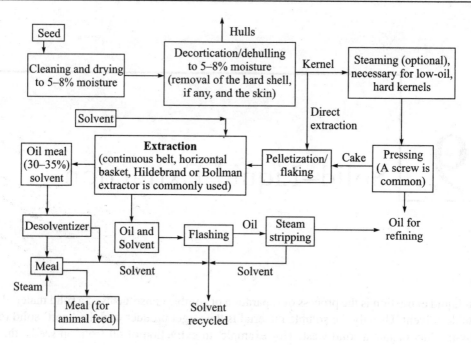

Figure 9.1 Solvent extraction of oilseeds.

9.1 CLASSIFICATION OF SOLID–LIQUID EXTRACTION SYSTEMS

Solid–liquid extraction may involve different physico-chemical mechanisms depending upon the characteristics of the solid (particle size, porosity or compactness, reactivity, solute content, etc.) and of the solvent. If the particle size of the solid is not small, there may be substantial diffusional resistance to transport of the solute within the solid. Whenever possible, the solid is broken down or disintegrated into particles or flakes (in the case of oil seeds, for example) to enhance the rate of extraction. Sometimes an acidic, alkaline or a complexing solution may be used for solubilization of the target substances. Rickles (1965) classified commercial solid–liquid extraction systems into the following categories.

Diffusional extraction

Almost the entire mass transfer resistance lies in the solid phase in such a case and hence the name *diffusional extraction*. An example of a system of this category is extraction of sugar from sugar beet. Sugar beets are cut into small pieces called 'cossettes' which are treated with warm water (70–75°C). Diffusion within the solid occurs through denatured cell walls and through the intersticial liquid. The solvent (water) also diffuses in the opposite direction, thus diluting the solute within the cells. The rate and time of extraction depend mainly upon the thickness of the pieces, the 'effective diffusivity' of the solute in the solid, and the concentration of sugar in the extracting liquor. Many other solid–liquid extraction systems in which the extraction rate is controlled by solid-phase diffusion of the solute, are encountered in food processing industries (Schwartzberg, 1980).

Washing extraction

If the solid particle size is pretty small, the solid-phase diffusional resistance becomes negligibly small. In such a case, extraction virtually becomes a process of *washing* the solid with the solvent. An example is extraction of oil from 'flakes' of oil seeds. Flakes are pretty thin (fraction of a millimetre). Further, during the flaking process much of the cells are ruptured and the diffusional resistance for transport of the solute within the solid becomes small. In washing extraction, a substantial amount of solvent is retained in the slurry after washing. The solute concentration in the liquid retained in the slurry is nearly the same as that in the bulk liquid.

Leaching

This involves dissolution of one or more substances from solid particles accompanied by chemical reaction(s). An acid, alkali or the solution of a complexing chemical is commonly used for solubilizing the target materials. Leaching of ores (oxides, carbonates, sulphides, etc.) is a major step in hydrometallurgy. Leaching of copper minerals by sulphuric acid or an ammoniacal solution, leaching of gold from its ores by sodium cyanide solution are typical examples (use of cyanides is less common nowadays because it is a severe pollutant). Low-grade ores are sometimes leached under drastic conditions. For example, a recently developed method of leaching low-grade nickel ore, called *nickel laterite*, uses sulphuric acid at 250°C and 650 psi pressure to dissolve the nickel (Hairston, 1999); cobalt is the by-product. An extraction vessel with acid resistant bricks or with titanium cladding may be used under such an extreme condition.

'Bioleaching' is a novel technique (Ciminelli et al., 2001) of dissolving ores, particularly the low-grade ones, carried out at near ambient condition without the use of chemical agents. Bacterial species like Thiobacillus Ferrooxidans and thermiphilic species such as Sulphobacillum, Acidianus, and Sulpholobus convert ores, particularly sulphide ores, to soluble sulphates. The process, though slow, is non-polluting since no sulphur dioxide is emitted unlike the conventional roasting process. Bioleaching is in commercial use for extraction of copper (about one-fifth of global extraction of copper is done by bioleaching), gold, zinc, nickel, etc.

Chemical extraction

This is functionally similar to the leaching operation but usually refers to recovering solutes from solids of organic nature. Recovery of gelatin from animal bones using an alkaline solution is an example of chemical extraction.

A few more commercially important solid–liquid extraction systems of the above categories are described in Table 9.1.

Table 9.1 Commercially important liquid–solid extraction systems (Rickles, 1965; Schwartzberg, 1980)

Solute(s)	Feed solid	Solvent/Product
(a) Diffusional extraction		
Soluble coffee	Coffee beans	Water
Fish oils	Fish meal, whole fish	Alcohols, hexane, etc. to produce fish protein concentrate
Sugar	Sugar beets	Water, to produce sugar
Water	Fruits	Sugar solution—for 'osmotic dehydration' of fruits

(Contd.)

Table 9.1   Commercially important liquid–solid extraction systems (Rickles, 1965; Schwartzberg, 1980)   [*Contd.*]

Solute(s)	Feed solid	Solvent/Product
(b) *Washing extraction*		
Vegetable oils	Oilseeds	Hexane, hydrocarbons
Flavours/Odours	Flowers	Ethanol
Sugar	Sugarcane	Water
Vanilla	Vanilla beans	Ethanol(35%)–Water(65%)
(c) *Leaching*		
Phosphoric acid	Phosphate rock	Sulphuric acid
Sodium aluminate	Bauxite	Caustic solution
Gold	Gold ore	Sodium cyanide
Copper	Copper ore	Sulphuric acid, complexing reagents
(d) *Chemical extraction*		
Gelatin	Bones and skins	Aqueous solution (pH 3 to 4)
Lignins	Wood chips	NaOH solution, sulphide or sulphite
Iodine	Seaweeds	Sulphuric acid
Pectin	Apple pumace (pulp)	Dilute acid

9.2   THE RATE OF SOLID–LIQUID EXTRACTION

The rate of extraction or 'leaching' of a solute from a solid substance depends upon a number of factors. A few important factors are described below.

9.2.1   Physical Characteristics of the Solid

The solute may remain distributed in the solid in different ways. The type of the solid matrix also varies—for example, it may be porous or nonporous, it may consist of plant or animal tissues. If the solute is distributed within an insoluble matrix of the 'inert' solid, it gradually dissolves and diffuses out leaving a porous structure. In some cases, the solid may be available as a slurry or a paste. If the solute has an affinity for the insoluble solid, it may remain partly adsorbed to it. Thus, the rate of extraction depends upon the nature and characteristics of the solid.

Admittedly, the rate of extraction becomes faster if the particle size of the solid is small or if the solid is porous. Since rigid solids like metal ores and most compact solids dissolve slowly, such materials are crushed and ground (about 60 to 100 mesh) before contacting with the solvent. Reactive solvents (for example, an acidic solvent) are sometimes used. The undissolved residue (often called *inerts*) may have a porous structure. But separation of the 'inerts' from the slurry may not always be easy (for example, separation of the residue after acidulation of phosphate ore in the process of manufacture of phosphoric acid). Materials of plant or animal origin are *not* generally smashed or disintegrated because the cell walls may be broken and thereby insoluble and undesired solid may come out. Separation of such insoluble colloidal solids may pose a problem. This is why sugar beets are sliced to thin pieces (but never smashed) and extraction of sugar is done with hot water. Transport of sugar occurs by 'osmotic passage' through the cell walls. In any case, the feed solid has to be 'prepared' in a suitable form or shape for quick extraction of most of the solute present in it.

9.2.2 Solvent

A solvent in which the solute has a high solubility is definitely preferred. But it should not dissolve the undesired solids. Further, the solvent should have a low viscosity, a low boiling point, and should be non-toxic and reasonably cheap. It is easier to remove a low-boiling solvent from the product liquor by 'flash vaporization'.

9.2.3 Temperature

Diffusivity of the solute in the solid as well as its miscibility with the solvent increases with temperature. Also, the viscosity of the solvent becomes less at an elevated temperature and it can penetrate into the interstices of the solid more easily. So the extraction rate increases with temperature. Heat sensitivity of the solute, volatility of the solvent and possible thermal effects on the inert or residual solid (for example, solubility, degradation, change in consistency, etc.) limit the temperature of extraction.

9.2.4 Agitation

Intense agitation increases the solid–liquid mass transfer coefficient and thereby increases the rate of extraction but may disintegrate the solid as well, causing a settling problem. However, if the solid phase offers the controlling resistance, the effect of agitation on the rate of extraction is not pronounced.

9.3 SOLID–LIQUID CONTACTING STRATEGY

The techniques of solid–liquid contacting may be broadly of two types: (i) fixed bed contact, and (ii) dispersed contact in an agitated tank or vessel.

9.3.1 Fixed Bed Contacting (Percolation)

The simplest equipment for fixed bed contacting is an open or closed vessel with a perforated support plate (also called *false bottom*) placed a little above the bottom. The solid rests on the support plate (Figure 9.2). The size of the perforations should be such that the extracting liquid can leave through it without much hindrance but the solid cannot. The liquid is fed at the top of the bed. Fixed bed contacting may be of two types: (i) spray percolation, and (ii) full immersion.

In spray percolation [Figure 9.2(a)], the liquid is distributed at the top and trickles down through the bed of solid. Extraction in a fixed bed is *not* generally a once-through process. The liquid leaving the bed is recirculated till a certain concentration is reached or till the solute concentration in the bed reduces to the desired extent. Repeated extraction with two or more fresh batches of solvent may be necessary in some cases. A common problem of fixed bed extraction by spray percolation is channeling of the solvent as it flows through the bed. As a result, there may be a number of pockets in the bed that do not come in good contact with the solvent and extraction remains incomplete.

In full immersion [Figure 9.2(b)], the solid is kept dipped in the liquid for a predetermined time after which it is drained and taken for recovery of the solute. Alternatively, the solvent enters the packed bed of the solid continuously at the bottom and leaves at the top, keeping the bed fully immersed. Recycling of the solution may be done if necessary.

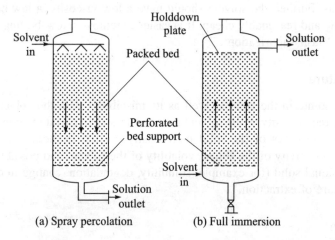

Figure 9.2 Schematics of fixed bed solid–liquid extraction.

9.3.2 Dispersed Contacting

In a disperse contact device, the solid and the extracting solvent are agitated in a vessel of suitable shape, size and design. Different types of agitators have been in use depending upon the characteristics of the solid. Solid–liquid contacting is followed by separation of the 'inerts' from the solution and recovery of the product from the solution as usual.

9.4 SOLID–LIQUID CONTACTING EQUIPMENT

Solid–liquid contacting may be done in a batch or a continuous equipment. The more common types of equipment are described below.

9.4.1 Batch Equipment

Percolation leaching (fixed bed contacting), which is a batch process, has already been briefly described in Section 9.3.1. A mechanically agitated tank for leaching is shown in Figure 9.3(a). A number of such tanks may be arranged in series to form a batch contact battery for oil extraction from seeds. After extraction is complete, the miscella (containing the oil, the solvent, and a little suspended solid) is removed. The residual solvent in the exhausted meal may be removed by passing steam through it. Air agitation of the content of a leaching tank is sometimes done. An air-agitated batch extractor, called the Pachuca extractor, is shown in Figure 9.3(b). This type is popular for metallurgical leaching. It is a vertical tank having an acid-resistant lining with a central draft tube through which air is bubbled. The rising bubbles lift the solid as well as the liquid, causing circulation of both. At the end of the batch time, the flow of air is stopped and the content is taken out and separated.

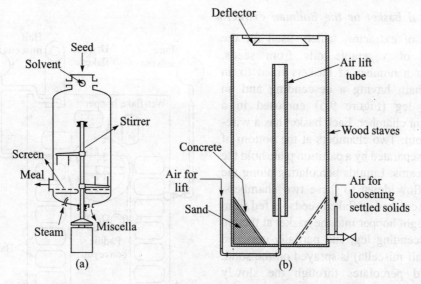

Figure 9.3 (a) A batch extraction vessel, and (b) the Pachuca extractor.

A multi-batch extraction unit uses a battery of batch contact vessels (Figure 9.4). Each vessel is charged with solids. Fresh solvent enters the vessel containing solids having the lowest solute concentration. It flows successively to vessels containing solids of higher solute content. At one end of the battery the relatively strong extract contacts a fresh batch of solid and the rich liquid from the vessel is taken for further processing. The exhausted solid leaves the battery at the other end. Typical movement of the solids is shown in the figure.

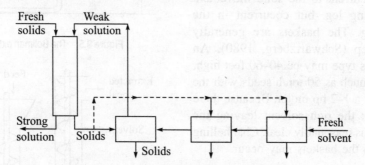

Figure 9.4 Multi-batch contact for solid–liquid extraction.

9.4.2 Continuous Contact Equipment

Several types of continuous contact extractors have been in use, particularly for vegetable oil extraction and in food processing industries (Rickles, 1965). The characteristics of continuous extractors have been described in detail by Schwartzberg (1980). Continuous extractors are generally operated in the countercurrent mode. For the same degree of extraction, a stronger extract solution can be obtained in the countercurrent operation. The more common continuous extractors are described below.

The vertical basket or the Bollman extractor

This type of extractor, widely used for the extraction of vegetable oils from seeds, consists of a number of baskets fixed to an endless chain having a descending and an ascending leg (Figure 9.5) enclosed in a vapour-tight chamber. Each basket has a wire-mesh bottom. Two chambers at the bottom of the vessel separated by a partition plate hold the extract streams. Liquids percolating along the two legs flow down to these two chambers. The solid (crushed or flaked seeds) is fed from a vapour-tight hopper into the basket at the top of the descending leg, and partially enriched solvent (half miscella) is sprayed on the solid. The liquid percolates through the slowly moving baskets and collects at one of the bottom compartments of the unit. Fresh solvent is sprayed on the top basket in the ascending leg and percolates through the rising baskets and collects in the other chamber at the bottom in the form of 'half-miscella', which is sprayed at the top basket of the ascending leg as stated before. Percolation of the liquid occurs countercurrent to the solid movement in the ascending leg, but cocurrent in the descending leg. The baskets are generally 0.5–0.7 m deep (Schwartzberg, 1980). An extractor of this type may be 40–60 feet high, can handle as much as 50 ton/h seeds with the chain driven by a 1–2 hp motor. Because there is no agitation, the rich solvent leaving the extractor remains reasonably clear. Channelling of the liquid in the baskets may occur.

The Hildebrand extractor

This is a vertical, total immersion extractor. It consists of a U-shaped screw conveyer fitted with three screws—one each in the vertical legs and one in the horizontal section of the barrel (Figure 9.6). The helical profiles of the screws are perforated to allow flow of the solvent. The solid is fed at the top of one of the legs and is propelled through the barrel. The

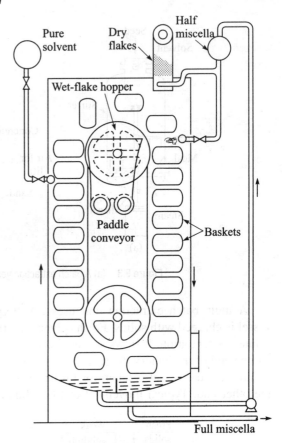

Figure 9.5   The Bollman extractor.

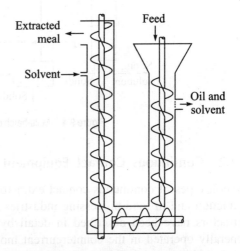

Figure 9.6   The Hildebrand extractor.

solvent is fed at the top of the other vertical leg and flows countercurrent to the solid through the perforations of the screws. This is an example of a continuous counter-current extraction device. The rich miscella is with-drawn through a strainer for further treatment and sol-vent separation. The major disadvantages of the device are: (i) a little overflow of the feed with the outgoing liquid, (ii) excessive disintegration of the solid if the feed is in the form of flakes, and (iii) occasional choking with fines.

The Bonotto extractor

A vertical Bonotto-type extractor is shown in Figure 9.7. It consists of a vertical column divided into a number of compartments by horizontal plates. Each plate has a slot that is oriented in the opposite side of the slot in an adjacent plate. The slots are like the downcomers in a distillation column. There is a scrapper on each plate. The scrappers are fixed to a shaft running axially through the column.

The solid enters the column at the top through a screw feeder. It moves from one plate to the next lower plate by the action of the scrapper. The solvent flows up through the column and the rich extract leaves at the top. A section of the column at the top is enlarged in diameter to reduce carryover of the solid. The exhausted solid is taken out through another screw conveyer at the bottom. The operation is somewhat similar to gas–liquid contacting in a tray tower.

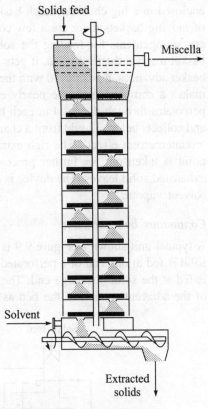

Figure 9.7 The Bonotto extractor.

Horizontal basket extractor

The type of horizontal basket extractor shown in Figure 9.8 (Schwartzberg, 1980) is widely used for oil extraction from seeds. It consists of a train of horizontal baskets fitted to a drive chain

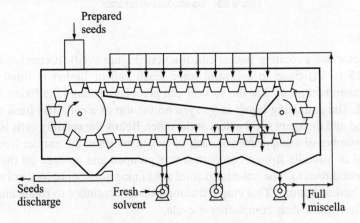

Figure 9.8 Continuous horizontal basket extractor.

enclosed in a big chamber. Each basket has a wire-mesh or perforated bottom. Below the train of moving baskets there are a few compartments on the floor of the enclosing chamber. There are arrangements for feeding the solid and spraying solvent on the baskets. When an empty basket reaches the feed point, it gets loaded with the solid from the feed hopper. As the loaded basket advances, it is sprayed with the full miscella from a bottom compartment. Before a basket makes a complete turn, the nearly exhausted solid is sprayed with fresh solvent. The liquid percolates through the solid in each basket, leaves through the perforated or wire-mesh bottom and collects below. Liquid from a chamber is pumped to the previous spray. This creates a partial 'countercurrent effect'. The rich extract from the collection chamber next to the solid feeding point is taken out for further processing (i.e. solvent separation and product recovery). The exhausted solid leaves. The device is enclosed in a vapour-tight housing to avoid leakage of the solvent vapour.

Continuous belt extractor

A typical unit shown in Figure 9.9 is used for extraction of sugar from sugarcane or beet. The solid is fed at one end of a perforated endless moving belt (Schwartzberg, 1980). Fresh solvent is fed at the solid discharge end. The liquid drains into a catch basin and is pumped to the top of the adjacent section of the bed as shown in the figure.

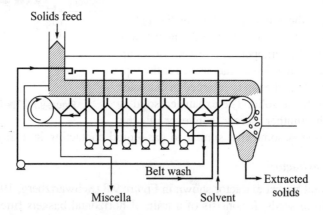

Figure 9.9   Continuous belt extractor.

Rotocel extractor

A rotocel extractor has a rotating basket construction (Figure 9.10). It consists of a number of cells (usually 15 to 18) fixed to a central rotor. Each cell or basket is fitted with a hinged perforated or screen bottom so that the solvent can percolate through the flakes of seeds or any other solid feed. The extracting liquid is sprayed on the top of a cell. The fresh solid enters the device at one end and the spent solid enters at the other. Below the rotating cells is a circular tank divided into a number of compartments, each of which receives the extract from one or more cells. The liquid or miscella from a compartment is pumped and sprayed on the next basket in the countercurrent direction. The exhausted solid containing some entrained solvent is removed by opening the hinged bottom. This emptied compartment continues to rotate and then receives an amount of fresh feed, thus completing a cycle.

Rotocel extractors have the advantages that the solid is not subject to attrition and counter-current extraction is achieved. Besides extraction of oils from flaked seeds, these are used for removing solubles from plant materials (like leaves, bark, etc.) and also for leaching of sugar beets. The construction of smaller units may be a little different from the one shown in Figure 9.10.

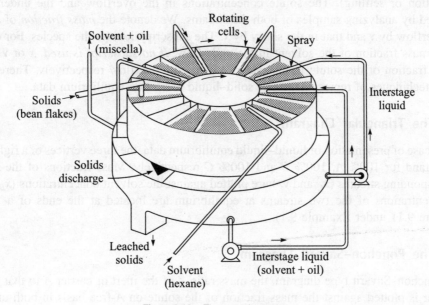

Figure 9.10   The rotocel extractor.

A few other types of solid–liquid extractors (Kennedy, Olier, Crown extractors, etc.) and their applications have been described by Schwartzberg (1980).

9.5 SOLID–LIQUID EXTRACTION EQUILIBRIUM

Consider an 'inert' (or 'carrier') solid A containing a soluble substance C distributed in it. A mass of the solid is kept in contact with the solvent B for a sufficient time. The following physicochemical phenomena may occur.

(a) If the solid is in the form of fine particles or flakes, the solid-phase diffusional resistance is small. Given sufficient time, the system will reach 'equilibrium'. Here equilibrium means that the concentration of the solute in the clear bulk solution will be equal to that in the liquid retained in the slurry. The amount of liquid or solution retained in the slurry depends upon the characteristics of the solid and the density and viscosity of the solution.

(b) If the solid is in the form of lumps or slices, the concentration of the bulk solution and that of the intersticial or retained solution will again be equal at 'equilibrium'. However, it may take a substantially longer time to attain equilibrium.

(c) If the solute reacts with a reagent present in the solution, leaching occurs till either the solute or the reagent is exhausted.

Solid–liquid extraction 'equilibrium data' for design calculations are reported in terms of the concentration of the solute in the clear liquid (called *overflow*) and the fraction of the liquid in the slurry (called *underflow*) and its concentration. Such data can be obtained by simple laboratory experiments (George, 1959). An amount of the solid is mixed with different amounts of the solvent and kept mixed for a period of time. The slurry is then separated from the mixture (by filtration or settling). The solute concentrations in the overflow and the underflow are determined by analyzing samples of both the streams. We denote the *mass fraction* of a species in the overflow by y and that in the slurry by x. The subscript denotes the species. For example, x_B is the mass fraction of the solvent in the underflow. *If no subscript is used*, x or y refers to the mass fraction of the solute in the underflow and the overflow respectively. There are two common techniques of representation of solid–liquid extraction equilibrium data.

9.5.1   The Triangular Diagram

As in the case of presentation of liquid–liquid equilibrium data, the three vertices of a right-angled triangle stand for 100% A, 100% B and 100% C respectively. Mass fractions of the solute in the corresponding streams (x_C and y_C) are plotted against the solvent concentrations (x_B and y_B). The concentrations of the two streams at equilibrium are located at the ends of a 'tie line' (see Figure 9.11 under Example 9.1).

9.5.2   The Ponchon–Savarit Diagram

In the Ponchon–Savarit type diagram, the mass ratio Z of the inert or carrier A to that of B and C together is plotted against the mass fraction of the solute on A-free basis in both underflow and overflow (i.e. Z versus X_C and Y_C).

Underflow:
$$X_C = \frac{x_C}{x_B + x_C}; \qquad Z = \frac{x_A}{x_B + x_C} \tag{9.1}$$

Overflow:
$$Y_C = \frac{y_C}{y_B + y_C}; \qquad Z = \frac{y_A}{y_B + y_C} \tag{9.2}$$

The kind of 'equilibrium' we describe here is not the same as thermodynamic equilibrium in case of other mass transfer operations. The composition of the sludge depends upon the settling time. If more time is allowed, the mass fraction of solid in the sludge will definitely be larger and that in the overflow will be smaller. The fraction of liquid retained in the sludge also depends upon the viscosity and density of the solution. With increasing density and viscosity of the solution, the fraction of liquid in the sludge will be more. Thus the 'equilibrium data' will depend upon the condition of the system — the particle size of the solid, the settling time allowed, and the density, viscosity and concentration of the solution. However, unless the inerts adsorb the solute, the concentrations of the overflow liquid and that retained in the sludge (on solid-free basis) are likely to be the same (i.e. $X_C = Y_C$).

A tie line on the right triangular equilibrium plot joins the compositions of the two phases in 'equilibrium'. If the liquid concentrations in the two phases on solid-free basis are equal, the tie lines on the X–Y–Z plane are vertical lines. The construction of solid–liquid 'equilibrium diagrams' is illustrated in Example 9.1.

EXAMPLE 9.1 (*Solid–liquid extraction equilibrium data*)   A set of experimental test data on solid–liquid extraction 'equilibrium' for the system *oil seed meal(A)–hexane(B)–oil(C)* is reported below. Mixtures of the 'components' at various overall composition are stirred in a laboratory vessel and then allowed to settle. Samples of the *overflow* (oil + solvent hexane + traces of the inert meal) and the *underflow* (inert meal + entrained solution) were drawn and analyzed. The following data were collected.

Overflow (100 kg), *solution*			Underflow (100 kg), *slurry*		
w_A (kg)	w_B (kg)	w_C (kg)	w'_A (kg)	w'_B (kg)	w'_C (kg)
0.3	99.7	0.0	67.2	32.8	0.0
0.45	90.6	8.95	67.1	29.94	2.96
0.54	84.54	14.92	66.93	28.11	4.96
0.70	74.47	24.83	66.58	25.06	8.36
0.77	69.46	29.77	66.26	23.62	10.12
0.91	60.44	38.65	65.75	20.9	13.35
0.99	54.45	44.56	65.33	19.07	15.6
1.19	44.46	54.35	64.39	16.02	19.59
1.28	38.50	60.22	63.77	14.13	22.10
1.28	34.55	64.17	63.23	12.87	23.90
1.48	24.63	73.89	61.54	9.61	28.85

Plot the 'equilibrium data' (a) as the right-triangular plot, and (b) as the 'Ponchon-Savarit' diagram.

Solution

(a) *Right-triangular diagram:*   The mass fraction of a component in the overflow is denoted by y and that in the underflow by x. In the given case, the values are directly obtainable from the above table. For example, from the last row of the table, mass fractions in the overflow are $y_A = 0.0148$, $y_B = 0.2463$, $y_C = 0.7389$; the corresponding concentrations in the underflow are $x_A = 0.6154$, $x_B = 0.0961$, $x_C = 0.2885$. 'Equilibrium' plots of the two streams are shown in Figure 9.11(a). The vertices of the right-angled triangle *ABC* represent: *A* (100% 'inerts', i.e. the solid free from oil and solvent); *B* (100% solvent); *C* (100% 'solute'). The plot of y_C versus y_B represents the overflow stream; that of x_C versus x_B represents the underflow streams (x_C and y_C are taken along the horizontal axis; x_B and y_B are taken along the vertical axis). The lines joining the corresponding points on the underflow and overflow curves are the tie lines. The tie lines pass through the origin.

Note: The solution phase contains traces of the inert solid (the meal). This occurs in many cases because settling is hardly perfect in practice. The entrained solid in the overflow increases with the oil concentrations (this occurs because of the increased density and viscosity of the solutions with increasing oil concentration). For this reason, the overflow curve lies slightly below the *hypotenuse*. If there is *no entrained solid* in the overflow, the curve should be a straight line along the hypotenuse.

The data show that the solution retained in the underflow per unit mass of inert increases with the concentration of the solution. For this reason the underflow line is slightly curved. If the fraction of solution retained is constant, the underflow line should be a straight line. However, the concentrations of oil (solid-free basis) in both the overflow and the underflow are the same. This indicates that the oil (solute) is not preferentially retained or adsorbed by the inert solid or meal.

(b) *'Ponchon–Savarit' diagram:* The given data are used to calculate $Y_C = w_C/(w_C + w_B)$, $Z = w_A/(w_C + w_B)$ for the overflow; $X_C = w'_C/(w'_C + w'_B)$, $Z = w'_A/(w'_C + w'_B)$ for the underflow. The calculated values of Z for both overflow and underflow are plotted versus X_C or Y_C to give the 'Ponchon-Savarit' type diagram, Figure 9.11(b). The values (tie-line data) are given below:

Y_C	0	0.09	0.15	0.25	0.30	0.39	0.45	0.55	0.61	0.65	0.75
Z	0.003	0.0045	0.0054	0.007	0.0078	0.0092	0.010	0.012	0.013	0.013	0.015

X_C	0	0.09	0.15	0.25	0.30	0.39	0.45	0.55	0.61	0.65	0.75
Z	2.05	2.04	2.02	1.99	1.965	1.93	1.90	1.80	1.76	1.72	1.6

Note: Since the overflow contains traces of the suspended solid, the overflow curve lies a little above the horizontal axis. If the overflow is absolutely clear, the overflow line will lie along the horizontal axis. The underflow line bends a little at higher concentrations X_C of the entrained solution. If the solution retained in the underflow (slurry) is independent of X_C, the line will be parallel to the horizontal axis.

The tie lines are also shown in Figure 9.11(b). Since the concentrations of the solution on 'solid-free basis' in the two streams are equal, the tie lines are parallel vertical lines. If the solution concentrations in the two streams are different, the tie lines will not be parallel.

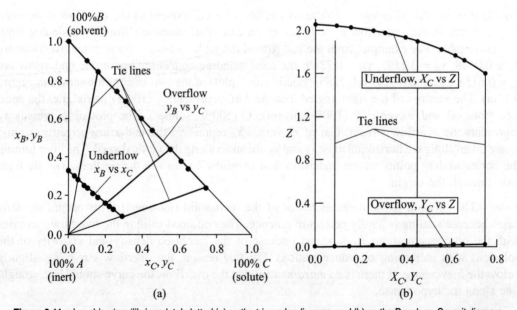

Figure 9.11   Leaching 'equilibrium data' plotted (a) on the triangular diagram, and (b) on the Ponchon–Savarit diagram.

9.6 SOLID–LIQUID EXTRACTION CALCULATIONS

Solid–liquid extraction calculations are often based on the concept of 'ideal stage'. If the clear solution leaving a contact stage has the same composition as that of the liquid retained in the sludge (or underflow), the stage is called *ideal*[†].

As in the case of many other mass transfer operations, the common strategies of solid–liquid contacting for extraction or leaching are: (i) batch contact, (ii) cross-current contact, and (iii) countercurrent contact. The important variables and parameters are: (i) the rate of processing of the solid feed; (ii) the solute content of the feed; (iii) the allowable solute concentration in the lean sludge leaving the extractor (or the fractional recovery of the solute); and (iv) the solvent rate and the concentration of solute in it, if any. Design calculations are based on material balance equations and the 'equilibrium data' for the particular system. The number of contact stages can be determined graphically using the right-triangular diagram or the Ponchon–Savarit type diagram. Analytical determination of the number of stages is possible under certain restrictive situations.

9.6.1 Batch Contact

In single-stage batch contact, the solid feed and the solvent are charged into an agitated vessel and kept in intimate contact for some time. The mixture is then allowed to settle. The clear solution (overflow) and the sludge (underflow) are separated. This is schematically shown in Figure 9.12. The flow rates and the concentrations of the input and output streams are also shown. Given the mass and the concentrations of the two input streams and the 'extraction

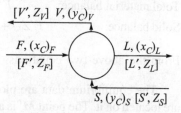

Figure 9.12 Single-stage batch contact.

equilibrium data', it is possible to calculate the concentrations and amounts of the two output streams (the overflow and the underflow) and also the fraction of the solute extracted. Graphical calculations are generally done, although algebraic calculations are possible in certain cases. The right-triangular diagram or the Ponchon–Savarit diagram can be used for graphical calculations.

Use of the right-triangular diagram

Here the total mass of a stream and the concentrations in mass fraction are used. Refer to Figure 9.12. We write the following balance equations:

Total mass balance: $\quad F + S = V + L = M \quad$ (*M* is the total mass of the two streams) (9.3)

Solute balance: $\quad F(x_C)_F + S(y_C)_S = L(x_C)_L + V(y_C)_V = M(x_C)_M \quad$ (9.4)

[†] This does not mean that the solution is 'saturated' or in equilibrium with the solute present in the solid, since the contact time allowed in a stage may not always be sufficient for establishment of such an equilibrium. Phenomena like the adsorption of the solute on the inerts or the imperfect settling of the sludge may be taken into account by incorporating a 'stage efficiency'. If experimental solid–liquid 'equilibrium data' collected in the laboratory are used for design of an industrial equipment operated under similar conditions, the stage efficiency is automatically taken into account.

The overall solute concentration of the mixture can be obtained from Eqs. (9.3) and (9.4) as

$$(x_C)_M = \frac{F(x_C)_F + S(y_C)_S}{F + S} \tag{9.5}$$

The equilibrium data are plotted on the right-triangular diagram. The points F and S giving the concentrations of these two streams are located on the diagram. The point M representing the mixture is also located on the line SF at $(x_C)_M$. Alternatively, the point M can be located on the line SF using the Lever Arm Rule. The terminals of the tie line through the point M give the solute concentrations $(x_C)_L$ and $(y_C)_V$ in the two output streams, L and V. The amounts of the output streams can be obtained by using the Lever Arm Rule or by material balance. The procedure is illustrated in Example 9.2.

Use of the Ponchon–Savarit diagram

The procedure is very similar to that described above. However, the mass of the streams are taken on 'solid-free basis', and their concentrations Z are taken as the mass of solid per unit mass of non-solid. The flow rates of the various streams are F', S', L', and V', all on 'solid-free basis'. We write the following material equations.

Total material balance: $F' + S' = L' + V' = M'$ (9.6)

Solid balance: $F'Z_{F'} + S'Z_{S'} = L'Z_{L'} + V'Z_{V'} = M'Z_{M'}$ (9.7)

From the above two equations, $Z_{M'} = \dfrac{F'Z_{F'} + S'Z_{S'}}{F' + S'}$ (9.8)

The equilibrium data are plotted on the Ponchon–Savarit diagram and the points F' and S' are located on it. The point M' is also located on the line $S'F'$, and the tie line through M' is drawn. The solid concentrations in the overflow $Z_{V'}$ and in the underflow $Z_{L'}$ are obtained from the extremities of the tie line (the subscript of Z indicates the stream concerned). The quantities of the overflow and the underflow are obtained by solving the material balance Eqs. (9.6) and (9.7). The procedure is illustrated in Example 9.2.

EXAMPLE 9.2 (*Solid–liquid extraction in a single-stage batch contactor*)   One thousand kilograms of crushed oil seeds (19.5% oil, 80.5% meal) is extracted with 1500 kg of 'pure' hexane in a batch extraction vessel. Calculate the fraction of the oil extracted using (a) the right-triangular diagram and (b) the 'Ponchon–Savarit diagram'. The equilibrium data given in Example 9.1 are applicable.

Solution

(a) *Calculation using the right-triangular diagram*

Refer to Figure 9.12. Given: $F = 1000$ kg; $S = 1500$ kg; $(x_C)_F = 0.195$; $(y_C)_S = 0$.

Total material balance: $F + S = M = L + V \Rightarrow M = 1000 + 1500 = 2500$.

Solute balance: $F(x_C)_F + S(y_C)_S = M(x_C)_M \Rightarrow (x_C)_M = [(1000)(0.195) + (1500)(0)]/2500 = 0.078$.

The points $F(x_A = 0.805, x_B = 0, x_C = 0.195)$ and $S(y_A = 0, y_B = 1, y_C = 0)$ are located on the diagram [see Figure 9.13(a)] in which the extraction 'equilibrium data' are also plotted. The point M representing the mixture of F and S lies on the line SF at $(x_C)_M = 0.078$. The tie line through the point M is drawn. The terminals of the tie line are the points $L(x_C = 0.0403,\ x_B = 0.29)$ and $V(y_C = 0.114,\ y_B = 0.884)$.

Total material balance [see Eq (9.3)]: $V + L = M = 1000 + 1500 = 2500$ (i)

Solute balance [see Eq. (9.4)]: $Vy_C + Lx_C = M(x_C)_M$

$\Rightarrow$ $(0.114)V + (0.0403)L = (0.078)(2500) \Rightarrow V + 0.3535L = 1710.5$ (ii)

Solving Eqs. (i) and (ii), $L = 1221$ kg, and $V = 1279$ kg

Amount of oil extracted $= Vy_C = (1279)(0.114) = 145.8$ kg

Initial amount of oil in the feed $= (1000)(0.195) = 195$ kg. Fraction extracted $= \boxed{74.8\%}$

(b) *Calculation using the Ponchon–Savarit diagram*

Given: $F' =$ amount of 'non-solid' in the feed $= (1000)(0.195) = 195$ kg; $(X_C)_{F'} =$ mass fraction of the solute in the feed on 'solid-free basis' $= 195/195 = 1$; $Z_{F'} =$ kg solid/kg non-solid $= 805/195 = 4.13$.

Similarly, $S' = 1500$, $(Y_C)_{S'} = 0$ (because the feed solvent is 'pure' or oil-free); $Z_{S'} = 0$.

By material balance, $M' = 195 + 1500 = 1695$; $Z_{M'} = (F'Z_{F'} + S'Z_{S'})/M' = 0.475$.

The 'equilibrium' data are plotted in Figure 9.13(b). The points $F'(1, 4.13)$ and $S'(0, 0)$ are located on the diagram. The point M' is located on the line $S'F'$ at $Z_{M'} = 0.475$. The tie line through the point M' is drawn. This is a vertical line with the terminal points L' and V'. It is found from the plot that

$Z_{L'} = 2.03$; $Z_{V'} \approx 0$; $(X_C)_{M'} = 0.115 = (X_C)_{L'} = (Y_C)_{V'}$ (since M', L' and V' are on the same vertical line).

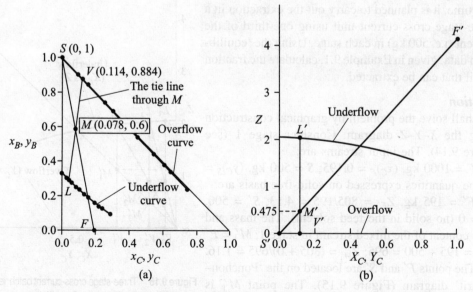

Figure 9.13 Single-stage batch 'leaching': (a) triangular diagram, and (b) 'Ponchon–Savarit' diagram.

Putting the values of different quantities in the material balance Eqs. (9.6) and (9.7), we get

$$L' = 396.6 \text{ kg; mass of the underflow} = L'(1 + Z_{L'}) = 396.6(1 + 2.03) = 1201.7 \text{ kg}$$

$$V' = M' - L' = 1695 - 396.6 = 1298.4 \text{ kg}$$

Mass of the overflow $= V'(1 + Z_{V'}) = (1298.4)(1 + 0) = 1298.4 \text{ kg}$ (*this is virtually solid-free*).

Fraction of the oil extracted $= (V')(Y_C)_{V'}/F' = (1298.4)(0.115)/195 = 0.736$, i.e. $\boxed{76.6\%}$

The small difference between the fractional extraction figures in parts (a) and (b) arises from the error in reading the values on the plots.

9.6.2 Cross-current Contact

The schematic of a three-stage cross-current contact unit is shown in Figure 9.14 (this is similar to Figure 4.16). The flow rates and the concentrations of the input and output streams to and from different stages are also shown. The underflow from the first stage is pumped to the second stage and so on. Extraction calculations can be done graphically as illustrated in Example 9.3.

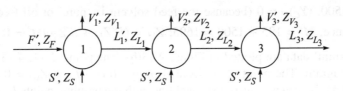

Figure 9.14 Multi-stage cross-current solid–liquid contact.

EXAMPLE 9.3 (*Cross-current solid–liquid extraction*)
Refer to Example 9.2. Instead of using the solvent at one time, it is planned to carry out the extraction in a three-stage cross-current unit using one-third of the solvent (i.e. 500 kg) in each stage. Using the 'equilibrium data' given in Example 9.1, calculate the fraction of oil that can be extracted.

Solution
We shall solve the problem by graphical construction using the X–Y–Z diagram. Consider stage 1 (see Figure 9.14). The input streams are:

$F = 1000$ kg, $(x_C)_F = 0.195$; $S = 500$ kg, $(y_C)_S = 0$. The quantities expressed on solid-free basis are:

$F' = 195$ kg, $Z_{F'} = 805/195 = 4.13$; $S' = 500$, $Z_{S'} = 0$ (no solid in the feed solvent). The mass and solid content of the mixed stream in stage 1, $M_1' = F' + S' = 195 + 500 = 695$; $Z_{M_1'} = (805 + 0)/695 = 1.16$.

The points F' and S' are located on the 'Ponchon–Savarit' diagram (Figure 9.15). The point M_1' is located on the line $S'F'$ such that $Z_{M_1'} = 1.16$. The tie

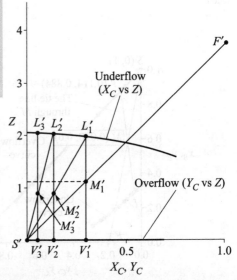

Figure 9.15 Three-stage cross-current batch 'leaching' calculation on the 'Ponchon–Savarit' diagram.

line $L_1'V_1'$ through M_1' ($L_1'V_1'$ is a vertical line for the given 'equilibrium data') is drawn. From the graph, $Z_{L_1'} = 1.96$, $Z_{V_1'} \approx 0$.

Writing a 'solid balance', we get

$$L_1'Z_{L_1'} + V_1'Z_{V_1'} = M_1'Z_{M_1'} \quad \Rightarrow \quad L_1'(1.96) + V_1'(0) = (695)(1.16) \Rightarrow L_1' = 411; \ V_1' = 284.$$

Now consider stage 2. The inputs to stage 2 are the streams L_1' and S'. If M_2' and $Z_{M_2'}$ are the amount and the concentration of the mixed stream, the point M_2' can be located on the line joining L_1' and S'.

$$M_2' = L_1' + S' = 411 + 500 = 911; \ Z_{M_2'} = [(411)(1.96) + (500)(0)]/911 = 0.884$$

The tie line $L_2'V_2'$ passing through M_2' is drawn. From the graph, $Z_{L_2'} = 2.02$, $Z_{V_2'} \approx 0$. Again, by a 'solid balance',

$$L_2'Z_{L_2'} + V_2'Z_{V_2'} = M_2'Z_{L_2'} = 805 \quad \Rightarrow \quad L_2' = 398.5; \ V_2' = 911 - 398.5 = 512.5$$

By the same procedure we can construct the tie line for stage 3.

$M_3' = L_2' + S' = 398.5 + 500 = 898.5$; $Z_{M_3'} = [(398.5)(2.02) + 500(0)]/898.5 = 0.896$. The point M_3' is located on the line joining L_2' and S'. The tie line through M_3' is drawn. This is a vertical line $L_3'V_3'$. The solute concentrations (on solid-free basis) in the streams are noted from the plot as

$$(X_C)_{L_3'} = (Y_C)_{V_3'} = 0.055 \qquad \text{and} \qquad Z_{L_3'} = 2.04$$

Also from a material balance,

$$(L_3')(Z_{L_3'}) + (V_3')(Z_{V_3'}) = (M_3')(Z_{M_3'}) \Rightarrow (L_3')(2.04) + (V_3')(0) = (898.5)(0.896)$$

$$\Rightarrow L_3' = 394.6; \ V_3' = 898.5 - 394.6 = 504$$

Mass of oil leaving with the underflow from stage 3 = $(L_3')(X_C)_{L_3'}$ = $(394.6)(0.055) = 21.7$ kg.

Fractional oil recovery = $(195 - 21.7)/195 = 0.89$, i.e. $\boxed{89\%}$

It has been found in Example 9.2 that the recovery of oil is about 75% if all the solvent is used in a single-stage.

9.6.3 Countercurrent Contact

An N-stage countercurrent extraction cascade is schematically shown in Figure 9.16. The flow rates are expressed on 'solid-free basis', and the solution concentrations in the overflow and in the underflow are given in mass fraction of the solute on 'solid-free basis' [X_C or Y_C, kg C/kg ($B + C$)].

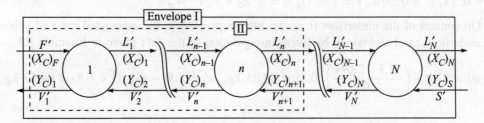

Figure 9.16 Countercurrent stage-wise solid–liquid extraction—material balance diagram.

An overall mass balance of $(B + C)$ and solute (C) balance on the entire battery (envelope I) are:

$(B + C)$ balance: $\qquad\qquad\qquad F' + S' = L'_N + V'_1 = M'$ (say) $\qquad\qquad$ (9.9a)

Solute (C) balance: $\qquad F'(X_C)_{F'} + S'(Y_C)_{S'} = L'_N(X_C)_{L'_N} + V'_1(Y_C)_{V'_1} = M'(X_C)_{M'}$ $\qquad$ (9.9b)

The quantity M' stands for the total amount of solvent (B) and solute (C) entering the battery, and $(X_C)_{M'}$ is the mass fraction of solute in it.

$$\Rightarrow \qquad\qquad (X_C)_{M'} = \frac{F'(X_C)_{F'} + S'(Y_C)_{S'}}{F' + S'} \qquad\qquad (9.10)$$

Now let us write down the mass balance equations for $(B + C)$ over the envelope II enclosing the first n stages.

$$F' + V'_{n+1} = L'_n + V'_1 \qquad\qquad\qquad (9.11)$$

$$\Rightarrow \qquad\qquad F' - V'_1 = L'_n - V'_{n+1} = L'_N - S' = \Delta \qquad\qquad (9.12)$$

Here Δ is a difference point having significance similar to that described in Section 8.4.3. From Eq. (9.12) it can be inferred that the point 'Δ' is in fact the point of intersection of the lines FV'_1 and $L'_N S'$. Also the points L'_n and V'_n lie at the extremities of a tie line for all n if the stages are 'ideal'.

In order to determine the number of ideal stages, the solid–liquid extraction 'equilibrium data' are plotted on the X–Y–Z plane. The points F', S', and L'_N are located on this Ponchon–Savarit diagram. The point M' is located on the line $F'S'$; $L'_N M'$ is joined and extended to meet the Y_C–Z curve at the point V'_1. The tie line through V'_1 has its other extremity at L'_1. From Eq. (9.12), it appears that the line joining Δ and L'_1 (for $n = 1$) intersects the Y_C–Z curve at V'_2. Proceeding this way, the number of stages required for a given degree of separation can be determined. This is illustrated in Example 9.4.

EXAMPLE 9.4 (*Number of stages for countercurrent leaching*) Crushed oil seeds containing 28 mass% oil is to be extracted with hexane to reduce the oil content to 0.8% in the underflow. One kilogram of the solvent is used per kg of the feed. Using the extraction 'equilibrium data' of Example 9.1, determine the number of stages required.

Solution
This calculation is based on 100 kg of the feed oil seed and 100 kg of the solvent. Following the usual notations,

$F = 100$ kg (28% oil); $S = S' = 100$ kg (oil free); $Z_{F'} = 72$ kg solid/0.28 kg oil $= 2.57$; $Z_{S'} = 0$; $(X_C)_F = 0.28/0.28 = 1.0$; $(Y_C)_S = 0$. $Z_S = 0$; $F' = 28$.

Oil content of the underflow from the Nth stage $= 0.8\%$; the associated mass of solvent in this underflow can be obtained by linear interpolation of the data given in Example 9.1.

$$w'_B = 32.8 - \left(\frac{32.8 - 29.94}{2.96}\right)(0.8) = 32.03 \text{ kg}; \quad w'_A = 100 - (32.03 + 0.8) = 67.17 \text{ kg}$$

$$(X_C)_N = \frac{w'_C}{w'_C + w'_B} = \frac{0.8}{0.8 + 32.03} = 0.0244$$

$$(Z)_{LN} = \frac{100 - (32.03 + 0.8)}{32.03 + 0.8} = 2.046$$

Solute concentration in the mixed stream M' is

$$(X_C)_{M'} = \frac{(28)(1.0) + 0}{100 + 28} = 0.219$$

Locate the points $F'(1, 2.57)$, $S'(0, 0)$ on the X–Y–Z plane and locate L'_N on the underflow curve for $(X_C)_N = 0.0244$. The graphical solution is shown in Figure 9.17.

Join $S'F'$ and locate the point M' [having an abscissa, $(X_C)_{M'} = 0.219$] on this line. Join $L'_N M'$ and extend it to meet the overflow line at V'_1. $L'_N S'$ and $F'V'_1$ are joined and extended to meet at the difference point 'Δ'.

The number of stages can now be determined by graphical construction in the usual way. Draw the tie line through V'_1 to meet the underflow line at L'_1 (the tie line is vertical in this case). Join $L'_1 \Delta$ that intersects the overflow line at V'_2 and so on.

The number of stages is found to be $\boxed{3}$.

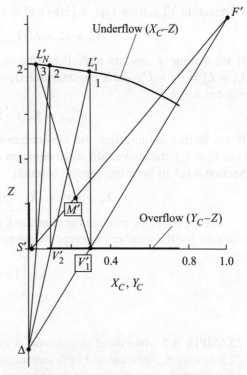

Figure 9.17 Countercurrent leaching—graphical construction of stages on the Ponchon–Savarit plot.

9.6.4 Analytical Determination of the Number of Stages for Constant Underflow

It is rather simple to determine the number of ideal stages for the case of constant underflow, i.e. if the solution retained per unit mass of inerts remains constant. Let us imagine a countercurrent extraction battery shown in Figure 9.18 (similar to Figure 9.16) in which L and V denote the total flow rates of the underflow and the overflow (on solid-free basis), and let X and Y be the corresponding mass fractions of the solute (the suffix C is omitted). Using the total flow rates and concentrations with appropriate suffixes, the total mass balance over envelope can be written as

$$V'_0 + L'_n = V'_{n-1} + L'_1 \tag{9.13a}$$

Solute (C) balance:
$$V'_0 Y_0 + L'_n X_n = V'_{n-1} Y_{n-1} + L'_1 X_1 \tag{9.13b}$$

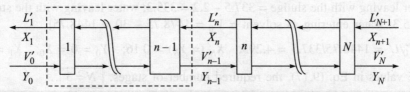

Figure 9.18 Countercurrent stage-wise solid–liquid extraction.

Eliminating V'_{n-1} from Eqs. 9.13(a) and 9.13(b),

$$(V'_0 + L'_n - L'_1)Y_{n-1} = L'_nX_n + (V'_0Y_0 - L'_1X_1) \tag{9.14}$$

If we assume a constant underflow (the amount of solution retained in the solid is constant, $L'_1 = L'_2 = \cdots = L'$) and a constant overflow ($V'_1 = V'_2 = \cdots = V'$) as well, the above equation reduces to

$$rY_{n-1} = X_n + rY_0 - X_1, \qquad r = V'_0/L' \tag{9.15}$$

If we further assume that the concentrations of the overflow and the underflow are equal (i.e. $X_n = Y_n$), the above difference equation can be solved following the procedure described in Section 4.6.3 to have the general solution

$$X_n = Kr^n + (X_1 - rY_0)/(1 - r), \quad K = \text{constant} \tag{9.16}$$

Putting $n = 0$, the value of the constant K can be found out. Again putting $n = N$, the following equation for the number of stages N can be obtained (Chen, 1964).

$$N = \frac{\log\left[1 + (r-1)\left(\dfrac{X_N - X_0}{X_1 - X_0}\right)\right]}{\log r} \tag{9.17}$$

EXAMPLE 9.5 (*Analytical determination of the number of stages*)   A solid feed containing 22% of solute, 3% water and 75% inerts (insolubles) is to be leached at a rate of 1 ton per hour with water in a countercurrent leaching cascade. The strong leachate leaving the unit should have 16% of the solute in it. Desired recovery of the solute in the feed is 99%. The overflow does not have any entrained inert in it, and the amount of solution retained in the sludge is 0.45 kg solution per kg inert. Analytically determine the number of stages required for the separation.

Solution
Mass of inerts = 750 kg/h; mass of solute entering = 220 kg/h; solution leaving with the inerts = (750)(0.45) = 337.5 kg/h = L'.

Mass of solute leaving with the sludge (for 99% recovery) = (220)(0.01) = 2.2 kg/h; solute concentration in the liquor entrained in the sludge leaving the battery = 2.2/337.5 = 0.00652 mass fraction (solid-free basis) = X_1.

The strong solution leaving the battery has 16% solute in it ($Y_N = 0.16$). We make a solute material balance.

$$\underset{\substack{\text{(Solute leaving} \\ \text{with the sludge)}}}{2.2} + \underset{\substack{\text{(Solute leaving with the} \\ \text{strong solution)}}}{[m_w - (337.5 - 2.2)](0.16/0.84)} = 220 \quad \Rightarrow \quad m_w = 1478.75 \text{ kg/h}$$

[*Note:* Water entering with the feed = 30 kg; m_w = water entering (including that present in the feed); water leaving with the sludge = 337.5 – 2.2 = 335.3; water leaving with the strong liquor = m_w – 335.3; water entering as solvent = V'_0 = 1478.75 – 30 = 1448.75]

$$\Rightarrow \quad r = V'_0/L' = 1448.75/337.5 = 4.293; \quad X_N (= Y_N) = 0.16; \quad Y_0 = 0 = X_0; \quad X_1 = 0.00652$$

Putting the values in Eq. (9.17), the required number of stages, $\boxed{N = 3}$.

The preceding techniques of determination of the number of stages can be used for the design of a continuous extractor (for example, a moving belt or even a moving basket extractor) if the 'equivalent length' of the extractor corresponding to a stage is defined and estimated. Thus, the length of a moving belt extractor for a particular separation is the product of the number of stages and the equivalent length. Since an extractor plant uses volatile solvents, due consideration should be given at the time of design to safety and health hazard. Disposal of the solid waste should also be taken care of.

9.7   SUPERCRITICAL FLUID EXTRACTION

Extraction of a solute from a solid (less frequently from a solution) using a supercritical fluid is a recent addition to separation technology. A fluid is called supercritical if both the temperature and pressure are above the critical values. At supercritical state, a fluid remains as a highly condensed phase and may have a density even more than its density in the liquid state. The state and density of CO_2, the most widely used supercritical solvent, is shown on the pressure–temperature plane in Figure 9.19. The constant density lines as well as the supercritical region are indicated. The density may be as high as 1200 kg/m^3.

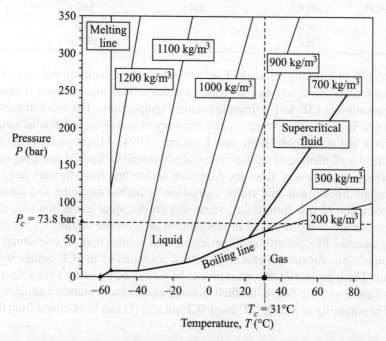

Figure 9.19   Pressure–temperature diagram for CO_2 (constant density lines are indicated).

A supercritical fluid (SCF) shares the properties of a gas and of a liquid. The solvent capacity increases greatly and the properties as a solvent change very rapidly with changes in temperature and pressure. While the viscosity remains an order of magnitude smaller than the normal liquid viscosity, the diffusivity of a solute in an SCF is about two orders of magnitude larger than that in the liquid. The diffusivity, viscosity and surface tension being highly favourable, the mass transfer characteristics, and hence the extraction rate also become highly favourable. The product may be easily separated from the extract by reduction of pressure when the solvent leaves as a gas which is compressed and recycled. Although carbon dioxide is the most important and widely used SCF, lower hydrocarbons (like ethylene, propylene, propane), chlorofluorocarbons, ammonia, etc. have been successfully used as supercritical solvents. There are quite a few remarkable advantages for which carbon dioxide has been the most attractive solvent for supercritical fluid extraction (SFE). It is inexpensive, non-toxic, non-flammable and available in high purity. It has sometimes been called the *cleanest solvent*. The critical constants of a few SFCs are given in Table 9.2.

Table 9.2   Critical properties of some supercritical solvents

Fluid	Normal boiling point (°C)	Critical constants		
		Pressure (bar)	Temperature (°C)	Density (g/cm³)
Carbon dioxide	−78.5	73.8	31.1	0.468
Ethylene	−103.7	50.4	9.3	0.2
Propylene	−47.7	46.2	91.9	0.23
Chlorotrifluoromethane	−81.4	39.2	28.9	0.58
Nitrous oxide	−89.0	71.0	36.5	0.457
Ammonia	−33.4	112.8	132.5	0.24

The high solvent capacity of an SCF is attributable to the closer packing of the solvent molecules which allow them to trap the solute molecules. This phenomenon is most prominent when the temperature is 1.01 to 1.2 times the critical temperature. The more important practical applications of SFE are for the extraction and recovery of active ingredients in natural products and in the food industries (McHugh and Krukonis, 1994; Mukhopadhyay, 2000). Typical applications are: decaffeination of tea and coffee (the Maxwell Coffee Co. has a big decaffeination plant in Houston); extraction of flavours, fragrance and aroma from flowers (e.g. jasmine and rose); food colour from plants and fruits; extraction of herbal medicine and antioxidants like β-carotene; extraction of oils from flaked seeds and grains; spice extraction (e.g. clove). Many newer applications are being explored in laboratories all over the world.

Solvent properties like polarity and interaction with solutes may be conveniently improved by the addition of a co-solvent. However, the critical constants of an SCF change in the presence of a co-solvent. These properties of a mixture can be estimated by using a suitable 'mixing rule'. The Peng–Robinson and the Soave–Redlich–Kwong equations of state are suitable for fugacity calculation. The solubility of a solute (2) in an SCF solvent (1) can be obtained from the following equation.

$$y_2 = \frac{P_2^s \exp[v_2^s(P - P_2^s)/RT]}{\bar{\phi}_2} \tag{9.18}$$

where $\bar{\phi}_2$ = the fugacity coefficient, P_2^s = saturation vapour pressure, and v_2^s = the molar volume of the solute.

A lot of work has been done on mass transfer during supercritical extraction. The schematic of an SCF unit is shown in Figure 9.20. It consists of three major units — the extractor, the solvent separator, and the recycle pump. Extraction in a packed bed is common. The solute-laden SCF from the extractor is cooled and goes to a precipitation chamber where the pressure is reduced to separate out the solute. Pressure reduction can be done in a number of stages if there are more solutes which are precipitated separately depending upon the pressure. Some fractionation of a mixture of solutes can be done in this way. The gaseous CO_2 is compressed, cooled and recycled to the extractor through a heat exchanger in order to heat it to the required temperature. Batch extraction is more common since continuous feeding of a solid and removal of the exhausted material is difficult in a high pressure system. However, a few continuous SFE units are reported to exist (McClain, 2000). Several studies have been reported on reactions in a superficial medium (example: oxidation of a waste material in superficial water).

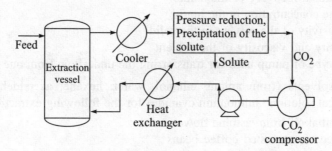

Figure 9.20 Schematic of a supercritical extraction unit.

Pure CO_2 is essentially inert to and compatible with most grades of carbon steel. But frequent presence of water in the solid-feed causes formation of carbonic acid and creates a corrosive environment. Type 300 and type 400 series stainless steel may be suitable materials of construction when water is present. Swelling of O-rings used for sealing is the cause of another practical problem in an SFE unit.

NOTATIONS

A, B, C	: 'inert solids', solvent and solute respectively
F, L, V	: total flow rate (or amount) of the feed, underflow and overflow respectively
F', L', V'	: flow rate (or amount) of the feed, underflow and overflow respectively on 'solid-free basis'
M, M'	: mass of two input streams, the total mass and that on 'solid-free' basis respectively
N	: number of stages
S, S'	: mass (or rate of flow) of the solvent, total and solid-free basis respectively
x, y	: mass fraction of a substance in the underflow and the overflow respectively
X, Y	: mass fraction of the solute in the underflow and the overflow on 'solid-free basis'
Z	: mass of 'inert solids' per unit mass of the rest in a stream

SHORT AND MULTIPLE CHOICE QUESTIONS

1. In which of the following equipment does extraction occur by the percolation process?
   - (i) Bollman extractor
   - (ii) Moving belt extractor
   - (iii) Pachuka extractor
   - (iv) Hildebrand extractor

2. Which of the following factors influences the fraction of liquid retained in the underflow or sludge?
   - (i) Boiling point of the solvent
   - (ii) Size and shape of the solid particles
   - (iii) Fractional recovery of the solute
   - (iv) Solute concentration in the liquid
   - (v) Diffusivity of the solvent in the solid
   - (vi) Density and viscosity of the solvent
   - (vii) The type of pump used for transferring the underflow from one settler to the next

3. Suggest solvents (from among ethanol, water, hexane, acetaldehyde, acetic acid, ammoniacal solution, ammonium cyanide) for the following extraction processes:
   - (i) Essential oil from jasmine flower
   - (ii) Coffee from roasted coffee beans
   - (iii) Gold from its ore
   - (iv) Copper from roasted ore
   - (v) Oil from peanut cake
   - (vi) Tea from tea leaves

4. Identify the controlling resistance in the following cases:
   - (i) Solubilization of sugar from cossets of sugar beet
   - (ii) Extraction of oil from fish meal
   - (iii) Leaching of copper ore by H_2SO_4

5. In a countercurrent leaching battery, the overflow from the stages are essentially solid-free. What is the slope of the Y_C–Z plot?
   - (i) Zero
   - (ii) Infinite
   - (iii) Negative and nonzero

6. If the solute concentrations (on 'solid-free basis') in the overflow and the underflow are equal, the tie lines are
   - (i) vertical   (ii) horizontal   (iii) of varying slope

7. A sludge is washed in a countercurrent cascade. The inerts have appreciable capacity of adsorption of the solute. While calculating the number of 'ideal stages', a student neglected adsorption. The correct number of ideal stages will be
   - (i) more than what he has calculated
   - (ii) less than what he has calculated
   - (iii) the same as what he has calculated.

8. One kilogram of sludge containing 0.5 kg CaCO$_3$, 0.15 kg NaOH and 0.35 kg water is mixed with 1 kg of water. The suspension is allowed to settle and the overflow and underflow are separated. The underflow has 0.3 kg solution retained per kg inerts. Calculate the amount and concentration of the solute in the overflow if it is free from solids.

9. If the fractional retention of solution in the underflow increases (other parameters remaining unchanged), the number of ideal stages required for a countercurrent washing job

   (i)   will be more
   (ii) will be less
   (iii) will not be affected.

10. What kind of diffusional phenomenon occurs within broken seeds during oil extraction?

    (i)   Diffusion of C (solute) through non-diffusing B (solvent)
    (ii) Non-equimolar counterdiffusion of B and C
    (iii) Equimolar counterdiffusion of B and C

11. Consider extraction of a solute by passing the solvent through a packed bed of the solid feed. The density of the liquid increases with the concentration of the solute in it. Which of the following strategies will reduce axial mixing in the liquid because of free convection?

    (i)   Upflow of the liquid through the bed
    (ii) Downflow of the liquid
    (iii) Pulsation of the liquid

12. What are the advantages and problems of carrying out extraction of a solid at an elevated temperature?

13. In solvent extraction of oil from seeds, which of the following forms of the solid gives the highest rate of extraction?

    (i)   Whole seeds
    (ii) Broken seeds
    (iii) Flakes of the seeds

14. If the solution retained in the solid has the same composition as that of the solid-free overflow, then the tie lines on the right-triangular plot

    (i)   are horizontal
    (ii) are vertical
    (iii) pass through the vertex representing 100% solid.

15. Suggest suitable extraction equipment for the extraction of

    (i)   oil from crushed soybean, peanut, saal seeds, rape seed cake, rice bran
    (ii) essential oil from flowers
    (iii) gelatin from acidified hides
    (iv) sugar from sugar beets
    (v)   pharmaceutical products from plant leaves, bark or root
    (vi) coffee from broken seeds.

16. Which of the following statements is correct for a supercritical extraction system?
    (i) The solute diffusivity is about 100 times that in a normal solvent.
    (ii) A supercritical fluid has a pretty large surface tension.
    (iii) The viscosity of an SCF is nearer to that of a gas than to a liquid.
    (iv) Propane has lower critical constants than ethylene.
    (v) A supercritical fluid penetrates even the smallest pore in a solid.
    (vi) Product separation from the extract is done by fractional distillation.
    (vii) Leakage from the system is hazardous if a hydrocarbon solvent is used.

17. Discuss the advantages of supercritical extraction. Name a few supercritical solvents. Why is carbon dioxide the most widely used solvent for this purpose? Give a few examples of practical applications. Which equations of state are suitable to describe the $P–V–T$ behaviour of an SCF?

18. Derive Eq. (9.17).

19. Draw the overflow ($X_C–Z$) and the underflow ($Y_C–Z$) curves for a system having the following characteristics—overflow: solids content = $0.1Y_C$ kg solid per kg solvent; underflow: solids content = $0.35 - 0.4X_C^2$, mass fraction of the slurry.

PROBLEMS

9.1 (*Drawing the underflow and underflow curves*)[1]   Oil is extracted from crushed seeds by a low-boiling hydrocarbon. The following experimental data are collected on the concentration and solid content of the overflow, and the solution retained in the underflow. The concentrations of both the streams are equal on 'solid-free basis'.

Overflow		Underflow
kg oil per kg clear solution	kg solid per kg solution	kg inerts per kg solution
0.0	0.00	0.67
0.05	0.002	0.66
0.20	0.005	0.64
0.25	0.007	0.625
0.30	0.01	0.60
0.35	0.013	0.58
0.40	0.017	0.55
0.45	0.022	0.51
0.50	0.029	0.46

Calculate and plot the experimental 'equilibrium data' (i) on a right-triangular diagram and (ii) as the Ponchon–Savarit diagram.

9.2 (*Cross-current liquid–solid contact*)[1]   Consider the system described in Problem 9.1. One thousand kilograms of crushed seeds containing 25% oil and 75% inerts is intimately mixed with 1800 kg of the hydrocarbon and adequate time for settling is allowed. Calculate (a) the mass of the underflow and that of the overflow, and (b) the fraction of the oil removed in the extract.

If the above extraction is done in two stages using 1500 kg of the solvent in each stage, calculate the mass fraction of residual oil in the final sludge.

9.3 (*Countercurrent contact*)[2]   Sodium hydroxide present in a $CaCO_3$ mud is to be recovered by countercurrent washing by water. The feed is one thousand kilograms per hour of the mud containing 44.3% inerts ($CaCO_3$), 33.5% NaOH, and 22.2% water. The clear solution leaving the extraction battery should have 15% NaOH in it, and 95% of the alkali is to be removed from the feed. The amount of solution retained in the mud is a function of its strength. The overflow is essentially solid-free.

Solution concentration (mass% NaOH)	0	5	10	15	20
Solution retained (kg per kg inert)	1.39	1.72	2.04	2.70	3.85

Calculate the rate of supply of wash water and the number of 'equilibrium stages'.

9.4 (*Countercurrent liquid–solid contact*)[3]   Experimental 'equilibrium data' on extraction of oil from a meal by using benzene are given below:

Mass fraction of oil (C) in solution	Mass fractions in the underflow		
y_C	x_C	x_A	x_B
0	0	0.67	0.33
0.1	0.0336	0.664	0.302
0.2	0.0682	0.660	0.272
0.3	0.1039	0.6541	0.242
0.4	0.1419	0.6451	0.213
0.5	0.1817	0.6366	0.1817
0.6	0.224	0.6268	0.1492
0.7	0.268	0.6172	0.1148

Two thousand kilograms per hour of the meal containing 26 mass% oil is extracted with 2100 kg/h of benzene. The underflow leaving the countercurrent cascade must not contain more than 0.015 mass fraction of oil. The feed benzene has 0.005 mass fraction oil in it. The overflow is essentially solid-free. Calculate the mass fraction in the rich extract leaving the cascade and the number of ideal stages required.

9.5 (*Constant retention of liquid in the underflow*)[3]   One thousand kilograms per hour of feed containing 15% solute, 2% water, and 83% inerts is extracted with water in a countercurrent cascade. The rich liquor leaving the cascade is to contain 15% of the solute. No carryover of the inerts in the overflow occurs. The underflow has a constant amount of 0.4 kg solution per kg inert. Also, the underflow leaving the cascade must not contain more than 0.005 kg solute per kg of inerts. Analytically determine the number of ideal stages required.

9.6 (*Leaching cascade of given Murphree efficiency*)[3]   Let us consider a countercurrent leaching cascade with constant underflow and no carryover of the inerts in the overflow. The stages are not 'equilibrium stages'. The stage efficiency is given by the Murphree efficiency defined below.

$$E_M = \frac{x_n - x_{n-1}}{x_n - x_{n-1}^*}$$

The flow rates of the feed and of the solvent, the fractional extraction of the solute and the fraction of liquid retained in the solid are given. Following Nguyen (1978) and assuming a 'linear equilibrium relationship' $Y_n^* = \alpha X_n$, determine the number of real stages required to achieve a given degree of separation.

9.7 (*Analytical determination of the number of stages, concentration dependent underflow*)[3]   Analytical determination of the number of stages in countercurrent leaching described in Section 9.6.4 can be extended to the case of variable underflow under certain conditions. For some systems it has been found (Chen, 1964) that the reciprocal of the fraction of liquid retained in the underflow can be expressed as a linear function of the concentration of the solute in the liquid. Analytically determine the number of ideal stages required for a given separation for such a system.

9.8 (*Analytical determination of the number of stages*)[2]   A solid having 20% solute, 2% water and the rest inerts is to be leached with water at a rate of 2 ton/h. The overflow leaving the countercurrent leaching cascade has 15% solute and no solid. The underflow carries 0.5 kg solution per kg inert independent of the solution concentration. If 97% of the solute is to be recovered, determine the number of ideal stages required.

9.9 (*Number of stages for countercurrent leaching*)[3]   A slurry of a seaweed is to be leached with hot water to recover a valuable protein. The slurry (48.1% solids, 49% water and 2.9% protein) enters a countercurrent leaching battery at a rate of 400 kg/h. Hot water enters at the other end at a rate of 500 kg/h. The underflow leaving the unit may have a maximum of 0.2% protein. Calculate the number of ideal contact stages required. The following 'equilibrium data' generated by laboratory tests (Chopey: *Chem. Engg. Calculations*, McGraw-Hill, 1994) may be used.

Extract (overflow) concentration, mass fraction			Slurry (underflow) concentration, mass fraction		
Water	Protein	Solids	Water	Protein	Solids
0.952	0.046	0.002	0.542	0.026	0.432
0.967	0.032	0.001	0.564	0.019	0.417
0.979	0.021	0.00	0.586	0.013	0.401
0.989	0.011	0.00	0.5954	0.0066	0.398
0.994	0.006	0.00	0.5994	0.0036	0.397
0.998	0.002	0.00	0.6028	0.0012	0.396

REFERENCES

Chen, N.H., 'Calculating theoretical stages in countercurrent leaching', *Chem. Engg.*, Nov. 23, 1964, 125–128.

Ciminelli, V.S., et al., *Biometallurgy — Fundamentals, Technology and Sustainable Development*, Elsevier Scientific, 2001.

George, W.J., 'Calculating number of stages graphically', *Chem. Engg.*, Feb. 9, 1959, 111–114.

Hairston, D., 'Leaching metal — For all its worth', *Chem. Engg.*, Nov. 1999, 28–31.

McClain, J., 'Processing with supercritical solvents', *Chem. Engg.*, Feb. 2000, 72–79.

McHugh, M., and V. Krukonis, *Supercritical Fluid Extraction*, 2nd ed., Butterworth, Oxford, 1994.

Mukhopadhyay, M., *Natural Extracts Using Supercritical Carbon Dioxide*, CRC Press, Florida, 2000.

Nguyen, H.X., 'Calculating actual stages in countercurrent leaching', *Chem. Engg.*, Nov. 6, 1978, 121–122.

Rickles, R.N., 'Liquid–solid extraction', *Chem. Engg.*, March 15, 1965, 157–172.

Schwartzberg, H.G., 'Continuous countercurrent extraction in the food industry', *Chem. Engg. Progr.*, April 1980, 67–85.

Schweitzer, P.A. (Ed.), *Handbook of Separation Techniques for Chemical Engineers*, 3rd ed., McGraw-Hill, 1997.

10

Humidification and Water Cooling

Industrial processes use a lot of water for cooling purposes. In the flow diagram of any chemical process, we see a pretty large number of heat exchangers, condensers and other types of coolers. In some of these equipment, heat exchange occurs between two process streams, generally for recovery of heat. But in many others, cooling water is used to extract unusable heat from process streams. Metallurgical plants and rolling mills also use a large volume of water for cooling. However, the largest users of cooling water are the power plants in which a huge quantity of low-pressure steam from the turbines is condensed in big condensers. Cooling water used in the industries are of two types—raw water and treated water. Raw water is directly drawn by pumps from natural water sources like rivers, lakes, etc. or is lifted from deep tube-wells. Treated water is obtained from a water treatment plant in which the raw water is freed from its hardness and dissolved substances. The problem of fouling and corrosion of the heat exchanger surfaces can be minimized if the treated water is used for cooling purposes.

Since water received at the 'battery limit' of a plant has its cost, the pumping and treatment costs being the most important, nobody can afford to throw it away after use. If raw water, which is much cheaper than the treated water, is available in plenty, 'once-through cooling' [Figure 10.1(a)] is sometimes used. But the hot water from an 'once-through cooling' system cannot always be discharged into a lake, river, canal, etc. Discharge of hot water causes thermal pollution and can severely affect the aquatic creatures and algae in the natural water. Above all, water is a resource and it has to be conserved like other natural resources.

Conservation of water in a plant is done by cooling the warm water from heat exchangers, reactors, etc. and reusing it as shown schematically in Figure 10.1(b) (Ahmed and Bayers, 2000). Only a small quantity of makeup water is necessary to compensate for the losses during use. The losses are mainly due to evaporative cooling. Cooling of warm water is done by direct contact with air in cooling towers. Water is fed at the top of a cooling tower and air is drawn at the bottom or through the side walls. Evaporative cooling of water occurs in the tower, the latent heat of vaporization being supplied mostly by the water itself. The air is humidified and the water is cooled. Air–water contacting has four major applications.

1. *Water cooling:* Air–water contacting is done mostly for the purpose of cooling the warm water before it can be reused.

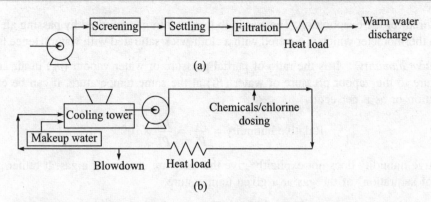

Figure 10.1 Cooling water systems: (a) once-through cooling, and (b) a cooling water curcuit.

2. *Humidification:* Air having a specified moisture content is necessary for some process applications—for example, in the drying of a solid under controlled condition. The process of increasing the moisture content of air is called 'humidification'. A humidifier is also used at the inlet of an air-ventilating system.

3. *Dehumidification:* Moist warm air may be relieved of a part of its moisture by contacting with water at a lower temperature. Dehumidification has use in air conditioning.

4. *Gas cooling:* A hot air stream can be cooled conveniently in contact with water. However, its content changes in the process.

Each of the above operations involves 'simultaneous transfer of heat and mass'. In water cooling, for example, the air flowing through the cooling tower is 'unsaturated'. Evaporation of water occurs and the water vapour is transported to the bulk of the air thereby increasing its humidity. The water temperature decreases, and some amount of heat transfer from the warm gas to the liquid occurs. Before dealing with the theoretical principles of simultaneous heat and mass transfer, we shall introduce several terms used in the description and calculation of humidification and water cooling. Water, the transferable component, is denoted by *A* and air is denoted by *B*.

10.1 TERMINOLOGY AND DEFINITIONS

'Temperature', 'humidity' and 'enthalpy' of air are the more important quantities in dealing with humidification. The rate of transfer of water vapour (generally to the air) depends upon the vapour pressure of the water and the moisture concentration in air. Two types of temperature— the 'dry-bulb' and the 'wet-bulb temperature'—are defined in connection with air–water contacting. Moisture concentration is expressed in terms of 'humidity' which can be defined in more than one ways.

Dry-bulb temperature: This is the temperature of air measured by a thermometer whose 'bulb is dry', i.e. not in touch with water or any other liquid. This is the true temperature of the air.

Wet-bulb temperature: It is the temperature attained by a small amount of evaporating water in a manner such that the sensible heat transferred from the air to the liquid is equal to the latent heat required for the evaporation. The wet-bulb temperature is measured by passing air over the bulb of a thermometer which is covered with a cloth-wick saturated with water. Hence the name.

Relative humidity: It is the ratio of partial pressure of water vapour (p_A) in air at a given temperature to the vapour pressure of water (P_A^v) at the same temperature. It can be expressed as a fraction or as a per cent.

$$\text{Relative humidity} = \frac{p_A}{P_A^v} = \frac{p_A}{P_A^v} \times 100\% \tag{10.1}$$

The relative humidity does not explicitly give the moisture content of a gas. It rather gives the 'degree of saturation' of the gas at a given temperature.

Absolute humidity (or simply humidity):   This is a direct measure of moisture content in a gas. The mass of water vapour per unit mass of the 'dry' gas is called its 'humidity' or 'absolute humidity'. These two terms are used interchangeably. We shall denote it by Y' (The notation Y generally indicates the gas-phase concentration in mole ratio unit. We use a prime to mean that the moisture content is given in *mass ratio unit*.). Suppose the partial pressure of moisture in air is p_A and the total pressure is P. Then

$$Y = \frac{p_A}{P - p_A} \text{ and } Y' = \frac{p_A}{P - p_A} \times \frac{18.02}{28.97} \frac{\text{kg water}}{\text{kg dry air}} \text{ [M.wt.: water = 18.02; air = 28.97]} \tag{10.2}$$

In industrial practice, the humidity is sometimes expressed in 'grains per pound of air' (1lb = 7000 grains).

Percentage humidity or percentage saturation: It is defined as

$$\text{Percentage humidity} = \frac{Y'}{Y_s'} \times 100\%; \qquad Y_s' = \frac{P_A^v}{P - P_A^v} \times \frac{18.02}{28.97} \tag{10.3}$$

Here Y' is the humidity (i.e. the absolute humidity) of a sample of air and Y_s' is its humidity at the same temperature and pressure if saturated with water vapour. The vapour pressure of water can be calculated using the Antoine equation given below.

$$\ln P_A^v(\text{bar}) = \frac{11.96481 - 3984.923}{T - 39.724} \qquad \text{where } T \text{ is in K} \tag{10.4}$$

Dew point: If a vapour–gas mixture is gradually cooled at a constant pressure, the temperature at which it just becomes saturated is called its 'dew point'. The partial pressure of water vapour in air is the same as the vapour pressure of water at this temperature. If the temperature is reduced even slightly, condensation occurs and droplets (dew) of water appear.

Humid volume: The humid volume v_H is defined as the volume of unit mass of 'dry' air with accompanying water vapour at a given temperature and pressure. If Y' is the humidity (i.e. absolute humidity) of a sample of air at atmospheric pressure and temperature T_G°C, i.e. ($T_G + 273$) K, its humid volume can be calculated from the following equation assuming ideal gas behaviour (volume of 1 kmol of a gas at 1 atm and 0°C = 22.4 m³).

$$v_H = \left(\frac{1}{28.97} + \frac{Y'}{18.02} \right) \times 22.4 \times \left(\frac{T_G + 273}{273} \right), \text{ in m}^3 \text{ per kg dry air} \tag{10.5}$$

Humid heat: The humid heat c_H is the heat energy required to raise the temperature of unit mass of 'dry air' with the accompanying water vapour by one degree. At ordinary temperature and pressure the heat capacity of dry air may be taken as 1.005 kJ/kg·K and that of water vapour as 1.88 kJ/kg·K. If the humidity of a sample of moist air is Y', its humid heat can be calculated from the following equation.

$$c_H = 1.005 + 1.88Y', \text{ in kJ/(kg dry air)(K)} \tag{10.6}$$

Enthalpy: Enthalpy of a sample of air appears in the energy balance equation of water cooling and many similar operations. Like humid volume and humid heat, it is also expressed on the basis of unit mass of dry air. Thus the statement "the enthalpy of a sample of air is H' kJ/kg" means that 1 kg of 'dry' air with accompanying water vapour has a heat content of H' kJ with respect to the specified reference states of air and water. The reference states may be chosen arbitrarily. The common choice is: dry air and liquid water, both at 0°C and 1 atm (1.013 bar) pressure.

An equation for the calculation of enthalpy of a stream of moist air at 1 atm pressure and of humidity Y' and temperature T_G°C is given below. It is assumed that Y' kg water is vaporized at the reference temperature (T_0°C) and mixed with 1 kg of dry air at the same temperature, T_0°C, to get $(1 + Y')$ kg moist air. If λ_0 is the latent heat of vaporization of water at the reference temperature, the enthalpy is given as

$$\underset{\text{(Enthalpy)}}{H'} = \underset{\text{(Latent heat)}}{Y'\lambda_0} + \underset{\text{(Sensible heat)}}{c_H(T_G - T_0)} \tag{10.7}$$

where c_H is the humid heat of the air.

If the reference temperature is 0°C, we take $\lambda_0 = 2500$ kJ/kg; c_H is given by Eq. (10.7). So the enthalpy is

$$H' = 2500Y' + (1.005 + 1.88Y')(T_G - T_0), \text{ in kJ per kg dry air} \tag{10.8}$$

The basis of Eq. (10.8) is schematically shown in Figure 10.2.

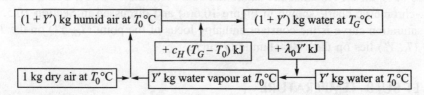

Figure 10.2 The basis of Eq. (10.8) illustrated (T_0°C = reference temperature).

10.2 ADIABATIC SATURATION TEMPERATURE

This is an important quantity in relation to air–water contacting. In order to explain the quantity, we use the air–water contacting arrangement shown in Figure 10.3. Water is continuously sprayed in the humdification chamber through the spray pipe. The water at the bottom of the chamber is recirculated by a pump as shown. An air stream continuously enters into the chamber and is brought in intimate contact with the water spray. The air stream attains thermal equilibrium with the water at temperature T_s and also gets saturated with water vapour at that temperature before it leaves the chamber. A small quantity of water at the temperature T_s may be fed

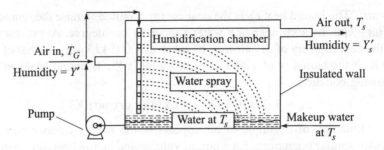

Figure 10.3   Schematic representation of adiabatic saturation of air.

continuously in order to compensate for the vaporization loss of water. The walls of the chamber are well-insulated and the system operates adiabatically. The temperature T_s attained by the air (which is the same as the temperature of water) is called the 'adiabatic saturation temperature'. (also denoted by T_{as}). Suppose Y' is the humidity of the inlet air and T_G is its temperature; λ_s is the heat of vaporization of water at the adiabatic saturation temperature, T_s. If T_s is also the reference temperature (chosen for convenience) and Y'_s is the humidity of the saturated exit air,

$$\text{Enthalpy of the inlet air} = c_H(T_G - T_s) + \lambda_s Y' \text{, in kJ per kg dry air}$$

$$\text{Enthalpy of exit air} = c_H(T_s - T_s) + \lambda_s Y'_s = \lambda_s Y'_s$$

Because the water temperature *does not* change, its enthalpy remains constant. The enthalpy of air also remains constant as there is no heat exchange with the surroundings. At steady state, we have

$$c_H(T_G - T_s) + \lambda_s Y' = \lambda_s Y'_s \quad \Rightarrow \quad (T_G - T_s) = (Y'_s - Y') \cdot \frac{\lambda_s}{c_H} \quad (10.9)$$

Equation (10.9) may be used to make a plot of Y' versus T_G for a given set of values of T_s and λ_s. Such a plot is called an 'adiabatic saturation curve'. It is slightly curved because of the dependence of c_H on Y'. An adiabatic saturation curve terminates on the 100% saturation curve of the 'psychrometric chart' shown in Figure 10.6(a) and discussed in Section 10.5. Thus, the adiabatic saturation curve is the constant enthalpy locus of the point (T_G, Y') on the T–Y plane. The point (T_s, Y'_s) lies on the 100% humidity curve.

10.3   WET-BULB TEMPERATURE

Consider a drop of water suspended in air at the tip of a thin wire. If the vapour pressure of water at the temperature of the drop is higher than the partial pressure of water vapour in the ambient air, evaporation of water will occur. The latent heat required for evaporation will be supplied: (i) partly by the surrounding air by convective heat transfer to the water drop, and (ii) partly by the water drop itself. The temperature of the drop falls as a result. As the temperature of the drop decreases with time, the vapour pressure of water in the drop also decreases causing a reduction in the partial pressure driving force and consequently in the evaporation flux. However, the temperature driving force for heat transfer from the ambient air to the water drop will increase. So the contribution of heat transfer from the ambient air towards the latent heat of vaporization of water will gradually increase. If sufficient time is allowed, the drop will eventually attain a steady-state temperature. At steady state, the heat flux from the ambient is equal to the latent heat required for the evaporation flux. The temperature of the drop does not decrease any further under this condition. This temperature of the drop is the wet-bulb temperature.

The wet-bulb temperature can be measured by a wet-bulb thermometer shown in Figure 10.4. One end of a wick wraps the thermometer bulb and the other end is dipped into a water pot. The wick remains wet by water by capillary action. The steady-state temperature of the wick indicated by the thermometer is the wet-bulb temperature. The dry-bulb temperature of air T_G and its humidity Y', primarily determine its wet-bulb temperature. However, factors such as air velocity and the shape of the thermometer bulb have some effect on the

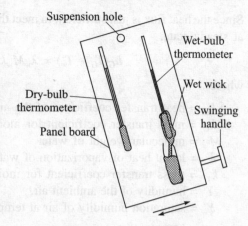

Figure 10.4   Sling thermometer.

wet-bulb temperature. At an air velocity above 30 km/h, the wet-bulb temperature depends upon the dry-bulb temperature and the humidity of the air only. The particular type of thermometer, called the 'sling thermometer' shown in Figure 10.4, gives the 'true' wet-bulb temperature. The thermometer is kept fixed on a panel that can swing rapidly so that a relative air velocity above 30 kmph may be maintained. A combination of a dry-bulb and a wet-bulb thermometer is called a *psychrometer*. Heat and mass transport through the air-film on the moist wick are illustrated in Figure 10.5.

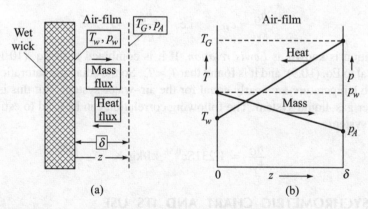

Figure 10.5   (a) Schematic of the wick and the air-film ; (b) the profile of temperature and partial pressure of water vapour in the air-film.

We determine below the quantitative relation of the wet-bulb temperature with the dry-bulb temperature, the humidity of the air, and the heat and mass transfer coefficients. If the steady-state temperature of the wick (i.e. the wet-bulb temperature) is T_w, and the vapour pressure of water at this temperature is p_w, the expressions for the heat flux and the evaporation mass flux can be written as

$$\text{Heat flux, } q = h_G(T_G - T_w); \text{ molar flux of water vapour, } N_A = k_G(p_w - p_A) \quad (10.10)$$

Since the heat flux is just sufficient to meet the requirement of latent heat of vaporization of water at steady state,

$$h_G(T_G - T_w) = \lambda_w M_w k_G(p_w - p_A) = \lambda_w k_{Y'}(Y'_w - Y') \tag{10.11}$$

where

h_G = heat transfer coefficient of the air-film
k_G = mass transfer coefficient for moisture transport through the air-film
M_w = molecular weight of water
λ_w = latent heat of vaporization of water
$k_{Y'}$ = mass transfer coefficient for moisture, in kg moisture/(m^2)(h)($\Delta Y'$)
Y' = humidity of the ambient air,
Y'_w = saturation humidity of air at temperature T_w.

From Eq. (10.11),

$$T_G - T_w = \frac{\lambda_w(Y'_w - Y')}{h_G/k_{Y'}} \tag{10.12}$$

The difference $T_G - T_w$ is called the 'wet-bulb depression'. The above equation can be used to calculate the wet-bulb temperature if h_G and $k_{Y'}$ are known or are estimated using a suitable correlation. The quantities T_w and Y'_w are related through the vapour pressure equation. However, the psychrometric data show that under moderate conditions the ratio of the heat and the mass transfer coefficient, $h_G/k_{Y'} = 0.227$ kcal/kg·°C. This is again equal to the humid heat of moist air c_H at moderate humidities. This very useful and interesting result can be expressed as

$$\frac{h_G}{k_{Y'}} \approx c_H \qquad \text{i.e.} \qquad \frac{h_G}{c_H k_{Y'}} \approx 1 \tag{10.13}$$

The above equation is known as *Lewis relation*. If it is combined with Eq. (10.12), we get an equation identical to Eq. (10.9), and it is found that $T_s \approx T_w$. So the adiabatic saturation temperature and the wet-bulb temperature are nearly equal for the air–water system. But this is certainly not true for any other gas–liquid system. The following correlation can be used to estimate the ratio $h_G/k_{Y'}$ for any system

$$\frac{h_G}{k_{Y'}} = 1.231 Sc^{0.56} \text{ kJ/kg·K} \tag{10.14}$$

10.4   THE PSYCHROMETRIC CHART AND ITS USE

The seven quantities, i.e. the dry-bulb temperature, the wet-bulb temperature, the relative humidity, the absolute humidity, the dew point, the enthalpy and the specific volume are all related. The psychrometric chart represents this interdependence. If any two of these quantities are known, the other five can be readily obtained from this chart shown in Figure 10.6(a) for the air–water system. The chart can be prepared by using the vapour pressure data or the equation for water and the definitions of the above quantities.

The use of the chart is illustrated on a portion of it reproduced in Figure 10.6(b). The dry-bulb temperature and one more quantity like humidity, relative humidity or wet-bulb temperature are generally used to specify the state or condition of a sample of air. If T_G is the air temperature and its humidity is Y', its state is denoted by the point a in Figure 10.6(b). It falls on the constant

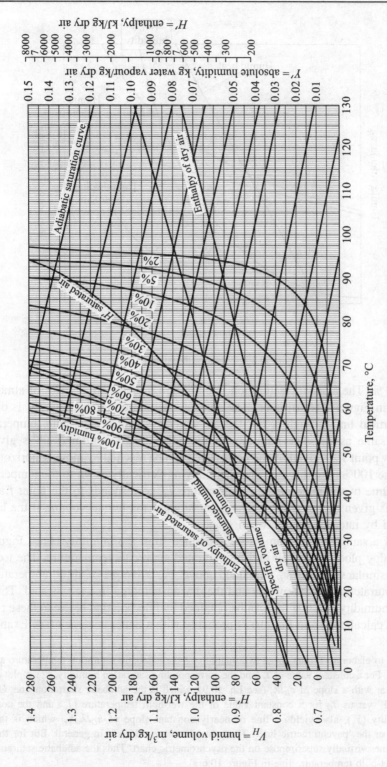

Figure 10.6 (a) Psychrometric chart for the air–water system at 1 atm total pressure.

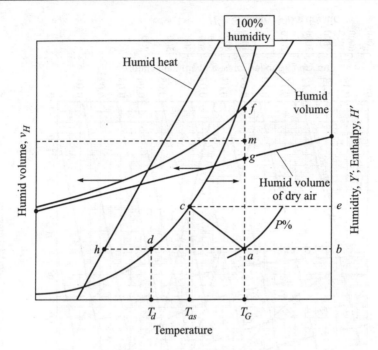

Figure 10.6(b)   Reading the humidity chart.

humidity line, $P\%$. The adiabatic saturation line through a [these are a series of almost parallel lines as shown in Figure 10.6(a)] is ac. The adiabatic saturation temperature T_{as} is obtained by drawing the vertical line through c. For the air–water system, the wet-bulb temperature T_w is practically the same as $T_{as}^{\dagger}$. The humidity of the adiabatically saturated air is given by the point e. The dew point T_d is given by the point d that can be reached by moving horizontally from the point a to the 100% humidity line and then moving vertically down to the temperature axis. The humid volume of saturated air at a temperature T_G corresponds to the point f and that of 'dry' air at T_G is given by the point g. The point m gives the humid volume if the humidity is Y'. It is reached by interpolation between g and f.

Enthalpy of a sample of air can also be obtained from the humidity chart. Figure 10.6(a) shows the enthalpy plots for dry air and for saturated air versus temperature. The technique of obtaining H' is similar to that of v_H explained above. For a sample of air at temperature T_G, the points on the saturated air enthalpy line and the dry air enthalpy line are located. The enthalpy of the air if the humidity is $(100Y')\%$ can be obtained by interpolation between these points. The enthalpy can be calculated from Eq. (10.7) probably with a better accuracy (see Example 10.1).

$\dagger$ It may be useful to elaborate further these two quantities—the adiabatic saturation temperature and the wet-bulb temperature. For a constant value of T_s (and the corresponding saturation humidity, Y_s'), a plot of Y' versus T_G is almost linear with a slope of c_H/λ_s (see Eq. 10.9), which is the adiabatic saturation line. On the other hand, a plot of Y' versus T_G for a constant value of the wet-bulb temperature (T_w) and the corresponding saturation humidity (Y_s'), also yields a line of nearly constant slope of $h_G/\lambda_w k_{Y'}$ which is the wet-bulb temperature line or the 'psychrometric line'. These two lines are different in general. But for the air–water system the two lines virtually superimpose on the psychrometric chart. Thus the adiabatic saturation line also represents the wet-bulb temperature line in Figure 10.6(a).

In fact, all the psychrometric quantities can be calculated using the given equations, although these can be directly read from the humidity chart.

EXAMPLE 10.1 (*Determination of psychrometric properties*) Determine the following psychrometric properties of a moist air sample having a dry-bulb temperature 27°C and a humidity of 0.015 kg/(kg dry air) using the psychrometric chart and/or the vapour pressure equation for water:

- (a) relative humidity
- (b) dew point
- (c) adiabatic saturation temperature
- (d) wet-bulb temperature
- (e) enthalpy
- (f) humid volume
- (g) humid heat

The Antoine equation for water is $\ln P_A^v$ (bar) $= 11.96481 - 3984.923/(T - 39.724)$. The total pressure is 1 atm.

Solution

Vapour pressure of water at 27°C (300.2 K) is $P_A^v = 0.0357$ bar (from the Antoine equation); p_A = the partial pressure of water vapour in the sample of air, and $P = 1.013$ (total pressure).

(a) Use Eq. (10.2). Humidity, $Y' = 0.015 = \dfrac{p_A}{P - p_A} \times \dfrac{18.02}{28.97} \Rightarrow p_A = 0.02385$ bar

Relative humidity $= (p_A/P_A^v) \times 100\% = (0.02385/0.0357) \times 100\% = \boxed{66.8\%}$.

(b) At the dew point, the sample of air will be just saturated, and the partial pressure of water vapour will be equal to its vapour pressure, i.e. $p_A = P_A^v = 0.02385$ bar. The corresponding temperature (from the Antoine equation), $T = 293.5$ K $= \boxed{20.3°C}$ is the dew point of the sample of air.

(c) Locate the point ($T = 27°C$, $Y' = 0.015$) on Figure 10.6(a) representing the condition or state of the air. Follow the adiabatic saturation line through this point (parallel to such lines on the psychrometric chart) to reach the 100% humidity or the saturation humidity curve to obtain the adiabatic saturation temperature of the given sample of air.

$T_{as} = \boxed{22.5°C}$; the corresponding saturation humidity, $Y_s' = \boxed{0.0172 \text{ kg/(kg dry air)}}$

(d) It is practically the same as the adiabatic saturation temperature, i.e.

$$T_w = \boxed{22.5°C}$$

(e) Enthalpy can be determined by three methods:

(i) Read the enthalpies of dry air and of saturated air at the given temperature from the psychrometric chart. Obtain the enthalpy of the given sample by interpolation. At the given temperature (27°C), enthalpy of dry air = 28.5 kJ/(kg dry air); that of saturated air (having a humidity 0.023) = 84 kJ/(kg dry air). By interpolation, the enthalpy of the given air sample of (humidity = 0.015) is

$$H' = 28.5 + (84 - 28.5)(0.015/0.023) = \boxed{64.7 \text{ kJ/(kg dry air)}}$$

(ii) The enthalpy calculated using Eq. (10.7) is

$$H' = 2500Y' + (1.005 + 1.88Y')(T - T_0)$$

$$= (2500)(0.015) + [1.005 + (1.88)(0.015)](27 - 0)$$

$$= \boxed{65.6 \text{ kJ/kg}}$$

[*Note:* The difference in enthalpy values between (i) and (ii) is due to error in reading the humidity chart.]

(iii) The enthalpy of a sample of air remains constant along the adiabatic saturation line. So the enthalpy of the given gas is the same as that of saturated air at T_{as} ($= 22.5°C$). From the chart,

$$H' = \boxed{64 \text{ kJ/kg}}.$$

Thus the values calculated by the three methods are *practically* the same.

(f) Humid volume can be determined by two methods:

(i) Using Eq. (10.5), $v_H = \left(\dfrac{1}{28.97} + \dfrac{0.015}{18.02}\right)(22.4)\left(\dfrac{27 + 273.2}{273.2}\right) = \boxed{0.87 \text{ m}^3/(\text{kg dry air})}$

(ii) Read the humid volumes of dry air and of saturated air at the given temperature from the psychrometric chart. Obtain the humid volume of the given sample by *interpolation*.

Humid volume of dry air $(27°C; Y' = 0) = 0.86 \text{ m}^3/(\text{kg dry air})$.

Humid volume of saturated air $(27°C, Y' = 0.023) = 0.88 \text{ m}^3/(\text{kg dry air})$.

Humidity of the given sample $(27°C, Y' = 0.015) = (0.88 - 0.86)\dfrac{0.015}{0.023}$

$$= \boxed{0.873 \text{ m}^3/(\text{kg dry air})}$$

(g) Humid heat can be easily calculated from Eq. (10.6).

$$c_H = 1.005 + 1.88Y' = 1.005 + (1.88)(0.015) = \boxed{1.033 \text{ kJ/(kg dry air)(°C)}}.$$

This quantity can also be determined from the chart by interpolation.

EXAMPLE 10.2 (*Estimation of the adiabatic saturation temperature of an organic liquid*)   It is a special feature of the air–water system that the wet-bulb temperature and the adiabatic saturation temperature are practically equal. This is not known to be so in any other gas–liquid pair. In this problem we calculate these quantities for the air–ethanol system. The temperature of the air is 30°C and it does not have any ethanol in it.

Given: diffusivity of ethanol in air, $D_{AB} = 0.145 \text{ cm}^2/\text{s}$ at 313 K and 1 atm; the vapour pressure equation of ethanol is $\ln P^v(\text{bar}) = 12.05896 - 3667.705/(T - 46.966)$, T in K; take other properties of air from the literature.

Solution

The wet-bulb temperature: It can be calculated from Eq. (10.12). The wet-bulb temperature is expectedly much lower than the bulk gas temperature of 30°C. It is desirable to take the value of Schmidt number at the mean film temperature. But this is not yet known. So we shall first calculate the wet-bulb temperature by taking the Schmidt number at 30°C. Once an estimate of the wet-bulb temperature is obtained, a more refined value can be obtained by taking the Schmidt number at the mean film temperature.

Properties of air at 30°C (303.2 K): density, $\rho = (28.97/22.4)(273.2/303.2) = 1.165 \text{ kg/m}^3$; viscosity, $\mu = 1.85 \times 10^{-5} \text{ Ns/m}^2$; diffusivity, $D_{AB} = (0.145)(303.2/313)^{1.5} \text{ cm}^2/\text{s} = 1.38 \times 10^{-5} \text{ m}^2/\text{s}$.

$$\text{Schmidt number of ethanol, Sc} = \frac{\mu}{\rho D_{AB}} = \frac{1.85 \times 10^{-5}}{(1.165)(1.38 \times 10^{-5})} = 1.151$$

From Eq. (10.14), $\dfrac{h_G}{k_{Y'}} = 1.231 \text{Sc}^{0.56} = (1.231)(1.151)^{0.56} = 1.332$ kJ/kg·K

Now we calculate the wet-bulb temperature from Eq. (10.12), $T_G - T_w = \dfrac{\lambda_w (Y_w' - Y')}{h_G / k_{Y'}}$

Given: $T_G = 30°C = 303.2$ K; $Y' = 0$ (no ethanol in bulk air); mol. wt. of ethanol = 46; its latent heat of vaporization (taken at 30°C), $\lambda_w = 970$ kJ/kg. Let $(P^v)_w$ be the vapour pressure of ethanol at its wet-bulb temperature T_w(K). From Eq. (10.12),

$$303.2 - T_w = \frac{(970)(Y_w' - 0)}{1.332}; \quad Y_w' = \frac{(P^v)_w}{P - (P^v)_w} \cdot \frac{46}{28.97}; \quad P = \text{total pressure} = 1.013 \text{ bar}$$

$$\Rightarrow \qquad 303.2 - T_w = \frac{970}{1.332} \times \frac{(P^v)_w}{1.013 - (P^v)_w} \cdot \frac{46}{28.97} = 1156 \times \frac{(P^v)_w}{1.013 - (P^v)_w}$$

$(P^v)_w$ is related to T_w by the vapour pressure equation. The above equation can be solved together with the given vapour pressure equation for ethanol by trial or numerically. The solution is $T_w = 278$ K = $\boxed{4.8°C}$.

Now we have an *estimate* of T_w. Next we recalculate the whole thing taking all the physical properties of the system at the 'mean gas film temperature', i.e. at $(30 + 4.8)/2 = 17.4°C$ = 290.6 K.

$$\text{At 290.6 K, } \rho = 1.212 \text{ kg/m}^3; \quad \mu = 1.65 \times 10^{-5} \text{ Ns/m}^2$$
$$D_{AB} = 1.3 \times 10^{-5} \text{ m}^2/\text{s}; \quad \text{Sc} = \mu/\rho D_{AB} = 1.05$$
$$h_G/k_{Y'} = 1.231 \text{Sc}^{0.56} = (1.231)(1.05)^{0.56} = 1.265$$

Since vaporization of the liquid occurs at its wet-bulb temperature, take the heat of vaporization of ethanol at the estimated wet-bulb temperature of 4.8°C, $\lambda_w = 985.6$ kJ/kg.

If the heat of vaporization λ_1 of a liquid is known at a particular temperature T_1 (K), its value at another temperature T_2 (K) can be calculated by using the following relation [see Reid et al. (1988), p. 228].

$$\lambda_2 = \lambda_1 \left(\frac{1 - T_{r2}}{1 - T_{r1}} \right)^{0.38}; \quad T_r = \text{the reduced temperature, } T/T_c; \quad \text{for ethanol, } T_c = 513.9 \text{ K}$$

We have

$$T_{r1} = T_1/T_c = 303.2/513.9 = 0.56; \quad \lambda_1 = 970 \text{ kJ/kg}; \quad T_{r2} = T_2/T_r = 278/513.9 = 0.541$$

From the above equation,

$$\lambda_2 = (970)[(1 - 0.541)/(1 - 0.56)]^{0.38} = 985.6 \text{ kJ/kg}$$

Using the above values of the relevant quantities and following the above procedure, we can obtain a refined value of the wet-bulb temperature, $T_w = \boxed{4°C}$.

Calculation of the adiabatic saturation temperature, T_{as}: We may make an estimate of T_{as} from Eq. (10.9) taking the relevant physical properties at the given air temperature (30°C) and then repeat the calculations taking the properties at the mean gas-film temperature. Alternatively, we can proceed with a guess value of T_{as} and the properties at the mean gas-film temperature. If the calculated value is not much different from the guess value, the second cycle of calculation to obtain a refined value may not be necessary. We follow this procedure here.

Take a guess value, $T_{as} = 3°C$. Mean temperature, $T_{av} = (30 + 3)/2 = 16.5°C$

$$\text{Working equation, Eq. (10.9):} \quad T_G - T_{as} = (Y'_{as} - Y')\frac{\lambda_{as}}{c_H} \tag{i}$$

If we know the values of λ_{as} and c_H, we can solve the above equation together with the vapour pressure equation to calculate T_{as}. We may get the value of λ_{as} at the guess temperature of 3°C following the method given in Reid et al. (1988) and used above. $\lambda_{as} = 985$ kJ/kg.

Determination of c_H: We take the value of 'humid heat' c_H at the mean humidity of air. Here 'humidity' means kg alcohol vapour per kg dry air. The vapour pressure of alcohol at the guess value of the liquid temperature (3°C) is calculated from the vapour pressure equation, $P^v = 0.01943$ bar.

Corresponding humidity = $Y'_s = [P^v/(P - P^v)] \times (46/28.97) = 0.03105$ (kg ethanol)/(kg dry air)

'Humidity' in the bulk air = $Y' = 0$;   Mean 'humidity' = 0.01552

Specific heat of alcohol vapour at the mean temperature (291.2 K) may be calculated using the relation given by Reid et al. (1988), Appendix A, p. 677.

$$c_p = 9.014 + 0.2141T - 8.39 \times 10^{-5}T^2$$
$$= 9.014 + (0.2141)(291.2) - 8.39 \times 10^{-5}(291.2)^2 = 64.25 \text{ kJ/kmol·K}$$
$$= 1.4 \text{ kJ/(kg alcohol)(K)}$$

Specific heat of dry air at the mean temperature = 1.007 kJ/kg·K

'Humid heat' (at $Y' = 0.01552$), $c_H = 1.007 + (0.0192)(1.4) = 1.034$ kJ/(kg dry air). Now putting all the values in Eq. (i), we have

$$303.2 - T_{as} = \frac{985}{1.034} \times \frac{p_{as}}{P - p_{as}} \times \frac{46}{28.97} = (1513)\frac{p_{as}}{P - p_{as}}$$

Solving the above equation together with the vapour pressure equation for alcohol (by trial or numerically), we obtain

$$T_{as} = \boxed{275.2 \text{ K} = 2°C}$$

This value is pretty close to the guess value of 3°C. No further calculation is necessary.

10.5   DESCRIPTION OF COOLING TOWERS—CONSTRUCTION AND OPERATION

A cooling tower is a special type of *heat exchanger* in which the warm water and the air are brought in direct contact for evaporative cooling. It must provide a very good contact of air and water in terms of the contact area and mass transfer coefficient of water vapour while keeping the air pressure drop low. In the early years of industrial development, cooling of warm water for reuse was done in 'spray ponds'. In a spray pond, as the name implies, a spray system located about six to eight feet above the water surface creates small droplets of warm water that cool down by evaporation in contact with air. This is a simple and easy process but requires a large pond area. It is inefficient (the effective heat transfer coefficient is about 3.5 Btu/h·ft^2·°F or 20 W/m^2·K), and creates the problem of entrainment and carryover of water droplets by air. The first water cooling tower was built in the USA by George Stocker in 1898. It was a wooden packed tower. Many changes in the design and construction of cooling towers have occurred since then. A brief history of development of cooling towers has been given by Willa (1997).

The important factors that govern the operation of a cooling tower are: (i) the dry-bulb and wet-bulb temperatures of the air; (ii) the temperature of warm water; (iii) the efficiency of contact between air and water in terms of the volumetric mass transfer coefficient ($k_Y \cdot \bar{a}$, see Section 10.7) and the contact time between the air and the water; (iv) the uniformity of distribution of the phases within the tower; (v) the air pressure drop; and (vi) the desired temperature of the cooled water. A tower is irrigated at the top through nozzles. A large air–water contact area and contact time are offered by a typical tower packing. Air may enter the tower driven by a density gradient (natural draft), may be pushed into the tower (forced draft) at the base or sucked into the tower (induced draft) assisted by a fan. Several types of cooling towers have been designed on the basis of the above factors and operating strategies. A number of models of each type are offered by the manufacturers. The more important types are classified (Figure 10.7) and described below.

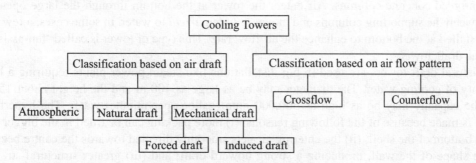

Figure 10.7 Classification of cooling towers.

10.5.1 Atmospheric Towers

An atmospheric tower consists of a big rectangular chamber with two opposite *louvered* walls. The tower is packed with a suitable *tower fill* (tower fills and louvers will be described later). Atmospheric air enters the tower through the louvers driven by its own velocity. An atmospheric tower is cheap but inefficient. Its performance largely depends upon the direction and velocity of wind.

10.5.2 Natural Draft Towers

A natural draft (also spelled 'draught') cooling tower (Figure 10.8) has a large reinforced concrete shell of hyperbolic shape (this is why such a tower is also called 'hyperbolic tower').

A small part of it near the bottom is filled with a high-void packing consisting of inclined wood or PVC battens of suitable size ($1'' \times 2''$ cross-section is common) fitted into slots along the supporting frames. Alternative layers of battens run in perpendicular directions. The warm water splashes to form droplets as it falls from one batten to the next lower. Evaporation, and the resulting cooling of water, occurs at the water-film on the battens as well as on the surface of a droplet. A few layers of batten placed above the water distributor act as the *drift eliminator*, which arrest fine water droplets (like the *dry packing* above the distributor in a packed tower) that tend to be carried away by the up-flowing air.

A natural draft tower is so called because natural flow of air occurs through the tower. Two factors are responsible for creating the natural draft: (i) a rise in temperature and humidity of air in the column reduces its density and (ii) the wind velocity at the tower

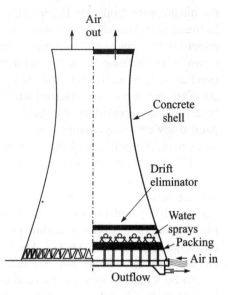

Figure 10.8   Counterflow natural draft tower.

bottom. The pressure drop across the tower is low (a fraction of an inch of water) and the air velocity above the packing may vary from 1–1.5 m/s. The concrete tower is supported on a set of reinforced concrete columns. Air enters the tower at the bottom through the large openings in between the supporting columns and moves *countercurrent* to water. In some cases, a few fans are installed at the bottom to enhance the air flow rate. This type of tower is called 'fan-assisted' natural draft tower.

Natural draft towers are used in big installations like steam power plants requiring a huge quantity of cooling water. The diameter may be as large as 100 m and the height about 150 m and the capacity may be as high as 500,000 gpm (gallons per minute) water. The hyperbolic shape is made because of the following reasons: (i) more packing can be fitted in the bigger area at the bottom of the shell; (ii) the entering air gets smoothly directed towards the centre because of the shape of the wall, producing a strong upward draft; and (iii) greater structural strength and stability of the shell is provided by this shape. The initial cost of a hyperbolic tower is high. However, the absence of a fan reduces the fixed cost and particularly the operating and maintenance costs making it economic over a long period of time.

10.5.3 Mechanical Draft Towers

Because of their huge shape, construction difficulties and cost, natural draft towers have been replaced by mechanical draft towers in many installations. Compact and relatively small size units of rectangular shape are now available and preferred in process industries and petroleum refineries. A mechanical draft tower uses fans to move the air through the tower. The two types of such towers are: (i) forced draft towers, and (ii) induced draft towers.

Forced draft towers

It has one or more fans located at the tower bottom to push air into the tower (Figure 10.9). This is why it is called *forced draft*. The air flows counter-current to water. The advantages of the forced draft system are the following: (i) A part of the velocity head of air thrown by the blower is converted to pressure head on entering into the tower. This makes the forced draft tower slightly more energy efficient than the induced draft type. (ii) The system is less susceptible to vibrations because the fans are installed near the ground on a solid foundation. The disadvantages of the forced draft system are: (i) the air flow through the packing or *fill* may not be uniform, particularly if the tower is big and a big fan is used; (ii) some of the warm and humid air may be recirculated back into the tower thereby reducing the performance (see Section 10.6.1). The recirculation rate becomes low if the wind velocity is high. Forced draft towers are not very popular except for small capacities.

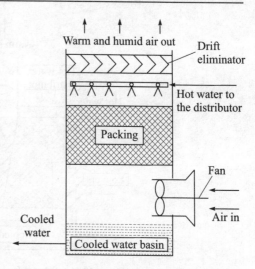

Figure 10.9   Schematic of a forced draft cooling tower.

Induced draft towers

An induced draft tower has one or more fans located at the top. The fans suck fresh air through the air inlets at the bottom. The air flow or draft is 'induced' by the suction created by the fans and hence the name. The induced draft tower may be of two types—crossflow and counterflow—depending upon the air inlet and flow pattern. In a 'counterflow induced draft tower' (Figure 10.10), a vertical movement of air countercurrent to the warm water occurs. The major advantage of this flow configuration is that the relatively dry air contacts the coldest water at the bottom, and the humid air contacts the warm water at the top of the tower. This ensures maximum average driving force for both heat and mass transfer. But more fan horsepower is required because of the restricted area of air flow at the bottom and, unlike the forced draft system, the velocity head of the air thrown out of the tower by the fan is dissipated.

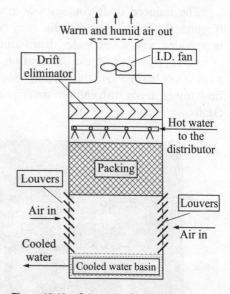

Figure 10.10   Schematic of a counterflow induced draft cooling tower.

The crossflow induced draft cooling tower provides horizontal air flow along the packed height (Figure 10.11). The air flow is crosscurrent to the down-flowing water. Louvers are provided all along the walls of the tower to allow the air to move in. For the same air flow rate, the tower requires less motor horsepower than the counterflow type. But the growth of algae on the fills is more because the tower interior gets more sunlight through the larger number of louvers.

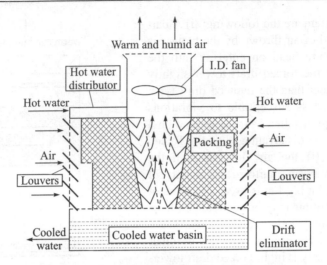

Figure 10.11 Schematic of a crossflow induced draft cooling tower.

The induced draft counterflow towers are nowadays built in compact cellular modules (Figure 10.12). Additional 'cells' may be added to increase the capacity if necessary. Each cell is provided with a fan, water distributor, and accessories. This is a big advantage of this type of towers. However, liquid distribution, in a crossflow tower is done by gravity flow through a hot water basin above the packing (see Figure 10.11) which may be easily cleaned. A counter-flow tower needs distribution under pressure through spray nozzles which are not so easy to clean.

Figure 10.12 A five-cell crossflow induced draft tower (Courtesy: Marley Cooling Tower).

Spray-filled towers

This is the simplest but the least efficient induced draft cooling tower. It does not have any 'fill' or packing. Water is sprayed at the top of a tall empty chamber. The fan at the top induces air flow through the tower countercurrent to the falling spray.

10.5.4 Structural Components and Materials of Construction

The major structural components of a cooling tower (Hensley, 1985) are: (i) the shell or the framework and casing walls, (ii) the tower fill, (iii) the louvers, (iv) the drift eliminator, (v) the water distributor, (vi) the cold water basin, (vii) the fan deck and fan cylinders, and (viii) mechanical equipment supports. Some of these components and their materials of construction are briefly described here.

The shell, the framework and casing walls

A natural draft tower has a hyperbolic reinforced concrete shell. A forced draft tower of rectangular shape has a framework made of concrete or wood which is enclosed by casing walls. Treated wood has been the material for the casing walls for many decades. Chromated copper arsenate (CCA) has been used for treating wood to protect it against bacterial degradation. Since arsenic is a severe pollutant, acid copper chromate (ACC) containing the salts of chromium, chromic acid and copper is now the preferred agent for wood treatment. These chemicals diffuse into the wood during treatment in a pressure vessel and are retained in it by weak complexation. Wood is relatively insensitive to chlorides and sulphides, but may get slowly degraded by excessive free chlorine.

Polyvinyl chloride (PVC) corrugated sheets have been tried for building casing walls. But relatively high thermal expansion characteristics of PVC have limited its use. Cement asbestos board (CAB) is a good material for walls, but it is substantially heavy and sometimes susceptible to chemical attack. Further, asbestos is classified as a carcinogen and its use is not allowed in many countries. The most favoured material for casing walls and louvers at present is the corrugated glass-fibre reinforced polyester (FRP or GRP). It is lightweight (10–12 oz/ft^2). The opaque variety guards against the algal growth within the tower by preventing the entry of sunlight. Ultraviolet protective additives are often used to extend its life. The FRP made from chlorinated polyesters has the inherent flame retardant ability.

The tower fill

The *tower fill* is the single most important component of a cooling tower. A good fill should promote a high contact surface and contact time between air and water while imposing little resistance and pressure drop on the air flow. The *fills* are broadly of two types: (i) splash-type fill, and (ii) film-type fill.

The splash-type fills (Figure 10.13) are traditional. This type of fill consists of staggered rows of 'splash bars'. Wood battens or slats of suitable size (0.5–1″ thick, 3–4″ wide, and 4–6′ long) were the only material used over the decades. The battens are fitted into slots along a supporting frame. The splash bars covered with thin water-films intercept the falling droplets. On hitting a splash bar, the droplets break. The contact time is greatly increased because of repeated interception of the droplets by the splash bars. Beginning 1950s, the wood has been gradually replaced by plastics. The advantages of plastic materials are their resistance to microbial attack, corrosion and erosion, compatibility with other materials, formability, high strength-to-weight ratio, and comparatively low cost. Plastics are also least susceptible to changes in the water condition. The most commonly used plastics for use in tower fills (in the form of battens or V-bars) are PVC, polypropylene, and FRP. Thin concrete slabs (1.5–2″ thick, 3–4″ wide), coated with water-resistant paints, are also used.

Splash fills are used in both crossflow and counterflow towers. These are not prone to clogging, create only a small air pressure drop and allow easy cleaning. The splash bars must be horizontal; sagging of the bars causes 'channeling' of air and water.

Figure 10.13   Splash-type fill—plastic splash bars (Courtesy: Marley Cooling Tower).

The film-type fill (also called *film-pack*; see Figure 10.14), which is similar to the structured packing (Section 5.11.2), consists of vertical corrugated sheets with a spacing of 18–25 mm. PVC is the most widely used material because it is inert and can be moulded easily into the desired shape. The sheets are glued to make rectangular units having sides about 1.5–2 m. The warm water spreads into thin films flowing along the fill surface. The air flows through the passage between the adjacent sheets.

The film-type fill is used in counterflow towers only and provides a higher cooling capacity for the same tower volume. Uniform spacing of the fill sheets is very important to ensure uniform distribution of air flow and to prevent 'channeling'. This type of tower fill is not recommended where the circulating cooling water contains foreign substances and debris.

Figure 10.14 Marley MC 75 counterflow film pack.

Louvers

Louvers (see Figures 10.10 and 10.11) are inclined blade or passage type assemblies fitted at the air inlet wall of a cooling tower to promote uniform air entry into the tower while preventing water splashout. Crossflow towers are always provided with louvers to allow uniform air flow all along the wall. Closely spaced and steeply sloped louvers are very effective for water containment. The most important louver materials are corrugated fire-retardant fibre-reinforced polyester and treated wood. Asbestos cement board louvers are also in use, but the use of this material is declining.

Drift eliminators

Water droplets carried over by the outgoing air are collectively called *drift*. It is like entrainment of liquid in the gas in a conventional packed tower. Drift causes loss of cooling water. It is also a potential nuisance in the region close to a cooling tower. Drift is more likely to occur in a tower using splash fills. A drift eliminator arrests the floating water droplets by *impaction* as the air passes through it. A few layers of slats placed in the frame above the water distributor may act as the drift eliminator. A 'honeycomb' type drift eliminator made from a plastic material (predominantly

PVC) with labyrinth passages for air is used by Marley Cooling Towers. By using an effective drift eliminator, the drift level can be reduced to 0.02% of the water flow or even less.

Fans

Cooling tower fans should deliver large volumes of air efficiently. The fan blades should be properly balanced to minimize vibration. Propeller type fans are generally used; centrifugal fans are used in rather small installations. The fan diameter ranges from less than a metre to as large as 10 metre. Larger fans are equipped with 'adjustable pitch blades' to regulate the air flow rate as per requirement in order to minimize wastage of electric power if there is a change in the cooling load. A drive shaft transmits power from the motor through a gear box. The fan rpm typically ranges between 150 and 400; the tip speed of the fan blade may be as high as 4000 m/min. FRP is the common material for fan blades. In induced draft towers the air thrown by the fan leaves through a tall 'fan stack' or 'fan cylinder' (Figure 10.15) of a smooth profile to ensure 'velocity recovery'.

Figure 10.15   Typical fibre-reinforced plastic fan cylinder (Courtesy: Marley Cooling Tower).

Water distribution

Water enters through a main header and is supplied to the individual compartments or cells of a mechanical draft tower. A spray distributor is common in counterflow towers. A crossflow tower uses an open distribution deck.

10.5.5 Interference and Recirculation

A number of cooling towers may have to be used if the hot water load is large. The towers are very often installed at one place in the plant for convenience. Interference and recirculation are two common problems with cooling towers placed in proximity. Some of the moist air leaving a tower may be sucked into another tower installed 'downwind' in the vicinity of the former [Figure 10.16(a)] affecting the performance. This is called 'interference'. Sometimes a part of the moist air from a tower may be sucked into itself by the 'forced-draft fan'. This is 'recirculation'

[Figure 10.16(b)]. The ratio of the 'plume velocity' to the 'wind velocity' is an important factor to determine the extent of recirculation. If this ratio is small, a forced-draft tower becomes more susceptible to recirculation [Figure 10.16(c)]. Both the phenomena of interference and recirculation reduce the enthalpy driving for cooling and adversely affect the performance of cooling towers.

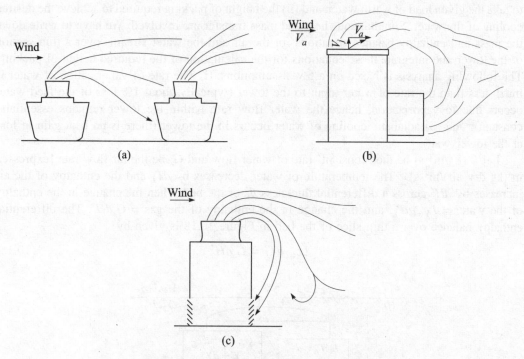

Figure. 10.16   (a) Interference; (b) and (c) recirculation.

10.5.6 Cooling Range and Approach

The difference in the temperatures of the inlet hot water and the outlet cooled water is called the 'range of cooling' or simply 'range'. The difference between the cooled water temperature leaving a tower and the wet-bulb temperature of the inlet air is the 'approach'. For example, if hot water is cooled from 40°C to 30°C by air of wet-bulb temperature 27°C, the range is 10°C and the approach is 3°C. If a small 'approach' is targeted, the height of packing increases rapidly. Theoretically, the approach is zero if a tower has an 'infinite' packed height. The range and approach are illustrated in Figure 10.17.

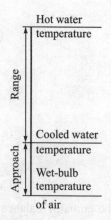

Figure 10.17 Cooling 'range' and 'approach' illustrated.

10.6 COOLING TOWER CALCULATIONS

An air–water contacting tower may have three major applications:
(i) evaporative cooling of warm water from the cooling water circuit in a plant, (ii) cooling of

a hot gas by direct contact with cool water, and (iii) dehumidification of a warm moist gas in contact with cool water. The design procedures are described below.

10.6.1 Sizing of a Cooling Tower

For sizing a cooling tower we primarily need to calculate: (i) the tower cross-section required to take the given load of warm water, and (ii) the height of packing required to achieve the desired cooling of the water. Simultaneous heat and mass transfer are involved. We have to write down the mass and enthalpy balance equations for the air and the water streams over a thin section of the tower and integrate these equations for the calculation of the required height of packing. The following analysis is based on a few assumptions: (i) The rate of vaporization of water is much less than the rate of water input to the tower (typically about 1% loss of the feed water occurs due to vaporization, hence the water flow rate within the tower remains essentially constant); and (ii) adiabatic cooling of water occurs in the tower (there is no heat gain or loss at the tower wall).

Let L (kg/m^2·s) be the 'constant' rate of water flow and G_s be the air flow rate [expressed in (kg dry air)/m^2·s].[†] The temperature of water decreases by dT_L and the enthalpy of the air increases by dH' across a differential thickness dz of the bed. Then the change in the enthalpy of the water = $Lc_{wL}dT_L$, and the change in the enthalpy of the gas = G_sdH'. The differential enthalpy balance over a thin slice of the bed in Figure 10.18 is given by

$$Lc_{wL}dT_L = G_sdH' \tag{10.15}$$

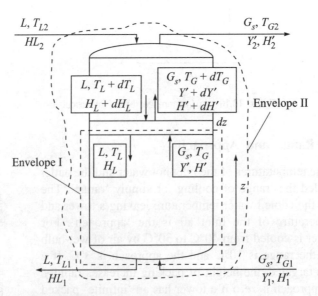

Figure 10.18   Mass and enthalpy balance in a cooling tower.

The enthalpy balance over the envelope I gives

$$Lc_{wL}(T_L - T_{L1}) = G_s(H' - H'_1) \tag{10.16}$$

[†] The flow rates L and G_s are on unit area basis, no prime (') is used.

Equation (10.16) is the *operating line* for the air–water contact. Since L, c_{wL} and G_s remain unchanged along the tower, it is a straight line on the T_L–H plane having a slope of Lc_{wL}/G_s. Also making an enthalpy balance over the entire tower, we get the following relation

$$Lc_{wL}(T_{L2} - T_{L1}) = G_s(H'_2 - H'_1) \qquad (10.17)$$

It appears from Eqs. (10.16) and (10.17) that the operating line may the obtained by joining the terminal points (T_{L1}, H'_1) and (T_{L2}, H'_2). The 'equilibrium curve' for the air–water system on the T_L–H' plane is the plot of enthalpy of saturated air versus the liquid temperature at equilibrium. As in other heterogeneous contacting, we assume that equilibrium prevails at the gas–liquid interface, i.e. the temperature and enthalpy of air at the air–water interface (T_{Li}, H'_i) lie on the equilibrium line. Typical operating and equilibrium curves are shown in Figure 10.19.

The rate of transfer of water vapour to air in the differential volume is

$$G_s dY' = k_{Y'}\bar{a}\, dz(Y'_i - Y') \qquad (10.18)$$

where

$k_{Y'}$ = mass transfer coefficient of water vapour
$\bar{a}$ = specific interfacial area of the air–water contact
Y'_i = humidity of air at the air–liquid interface.

We shall use two other relations in the following analysis.

The decrease in the temperature of the gas because of sensible heat transfer to the water is given by

$$-G_s c_H dT_G = h_G \bar{a}\, dz(T_G - T_i) \qquad (10.19)$$

The differential form of Eq. (10.7) is multiplied by G_s and then Eqs. (10.18) and (10.19) are used to yield

$$G_s dH' = G_s \lambda_0 dY' + G_s c_H dT_G = G_s \lambda_0 dY' - h_G \bar{a}\, dz(T_G - T_i)$$
$$= -h_G \bar{a}\, dz(T_G - T_i) + \lambda_0 k_{Y'}\bar{a}\, dz(Y'_i - Y') \qquad (10.20)$$
$$\Rightarrow \qquad G_s dH' = k_{Y'}\bar{a}\, dz[(h_G/k_{Y'})(T_i - T_G) + \lambda_0(Y'_i - Y')] \qquad (10.21)$$

Using the result $(h_G/k_{Y'}) = c_H$ in the above equation,

$$G_s dH' = k_{Y'}\bar{a}\, dz[c_H(T_i - T_G) + \lambda_0(Y'_i - Y')]$$
$$= k_{Y'}\bar{a}\, dz[\{Y'_i\lambda_0 + c_H(T_i - T_0)\} - \{\lambda_0 Y' + c_H(T_G - T_0)\}]$$

Using the definition of enthalpy of the gas [see Eq. (10.7)],

$$G_s dH' = k_{Y'}\bar{a}\, dz(H'_i - H') \qquad (10.22)$$

The above equation is unique in the sense that the change in the energy content of the gas over the differential thickness dz is expressed in terms of a transport coefficient and the 'enthalpy driving force'. The height of packing in the cooling tower can be obtained by integrating the above equation.

$$\int_{H'_1}^{H'_2} \frac{dH'}{H'_i - H'} = \frac{k_{Y'}\bar{a}}{G_s} \int_0^z dz = \frac{k_{Y'}\bar{a}}{G_s} z \qquad (10.23)$$

Invoking the concept of transfer units, we can define

$$N_{tG} = \int_{H'_1}^{H'_2} \frac{dH'}{H'_i - H'} \quad \text{and} \quad H_{tG} = \frac{G_s}{k_{Y'}\bar{a}} \tag{10.24}$$

where

N_{tG} = number of gas-enthalpy transfer units

H_{tG} = height of a gas-enthalpy transfer unit.

Height of the packed section,

$$z = H_{tG}N_{tG} \tag{10.25}$$

The volumetric mass or enthalpy transfer coefficient ($k_{Y'}\bar{a}$) should be known or has to be estimated from a suitable correlation. So the height of a transfer unit may be calculated from the given gas mass flow rate. In order to determine the number of transfer units, the integral in Eq. (10.24) is to be evaluated. There is no direct relation available between the enthalpy of the bulk gas H' and that at the interface H'_i. So the integral cannot be evaluated analytically. For numerical or graphical evaluation of the integral, we have to know the values of H'_i (the enthalpy of air at the condition of the air–liquid interface or the 'interfacial enthalpy') for a set of values of H' within the range of enthalpy values given by the operating line ($H'_1 \le H' \le H'_2$). The values of H'_i can be obtained by following a procedure similar to that for the determination of the interfacial gas-phase concentration of a solute described in Section 6.4.1.

If $h_L\bar{a}$ is the volumetric individual heat transfer coefficient on the water-side of the interface, a differential heat balance equation over a small section of the packing gives

$$Lc_{wL}dT_L = h_L\bar{a}\, dz(T_L - T_{Li}) \tag{10.26}$$

Combining Eqs. (10.15), (10.22) and (10.26),

$$k_{Y'}\bar{a}\, dz(H'_i - H') = -h_L\bar{a}\, dz(T_{Li} - T_L) \Rightarrow \frac{H'_i - H'}{T_{Li} - T_L} = -\frac{h_L}{k_{Y'}} \tag{10.27}$$

The above equation indicates that a line of slope $-h_L/k_{Y'}$ emanating from a point (T_L, H') on the operating line meets the equilibrium line at the point (T_{Li}, H'_i) that represents the liquid temperature and air humidity at the gas–liquid interface. A very similar procedure was used in Section 6.4.1 for the determination of the interfacial concentrations of the gas and the liquid phases at a section of a gas absorption column if both the phases offer resistance to mass transfer. If a set of parallel lines of slope $-h_L/k_{Y'}$ are drawn from several points on the operating line, a set of values of (H', H'_i) can be obtained. These values can be used to numerically or graphically evaluate the integral in Eq. (10.24). The value of the integral is the number of gas-phase transfer units, N_{tG}.

An alternative form of N_{tG} can be obtained by substituting $G_s dH' = Lc_{wL}dT_L$ [see Eq. (10.15)] in Eq. (10.22).

$$Lc_{wL}dT_L = k_{Y'}\bar{a}\, dz(H'_i - H') \Rightarrow \int_{T_{Li}}^{T_{Lo}} \frac{dT_L}{H'_i - H'} = \frac{k_{Y'}\bar{a}}{Lc_{wL}} \int_0^z dz = \frac{k_{Y'}\bar{a}}{Lc_{wL}} z \tag{10.28}$$

The above integral of the inverse of the enthalpy driving force also represents a type of transfer units. Kern (1950) preferred to call it the number of 'diffusion units' (NDU). The procedure of evaluation of the NDU is similar to N_{tG}.

A simplified design equation based on the overall enthalpy transfer coefficient

If an overall enthalpy transfer coefficient $K_{Y'}$ is used, the differential mass balance Eq. (10.22) becomes

$$G_s dH' = K_{Y'} \bar{a} \, dz (H'^* - H') \tag{10.29}$$

Here H'^* is the enthalpy of the saturated air at a temperature equal to the bulk liquid temperature, T_L.

On integration,

$$\int_{H_1'}^{H_2'} \frac{dH'}{H'^* - H'} = \frac{K_{Y'} \bar{a}}{G_s} \int_0^z dz = \frac{K_{Y'} \bar{a}}{G_s} z \tag{10.30}$$

The above integral is the number of overall gas-phase enthalpy transfer units.

$$\int_{H_1'}^{H_2'} \frac{dH'}{H'^* - H'} = N_{tOG}; \quad \frac{G_s}{K_{Y'} \bar{a}} = H_{tOG}; \quad z = N_{tOG} H_{tOG} \tag{10.31}$$

The above method is often called the 'Marked method' and the integral representing N_{tOG}, the 'Marked Integral'.

Expression of the overall enthalpy transfer coefficient in terms of the individual coefficients

If the individual gas-phase enthalpy transfer coefficient $k_{Y'}$ and the liquid-phase heat transfer coefficient h_L are known, these can be combined to express the overall coefficient (compare with Section 4.4).

Since T_L is the bulk water temperature and T_{Li} is the temperature at the air–water interface, the flux of energy transport from the liquid may be written as

$$q = k_{Y'}(H_i' - H') = h_L(T_L - T_{Li}) = K_{Y'}(H'^* - H') \tag{10.32}$$

Driving force: $\qquad (H'^* - H') = (H'^* - H_i') + (H_i' - H') \tag{10.33}$

From Eqs. (10.32) and (10.33),

$$\frac{q}{K_{Y'}} = q\frac{H'^* - H_i'}{h_L(T_L - T_{Li})} + \frac{q}{k_{Y'}} \Rightarrow \frac{1}{K_{Y'}} = \frac{H'^* - H_i'}{h_L(T_L - T_{Li})} + \frac{1}{k_{Y'}} \tag{10.34}$$

If the individual coefficients $k_{Y'}$ and h_L are known, the overall coefficient $K_{Y'}$ can be determined. The quantity $(H'^* - H')$ gives the overall enthalpy driving force for the water cooling process.

Step-by-step design procedure (also see Examples 10.3 and 10.4)

(a) Specify the inlet and outlet temperatures and the flow rate of warm water. These quantities are governed by the requirement of cooling water in the heat exchangers and other cooling devices in a plant.

(b) Select the design values of the dry-bulb and the wet-bulb temperature of air at the proposed geographical location of the cooling tower. The relevant data are available at the weather office in the region.

(c) Draw the 'equilibrium curve', i.e. the saturation–humidity curve. The enthalpy data can be calculated using the vapour pressure equation for water and the physical properties of air and water vapour [see Eq. (10.8)].

(d) Locate the lower terminal of the operating line Q on the T_L–H' plane by the point (T_{L1}, H_1'). This point indicates the condition at the bottom of the tower in the case of water cooling.

(e) Draw a tangent to the equilibrium line through the point Q. The slope of this tangent gives the ratio of the liquid and the minimum gas flow rates [see Eq. (10.16)]. The water rate is given. The minimum air rate is calculated. The actual air rate taken is usually 1.25 to 1.5 times the minimum. This step is not relevant if the air rate is given.

(f) The upper terminal of the operating line is located by the point $P(T_{L2}, H_2')$. It is the point where the operating line of the slope determined in step (e) meets the vertical line through T_{L2}. It can also be located by calculating the top end enthalpy H_2' from Eq. (10.17).

(g) Evaluate the integral in Eq. (10.24) or (10.28). This is the number of gas-phase enthalpy transfer units. The volumetric transfer coefficients $k_{Y'}\bar{a}$ and $h_L\bar{a}$ are required for this purpose. As described above, a set of parallel lines (sometimes called *tie lines*) of slope $-h_L\bar{a}/k_{Y'}\bar{a}$ is drawn between the operating line and the equilibrium line. The values of H' and H_i' are taken from the terminals of these lines. The integral is evaluated numerically or graphically.

(h) If the overall enthalpy transfer coefficient $K_{Y'}$ is known and used, the 'tie lines' are vertical. For a given value of H', the value of H'^* is given by the point on the equilibrium line vertically above it. The integral in Eq. (10.31) gives the number of overall transfer units in this case.

(i) The height of a transfer unit ($G_s/k_{Y'}\bar{a}$ or $G_s/K_{Y'}\bar{a}$) is calculated from Eq. (10.24) or (10.31). The packed height is the product of the height of a transfer unit and the number of transfer units.

The approximate packed heights of towers for different values of approach and cooling range are given below:

Approach to wet-bulb temperature (°F)	Cooling range (°F)	Packed height (ft)
15–20	25–35	15–20
10–15	25–35	25–30
5–10	25–35	35–40

EXAMPLE 10.3 (*Calculation of the height of packing, substantial liquid-phase heat transfer resistance*)   Warm water at 45°C is to be cooled to 30°C by countercurrent contact with air in a tower packed with wood slats. The inlet air has a dry-bulb temperature of 31°C and a wet-bulb temperature of 22°C. The mass flow rate of water is 6000 kg/m²·h and that of air is 1.4 times the minimum. The individual gas-phase mass transfer coefficient is $k_{Y'}\bar{a} = 6000$ kg/(m³)(h)($\Delta Y'$). The volumetric water-side heat transfer coefficient is given by $h_L\bar{a} = 0.059L^{0.51}G_s$, in kcal/m³·h·K, where L and G_s are mass flow rates of water and air (dry basis).

Determine (a) the dry air flow rate to be used, (b) the height of packing, and (c) the wet-bulb depression at the bottom of the tower.

Solution

(a) Inlet air: $T_G = 31°C$; $T_w = 22°C = T_{as}$; humidity [from Figure 10.6(a)], $Y_1' = 0.01295$ kg/kg

$$\text{Enthalpy, } H_1' = 2500Y_1' + (1.005 + 1.88Y_1')(31 - 0) = 64.3 \text{ kJ/(kg dry air)};$$

$$\text{Exit water temperature, } T_{L1} = 30°C$$

Draw the saturation humidity curve (the equilibrium line) from the calculated values of saturation enthalpies at different temperatures (the procedure is illustrated in Example 10.1), as shown in Figure 10.19. For example, take $T_L = 35°C$ (= 308.2 K). Vapour pressure of water at this temperature, $P^v = 0.05625$ bar, and

$$Y' = [(0.05625)/(1.013 - 0.05625)] [18.02/28.97] = 0.03657 \text{ (kg moisture)/(kg dry air)}.$$

Enthalpy of saturated air at 35°C [ref. temp. = 0°C; see Eq. (10.8)]

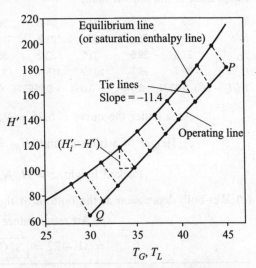

$$= (2500)(0.03657) + [1.005 + (1.88)(0.03657)]35$$

$$= 129 \text{ kJ/(kg dry air)}$$

Locate the point Q (30°C; 64.3 kJ/kg) on the T_L–H' plane (Q is the lower terminal of the operating line). In order to determine the minimum air rate, draw the tangent to the equilibrium line from the point Q (not shown in Figure 10.19).

$$\text{Slope of the tangent} = 10.76 = \frac{Lc_{wL}}{G_{s,\,min}}$$

$$c_{wL} = 4.187 \text{ kJ/kg·K}$$

$$L = 6000 \text{ kg/m}^2\text{·h}$$

$$\Rightarrow \qquad G_{s,\,min} = 2335 \text{ kg/m}^2\text{·h}$$

Actual air rate to be used,

Figure 10.19 Equilibrium and operating lines.

$$G_s = 1.4G_{s,\,min} = (1.4)(2335)$$

$$= \boxed{3270 \text{ kg/m}^2 \cdot \text{h(dry basis)}}$$

(b) Given, feed water temperature, $T_{L2} = 45°C$. Determine H_2' (enthalpy of the exit air stream) from the equation of the operating line, Eq. (10.17).

$$Lc_{wL}(T_{L2} - T_{L1}) = G(H_2' - H_1') \Rightarrow (6000)(4.187)(45 - 30) = (3270)(H_2' - 64.3)$$

$$\Rightarrow \qquad H_2' = 179.6 \text{ kJ/kg}$$

Locate the point P (45°C, 179.6 kJ/kg) which is the upper terminal of the operating line. Join PQ.

[The point P can be reached by an alternative method. Calculate the actual slope of the operating line ($10.76/1.4 = 7.685$ in this case). A line of this slope drawn through the point Q meets the vertical line through $T_L = 45°C$ at the point P which is the upper terminal of the operating line.]

Calculate the liquid-phase heat transfer coefficient from the given correlation.

$$h_L \bar{a} = (0.059)(6000)^{0.51}(3270) = 16,300 \text{ kcal/h·m}^3\text{·°C} = 68,260 \text{ kJ/h·m}^3\text{·°C}$$

$$\text{Slope of the 'tie lines'} = -h_L \bar{a}/k_Y \bar{a} = -68,250/6000 = -11.4$$

A set of tie lines of this slope (-11.4) is drawn from several points on the operating line (including the terminal points) as shown in Figure 10.19. Any such line meets the equilibrium line at (T_{Li}, H_i'). The set of points (H', H_i') thus obtained are given below. The values of $1/(H_i' - H')$ are plotted against T_L and the integral in Eq. (10.28) is evaluated graphically. The graphical integration is not shown here.

T_L	30	31.45	33	34.8	36.5	38.2	39.7	41.5	43.1	45
H'	64.3	75	87.2	101.2	114	127.5	138.7	152.6	165	179.6
T_{Li}	27.8	29.5	31.2	33.2	35.1	37	38.4	40.2	41.7	43.5
H_i'	89.7	96.7	105.7	118	130	142.5	153.5	168	181.1	196.7
$1/(H_i' - H')$	0.0394	0.0461	0.054	0.0595	0.0625	0.0667	0.0676	0.0641	0.0621	0.0585

$$\text{Area under the curve} = 6.76 = N_{tG} = \text{number of gas-phase transfer units}$$

$$\text{Height of a transfer unit, } H_{tG} = G_s/k_Y \bar{a} = 3270/6000 = \boxed{0.545 \text{ m}}$$

$$\text{Packed height, } z = H_{tG} N_{tG} = (0.545)(6.76) = \boxed{3.68 \text{ m}}$$

(c) Wet-bulb depression at the bottom of the tower

$$= \text{Air temperature} - \text{Wet-bulb temperature}$$

$$= 31 - 22 = \boxed{9°C}$$

10.6.2 Determination of the Gas Temperature Profile

In most cases, the temperature of the warm feed water (T_{w2}) to a cooling tower is well above that of the ambient air (T_{G1}). However, the temperature of the cooled water (T_{w1}) may be above or below T_{G1}. In either case, the heat supplied by the warm water is mostly utilized to vaporize water at the air–water interface. If $T_{G1} > T_{w1}$, a small part of the heat of vaporization comes from the air and its temperature decreases with height in the lower part of a cooling tower followed by a rise in contact with the warm water. However, if $T_{G1} < T_{w1}$, the air temperature increases continuously along the height.

The bulk liquid temperature at any axial position in the tower can be determined by a slight manipulation of Eq. (10.28). But the determination of the bulk gas temperature is not straightforward. It can be determined by the following graphical procedure.

Dividing Eq. (10.22) by Eq. (10.19),

$$-\frac{G_s \, dH'}{G_s c_H \, dT_G} = \frac{k_{Y'} \bar{a} \, dz (H_i' - H')}{h_G \bar{a} \, dz (T_G - T_i)}$$

Using the result $h_G/k_{Y'} = c_H$ for the air–water system,

$$\frac{dH'}{dT_G} = \frac{H_i' - H'}{T_G - T_i} \tag{10.35}$$

A step-by-step procedure for the determination of the gas temperature profile in a cooling tower using the above equation is given by Skelland (1974). This is illustrated in Example 10.4.

EXAMPLE 10.4 (*Determination of packed height, the overall coefficient being given*) A cooling tower receives warm water at 43°C at a mass flow rate of 7000 kg/m²·h. A cooling range of 13°C is to be achieved by countercurrent contact with air. The air enters at a rate of 4200 kg/m²·h at a dry-bulb temperature of 31°C and a humidity of 0.01516 kg/(kg dry air). The overall volumetric mass transfer coefficient is $K_{Y'}\bar{a} = 2500$ kg/(m³)(h)($\Delta Y'$).

(a) Determine the number of overall gas-phase transfer units and the height of packing.

(b) Plot the gas temperature profile along the tower.

Solution
(a) Dry-bulb temperature of air, $T_G = 31°C$

Humidity, $Y_1' = 0.01516$; enthalpy, $H_1' = 70$ kJ/(kg dry air), calculated; cooling range = 13°C

Water temperature: inlet, $T_{L2} = 43°C$; outlet, $T_{L1} = 43 - 13 = 30°C$

Water feed rate, $L = 7000$ kg/h·m²

Total rate of air input = 4200 kg/h·m²(on dry basis)

$G_s = 4200/1.01516 = 4137$ (kg dry air)/m²·h

Heat balance [see Eq. (10.17)]: $(7000)(4.187)(43 - 30) = (4137)(H_2' - 70)$

$\Rightarrow \qquad\qquad H_2' = 162$ kJ/(kg dry air)

Draw the 'equilibrium line' and draw the operating lines through the points $Q(30, 70)$ and $P(43, 162)$.

The integral in Eq. (10.31) is now evaluated graphically. A set of vertical lines (tie lines) are drawn between the operating line and the equilibrium line [Figure 10.20(a)]. A set of points (H', H'^*) obtained from the terminals of these lines are tabulated. Graphical integration is shown in Figure 10.20(b).

T_L	30	33	35	37	39	41	43
H'	70	84.5	99.6	115.2	130.2	145.5	162
H'^*	105	117	129	143	158.7	175.5	196
$1/[H'^* - H']$	0.0286	0.0308	0.034	0.036	0.0351	0.0333	0.0295

Area under the graph, $\int_{H_1'}^{H_2'} \frac{dH'}{H'^* - H'} = N_{tOG} = 3.04$; $H_{tOG} = \frac{G_s}{K_{Y'}\bar{a}} = \frac{4137}{2500} = 1.655$ m

Packed height, $z = (1.665)(3.04) = \boxed{5.06 \text{ m}}$

(b) The gas temperature profile may be obtained by discrete graphical construction on the $H'-T_G, T_L$ plane following the principles described in Section 10.7.2. Refer to Figure 10.20(c).

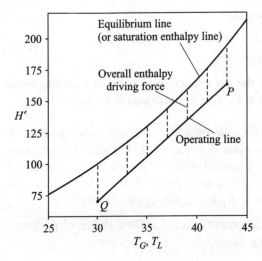

Figure 10.20(a) Equilibrium and operating lines.

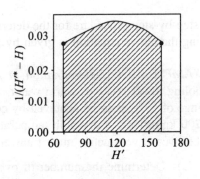

Figure 10.20(b) Graphical integration for N_{tOG}.

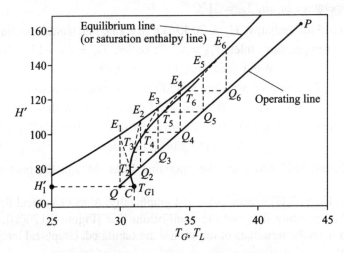

Figure 10.20(c) Gas temperature profile along the tower.

(i) The inlet state of the gas is given by the point C (H_1', T_{G1}). A vertical line through the end of the operating line, Q, meets the 'equilibrium line' at the point E_1 which denotes the interfacial condition at the bottom (*neglecting the liquid-phase resistance*).

(ii) Join CE_1. Equation (10.35) stipulates that the gas temperature in the 'film' follows the line CE_1.

(iii) Move a 'small' distance to the point T_2 along CE_1. Move horizontally to Q_2 on the operating line and then move vertically to E_2 on the equilibrium line; the point E_2 gives the interfacial condition when the bulk gas temperature is T_2. In the next step the bulk gas temperature changes along T_2E_2, and so on. Proceeding in this way, the gas temperature profile can be obtained as shown in Figure 10.20(c).

It may be noted that the temperature difference between the gas and the liquid decreases quickly along the bed, although the enthalpy driving force does not decrease much.

10.6.3 Dehumidifiaction and Cooling of a Hot Moist Gas

Dehumidification and cooling of a hot, moist gas stream can be conveniently done by direct contact with cool water in a packed tower. This is a practically useful technique adopted in many applications. Consider the case of drying of a moist solid prone to air-oxidation. Drying may be done in contact with a hot inert gas, say N_2. The gas (N_2) has value and cannot be discarded after use. It is recycled. For this purpose, the warm and moist gas from the dryer is needed to be dehumidified (otherwise it cannot be used again). This can be done in direct contact with cool water in a tower. The dehumidified gas is heated again (using a steam heater, for example) and recycled to the dryer.

There are many uses of air of controlled humidity typically in pharmaceutical industries and for the storage of hygroscopic materials (e.g. fertilizers like urea, ammonium nitrate, etc.). A cooling tower cannot supply dehumidified air for such cases. Dehumidification by chilling or by a desiccant is preferred in practice (Harrison and Simkins, 1997; Speltz, 1998).

The procedure of calculation of packed height is very similar to that of water cooling described in the previous section. The operating line is given by Eq. (10.17). The only difference is that for dehumidification, the operating line lies above the equilibrium line on the T_L–H' plane so that transport of moisture as well as sensible heat occurs from the gas- to the liquid-phase. The water temperature increases down the column.

10.6.4 Humidification and Gas Cooling with Water at the Adiabatic Saturation Temperature

In some applications, a hot gas having a rather small quantity of moisture may have to be cooled. This can be done in a conventional heat exchanger by indirect contact with a cold fluid, for example, cooling water. If an *increase* in the moisture is *not undesirable*, cooling may be conveniently done by direct contact with cool water. The gas is cooled, but simultaneously gets humidified. In such an arrangement in practice, the water in the gas cooling tower is continuously recycled with the addition of makeup water to compensate for the evaporation loss (Figure 10.3). If we neglect heat loss or gain through the tower wall, cooling of the gas will follow the adiabatic saturation temperature line. The gas temperature will *approach* its adiabatic saturation temperature, T_{as}, at the exit or top end of the tower. So, at the steady-state operating condition, the cooling water will effectively remain at its adiabatic saturation temperature.

The temperature and humidity of the gas change along the adiabatic saturation line, but its enthalpy remains constant. The liquid temperature also remains constant at T_{as}. So the terminals of the operating line merge and the operating line shrinks to a point on the equilibrium line. The enthalpy driving force is zero as a result. So the design calculation is to be based on either the temperature or the humidity driving force. If we use the humidity driving force as the basis of calculation, we take help of the following differential mass balance equation

$$G_s dY' = k_{Y'}\bar{a}\,(Y'_{as} - Y')dz \tag{10.36}$$

Integrating $\quad G_s \int_{Y'_1}^{Y'_2} \dfrac{dY'}{Y'_{as} - Y'} = k_{Y'}\bar{a}\,z \Rightarrow z = \dfrac{G_s}{k_{Y'}\bar{a}} \ln \dfrac{Y'_{as} - Y'_1}{Y'_{as} - Y'_2} = H_{tG}N_{tG} \tag{10.37}$

Example 10.5 shows an application of the above equation.

EXAMPLE 10.5 (*Humidification of a moist gas with water at the adiabatic saturation temperature*)   Nitrogen gas (dry-bulb temp. = 70°C; wet-bulb temp. = 30°C; pressure = 1 atm) is supplied to a cooling tower at a rate of 5500 m³/h·m². The water is continuously recirculated (with necessary makeup to compensate for the vaporization loss) and its temperature is maintained essentially at the adiabatic saturation temperature of the gas. The humidified gas leaves the tower 97% saturated. Calculate (a) the rate of supply of makeup water, (b) the number of overall gas-phase transfer units, and (c) the packed height if the overall volumetric mass transfer coefficient is given as $K_{Y'}\bar{a}$ = 2850 kg/(h)(m²)($\Delta Y'$).

Hints: Vapour pressure of water at 30°C = 0.04244 bar; humidity of saturated N_2 at 30°C = 0.0281.

Enthalpy of saturated N_2 at 30°C [from Eq. (10.7)] = 102 kJ/(kg dry gas) = enthalpy of the feed N_2 at 70°C (since the hot gas gets 'adiabatically' saturated). If the humidity of the feed nitrogen is Y_1',

$$102 = 2500Y_1' + c_H(70) \quad [c_H = \text{humid heat of nitrogen}] \Rightarrow Y_1' = 0.012 \text{ kg/(kg dry nitrogen)}.$$

Since the nitrogen leaving the tower is 97% saturated, $Y_2' = (0.97)(0.0281) = 0.0273$.

From Eq. (10.37), $N_{tOG} = 3$. $H_{tOG} = G_s/K_{Y'}\bar{a}$ = 1.952 m; z = 5.85 m.

10.7   SOME ADDITIONAL INFORMATION ON COOLING TOWERS

10.7.1   Blowdown

About 1–2% of the water circulating through the cooling tower evaporates in the cooling process. This leads to a buildup of the total dissolved solids (TDS) in the water. The TDS content has to be kept below a certain limit in order to avoid excessive fouling of heat exchangers and other water-cooled equipment. This is done by 'blowdown', i.e. by continuously discarding a part of the circulating water (Figure 10.1). Makeup water is simultaneously added to compensate for the blowdown, evaporation and other losses like drift loss and leakages. The blowdown rate may be calculated using the following simple equation.

Let B = blowdown rate; E = rate of evaporation loss; D = rate of losses due to 'drift' and leakages; C_1 = dissolved solid concentration in the makeup water; C_2 = that in the circulating water; M = makeup water rate.

Total water balance: $$M = B + D + E \tag{10.38}$$
Solids balance: $$MC_1 = (B + D)C_2 + (E)(0) \tag{10.39}$$

The water vaporized (E) does not have any solids in it, and the TDS in the blowdown and in the drift is the same as that in the circulating water. From the above equations,

$$(B + D + E)C_1 = (B + D)C_2 \Rightarrow B = \frac{E - D(r-1)}{r-1}; r = \frac{C_2}{C_1} \tag{10.40}$$

Once the blowdown rate B is known, the makeup rate M may be calculated from Eq. (10.39).

The evaporation loss may be estimated by a thumb rule (Hensley, 1985) as follow:

$$E = \text{(water flow rate, gpm)(range, °F)(0.0008), in gallon per minute (gpm)} \quad (10.41)$$

EXAMPLE 10.6 (*Blowdown calculation*) An induced draft crossflow tower is rated to cool 15,000 gpm of water from 40°C to 29°C. The total solids concentration must not exceed 900 ppm. The TDS of the makeup water is 300 ppm. About 0.1% of the water is lost by 'drift' from the tower and leakages in the circulation system. Calculate the blowdown and makeup rate.

Solution

$$\text{The range} = 40 - 29 = 11°C = 19.8°F$$

Evaporation rate, $E = (15,000)(19.8)(0.0008) = 237.6$ gpm [from Eq. (10.41)]

Drift and leakages, $D = 0.1\%$ of 15,000 gpm = 15 gpm; $r = C_2/C_1 = 900/300 = 3$

Blowdown rate [Eq. (10.40)], $B = [237.6 - (15)(3 - 1)]/(3 - 1) = 104$ gpm

Makeup water rate, $M = B + D + E = 104 + 15 + 237.6 = 356.6$ gpm

10.7.2 The Problem of Legioellosis

A cooling tower offers an environment congenial for the growth of a rod-shaped bacteria called *legionella pneumophila* that causes respiratory diseases. Infection may be caused by mist of drift from a cooling tower. The disease is reported to have claimed lives in many places. Cooling tower water must be tested periodically for the presence of this bacteria. Dosing of ozone, hydrogen peroxide, or the use of a UV source have all been found to be useful to control the growth of this bacteria. Also, a cooling tower must be cleaned periodically and stagnant pockets of water must be avoided (Ondrey et al., 1999; Silverberg, 1997). In some countries a code of practice (COP) for cooling tower operation has been introduced (Ondrey et al., 1999) to check the problems of bacterial growth, plume, etc.

10.7.3 Typical Values of Design Variables

The practical values of the important design variables and parameters of cooling towers are given below.

Range = 8–15°C; approach = 5–6°C; evaporation loss = 1.5–2%; drift loss = 0.02–0.2%; overall volumetric gas-phase mass transfer coefficient, $K_Y\bar{a} = 1500$–3000 kg/(h)(m^2)($\Delta Y'$); packing depth = 5–10 m for splash packings, 1.5–2 m for filmpack; liquid mass flow rate = 2–5 gallon/min·ft^2; $L/G = 0.75$ to 1.5; free space above the drift eliminator = 2–3 m; height of the fan stack (or fan cylinder) = 3–5 m; spacing of corrugated sheets in a film pack = 19–25 mm.

NOTATIONS

$\bar{a}$	: specific interfacial area of contact between water and air, m^2/m^3
A	: water vapour

B	: air; blowdown rate, kg/s
c_H	: humid heat, kJ/(kg dry air)(K)
c_{wL}	: heat capacity of the liquid (water), kJ/kg·K
G_s	: air (gas) flow rate, kg/m²·s (dry basis)
h_G	: gas-phase heat transfer coefficient, kJ/(m²)(s)(K)
k_G	: gas-phase mass transfer coefficient, kg/(m²)(s)(Δp_A)
$k_{Y'}$	: gas-phase mass transfer coefficient, kg/(m²)(s)($\Delta Y'$)
$K_{Y'}$	: overall gas-phase mass transfer coefficient, kg/(m²)(s)($\Delta Y'$)
H'	: enthalpy of air, kJ/(kg dry air)
H'^*	: enthalpy of the gas saturated with water vapour at the bulk liquid temperature, kJ/(kg dry air)
L	: liquid (water) flow rate, kg/m²·s
p	: partial pressure, bar
P	: total pressure, bar
P^v	: vapour pressure, bar
T	: temperature, K
v_H	: humid volume, m³/(kg dry air)
Y	: humidity of air, (kmol moisture)/(kmol dry air)
Y'	: humidity of air, (kg moisture)/(kg dry air)
Y_s'	: humidity of saturated air, (kg moisture)/(kg dry air)
z	: packed height (m), vertical coordinate
λ_0	: latent heat of water at the datum temperature (T_0), kJ/kg

Subscripts

as	: adiabatic saturation
i	: interface
L	: liquid
s	: satuaration
w	: wet bulb

SHORT AND MULTIPLE CHOICE QUESTIONS

(Use the Antoine Equation for vapour pressure of water, if necessary)

1. Which of the following does a cooling tower help us to achieve?
   (i) Once-through use of cooling water

    (ii)   Conservation of water

    (iii)   Keeping the cooling water clean

2. What is the maximum possible humidity of air at 30°C and 1.3 atm pressure?

    (i) 0.042   (ii) 0.009   (iii) 0.0207 kg/(kg dry air)

3. If warm water is cooled by 5°C, the evaporation loss of water is about

    (i) 0.85%   (ii) 0.1%   (iii) 10%

4. The drift or windage loss of water in an atmospheric type tower is about

    (i) 3–5%   (ii) 0.1–0.2%   (iii) more than 5%

5. The rate of increase of saturated humidity of air with temperature at 1 atm and 25°C is

    (i) 0.0594   (ii) 0.00527   (iii) 0.00124

6. In a cooling tower terminology, the 'range' means

    (i)   the reduction in temperature of the warm water

    (ii)   the difference between the maximum and minimum air flow rates

    (iii)   the change in the air temperature.

7. In a cooling tower, T_{wi} = inlet water temp., T_{wo} = outlet water temp., T_{Gi} = inlet air temp., T_{Go} = outlet air temp., T_{as} = adiabatic saturation temperature of air. Then the 'approach' is

    (i) $T_{wo} - T_{wi}$ (ii) $T_{wo} - T_{as}$ (iii) $T_{as} - T_{Go}$

8. In a mechanical draft cooling tower, the L/G ratio generally lies between

    (i) 1–4   (ii) 0.75–1.5   (iii) 0.25–0.75

9. Which of the following is a *likely value* of $K_{Y'}\bar{a}$?

    (i) 1 lb/(h)(ft^3)($\Delta Y'$)   (ii) 1 lbmol/(s)(ft^3)($\Delta Y'$)   (iii) 125 lb/(h)(ft^3)($\Delta Y'$)

10. At a particular section of a cooling tower, the temperatures are: bulk liquid, T_L = 42°C; liquid interface, T_{Li} = 39°C; bulk gas, T_G = 36°C. The bulk humidity is H' = 135 kJ/(kg dry air). What is the value of $h_L/k_{Y'}$ (kJ/kg·°C)?

    (i) 1.0   (ii) 3.97   (iii) 7.17

11. Air saturated with water vapour at 25°C is heated to 40°C at constant pressure. How does its humidity, dew point and humid heat change as a result?

12. We have two samples of moist air. Sample 1: temp. = T_1°C, enthalpy = H_1'; sample 2: temp. = $2T_1$°C, enthalpy, = H_2'. The wet-bulb temperatures of the samples are equal. Then:

    (i) $H_2' = 2H_1'$ (ii) $H_2' = H_1'$ (iii) $H_2' < H_1'$

13. If the 'approach' in a cooling tower is smaller, the height of the packed section will

    (i)   be less

    (ii)   be more

    (iii)   remain unaffected.

14. Partial recirculation of warm and humid air leaving a tower is *more likely* to occur in

    (i)   a natural draft tower

(ii)   a forced draft tower

(iii)   an induced draft tower.

15. A long horizontal spray chamber receives air of dry-bulb temperature T_G and wet-bulb temperature T_w. The makeup water enters at a temperature $T_L < T_w$. Make a sketch of the air temperature and humidity profile along the length of the spray chamber.

16. 'Blowdown' of water from a cooling tower is done in order to
    (i)   regulate the total dissolved solids
    (ii)   control the cooling water temperature
    (iii) prevent growth of algae.

17. The most preferred material for the casing walls of a cooling tower is
    (i) PVC   (ii) FRP   (iii) CAB   (iv) wood   (v) steel.

18. The most preferred material for tower fill is
    (i) wood   (ii) concrete   (iii) PVC   (iv) chrome steel.

19. The air flow rate remains constant along the packing in a
    (i)   hyperbolic tower
    (ii)   counterflow tower
    (iii) tower with louvered walls
    (iv)   crossflow tower.

20. Which type of tower is most favoured in the chemical process industries?
    (i)   Induced draft tower
    (ii)   Hyperbolic tower
    (iii) Spray tower without a fill

21. Which of the following tower fill is most susceptible to clogging?
    (i)   Wood packing
    (ii)   Splash fill
    (iii) Corrugated film-pack

22. The *most important function* of louvers is
    (i)   to protect against algal growth
    (ii)   to allow air flow while preventing water splashout
    (iii) to enhance the structural strength of the walls.

23. In which of the following types of towers is vibration of the fans more likely to occur?
    (i)   Forced draft
    (ii)   Fan-assisted natural draft
    (iii) Induced draft

24. Which of the following is an appropriate driving force in the air–water direct contact cooling operation? Difference in:
    (i)   enthalpy
    (ii)   partial pressure
    (iii) temperature.

25. What is Lewis number? Show that its value for the air–water system is nearly unity if the moisture content is not high.

26. Can a forced draft cooling tower operate with crossflow of air?

27. It is required to enhance the capacity of an existing counterflow induced draft tower with wooden splash bar packing. Discuss the effectiveness of the following changes to *retrofit* the tower?
    (i) Fit the walls with louvers in order that it operates as a crossflow tower
    (ii) Change the fill by film-packs and increase the fan capacity if needed
    (iii) Recirculate a part of the cold water to the tower
    (iv) Change the fan stack and install a larger capacity fan
    (v) Relocate the fan at the bottom to change it to a 'forced draft' tower
    (vi) Modify the water distribution system by increasing the number and diameter of the nozzles and placing the nozzles more uniformly.

28. A cooling tower is designed on the basis of a wet-bulb temperature of 19°C. If the actual wet-bulb temperature on a day is 22°C, the cooled water temperature will be
    (i) higher than the design temperature
    (ii) lower than the design temperature
    (iii) between 19°C and 22°C.

29. Name a few industries that have a large cooling load.

30. A cooling tower fan has a diameter of 8 m and the speed is 200 rpm. What is the 'tip speed' of the fan blades?
    (i) 5 km/min   (ii) 2 km/s   (ii) 10 km/h

31. Discuss the energy efficiencies of the forced and induced draft towers, particularly considering the velocity and pressure heads of the air. What is 'velocity recovery' mentioned in Section 10.5.4?

32. What kinds of water loss occur during cooling in a tower? What is 'blowdown'? Why is it done?

33. How does the packed height depend upon the cooling range and the approach? At a particular geographical location, the wet-bulb temperature of air is known to vary from a minimum of 15°C to a maximum of 31°C. Which temperature do you take into account for cooling tower design? Why?

34. If the 'tie-lines' between the saturation humidity line and the operating line on the T_L–H' plane are vertical, then
    (i) the bulk air is saturated
    (ii) the gas-film coefficient for enthalpy transport is very large
    (iii) the liquid side heat transfer coefficient is very large.

35. What are the important factors that influence design and operation of a cooling tower?

36. List out the advantages and limitations of forced draft and induced draft cooling towers.

37. If nearly saturated air at 45°C is contacted with water at 25°C in a tower, which of the following will occur?

(i) Humidification of air

(ii) Dehumidification of air

(iii) A rise in the outlet water temperature

(iv) Evaporation loss of water

(v) Cooling of the water

38. Natural draft hyperbolic cooling towers may be erected at a small separation (centre-to-centre distance as low as 1.5 times the base diameter may be allowed). But the mechanical draft towers need to be widely separated. The reason is:

(i) A mechanical draft tower needs more frequent cleaning and maintenance compared to a hyperbolic tower.

(ii) A mechanical draft tower emits more drift and hence should be widely separated.

(iii) As compared to mechanical draft towers, a hyperbolic tower emits moist air much above the ground level and there is little possibility of its recirculation.

39. Which of the following is a *likely value* of the superficial air velocity in a hyperbolic tower?

(i) 10 m/s   (ii) 1 m/s   (iii) 0.1 m/s

40. The sections of three-louvered casing walls of a forced draft tower are sketched below (Figure 10.21). Which sketch shows the correct orientation of the louvers? What are the problems with the other two orientations?

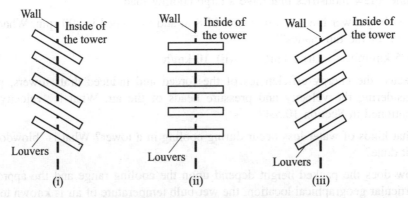

Figure 10.21   Three orientations of the louvers.

41. Why does the internal passage for moist air in a crossflow induced draft tower have a V-shape? Why does such a tower need less fan power than the counterflow one for the same air rate?

42. What is the benefit of providing a slightly tapered 'fan stack' in an induced draft tower?

43. A stream of air is (i) heated from temperature T_1 to T_2, (ii) fed to a dryer where it undergoes adiabatic saturation to temperature T_{as}, and (iii) dehumidified and cooled to T_1 for heating and recycling. Make a sketch of the loop representing the above steps on the T–Y' plane.

44. Why does a big natural draft cooling tower have a hyperbolic shape?

45. What are the common packings and materials for a cooling tower? What is the recent trend in this direction?

PROBLEMS

10.1 (*Determination of psychrometric properties*)[1] A sample of air has a dry-bulb temperature of 33°C and wet-bulb temperature of 23°C. The total pressure is atmospheric. (a) Determine its psychrometric properties—humidity, enthalpy, dew point, humid volume, and humid heat. (b) If the sample of air is heated to 50°C, what will be its wet-bulb temperature? (c) How much heat is rejected if 1 kg of air (dry basis) is cooled down from 33°C to 15°C? (d) If the air sample is heated to 50°C and its pressure doubled, what would be its relative humidity and dew point?

10.2 (*Psychrometric properties*)[2] Air (dry-bulb temp. = 34°C; wet-bulb temp. = 23°C) is contacted with a sufficient quantity of water at 23°C in a spray chamber. The water is recycled. Air leaves the chamber 95% saturated. Determine the temperature, the relative humidity and the wet-bulb temperature and enthalpy of the exit air.

10.3 (*Heat load in a cooling tower*)[2] The central air-conditioning installation of a building discards 50 m^3 of air per minute and draws the same volume of fresh air at 27°C (wet-bulb temp. = 20°C). This air is cooled to 12°C (saturated) before it enters the cold air duct. Calculate the corresponding hourly heat load. The water condensate leaves at 3°C.

10.4 (*Cooling tower calculations*)[3] A tray dryer receives 100 m^3/min hot air at 90°C with a humidity of 0.02 kg moisture per kg dry air at 1 atm pressure. The air leaves the dryer at 50°C. A part of this air is recirculated after mixing with fresh air (dry-bulb temperature 27°C; wet-bulb temperature 20°C) and heating in a steam heater to 90°C. If 5% of the heat supplied by condensing steam in the air heater is lost, calculate the rate of condensation of steam. The steam is saturated at 5 kg/cm^2 gauge. It may be assumed that humidification and cooling of the air within the dryer follows the adiabatic saturation line. Heat of condensation of steam at 5 kg/cm^2 gauge is 2080 kJ/kg.

10.5 (*Psychrometric properties*)[2] Warm air at 80°C with 0.035 kg moisture per kg dry air is to be supplied to a rotary dryer at a rate of 6000 kg/h. Atmospheric air at 30°C and 65% relative humidity is heated to a temperature T and then adiabatically humidified to the desired moisture content for further heating before supply to the dryer. Determine (a) the temperature T and the total heat load, (b) the adiabatic saturation temperature, and (c) the psychrometric condition of the air fed to the dryer.

10.6 (*Psychrometric calculations*)[3] A stream of air (dry-bulb temperature = 70°C; wet bulb temperature = 60°C) is dehumidified and cooled in contact with water entering at 26°C. The outlet air is *essentially* at thermal equilibrium with the water. Calculate the wet-bulb temperature of the outlet air and the moisture removed per kg of dry air.

10.7 (*Determination of the minimum air rate*)[3] A cooling tower of 100 m^2 cross-section is required to cool warm water from 42°C to 29°C at a rate of 225,000 gph. The ambient air at 32°C has a wet-bulb temperature of 22°C and the air rate is 6000 kg/h·m^2. Determine the minimum air rate and the overall gas-phase enthalpy transfer units.

10.8 (*Tower height*)[3] A cooling tower is to be designed to cool water from 45°C to 30°C by countercurrent contact with air of dry-bulb temperature 30°C and wet-bulb temperature of 25°C. The water rate is 5500 kg/h·m^2 and the air rate is 1.25 times the minimum.

Determine the tower height if the overall mass transfer coefficient is $K_{Y'}\bar{a}$ = 2500 kg/ h·m³. Comment on the expected outlet water temperature from the tower in winter when the dry-bulb temperature is 20°C and the wet-bulb temperature drops down to 15°C, the other parameters remaining unchanged.

10.9 (*Tower design*)[3]   Warm moist air (dry-bulb temperature = 85°C; wet-bulb temperature = 46°C) enters a tower at a rate of 5000 kg/h·m². It is to be cooled and dehumidified to a wet-bulb temperature of 31°C using water available at 26°C. The overall gas-phase mass transfer coefficient is estimated to be 2300 kg/h·m². The water rate is 1.25 times the minimum. Calculate (a) the water rate and its outlet temperature, (b) the water condensed per hour, and (c) the packed height.

10.10 (*Humidification of a gas with water at the adiabatic saturation temperature*)[3]   A stream of air (dry-bulb temperature = 80°C; wet-bulb temperature = 27°C; 4000 kg/h·m², dry basis) is contacted with water maintained at the adiabatic saturation temperature of the gas. The gas leaves the tower 95% saturated. Calculate the overall gas-phase transfer units and the makeup water to be supplied.

10.11 (*Blowdown calculation*)[2]   A cooling tower has a rating of 10,000 gph of warm water to be cooled from 45° to 28°C. The TDS of the water in circulation should be limited to 600 ppm and that of the makeup water is known to be 250 ppm. Estimate the rate of blowdown and the makeup water necessary.

10.12 (*Mass and energy balance in a dryer*)[2]   Air at 25°C and 70% relative humidity is heated in an air heater and the hot air is supplied to a dryer. Three hundred kilogram of moisture is removed from the dryer per hour. It is desired that the moist air should leave the dryer at T_G = 55°C and T_w = 40°C. Heat required for warming up of the wet solid and the heat losses taken together amount to 15% of that necessary for evaporation of water in the dryer. Calculate the temperature and flow rate of the hot air supplied to the dryer.

Saturated steam at 5 atm gauge is used for air heating, and the overall heat transfer coefficient is 32 W/m²·°C. Calculate the area of the air heater. *Given:* latent heat of vaporization of water in the dryer = 2370 kJ/kg; latent heat of vaporization of saturated steam at 5 atm gauge = 2100 kJ/kg.

10.13 (*Psychrometric properties of the mixture of two air streams*)[1]   Two air streams are mixed before feeding to a dryer in order to have proper humidity control. Stream 1: flow rate = 2 kg/s, temperature = 50°C, relative humidity = 30%; stream 2: flow rate = 3 kg/s, temperature = 25°C, relative humidity = 50%. Calculate the enthalpy, humidity, and temperature of the mixed air stream. The total pressure is 1 atm.

REFERENCES

Ahmed, S., and J. Bayers, 'Design basis for cooling systems', *Chem. Engg.*, Jan. 2000, 78–83.

Burger, R., 'Cooling towers—The often overlooked profit center', *Chem. Engg.*, May 1993, 100–104.

Cribb, G., 'Liquid phase resistance in water cooling', *Brit. Chem. Engr.*, May 1959, 264–266.

Harrison, L., and D. Simkins, 'Don't sweat it—Dehumidify', *Chem. Engg.*, Aug. 1997, 80–87.

Hensley, J.C., *Cooling Tower Fundamentals*, Marley Cooling Tower, Kansas, USA, 1985.

Hensley, J.C., 'Maximize tower power', *Chem. Engg.*, Feb. 1992, 74–82.

Jackson, B., 'Liquid phase resistance in water cooling', *Brit. Chem. Engr.*, Nov. 1958, 598–600.

Kern, D.Q., *Process Heat Transfer*, McGraw-Hill, New York, 1950.

McKelvey, K.K., and M. Brooke, *The Industrial Cooling Tower*, Elsevier, Amsterdam, 1959.

Ondrey, G. et al., 'COP's put heat on cooling towers', *Chem. Engg.*, Aug. 1999, 29–33.

Reid, R.C. et al., *Properties of Gases and Liquids*, McGraw-Hill, New York, 1988.

Silverberg, P.M., 'How to fight *legionellosis*', *Chem. Engg.*, Nov. 1997, 92–96.

Skelland, A.H.P., *Diffusional Mass Transfer*, John Wiley, New York, 1974.

Speltz, K., 'Properly select and design a process dehumidifier', *Chem. Eng. Progr.*, Nov. 1998, 65–70.

Suptic, D.M., 'Reduce the plume from cooling towers', *Chem. Engg.*, Jan. 2000, 105–108.

Thomas, W.J., and P. Houston, 'Simultaneous heat and mass transfer in cooling towers', *Brit. Chem. Engr.*, March 1959, 160–163; April 1959, 217–222.

Willa, J.L., 'Improving cooling towers', *Chem. Engg.*, Nov. 1997, 92–96.

11 | Drying of Wet Solids

The removal of moisture from a wet solid, a solution or a gas to make it 'dry' is often necessary in various industrial operations, particularly in chemical process industries. Examples are numerous. In the last stage of sugar production, washed and centrifuged sugar crystals are dried to get the finished product ready for packaging. Drying of leather under controlled conditions is an important step in leather processing. Soap bars are dried to reduce the moisture content. Milk is dried in a spray chamber to produce milk powder. In all these cases the wet material loses moisture in *direct contact* with a hot gas. The hot gas supplies the energy required for drying and also carries away the moisture released by the solid. There are examples in which heat-sensitive materials are dried by expulsion of moisture under vacuum. Direct contact of a heat-sensitive material with a hot gas is avoided; heat is supplied by a heating medium (generally a hot gas) through the wall of the drier. In a few other cases, particularly in some organic chemical industries, a liquid other than water may have to be removed from a wet solid. Thus, 'drying' may be defined as an operation in which the liquid, generally water, present in a wet solid (or a suspension or even a solution) is removed by vaporization to get a relatively liquid-free solid product. Drying of a solid does not demand ŏr ensure complete removal of the moisture. Sometimes it is desirable to retain a little moisture in the solid after drying (example: moisture is not removed totally during the drying of a soap bar, many foodstuff, etc.).

Drying involves liquid–solid separation. It is rather easy to distinguish drying from other liquid–solid separation operations like filtration, settling, centrifugation, etc. The latter operations are relatively simple; the liquid is removed by mechanical means. But considerable amount of liquid is still retained in the solid. This residual liquid can be removed by drying. There are many examples of separation of water from solutions which are *not* called drying. The removal of water from a purified soap lye to make glycerin is called 'evaporation' (and not drying) because the final product is not a solid. Similarly, the production of condensed milk involves evaporation, but the production of milk powder involves drying.

There are other examples of removal of moisture from gases and liquids which are conventionally called drying but do not come under the scope of this chapter. Dehydration of a gas by absorption or adsorption of the moisture is often called 'drying'. Natural gas is 'dried' by absorption of the moisture in triethylene glycol in a tray tower (this is a 'gas absorption' operation). Similarly, air is 'dried' by adsorption of the moisture in silica gel. The removal of small amounts of dissolved moisture from benzene (before chlorination of benzene, for example) is carried out in a distillation column. The process is called 'drying of benzene'.

11.1 PHYSICAL MECHANISM OF DRYING

Drying is basically governed by the principles of transport of heat and mass. When a moist solid is heated to an appropriate temperature, moisture vaporizes at or near the solid surface and the heat required (sensible heat and the heat of vaporization) for drying is usually supplied by a hot gas (exceptions: microwave drying, freeze drying, etc.). As soon as some of the surface moisture vaporizes, more moisture is transported from inside the solid to its surface. Moisture can move within a solid by a variety of mechanisms depending upon the nature and type of the solid and its state of aggregation. Various types of solids may have to be handled for drying—crystalline (sugar, salt, etc.), granular, beads (moist polymer beads), powders, sheets, slabs, filter-cakes, etc. The mechanism of moisture transport in different solids may be broadly classified into (i) transport by capillary forces, (ii) liquid diffusion, (iii) pressure induced transport, and (iv) vapour diffusion. The mechanism that dominates depends on the nature of the solid, its pore structure and the rate of drying. Also, different mechanisms may come into play and dominate at different stages of drying of the same material.

In granular and porous solids with an open pore structure, moisture transport occurs due to capillary forces so long as there is enough moisture in the bulk of the solid. The capillary structure of a bed is often nonuniform. The larger capillaries are emptied first, but the smaller ones continue to supply liquid to the drying surface. Simultaneously some drying gas enters into the solid through free passages and cracks. The pore volumes and interstices vacated by the liquid are thus occupied by the gas–vapour mixture and the volume of such gas-filled space increases as drying proceeds. The states of a moist granular solid at different stages of drying are shown in Figure 11.1.

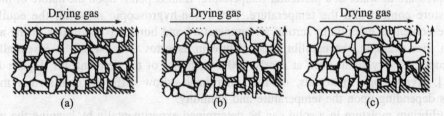

Figure 11.1 Stages of drying of a moist solid: (a) the solid is uniformly wet, (b) the upper region is partly dry, (c) the upper region of the solid is dry. The resistance to moisture diffusion increases from (a) to (b) to (c) and the drying rate decreases. The vertical arrows indicate the direction of moisture diffusion.

Some solids undergo significant shrinkage on drying. If the drying rate is high, the outer layer dries up fast, contracts and thereby generates a compressive force to squeeze out moisture from the interior. This is pressure-induced transport of liquid within the solid. For colloidal, gelatinous and some other materials that have an appreciable affinity for water, moisture transport occurs by molecular diffusion of liquid. As drying proceeds, the water concentration near the surface decreases. This creates the driving force for water diffusion from within the moist medium towards its exposed surface. At a low moisture content in a solid, which is inherently porous or in which pores are generated in course of drying, vaporization may even occur appreciably below the surface. The vapour thus produced has to diffuse out of the solid. This is what is called 'vapour diffusion'.

Broadly, three transport resistances play important roles in the drying process. These are: (i) the resistance to liquid or vapour transport inside the solid, (ii) the resistance to convective mass transfer of vapour from the surface of the solid to the bulk of the gas, and (iii) the resistance to convective heat transfer from the bulk of the drying gas to the solid surface. Because the solid temperature rises during drying, a conduction heat transfer resistance also becomes important, particularly at a low moisture content of the solid. More than one of these resistances are frequently found to become significant.

Another phenomenon may occur in the drying of certain solids like a soap bar. If drying is rapid, the outer surfaces lose moisture very quickly, become hard and impervious to moisture. Under such a condition, drying almost stops although sufficient moisture is still there inside. This is called 'case hardening'. A controlled rate of drying by adjustment of the temperature and humidity of the drying gas is necessary to avoid such a phenomenon and to get a product of desired moisture content.

11.2 DRYING EQUILIBRIA

Drying equilibrium means the relation between the moisture content of a solid and the humidity of the ambient drying medium at equilibrium. Like other mass transfer operations, drying or loss of moisture by vaporization occurs till the moisture content of the solid is more than the equilibrium value under the prevailing state (temperature and moisture content) of the ambient medium. The moisture present in a solid exerts a pressure which is equal to or less than the vapour pressure of water at a particular temperature. It all depends upon the nature of the solid, its moisture content and the temperature. For a non-hygroscopic material, the equilibrium moisture content is essentially zero at all temperature and humidity conditions of the ambient medium. For example, the equilibrium moisture in asbestos fibre, which is essentially non-hygroscopic, is very small even at nearly 100% humidity of the ambient gas [Figure 11.2(a), curve-1]. Hygroscopic materials, on the other hand, show different equilibrium moisture contents depending upon the temperature and humidity.

Equilibrium moisture in a solid can be determined experimentally by keeping the material suspended in a gas of a constant humidity and temperature for a sufficiently long time. Weights of the solid at equilibrium as well as in 'bone dry'[†] condition are to be noted. Moisture content is generally expressed as the mass of moisture per unit mass of bone dry solid. Below a certain moisture content and at a particular temperature, the vapour pressure of moisture over a moist solid becomes less than the vapour pressure of pure water at that temperature. All moisture below this threshold value is called 'bound moisture' and that above is called 'unbound moisture'.

[†] A solid totally free from moisture is called 'bone dry'.

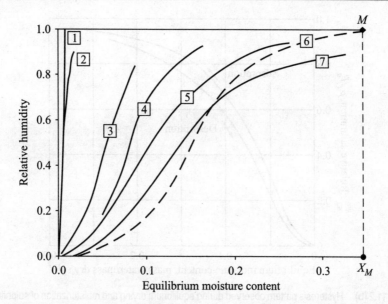

Figure 11.2 (a)   Equilibrium moisture isotherms for selected substances at room temperature: (1) asbestos fibre, (2) PVC, (3) wood, (4) Kraft paper, (5) jute, (6) wheat, and (7) potato.

Equilibrium moisture contents of a few substances are plotted in Figure 11.2(a) against the relative humidity of the ambient medium to get 'moisture isotherms'. Consider the point M on curve-6 for wheat at which the relative humidity is $R_{HM} = 1$, and the moisture content is X_M. On the right of M, the curve is horizontal. For a moisture content of the solid equal to or more than X_M, the equilibrium vapour pressure exerted by the solid is equal to the vapour pressure of water at the temperature concerned (i.e. $R_H = 1$). At a moisture content less than X_M, the solid exerts a vapour pressure of water less than that of pure water. All the moisture in the solid above X_M is 'unbound'; that below X_M is 'bound' moisture.

A solid which is hygroscopic or which adsorbs moisture shows a relatively high equilibrium moisture content. Even a microporous solid may have a large equilibrium moisture because a liquid filled in a capillary exerts a vapour pressure less than the normal vapour pressure of the liquid [see the Kelvin equation, Eq. (14.2)]. Some solids exhibit different equilibrium moisture relationships depending upon whether it is undergoing drying or it is absorbing moisture. This is a phenomenon of 'closed loop hysteresis' (Keey, 1972) shown in Figure 11.2(b).

The equilibrium vapour pressure exerted by the moisture present in the solid at the same moisture content is larger in the case of moisture uptake than in the case of drying. The phenomenon may be explained by taking the help of the Kelvin equation. Vaporization and condensation are not reversible within fine capillaries. When drying occurs, the capillaries are already liquid-filled and the vapour pressure is less than normal. In the case of moisture uptake, however, adsorption occurs on the pore walls, but a meniscus is not immediately formed. The lower curve (drying equilibrium curve) is useful for drying calculations. The upper curve is useful in calculating the time for moisture uptake—for example, to calculate the time within which a hygroscopic solid should be packaged after drying.

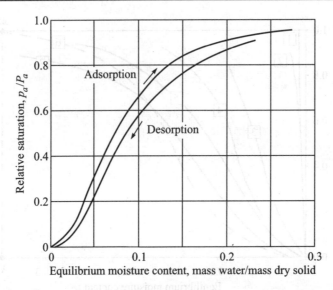

Figure 11.2 (b)   Hysteresis pattern observed during equilibrium drying and moisturization of sulphite pulp.

11.3   IMPORTANT DEFINITIONS AND TERMS

The more important quantities and terms in relation to drying are explained below.

Moisture content: As stated before, the moisture content is the quantity of moisture in a wet solid generally expressed in the mass ratio unit (kg moisture per kg dry solid). However, it can also be expressed as a mass fraction or per cent.

Bound moisture: The amount of moisture in a solid that exerts a vapour pressure less than the normal vapour pressure of water at the given temperature is called bound moisture.

Unbound moisture: The amount of moisture in a wet solid in excess of the bound moisture is called unbound moisture. Unbound moisture exerts a vapour pressure equal to that of water at the given temperature.

Equilibrium moisture: The moisture content in a solid that can remain in equilibrium with the drying medium of a given relative humidity at a given temperature is called equilibrium moisture.

Free moisture: The moisture in a wet solid in excess of the equilibrium moisture is called free moisture. Only free moisture can be removed by drying under a given set of conditions (the temperature and humidity of the drying gas).

These terms are also illustrated in Figure 11.3. A solid of initial moisture content X_i is being dried in contact with a gas of relative humidity R_H^*. The water present in the solid exerts a vapour pressure equal to that of 'pure' water till a moisture content of X_b is reached. So $(X_i - X_b)$ is the unbound moisture content of the wet solid. As the moisture concentration decreases below X_b, the vapour pressure exerted by the water remaining in the solid also decreases. As the moisture content reaches the equilibrium moisture content X^*, the vapour pressure of moisture

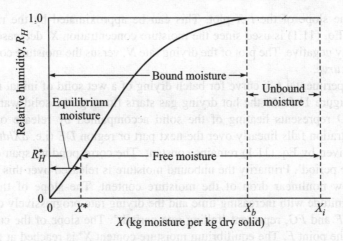

Figure 11.3   Different types of moisture in a wet solid.

over the solid becomes equal to the partial pressure of water vapour in the drying gas (the corresponding relative humidity is R_H^* in Figure 11.3). Hence X_b is the bound moisture, $X_i - X^*$ is the free moisture content (all expressed as kg moisture per kg dry solid).

11.4   THE DRYING RATE CURVE

The time required for drying of a moist solid to a final moisture content can be determined from a knowledge of the rate of drying under a given set of conditions. The drying rate of a solid is a function of temperature, humidity, flow rate and transport properties (in terms of Reynolds number and Schmidt number) of the drying gas. The drying rate has to be determined experimentally. A simple setup for the purpose is shown in Figure 11.4. The moist solid is taken on a pan and kept suspended in the drying chamber through which the drying gas is passed at a given flow rate. The change in mass of the solid with time is recorded. The mass of the 'bone dry' solid is determined separately. Let W_s = mass of the 'bone dry' solid, a = drying area (when the drying gas flows over the wet solid, the drying area is the exposed area of the mass taken on the pan), and X = moisture content at any time t. Then the rate of drying is given as

$$N = -\frac{W_s}{a}\frac{dX}{dt} \approx -\frac{W_s}{a}\frac{\Delta X}{\Delta t} \quad \frac{\text{kg moisture}}{\text{m}^2 \cdot \text{s}} \tag{11.1}$$

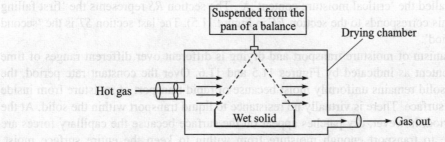

Figure 11.4   Schematic of a simple laboratory batch drying experiment.

Here dX/dt is the slope of the t–X plot. This can be approximated by the ratio $\Delta X/\Delta t$. The negative sign in Eq. (11.1) is used since the moisture concentration X, decreases with time and dX/dt is inherently negative. The plot of the drying rate N, versus the moisture content X, is called the *drying rate curve*.

A typical experimental t–X curve for batch drying of a wet solid of initial moisture content X_i is shown in Figure 11.5. As the hot drying gas starts flowing, the solid warms up. The part of the curve X_iD represents heating of the solid accompanied by release of moisture. The moisture concentration falls linearly over the next part or region DE (i.e. dX/dt = constant). So the drying rate given by Eq. (11.1) remains constant. The corresponding span of time is called the 'constant rate period'. Primarily the unbound moisture is released over this period. Sections EF and FG show nonlinear drop of the moisture content. The slope of the curve (dX/dt) decreases in magnitude with increasing time and the drying rate progressively diminishes. Both these sections, EF and FG, represent 'falling rate periods'. The slope of the curve may have a discontinuity at the point F. The equilibrium moisture content X^* is reached at the point G after which the curve becomes flat indicating no further loss of moisture.

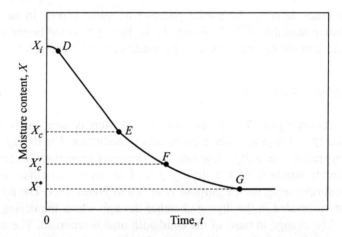

Figure 11.5   Change in the moisture content of a solid in batch drying.

The drying rate curve corresponding to the t–X curve of Figure 11.5 is shown in Figure 11.6. Over the section PQ in Figure 11.6, the solid gradually gets heated and the rate of drying increases. Over the section QR, the rate of drying remains constant at N_c. The moisture content at the point R in Figure 11.6 (or the corresponding point E in Figure 11.5) where the constant rate period terminates is called the 'critical moisture content' X_c. The section RS represents the 'first falling rate period' (this corresponds to the section EF in Figure 11.5). The last section ST is the 'second falling rate period'.

The mechanism of moisture transport and drying is different over different ranges of time or moisture content as indicated by Figures 11.5 and 11.6. Over the constant rate period, the surface of the solid remains uniformly moist because of rapid transport of moisture from inside the solid to its surface. There is virtually no resistance to liquid transport within the solid. At the end of this period, however, dry patches appear on the surface because the capillary forces are no longer able to transport enough moisture from within to keep the entire surface moist. Unsaturated surface drying occurs during the first falling rate period. The drying rate is governed

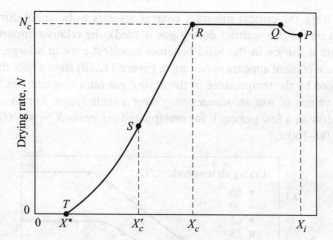

Figure 11.6 A typical drying rate curve.

by the combined transport resistances of moisture inside the solid and that outside the solid [i.e. the resistances described by steps (i) and (ii) in Section 11.1 act in series]. The moisture content of the solid becomes quite low in the second falling rate period given by *FG* (Figure 11.5), where the internal diffusion of moisture essentially controls the rate of drying.

It is to be noted that the critical moisture content of a wet solid is not a constant quantity. It depends upon a number of factors like (i) the pore structure and particle size of the solid, (ii) the thickness of the bed of wet solid, and (iii) the drying rate. The last factor, in turn, depends upon the temperature, the humidity and the flow rate of the drying gas. The critical moisture content may be viewed as a point of transition of the nature and magnitude of the mass transfer resistance in relation to drying. If the particle size of the solid is small, the intra-particle resistance to moisture transport is less. So the constant rate of drying continues for a longer period. As a result, the critical moisture content appears to be less than that for the drying of larger particles of the same material. If the solid has more open and large pores, or if the depth of the bed is

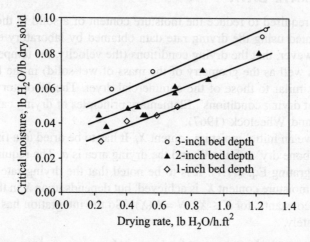

Figure 11.7 (a) Sand drying with superheated steam—effects of constant drying rate and bed thickness on critical moisture content [Wenzel, *I&EC, 43* (1951) 1829].

small [Figure 11.7(a)], the critical moisture content appears to be small. Similarly, at a larger drying rate (for example, if a warmer drying gas is used), the relative importance of resistance to internal moisture diffusion in the solid becomes manifest even at a larger moisture content. The critical moisture content appears to be larger. Figure 11.7(b) shows how the critical moisture content is influenced by the temperature of the drying gas (at a constant wet-bulb temperature). Critical moisture values of wet substances vary over a wide range. For example, for a bed of sand it may be as low as a few per cent; for precipitated pigments $X_c \sim 40\text{--}60\%$; for leather and wallboard, $X_c \sim 100\text{--}160\%$.

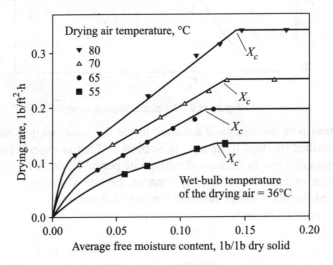

Figure 11.7 (b)   Effect of drying air temperature on the drying rate of asbestos pulp in air [McCready et al., Trans. *AIChE J.*, *29* (1933) 131].

11.5   CALCULATION OF THE DRYING TIME FROM THE DRYING RATE DATA

The time of drying required to reduce the moisture content of a solid to the desired extent in a dryer can be calculated using the drying rate data obtained by laboratory experiments. It must be remembered, however, that the drying conditions (the velocity, the temperature, the humidity of the drying gas as well as the geometry of the mass of wet solid) in the laboratory apparatus have to be closely similar to those of the commercial dryer. The laboratory tests are generally done under 'constant drying conditions'. Elementary principles of drying calculations have been discussed by Tsao and Wheelock (1967).

Let the solid have an initial moisture content X_i. It has to be dried to a final moisture content of X_f. The mass of 'bone dry' solid is W_s and the drying area is a. The required drying time may be obtained by integrating Eq. (11.1). It is to be noted that the drying rate N remains constant at N_c till the critical moisture content X_c is achieved, but depends upon X in the falling rate period [$X \geq X_c$, $N = N_c$ (= constant); for $X \leq X_c$, $N = N(X)$]. So the integration has to be done over the two intervals separately.

$$t = -\frac{W_s}{a} \int_{X_i}^{X_f} \frac{dX}{N} = \frac{W_s}{a} \int_{X_f}^{X_i} \frac{dX}{N} = \frac{W_s}{a} \int_{X_c}^{X_i} \frac{dX}{N} + \frac{W_s}{a} \int_{X_f}^{X_c} \frac{dX}{N} = \frac{W_s}{a} \int_{X_c}^{X_i} \frac{dX}{N_c} + \frac{W_s}{a} \int_{X_f}^{X_c} \frac{dX}{N} \quad (11.2)$$

The second integral may be evaluated graphically or numerically if the tabular data for N versus X are available. In the simplest case, if the drying rate N decreases with X as a linear function ($N = pX + q$, say) over the falling rate period, the time of drying may be expressed as

$$t = \frac{W_s(X_i - X_c)}{a N_c} + \frac{W_s}{a} \int_{X_f}^{X_c} \frac{dX}{pX + q} = \frac{W_s(X_i - X_c)}{a N_c} + \frac{W_s}{a p} \ln \frac{pX_c + q}{pX_f + q}$$

$$= \frac{W_s(X_i - X_c)}{a N_c} + \frac{W_s}{a p} \ln \frac{N_c}{N_f} \qquad (11.3)$$

since $N_c = pX_c + q$ and $N_f = pX_f + q$, $p = (N_c - N_f)/(X_c - X_f)$. On substitution,

$$t = \frac{W_s(X_i - X_c)}{a N_c} + \frac{W_s}{a} \frac{X_c - X_f}{N_c - N_f} \ln \frac{N_c}{N_f} = t_c + t_f \qquad (11.4)$$

Here t_c = constant rate drying time, and t_f = falling rate drying time. Equation (11.4) may be expressed in a slightly different form by noting the fact that the drying rate $N = 0$ at the equilibrium moisture, $X = X^*$. Thus,

$$0 = pX^* + q \quad \Rightarrow \quad q = -pX^*$$

$$\Rightarrow \quad \frac{N_c}{N_f} = \frac{pX_c + q}{pX_f + q} = \frac{pX_c - pX^*}{pX_f - pX^*} = \frac{X_c - X^*}{X_f - X^*}$$

and

$$\frac{X_c - X_f}{N_c - N_f} = \frac{X_c - X_f}{(pX_c + q) - (pX_f + q)} = \frac{1}{p} = \frac{X_c - X^*}{N_c}$$

Substituting these results in Eq. (11.4),

$$t = t_c + t_f = \frac{W_s(X_i - X_c)}{a N_c} + \frac{W_s}{a} \frac{X_c - X^*}{N_c} \ln \frac{X_c - X^*}{X_f - X^*} \qquad (11.5)$$

The drying rate is zero when $X = X^*$. Hence if the falling rate of drying is linear in X, it is proportional to $(X - X^*)$. If there are two falling rate periods over which the drying rates are known, the functions of the moisture content X in Eq. (11.2) should be integrated accordingly (see Problem 11.2). If the drying rate data (N versus X) are available in a tabular form, it is convenient to determine the drying time by graphical integration.

EXAMPLE 11.1 A wet solid of 28% moisture is to be dried to 0.5% moisture in a tray dryer. A laboratory test shows that it requires 8 hours to reduce the moisture content of the same solid to 2%. The critical moisture content is 6% and the equilibrium moisture is 0.2%. The falling rate of drying is linear in the free moisture content. Calculate the drying time of the solid if the drying conditions similar to those in the laboratory test are maintained. All moistures are expressed as per cent of 'bone dry' mass of the solid.

Solution
Use Eq. (11.5). *Given:* $X_c = 0.06$; $X^* = 0.002$; $X_i = 0.28$.

For the laboratory test, final moisture, $X_f = 0.02$; time of dryimg, $t = 8$ h. Putting in Eq. (11.5),

$$8 = \frac{W_s}{a\,N_c}\left[(0.28 - 0.06) + (0.06 - 0.002)\ln\left(\frac{0.06 - 0.002}{0.02 - 0.002}\right)\right] \Rightarrow \frac{W_s}{a\,N_c} = 27.8$$

Required time of drying to 0.5% moisture (i.e. $X_f = 0.005$) is

$$t = \frac{W_s}{a\,N_c}\left[(0.28 - 0.06) + (0.06 - 0.002)\ln\left(\frac{0.06 - 0.002}{0.005 - 0.002}\right)\right]$$

$$\Rightarrow \qquad\qquad t = (27.8)(0.392) = \boxed{11\,\text{h}}$$

11.6   CLASSIFICATION OF DRYING EQUIPMENT

A wide variety of moist solids, slurries and solutions are required to be dried in commercial practice. Different types of dryers are available to suit specific needs. The performance of a drying equipment depends upon how good the contact between the wet solid and the drying gas is. The gas–solid contact in dryers may occur in a number of ways. For example:

(a)   The wet solid may be taken in a number of trays; the trays are stacked in the drying chamber maintaining a gap or clearance so that the drying gas may be passed over the exposed top surface of the solid spread on a tray. This is called 'cross-circulation drying'. The drying rate is low because moisture is transported to the drying surface by diffusion through the layer of moist solid. [Example: tray dryer]

(b)   The wet solid may be taken on a perforated (or screened-bottom) tray or on a moving belt. The hot drying gas passes *through* the bed of the solid. This is called 'through-circulation drying'. Because all the wet solid particles are exposed to the gas, the effective drying area and the drying rate are much larger than in the case of cross-circulation drying. [Example: conveyer or band dryer]

(c)   The solid may move through a slightly inclined rotating shell. The solid is simultaneously lifted by a number of 'flights' fitted to the inner wall of the shell and showered in the hot drying gas flowing through the shell. [Example: rotary dryer]

(d)   The wet solid is taken in a cylindrical vessel of suitable design. The drying gas flows at a considerably high velocity such that the wet solid is dried under 'suspended' or 'fluidized' condition. Drying occurs uniformly and at a high rate. [Example: flash dryer; fluidized-bed dryer]

(e)   If the feed is a solution or a slurry, it may be sprayed as fine droplets to ensure efficient contact with the hot gas (example: spray dryer). A thick liquid or slurry may be fed on the surface of a heated rotating drum where it spreads on the surface and gets dried thereon (example: drum dryer).

Many industrial dryers work on the above strategies of contacting the feed (i.e. the material to be dried) with the drying gas. However, the modes of operation of and energy supply to the dryers vary. Industrial dryers may be classified on one or more of these basis.

(a) *Mode of operation:* A dryer may operate batch-wise or in the continuous mode. Correspondingly the dryers may be classified as batch or continuous. A batch dryer has a low equipment and installation cost, it is easy to operate, and is more versatile in possible applications. If necessary, the same dryer may be used to dry different materials. Batch dryers are generally suitable for small production capacities.

(b) *State of the wet solid:* The wet feed to a dryer may range from a liquid solution, a slurry, a paste, or a filter-cake to free-flowing powders, granular or fibrous solids or lumps. Dryers may be classified on this basis too.

(c) *Method of energy supply:* Heat energy required for drying may be supplied directly by a hot drying gas, or it may be supplied indirectly through the wall of the dryer from a hot gas flowing outside the wall. The dryers are correspondingly called 'direct-heat' or 'indirect heat dryers'. In some cases an inert gas may flow through the dryer in direct contact with the wet solid, but it is not hot and does not supply any energy. It rather acts as a carrier of the vapour generated during drying. Heat is supplied from outside the wall.

The important types of dryers are classified and listed in Figure 11.8. The construction and operational features of selected dryers are described below. More details are available in Sloan et al. (1967). Details of drying principles and equipment have been discussed by Keey (1972) and Cook and DuMont (1991). Description and applications of many novel drying equipment are available in the literature of Wolverine, Proctor and Schwartz, USA.

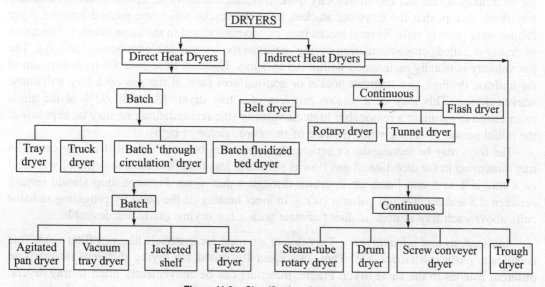

Figure 11.8 Classification of common dryers.

11.7 DIRECT-HEAT BATCH DRYERS: TRAY AND TRUCK DRYERS

The direct-heat batch dryer is simple in construction and includes trays, trucks, shelf and cabinet dryers which are similar in construction, operation and application. The wet material is spread evenly on a number of trays which are stacked one over another inside an insulated cabinet (Figure 11.9). The drying gas (usually air) is heated in contact with steam coils. A blower fitted

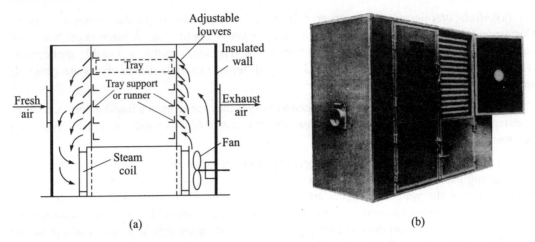

Figure 11.9   (a) Inside a tray dryer; (b) a standard 20-tray dryer (Courtesy: Wolverine, Proctor & Schwartz).

inside the cabinet forces the hot gas over the trays. A part of the gas circulates inside the cabinet and the rest leaves the dryer carrying the evaporated moisture. The temperature, the humidity and the velocity of air may be regulated as required by adjusting the gas flow rate, the recirculation rate and the steam rate. Adjustable vanes on both ends of a tray are used to regulate the recirculation rate and the air velocity over it. A batch truck dryer operates like an ordinary tray dryer, except that the trays are stacked upon the trucks which are pushed into the dryer cabinet over pairs of rails. Several trucks may be accommodated in the same cabinet. The mode of drying is called 'cross-circulation drying' because the hot gas is blown across the trays. The gas velocity is usually maintained within 0.3 to 3 m/s. Uniform flow over the trays is required for uniform drying. Any stagnant pocket or non-uniform flow of the gas on a tray will cause uneven drying. This may be a serious problem of a tray dryer. About 80–95% of the air is recirculated to maintain a reasonably high air velocity (the recirculation rate may be kept low at the initial period of drying when the rate of moisture release is high).

The trays may be rectangular or square, the area varies between 0.5 and 1 m² per tray. The tray dimension in the direction of gas flow is generally less than 0.75 m. The depth of wet solid on a tray is 1 to 5 cm. Fresh air is drawn through a dust filter. Pressure drop should remain between 2.5 and 5 cm water column (w.c.). Indirect heating of the solid by providing radiator coils above each tray is done if direct contact with a hot drying gas is not desirable.

Applications and advantages: Tray dryers are used for materials like wet filter-cake, fine chemicals, pasty substances, etc. These are specially suited for drying different materials in different batches in the same dryer. Fragile materials can be conveniently dried in tray dryers. The advantages of tray dryers are: low cost, less space requirement, ease of cleaning, accessibility and good control of drying conditions. Formation of stagnant air pockets in some regions, which leads to non-uniform drying, may be a problem with tray dryers. Perforated trays may be used instead of solid-bottom trays when the material to be dried is granular. In this design a large part of the air or gas flows *through* the bed. This is called the 'through-circulation' mode of drying because the gas flows through the solid. The most serious disadvantage of tray dryers is the high operating cost, particularly the cost of labour for loading and unloading of the trays.

11.8 DIRECT-HEAT CONTINUOUS DRYERS

Drying occurs at a faster rate in a direct-heat continuous unit. The wet materials spread on trays are loaded on trucks which move slowly through the drying chamber and get dried by the time a truck leaves the chamber. In another design, the solid may form a thin bed on a moving perforated belt through which the drying gas flows.

11.8.1 Tunnel Truck Dryers

These are direct-heat continuous dryers similar to batch tray or truck dryers, except that trucks loaded with trays move through a long tunnel. The trucks are put into the tunnel one after another at a regular time interval and are pulled by a chain towards the other end of the tunnel. Each truck takes a certain time to traverse the length of the tunnel. This is the drying time (including the time for preheating). A fixed number of trucks remain in the tunnel at any time. Tracks or rails are provided in the tunnel for the trucks to advance smoothly. Hot air flows through the tunnel cocurrent or countercurrent to the trucks. Fans are sometimes provided on the tunnel wall to blow the hot air across the trays on the trucks. Steam coils may be provided in the tunnel for air heating. A part of the air is usually recycled as in a batch tray dryer. The isometric view of a tunnel truck dryer is given in Figure 11.10(a). The schematic end view is given in Figure 11.10(b) in which only one truck is seen; others are behind it. The side view of the dryer in which the drying air is in counterflow is shown in Figure 11.10(c).

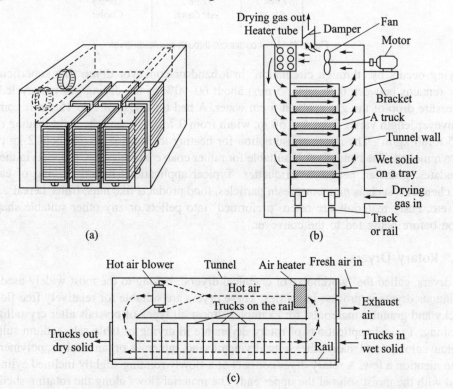

Figure 11.10 Tunnel truck dryer: (a) Isometric view, and (b) end view. (c) A countercurrent tunnel dryer.

Tunnel truck dryers are used extensively in the ceramic industry for drying pottery and ceramic ware. Use in the chemical industry is not common. However, these may also be used for drying of crystals, filter-cakes, and pasty materials.

11.8.2   Belt (Also Called Band) or Conveyer Dryer

A band dryer is also a direct-heat continuous type dryer (Figure 11.11). It basically consists of a perforated moving belt (a screen or a perforated steel belt; the minimum size of the openings is 30 mesh) onto which the wet solid is fed at one end. The belt moves into a drying cabinet and the hot gas passes through the layer of moist solid. The solid is carried through the cabinet and discharged at the opposite end. A uniform rate of feeding and distribution of the material over the conveyer is necessary in order to prevent a higher flow rate of drying air through the thinner regions of the bed. Maldistribution of air flow leads to uneven drying of the solid.

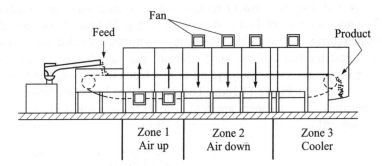

Figure 11.11   A continuous through-circulation dryer.

Drying occurs by 'through circulation' in a band or conveyor dryer. The superficial gas velocity remains between 0.25 and 1.5 m/s; about 60–90% of the drying gas is recycled. The total pressure drop of the gas is about 5 cm water. A bed thickness of 3 to 15 cm is common. The conveyer length varies from 4 to 50 m, width from 0.7 to 4 m, and the solid loading ranges from 15 to 80 kg/m^2. The steam consumption for heating the drying gas in about 2 kg per kg moisture removed. The band dryer is suitable for rather coarse particles, i.e. products in the form of extrudates, granular, pellets or briquettes. Typical applications include drying of catalyst pellets, chemicals such as pigments, resin particles, food products like nuts, fruits, cereals, sliced carrots, etc. Pasty materials are often 'preformed' into pellets or any other suitable shape by extrusion before being fed to the conveyer.

11.8.3   Rotary Dryers

Rotary dryers, called the 'workhorse of chemical dryers', belong to the most widely used class of continuous dryers in process industries. These dryers are suitable for relatively free-flowing, non-sticky and granular materials; for example, almost all types of crystals after crystallization and washing. Typical applications of rotary dryers are in drying of table salt, sodium sulphate, ammonium sulphate and many other salts, drying of sand, minerals, organic solids, polymer resin beads, to mention a few. A rotary dryer consists of a slowly rotating slightly inclined cylindrical shell fed with the moist solid at the upper end. The material flows along the rotating shell, gets dried and leaves the dryer at the lower end.

Supply of heat to the wet solid may be done directly or indirectly. Accordingly, a rotary dryer is called 'direct heat rotary dryer' or 'indirect heat rotary dryer'. In a dryer of the former type, the wet solid is dried in direct contact with a hot gas flowing parallel or countercurrent to the moving solid. In an indirect heat dryer, on the other hand, heat is supplied through the shell wall of the dryer by a hot flue flowing outside. Heat supply may also be done by steam condensing in a jacket around the shell or in heating tubes provided within the shell. A low flow rate of air or an inert gas is maintained within the shell to carry away the evaporated water. Both kinds of dryer are shown schematically in Figure 11.12.

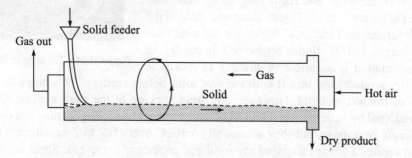

Figure 11.12 Schematic picture of a direct-heat countercurrent rotary dryer.

Construction and operating features

A direct heat countercurrent rotary dryer assembly is shown in Figure 11.13. The major parts of such a dryer are also shown. The shell is made of a suitable metal or alloy. The major 'internals' are the 'flights' running along the shell of the dryer. It is essential to keep the solid mixed as it flows in order to avoid agglomeration or formation of lumps. The flights do this job (Figure 11.14). As the shell rotates, the flights lift the flowing solid and shower it in the air stream

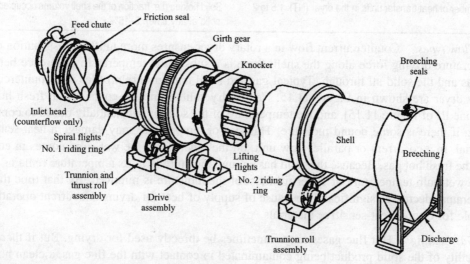

Figure 11.13 A direct heat countercurrent rotary dryer assembly (the flights for lifting the solid and the major mechanical components like the drive, the girth gear, and the trunnion roll supporting the rotating shell are also shown).

so as to avoid agglomeration. This also ensures a good contact between the solid and the hot gas and continuously exposes the solid so that drying of the particles occurs uniformly. The drying rate is intermediate between tray dryers and fluidized-bed dryers. The flights project radially from the shell wall. These may be straight or may have a 45° or 90° 'lip'. These are called straight, 45°- or 90°-flights. For drying granular materials, 45°- or 90°-flights may be used throughout the drying length of the shell. But for drying sticky materials, the suitable flights are: straight flights along one-third of the shell length for the feed end, 45°-flights for the next one-third of the length, and 90°-flights for the rest. In the drying of sticky materials it is an effective strategy to recycle a

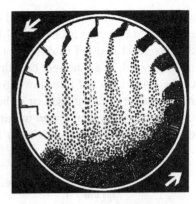

Figure 11.14   The flights for lifting the solids.

part of the dry product, and mix it with the wet solid before feeding. This helps to reduce the 'stickiness' of the wet material. However, any solid sticking to the shell wall or the flights is usually disengaged by 'external shell knockers' (see Figure 11.13). Flights may run continuously along the length of a dryer, but they are usually 'offset' every 0.7 to 2 m length. This type of construction creates a better mixing of the solid and contact with the gas. Some information on dimensions and operating parameters of rotary dryers is given in Table 11.1.

Table 11.1   Practical ranges of dimensions and operating parameters of rotary dryers

Internal diameter of the shell: D = 1 to 10 ft	Length, L = $4D$ to $15D$
Radial flight height: $D/12$ to $D/8$; shell rpm: 4 to 5	Peripheral shell speed: 50–100 ft/min
The flight count per circle: $2.4D$ to $3D$ (D in ft)	
Inclination of the shell to the horizontal: up to 8 cm/m	Average solid retention time: 5 min to 2 h
Mass flow rate of the drying gas: 300 to 5000 lb/h·ft^2	Drying capacity: 0.4 to 2.5 lb moisture/(h)(ft^3 dryer volume)
Number of heat transfer units in the dryer (NT): 1.5 to 2	Solid holdup (i.e. fraction of the shell volume occupied by the solid at any time): 5–15%

Flow types: Countercurrent flow in a rotary dryer ensures more uniform distribution of the temperature driving force along the shell; there is a substantial temperature difference between the gas and the solid all through. Typical gas and solid temperature profiles in a countercurrent rotary dryer are shown in Figure 11.15. Nearly dry solid comes in contact with fresh hot gas (in Zone III of Figure 11.15), and the temperature of the solid is substantially raised to complete drying if there is some bound moisture. This rise of temperature may damage a heat-sensitive material. In a cocurrent or parallel flow unit, on the other hand, the wet solid comes in contact with the fresh hot gas. Because the solid has enough moisture in it, its temperature remains close to the wet-bulb temperature of water till most of the moisture is removed. By that time the gas temperature decreases significantly because of supply of heat for drying. Cocurrent operation is suitable for drying heat-sensitive materials.

Gas heating: Hot flue gases may sometimes be directly used for drying. But if there is a possibility of the solid product being contaminated in contact with the flue gas, a clean heating gas is necessary. Air or nitrogen may be heated in a gas- or oil-fired heater or in a finned-tube steam-heater and fed to the dryer.

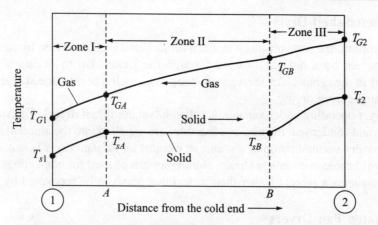

Figure 11.15 Solid and gas temperature profiles in a countercurrent rotary dryer.

Solid feeding: The solid-feeder should push the wet solid into the drier at the top end but should not allow the drying gas to escape through it. A screw feeder is most convenient because it acts as a 'gas-seal' too. A conveyer-mixer may be used if a part of the dry product is mixed with a sticky feed to reduce its stickiness. A chute extending into the shell may also be used for feeding (see Figure 11.13).

Dust collection: The exit gas from a rotary dryer often carries over or entrains considerable amounts of fines. If the carryover of dust is substantial, the gas is led to a cyclone or a bag filter to separate the fines. If there is excessive dusting, the mass flow rate [(kg)/(s)(m^2) of the dryer cross-section)] of the hot gas is kept low. The majority of rotary dryers operate at gas velocities below 2 m/s.

Support and drive of the dryer: A full-scale rotary dryer has a huge weight and is supported on assemblies of trunnion and thrust roll. Anti-friction pillow blocks are used in modern installations. A motor of high rating rotates the dryer through a speed reduction device and a girth gear on the periphery of the shell. The shell is properly insulated against heat loss to the ambient.

Heat efficiency: The fraction or percentage of the thermal energy of the hot gas that is utilized for drying is called the 'heat efficiency' or 'thermal efficiency' of the dryer. The rest of the supplied energy leaves the dryer with the gas or is lost to the ambient. Heat efficiency of a rotary dryer may vary from about 20% to 80% depending upon the operating temperature.

11.9 INDIRECT-HEAT BATCH SYSTEMS

This class of equipment includes jacketed-shelf dryers, rotary vacuum dryers, agitated pan dryers, freeze dryers, etc. They find applications in fields ranging from drugs, fine chemicals, paints, varnishes and plasticizers to substances that cannot tolerate exposure to the hot drying gas for possible degradation or damage of quality. Characteristics and selection of dryers of this category have been discussed by Lattman and Laible (2000).

11.9.1   Jacketed-shelf Dryers

As the name implies, the wet substance is taken on jacketed shelves heated by steam, hot water, oil, Dowtherm,[†] or by a hot gas flowing through the jacket. Up to twenty shelves may be accommodated in the cabinet. An inert gas flowing at a small rate over the shelves picks up the vapour generated during drying.

   A shelf dryer operating under vacuum is called a 'vacuum shelf dryer'. The vapour is drawn through a pipe and condensed; the non-condensibles are expelled into the ambient by the vacuum device (a wet or dry vacuum pump or a steam jet ejector). A vacuum dryer is suitable (i) for heat sensitive and oxidizable materials (a stream of nitrogen can be used for *blanketing*), and (ii) when the wet solid contains a solvent (other than water) that needs to be recovered by condensation.

11.9.2   Agitated Pan Dryers

An agitated pan dryer is a bowl or a shallow cylindrical vessel (1 to 3 m in diameter) provided with a slow-moving stirrer (2 to 20 rpm). Heating is done by steam or a hot fluid flowing through a jacket on the pan. A vapour collection hood is fitted above the pan. The vapour generated may be vented or may be drawn and condensed under vacuum if recovery of the vapour is desired. It is suitable for both granular and pasty materials. The type of agitator and its rpm depend upon the material to be dried.

11.9.3   Conical Vacuum Dryer

The conical vacuum dryer (Figure 11.16) is provided with a heating jacket and a slow-moving agitator for the wet solid. A moderate vacuum, generally not below 10 mm Hg, is used. The vapour drawn by the vacuum device may be condensed if recovery is desired. The conical shape allows faster discharge of the dry product through the bottom. This kind of dryer is used for drying powders, dyes, chemicals, and pharmaceuticals.

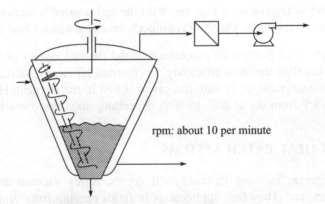

rpm: about 10 per minute

Figure 11.16   Schematic of an agitated conical vacuum dryer.

[†] 'Dowtherm' is a common heat-transfer fluid (see Dutta, 2001).

11.10 INDIRECT-HEAT CONTINUOUS DRYERS

In indirect-heat continuous dryers, heat transfer to the wet material occurs by conduction through the wall of the dryer. Steam, hot water, oil or a gas may be used as the heating medium. Electrical heating may also be done. This type of dryer is particularly suited if the solvent vapour is to be recovered or an inert atmosphere is to be maintained to prevent damage or oxidation of the product. Dusting materials can also be handled satisfactorily. The cutaway view of a steam-tube rotary dryer is shown in Figure 11.17.

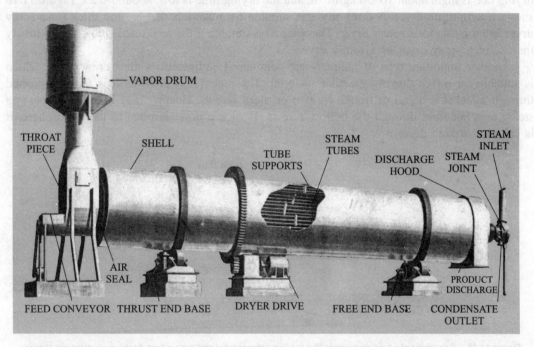

Figure 11.17   Cutaway view of an indirect heat rotary dryer (*Courtesy:* Swenson Technology, Monee, IL., USA).

11.10.1 Indirect-heat Rotary Dryer

Indirect-heat rotary dryer is basically similar to the direct-heat type except that the heating medium does not come in direct contact with the solid or the drying gas. This gives a better thermal efficiency that may be as high as 95%, and loss of heat through the heating gas is much less. The exit temperature of the gas may be substantially reduced if two passes of the gas are used. Supply of heat may be done through the shell wall or through tubes provided within the shell.

Indirect heat or steam-tube rotary dryers are used where a clean and inert heating atmosphere is to be maintained. For example, drying of terephthalic acid[†] (powder, ~150 mesh) in the final stage of its production is done in a steam-tube rotary dryer. Oxygen-lean vent gas (less than 6% oxygen) from the *p*-xylene oxidation reactor is stripped of the organic vapour and passed through the dryer. Direct drying by hot air cannot be done since degradation of the material occurs.

[†] It is a bulk organic chemical made by liquid-phase air oxidation of *p*-xylene. It is used for the production of polyethylene terephthalate (PET).

11.10.2 Drum Dryer

A drum dryer consists of one or two steam-heated rotating drums. The feed, a solution or a slurry, forms a thin layer on the drum. The film thickness can be controlled by an adjustable blade (for a single-drum unit) or by adjusting the gap between the drums (for a twin-drum unit). The feed gets dried in contact with the heated drums. A gas, normally air, may be blown over the surface for quick removal of moisture. The dry product is scrapped off as flakes, 1–3 mm thick, from the drum surface by a knife. The speed of rotation in rpm varies between 1 and 24. The drying rate is high, about 10–30 kg/m²·h, and the drying time is low, about 3–12 s. Figure 11.18 shows a twin-drum dryer. A drum dryer is suitable for materials that are too thick for a spray dryer and too thin for a rotary dryer. These are also suitable if the feed rate is too small to justify the use of a spray dryer or a rotary dryer.

Another important type of indirect-heat continuous equipment is the 'screw dryer' which is suitable for a free-flowing granular material. The material is dried as it is fed and pushed through a jacketed barrel or trough by two or more screws. Heating may be done by passing steam or a hot fluid through the hollow screws. If such a dryer is open to the atmosphere, it is called a 'trough dryer'.

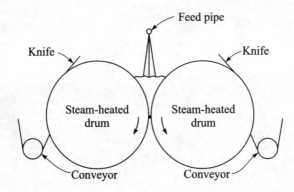

Figure 11.18 Schematic of a twin-drum dryer (the feeding arrangement and the product discharge system are shown).

11.10.3 Freeze Dryer

The technique of freeze drying is adopted for dehydrating heat-sensitive and perishable materials like seafood, meat, fruits, vegetables, pharmaceuticals, etc. The material is first frozen so that the liquid (water) gets separated by crystallization in the form of ice. The simplest freeze dryer is a vacuum shelf-type unit operated at an absolute pressure less than about 0.8 mm Hg. The temperature may be –20°C or even less. The ice crystals in the solid sublimate under vacuum and the vapour is condensed at about –60°C. Heat of vaporization may be supplied through 'ribs' on a tray. The driving force for sublimation of ice is the difference between the sublimation vapour pressure and the condenser pressure. The drying rate is low, about 0.2–2 kg/m²·h. Shrinkage of the material does not occur in freeze drying and the freeze-dried product can be instantly and fully rehydrated when it is used (Ruthven, 1997). A simple theoretical analysis of the freeze drying of a slab is given in Section 11.14.

11.11 AIR-SUSPENDED DRYING SYSTEMS

Air-suspended dryers include flash, fluidized-bed and spray dryers. The drying is uniform, the drying rate is rapid, and a small contact time is sufficient.

11.11.1 Flash Dryers

The flash dryer, also called 'pneumatic conveyer', essentially consists of a vertical conveyer pipe into which the wet solid is fed near the bottom generally through a screw feeder (Figure 11.19). Hot air enters the dryer at a point below the solid feed point at a velocity of 20 to 30 m/s that should be high enough to convey the solid through the dryer. A small residence time (1 to 10 s, usually around 3 s) is allowed for drying of the solid. The drying rate is very high (this is why it is called a *flash dryer*), but the solid temperature does not rise much because of the very short contact time. Often the solid temperature remains at the wet-bulb temperature of the drying gas. A flash dryer is used for drying of heat-sensitive or easily oxidizable materials (proteins, animal feed); it is ideally suited for removal of surface moisture (for example, for drying of polymer beads—PVC, polyethylene, polypropylene, polystyrene). A cyclone at the top separates the solid from the gas. The inlet gas temperature is high. Drying occurs very rapidly and the solid remains nearly at the wet-bulb temperature of the gas. Flash dryers and their modified versions are used for drying of corn, some food materials, clays, inorganic salts, polymer beads, etc. A flash dryer is unsuitable for large or heavy particles. Its special advantage is that no separate arrangement is necessary for transporting the dried product. It is carried away to the collection vessel by the drying gas itself. The operating features, the advantages and applications of this kind of dryer have been discussed by Christiansen and Sardo (2001).

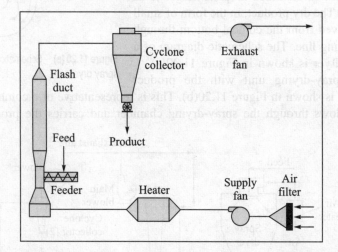

Figure 11.19 Schematic of a flash drying unit (Christiansen and Sardo, 2001).

11.11.2 Fluidized-bed Dryer

Free-flowing moist solids are sometimes dried in a fluidized-bed dryer. The working principle is simple. The solid is fed continuously into the dryer by a screw feeder and is kept fluidized by the stream of hot drying gas. The dry product is also continuously removed through a nozzle at an appropriate location. The fines carried over by the gas are separated in a cyclone separator or a bag filter. A fluid-bed dryer is widely used to dry a variety of materials such as minerals, pharmaceuticals, seeds, cereals, grains, spices, potato flakes, fish meal, waste materials, etc.

11.11.3 Spray Dryers

As the name indicates, a spray dryer is used to dry the atomized droplets of a feed that may be a solution or a slurry of fine particles. It consists of a big drying chamber (may be even 15 m diameter and 35 m tall) in which the feed is introduced through an atomizer at the top. The hot gas is introduced either at the top or at the bottom (the gas flow is accordingly called cocurrent or countercurrent). The hot gas temperature may be as high as 700°C but normally it is kept within 250–280°C. Drying of the droplets dispersed in the hot gas occurs in a very short contact time of a few seconds. Atomization of the feed is done by a rotating disk, a high pressure nozzle or a two-fluid nozzle. A rotating or whirling disk is preferred in the chemical industry. The liquid or slurry is fed onto the disk at the centre which is centrifugally accelerated and then ejected from the periphery of the disk at a speed of 80–200 m/s. The disk may be plane or vaned, its velocity ranges from 3000 to 20,000 rpm. Even the slurry of an abrasive solid or a paste can be atomized by using a whirling disk without erosion. It is also considerably flexible with respect to feed rate and properties. The size of atomized droplets ranges from 10 to 20 microns. The dry product, in the form of small particles, is removed from the conical bottom through a product conveying line. The schematic diagram of a cocurrent spray dryer is shown in Figure 11.20(a).

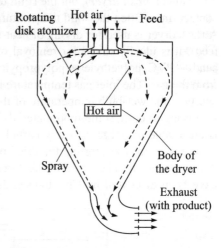

Figure 11.20 (a)   Schematic diagram of a cocurrent spray dryer.

A typical spray-drying unit with the product collection system is shown in Figure 11.20(b). This is representative of a commercial unit. The hot drying gas flows through the spray-drying chamber and carries the product to the first

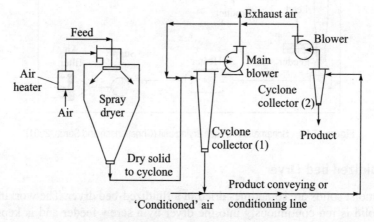

Figure 11.20 (b)   A spray drying unit.

cyclone separator. If necessary, a secondary stream of air (or gas) of controlled humidity is used to convey the product out of the cyclone. The product cools down in contact with the conveying gas and is separated in a second cyclone. The conveying gas is then led to the first cyclone along with the drying gas (that comes out of the spray chamber and is laden with product particles), and is ultimately vented out. Mixing of the gas streams in cyclone-1 helps in product cooling. Bag filters are sometimes used in series with the cyclone separator for better separation of the fines.

Because of the very short contact time between the droplets and the drying gas, a spray dryer is suitable for drying heat-sensitive materials. It is also used to dry a variety of other liquids. Typical examples are: milk ($d_p \sim 60\ \mu$m), egg, coffee ($d_p \sim 300\ \mu$m), tea, tannin, some polymeric resins pharmaceuticals, organic and inorganic chemicals, soap, detergent, etc.

The dryers described above are the more common types. Many other dryers are in use for specific purposes and may not use a drying gas for supply of heat and carrying away the vapour. For example, a 'microwave dryer' uses long wavelength radiation of the order of radio waves. The material is heated throughout by the radiation that penetrates into it. Applications range from binding and drying wood and plywood to textile skeins, food products, and pharmaceuticals. The technique is expensive but ensures uniform drying (in an inert, isolated atmosphere) and good product quality. ·

11.12 DRYING CALCULATIONS

We discussed in Section 11.5 how the time of drying of a solid from a given initial moisture content to a desired final moisture can be calculated if we have the following data: (i) experimental drying rate in the constant rate period N_c, (ii) the nature of dependence of the falling rate of drying on the moisture content, and (iii) the critical and the equilibrium moisture content X_c and X^*. The experimental drying data need to be collected under similar conditions.

It is nevertheless possible to calculate the drying rate and the drying time under a given set of conditions using the well-known principles of heat and mass transfer. Such calculations are not always accurate enough for the purpose of design of dryers because of limitations of the correlations used and the simplifying assumptions made (Nonhebel and Moss, 1971; Williams-Gardener, 1971). But these give at least an approximate idea of the drying rate and the drying time for a preliminary design. In most cases, the design of a dryer is still done on the basis of data from a pilot unit of a full-scale existing equipment. We discuss below the application of the basic heat and mass transfer principles to drying calculations and dryer design.

11.12.1 Cross-circulation Drying

As stated before, the flow of the drying gas over the wet material on the trays in a tray dryer is called *cross-flow*. The gas enters at one end of a tray, flows over the material while supplying heat to the solid and picking up moisture in return, and leaves at the other end. This is schematically shown in Figure 11.21. Some of the notations used are also shown in the figure. The dry-bulb temperature of the drying gas at the inlet to a tray is T_{Gi} and its humidity[†] is Y_i (the subscript

---

[†] The notation Y stands for the humidity of the gas in terms of (kg moisture)/(kg dry gas). It is the same as Y' in Chapter 10.

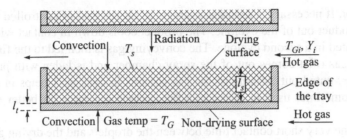

Figure 11.21   Cross-circulation drying in a tray dryer.

i means inlet). The temperature of the solid is T_s and the corresponding saturation humidity is Y_s. Heat transfer from the drying gas to the wet solid occurs mainly by convection at the top open surface (we call it the *drying surface*). Some amount of heat transfer to the drying surface also occurs through the tray wall and conduction through the wet solid and possibly by radiation from the upper tray surface. The overall heat transfer coefficient can be obtained as follows.

Convective heat transfer coefficient at the tray bottom (this is a *non-drying surface*) = h_c

Thickness of the wet solid layer = l_s;   thermal conductivity = k_s

The combined coefficient h_b for heat transfer to the drying surface from the tray bottom is given by

$$\frac{1}{h_b} = \frac{1}{h_c} + \frac{l_s}{k_s} \quad \Rightarrow \quad h_b = \frac{h_c k_s}{k_s + h_c l_s} \tag{11.6}$$

Here the thermal resistance of the tray wall has been neglected since it is very small for all practical purposes. If we take into account the area of the edges of the tray, the heat transfer area of the non-drying surface is a little larger than that of the drying surface. Heat gain by radiation has not been included in the above equation. However, this factor is illustrated in Example 11.3.

Case I — *The temperature and humidity of the drying gas remain constant:*   If the gas flow rate is *high*, its temperature and humidity may be assumed to remain reasonably constant over a tray. The combined heat flux at the drying surface (including that from the tray bottom), $q = (h_c + h_b)(T_i - T_s)$ and the mass flux or drying rate, $N_c = k_Y(Y_s - Y_i)$. If λ_w = heat of vaporization of water (kJ/kg), the fluxes are to be related as

$$N_c = k_Y(Y_s - Y_i) = (h_c + h_b)(T_{Gi} - T_s)/\lambda_w \quad \Rightarrow \quad \frac{(Y_s - Y_i)\lambda_w}{h_c/k_Y} = \left(1 + \frac{h_b}{h_c}\right)(T_{Gi} - T_s) \tag{11.7}$$

The quantity h_c/k_Y is approximately equal to the humid heat of water, c_H (see Chapter 10). The equation has two unknowns (T_s and Y_s). It can be solved in combination with the saturation humidity-temperature relation for water graphically or by trial-and-error (see Example 11.3). The constant drying rate [$N_c = k_Y(Y_s - Y_i)$], for the removal of the bound moisture can be calculated easily. If W_s is the weight of 'bone dry' solid and a is the area of the drying surface, the constant rate drying period t_c is

$$t_c = \frac{W_s(X_i - X_c)}{a N_c} \qquad (X_i = \text{initial moisture}, X_c = \text{critical moisture}) \tag{11.8}$$

A simple equation for the falling rate drying time can now be determined (i) if the drying rate decreases linearly with the moisture content and (ii) if 'unsaturated surface drying' occurs. The latter condition means that dry patches appear on the surface, which grow in size with time. Drying occurs *predominantly* from the moist areas on the surface. The temperature of the wet surface is given by Eq. (11.7) as before. The length of the falling rate period can be written like the second term on the right-side of Eq. (11.5).

From Eqs. (11.5) and (11.7),

$$t_f = \frac{W_s}{a} \frac{X_c - X^*}{N_c} \ln \frac{X_c - X^*}{X_f - X^*} = \frac{W_s}{a} \frac{X_c - X^*}{k_Y(Y_s - Y_i)} \ln \frac{X_c - X^*}{X_f - X^*}$$

$$= \frac{W_s}{a} \frac{\lambda_w(X_c - X^*)}{(h_b + h_c)(T_{Gi} - T_s)} \ln \frac{X_c - X^*}{X_f - X^*} \tag{11.9}$$

The total drying time per batch is $t = t_c + t_f + t_d$, where t_d is the 'downtime' (the time required for loading and unloading of the trays in the dryer). It is to be noted that if heat transfer from the tray bottom to the solid surface by conduction is neglected (i.e. h_b is pretty small), T_s is essentially the same as the wet-bulb temperature of the drying air. Heat transfer to the solid by radiation may also occur in some designs. Example 11.3 illustrates this.

Case 2 — *The temperature and humidity of the gas vary along the tray:* In the analysis of the drying rate given under Case 1, we have tacitly assumed that the temperature and humidity of the drying gas remain essentially constant over a tray. This assumption holds good if the gas flow rate is pretty high. If not, the gas temperature decreases and its humidity increases in the direction of gas flow. As a result, the temperature and concentration driving forces change and the drying rate also varies along the tray. The drying rate will be the highest at the inlet to the open space above a tray and the minimum at the exit from a tray . A theoretical analysis of the changing rate of drying along a tray is done below by making a differential heat balance over a thin strip of the solid layer on a tray.

Let b be the breadth of a tray and w be the gap between two adjacent trays for gas flow. The cross-section for gas flow is $b.w$ and the total gas flow rate over a tray is $G'_s.b.w$ (kg/s) where G'_s [++] is the mass flow rate of the gas on dry basis [kg dry air/(m^2·s)]. The specific heat (humid heat) of the gas is c_H. Let us refer to Figure 11.22 and note the other symbols used therein: z = the local distance from the gas-inlet end of the tray; T_G = local temperature of the gas; T_s = surface temperature of the solid; l_s = thickness of the solid. An amount of heat dQ is transferred from the gas to the solid over a thin strip of area $b.dz$. The gas temperature drops by dT_G as a result. The following heat balance equation may be written.

$$dQ = -G'_s(bw)c_H \, dT_G = h_c b \, dz (T_G - T_s) \tag{11.10}$$

Since we have neglected heat transfer by conduction through the tray bottom, the solid temperature T_s is the same as the wet-bulb temperature or the 'adiabatic saturation temperature'. It remains unchanged even when the gas temperature and humidity change along the tray. Equation (11.10) can be integrated from the inlet gas temperature T_{Gi} to the outlet temperature

---

[++]Notation for gas flow rates: G, G_s = gas flow rate, total and moisture-free basis respectively, kg/h; G', G'_s = gas flow rate per unit area, total and moisture-free basis respectively, kg/h·m^2.

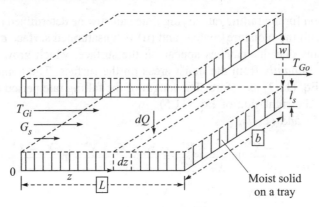

Figure 11.22   A thin strip on the drying surface.

T_{Go} over the length of the tray L.

$$-\int_{T_{Gi}}^{T_{Go}} \frac{dT_G}{T_G - T_s} = \frac{h_c}{G'_s \, w \, c_H} \int_0^L dz \quad \Rightarrow \quad \ln \frac{T_{Gi} - T_s}{T_{Go} - T_s} = \frac{h_c \, L}{G'_s \, w \, c_H}$$

$\Rightarrow \qquad\qquad L = \left(\dfrac{G'_s w c_H}{h_c}\right) \ln \dfrac{T_{Gi} - T_s}{T_{Go} - T_s} = (H_{tG})_h \, (N_{tG})_h \qquad\qquad (11.11)$

where $\qquad \ln \dfrac{T_{Go} - T_s}{T_{Gi} - T_s} = (N_{tG})_h \quad$ and $\quad \dfrac{G'_s \, w \, c_H}{h_c} = (H_{tG})_h \qquad\qquad (11.12)$

Note that $(N_{tG})_h$ = number of gas-phase heat transfer units, and $(H_{tG})_h$ = length of a gas-phase heat transfer unit. The product of these two quantities is the length of the tray [see Eq. (11.11) above]. From Eq. (11.11),

$$1 - \frac{T_{Gi} - T_{Go}}{T_{Gi} - T_s} = \exp[-L/(H_{tG})_h]$$

$\Rightarrow \qquad\qquad T_{Gi} - T_{Go} = (T_{Gi} - T_s)(1 - \exp[-L/(H_{tG})_h]) \qquad\qquad (11.13)$

The rate of heat transfer to the solid = $Q = G'_s(bw) \, c_H (T_{Gi} - T_{Go})$; area of the tray, $a = bL$
The average rate of vaporization of moisture per unit drying area = $Q/a\lambda_w$

Determination of the constant rate drying time

Rate of drying in the constant rate period, $N_c = \dfrac{Q}{a\lambda_w} = \dfrac{G_s(bw)c_H(T_{Gi} - T_{Go})}{a\lambda_w}$

The quantity of 'unbound moisture' to be removed during the constant rate period,
$M_c = al_s(\rho_s)(X_i - X_c) = W_s(X_i - X_c)$; $a \cdot l_s$ = volume of the solid; ρ_s = bulk density of the solid (dry basis).
Drying time for the removal of unbound moisture (i.e. the *constant rate drying time*),

$$t_c = \frac{M_c}{a N_c} = \frac{a(l_s)(\rho_s)(X_i - X_c)(\lambda_w)}{G'_s \, bw c_H(T_{Go} - T_{Gi})}$$

$$= \frac{W_s(X_i - X_s)\lambda_w}{bw\,G'_s\,c_H(T_{Gi} - T_s)(1 - \exp[-L/(H_{tG})_h])} \tag{11.14}$$

The drying time for the falling rate period can be determined following the usual procedure. If we assume that the falling rate of drying is proportional to $(X - X^*)$, $X \leq X_c$, the falling rate time of drying is

$$t_f = \frac{W_s}{a}\,\frac{X_c - X^*}{N_c}\,\ln\frac{X_c - X^*}{X_f - X^*}$$

$$= \frac{W_s(X_c - X^*)\lambda_w}{bw\,G'_s\,c_H(T_{Gi} - T_s)(1 - \exp[-L/(H_{tG})_h])}\,\ln\frac{X_c - X^*}{X_f - X^*} \tag{11.15}$$

The value of the forced convection heat transfer coefficient h_c is required for using the above equations for calculation of the rate or time of drying. A correlation for the Nusselt number for boundary layer heat transfer over a flat plate is not quite appropriate since the flow channel has a rather narrow width and the surface of the wet solid is not at all smooth. The following empirical correlation may be used to estimate the heat transfer coefficient h_c.

$$h_c = 0.0204(G')^{0.8} \quad \text{where } G' \text{ is in kg/h·m}^2 \text{ and } h_c \text{ is in W/m}^2\text{·K} \tag{11.16}$$

EXAMPLE 11.2 (*Cross-circulation drying of a granular material*)   A granular wet solid is taken on a tray (1 m × 0.6 m) and dried in a stream of hot air (120°C; humidity = 0.02 kg per kg dry air; velocity, u = 4.5 m/s). The initial moisture content of 28% (dry basis) is to be reduced to 0.5%. From laboratory tests it is known that the critical moisture content is 12% and the equilibrium moisture is negligible. The falling rate of drying is linear in the moisture content. If the solid loading (dry basis) is 35 kg/m^2, calculate the drying time. Assume that the air flow is 'large' and its temperature drop across the tray is 'small'.

Solution
The convective heat transfer coefficient h_c is to be calculated first to find out the constant rate drying. It is *assumed* that heat transfer and drying occur at the top open surface only (i.e. no conduction or radiation).

Air temperature (assumed constant), T_G = 120°C = 393 K; pressure = 1 atm.

Using the ideal gas law, humid volume of air for Y_G = 0.02 is

$$v_H = \frac{RT_G}{P}\left(\frac{1}{29} + \frac{1}{18}\right) = \frac{(0.0821)(393)}{1.0}\left(\frac{1}{29} + \frac{1}{18}\right) = 1.148 \text{ m}^3/(\text{kg dry air})$$

Density of air, ρ_G = 1.02/1.148 = 0.888 kg/m^3
Mass flow rate of the gas, G' = $u\rho_G$ = (4.5)(3600)(0.888) = 14,386 kg/m^2·h
Use Eq. (11.16) to calculate the heat transfer coefficient,

$$h_c = 0.0204(G')^{0.8} = (0.0204)(14,386)^{0.8} = 43.3 \text{ W/m}^2\text{·K}$$

Temperature of the solid in the constant rate period = adiabatic saturation temperature of air (at T_G = 120°C; humidity, Y_G = 0.02); wet-bulb temperature of air, T_w = 41.5°C = T_s; saturation humidity at 41.5°C, Y_s = 0.0545 kg/(kg dry air). The temperature of the air is *assumed* constant.

Constant drying rate, $N_c = \dfrac{h_c(T_G - T_w)}{\lambda_w} = \dfrac{(43.3)(120 - 41.5)}{(2400)(1000)} = 1.412 \times 10^{-3}$ kg/m^2·s

$$= 5.08 \text{ kg/m}^2 \cdot \text{h}$$

Given moisture contents: $X_i = 0.28$; $X_c = 0.12$; $X^* = 0$; $X_f = 0.005$; solid loading, $W_s/a = 35$ kg/m^2.

Unbound moisture to be removed $= (W_s/a)(X_i - X_c) = (35 \text{ kg/m}^2)(0.28 - 0.12) = 5.6$ kg/m^2

Constant rate drying time, $t_c = (5.6 \text{ kg/m}^2)/N_c = (5.6 \text{ kg/m}^2)/(5.08 \text{ kg/m}^2 \cdot \text{h}) = 1.102$ h

Falling rate drying time [see Eq. (11.5)],

$$t_f = \frac{W_s}{a} \frac{X_c - X^*}{N_c} \ln \frac{X_c - X^*}{X_f - X^*} = (35)\left(\frac{0.12 - 0}{5.08}\right) \ln\left(\frac{0.12 - 0}{0.005 - 0}\right) = 2.627 \text{ h}$$

Total drying time $= t_c + t_f = 1.102 + 2.627 = \boxed{3.75 \text{ h}}$

EXAMPLE 11.3 (*Calculation of cross-circulation drying time; heat supply by convection and radiation*)   A wet solid is dried on a tray dryer (0.6 m × 0.7 m), the dimension of the tray in the direction of air flow being 0.6 m. Cross-flow of the drying air over the tray occurs (temperature = 110°C, humidity = 0.017, velocity = 3 m/s). The solid receives radiant heat from a heated plate at 250°C placed above it. The surface of the solid and the hot plate may be assumed to be in 'full view' of each other (this is reasonable since the gap between them is small). Also given: the solid layer thickness, $l_s = 2.5$ cm; thermal conductivity of the solid, $k_s = 0.3$ W/m·K; emissivity of the solid, $\varepsilon_s = 0.85$; thickness of the tray deck, $l_m = 2$ mm; thermal conductivity of the tray material, $k_m = 22$ W/m·K. Calculate the surface temperature of the solid and the constant rate of drying. State clearly any assumption made for solving the problem.

Solution

The following assumptions are made: (i) the temperature and humidity of the gas remain constant over the tray, and (ii) heat transfer to the solid through the edges of the tray is negligible.

Putting $T_G = 110°C = 383$ K and $Y_i = Y_G = 0\ 0.017$ in Eq. (10.6), humid volume of the gas, $v_H = 1.114$ m^3/(kg dry air).

Density of the gas, $\rho_G = 1.017/1.114 = 0.913$ kg/m^3; air velocity, $u = 3$ m/s; gas mass flow rate, $G' = u.\rho_G = (3)(0.913)(3600) = 9860$ kg/m^2·h

Calculate the convective heat transfer coefficient from Eq. (11.16):

$$h_c = (0.0204)(9860)^{0.8} = 32 \text{ W/m}^2 \cdot \text{K}$$

Since heat transfer occurs by conduction and radiation as well, the surface temperature T_s of the solid will be greater than the wet-bulb temperature of the gas. It can be calculated from the relation between the rates of heat and mass transfer as discussed before. Total heat gain by the solid occurs by a combination of *convection, conduction* and by *radiation*. To obtain the 'radiation heat transfer coefficient' we need to know the surface temperature which is in fact a quantity to be found out. So an *iterative approach* has to be adopted. We start with an assumed surface temperature of $T_s = 51°C$. This will be corrected if necessary after the first cycle of calculation.

Radiant surface temperature, $T_R = 250°C = 523$ K; view factor $= 1$; radiant heat flux $= \varepsilon_s \sigma(T_R^4 - T_s^4)$

Radiant heat transfer coefficient,

$$h_R = \frac{\varepsilon_s \sigma (T_R^4 - T_s^4)}{T_R - T_s} = \frac{(0.85)(5.669 \times 10^{-8})(523^4 - 324^4)}{523 - 324} = 15.3 \text{ W/m}^2 \cdot \text{K}$$

The effective coefficient of heat transfer through the bottom of the tray can be obtained from Eq. (11.16), considering the resistance of the metal wall as well.

$$\frac{1}{h_b} = \frac{1}{h_c} + \frac{l_m}{k_m} + \frac{l_s}{k_s} = \frac{1}{32} + \frac{0.002}{22} + \frac{0.025}{0.3}$$

$$= 0.0312 + 0.00091 + 0.0833 \Rightarrow h_b = 8.66 \text{ W/m}^2 \cdot \text{K}$$

[Note that the metallic tray deck offers a very small heat transfer resistance and could be neglected.]

Total heat flux, $q = (h_c + h_b)(T_G - T_s) + h_R(T_R - T_s) = N_c \cdot \lambda_w = k_Y(Y_s - Y_G)\lambda_w$

$$\Rightarrow \qquad \left(1 + \frac{h_b}{h_c}\right)(T_G - T_s) + \frac{h_R}{h_c}(T_R - T_s) = \frac{(Y_s - Y_G)\lambda_w}{h_c/k_Y}$$

$$\Rightarrow \qquad \left(1 + \frac{8.66}{32}\right)(110 - T_s) + \frac{15.3}{32}(250 - T_s) = \frac{(Y_s - 0.017)2380}{1.037} \frac{\text{kJ/kg}}{\text{kJ/kg} \cdot \text{K}}$$

$[h_c/k_Y = c_H = $ humid heat of the air $= 1.005 + (1.88)(0.017) = 1.037$ kJ/kg·K; $\lambda_w = 2380$ kJ/kg at 51°C]

$$\Rightarrow \qquad 2305(Y_s - 0.017) = 259.3 - 1.7486T_s \quad \Rightarrow \quad Y_s = 0.1295 - 0.00076T_s \qquad \text{(i)}$$

Y_s is the saturation humidity at temperature T_s. So Eq. (i) above has to be solved in combination with the saturation humidity curve by trial or graphically. The equation for the saturation humidity curve can be written using the vapour pressure equation of water.

$$\ln p^v = 11.96481 - \frac{3984.923}{T_s - 39.724}$$

$[p^v = $ vapour pressure of water in bar; $T_s = $ surface temp. in K] (ii)

Then saturation humidity of air at temperature T_s is

$$Y_s = \left(\frac{p^v}{1.013 - p^v}\right)\left(\frac{18}{29}\right) \tag{iii}$$

Equations (i), (ii) and (iii) are solved together graphically. The T_s–Y_s curve can be drawn from Eqs. (ii) and (iii). Equation (i) is plotted on the same graph; T_s and Y_s are obtained from the point of intersection. This is shown in Figure 11.23. The calculated data for the T_s–Y_s curve are given below.

T_s(°C)	44	46	48	50	52
p^v [at T_s, calculated from Eq. (ii)]	0.0901	0.09986	0.1105	0.1221	0.1348
Y_s [calculated from Eq. (iii)]	0.0606	0.0679	0.076	0.0851	0.0953

The solutions for T_s and Y_s are: $T_s = 51$°C; $Y_s = 0.0809$. (which is acceptable)

T_s is the same as assumed value. No further correction or iteration is necessary. The heat flux to the solid surface,

$$q = (8.66 + 32)(110 - 51) + (15.3)(250 - 51) = 5444 \text{ W/m}^2$$

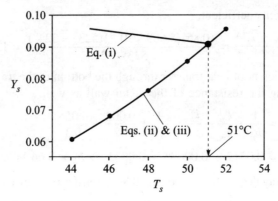

Figure 11.23 T_s–Y_s plots.

The constant drying rate,

$$N_c = \frac{q}{\lambda_w} = \frac{5444}{(2380)(1000)} \frac{\text{J/m}^2 \cdot \text{s}}{\text{J/kg}} = 2.287 \times 10^{-3} \text{ kg/m}^2 \cdot \text{s} \boxed{= 8.23 \text{ kg/m}^2 \cdot \text{h}}$$

11.12.2   Through-circulation Drying

In through-circulation drying, the hot drying gas flows through a shallow bed of the wet solid. Such a process occurs in a belt (or band or conveyer) dryer (Section 11.8.2) or even on a perforated-tray batch dryer. The hot air generally enters the bed at the top, flows through the wet solid, picks up moisture, and leaves at the bottom (flow may occur from bottom to the top as well). The rate of drying is maximum where the hot gas enters the bed at the beginning since the driving force (in terms of difference in temperature or in humidity) is the largest there. The rate of drying decreases along the direction of gas flow.

A simplified physical picture of the drying process is given in Figure 11.24 in which the bed is visualized to consist of three zones. As the flow of the hot gas starts, a region near the entry (zone I) loses moisture quickly and after some time this region will have bound moisture only. Since the gas entering zone II is already loaded with considerable amount of moisture picked up from zone I, the drying rate there is predictably lower. There will be little or no evaporation of moisture in zone III at the beginning. On the whole, the local moisture content in the bed increases along the direction of drying gas flow but the drying rate decreases. As drying proceeds, the lengths of the zones change. Zone I will have very little moisture left in it after some time. The thickness of this zone increases with time and removal of the bound moisture begins, but zones II and III shrink and eventually disappear. The phenomenon is qualitatively similar to desorption of a gas from a packed bed (Chapter 12). It

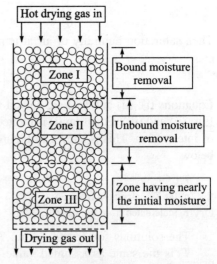

Figure 11.24   Three zones in the initial stages of 'through-circulation' drying.

should be remembered that no such zones exist in reality. In other words, the boundaries between zones are diffuse. We visualize the zones for the sake of explaining the mechanism of drying.

Here we develop simple equations for the determination of the rate of drying and the drying time for through-circulation drying of a bed. We consider a thin slice of the bed of unit cross-sectional area and of thickness dz. The mass transfer coefficient for moisture transport is k_Y and the drying area (i.e. the outer surface area of the particles) per unit bed volume is $\bar{a}$. If the increase in the humidity of the gas is dY as it passes through the thin slice of the bed, the following differential mass balance equation may be written (as before it is assumed that the solid is moist and is at the adiabatic saturation temperature of the drying gas).

$$G'_s dY = k_Y (\bar{a}\, dz)(Y_s - Y) \tag{11.17}$$

Here G'_s is the mass flow rate of the gas (kg/m^2·h, dry basis), and Y is its 'local' humidity of the bulk gas. If the humidity of the drying gas changes from Y_i(inlet) to Y_o(exit) across the bed of thickness l_s, the above equation may be integrated to the following form

$$\int_{Y_i}^{Y_o} \frac{dY}{Y_s - Y} = \int_0^{l_s} \frac{k_Y \bar{a}\, dz}{G'_s} = \frac{k_Y \bar{a}}{G'_s} l_s \Rightarrow \ln \frac{Y_s - Y_i}{Y_s - Y_o} = \frac{k_Y \bar{a}}{G'_s} l_s \tag{11.18a}$$

Let us call $\ln \dfrac{Y_s - Y_i}{Y_s - Y_o} = (N_{tG})_m$, $\dfrac{G'_s}{k_Y \bar{a}} = (H_{tG})_m$ and $(N_{tG})_m \cdot (H_{tG})_m = l_s$ = thickness of the bed.

Here

$(N_{tG})_m$ = 'number of gas-phase mass transfer units' for moisture transport

$(H_{tG})_m$ = 'height of a transfer unit'.

Equation [11.18(a)] may be rearranged as

$$\frac{Y_s - Y_o}{Y_s - Y_i} = \exp[-(N_{tG})_m] \Rightarrow 1 - \frac{Y_o - Y_i}{Y_s - Y_i} = \exp[-(N_{tG})_m]$$

$$\Rightarrow \qquad (Y_o - Y_i) = (Y_s - Y_i)(1 - \exp[-(N_{tG})_m]) \tag{11.18b}$$

Constant rate drying time: Consider 1 m^2 of bed cross-section. Bed volume = $(1.l_s)$ m^3; mass transfer area of the solid = $\bar{a}.l_s$ m^2.

If N_c is the constant drying rate,

$$\text{rate of mass transfer} = (\bar{a}\, l_s) N_c = G'_s (Y_o - Y_i) = G'_s (Y_s - Y_i)(1 - \exp[-(N_{tG})_m])$$

and

$$N_c = \frac{G'_s (Y_s - Y_i)}{\bar{a}\, l_s} [1 - \exp[-(N_{tG})_m]] \tag{11.19}$$

The moisture to be removed in the constant rate period per unit bed cross-section,

$$M_c = (1.l_s \cdot \rho_s)(X_i - X_c)$$

Drying time, $\qquad t_c = \dfrac{l_s \rho_s (X_i - X_c)}{(\bar{a}\, l_s) N_c} = \dfrac{l_s \rho_s (X_i - X_c)}{G'_s (Y_s - Y_i)[1 - \exp[-(N_{tG})_m]]} \tag{11.20}$

Falling rate drying time: This can be written following Eq. (11.5) if the falling rate of drying is linear in the concentration of bound moisture.

$$t_f = \frac{l_s \rho_s (X_c - X^*)}{G'_s (Y_s - Y_i)[1 - \exp[-(N_{tG})_m]]} \ln \frac{X_c - X^*}{X_f - X^*} \tag{11.21}$$

In the above analysis the moisture concentration in the bed at any instant has been implicitly assumed to remain uniform. This assumption is reasonable only for a thin bed.

Mass transfer correlations: In order to calculate the rate of drying by using the above equations, it is necessary to know either of the transport coefficients (the coefficient of heat transfer or mass transfer) or the height of a transfer unit. A few empirical correlations are available for this purpose.

For through-circulation drying in a shallow bed of wet solid (particle size 3 to 20 mm), the following approximate correlation for the height of a gas-phase mass transfer unit may be used.

$$(H_{tG})_m = l_s/(N_{tG})_m = G_s'/k_Y \bar{a} = 2.5(d_p G_s')^{0.41}/\bar{a} \tag{11.22}$$

The coefficient of heat transfer can be estimated by using either of these correlations.

$$h_c = 0.151(G')^{0.59}/(d_p)^{0.41} \qquad \text{for} \qquad d_p G'/\mu_G > 350 \tag{11.23}$$

$$h_c = 0.214 \, (G')^{0.49}/(d_p)^{0.51} \qquad \text{for} \qquad d_p G'/\mu_G < 350 \tag{11.24}$$

When G' (given as kg/m^2·h) changes appreciably along the bed, an average value may be used in any of the above equations. The above equations are applicable to a bed of spherical particles. In practice, particles are rarely spherical except probably for some catalyst pellets. An equivalent or effective diameter needs to be used for non-spherical particles. If the pellets are cylindrical of length l_c and diameter d_c, the effective diameter and specific surface area can be calculated by the following equations.

$$d_p = (d_c l_c + 0.5 d_c^2)^{1/2} \qquad \text{and} \qquad \bar{a} = [4(1 - \varepsilon)(l_c + 0.5 d_c)]/(d_c l_c)$$

EXAMPLE 11.4 (*Through-circulation drying of a wet solid*)   A bed of solid, 4 cm thick, containing moist pellets of average size 4 mm is to be dried by through-circulation of hot air (temperature = 120°C; humidity = 0.01 kg/(kg dry air); superficial velocity = 1 m/s). The initial moisture is 28%, the critical moisture is 12% and the equilibrium moisture is negligible. The falling rate of drying is linear in the moisture content. If the bed density is 750 kg/m^3 dry solid, and the surface area of the solid is 600 m^2/m^3 of bed volume, determine the time of drying of the material to 0.5% moisture. (All moistures are on dry basis.)

Solution

To select the correlation to be used for the estimation of the heat transfer coefficient, we need to evaluate the Reynolds number first. Take the thermophysical properties of air at the inlet temperature (120°C): density, $\rho_G = 0.888$ kg/m^3; $\mu_G = 2.2 \times 10^{-5}$ N·s/m^2; particle size, $d_p = 4$ mm = 0.004 m.

Particle Reynolds number, Re $= d_p V \rho_G/\mu_G = (0.004)(1.0)(0.888)/(2.2 \times 10^{-5}) = 161$

Use Eq. (11.24) to calculate the heat transfer coefficient,

$$h_c = 0.214(G)^{0.49}/(d_p^{0.51}) = (0.214)[(1.0)(0.888)(3600)]^{0.49}/(0.004)^{0.51}$$
$$= 186.5 \text{ W/m}^2 \cdot \text{K}$$

The wet-bulb temperature of the drying air ($T_{Gi} = 120$°C, $Y_i = 0.01$) is

$$T_w = 38°\text{C} = T_s$$

Heat of vaporization of water at 38°C, $\lambda_w = 2400$ kJ/kg; saturation humidity, $Y_s = 0.0445$

Assume $h_c/k_Y = c_H$ = humid heat of the drying air

$$= (1.005 + 1.88Y) = [(1.005) + (1.88)(0.01)] \text{ kJ/kg·K} = 1043 \text{ J/kg·K}$$

$$\Rightarrow \qquad k_Y = h_c/c_H = (186.5 \text{ W/m}^2\text{·K})/(1043 \text{ J/kg·K}) = 0.179 \text{ kg/m}^2\text{·s}$$

Given: $\bar{a} = 600 \text{ m}^2/\text{m}^3$; bed thickness, $l_s = 4 \text{ cm} = 0.04 \text{ m}$; $X_i = 0.28$; $X_c = 0.12$; $X^* = 0$; $X_f = 0.005$

The number of mass transfer units,

$$(N_{tG})_m = \frac{k_Y \bar{a}}{G_s'} l_s = \frac{(0.179)(600)}{(1.0)(0.888)}(0.04) = 4.84$$

From Eq. [11.18(b)],

$$(Y_o - Y_i) = (Y_s - Y_i)(1 - \exp[-(N_{tG})_m])$$

$$= (0.0445 - 0.01)[1 - \exp(-4.84)] = 0.03423 \text{ kg/(kg dry air)}$$

Rate of moisture removal in the constant rate period

$$N_c = G_s'(Y_o - Y_i) = [(1.0)(0.888)(3600)](0.03423)$$

$$= 109 \text{ kg/(m}^2 \text{ tray area)(h)}$$

Solid loading in the bed (kg dry solid per m^2 tray area)

$$= (1 \text{ m}^2)(0.04 \text{ m})(750 \text{ kg/m}^3) = 30 \text{ kg/m}^2$$

The constant rate drying period, $t_c = (30)(0.28 - 0.12)/(109) = 0.044 \text{ h}$

The falling rate drying period,

$$t_f = \frac{W_s}{a} \frac{(X_c - X^*)}{N_c} \ln \frac{X_c - X^*}{X_f - X^*}$$

$$= (30) \frac{0.12 - 0}{109} \ln \frac{0.12 - 0}{0.005 - 0} = 0.105 \text{ h}$$

Total drying time, $t = t_c + t_f = 0.044 + 0.105 = 0.149 \text{ h} = \boxed{9 \text{ min}}$

11.12.3 Material and Energy Balances in Continuous Dryers

Material and energy balances are integral parts of design calculations of all kinds of dryers including the continuous dryers. Let us refer to Figure 11.25 showing the flow rates and enthalpies of the gas and the solid streams entering or leaving a continuous countercurrent dryer.

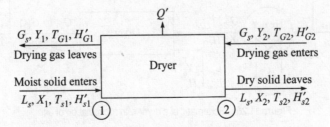

Figure 11.25 Input and output streams in a continuous dryer.

Here G_s = flow rate of air (dry basis, kg/h); L_s = flow rate of the solid (kg/h, dry basis); H = humidity of air [(kg H_2O)/(kg dry air)]; Q' = rate of heat lost (kJ/h).

Material balance equation: $G_sY_2 + L_sX_1 = G_sY_1 + L_sX_2$ (11.25)

Energy balance equation: In order to write down the energy balance equation, the heat contents of the gas and the solid streams are to be expressed with respect to a reference or datum temperature. If H'_s denotes the enthalpy of the solid (kJ per kg dry solid) and H'_G, that of the gas (kJ per kg dry gas),

$$G_sH'_{G2} + L_sH'_{s1} = G_sH'_{G1} + L_sH'_{s2} + Q'$$ (11.26)

Taking T_0 as the reference temperature, the enthalpies of the gas and the solid streams are:

$$H'_s = c_{ps}(T_s - T_0) + Xc_{pl}(T_s - T_0) = c_{ps}(T_s - T_0) + 4.187X(T_s - T_0)$$ (11.27)

$$H'_G = c_{pG}(T_G - T_0) + Yc_{pv}(T_G - T_0) + Y\lambda_w$$

$$= (1.005)(T_G - T_0) + 1.88Y(T_G - T_0) + 2500Y$$ (11.28)

where c_{ps}, c_{pl}, c_{pG}, c_{pv} are specific heats of the solid, the liquid (water), the dry gas (air), and of the vapour (water vapour) respectively (in kJ/kg·K); λ_w = heat of vaporization of water at the reference temperature = 2500 kJ/kg (at the reference temperature $T_0 = 273$ K).

EXAMPLE 11.5 (*Material and energy balance on a continuous dryer with air recirculation*)   A non-hygroscopic filter cake is to be dried in a continuous countercurrent dryer from 30% moisture to 2% moisture (wet basis) at a rate of 1000 kg per hour. The material enters the dryer at 27°C and leaves at 52°C. Fresh air is mixed with a part of the moist air leaving the dryer and heated to a temperature of 120°C in a finned air heater using low pressure steam (4 kg/cm², gauge). Calculate (a) the rate of flow of fresh air, (b) the fraction of the air leaving the dryer that is recycled, (c) the theoretical steam requirement, and (d) the heat loss from the dryer, if any. The following data and information are given: temperature of fresh air = 29°C; humidity = 0.018 kg/(kg dry air); humidity of the air leaving the heater = 0.03 kg/kg; humidity and temperature of the air leaving the dryer = 0.05 kg/kg, 70°C; specific heat of the dry solid = 920 J/kg·K.

Solution

The material and energy flow diagram of the drying system is shown in Figure 11.26.

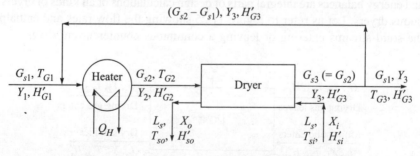

Figure 11.26   Schematic of a dryer with recirculation of air.

We have:
$$T_{G1} = 29°C, \quad Y_1 = 0.018, \quad H'_{G1} = 75.13$$
$$T_{G2} = 120°C, \quad Y_2 = 0.03, \quad H'_{G2} = 202.4$$
$$T_{G3} = 70°C, \quad Y_3 = 0.05, \quad H'_{G3} = 201.93 \text{ kJ/kg}$$

[Calculation of the enthalpy values are shown below.]

Basis of calculation: 1 h operation

Mass of the solid (dry basis), $\quad L_s = 1000(1 - 0.3) = 700$ kg
$$X_i = (1000)(0.3)/700 = 0.429$$
$$X_o = 0.02/0.98 = 0.0204$$

Specific heat of the dry solid, $c_{ps} = 0.92$ kJ/kg·K; $\quad T_{si} = 27°C; \quad T_{so} = 52°C$
$$H'_{si} = 73.26 \text{ kJ/kg}; \quad H'_{so} = 52.27 \text{ kJ/kg}$$

Calculation of enthalpy values (reference temperature = 0°C):

$$H'_{si} = [c_{ps} + (X_i)(4.18)](T_{si} - 0) = [0.92 + (0.429)(4.18)](27 - 0)$$
$$= 73.26 \text{ kJ/(kg dry solid)}$$

$$H'_{so} = [c_{ps} + (X_o)(4.18)](T_{so} - 0) = [0.92 + (0.0204)(4.18)](52 - 0)$$
$$= 52.27 \text{ kJ/(kg dry solid)}$$

$$H'_{G1} = [1.005 + (1.88)Y_1](T_{G1} - 0) + 2500Y_1$$
$$= [1.005 + (1.88)(0.018)](29 - 0) + (0.018)(2500) = 75.13 \text{ kJ/kg}$$

$$H'_{G2} = 1.005 + (1.88)(0.03)](120 - 0) + (0.03)(2500) = 202.4 \text{ kJ/(kg dry air)}$$

$$H'_{G3} = 1.005 + (1.88)(0.05)](70 - 0) + (0.05)(2500) = 201.93 \text{ kJ/kg}$$

Material balance of moisture over the dryer

$$G_{s2}(Y_3 - Y_2) = L_s(X_i - X_o) \Rightarrow G_{s2}(0.05 - 0.03) = 700(0.429 - 0.0204) = 286.02$$
$$\Rightarrow \qquad\qquad G_{s2} = 14,301 \text{ kg dry air}$$

(a) and (b) Fresh air rate (G_{s1}) and the fraction of air recycled

The material balance of water at the heater inlet is

$$G_{s1}Y_1 + (G_{s2} - G_{s1})Y_3 = G_{s2}Y_2 \Rightarrow G_{s1}(0.018) + (14,301 - G_{s1})(0.05) = (14,301)(0.03)$$
$$\Rightarrow \qquad (0.018)G_{s1} - (G_{s1})(0.05) + 286.02 = 0 \Rightarrow G_{s1} = 8938 \text{ kg dry air}$$

Air recycled, dry basis = $G_{s2} - G_{s1} = 14,301 - 8938 = \boxed{5363 \text{ kg/h}}$

Fraction of the air from the dryer recycled = $5363/14,301 = \boxed{37.5\%}$

(c) Theoretical steam requirement

We make an energy balance over the air heater as

$$G_{s1}H'_{G1} + (G_{s2} - G_{s1})H'_{G3} + Q_H = G_{s2}H'_{G2}$$
$$\Rightarrow \qquad (8938)(75.13) + (14,301 - 8938)(201.93) + Q_H = (14,301)(202.4)$$

$\Rightarrow$ $$Q_H = 1.14 \times 10^6 \text{ kJ/h}$$

Latent heat of steam at 4 kg/cm^2 gauge, $\lambda_w = 2110$ kJ/kg

$$\text{Steam requirement} = Q_H/\lambda_w = (1.14 \times 10^6 \text{ kJ/h})/(2110 \text{ kJ/kg})$$

$$= \boxed{540 \text{ kg/h}}$$

(d) Calculation of heat loss: Energy balance over the dryer is made as

$$G_{s2}H'_{G2} + L'_s H'_{si} = G_{s2}H'_{G3} + L_s H'_{so} + Q_D$$

$$(14{,}301)(202.4) + (700)(73.26) = (14{,}301)(201.93) + (700)(52.27) + Q_D$$

$\Rightarrow$ $$Q_D = \boxed{21{,}410 \text{ kJ/h}}$$

11.12.4 Drying Time in a Continuous Countercurrent Dryer

For the purpose of mass and heat transfer calculations as well as for calculation of drying time, a continuous countercurrent dryer can be considered to consist of a few zones. Refer to Figure 11.27 in which the dryer has been divided into three zones (compare with Figure 11.15 for a rotary dryer).

Wet solid enters zone I at a rate of L_s kg/h (dry basis) and the hot gas enters at the opposite end of the dryer. The temperature, the moisture content and the enthalpy of the gas and of the solid at the boundaries between the zones are shown in the figure. Drying occurs in zones I and II, while heating of the dry solid, if necessary, occurs in zone III. The whole surface of the solid remains moist over zone I (as it happens during the constant rate drying period in a batch equipment). The critical moisture content X_c is reached at the boundary 2. Dry patches appear on the surface (unsaturated surface drying) while the solid passes through zone II, and the fraction of surface covered by the patches increases as the solid advances. This is comparable with batch drying in the falling rate period. The drying rate depends upon the moisture content of the solid in this zone. The solid has a rather small concentration of moisture at the boundary 3. In zone III, it is just heated to the desired outlet temperature; virtually no drying takes place. The solid temperature is assumed to be at the wet-bulb temperature of the gas over zones I and II. It is to be noted that in some cases it may take some time for the feed solid to get warmed up to the wet-bulb temperature. If it is so, another zone has to be considered. This is neglected in the following analysis since this time is usually small. The surface area of drying is a' m^2/(kg dry solid).

Zone III: We follow the notations given in Figure 11.27. The terminal conditions (temperature and moisture content) of the two streams are either given or can be obtained by overall material and energy balance. The heat load Q_3 for raising the temperature of the 'dry solid' from T_{s3} ($= T_w$) to T_{s4} and the temperature driving forces at the boundaries are:

$$Q_3 = L_s c_{ps}(T_{s4} - T_{s3}); \quad (\Delta T)_3 = T_{G3} - T_{s3}; \quad (\Delta T)_4 = T_{G4} - T_{s4} \tag{11.29}$$

If $(\Delta T)_m$ is the log-mean temperature difference, the heating time in this zone is given by

$$t_{\text{III}} = \frac{Q_3}{(L_s a') h_c (\Delta T)_m} \tag{11.30}$$

Both the temperatures T_{s3} and T_{G3} at the boundary 3 are unknown. The energy balance equation, Eq. (11.31) given below is not sufficient to calculate both the temperatures. However, the humidity of the gas remains the same over the zone since no moisture removal occurs ($Y_3 = Y_4$). It is also known that T_{s3} is the wet-bulb temperature corresponding to the gas at temperature T_{G3} and humidity Y_3. Given these conditions, we start with a *guess value* of T_{s3} ($= T_w$) and calculate H'_{G3}, and therefrom the gas temperature T_{G3}, and check if the corresponding wet-bulb temperature matches the assumed T_{s3}. This is a trial-and-error procedure.

$$G_s(H'_{G4} - H'_{G3}) = L_s(H'_{s4} - H'_{s3}) \tag{11.31}$$

Zone I: For convenience of theoretical analysis, we calculate the drying time for this zone before that of zone II. Since the moisture content of the solid changes from X_1 to X_c and the condition of the gas at boundary 1 is known, the humidity of the gas at boundary 2 (Y_2) can be calculated by a moisture balance. The solid is at the wet-bulb temperature and the corresponding saturation humidity is Y_s. If the local humidity of the gas is Y, then the local drying rate N is given by

$$N = k_Y(Y_s - Y) = -\frac{L_s}{L_s a'}\frac{dX}{dt} \quad \left[\frac{L_s}{L_s a'} \text{ is equivalent to } \frac{W_s}{a} \text{ in Eq. (11.2)}\right] \tag{11.32}$$

Putting $L_s\, dX = G_s\, dY$, and integrating over the zone, the drying time t_I can be obtained.

$$t_I = \frac{G_s}{k_Y(L_s a')} \int_{Y_2}^{Y_1} \frac{dY}{Y_s - Y} = \frac{G_s}{k_Y(L_s a')} \ln \frac{Y_s - Y_2}{Y_s - Y_1} \tag{11.33}$$

Zone II: The moisture content of the solid is below the critical moisture ($X < X_c$) over this zone and the drying rate depends upon X. We assume that the drying rate is proportional to the free moisture, i.e. ($X - X^*$).

$$N = k_Y(Y_s - Y)\frac{X - X^*}{X_c - X^*} = -\frac{L_s}{L_s a'}\frac{dX}{dt} = \frac{G_s}{L_s a'}\frac{dY}{dt} \tag{11.34}$$

$\Rightarrow$ Drying time, $\quad t_{II} = \dfrac{G_s(X_c - X^*)}{(L_s a')k_Y} \displaystyle\int_{Y_3}^{Y_2} \dfrac{dY}{(Y_s - Y)(X - X^*)} \tag{11.35}$

To integrate, we can express X in terms of Y by writing the following moisture balance.

$$L_s(X - X_4) = G_s(Y - Y_4) \quad \Rightarrow \quad X = X_4 + (G_s/L_s)(Y - Y_4) \tag{11.36}$$

$\Rightarrow$ Drying time, $\quad t_{II} = \dfrac{G_s(X_c - X^*)}{(L_s a')k_Y} \displaystyle\int_{Y_3}^{Y_2} \dfrac{dY}{(Y_s - Y)[(X_4 - X^*) + (G_s/L_s)(Y - Y_4)]}$

If $X^* \approx 0$, drying time, $\quad t_{II} = \dfrac{G_s X_c}{(L_s a')k_Y} \dfrac{1}{X_4 + (G_s/L_s)(Y_s - Y_4)} \ln \dfrac{X_c(Y_s - Y_3)}{X_4(Y_s - Y_2)} \tag{11.37}$

The above simple analysis of a countercurrent continuous dryer can be used for many design calculations with necessary modification.

EXAMPLE 11.6 (*Drying time in a continuous counterflow dryer*)   A wet solid having 25% moisture is to be dried at a rate of 1000 kg/h to 1% moisture in a continuous countercurrent dryer. The drying air enters at 100°C at a rate of 12,000 kg/h (dry basis) with a humidity of 0.025 kg per kg dry air and the dry solid leaves at 60°C. The temperature of the wet solid entering the dryer is nearly the same as the adiabatic saturation temperature of the air leaving the dryer. Following data and information are available: gas-phase mass transfer coefficient for drying of the solid, $k_Y = 150$ kg/m^2·h; effective surface area of the solid = 0.065 m^2/kg dry solid; specific heat of the solid, $c_{ps} = 0.96$ kJ/kg K; critical moisture of the solid is 8%; the equilibrium moisture is negligible. All moistures are on wet basis. Calculate the drying time.

Solution

The dryer may be considered to consist of three zones: zone I—removal of moisture above X_c; zone II—removal of moisture below X_c; zone III—heating of the solid to its exit temperature of 60°C. The solid remains at the adiabatic saturation temperature of the drying gas in zones I and II.

Refer to Figure 11.27. *Given:* wet solid entering = 1000 kg/h; dry solid entering, $L_s = 1000$ $(1 - 0.25) = 750$ kg/h; $X_1 = 25/75 = 0.333$; $X_4 (= X_3) = 1/99 = 0.0101$; $X_c = 0.08/0.92 = 0.087$; $X^* \approx 0$; $G_s = 12{,}000$ kg/h (dry basis); $T_{G4} = 100$°C; $Y_4 (= Y_3) = 0.025$; $T_{s4} = 60$°C; $c_{ps} = 0.96$ kJ/(kg dry solid)(K).

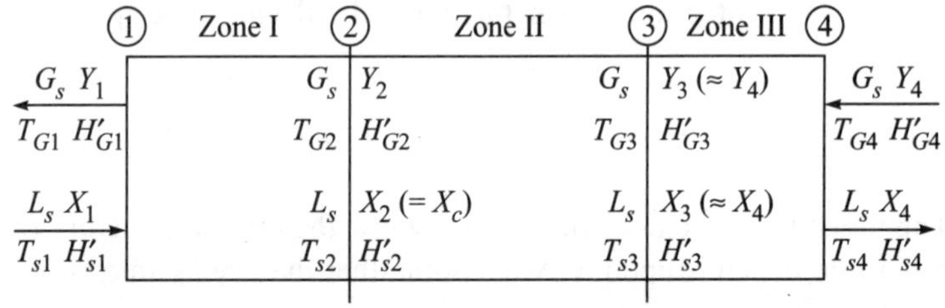

Figure 11.27   Three zones of a continuous countercurrent dryer.

By an overall moisture balance:

$$G_s(Y_1 - Y_4) = L_s(X_1 - X_4) \Rightarrow 12000(Y_1 - 0.025) = 750(0.3333 - 0.0101) \Rightarrow Y_1 = 0.0452$$

Humid heat of air in zone III: $c_H = 1.005 + (1.88)(0.025) = 1.052$ kJ/(kg dry air)(K)

Calculated enthalpy values (ref. temp. = 0°C; *assume* inlet temperature of the solid, $T_{s1} = 40$°C):

$$H'_{s1} = [c_{ps} + (0.333)(4.187)](T_{s1} - 0) = [0.96 + (0.333)(4.187)](40)$$
$$= 94.2 \text{ kJ/(kg dry solid)(K)}$$

$$H'_{s4} = [c_{ps} + (0.0101)(4.187)](T_{s4} - 0) = [0.96 + (0.0101)(4.187)](60)$$
$$= 60.14 \text{ kJ/(kg dry solid)(K)}$$

The gas temperature T_{G3} can be calculated by heat balance over zone III

$$G_s c_H(T_{G4} - T_{G3}) = L_s(H'_{s4} - H'_{s3})$$

$$\Rightarrow \qquad (12{,}000)(1.052)(100 - T_{G3}) \approx (750)(0.96)(60 - 40) \qquad \Rightarrow T_{G3} = 99\text{°C}$$

Since the heat load of this zone is small, the hot gas temperature does not change much.

Heat transfer calculations in zone III

Rate of heat transfer from the gas, $Q_3 = G_s c_H (T_{s4} - T_{s3})$

$$= (12,000)(1.052)(100 - 99) = 12,620 \text{ kJ/h}$$

Heat transfer coefficient, $\qquad h_c = k_Y c_H = (150)(1.052) = 158 \text{ kJ/m}^2 \cdot \text{h} \cdot \text{K}$

Temperature driving force, $\qquad \Delta T_4 = 100 - 60 = 40°C; \quad \Delta T_3 = 99 - 40 = 59°C$

Log mean driving force, $\qquad (\Delta T)_m = \dfrac{\Delta T_3 - \Delta T_4}{\ln(\Delta T_3 / \Delta T_4)} = \dfrac{59 - 40}{\ln(59/40)} = 49°C$

Time of heating, $\qquad t_{III} = Q_3 / [(L_s a')(h_c)(\Delta T)_m]$

$$= 12,620/[(750 \times 0.065)(158)(49)]$$

$$= 0.0334 \text{ h} \ (= 2 \text{ min})$$

Calculation of drying time in zone II

Adiabatic saturation temperature of the gas in zone II and zone I (corresponding to the dry-bulb temperature 99°C and humidity 0.025 of the gas at boundary 3) = 40°C (this is the same as the *guess value*).

Overall energy balance: $G_s(H'_{G4} - H'_{G1}) = L_s(H'_{s4} - H'_{s1})$ [$H'_{G4} = 167.7$ kJ/kg; calculation not shown.]

$\Rightarrow \qquad (12,000)(167.7 - H_{G1}) = 750(60.14 - 94.2)$

$\Rightarrow \qquad H_{G1} = 169.8 \text{ kJ/(kg dry air)}$

$\qquad H_{G1} = 169.8 = [1.005 + (1.88)(0.0452)](T_{G1} - 0) + (0.0452)(2500)$

$\Rightarrow \qquad T_{G1} = 52°C$

Moisture content of the solid at the boundary 2 is $X_2 = X_c$ (critical moisture) = 0.087

$H'_{s2} = [0.96 + (0.087)(4.187)](40 - 0) = 53 \text{ kJ/(kg dry solid)}; \ H'_{s3} = 40 \text{ kJ/(kg dry solid)}$

Material balance:

$$G_s(Y_2 - Y_3) = L_s(X_2 - X_3)$$

$\Rightarrow \qquad (12,000)(Y_2 - 0.025) = (750)(0.087 - 0.0101) \Rightarrow Y_2 = 0.0298$

$$H'_{G3} = [1.005 + (1.88)(0.025)](99 - 0) + (0.025)(2500)$$

$$= 166.6 \text{ kJ/(kg dry air)}$$

Energy balance:

$$G_s(H'_{G3} - H'_{G2}) = L_s(H'_{s3} - H'_{s2})$$

$\Rightarrow \qquad (12,000)(166.6 - H'_{G2}) = (750)(40 - 53)$

$\Rightarrow \qquad H'_{G2} = 167.4 = [1.005 + (1.88)(0.0298)](T_{G2} - 0) + (0.0298)(2500)$

$\Rightarrow \qquad T_{G2} = 87.5°C$

At $T_s = 40°C$, $Y_s = 0.05$.

Drying time [Eq. (11.37); put $Y_s = 0.05$ at the solid temperature, $T_s = 40°C$],

$$t_{II} = \frac{(12000)(0.087)}{(750 \times 0.065)(150)} \frac{1}{(0.0101) + (12000/750)(0.05 - 0.025)} \ln \frac{(0.05 - 0.025)(0.087)}{(0.05 - 0.0298)(0.0101)}$$

$$= 0.824 \text{ h}$$

Calculation of the drying time in zone I

$Y_2 = 0.0298$; $Y_1 = 0.0452$; solid temperature $= 40°C$; $Y_s = 0.05$.

Using Eq. (11.33),

$$t_I = \frac{12000}{(750 \times 0.065)(150)} \ln \frac{0.05 - 0.0298}{0.05 - 0.0452} = 2.357 \text{ h}$$

Total time $= 0.0334 + 0.824 + 2.357 = \boxed{3.21 \text{ h}}$

11.13   PRELIMINARY DESIGN OF A ROTARY DRYER

It is difficult, if not impossible, to design a rotary dryer on the basis of fundamental principles only. The available design correlations are a few in number and may not prove to be satisfactory for many systems. The design of a rotary dryer (and also of most other dryers) is better done by using the pilot plant test data or the full-scale operating data of a dryer of similar type together with the available design correlations. A fairly large number of variables are involved. The capacity in terms of the solid to be dried per hour, the inlet and exit moisture contents of the solid, the critical and equilibrium moisture contents, the temperature and humidity of the drying gas are generally the known or given quantities. The process design engineer has to make mass and energy balance calculations, calculate the required rate of hot drying gas, the shell diameter and length, the solid hold-up and retention time, the number, the height and type of lifting flights, the peripheral speed (rpm) of the shell, etc. The design procedure based on the basic principles, and available correlations, is briefly discussed below. Here we assume that the solid has unbound moisture only and in zone II (see Figure 11.15) the solid is at the wet-bulb temperature of the gas. Heat losses from the dryer surface are neglected. Some of the notations used are shown in Figure 11.15.

(a)   The capacity of the dryer (solid drying rate, L_s kg/h, dry basis, the terminal moisture contents, X_1 and X_2, and the temperatures, T_{s1} and T_{s2}) is known. The drying gas flow rate, its temperature and humidity are decided considering a number of factors. However, the following moisture and enthalpy balance equations need to be satisfied.

$$G_s(Y_1 - Y_2) = L_s(X_1 - X_2) \tag{11.38}$$

$$G_s(H'_{G2} - H'_{G1}) = L_s(H'_{s2} - H'_{s1}) \tag{11.39}$$

(b)   Distributions of the gas and the solid temperatures in an 'ideal' rotary dryer are qualitatively shown in Figure 11.15. The temperature of the wet solid is raised to the wet-bulb temperature ($T_w = T_{sA} = T_{sB}$) of the drying gas (corresponding to its temperature and the humidity) in zone I. However, we assume that practically no evaporation of water occurs in this region. The temperature of the solid remains constant over zone II if the solid has unbound moisture only. This zone is responsible for drying of the solid. At the end of zone II, the solid is practically dry and its temperature rises from T_{sB} to T_{s2} in zone III, but only little drying occurs there.

(c)   The gas and solid temperatures at the boundaries are obtained by moisture and energy balances in much the same way as described in Section 11.12.4. Now the number of heat transfer units for each zone is calculated. For the zone II, for example, the number of heat transfer units is given by

$$(N_{tG})_{h,\text{II}} = \frac{T_{GB} - T_{GA}}{\Delta T_m}; \quad \text{where} \quad \Delta T_m = \frac{(T_{GB} - T_{sA}) - (T_{GA} - T_{sA})}{\ln[(T_{GB} - T_{sA})/(T_{GA} - T_{sA})]} \quad (11.40)$$

Here $(T_{GB} - T_{sA})$ and $(T_{GA} - T_{sA})$ are called the wet-bulb depression at the two ends of zone II.

(d) The lengths of heat transfer units L_T for the three zones are calculated. A few correlations are available for the estimation of L_T. The total length of the dryer is given by

$$L = (L_T)_{\text{I}}(N_{tG})_{\text{I}} + (L_T)_{\text{II}}(N_{tG})_{\text{II}} + (L_T)_{\text{III}}(N_{tG})_{\text{III}} \quad (11.41)$$

(e) The shell diameter is calculated from the dry gas flow rate [calculated in step (a)] and a suitable gas velocity or gas mass flow rate. The choice may be guided by the maximum gas velocity beyond which substantial entrainment or 'dusting' of the fines in the solid occurs.

A few correlations useful for the design of a rotary dryer are given below.

Volumetric gas–solid heat transfer coefficient (Treybal, 1980):

$$U\bar{a} \ (\text{W/m}^3 \cdot \text{K}) = 237(G')^{0.67}/d \quad (11.42)$$

Length of a transfer unit (Treybal, 1980) $\quad L_T = G'c_H/(U\bar{a}) \quad (11.43)$

$\quad$ (Tsao and Wheelock, 1967): $L_T = 0.0063 c_H d G_s^{0.84} \quad (11.44)$

Solid retention time (from Perry's *Handbook*, 7th ed., 1997):

$$\theta = \frac{0.23L}{S N^{0.9} d} \pm 1.97 \frac{BLG'}{F} \quad (11.45)$$

[θ = retention time (min); L = dryer length (m); S = slope of the dryer (m/m); N = speed (rpm); G' = gas mass flow rate (kg/m²·h); F = feed rate (kg/m²·h, dry basis); $B = 5(d_p)^{-0.5}$, d_p = weight-average particle diameter (microns); d = dryer diameter (m)]. In Eq. (11.45), the positive sign is for counterflow, and the negative sign is for parallel flow of the gas and the solid.

EXAMPLE 11.7 (*Sizing of a rotary dryer*)   A moist non-hygroscopic granular solid at 26°C is to be dried from 20% initial moisture to 0.3% final moisture (wet basis) in a rotary dryer at a rate of 1500 kg/h. Hot air enters at 135°C with a humidity of 0.015. The exit solid temperature must not exceed 110°C and the air velocity must not exceed 1.5 m/s in order to avoid dusting of the solid. Specific heat of the dry solid is $c_{ps} = 0.85$ kJ/kg·K. Suggest the diameter, the length and the other parameters of the dryer.

Solution

Basis of calculation is 1 hour operation.

$\quad$ Mass of dry solid, $L_s = (1500)(1 - 0.2) = 1200$ kg/h; moisture in the wet solid, $X_1 = 20/80 = 0.25$; moisture in the dry solid, $X_2 = 0.3/99.7 = 0.00301$.

$\quad$ Water evaporated, $m_s = L_s(X_1 - X_2) = (1200)(0.25 - 0.00301) = 296.4$ kg

$\quad$ Refer to Figure 11.15. *Given*: $T_{s1} = 26°C$; $T_{G2} = 135°C$; $Y_2 = 0.015$

We *assume* that the exit temperature of the gas is $T_{G1} = 60°C$ and that of the solid is $T_{s2} = 100°C$. These values are to be checked later on.

Calculated enthalpy values of different streams (Ref. temp. = 0°C)

$H'_{s1} = [c_{ps} + (4.187)X_1](T_{s1} - 0) = [0.85 + (4.187)(0.25)](26 - 0) = 49.31$ kJ/(kg dry solid)

$H'_{s2} = [c_{ps} + (4.187)X_2](T_{s2} - 0) = [0.85 + (4.187)(0.00301)](100 - 0) = 86.2$ kJ/(kg dry solid)

$H'_{G2} = [1.005 + (1.88)(0.015)](135 - 0) + (0.015)(2500) = 177$ kJ/kg

$H'_{G1} = (1.005 + 1.88Y_1)(60 - 0) + (2500)Y_1 = 60.3 + 2613Y_1$

Overall mass balance

$G_s(Y_1 - Y_2) = L_s(X_1 - X_2) \Rightarrow G_2(Y_1 - 0.015) = 296.4 \Rightarrow G_s = 296.4/(Y_1 - 0.015)$

$L_s(H'_{s2} - H'_{s1}) = G_s(H'_{G2} - H'_{G1}) \Rightarrow 1200(86.2 - 49.31) = \dfrac{296.4}{Y_1 - 0.015}(177 - 60.3 - 2613Y_1)$

$\Rightarrow \qquad Y_1 = 0.04306$ and $G_s = 296.4/(Y_1 - 0.015) = 10{,}560$ kg/h

Calculation of the shell diameter

Humid volume of the inlet gas (135°C, $Y_2 = 0.015$), $v_{H2} = 1.183$ m³/(kg dry air)

Humid volume of the exit gas (60°C, $Y_1 = 0.04306$), $v_{H1} = 1.008$ m³/(kg dry air)

The maximum volumetric gas flow rate (this occurs at end 2 in Figure 11.15)

$$= G_s v_{H2} = (10{,}560)(1.183) = 12{,}490 \text{ m}^3/\text{h} \Rightarrow 3.47 \text{ m}^3/\text{s}$$

Take the maximum superficial air velocity to be 1.2 m/s (this is 20% less than the maximum allowable velocity since part of the dryer is filled with the moving solid, and the entire cross-section is not available for gas flow). If d is the dryer diameter,

$$(\pi d^2/4)(1.2) = 3.686 \Rightarrow d = \boxed{1.98 \text{ m}}. \quad \text{Select a 2-m diameter shell.}$$

Calculation of the number of heat transfer units

The dryer is considered to consist of three zones as shown in Figure 11.15. The temperature and humidity or moisture content of the streams can be obtained by material and energy balance.

Zone III: Only heating of the solid occurs in this zone; there is little water left for vaporization. At the boundary between zones III and II, the solid is at T_{sB}, the wet-bulb temperature of the air at that location. Assume $T_{sB} (= T_{SA}) = 41°C$ (this value is to be checked and modified later, if necessary).

Enthalpy of the solid at the inlet to zone III,

$$H'_{sB} = [0.85 + (0.00301)(4.187)](41 - 0) = 35.37 \text{ kJ/(kg dry solid)}$$

Humid heat of the gas entering zone III, $c_{HB} = [1.005 + (1.88)(0.015)] = 1.033$ kJ/kg·K (this remains constant in zone III, since the humidity does not change in this section).

Heat balance over zone III: $L_s(H'_{s2} - H'_{sB}) = G_s(c_{HB})_{III}(T_{G2} - T_{GB})$

$$\Rightarrow \qquad (1200)(86.2 - 35.37) = (10{,}560)(1.033)(135 - T_{GB}) \Rightarrow T_{GB} = 129°C$$

Adiabatic saturation temperature of air entering zone II (129°C and humidity of 0.015) is 41.3°C. This is fairly close to the guess value of 41°C and $T_{SA} = T_{SB} = 41°C$ is not changed.

At the boundary B, $\Delta T_B = 129 - 41 = 88°C$; at end 2, $\Delta T_2 = 135 - 100 = 35°C$

Log mean temperature in zone III, $(\Delta T)_m = \dfrac{88 - 35}{\ln(88/35)} = 57.5°C$

Number of heat transfer units, $(N_{tG})_{III} = \dfrac{T_2 - T_{GB}}{(\Delta T)_m} = \dfrac{135 - 129}{57.5} = 0.104$

Zone II: In order to calculate $(N_{tG})_{II}$, we need the value of T_{GA}. This can be obtained by heat balance.

$H'_{GB} = [1.005 + 1.88Y_B](129 - 0) + (2500)(Y_B) = 170.8$ kJ/kg. (since $Y_B = 0.015$)

$H'_{sA} = [0.85 + c_{ps}X_1](T_{sA} - 0) = [0.85 + (4.187)(0.25)](41) = 77.77$ kJ/(kg dry solid)

Enthalpy balance: $L_s(H'_{sB} - H'_{sA}) = G_s(H'_{GB} - H'_{GA})$

$\Rightarrow$ $\quad\quad\quad\quad (1200)(35.37 - 77.77) = (10,560)(170.8 - H'_{GA})$

$\Rightarrow H'_{GA} = 175.6 = [1.005 + (0.04306)(1.88)](T_{GA} - 0) + (0.04306)(2500) \Rightarrow T_{GA} = 63°C$

Temperature differences: At section A, $(\Delta T)_A = 63 - 41 = 22°C$; $(\Delta T)_B = 88°C$

$$(\Delta T)_m = \frac{88 - 22}{\ln(88/22)} = 47.6$$

Number of heat transfer units, $(N_{tG})_{II} = \dfrac{T_{GB} - T_{GA}}{(\Delta T)_m} = \dfrac{129 - 63}{47.6} = 1.386$

Before calculating $(N_{tG})_I$, let us check the validity of the assumed value of the exit gas temperature, $T_{G1} = 60°C$, by making an energy balance over zone I. Putting the values of different quantities in Eq. (11.39),

$$10,560(175.6 - H'_{G1}) = 1200(77.77 - 49.31) \quad \Rightarrow \quad H'_{G1} \Rightarrow T_{G1} = 59.6°C,$$

matches the assumed value.

Zone I: $(\Delta T)_1 = 60 - 26 = 34°C$; $(\Delta T)_A = 22°C$; $(\Delta T)_m = \dfrac{34 - 22}{\ln(34/22)} = 27.5$

Number of heat transfer units, $(N_{tG})_I = \dfrac{T_{GA} - T_{G1}}{(\Delta T)_m} = \dfrac{63 - 60}{27.5} = 0.109$

Total number of heat transfer units $N_{tG} = 0.104 + 1.386 + 0.109 = 1.53$ (this lies within the usual range)

Length of a transfer unit

Average gas mass flow rate = $[(10,560)(1.015) + (10,560)(1.04306)]/2 = 10,867$ kg/h

The gas mass flow rate, $G' = (10,867/3600)/(\pi/4)(2)^2 = 0.961$ kg/m$^2 \cdot$s

Volumetric heat transfer coefficient [Eq. (11.42)],

$$U\bar{a} = \frac{237(G')^{0.67}}{d} = \frac{(237)(0.961)^{0.67}}{2} = 115 \text{ W/m}^3 \cdot \text{K}$$

Humid heats at the ends: $c_{H2} = 1.005 + (1.88)(0.015) = 1.033$

$$c_{H1} = 1.005 + (1.88)(0.04306) = 1.083$$

Average humid heat, $c_H = (1.033 + 1.083)/2 = 1.058$ kJ/kg·K = 1058 J/(kg dry air)(K)

Length of a heat transfer unit Eq. (11.43), $L_T = \dfrac{G'c_H}{U\bar{a}} = \dfrac{(0.961)(1058)}{115} = 8.84$ m

Length of the dryer, $L = (N_{tG})(L_t) = (1.56)(8.84) = 13.8$ m

Select a $\boxed{\text{2 m diameter, 15 m long dryer}}$.

Note: If Eq. (11.44) is used, we get $L_T = 12.8$ m which is 50% longer than that obtained from Eq. (11.43). The available correlations are not very accurate beyond the systems and the dryer type used to develop these. As a result, only approximate sizing of a rotary dryer is possible by taking the help of these correlations.

11.14 FREEZE DRYING CALCULATIONS

Freeze drying (also called 'freeze dehydration') is an important drying technique especially suitable for food materials. Since drying occurs at subzero temperature, there is no risk of product degradation and possibly a loss of flavour and aroma. Besides, the texture of the material remains intact making it more acceptable to the customers. The process of 'rehydration' is also simple. The freeze drying process involves initial freezing of the material which is followed by sublimation of ice and removal of water vapour under vacuum. The equipment basically consists of an evaporator-condenser assembly and a vacuum device such as a vacuum pump or an ejector. The heat of sublimation is sometimes supplied by radiation from an appropriately placed hot plate. As drying proceeds, the 'ice-front' gradually recedes within the material leaving a dried porous product layer. A simple theoretical analysis of freeze drying of a material in the form of a slab is given below (Sandal et al., 1967).

Figure 11.28 shows a slab of thickness L undergoing freeze drying from both surfaces. It has a frozen interior with a dry product layer of thickness l on either side at any instant t, so that the ice-front is located at a distance l from the surface. It is assumed that heat and mass transfer (to or from the slab) occurs by a combination of conduction, convection and diffusion. The drying phenomenon constitutes an unsteady state 'moving boundary problem'. However, for the sake of simplicity we make a 'pseudo-steady state' approximation of the heat and mass transport processes. Let us use the following notations:

T_s = temperature at the ice front within the slab
T_f = temperature of the fluid within the dryer
k_s = thermal conductivity of the dried solid layer
h_c = convective heat transfer coefficient at the surface of the slab
P_s^v = sublimation pressure of ice at the ice-front within the solid
p_f = partial pressure of moisture in the bulk fluid
D_w = effective diffusivity of moisture in the dry layer
k_G = mass transfer coefficient of moisture
λ_w = heat of sublimation of water per kg.

The heat flux, q (W/m$^2 \cdot$°C) and mass flux, N_w (kmol water vapour/m$^2 \cdot$s) at the surface may be expressed as

$$q = \frac{T_f - T_s}{(l/k_s) + (1/h_c)}; \qquad N_w = \frac{P_s^v - p_f}{(1/k_G) + (l \cdot RT/D_w)} \qquad (11.46)$$

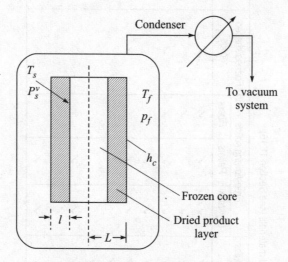

Figure 11.28 A slab undergoing freeze drying.

Consider *unit area of the slab* and neglect the area of the edges. If v_w is the volume of material that contains 1 kg of frozen water in it, the moles of water in the solid at any time is $(L - 2l)/(v_w M_w)$ kmol. The rate of drying (considering both the surfaces) is

$$2N_w \text{ (kmol water/m}^2 \cdot \text{s)} = -\frac{d}{dt}\left(\frac{L - 2l}{v_w M_w}\right) \Rightarrow N_w = \frac{1}{v_w M_w}\frac{dl}{dt} \qquad (11.47)$$

$$\Rightarrow \qquad \frac{dl}{dt} = v_w M_w N_w = v_w M_w \frac{q}{\lambda_w M_w} = \frac{v_w}{\lambda_w}\frac{T_f - T_s}{(l/k_s) + (1/h_c)} \qquad (11.48)$$

Integrating from $t = 0$, $l = 0$, to $t = t$, $l = l$, the drying time is expressed as

$$t = \frac{\lambda_w}{v_w(T_f - T_s)}\left(\frac{l^2}{2k_s} + \frac{l}{h_c}\right) \qquad (11.49)$$

The time for complete drying t_f can be obtained by putting $l = L/2$. Thus,

$$t_f = \frac{\lambda_w}{v_w(T_f - T_s)}\left(\frac{L^2}{8k_s} + \frac{L}{2h_c}\right) \qquad (11.50)$$

The rate of freeze drying is generally controlled by the rate of heat transfer. Hence the above equation is useful for calculation of the drying time.

Table 11.2 Dryer selection for various feed materials (see Section 11.15)

Dryer type	Liquids		Pastes	Cake	Powder	Granules	Free-flowing solids			Formed/shaped solids	Heat-sensitive solids
	Solution	Slurry					Crystals	Pellets	Fibers		
Tray				✓	✓	✓	✓	✓	✓	✓	
Tunnel truck				✓	✓	✓	✓	✓	✓		
Belt conveyer						✓	✓	✓	✓	✓	
Rotary				✓	✓	✓	✓	✓			
Vacuum shelf				✓	✓	✓	✓	✓		✓	✓
Agitated pan			✓	✓	✓	✓					
Conical vacuum			✓	✓		✓					
Flash							✓	✓			✓
Spray	✓	✓									✓
Fluidized bed						✓	✓	✓			✓

11.15 DRYER SELECTION

Given a large variety of dryers available from different vendors, the selection of the most suitable dryer for a particular application needs a lot of consideration. The nature of the material (moisture content, state, heat sensitivity, whether sticky or free-flowing, fragility, etc.), the drying capacity, the final product quality, the allowable drying rate and many other factors govern the selection of a dryer. The operating conditions of a dryer may have to be adjusted depending upon the type of material. For example, if a controlled drying rate is desired, partial recycle of the exhaust drying gas is done to regulate the humidity and the drying rate (Cook, 1996). A dryer selection guide was suggested long ago by Parker (1963). Dryer selection has also been discussed in some detail by van't Land (1984) and by Kimball (2001). The optimization of dryer performance has been discussed by Liptak (1998). A simple guide to dryer selection is given in Table 11.2.

NOTATIONS

A, a	: drying area (m^2), specific surface area per unit bed volume (m^2/m^3)
b	: breadth of a tray, m
c_H	: humid heat, kJ/(°C)(kg dry air)
d_p	: particle diameter, m
G'	: gas flow rate, kg/m^2·h
G_2	: gas rate (dry basis), kg/h
h_b	: equivalent heat transfer coefficient to account for the heat flux through the bottom of the drying tray
h_c	: convective heat transfer coefficient, W/m^2·°C
k_s	: thermal conductivity of the solid, W/m·°C
k_Y	: mass transfer coefficient, kg/m^2·ΔY
H	: enthalpy, kJ/kg
l_s	: depth of solid on a tray, m
L	: length of a tray in the direction of flow of the drying gas, m
L_s	: solid rate (dry basis), kg/h
L_T	: length of a heat transfer unit in a rotary dryer
N, N_c	: moisture flux, constant drying rate, kg/m^2·s
N_{tG}, H_{tG}	: number and height (in m) of transfer units
Q	: rate of heat transfer to the solid, heat input or output rate, W
R_H	: relative humidity of the drying gas
t	: time, s
t_c, t_f	: constant rate and falling rate drying time, s
T, T_G, T_s	: temperature, gas temperature and solid temperature, °C, °F or K
w	: gap between two adjacent trays for gas flow (Figure 11.22)

W_s	: mass of solid (normally on dry basis) taken for drying, kg
X	: moisture content, (kg moisture)/(kg dry solid)
X_i, X_f, X_c, X^*	: initial, final, critical and equilibrium moisture content
Y	: absolute humidity of the drying gas, (kg moisture)/(kg dry gas)
z	: axial coordinate in the direction of gas flow

SHORT AND MULTIPLE CHOICE QUESTIONS

1. Which of the following is a probable value of the equilibrium moisture of sand at 40°C and 70% relative humidity of the ambient air?

   (i) 1.0   (ii) 0   (iii) 0.3 kg/(kg dry sand)

2. Which of the following substances may undergo 'case-hardening' if the drying rate is fast?

   (i)   Sand
   (ii) Soap bar
   (iii) Wood chips
   (iv) Clay brick
   (v)   Wet PVC beads

3. During air-drying at 30°C, the critical moisture content of a 5 cm thick layer of 200–325 mesh sand is found to be 0.06 kg water per kg dry sand. Which of the following is a probable value of the critical moisture content of

   (a) 10 cm thick layer of the same material at the same temperature:

   (i) 0.01   (ii) 0.06   (iii) 0.1 kg/(kg dry sand)

   (b) 5 cm thick bed of sand of 50–150 mesh size range:

   (i) 0.04   (ii) 0.06   (iii) 6.0

   (c) 5 cm thick bed, 200–325 mesh, air of the same humidity but 50°C temperature:

   (i) 0.08   (ii) 0.06   (iii) 0.02

4. A pigment is dried in a cross-flow tray dryer with air of temperature 50°C and humidity 0.015. There is virtually no radiation or conduction heat transfer to the solid. During constant rate drying, the surface temperature of the solid would be

   (i) 28°C   (ii) 35°C   (iii) 41°C

5. A gas flows over a tray containing a wet solid having 30% moisture on dry basis. The width of the gap for gas flow between the two consecutive trays is 5 cm and the tray size is 1 m × 1 m. The solid is assumed to be at the wet-bulb temperature of the gas. The ratio of the number of mass transfer unit to that of heat transfer unit is

   (i) 1.5   (ii) 0.72   (iii) 1.0

6. Consider constant-rate drying of a moist solid on a tray. Substantial heat transfer to the solid occurs from the tray floor. If the wet-bulb temperature of the drying gas is T_w and the surface temperature of the solid is T_s, then

   (i) $T_s < T_w$ (ii) $T_s = T_w$ (iii) $T_s > T_w$

7. The convective heat transfer coefficient h_c for through-circulation drying of a solid is estimated to be 150 W/m^2·K. What would be the mass transfer coefficient k_Y for moisture transport from the surface of a particle to the bulk of air having a humidity of 0.018?

 (i) 520 kg/m^2·h   (ii) 0.1 kg/m^2·s   (iii) 50 kg/m^2·min

8. A solid is to be dried in the falling rate period from the critical moisture content X_c to one-tenth of it $(X_c/10)$. The equilibrium moisture is negligible. If the falling rate is linear in X, the drying time is t_1; if the drying rate varies as X^2, the drying time is t_2. Then $t_1/t_2 =$

 (i) 1.0   (ii) 0.521   (iii) 0.256

9. A drying gas in cross-flow enters at one end of a stack of trays at 90°C and leaves at 70°C. The temperature of the drying surface of the solid is 33°C. What is the number of heat transfer units?

 (i) 4.3   (ii) 0.43   (iii) 0.27

10. The number of gas-phase heat transfer units in through-circulation drying of a solid is 3.5. The gas temperature decreases by 35°C across the bed. What is the log mean temperature driving force?

 (i) 10°C   (ii) 38.5°C   (iii) 30°C

11. Which of the following determine the maximum air velocity in a rotary dryer for the drying of relatively fine particles?

 (i) The blower horsepower
 (ii) The diameter of the tower
 (ii) Dusting of the solid
 (iv) The type of 'flights' used

12. What kind of flow strategy is preferred for drying a heat-sensitive substance in a continuous dryer?

 (i) Crosscurrent flow
 (ii) Cocurrent flow
 (iii) Countercurrent flow

13. What type of flight is used in a rotary dryer processing a sticky solid?

 (i) 90°-flight   (ii) 45°-flight   (iii) straight flight

14. Can the moisture content of a solid (dry basis) be above 100%?

15. Which of the following parameters affects the equilibrium moisture content of a solid?

 (i) Density of the solid
 (ii) Temperature
 (iii) Humidity of the ambient air
 (iv) Time of contact of the solid with the ambient gas
 (v) Critical moisture content of the solid
 (vi) Nature of the solid and its particle size

16. Which of the following offers negligible transport resistance during the constant rate drying of a porous solid?

   (i)   Capillary diffusion of water

   (ii) Vapour diffusion within the pores

   (iii) Gas phase transport of moisture

17. Which of the following is a probable value of the number of heat transfer units in a rotary dryer?

   (i) 1.8   (ii) 27   (iii) 0.05

18. The common range of the value of the length/diameter ratio of a rotary dryer is

   (i) 0.1–2.5   (ii) 4–15   (iii) 20–200

19. What kind of dryer do you suggest for drying of the following substances?

   (i)   Milk

   (ii)   A slurry of basic chrome sulphate

   (iii) Table salt in the final stage of production

   (iv)   Sugar crystals

   (v)   Detergent slurry for the production of detergent powder

   (vi)   Soap bars

   (vii) 5 mm size catalyst pellets

   (viii) Moist PVC beads

   (ix)   'Green' ceramic wares

   (x)   Large quantities of fibre board

   (xi)   Terephthalic acid crystals

   (xii) An antibiotic

   (xiii) Ammonium sulphate crystals (8 ton/h)

   (xiv) Tobacco leaves (in a large scale and on a continuous basis)

   (xv)   Food products like cereals, carrot slices, potato slices (about 2 ton/h, continuous)

20. The rate of crossflow drying of a solid at an instant in the falling rate period is 1.5 kg/m^2·h. The drying surface temperature is 35°C, the gas-phase mass transfer coefficient of water vapour, $k_Y = 120$ kg/m^2·h, and the humidity of the drying air, $Y_G = 0.018$ kg/(kg dry air). If unsaturated surface drying of the solid occurs, estimate the fraction of the drying area covered by dry patches. What simplifyimg assumptions have to be made?

21. Transport of liquid from inside a solid to the drying surface occurs by 'liquid diffusion' if the material is

   (i)   highly porous and non-hygroscopic

   (ii) non-porous, hygroscopic

   (iii) almost dry.

22. The amount of free moisture in a solid

   (i)   must be greater than the unbound moisture

   (ii) less than the critical moisture

   (iii) may be more than the bound moisture

   (iv) is none of these.

23. Cylindrical pellets of a catalyst support are soaked in the solution of an inorganic salt for 'impregnation'. How does the drying rate of the material compare with that of the same material but soaked in water (under identical drying conditions)?

    (i) larger   (ii) equal   (iii) smaller

24. The drying rate curves of a few solids are given in Figure 11.29. Identify the possible mechanism of drying in the falling rate periods.

25. A solid is being dried in a tray dryer. The hot gas flowing over the solid has a virtually constant temperature T_i. The solid temperature T_o changes with time. Which of the curves in Figure 11.30 is a reasonable representation of the variation of $(T_i - T_o)$ with time?

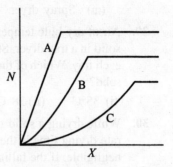

Figure 11.29

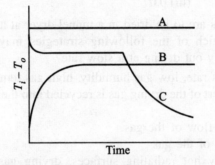

Figure 11.30

26. Draw and qualitatively explain the typical moisture concentration profiles in a packed bed of wet solid under the through-circulation drying condition:

    (i)   A short while after the drying gas flow starts
    (ii) After a considerable fraction of the free moisture is removed

27. The solid hold-up in a rotary dryer remains in the range:

    (i) 5–15%   (ii) 25–35%   (iii) 50–70%

28. Which of the following dryers may be suitable for drying of the substances (a), (b), and (c)?

    (a) A heat-sensitive material at a rate of 100 kg/h:
        (i)   Vacuum tray dryer
        (ii) Cocurrent rotary dryer
        (iii) Fluidized bed dryer

    (b) Fragile crystals at a rate of 500 kg/h:
        (i)   Countercurrent rotary dryer
        (ii) Belt-conveyer dryer
        (iii) Agitated pan dryer

(c) Three dyes produced alternately in a plant at a maximum rate of 700 kg/day:
- (i) Flash dryer
- (ii) Tray dryer
- (iii) Spray dryer

29. Air of dry-bulb temperature 100°C and wet-bulb temperature 38°C flows over the moist solid in a tray dryer. Steam pipes carrying saturated steam at 10 kg/cm^2 are placed above each tray. Which of the following is a likely value of the surface temperature of the moist solid?

    (i) 35°C   (ii) 38°C   (iii) 46°C

30. While drying a solid from 33% to 1% moisture (dry basis), it is found that the constant rate drying time is the same as the falling rate drying time. The equilibrium moisture is negligible. If the falling drying rate is linear in the moisture content, what is the critical moisture content of the solid?

    (i) 0.18   (ii) 0.1   (iii) 0.07

31. Green ceramic wares are to be dried in a tunnel dryer at a slow rate to avoid possible case-hardening. Which of the following strategies may be adopted, singly or in combination, to carry out drying at a slow rate?
- (i)   Low drying gas rate, low gas humidity, high gas temperature
- (ii) A substantial part of the drying gas is recycled into the dryer to maintain a high gas humidity
- (iii) Countercurrent flow of the gas
- (iv) Cocurrent flow of the gas
- (v) Heat supply by hot radiating surfaces, drying gas is at nearly atmospheric temperature

32. The crystals moist with an organic liquid are to be dried and the vapour has to be recovered. Which of the following types of dryer would be appropriate?
- (i)   Direct-heat dryer
- (ii) Indirect-heat dryer
- (iii) Batch dryer
- (iv) Any dryer with the solid suspended in the gas (e.g. a fluid-bed dryer)

33. If the dimension of a tray in the direction of flow of the drying gas is large (say, more than 0.75 m), which of the following may happen?
- (i)   There may be excessive dusting.
- (ii) The drying rate at the gas-exit end of the tray will be substantially low.
- (iii) Mechanical handling of the trays may be difficult.

34. Draw and explain the typical gas and solid temperature profiles for drying of a
- (i) hygroscopic solid
- (ii) non-hygroscopic solid in a cocurrent rotary dryer.

35. An indirect-heat rotary dryer (say a steam-tube rotary dryer) is often found to be more 'energy efficient' than the direct heat dryer. How can this be explained?

36. Tsao and Wheelock (1967) cited the correlation $L_T = 0.1c_H d(G')^{0.84}$ for the length of a heat transfer unit in a rotary dryer [L in ft; c_H in Btu/lb·°F ; d, the dryer diameter, in ft, and G' in lb/ft^2·h]. Show that the correlation reduces to Eq. (11.44) if the quantities are expressed in SI units.

37. Explain the functions of the following components of a rotary dryer.
   (i) Flights
   (ii) Shell knocker
   (iii) Friction seal
   What is the disadvantage of using a girth gear to rotate the shell?

PROBLEMS

11.1 (*Calculation of the drying time, the constant drying rate being given*)[1]   A granular wet solid is dried on a tray dryer under cross-flow of hot air from 30% initial moisture to 1% final moisture. The solid loading is 35 kg dry solid per m^2 tray area. The constant drying rate is $N_c = 4.5$ kg/m^2·h. The critical moisture is 10% and the equilibrium moisture is 0.2%. (a) Calculate the total drying time if the falling rate is linear in moisture content. (b) What is the drying rate when the moisture content is 5%? All moisture concentrations are expressed on dry basis [kg/(kg dry solid)].

11.2 (*Calculation of the drying time when there are two falling rates*)[2]   A wet solid having 32% moisture (dry basis) is to be dried on a tray dryer to a final moisture of 1%. The solid loading is 30 kg dry solid per m^2 tray area. There are two critical moisture values— $X_{c1} = 0.183$, and $X_{c2} = 0.097$. A laboratory test gives a drying rate of 4 kg/m^2·h in the constant rate period. In the first falling rate period, the drying flux is linear in the moisture content; in the second falling rate, the drying flux varies as the square of the moisture content. The equilibrium moisture is negligible. Calculate the drying time if the drying conditions are the same as in the laboratory test. Mention any assumption made.

11.3 (*Drying time calculation from experimental drying time data*)[1]   In the laboratory drying test of a granular, hygroscopic wet solid, it took 8.5 hours to dry the solid from 28% to 2% moisture with a solid loading of 20 kg/m^2. Given, $X_c = 0.1$, $X^* = 0.005$, and the falling rate of drying being linear in the moisture content (all moistures are on dry basis), calculate the time required for drying the material from 25% to 1.5% moisture under similar drying conditions. What are the highest and the lowest drying rates?

11.4 (*Drying time calculation from laboratory drying time data*)[1]   In a laboratory drying test, a square fibre board (size = 30 cm × 18 cm × 2 cm; dry mass = 10 kg; initial moisture content = 25%) with edges sealed is placed in a flowing stream of hot air. The drying rate remains constant at 2 kg/m^2·h till a moisture content of 10.7% (dry basis) is reached. The total drying time to reduce the moisture content to 1.52% was 2 hours. The equilibrium moisture, measured separately under the same conditions is 0.5%, dry basis.

   It is required to determine the drying time of another board, 1 m × 1 m × 2 cm, from 35% initial moisture to 1% final moisture under similar drying conditions. Calculate the drying time. The drying rate is known to be linear in the falling rate period. All moistures are on wet basis unless stated otherwise.

11.5 (*Through-circulation drying of moist pellets*)[2] Cylindrical catalyst pellets (length = diameter = 5 mm) are to be dried by the through-circulation of hot air [temperature = 90°C; humidity = 0.018 kg/(kg dry air)] at a superficial velocity of 0.8 m/s through a 30 mm thick bed of the wet pellet having 36% moisture. The solid is non-hygroscopic; the critical moisture content is 12% and the equilibrium moisture is negligible. The dried product is unloaded at 70°C with 0.2% moisture. The falling rate of drying is linear in moisture content. All moistures are on dry basis. Density of the bed of dry solid = 600 kg/m^3; specific heat = 0.4 kJ/kg·°C; and the effective surface area of drying = 400 m^2/m^3. Calculate (a) the initial rate of drying, (b) the total drying time, and (c) the time of heating of the dry solid to 70°C.

11.6 (*Drying time for crossflow of the gas*)[2] Ten kilograms of a solid having 30% moisture (wet basis) is dried on a tray under cross-flow of air (dry-bulb temperature = 100°C; wet-bulb temperature = 35°C) at a velocity of 2 m/s. The following data and information are available: tray area = 0.5 m^2; X_c = 10%; and X^* = 0.5% (both dry basis). Calculate the time required for drying the solid to a final moisture of 0.01 kg/(kg dry solid).

11.7 (*Drying of a solid having two critical moisture contents*)[3] In the course of drying of a solid, two falling rate periods were identified with critical moisture values X_{c1} = 0.1 and X_{c2} = 0.05. The first falling rate is linear in X, and the drying rate varies as X^2 in the second falling rate. The equilibrium moisture is small. If the solid is to be dried to a moisture content of 0.5%, calculate the ratio of the times required for drying in the two falling rate regimes.

11.8 (*Calculation of X_c from the drying times*)[3] A solid is dried from X_i = 0.3 to X_f = 0.003. The equilibrium moisture is negligible and the falling rate of drying is linear in moisture content. Calculate the critical moisture content of the solid under the particular drying conditions if (a) the drying time of the constant rate period is the same as that of the falling rate period, and (b) if the time of constant rate drying is half that of the falling rate drying.

11.9 (*A tray dryer subjected to heat transfer by conduction, convection and radiation*)[3] A tray dryer having a stack of trays (0.6 m × 0.6 m) is loaded with a 3 cm thick bed of wet solid on each. The drying gas (air at 100°C, wet-bulb temperature = 35°C) flows over the trays at a sufficiently high rate so that drop in the air temperature is small. The wet material on the tray receives heat by convection from the air flowing over the open surface, by radiation from the bottom of the tray above, and from the tray floor by conduction through the solid bed. The following data are given: density of dry solid, ρ_s = 1200 kg/m^3; thermal conductivity of the solid, k_s = 0.12 W/m·K ; X_i = 0.35; X_c = 0.12; X^* = 0.005; X_f = 0.01. The radiating and the absorbing surfaces are both considered as blackbodies for simplicity. If the convective heat transfer coefficient is estimated as 20 W/m^2·°C, calculate the drying time.

11.10 (*Calculation of drying time, the constant drying rate given*)[2] In a small textile processing unit, dyed and washed cotton yarn is dried in an insulated chamber through which hot air is blown. Bundles of yarn are kept suspended from the roof of the chamber. Two hundred kilograms of wet yarn with 1kg water per kg yarn is taken in a batch. Air at 25°C (wet-bulb temperature = 15°C) is heated to 65°C before it enters the chamber. Assume that the air flow rate is large enough for its temperature and humidity to remain essentially constant.

From the operating data it is known that the constant rate of drying under the given conditions is 0.5 kg moisture per hour per kg of dry yarn. The critical moisture is $X_c = 0.15$, and the equilibrium moisture is $X^* = 0.001$. Calculate the time required for drying the yarn to a final moisture of $X_f = 0.003$ if the falling rate of drying is linear in X.

11.11 (*Two falling rates of drying*)[3] The following values of drying parameters were obtained from the experimental data on batch drying of a granular solid taken on a tray and placed in a stream of hot air. There were two falling rates, both linear, in the moisture content (in kg moisture per kg dry solid). Constant drying rate, $N_c = 2.5$ kg/m²·h; first critical moisture, $X_{c1} = 0.18$; second critical moisture, $X_{c2} = 0.1$; equilibrium moisture, $X^* = 0$. At a solid loading of 7 kg (dry basis) per square metre, it took 1.68 h to dry it from the second critical point to a final moisture of $X_f = 0.03$. Using the above data and information, calculate the time required to dry the material from an initial moisture of $X_i = 0.35$ to a final moisture of $X_f = 0.01$ under the conditions of the experiment.

11.12 (*Drying time in a tray dryer, heat supply by convection and conduction*)[3] A moist solid is to be dried on a tray dryer from a moisture content of $X_i = 0.4$ to $X_f = 0.012$. Air at 90°C and humidity $Y_G = 0.015$ (kg moisture per kg dry air), flows over the solid at a velocity of 3 m/s. The critical moisture of the solid is $X_c = 0.015$, the equilibrium moisture is $X^* = 0.008$, and the falling rate is linear in moisture content. The solid receives heat by convection at the open surface and from the tray bottom by conduction through the layer of solid. The thickness of the solid layer is 3 cm, and the thermal conductivity of the material is 2 W/m·°C. The radiation effect can be neglected. Calculate the drying time required. What fractional reduction in drying time can be achieved by increasing the air velocity by 50%?

11.13 (*Belt dryer calculation for once-through flow of the hot gas*)[3] A granular material is to be dried at a rate of 1300 kg/h (dry basis). The properties of the solid are: particle size, $d_p = 5$ mm (almost spherical); specific surface area of the particles, $\bar{a} = 500$ m²/m³ of bed volume; $X_i = 0.6$; $X_c = 0.2$; $X^* = 0.01$; the falling rate is linear in X, and the bulk density of dry solid, $\rho_s = 900$ kg/m³. A band dryer with a 2 m wide and 10 m long porous belt is available. It is suggested that hot air at $T_G = 90$°C and of humidity $Y_G = 0.015$ would be passed through the bed ('through circulation') of thickness, $l_s = 3.5$ cm at a superficial velocity of 1 m/s. Can the dryer perform the job? What belt speed should be used?

11.14 (*Enthalpy balance in a continuous dryer*)[2] A continuous dryer receives 1200 kg/h of a wet solid having 40% moisture (wet basis) at 26°C. The dried product leaves at 45°C with 1% moisture (dry basis), and the exhaust air leaves at 65°C and $Y = 0.043$. In order to regulate the drying rate, a part of the exhaust air is recirculated and mixed with fresh air at 28°C and $Y = 0.013$. The mixed gas enters an air heater to which the saturated steam is supplied at 155°C. The hot air from the heater enters the dryer at 120°C and $Y = 0.023$. Determine the rating of the air heater. What is the rate of heat loss from the dryer? If the heat transfer coefficient for air heating is 30 W/m²·°C, calculate the required area of the heater.

11.15 (*Drying time in a countercurrent dryer*)[3]   A solid having 30% moisture is to be dried in a continuous countercurrent tunnel dryer at a rate of 1500 kg/h (dry basis). It remains at the wet-bulb temperature of the drying gas all through the dryer. The critical moisture is 12%; the equilibrium moisture is negligible. The dried solid leaves with 0.8% moisture without further heating. *Given:* surface area for drying = 0.08 m²/(kg dry solid); specific heat of the dry solid, c_{ps} = 1 kJ/kg·°C; drying gas (temperature = 150°C, humidity = 0.02) is supplied at a rate of 15,000 kg/h; mass transfer coefficient, k_Y = 115 kg/m²·h·ΔY. All moistures are on wet basis. Calculate the drying time. What is the theoretical minimum air rate for this service?

11.16 (*A belt dryer with counterflow of the gas*)[3]   A moist solid is dried in a belt dryer with the hot air flowing over the bed countercurrent to the solid. This flow configuration is selected to ensure a slow rate of drying. The solid, which is at the wet-bulb temperature of the drying gas, is supplied at a rate of 1000 kg/h (dry basis) and leaves at 65°C. *Given:* bulk density of the dry solid = 700 kg/m³; depth of the bed over the belt, l_s = 4 cm; breadth of the belt = 2 m; X_i = 0.2; X_c = 0.08; X_f = 0.01; X^* = 0; rate of supply of hot air = 12,000 kg/h (dry basis); temperature, T_G = 140°C having humidity Y = 0.017. Calculate the belt speed and the length of the dryer.

11.17 (*Diameter and rpm of a drum dryer*)[3]   It is planned to dry a thick slurry using a horizontal single drum dryer dipped to an angle of 45° in a trough containing the feed. A layer of the slurry, 2 mm thick, will be drawn by the rotating drum and the dry material will be scrapped from the surface by a doctor's blade from the other side of the drum (Figure 11.31). Low pressure steam condenses in the drum and the drying surface temperature of the layer is maintained at 75°C. Hot air at about 85°C flows through a passage over the slurry layer to carry away the water vapour. However, the heat transfer to the slurry from the gas is small and can be neglected. The system resembles a continuous cocurrent flow dryer. The required production rate is 50 kg solid per hour (dry basis) per metre length of the drum. The other relevant data are: X_i = 0.8; X_f = 0.03; X_c = 0.15; X^* ≈ 0; Y_1 = 0.015; rate of supply of hot air = 7.0 kg (dry basis) per kg dry solid; and k_Y = 160 kg/h·m²·ΔY. Suggest a drum diameter and rpm of the drum.

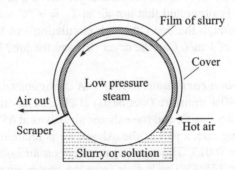

Figure 11.31   Schematic of a drum dryer.

11.18 (*Sizing of a rotary dryer*)[2]   A fine granular solid is to be dried at a rate of 600 kg/h from 22% to 0.2% moisture (all wet basis) in a countercurrent rotary dryer using hot air at

110°C of humidity 0.012 kg/(kg dry air). The moist solid fed to the dryer is at 25°C and the dried solid leaves at 80°C. The moisture in the solid is unbound. In order to avoid dusting, the gas velocity should not exceed 1.7 m/s. The specific heat of the dry solid is 0.9 kJ/kg·°C. Suggest a dryer size.

11.19 (*Sizing of a rotary dryer*)[2] A wet solid at 28°C with 25% moisture (wet basis) is to be dried in a direct-heat countercurrent rotary dryer. Hot air at 175°C containing 0.01 kg moisture per kg dry air is available and an output of 500 kg dry solid per hour is required. The heat capacity of the solid is 0.85 kJ/(kg dry solid)(K). The velocity of the gas must not exceed 1.5 m/s. Estimate the diameter and length of the drier. Given the following data and information, calculate the anticipated solid holdup: rpm, $N = 4$; slope, $S = 1$ in 16; particle size of the solid, $d_p = 0.5$ mm.

11.20 (*Calculation of drying rate and time from laboratory data*)[2] Test drying of 4.2 kg wet solid is done in a laboratory apparatus under constant drying conditions. The area for drying is 0.1 m^2, and the mass of the dry solid is 3.0 kg. The humidity of the drying gas is 0.015 kg per kg dry air. From the drying data given below, calculate the drying rates at different moisture contents of the solid. Plot the t–W and X–N curves.

t (h)	0	0.25	0.50	0.75	1.0	1.25	1.5	1.75	2.0	2.25	2.5
W (kg)	4.2	4.145	4.091	4.035	3.978	3.920	3.868	3.811	3.756	3.704	3.653
t (h)	2.75	3.0	3.25	3.5	3.75	4.0	4.25	4.5	4.75	5.0	5.5
W (kg)	3.605	3.558	3.516	3.480	3.448	3.421	3.394	3.368	3.345	3.323	3.285
t (h)	6.0	6.5	7.0	7.5	8.0						
W (kg)	3.253	3.226	3.202	3.183	3.166						

(a) Determine from the X–N plot, the critical moisture and the equilibrium moisture. How is the drying rate related to the moisture content in the falling rate period?

(b) During the constant rate period, the surface temperature of the wet solid is estimated to be 46°C. Calculate the mass transfer coefficient for drying.

(c) If 'unsaturated surface drying' occurs in the falling rate period, what fraction of the surface is covered by 'dry patches' when the moisture content of the solid is 0.15 kg/(kg dry solid)?

(d) If the same solid is required to be dried from 25% to 3% moisture (wet basis), under the same drying conditions, calculate the drying time.

11.21 (*Time of freeze-drying*)[1] A 2-cm thick slab of a food material having 130% moisture (dry basis) is to be freeze-dried to almost bone-dry condition. The following data and information are available: bulk density of the bone-dry solid = 0.4 gm/cm^3; thermal conductivity of the dry solid = 1.25×10^{-5} kcal/m.s.K; effective coefficient of heat transfer to the solid surface = 70 kJ/m^2·h·K; temperature of the fluid medium in the dryer = -8°C; condenser temperature = -30°C; heat of sublimation of ice (at -30°C) = 620 cal/gm. The solid does not under go any shrinking. If the drying process is heat transfer controlled, calculate the drying time.

REFERENCES

AIChE, *Spray Dryers—A Guide to Performance Evaluation*, 2nd ed., New York, 2003.

Christiansen, O.B., and M.S. Sardo, 'Find the optimum flash dryer,' *Chem. Eng. Progr.*, *97*, August, 2001, 54–58.

Cook, E.M., and H.D. DuMont, *Process Drying and Practice*, McGraw-Hill, New York, 1991.

Cook, E.M., 'Process calculations for partial recycle dryers,' *Chem. Engg.*, April 1996, 82–89.

Keey, R.B., *Drying Principles and Practice*, Pergamon Press, 1972.

Kimball, G., 'Direct vs. indirect drying: optimizing the process,' *Chem Engg.*, May 2001, 74–81.

Lattman, M., and R. Laible, 'Batch drying: the 'indirect solution' to sensitive drying problems', *Chem. Engg.*, November 2005, 34–39.

Liptak, B., 'Optimizing drying performance', *Chem. Engg.*, February 1998, 110–114; March 1998, 96–104.

Masters, K., *Spray Drying Handbook*, 5th ed., Longman, 1991.

Nonhebel, G., and A. Moss, *Drying of Solids in the Chemical Industry*, CRC Press, 1971.

Parker, N.H., 'Aids to dryer selection,' *Chem. Engg.*, June 24, 1963, 115–119.

Ruthven, D.M. (Ed.), *Encyclopedia of Separation Technology*, John Wiley, New York, 1997.

Sandal, O.C. et al., 'The relationship between transport properties and rates of freeze drying of poultry meat', *AIChE J.*, *13*(1967) 428.

Sloan, C.E., T.D. Wheelock, and G.T. Tsao, 'Drying', *Chem. Engg.*, June 19, 1967, 167–200.

Treybal, R.E., *Mass Transfer Operations*, 3rd ed., McGraw-Hill, 1980.

Tsao, G.T., and T.D. Wheelock, 'Drying theory and calculations', *Chem. Engg.* June 19, 1967, 201–214.

van't Land, C.M., 'Selection of industrial dryers,' *Chem. Engg.*, March 5, 1984, 53–61.

Williams-Gardener, A., *Industrial Drying*, Leonard Hill, London, 1971.

12 | Adsorption

Adsorption may be defined as selective concentration or retention of one or more components of a mixture on a solid surface. The solid that adsorbs a component is called the *adsorbent*, and the component adsorbed is called the *adsorbate*. The adsorption process is a result of interaction between the adsorbate molecules and the surface (or pore wall) of the adsorbent. The selective transfer of some of the molecules of a mixture to the surface or into the bulk of a solid (or a liquid) is called *sorption*. The term sorption is used in a more general sense and includes both *adsorption* and *absorption*. When the sorbed molecules or atoms remain concentrated or accumulated at or near the surface, the process is called *adsorption*. But if these sorbed molecules are distributed throughout a liquid phase, the process is called *absorption*. The uptake of a gas or a liquid by a polymer is also called *sorption*. The adsorption phenomenon provides an excellent method of separation of a variety of fluid mixtures, particularly at low concentrations, and as such it is recognized as an important mass transfer operation. It may be noted that adsorption may occur on a liquid surface too, but it is of less practical importance than adsorption in a solid.

Adsorption of a substance on a solid surface occurs because of an 'affinity' of the surface for the particular substance. It is natural that the surface will have varying affinity for different substances. For example, activated alumina has a strong affinity for moisture, but not for hydrocarbons. Thus, a judiciously selected adsorbent preferentially adsorbs the targeted compounds from a mixture thereby acting as a medium of separation.

One way of classification of adsorption is based on how strong the interaction between the adsorbent and the adsorbate is. If the force of interaction is rather weak, the type of adsorption is called *physical adsorption* (also called *physisorption*). The forces of physical adsorption are Van der Waal's force (or dispersion force) and electrostatic force, and the heat of adsorption is at best a few times (1–4 times) the heat of vaporization of the component concerned. On the other hand, if the interaction between a solute and the adsorbent is very strong, a chemical bond may be formed between them. This is called *chemical adsorption* or *chemisorption*. The heat of chemisorption is considerably larger than that of physical adsorption. Chemisorption occurs as an essential step of a heterogeneous catalytic reaction. For example, chemisorption of nitrogen occurs on the surface of promoted iron catalyst during the ammonia synthesis reaction. Physical adsorption is reversible, but chemisorption may not be so.

The reverse of adsorption is called *desorption* (it may be recalled that the reverse of absorption is also called desorption). The 'reversible' nature of physical adsorption is the basis of its exploitation for separation of mixtures. In some applications, the adsorbed species may have material value and its separation is followed by recovery. A typical example is the recovery of a hydrocarbon from a waste gas stream by adsorption. In other cases the adsorbed species may not have any value and the question of the recovery of species or regeneration of the adsorbent is not relevant. For example, the spent adsorbent after removal of impurities from vegetable oils cannot be reused and is discarded. In a majority of cases, the spent or loaded adsorbent bed is 'regenerated' by desorption of the solute and is used again. However, the regenerated bed may not always fully regain its original capacity for adsorption. An adsorbent like active carbon is discarded after varying number of adsorption–desorption cycles depending upon the feed and the adsorbent. Sometimes a bed of adsorbent is used for months or even a year.

Pressure (or concentration) and temperature are the two most important variables that determine the amount of a solute adsorbed per unit mass of the adsorbent at equilibrium. Adsorption is favoured at a higher pressure and a lower temperature. Conversely, a lower pressure or a higher temperature favours desorption. In industrial practice, a feed mixture to be separated is first brought in contact with the adsorbent in a vessel when adsorption of one or more of the components occurs. When the bed gets nearly exhausted or saturated, the flow of the feed is stopped and the bed is subjected to desorption or regeneration. A suitable carrier or regenerating gas is passed through the bed, and after some time, most of the adsorbed molecules are removed. The bed becomes 'regenerated' and ready for adsorption again. Two vessels with packed beds of adsorbents are commonly used to do the job as shown in Figure 12.1. The beds operate in cycles. When bed-1 receives the feed and operates in the adsorption mode, bed-2 receives the carrier or purge gas and operates in the regeneration mode. After a half-cycle, switching over of the feed and the regenerating medium is done. Bed-2, regenerated by this time, starts receiving the feed and bed-1 is subjected to regeneration. A complete cycle consists of an adsorption and a desorption or regeneration step.

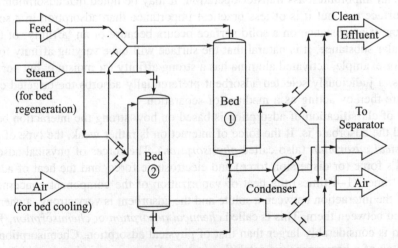

Figure 12.1   Flow diagram of a dual-bed adsorption-desorption system.

Regeneration may be done by heating the bed (by passing a hot carrier or purge or stripping gas like superheated steam through it) or by reducing the pressure in the bed (vacuum regeneration). The former strategy is called *thermal regeneration* or *temperature swing* or *thermal swing adsorption* (TSA) and the latter is called *pressure swing adsorption* (PSA). These strategies will be discussed in detail later in this chapter. If thermal regeneration is done, it is necessary to cool the bed (by passing a cool gas through the bed, for example) before it goes for adsorption again. In Figure 12.1, steam is the regenerating (or stripping) medium. In the case of liquid–solid adsorption, the spent adsorbent bed is regenerated by passing a solvent through the spent bed, often in the reverse direction. This is called *backwashing*.

12.1 COMMERCIAL ADSORBENTS AND THEIR APPLICATIONS

The use of adsorption as a purification technique is pretty old. A few examples of use of wood char in ancient Egypt and also in Japan for purifying medicinal substances and water have been cited by Suzuki (1990). Two hundred years ago, bone charcoal and wood charcoal were used for the decolourization and refining of sugar. Now adsorption is a very imporatnt technique of separation and purification of gases and liquids (Knaebel, 1995; Keller, 1995; Notaro et al., 1999), and also for the treatment of water and wastewater (Eckenfelder, 2000). Several commercially important adsorbents, their characteristics and applications are given in Table 12.1. Four common commercial adsorbents are: (i) activated carbon, (ii) zeolites or molecular sieves, (iii) silica gel, and (iv) activated alumina. Their global sales also come in this order. The characteristics, the important methods of preparation and typical applications of these materials are described below (Keller et al., 1987; Kovach, 1997; Suzuki, 1990).

12.1.1 Activated Carbon

It is a microcrystalline non-graphitic form of carbon. A variety of carbonaceous raw materials are used for the preparation of activated carbon. The common starting materials for 'decolourizing activated carbon' are lignin, lignite, peat, wood, saw dust, etc. These materials are generally mixed with an alkali metal sulfate, carbonate or phosphate, or zinc chloride and then calcined at 500–900°C. The calcined mass is washed, filtered and dried. The variety of activated carbons used for vapour or gas adsorption are made from nut shells (mostly coconut shell), rice hull, peat, refinery residue, or coal. These materials are initially calcined at 400–500°C, and then subjected to controlled oxidation and 'activation' at 800–1000°C in a stream of steam, carbon dioxide, or even flue gas. The last step of preparation is also responsible for the development of micropores.

Activated carbon has considerable hydrophobic character. But it contains some oxygen complexes at the surface (also called 'surface oxide groups') which are formed during the activation stage. The oxide groups may be of different types: carboxylic, lactone, phenolic and carbonyl groups (Suzuki, 1990). Such surface oxides impart some surface polarity or hydrophilicity to activated carbon.

The commercially used activated carbon may be of two important types: 'powdered activated carbon' (PAC), and 'granular activated carbon' (GAC). Powdered activated carbon has an average particle size in the range 15 to 25 μm. For such small size particles, intraparticle diffusional resistance may not become the rate-limiting step. The surface area ranges from 200 to above

Table 12.1 Commercially important adsorbents and their characteristics (Keller, 1995)

Adsorbent	Characteristics	Commercial uses	Strengths	Weaknesses
Activated carbon	Hydrophobic surface, favours organics over air or water	Removal of organic pollutants from aqueous or gaseous effluents	Cheapest hydrophobic adsorbent, workhorse of pollution control	Difficult to regenerate if fouling occurs, may catch fire during air regeneration.
Carbon molecular sieve (CMS)	Separates on the basis of difference in intraparticle diffusivity	Production of N_2 from air	The only practical adsorbent for selective adsorption of O_2 over N_2	The only commercial application is in air separation
Silica gel	High capacity hydrophilic adsorbent	Drying of air and other gases	Higher capacity than zeolite molecular sieves (ZMS)	Not very effective if the moisture level has to be reduced to very low
Activated alumina	High capacity, hydrophilic adsorbent	Drying of gas streams	Higher capacity than ZMS	Not as effective as ZMS for the removal of moisture in traces
Zeolite molecular sieve (ZMS)	Hydrophilic surface, polar regular channels	Dehydration, air separation, separation of molecules based on size and shape	Separation of molecules based on both polarity and geometry	Lower adsorption capacity than many other adsorbents
Silicalite	Hydrophobic surface	Removal of organics from gas streams	Can be regenerated by burning more easily	Quite expensive
Polymer adsorbents	Styrene/divinyl benzene copolymer is most common	Removal of organics from gas streams	Less prone to fouling than activated carbon	Much more costly than activated carbon

1000 m²/g, and the void volume above 0.45 cm³/g. One of the indicators of adsorption capacity is the 'iodine number'[†]. The main uses of PAC are decolourization of food products (examples: sugar refining for the removal of colouring matters, wine production, production of sodium glutamate), water treatment (drinking water as well as wastewater), refining of vegetable oils and fats.

Granular activated carbon is available as crushed granules or as pellets. Pellets are prepared from PAC by using a binder such as coal tar pitch. The GAC, in the form of beads, is prepared by carbonizing beads of petroleum pitch. The size of the granules or pellets varies depending upon the application. For gas separation, 4 to 6 mm pellets or 4/8 to 10/20 mesh granules are used. Typical applications are found in solvent recovery from vent gases (like alcohols, ketones, chlorinated hydrocarbons, lower hydrocarbons, and aromatics like benzene, toluene, xylenes, etc), air purification, flue gas desulphurization, etc. For liquid separation, the smaller size granules or pellets (12 to 42 mesh) are preferred in order to keep the intraparticle diffusional resistance low. Operational requirements relating to handling, pressure drop, elutriation and abrasion during backwashing or regeneration also limit the particle size. Applications in liquid separation include removal of organics from water, removal of trace contaminants and odour from drinking water, and wastewater treatment (Cooney, 1999; Metcalfe and Eddy, 2003). Active carbon is used as an adsorptive medium in sampling tubes for gases and in protective equipment such as respiratory cartridges (see for example, Yoon and Nelson, 1984, for an analysis of adsorption kinetics in a respiratory cartridge).

Pore size distribution and surface area, outer surface qualities and chemical composition all strongly affect the capacity, the selectivity, the regenerability, the kinetics of adsorption, the compatibility and the cost of activated carbon. The specific surface area ranges from 300 to 1500 m² per gram. The apparent density of activated carbon varies from 400 to 600 kg/m³ and the ash content varies from 2 to 25% (Knaebel, 1995).

Activated carbon is also prepared in the form of fibres by carbonizing synthetic fibres of phenolic resins, polyacrylonitrile or viscose rayon. The fibre diameter ranges from 7 to 15 μm. The diffusional resistance within a fibre remains pretty small.

12.1.2 Molecular Sieves (or Synthetic Zeolites)

Molecular sieves or 'synthetic zeolites' are crystalline aluminosilicates of metals like sodium, potassium, magnesium or calcium. These are inorganic crystalline polymers with the three-dimensional interacting network structure of AlO_4 and SiO_4 tetrahedra linked through oxygen atoms (Ruthven, 1984). The structure contains interstitial voids and connecting channels which are occupied by cations and water molecules. A pretty large variety of natural zeolites (for example, chabazite, mordenite, etc.) is found to have remarkable adsorption capacities. This has led to an extensive research work on the synthesis of zeolites. Nowadays, molecular sieves or synthetic zeolites are used not only for the purification and recovery of certain substances but also for the fractionation of mixtures.

[†] 'Iodine number' is an indicator of the 'activity' of a sample of active carbon used for adsorption of compounds and pollutants from water. An amount of the sample is contacted with a standard solution of iodine. The milligrams of iodine adsorbed per gram of carbon is its iodine number (ASTM-D4607). For gas separation applications, the 'activity' is measured in terms of the quantity of carbon tetrachloride adsorbed by a sample of active carbon expressed as mass% (ASTM-D3467).

Synthetic zeolites

The starting materials for zeolite preparation are sodium aluminate, silicate and hydroxide, alumina trihydrate (Al_2O_3, $3H_2O$), colloidal silica and silicic acid. The reaction among the ingredients is followed by gel formation under controlled conditions. The gel is crystallized very slowly. The crystalline product is filtered, washed and then ion-exchanged to replace sodium by other suitable cations to the desired degree. The final product may be in the form of powder or pellets. To prepare the latter, the powder is mixed with a clay binder, made into pellets, dried and then fired to get the final product.

Commercial molecular sieves are generally of types A or X. There are three categories under type A—namely, 3A, 4A and 5A (3A means a variety having a nominal pore diameter of 3 Å). It has the general formula $Na_{12}(Al_2O_2)_{12}(SiO_2)_{12} \cdot nH_2O$. The type 4A sieves are prepared in the sodium form. The replacement of sodium by potassium ions gives 3A sieves; sodium is replaced by calcium ions in 5A sieves. The value of n may be as high as 27. The type X molecular sieve may be 10X (nominal pore diameter = 8 Å) or 13X (nominal pore diameter = 10 Å). The general formula is $Na_{12}(Al_2O_2)_{86}(SiO_2)_{106} \cdot nH_2O$. Exchange of sodium ions by other metal ions may be done easily. The value of n for type X sieve may be as high as 276. The framework structures of zeolite are schematically shown in Figure 12.2(a).

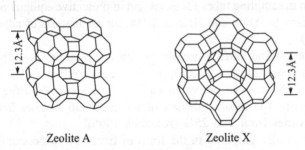

Zeolite A   Zeolite X

Figure 12.2(a)   The framework structures of zeolite.

The molecular sieves have both adsorption and catalytic properties. The type A sieves are widely used as dehydrating agents. But novel uses of these materials are based on their ability to 'sieve' molecules depending on their relative sizes and the pore diameters of the adsorbent (this is why these are called *molecular sieves*). The type 5A material is used for the separation of *n*-paraffins from their branched or cyclic counterparts (a straight-chain hydrocarbon molecule can enter the pores and get adsorbed, but a branched or cyclic compound cannot). The type 10X molecular sieve is used for the separation of aromatics. The type 13X is used for the removal of H_2O and CO_2 from gases, the removal of H_2S from natural gas (sweetening), and the removal of mercaptans from petroleum fractions. Molecular sieves are also widely used as catalysts, and their catalytic property considerably depends upon their ability of selective adsorption.

Carbon molecular sieves

The carbon molecular sieves (CMS) are largely used for N_2 production by employing the pressure swing adsorption (PSA) method. The modern method of manufacture of a CMS starts with bituminous coal which is oxidized in air below its ignition temperature. It is powdered, mixed with a polymeric binder and pelletized. The pellets are carbonized and further processed. A CMS adsorbs O_2 much faster than it can absorb N_2. A huge amount of CMS is used in N_2 production.

12.1.3 Silica Gel

Pure silica is a chemically inactive non-polar material. But when it has a hydroxyl (silanol) functional group, the surface becomes very polar and hydrophilic [Figure 12.2(b)]. This material is called *silica gel*. It is prepared from sodium silicate which is neutralized by sulphuric acid to yield a colloidal solution of silicic acid (3 to 5 nm particle size). The colloidal product is coagulated to form a hydrogel which is subjected to controlled dehydration followed by crushing and sieving. Spherical silica gel particles are prepared by spray drying of the hydrogel in hot air.

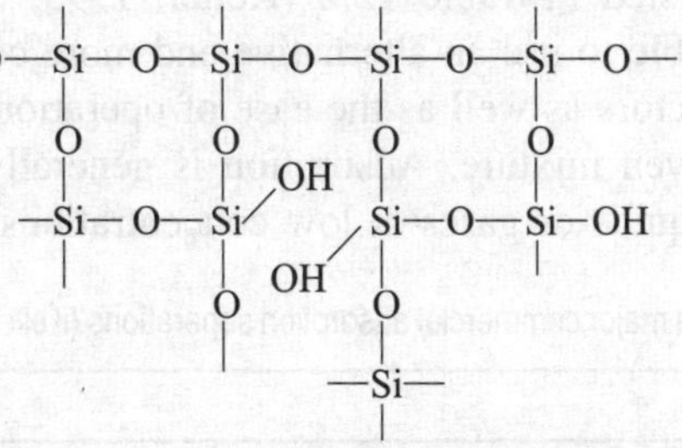

Figure 12.2(b) Network structure of silica gel.

Silica gels of two types of pore distribution (types A and B) are commercially more important. The type A has pores in the range 2–3 nm diameter and specific surface area of about 650 m^2 per gram. The type B has considerably larger pores (about 7 nm) and has specific surface area of about 450 m^2 per gram. The porosity is about 50–55%. Silica gel retains about 4–6% water when heated to about 350°C. If it loses this water on further heating, it no longer remains hydrophilic and loses the capacity to adsorb water. The adsorbed water molecules bind to 'silanol' groups in the adsorbent ($\equiv$Si–OH·OH$_2$; see Yang, 1987). The main uses of silica gel are for drying of air and natural gas, drying of liquid hydrocarbons, and other gases. A crystalline and non-hydrophilic form of silica, called *silicalite*, is useful for the adsorption of organics.

12.1.4 Activated Alumina

This is basically a highly porous alumina (generally γ-alumina; the highly stable form, α-alumina, is much less active). Activated alumina is chemically inert to most gases and vapours and has a high resistance to shock and abrasion. It is manufactured from precipitated aluminum hydroxide gel that may be obtained by ammoniation of an aluminium salt like sulphate, or by acidification of a solution of sodium aluminate. The hydroxide is washed, dried and made in the form of granules or spheres. This is followed by activation in a stream of air at an elevated temperature when the material is dehydrated to about 6% moisture content and develops a porous structure. The physical characteristics of activated alumina are: pore size: 1.5–6 nm; fractional porosity: around 0.4; specific surface area: 200–400 m^2/g; bulk density: 700–900 kg/m^3. The common shapes are balls (1–8 mm dia), granules and extrudates or pellets (2–4 mm dia), and powder.

This material is widely used as a dehydrating agent for both gases and liquids; the moisture adsorption capacity varies from 0.07 to 0.25 kg water per kg alumina. The important specific uses are: drying of air (in an air liquefaction plant, for example), hydrocarbons, sulphur dioxide, refrigerants, drying of liquids such as kerosene, gasoline, aromatics, etc. The adsorbents can be reactivated many times by heating to an elevated temperature (177–316°C) without any appreciable loss of activity.

12.1.5   Applications of Adsorbents

A few applications of adsorbents have been given in Table 12.1. There are certain separation or purification problems for which adsorption is the unique solution. A number of commercial adsorption processes are listed in Table 12.2 (Keller, 1995; Shanley, 2000). For some gas purification jobs, it is possible to use an alternative and more common process like absorption or distillation. Economic factors as well as the ease of operation determine the selection of the separation process for a given mixture. Adsorption is generally preferred for the removal or recovery of solutes from liquids or gases at low concentrations (generally 1000 ppm or less).

Table 12.2   Some major commercial adsorption separations (Keller, 1995; Shanley, 2000)

Separation	Adsorbent
Gas Bulk Separation	
Normal paraffins/*iso*-paraffins, aromatics	Zeolite
N_2/O_2	Zeolite
O_2/N_2	Carbon molecular sieve
CO, CH_4, N_2, Ar, NH_3 from H_2	Zeolite, activated
Hydrocarbons from emissions	Activated carbon
Gas Purification	
H_2O/cracker gas, natural gas, synthesis gas	Silica gel, alumina, zeolite
CO_2/C_2H_4, natural gas	Zeolite
Hydrocarbons, solvents/vent streams	Activated carbon
Sulphur compounds/natural gas, H_2, liquefied petroleum gas, etc.	Zeolite
SO_2/vent streams	Zeolite
Indoor air pollutants (VOC's)/air	Activated carbon
Tank vent emissions/air or N_2	Activated carbon
Odours/air	Activated carbon
Liquid Bulk Separation	
Normal paraffins/*iso*-paraffins, aromatics	Zeolites
p-Xylene/*o*-xylene, *m*-xylene	Zeolite
Detergent-range olefins/paraffins	Zeolite
Fructose/glucose	Zeolite
Liquid Purification	
H_2O/organics, oxygenated organics, halogenated organics	Silica gel, alumina, zeolite
Organics, halogenated organics/H_2O	Activated alumina, silica gel
Odour and taste bodies/H_2O	Activated carbon
Sulphur compounds/organics	Zeolite
Colour contaminants/petroleum fractions, syrups, vegetable oils	Activated carbon
Fermentation products/fermenter effluents	Activated carbon

Separations in which the adsorbate concentration in the feed is a few per cent are called *bulk separation*; if the feed contains less than a per cent of the substance to be separated, the process is called *purification*. Adsorption is widely used as an alternative to distillation when the latter becomes energy-intensive (example: air separation). It is also preferred in the following situations (Keller, 1995): (i) if the relative volatility is less than 1.5, (ii) if the distillation temperature is very low (cryogenic condition) or very high (above 300°C), (iii) if the operating pressure is less than about 2 kPa or greater than about 5 MPa, (iv) if undesirable reactions occur during distillation, and (v) if the high boiling compounds are to be separated.

The UOP's Sorbex Simulated Moving Bed Technology has got good commercial success for separation of difficult mixtures like *p*-xylene/C8 aromatics (Parex process), *n*- and *iso*-paraffins of close molecular weights (Molex process), fructose-glucose (Sarex process), etc. Regeneration of the bed is done by the displacement-purge adsorption (DPA) technique (Keller, 1995).

A large quantity of activated carbon is used for drinking water purification and for wastewater treatment. The details are available in Metcalfe and Eddy (2003) and Eckenfelder (2000).

12.2 CHARACTERISTICS AND PROPERTIES OF ADSORBENTS

The following three important attributes of an adsorbent make it suitable and effective for separation of a mixture: (i) selectivity, (ii) adsorption capacity, and (iii) reversibility of adsorption. An adsorbent must selectively bind the target component(s). For some adsorbents, selectivity is governed by the difference in affinity (or even by the difference in the rate of diffusion in the pores) of the target molecules from that of other molecules for the active sites of adsorption. Adsorbents being highly porous substances, most of the uptake occurs within an adsorbent pellet or particle. Different components are likely to diffuse into a pellet at different rates giving rise to selectivity for the molecules that diffuse faster. Selectivity due to differences in the rate of diffusion and adsorption is sometimes called *kinetic selectivity*. Further, the molecular size and the shape of the components in a mixture vary. Thus, some of the components may not enter the pores of an adsorbent particle if the molecular size is larger than the pore size. Separation occurs primarily by size exclusion in such a case. The above three factors—affinity, intraparticle diffusion rate, and size—determine the selectivity individually or collectively.

An adsorbent must have a reasonably high capacity of adsorption so that the adsorbent required for a separation job is not large. The adsorption capacity, in turn, depends primarily upon the affinity of adsorption and the specific surface area (m^2/g). The adsorption capacity may slowly decrease on repeated use and regeneration. Reversibility of adsorption is a necessary condition if the selectively adsorbed substance is to be recovered or the adsorbent is to be regenerated and reused. But adsorption need not be reversible if the recovery of the adsorbent is not desired and if it is discarded after use.

The other important characteristics of an adsorbent are: (i) particle size and its distribution, (ii) porosity and pore-size distribution, (iii) specific surface area, and (iv) structural strength and stability. A good adsorbent must have a high porosity and a narrow pore-size distribution. The last factor is especially important for size-selective adsorbents like zeolites. Pores have been broadly classified as *micropores* (less than 20 Å dia), *mesopores* (20–500 Å dia), and *macropores* (pore dia larger than 500 Å or 0.05 μm).

The measurement of porosity or fractional void volume is not very difficult. The porosity of a particle is given by $\varepsilon_p = 1 - (\rho_p/\rho_s)$, where ρ_p = particle density, and ρ_s = true density of the solid. The measurement of pore-size distribution may be done by mercury penetration in an instrument called *mercury porosimeter*. The working principle of the instrument is based on the following equation that gives the pressure P to be applied on a liquid to fill the pores of radius larger than r'.

$$r' = -\frac{2 \times 10^6 \sigma \cos\theta}{P} \qquad (12.1)$$

where

    σ = surface tension of mercury (0.47 N/cm at 298 K)

    θ = the contact angle between mercury and the sample surface

    P = pressure to be applied, in N/m^2

    r' = radius of the pore, in μm.

A small amount of the sample is put in the *penetrometer* (it is the name of the sample holder which is gradually filled with mercury) and evacuated to a high vacuum. Mercury is then allowed to enter the penetrometer. The free space is first filled with mercury. As the pumping pressure of mercury is increased, it starts filling the pores. The volume of mercury that enters the penetrometer is measured against the applied pressure. The radius of the smallest pores filled corresponding to an applied pressure is calculated from the above equation. The mercury penetration data can be plotted as cummulative pore volume versus the minimum pore diameter. Another method, particularly suitable for micropores, is the nitrogen adsorption method carried out at the liquid nitrogen temperature (–196°C). Adsorption of nitrogen occurs on the walls of large pores and 'capillary condensation' (see Section 14.2.4) in the small pores. Using the adsorption isotherm of nitrogen and the amount of nitrogen adsorbed, the pore-size distribution can be determined. The determination of the specific surface area of an adsorbent is discussed in Section 12.5.

12.3 ADSORPTION EQUILIBRIA

Let us recall our discussion on equilibrium in a gas–liquid system in Section 4.2. If the vessel shown in Figure 4.1 and referred to in Section 4.2 contains some solid adsorbent instead of the liquid, and if the gas phase contains an adsorbable component, adsorption and desorption of molecules will occur simultaneously. But if an experiment starts with a fresh lot of adsorbent, the rate of adsorption will be more than the rate of desorption for some time. Eventually, these rates will become equal and adsorption equilibrium will be established. At a constant temperature, the amount adsorbed per unit mass of the adsorbent depends upon the partial pressure of the adsorbent in the gas phase (or on the concentration, in the case of adsorption from a solution). The equilibrium relation between the amount adsorbed q (mass adsorbed per unit mass of the adsorbent) and the concentration C (or partial pressure p) of the adsorbate or solute at a constant temperature T, is called an *adsorption isotherm*.

$$q = q(C) \qquad \text{(at a constant temperature } T) \qquad (12.2)$$

This functional relation depends upon temperature. A plot of the equilibrium adsorbent loading q versus temperature T at a constant pressure of the adsorbent is called an *isobar* (Kovach,

1997). Similarly, a plot of the logarithm of the concentration (ln C) or the partial pressure (ln p) of the solute in the fluid versus the inverse of absolute temperature ($1/T$) for a constant loading q of the adsorbent is called an *isostere* (see Example 12.1).

$$C = \psi(1/T) \qquad \text{or} \qquad p = \psi'(1/T) \qquad \text{(at constant } q) \qquad (12.3)$$

Different types of adsorption isotherms occur for various adsorbent–adsorbate pairs. Braunauer et al. (1940) identified five basic types of adsorption isotherms shown in Figure 12.3(a). These isotherms represent the following situations.

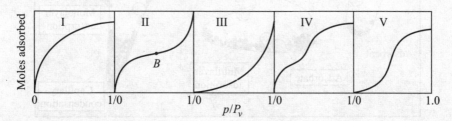

Figure 12.3(a)   Five basic types of isotherms identified by Braunauer et al., 1940 (p = sorbate pressure; P_v = saturation vapour pressure of the sorbate).

Type I: Such an isotherm represents a system in which adsorption proceeds at best up to the formation of a mono-molecular layer of adsorbate. It is concave downwards. The adsorption technique is mostly used to remove solutes present in low concentrations; a type-1 isotherm ensures a relatively high solute loading in the solid at such concentrations. Hence an isotherm of this type is called 'favourable'; example: oxygen adsorption on carbon black at −183°C. Many common gas–solid adsorption systems exhibit this behaviour.

Type II: An indefinite multilayer (BET type) forms after completion of the monolayer; the point B at the knee of the curve indicates complete monolayer formation. Such a behaviour is pretty common in the case of physical adsorption; example: adsorption of water vapour on carbon black at 30°C.

Type III: This is a relatively rare type of isotherm. The amount of gas adsorbed increases indefinitely as its relative saturation (p/P_v) approaches unity; the heat of adsorption is equal to or less than the heat of liquefaction of the adsorbate. The isotherm is convex downwards and is 'unfavourable', since the solute loading is low at a small concentration in the fluid; example: adsorption of N_2 on ice.

Types IV and V: These isotherms have alternating convex and concave regions and reflect the phenomenon of capillary condensation within the pores.

Mono- and multi-layer adsorption of a binary gas mixture on a porous adsorbent as well as capillary condensation are illustrated in Figure 12.3(b).

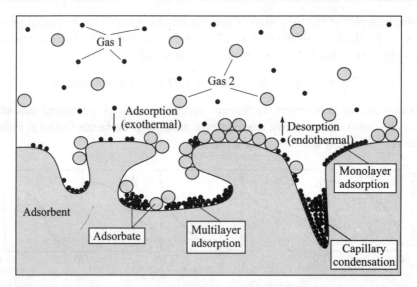

Figure 12.3(b)   Mono- and multi-layer adsorption and capillary condensation illustrated (Courtesy: RUBOTHERM Gmbh, Germany).

A few mathematical forms of adsorption isotherms, which can be fitted with physical adsorption data, have been proposed (Young and Crowell, 1962). The more important ones have been cited by Ismadji and Bhatia (2000). Some of the isotherms have reasonable theoretical basis while the others are purely empirical.

12.3.1   Langmuir Isotherm

The Langmuir isotherm (1918) is based on the simplest model of physical adsorption which assumes that (i) the molecules are adsorbed at discrete active sites on the surface, (ii) each active site adsorbs one molecule only, (iii) the adsorbing surface is energetically uniform, and (iv) there is no interaction among the adsorbed molecules. As a result, the rate of capture of adsorbate molecules by the surface is proportional to the fraction of uncovered area, $(1 - \theta)$, and to the partial pressure p or concentration of the adsorbate. The rate of desorption is proportional to the fraction of surface covered only, i.e. θ. Therefore,

$$\text{Rate of capture or adsorption} = k_1 p(1 - \theta); \quad \text{rate of escape or desorption} = k_2 \theta$$

At equilibrium, $k_1 p(1 - \theta) = k_2 \theta$ $\Rightarrow$ $\theta = \dfrac{k_1\, p}{k_2 + k_1\, p} = \dfrac{Kp}{1 + Kp}$ 　　　　(12.4)

If we write $\theta = \dfrac{q}{q_m}$,

$$q = q_m \frac{Kp}{1 + Kp} \quad \text{(where } K = k_1/k_2) \tag{12.5}$$

The above equation represents the Langmuir isotherm which has two 'adjustable parameters', q_m and K.

Here q = amount of gas adsorbed at equilibrium per gram of adsorbent at a partial pressure p; and q_m = maximum quantity of gas adsorbed per gram of adsorbent (at a *large* pressure).

At a low partial pressure of the adsorbate ($Kp \ll 1$),

$$q = q_m Kp = K_H p \tag{12.6}$$

The above equation is of the form of *Henry's law*; K_H is the 'Henry's law constant' for adsorption. This particular form represents a 'linear isotherm'.

At a large pressure ($Kp \gg 1$), $q = q_m$ and the fractional coverage of the adsorption sites is $\theta = 1$.

The Langmuir equation, Eq. (12.5), can be rearranged in the form

$$\frac{p}{q} = \frac{1}{q_m K} + \frac{p}{q_m} \tag{12.7}$$

If the Langmuir model applies to a particular system, a plot of the experimental data in the form of p/q versus p should yield a straight line of slope $1/q_m$ and intercept $1/q_m K$. From the values of the slope and the intercept, the parameters q_m and K can be calculated.

12.3.2 Freundlich Isotherm

This is an *empirical* isotherm which assumes that the amount adsorbed at equilibrium has a power law dependence on the partial pressure (or concentration) of the solute, i.e.

$$q = K' p^{1/n} \tag{12.8}$$

This is also a two-parameter isotherm; K' and n are the 'adjustable parameters'. The value of n usually varies between 1 and 5; for $n = 1$, the Freundlich isotherm (1926) takes the form of the Henry's equation, Eq. (12.6). These parameters can be evaluated from a 'log-log plot' of q versus p that should be a straight line of slope $1/n$ and intercept $\log K'$. The Freundlich isotherm represents adsorption on a surface that is energetically non-uniform. As a result, the heat of adsorption at different sites is not the same. Despite the fact that the isotherm is practically useful and can fit experimental adsorption data for many systems (for adsorption from a gas as well as from a solution), it is thermodynamically inconsistent in the sense that it does not give a finite value of the Henry's law coefficient as the concentration or partial pressure tends to zero (Knaebel, 1999).

12.3.3 Toth Isotherm

This is an empirical isotherm useful for the correlation of equilibrium adsorption data on heterogeneous adsorbents like activated carbon.

$$q = q_m \frac{p}{(b + p^n)^{1/n}} \tag{12.9}$$

It is again a three-parameter isotherm that reduces to the Henry-type equation at low pressure (or small concentration) of the solute. Valenzuela and Myers (1989) used this isotherm to correlate adsorption data for a large number of systems.

12.3.4   Sips Isotherm

This isotherm equation combines the Langmuir and the Freundlich equation in the following form.

$$q = q_m \frac{(K''p)^{1/n}}{1 + (K''p)^{1/n}} \tag{12.10}$$

Here q_m = adsorption capacity, and K'' is called the *affinity coefficient*. The parameter n gives a measure of the system heterogeniety.

12.3.5   BET Equation

The Braunauer–Emmet–Teller equation (Braunauer et al., 1938) can represent multilayer adsorption equilibrium for many systems. The equation is given as

$$q = q_m \frac{c\chi}{(1 - \chi)[1 + (c' - 1)\chi]} \tag{12.11}$$

Here

- q = quantity of gas adsorbed, in gram per gram of adsorbent
- q_m = quantity of gas to be adsorbed to form a monolayer on the surface, in gram per gram of adsorbent
- $\chi = p/P_v$
- P_v = vapour pressure of the adsorbate at the given temperature
- c' = a temperature dependent constant for a particular gas–solid system.

The BET equation is based on the assumption that the heat of adsorption remains constant till the formation of a monolayer is complete. For the secondary layer, the heat of adsorption is assumed to be equal to the heat of liquefaction of the adsorbate. This is an extremely useful equation for the determination of the specific surface area of a solid. The common procedure involves the measurement of the amount of N_2 adsorbed per gram solid at different pressures at its normal boiling point ($-196°C$). Example 12.2 illustrates the method of calculation of specific area from such data.

A few other useful isotherms—the Dubinin–Radushkevich isotherm, UNILAN isotherm, etc. —have been described by Valenzuela and Myers (1989) and Knaebel (1995).

12.3.6   Multicomponent Adsorption Equilibrium

The simplest approach to describing adsorption equilibrium in a multicomponent system is to extend the Langmuir model.

$$q_1 = q_{1m} \frac{b_1 p_1}{1 + b_1 p_1 + b_2 p_2 + \cdots} ; \qquad q_2 = q_{2m} \frac{b_2 p_2}{1 + b_1 p_1 + b_2 p_2 + \cdots} \tag{12.12}$$

It appears that the amount of a component (say, component 1) adsorbed at equilibrium at a partial pressure p_1 is less than that if no other adsorbable components were present. In other words, the presence of another component competing for active sites reduces the equilibrium adsorption of a component. A separation factor for component 1 in a mixture of 1 and 2 can be defined as

$$\alpha_{12} = \frac{x_1/y_1}{x_2/y_2} \tag{12.13}$$

where x is the mole fraction of a component in the adsorbed phase and y is that in the fluid phase at equilibrium.

Though simple, Eq. (12.12) is not quite successful in correlating or predicting multicomponent adsorption equilibrium. A Langmuir–Freundlich combined model has been found to be more effective.

$$q_i = q_{im} \frac{b_i p_i^{ni}}{1 + b_1 p_1^{n1} + b_2 p_2^{n2} + \cdots + b_i p_i^{ni} + \cdots} \tag{12.14}$$

The most successful approach to predicting multicomponent adsorption equilibrium from single component isotherm data is known as the Ideal Adsorbed Solution (IAS) theory, first proposed by Myers and Prausnitz (1965). The theory is based on the assumption that the adsorbed phase is thermodynamically 'ideal' in the sense that the equilibrium partial pressure exerted by an adsorbed component is the product of its mole fraction in the adsorbed phase and the equilibrium pressure of the pure component at the same 'spreading pressure'. A few other theories, including the 'potential theory', have been proposed to interpret multicomponent adsorption. These have been reviewed by Do, 1997.

12.4 HEAT OF ADSORPTION

Adsorption is an exothermic process. This can be established from the following basic thermodynamic equation:

$$\Delta F = \Delta H - T\Delta S \tag{12.15}$$

Adsorption being a spontaneous process, the free energy change ΔF is negative. The adsorbed molecules being in a more orderly state, the entropy change ΔS is also negative. So, the enthalpy change ΔH for adsorption must be negative, and hence the process is exothermic.

Heat of adsorption may be of three types: (i) differential heat of adsorption, (ii) integral heat of adsorption, and (iii) isosteric heat of adsorption. The total enthalpy change during adsorption from zero adsorption loading to a specified final loading at a constant temperature is the integral heat of adsorption. The differential heat of adsorption is the rate of change of the integral heat of adsorption with adsorbent loading. The isosteric heat of adsorption is the most important type of heat of adsorption from a practical point of view. An expression for this quantity can be obtained from the Clausius–Clapeyron equation:

$$(\Delta H)_{iso} = -RT^2 \frac{d \ln p}{dT} = R \frac{d \ln p}{d(1/T)} \tag{12.16}$$

(at a particular temperature, pressure and adsorbent loading)

The isosteric heat of adsorption can be determined from Eq. (12.16) if the adsorption isotherm data are available at different temperatures. If the active sites on an adsorbent are energetically homogeneous and if there is no interaction among the adsorbed molecules, the isosteric heat of adsorption is independent of adsorbent loading. For many solute-adsorbent pairs, the heat of physical adsorption is substantial—from a few kcal per gmol to 10 kcal/gmol. An adsorption isotherm, an isostere and determination of the heat of adsorption are illustrated in Example 12.1.

EXAMPLE 12.1   Ray and Box [*Ind. Eng. Chem.*, 42(1950) 1315] reported the following data on adsorption of pure propane on Columbia grade L activated carbon at different temperatures and pressures.

T = 311 K		T = 338.7 K		T = 394 K		T = 422 K	
p	q	p	q	p	q	p	q
2.266	1.044	6	1.069	7.067	0.7099	13.07	0.6798
15.6	2.819	27.2	2.469	38.67	1.677	41.73	1.264
31.74	3.48	53.2	3.078	83.21	2.238	71.07	1.611
59.6	3.968	92.67	3.512	98.54	2.37	96.27	1.831
89.74	4.207	99.97	3.635	99.97	2.4	99.97	1.894
99.97	4.342	244.8	4.188	303.4	3.251	313.7	2.785
293	4.94	424	4.475	482.6	3.599	493	3.144

p = pressure of propane (kPa); q = amount of propane adsorbed at equilibrium (millimol/g carbon).

(a) Draw the adsorption isotherms (q vs. p) at the above four temperatures, and the adsorption isosters (ln p vs. $1/T$) at constant solute loadings of q = 2.0, 2.5, 3.0 and 3.5 (mmol/g carbon).

(b) Test the applicability of the Langmuir and the Freundlich isotherms for the given data.

(c) Determine the isosteric heat of adsorption.

Solution

(a) The adsorption isotherms (q vs. p) at the four given temperatures are plotted in Figure 12.4(a). An adsorption isoster is a plot of the equilibrium pressure (ln p) of the solute versus $1/T$ at a constant loading of the solute in the solid. Horizontal lines are drawn through q = 2.0, 2.5, 3.0 and 3.5 on Figure 12.4(a). The T–p data are obtained from the intersection of such a line with the isotherms. For example, the data obtained from the figure for a constant value of q = 3.0 are:

Values of the pair (T, p) for q = 3.0:: (311, 17.5), (338.7, 48.75), (394, 225), (422, 408.75).

The isosters for q = 3.0 and also for three other values of solute loading are plotted in Figure 12.4(b).

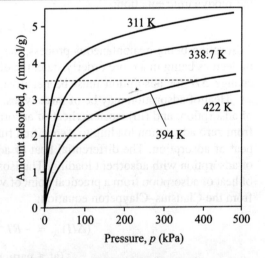

Figure 12.4(a) Adsorption isotherms of propane on activated carbon at different temperatures (Ray and Box, 1950).

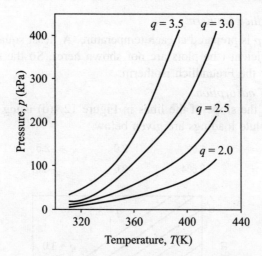

Figure 12.4(b) Adsorption isosters for different loadings q of propane on activated carbon.

(b) (i) *Fitting of the Langmuir isotherm*

Following Eq. (12.7), the values of p/q versus p are plotted at the four given temperatures in Figure 12.4(c). A 'least square line' is fitted through each set of data points, and the model parameters q_m and K of the Langmuir isotherm are obtained from the slope and the intercept of each line. The 'correlation coefficient' values for data fit given below are excellent and show the goodness of the fit.

Temperature,	$T =$	311 K	338.7 K	394 K	422 K
	$q_m =$	5.426	4.719	3.932	3.587
	$K =$	0.0509	0.0369	0.0182	0.0125
Correlation coeff.,	$\sigma^2 =$	0.998	0.999	0.995	0.994

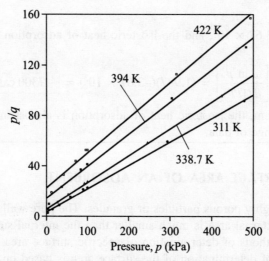

Figure 12.4(c) Fitting of Langmuir isotherm (Ray and Box, 1950).

(ii) *Fitting of the Freundlich isotherm*

A plot of ln q versus ln p is prepared at each temperature. A 'least square fit' of the data shows a poor correlation coefficient (the plots are not shown here). So the reported adsorption data cannot be fitted well by the Freundlich isotherm.

(c) *The isosteric heat of adsorption*

It can be obtained from the slope of the lines in Figure 12.4(d) using Eq. (12.16). The values obtained for different solute loadings are given below.

Solute loading, $q =$	1.5	2.0	2.5	3.0	3.5
$10^3 \times d(\ln p)/d(1/T) \quad =$	−3.684	−3.6	−3.57	−3.73	−3.76

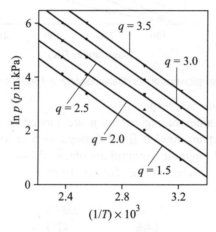

Figure 12.4(d) Plots of ln p versus $1/T$ (at constant q) for the determination of isosteric heat of adsorption.

It appears that the plots of ln p versus $1/T$ are almost parallel [Figure 12.4(d)]. The average slope is

$$\frac{d(\ln p)}{d(1/T)} = -3.67 \times 10^3,$$ and the isosteric heat of adsorption is [see Eq. (12.16)]

$$[\Delta H]_{\text{iso}} = R\left[\frac{d\ln p}{d(1/T)}\right] = (1.987)(-3.67 \times 10^3) = \boxed{-7300 \text{ cal/gmol}}$$

For this particular system, the isosteric heat of adsorption is almost independent of the solute loading in the given range of data.

12.5 SPECIFIC SURFACE AREA OF AN ADSORBENT

Good adsorbents are highly porous particles or granules. The pore walls primarily contribute to the surface area; the external area is much smaller than the internal surface area due to pores. There are different methods of determination of specific surface area.

A simple method of determination of the surface area is based on the adsorption capacity corresponding to a monomolecular layer. The latter is obtained by fitting the Langmuir isotherm or the BET isotherm to the adsorption data. The projected area α of an adsorbed molecule can be calculated from the following equation, i.e. Eq. (12.17).

$$\alpha = 1.09\left(\frac{M}{N\rho}\right)^{2/3} \tag{12.17}$$

where

M = molecular weight of the adsorbate
ρ = density of the adsorbate in the liquid phase
N = Avogadro's number

The specific surface area is given by

$$S_g = q_m N\alpha \qquad (q_m = \text{gmol adsorbed per g adsorbent}) \tag{12.18}$$

It is easy to fit the BET equation to a given set of data in order to calculate q_m. Putting $\chi = p/P_v$, Eq. (12.11) can be recast as

$$\frac{p}{q(P_v - p)} = \frac{1}{c'q_m} + \frac{(c'-1)p}{c'q_m P_v} \tag{12.19}$$

If the BET model is applicable to an adsorbent–adsorbate pair, a plot of $p/[q(P_v - p)]$ versus p/P_v should yield a straight line. The quantity q_m (= amount adsorbed in the solid corresponding to a monomolecular layer) can be calculated from the slope and the intercept of the line. Now the specific surface area can be calculated from Eq. (12.18). The technique is illustrated in Example 12.2.

EXAMPLE 12.2 The following data have been collected on equilibrium adsorption of nitrogen on an oxidation catalyst at 77.4 K, the normal boiling point of nitrogen. Determine the specific surface area of the catalyst by the BET technique.

p (pressure of N_2, mm Hg)	v (volume of N_2 adsorbed, cm^3 at NTP per 100 g solid)
10	71.3
20	142.2
40	287.7
100	679.4
150	1025
200	1053
250	1175
300	1316
350	1996
400	3451
500	5283

Solution

At $T = 77.4$ K, vapour pressure of N_2, $P_v = 760$ mm Hg. We have to prepare a plot of

$p/[v(P_v - p)]$ versus p/P_v using the above data. [Note that the amount of N_2 adsorbed has been expressed in cm^3 rather than in mmol.]

p	p/P_v	$p/[v(P_v - p)]$
10	0.0132	0.0187
20	0.0263	0.019
40	0.0526	0.0193
100	0.1316	0.0223
150	0.1974	0.024
200	0.263	0.025
250	0.329	0.028
300	0.3947	0.030
350	0.4605	0.0293
400	0.5263	0.0322
500	0.6579	0.0364

Figure 12.5 shows a plot of $p/[v(P_v - p)]$ versus p/P_v which is linear with a slope $S' = 0.0249$ and intercept $I' = 0.0187$. Then the amount adsorbed per gram to form a monolayer is

$$q_m = \frac{1}{S' + I'} = \frac{1}{0.0249 + 0.0187} = \frac{1}{0.0436} = 22.94 \text{ cm}^3/\text{g adsorbent}$$

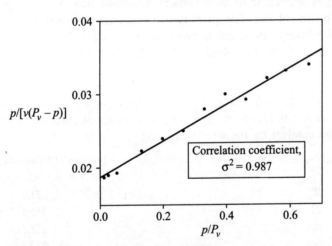

Figure 12.5   BET plot.

For liquid N_2, $\rho = 0.0808$ g/cm^3. Also, $M = 28$ and $N = 6.023 \times 10^{23}$.
Therefore,

$$\alpha = 1.09 \left(\frac{M}{N\rho} \right)^{2/3} = 1.09 \left[\frac{28}{(6.023 \times 10^{23})(0.0808)} \right]^{2/3} = 1.625 \times 10^{-15}$$

$$\Rightarrow \qquad S_g = \left(\frac{q_m N}{V} \right) \alpha = \frac{(22.94)(6.023 \times 10^{23})}{22,414} (1.625 \times 10^{-15})$$

$$= 1.002 \times 10^6 \text{ cm}^2/\text{g} = \boxed{100.2 \text{ m}^2/\text{g}}$$

12.6 SELECTION OF ADSORBENTS

The availability of a *good* adsorbent is vital to the success of an adsorption process. A few criteria for the selection of adsorbents and adsorption process are discussed below.

(a) *Ease of separation:* If the relative volatility of the components in a mixture is close to unity, both capital and operating costs of a distillation column may be prohibitive and adsorption may be an attractive choice.

(b) *Solute concentration:* A low concentration of the target component in the feed tilts the balance in favour of adsorption. For example, to treat an aqueous organic at low concentration by distillation, the entire mass has to be vaporized and the vapour is to be condensed in the overhead condenser. This entails a huge energy consumption. Adsorption may provide an easy and simpler solution to the problem. This is particularly effective in the treatment of a variety of aqueous waste streams, and also in the treatment of waste gaseous streams containing organics.

(c) *Process conditions:* Separation by adsorption may be desirable if only mild process conditions are allowed for the separation. This becomes relevant if the product is susceptible to thermal deterioration or damage.

(d) *Adsorbent criteria:* As mentioned in Section 12.2, a good adsorbent must have (i) a high adsorption capacity, (ii) reversibility of adsorption, (iii) selectivity, (iv) easy regenerability, (v) low cost, (vi) insolubility, and (vii) good mechanical strength when used in bead or pellet form. Among these factors, 'capacity' is usually the most important factor. It is expressed as the volume or mass of the solute adsorbed per unit mass of the adsorbent.

12.7 BATCH ADSORPTION IN A STIRRED VESSEL

Removal of a solute or an impurity from a solution can be carried out in a batch stirred vessel or in a packed bed of solid. The former technique is convenient if the adsorbent particles are fine. Again, for fine particles the resistance due to pore diffusion may be fairly small, and the adsorption process may be controlled by the external transport resistance. If the relevant properties of the solid and of the liquid (particle size, density and porosity, liquid properties), the adsorption equilibrium (in terms of an adsorption isotherm), and a suitable mass transfer correlation are known, it is not difficult to design a stirred vessel on the basis of first principles for a given degree of separation. Example 12.3 illustrates the procedure.

EXAMPLE 12.3 (*Batch adsorption in a stirred vessel*) Adsorption equilibrium data for the decolourization of a sample of waste oil using a special type of clay collected from a set of laboratory experiments could be fitted by a Henry's law type relation—$Y = 4.2 \times 10^{-4} X^*$, where Y = number of 'colour units' per kg oil, and X^* = number of 'colour units' per kg clay in equilibrium. One thousand kilograms of a waste oil having an initial colour concentration of 50 units has to be treated to reduce the concentration to 1 colour unit. The adsorbent has an effective specific surface area of 25 m^2/kg, and the surface mass transfer coefficient is $k_L = 5.2 \times 10^{-6}$ m/s (on the solid-phase concentration basis). The density of the oil is 950 kg/m^3.

(a) Calculate the minimum quantity of adsorbent required.
(b) What is the required contact time if 1.2 times the minimum amount of adsorbent is used?

Solution

(a) If the desired separation is to be performed by using the minimum quantity of clay, the system must reach equilibrium at the end of the treatment.

The total units of colour removed $= L_s(Y_i - Y_f) = 1000(50 - 1) = 49,000$ units

Here L_s = mass of the liquid; $Y_i = 50$, and $Y_f = 1.0$ are the initial and final colour concentrations. The equilibrium colour concentration in the clay phase is obtained from the given equilibrium relation.

$$X^* = Y/(4.2 \times 10^{-4}) = 2381Y \Rightarrow \quad X^* = (2381)(1) = 2381 \text{ units per kg clay}$$

If W is the mass of clay used, $49,000/W = X^* = 2381 \Rightarrow W = 49,000/2381 = \boxed{20.6 \text{ kg}}$

(b) Mass of adsorbent used (1.2 times the minimum) $= (20.6)(1.2) = 24.72$ kg

At any time t, let the colour concentration in the oil be Y units/kg.

$\Rightarrow$ units of colour in 1000 kg oil $= 1000Y$, and the units of colour removed $= (1000)(50 - Y)$.

Colour concentration in the clay (at time t), $X = (1000)(50 - Y)/24.72 = 40.45(50 - Y)$; equilibrium conc., $X^* = 2381Y$.

By an unsteady state mass balance,

$$-\frac{d}{dt}(1000Y) = a'm_s k_L(X^* - X)$$

$$= \left(25 \frac{\text{m}^2}{\text{kg}} \times 24.72 \text{ kg}\right)\left(5.2 \times 10^{-6} \frac{\text{m}}{\text{s}}\right)[2381Y - (40.45)(50 - Y)]$$

$$\Rightarrow \qquad -\frac{dY}{dt} = 3.214 \times 10^{-6}(2421.45Y - 2022.5)$$

Integrating from $t = 0$, $Y = 50$ to $t = t$, $Y = 1$ (the final concentration of colour in the oil),

$$-\int_{50}^{1} \frac{dY}{2421.45Y - 2022.5} = 3.214 \times 10^{-6} \int_0^t dt$$

$$\Rightarrow \qquad \frac{1}{2421.45} \ln \frac{(2421.45)(50) - 2022.5}{2421.45 - 2022.5} = 3.214 \times 10^{-6} t$$

$$\Rightarrow \quad \text{the required time, } t = 732 \text{ s} = \boxed{12.2 \text{ min}}$$

12.8 ADSORPTION IN A FIXED BED

Most industrial gas adsorption operations are carried out in a fixed bed of adsorbent following the adsorption-regeneration strategy described at the beginning of this chapter. Separation or removal of a solute from a liquid solution by adsorption is also frequently done in a fixed bed.

An adsorption isotherm for a solute–adsorbent pair only indicates the capacity of uptake of the solute by the adsorbent at equilibrium under a given set of physical conditions (for example, temperature, pressure, solute concentration, etc.). But an isotherm does not speak about the rate or 'the kinetics of adsorption'.[†] A knowledge of both equilibrium and kinetics of adsorption is required for the *sizing* of an adsorption bed or column.

The rate of adsorption in a bed or a part thereof depends upon a number of factors. There are broadly two mass transfer resistances in series: (i) the resistance to transport of the solute from the bulk of the gas to the surface of an adsorbent particle presumably through a stagnant film of the gas, and (ii) that due to diffusion of the solute through the pores (macro-, meso- and micro-pores) of an adsorbent particle to reach the adsorption sites within the particle. Adsorption of the solute molecules at the active sites may also offer a resistance that may be called *adsorption kinetic resistance*. This resistance can be neglected if the intrinsic adsorption rate is fast. Thus, generally there is a concentration gradient of the solute within a particle. Also, if we look at the bed as a whole, the concentration of the solute in the gas decreases along the length of the bed because the solute is removed from the flowing carrier gas by adsorption in the bed. Both these spatial changes in concentration (within a particle as well as along the bed) depend upon time. Therefore, a rigorous theoretical analysis of the adsorption rate process and the solute concentration in the bed involves two differential equations obtained by an unsteady state mass balance—one for the solute concentration within a particle and another for that along the bed (Ruthven, 1984). Derivation of these equations will be taken up in Section 12.10. Now we make an attempt to present a simplified physical description of the adsorption process in a fixed bed based on the concept of a 'mass transfer zone' (MTZ) suggested by Michaels (1952) and others.

12.8.1 Mass Transfer Zone (MTZ) and Breakthrough

Here we look at the adsorption process in a packed bed from a macroscopic point of view (Lukchis, 1973). Let the concentration of the solute in the feed stream be C_o, that in the bulk gas (or fluid) at any axial position z in the bed be C. The adsorbent concentration in the solid in equilibrium with the feed (i.e. *saturated* bed) is q_o. The solute concentration in the adsorbent is q at the axial position z in the bed. The corresponding local non-dimensional solute concentration in the bed is $x' = q/q_o$; the dimensionless bed concentration at equilibrium (or saturation) is $x' = 1$.

When the flow of feed into a fresh or regenerated bed (total length of the bed = L) starts, the initial rate of adsorption, particularly near the bed entrance, is pretty fast. As the gas flows through the bed, the concentration of the solute in it decreases because of adsorption. The solute concentration in the adsorbent also decreases along the length and a transient (or time dependent) concentration profile of the adsorbed solute in the bed develops. The solute concentrations in the fluid and in the solid change along the bed at any time, and also with time at any location in the bed [i.e. $C = C(z, t)$, and $q = q(z, t)$]. Such concentration profiles at times $t = 0+$ and $t = t_1$ are shown in Figure 12.6(a). At a small time ($t = 0+$), no part of the bed is 'saturated'. At a later time $t = t_1$, the bed gets saturated near the inlet (i.e. $x' = q/q_o = 1$ at $z = 0$), but the adsorbed

---

[†] Equilibrium and kinetics of a process are mutually independent. For example, if we consider a chemically reactive system, the equilibrium constant indicates the theoretical maximum conversion. But it is in no way related to the kinetics or the rate of reaction. The latter again indicates how fast the reaction can proceed at a given concentration of the reactant and at a particular temperature but is totally silent about the maximum or equilibrium conversion attainable. The same applies to adsorption phenomenon as well.

solute concentration decreases along the bed up to $z = L_1'$. Adsorption of the solute occurs in the unsaturated section of the bed, $0 < z < L_1'$ [see Figure 12.6(a)]. The section $0 < z < L_1'$ is called the *mass transfer zone* (MTZ). Beyond $z = L_1'$, the gas is virtually solute-free and no adsorption occurs there. Hence, for $z > L_1'$ the bed practically remains as fresh as it was at the beginning.

Since flow of the feed and adsorption continue to occur simultaneously, a section of the bed near the inlet gets saturated or equilibriated after some time. Thus at time t_2, the section of the bed of length L_2 becomes 'saturated' with a concentration $q = q_o$. No further adsorption occurs in this section. By this time the MTZ has moved forward and now, at time $t = t_2$, it stretches over the distance $L_2 < z < L_2'$. The situation is depicted in Figure 12.6(b). After still some more time, at $t = t_3$, the length of the saturated zone increases to $z = L_3$; the MTZ has moved still further and now it occupies the region $L_3 < z < L_3'$. The region $L_3' \leq z \leq L$ virtually remains fresh [Figure 12.6(c)]. Thus the mass transfer zone moves along the bed with time like a wave. The 'S-shaped' curves shown in Figure 12.6 are called the *mass transfer wave front*.

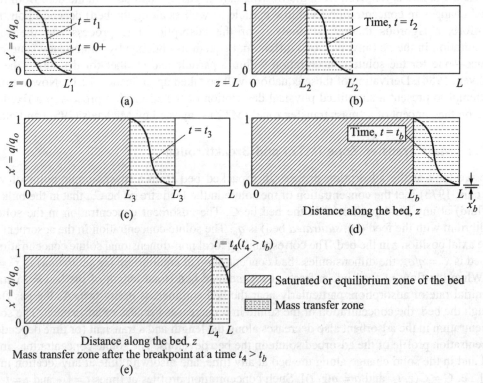

Figure 12.6 Solid phase concentration profile at different times. The part (d) shows the concentration profile at the breakthrough time, t_b, and the part (e) shows that after t_b.

Figure 12.7 shows how the concentration of the gas changes with time at different locations in the bed. Let us consider the curve for $z = L_3$ in conjunction with Figure 12.6(c). At time $t = t_3'$, the leading edge of the mass transfer zone reaches the axial position L_3 in the bed and the concentration of the adsorbed solute at $z = L_3$ is negligibly small at that moment. The solute concentration in the gas is negligibly small too. However, the solute concentration in the flowing gas gradually builds up and the adsorbed solute concentration in the bed at $z = L_3$ also increases with time. The mass transfer zone moves on. At time $t = t_3$, the dimensionless solute concentration in the gas becomes $y' = 1$ (the same as the concentration of the feed), and the adsorbed solute concentration reaches the equilibrium or saturation value (i.e. $x' = 1$); the rear end of the mass transfer zone has now reached $z = L_3$. The time variation of the gas-phase solute concentration is shown by the S-shaped curve for $z = L_3$ in Figure 12.7. Similar curves (y' vs. t) at a few other locations are also shown in Figure 12.7.

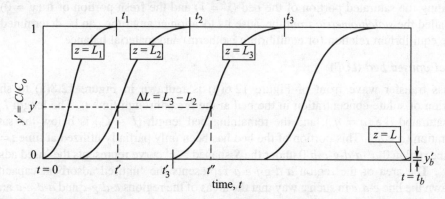

Figure 12.7 Concentration history of the solute in the gas at different axial positions (y'_b = normalized concentration at breakthrough).

Breakthrough

Let us consider Figure 12.6(d) which shows the concentration profile of the adsorbed solute in the bed at the time t_b and the mass transfer zone ($L_b \leq z \leq L$). At this time the leading edge of the mass transfer zone reaches the top of the packed section ($z = L$) such that the dimensionless concentration of the solute in the solid at the top of the bed has a small value, say x'_b. Correspondingly, at time $t = t_b$, the effluent gas from the bed also has a small but measurable concentration of the solute, $C = C_b$ (see Figure 12.7). This phenomenon of appearance of a small but detectable concentration in the effluent from the bed is called *breakthrough*. The term implies that the solute in the gas has been able to break through the barrier of the bed of adsorbent. The time t_b required for appearance of the solute in the effluent is called the *breakthrough time* and $C = C_b$ is called the *breakthrough concentration*. The breakthrough concentration is rather arbitrarily defined. It may be either the 'minimum detectable concentration' or the 'maximum permissible concentration' of the solute in the effluent from the bed.

Equilibrium time

If the flow of the feed is continued even after occurrence of the breakthrough (i.e. after time t_b), the solute concentration in the effluent increases and the thickness of the mass transfer zone decreases. The MTZ and the solute concentration profile in it at time t_4 ($t_4 > t_b$) is shown in Figure 12.6(e). Eventually, the rear of the mass transfer zone will reach the top of the bed, $z = L$. The whole bed will then be saturated, i.e. be in equilibrium with the gas at the feed concentration, C_o. The time required for this is called the *equilibrium time* t_e.

Stoichiometric front (SF)

The existence of the mass transfer zone is a direct consequence of the mass transfer resistance (i.e. the combined resistance of external convection and pore diffusion in the adsorbent) and the adsorption kinetic resistance in the bed. If the total resistance is larger, the overall process will be slower and the solute-laden gas will have to move through a longer section of the bed to get stripped of the solute. In other words, the length of the mass transfer zone will be larger. On the other hand, if the total resistance to mass transfer and adsorption is less, the overall process of adsorption will be faster and the length of the mass transfer zone will be smaller. In the limiting or *ideal* case of zero total resistance (if the overall process of adsorption is *extremely fast*), the thickness of the mass transfer zone will be negligibly small, and it will effectively be just a line demarcating the saturated portion of the bed ($x' = 1$) and the fresh portion of it ($x' \approx 0$)[†]. This line is called the *stoichiometric front*, because its location at any time can be determined simply from the equilibrium relation (or equilibrium isotherm) and material balance.

Length of unused bed (LUB)

The mass transfer wave front of Figure 12.6(d) is redrawn in Figure 12.8(a) to show the distribution of solute concentration in the bed at the breakthrough time t_b. The length L_b of the bed is saturated (i.e. $q = q_o$), and the remaining bed length ($L - L_b$) is below the saturation concentration ($q < q_o$). This portion of the bed has been only partially utilized at time $t = t_b$. The area of the region $0\text{-}a'\text{-}a\text{-}d\text{-}g\text{-}c\text{-}b\text{-}0$ under the S-shaped $z\text{-}x'$ curve represents the 'used adsorption capacity'. The area of the region $a\text{-}d\text{-}g\text{-}f\text{-}e\text{-}a$ represents the 'unused adsorbent capacity'. We have drawn the line $c\text{-}d\text{-}e$ in such a way that the areas of the regions $c\text{-}d\text{-}g\text{-}c$ and $a\text{-}d\text{-}e\text{-}a$ are equal. So the line $c\text{-}d\text{-}e$ can be considered as the 'equivalent stoichiometric front'. An amount of the adsorbent required to fill the bed length ($L - L_s$) remains effectively unused. This length ($L - L_s$) is called the *length of unused bed* or LUB. Thus if the feed flow is continued up to the breakthrough time t_b, virtually all the solute entering the bed gets captured. On further continuation of the feed flow, the solute shows up in the effluent with gradually increasing concentration. At time t_e, the effluent concentration becomes equal to the feed concentration. This means that the entire bed becomes saturated at the time t_e, which is the equilibriation time [see Figure 12.8(b)].

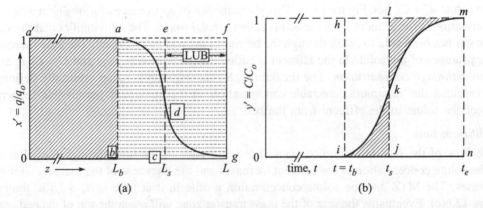

Figure 12.8   (a) The mass transfer zone at the breakthrough time ($t = t_b$), and (b) the concentration of the solute in the effluent as a function of time.

[†] A regenerated bed is likely to have a small concentration of residual solute left in it.

Stoichiometric time

What is the time required for the stoichiometric front to reach the top of the bed? This may be determined from the effluent concentration plot shown in Figure 12.8(b). The line j-k-l has been drawn in such a way that the areas of the regions i-j-k-i and k-l-m-k are equal. Had the MTZ been as thin as a line, it would have reached the top of the bed at time t_s. The time t_s is called the *stoichiometric time*. The progress of the MTZ and the stoichiometric front are also shown in Figure 12.9.

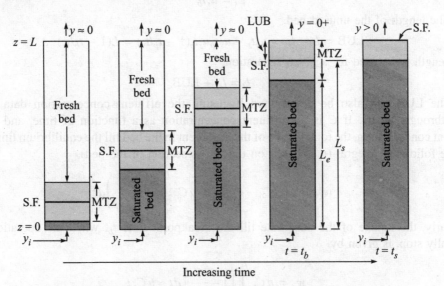

Figure 12.9 Propagation of the MTZ and the SF through a packed bed of adsorbent.

12.8.2 Design Calculation Using LUB

The design of a packed adsorption column by the LUB method requires experimental adsorption data usually collected from a laboratory setup under *identical* flow conditions, feed concentration, pressure and temperature. Since the determination of the bed concentration profile is very difficult, only the effluent concentration is measured over a period of time to prepare a breakthrough plot like Figure 12.8(b). The breakthrough time t_b is measured directly; the stoichiometric time t_s is determined so that the area i-j-k-i is equal to the area k-l-m-k.

The velocity of the wave front or the stoichiometric front (u_s) can be determined by different but basically similar methods.

(i) If t_s is determined by matching the areas [see Figure 12.8(b)], u_s can be calculated from

$$L = u_s t_s \qquad (12.20a)$$

(ii) If the mass transfer wave front is *symmetric* and t_m is the time when the effluent from the bed attains $C/C_o = 0.5$, u_s can be calculated from the equation

$$L = u_s t_m \qquad (12.20b)$$

(iii) A more reliable method is to collect and use the breakthrough data from the two beds of different lengths but operated under identical conditions. If L_1 and L_2 are the bed lengths and t_{s1} and t_{s2} are the corresponding stoichiometric times, we can obtains u_s from the following equation [see Problem 12.11].

$$u_s = \frac{L_2 - L_1}{t_{s2} - t_{s1}} \tag{12.20c}$$

For design of an adsorption bed, it is necessary to determine the LUB. If t_b is the experimental breakthrough time, the length of the saturated bed is

$$L_s = u_s t_b \tag{12.21}$$

And the length of the unused bed,

$$\text{LUB} = L - L_s = u_s t_s - u_s t_b u_s t_s (1 - t_b/t_s) = L(1 - t_b/t_s) \tag{12.22}$$

Bed length to be used for a given separation,

$$L = L_s + \text{LUB} \tag{12.23}$$

The LUB can also be determined by using the effluent concentration data after the breakthrough occurs. If C is the effluent concentration as a function of time, and C_o is the influent concentration, the total uptake of the adsorbent in the bed till the equilibrium time is given by the following integral (it is based on unit cross-section of the bed).

$$w_1 = u \int_0^{t_e} (C_o - C)dt = u C_o \int_0^{t_e} \left(1 - \frac{C}{C_o}\right)dt \tag{12.24}$$

Similarly, the uptake of the adsorbate till the breakpoint time t_b, when the operation should normally stop, is given by

$$w_2 = u C_o \int_0^{t_b} \left(1 - \frac{C}{C_o}\right)dt \approx u C_o t_b \tag{12.25}$$

The fractional utilization of the bed capacity is w_2/w_1 and the LUB is given as

$$\text{LUB} = (1 - w_2/w_1)L \tag{12.26}$$

In order to calculate the bed height for a certain separation, the time of operation is first fixed. The next steps are:

(a) Calculate u_s and LUB from the experimental data using Eqs. (12.21) and (12.22) or Eq. (12.26).
(b) From the measured breakthrough time and the time-concentration data for the effluent, calculate L_s of the bed to be designed using Eq. (12.21), add the LUB to it, and get the required bed height. On the other hand, given a bed height, the breakthrough time can be calculated. If the time-concentration data are collected over a limited period of time, u_s, t_s and LUB can be computed after extrapolating the data, although with a risk of involving errors.

Example 12.4 illustrates the procedure.

EXAMPLE 12.4 (*Calculation of the bed height by the LUB method*) Vinyl chloride is a bulk organic chemical required for the production of polyvinyl chloride (PVC), a widely used polymer. Since vinyl chloride is a toxic and carcinogenic volatile organic compound (VOC), it must be removed from any waste gas stream containing this compound. Adsorption in a packed bed of activated carbon is a practical method of its removal from an emission. The following experimental breakthrough data for adsorption of vinyl chloride on granular activated carbon (GAC) at 20°C and essentially atmospheric pressure were collected by Lin et al. [*J. Env. Eng.*, March 1996, p. 169].

Time, t (min) =	141	154	166.7	189.7	205	225.6	246	261	282	297	318	338	350
y/y_i =	0	0	0.018	0.144	0.223	0.411	0.587	0.692	0.807	0.894	0.966	0.99	1.0

Details of the experimental parameters are: bed length, $L = 15.2$ cm; bed diameter, $d = 2.3$ cm; gas flow rate = 80 cm^3/s at 1 atm and 20°C; bed porosity, $\varepsilon = 0.36$; interstitial gas velocity = 0.535 m/s; vinyl chloride concentration in the feed = 190 ppm (by volume); y_i = mole fraction of the solute in the feed gas and y is that in the effluent.

(a) Calculate the length of the mass transfer zone, the velocity of the stoichiometric front and the saturation capacity of the bed at the influent gas concentration. (b) A waste gas stream containing 190 ppm (by volume) vinyl chloride is to be treated with activated carbon in a packed bed at a rate of 20 m^3/min to reduce its concentration by 98%. Using the above breakthrough data, determine the bed diameter, the height and pressure drop if an adsorption period of 10 h is allowed. The superficial gas velocity to be used is the same as that of the experimental study.

Solution

(a) The experimental breakthrough data are plotted in Figure 12.10. The time t_s is determined in a way that the areas of the shaded portions are equal. This gives $t_s = 238$ min. At this time the equivalent length of the saturated bed = 15.2 cm. Therefore,

Velocity of the stoichiometric front [(Eq. 12.20)], $u_s = 15.2/238 = $ $\boxed{0.0639 \text{ cm/min}}$

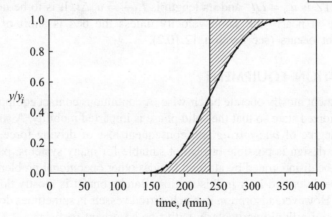

Figure 12.10 Plot of the breakthrough data.

Breakthrough time in the experimental column, $t_b \approx 165$ min (when the effluent concentration ≈ 0.02)

$$\Rightarrow \qquad \text{LUB} = L_s\left(1 - \frac{t_b}{t_s}\right) = (15.2)\left(1 - \frac{165}{238}\right) = \boxed{4.66 \text{ cm}}$$

The mass transfer wave front is nearly symmetric. Length of MTZ = 2 × LUB = $\boxed{9.32 \text{ cm}}$

(b) The superficial velocity in the experimental column

$$u_o = \frac{80}{(\pi/4)d^2} = \frac{80 \text{ cm}^3/\text{s}}{(\pi/4)(2.3)^2 \text{ cm}^2} = 19.25 \text{ cm/s} = 0.1925 \text{ m/s (at } 20°\text{C, 1 atm)}$$

This same superficial velocity is used in the *full-scale column*.

Flow rate = 20 m³/min = (20)(293/273) = 21.46 m³/min at 20°C.

Bed cross-section = $\left(\frac{21.46}{60} \text{ m}^3/\text{s}\right)(0.1925 \text{ m/s}) = 1.86 \text{ m}^2$; bed diameter = $\left[\left(\frac{4}{\pi}\right)(1.86)\right]^{1/2}$

$$= \boxed{1.54 \text{ m}}$$

Adsorption time allowed = 10 h

Bed height = (10 × 60 min)(0.0639 cm/min) + LUB = 38.34 + 4.66 cm = $\boxed{0.43 \text{ m}}$

The LUB method has a few limitations: (a) it assumes isothermal operation; (b) a bed can be designed only if experimental effluent concentration data (i.e. breakthrough data) are available; (c) both experimental and full-scale beds should operate under similar flow conditions and should be long enough to ensure a stable MTZ. An experimental bed of at least 5 cm diameter and a packing depth not less than five times the length of MTZ should be used. For a short bed, which is unlikely to have a stable MTZ, the breakthrough time can be calculated following Rosen (1954).

The length and velocity of the MTZ can also be calculated from the experimentally determined concentration of the effluent from the bed over a period of time. Let t^* be the time at which the effluent has a concentration of $C_o/2$; Δt is the time interval measured from the breakthrough time, required for the effluent concentration to reach the feed concentration value, C_o. Then the velocity of the MTZ is $u_m = L/t^*$ and its length is $L_{MTZ} = u_m\Delta t$. It is to be noted that the MTZ and the SF move at nearly the same velocity unless the bed is short or spreading of the concentration front occurs (see Section 12.10.2).

12.9 ADSORPTION EQUIPMENT

Adsorption equipment mostly operate batch-wise. A continuous contact equipment must have the adsorbent in a fluidized state so that the solid phase is imparted mobility. A simple fluidized bed involves a high degree of *backmixing* and consequent loss of driving force. A countercurrent multiple tray-type design is possible but is not suitable for many systems, particularly because the particles may be disintegrated by attrition besides other operational problems. A novel design of this kind will be described later in this section. Batch contact is mostly done in packed beds (see Figure 12.1). However, adsorption in batch stirred vessels is sometimes done for purification of small quantities of a liquid particularly with fine adsorbent particles.

A packed adsorption equipment consists of a cylindrical shell provided with (i) a support grid for holding the solid adsorbent while allowing the gas or the liquid to flow through it, (ii) inlet and outlet nozzles for the fluid, and (iii) a suitable arrangement for distribution of the fluid to ensure reasonably uniform flow through the bed (Johnston, 1972). The feed gas must be freed from particulates (dust particles and oil droplets) by using a coalescing filter upstream. A filter on the downstream side is also necessary to retain any particles that may come from the bed. Carbon steel is the common material of construction of an adsorption vessel, although another suitable material may have to be used if the environment is corrosive. The cost of a vessel per unit volume increases rapidly with diameter particularly if it operates under pressure. Another factor to be considered in selecting the diameter is the pressure drop across the bed. The vessel needs insulation to prevent heat loss (and for personal protection) if thermal regeneration of the spent adsorbent bed is done. Most such vessels are installed vertically, although the pressure drop may be high for a tall vessel. Flow distribution is more uniform in a vertical vessel. The feed flows downwards to avoid fluidization of the bed if there is a sudden surge in the flow rate. Further, if the feed contains a mixture of high and low boiling substances, the vessel may have two sections with a separating grid. In such a case, the feed enters at the bottom, the higher boiling substances are adsorbed in the lower section and the lower boiling compounds are adsorbed in the upper section. The spent beds can be regenerated separately. Pressure drop for flow of a gas through a packed bed of solid may be calculated using the Ergun equation (Gamane and Lannoy, 1996).

Two types of support are common. A grid with one or more layers screen of decreasing pore size may support the adsorbent bed. Alternatively, a few layers of ceramic balls of graded sizes may hold the bed. The openings at the top of the support layer must be smaller than the adsorbent particle size, and flow distribution in the bed must be reasonably uniform (otherwise there will be dead zones in the bed). This may be achieved by providing baffle plates at the inlet and exit nozzles or by making slots on the nozzles so that the fluid is released radially and then flows axially (Figure 12.11).

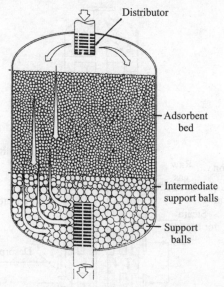

Figure 12.11 Construction of a packed adsorption bed. Bed support: ceramic balls of two sizes; radial gas distributor.

Butterfly valves are mostly used in the pipelines if the feed is a gas. The gasket should be compatible with the solute in the gas, particularly if a solvent vapour is to be recovered in the bed. Leakage of the valves is a common problem. Enough care should be taken to avoid breakage of the particles during loading and unloading. Breakage of particles creates fines and causes a lot of problems (loss of adsorbent, carryover of solid particles in the cleaned gas, etc.). Vacuum loading and unloading are sometimes used. Downflow of the fluid during adsorption and upflow for regeneration are common. Generation of local hot spots and spontaneous ignition have been reported for activated carbon beds in some cases. Typical ranges of operating parameters (Kovach, 1997) for packed-bed adsorption are given in Table 12.3.

Table 12.3   Typical ranges of operating parameters for gas adsorption in a packed bed

Parameter	Range of values
Superficial gas velocity	0.2–0.5 m/s
Adsorbent bed height	0.3–1.5 m (3 to 10 times the MTZ)
Adsorption time (for TSA)	0.5–8 h
Feed concentration	0.01–0.5% by volume
Adsorbent particle size	0.5–10 mm
Adsorbent bed voidage	38–50%
Steam-adsorbate ratio for regeneration	2:1 to 8:1
Steam regeneration temperature	105–110°C
Inert gas regeneration temperature	100–300°C
Regeneration time	About half of adsorption time

A novel continuous moving bed adsorber was developed by Kureha Chemical Co. of Japan in the 1970s. It has a few 'trays' in the upper section (Figure 12.12) containing the fluidized

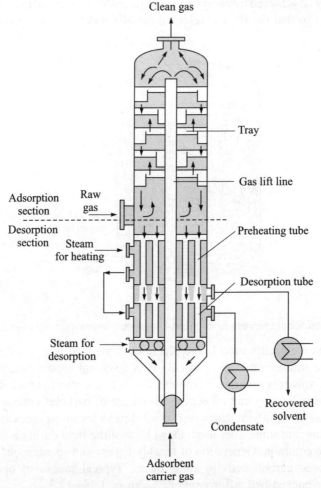

Figure 12.12   A continuous moving-bed adsorption unit.

adsorbent particles that continuously move down through the 'downcomers'. Adsorption occurs in this upper section. As the solid moves down to the lower desorption section, it enters an array of steam-heated desorption tubes. The product recovered by desorption is condensed. A carrier gas recycles the regenerated adsorbent to the top of the adsorber through a central pipe. The adsorbent particles must be hard and resistant to abrasion. The device is in use in many plants for the removal and recovery of small amounts of solvent vapour from vent gases. Another continuous adsorption device with a 'monolithic' adsorbent block mounted on a rotating wheel is described by Keller (1995).

12.10   ADSORPTION DYNAMICS

The sizing of a packed (or fixed) bed for adsorption of a solute from a feed gas by the LUB method depends entirely upon experimental adsorption and breakthrough data collected by using a prototype laboratory or pilot scale column. It does not quantitatively deal with the mass (and also heat) transfer phenomena occurring in the bed, the kinetics of adsorption and adsorption equilibrium. No theoretical analysis of the dynamics of the adsorption process is involved in the LUB method. Adsorption dynamics of a column means how the solute concentrations in the bulk fluid and within a porous adsorbent particle or pellet change with time and position in the column. A brief analysis of the phenomenon and the related theoretical principles are discussed below.

12.10.1   One-dimensional Model

The adsorption phenomenon in a packed or fixed bed of solid can be physically described as follows:

- As the feed gas moves through the bed, the concentration of the solute in the gas decreases along the bed (i.e. in the axial direction) because of adsorption of the solute in the solid. In this model the fluid concentration is assumed to be uniform at all points on the cross-section of the bed at any axial position. As such the solute concentration does not depend upon the radial position in the bed. The model is therefore called *one-dimensional model*.
- At any point of the bed, the solute molecules are transported from the bulk gas to the surface of a pellet by convective mass transfer through a *gas film* around a particle.
- While a little of the solute gets adsorbed on the outer surface of a pellet, most of it diffuses into the pellet through the pores in it.
- As the solute molecules diffuse through the pores within a pellet, they are simultaneously adsorbed on the walls of the pores following the adsorption kinetics of the solute.

We shall now develop the differential equations for the time-dependent concentration distribution of the solute for both the gas and the fixed bed. It is assumed that the adsorbent is available in the form of uniform-sized spherical beads or pellets of radius r_o (diameter = $d_p = 2r_o$).
We use the following notations:

C = local concentration of the solute in the *bulk* of the carrier gas; it is a function of axial position and time [i.e. $C = C(z, t)$]

ε_b = porosity of the packed bed (i.e. the interstitial void volume per unit volume of the bed; this void volume does not include the internal pore volume in the pellets)

u = interstitial fluid velocity in the bed [= (volumetric gas flow rate)/(cross-section of the bed)(ε)]

D_E = axial dispersion coefficient of the solute in the bed

z = distance from the feed end of the bed

t = time

J_o = solute flux (kmol/m²·s) to the surface of a pellet from the bulk of the gas

ρ_b = bulk density of the bed (kg adsorbent per m³ of bed volume)

c = local fluid-phase concentration of the solute within the pores of a particle [it is a function of the radial position within a spherical pellet, $c = c(r)$]

q = local adsorbed solute concentration within a particle (kmol solute per kg adsorbent), i.e. local solute loading

D_e = effective diffusivity of the solute in the pores

$\bar{a}$ = external surface area of the particles per unit volume of the bed[†]

ε_p = the internal porosity of the particles (it is the pore volume per unit volume of the solid)

J = rate of disappearance of the solute by adsorption within a pellet (expressed as kmol solute adsorbed per m³ of the volume of adsorbent per unit time).

The following derivation is based on unit cross-section of the bed. First, we shall derive the equation for the unsteady state concentration distribution of the solute in the gas along the bed. We consider a thin slice of the bed of thickness Δz at a distance z from the feed end of the bed (note that the volume of the slice is also Δz) as shown in Figure 12.13. The solute entering the slice at any time t will (i) be partly adsorbed in the slice, (ii) partly get accumulated in the interstitial fluid in the slice, and (iii) partly leave the slice by *bulk flow* and by *axial dispersion*. Let us identify the various transport rates so that we can make an

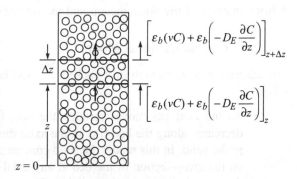

Figure 12.13   Differential mass balance over a section of the bed.

unsteady state mass balance over the slice (*per unit cross-section of the bed*).

Rate of input of the solute to the slice (at z) = $\varepsilon_b(uC)\big|_z$ [The notation "$\big|_z$" means evaluated at z.]

Rate of input of the solute to the slice by axial dispersion = $\varepsilon_b(-D_E \partial C/\partial z)\big|_z$

Rate of output of the solute from the slice at $z + \Delta z$ = $\varepsilon_b(uC)\big|_{z+\Delta z}$

Rate of output of the solute from the slice by axial dispersion = $\varepsilon_b(-D_E \partial C/\partial z)\big|_{z+\Delta z}$

Rate of removal of the solute from the gas by adsorption in the slice = $\Delta z\,\bar{a}\,J_o$

Rate of accumulation of the solute in the interstitial fluid = $\varepsilon_b \Delta z(\partial C/\partial t)$

[†] For a single particle, volume $v_p = (4/3)\pi r_o^3$; area $a_p = 4\pi r_o^2$. External area per unit volume of the solid = a_p/v_p = $3/r_o$. Volume fraction of the solid in the bed = $1 - \varepsilon$. External area of the particles per unit volume of the bed, $\bar{a} = 3(1 - \varepsilon)/r_o$, m²/m³.

An unsteady state mass balance over the slice yields

$$\varepsilon_b(vC)\big|_z + \varepsilon_b(-D_E \partial C/\partial z)\big|_z - \varepsilon_b(vC)\big|_{z+\Delta z} - \varepsilon_b(-D_E \partial C/\partial z)\big|_{z+\Delta z}$$
$$= \Delta z \bar{a} J_o + \varepsilon_b \Delta z (\partial C/\partial t) \tag{12.27}$$

Dividing by Δz throughout and taking the limit $\Delta z \to 0$,

$$\varepsilon_b D_E \frac{\partial^2 C}{\partial z^2} - \varepsilon_b u \frac{\partial C}{\partial z} - \bar{a} J_o = \varepsilon_b \frac{\partial C}{\partial t}$$

$$\Rightarrow \qquad D_E \frac{\partial^2 C}{\partial z^2} - u \frac{\partial C}{\partial z} - \frac{3(1-\varepsilon_b)}{\varepsilon_b r_o} k_c [C - c(r_o)] = \frac{\partial C}{\partial t} \tag{12.28}$$

Here k_c = the mass transfer coefficient at the external surface of a pellet; the solute flux is $J_o = k_c[C - c(r_o)]$ where $c(r_o)$ is the solute concentration at the pore mouth, $r = r_o$ (i.e. the solute concentration at the pellet surface). If $\bar{q}$ is the average concentration of the solute in a pellet, Eq. (12.28) can be written in an alternative form.

$$D_E \frac{\partial^2 C}{\partial z^2} - u \frac{\partial C}{\partial z} - \frac{1-\varepsilon_b}{\varepsilon_b} \rho_p \frac{\partial \bar{q}}{\partial t} = \frac{\partial C}{\partial t} \tag{12.29}$$

Now we write down the equation for concentration distribution of the solute within the pores of an adsorbent particle at any axial position z. The equation can be derived by making an unsteady state mass balance of the solute over a thin spherical shell within the adsorbent pellet.

$$D_e \left(\frac{\partial^2 c}{\partial r^2} + \frac{2}{r} \frac{\partial c}{\partial r} \right) - J = \varepsilon_p \frac{\partial c}{\partial t} \tag{12.30}$$

Here J is the local rate of adsorption of the solute within a pellet per unit volume of the solid. It is a function of the local solute concentration in the gas phase within the pores (c) and the local adsorbate concentration in the solid (q), i.e. $J = J(c, q)$.

The above equations for concentration distribution of the solute in a pellet as well as that along the bed are to be solved together, subject to appropriate *initial* and *boundary* conditions in order to find out the breakthrough pattern for the system. This can be done only numerically for the general case, although analytical solutions for simplified and limiting cases have been reported (Ruthven, 1984; Yang, 1987). If the effects of axial dispersion are neglected, Eq. (12.29) takes the following simple form

$$\frac{\partial C}{\partial t} + u \frac{\partial C}{\partial z} + \frac{1-\varepsilon_b}{\varepsilon_b} \rho_p \frac{\partial \bar{q}}{\partial t} = 0 \tag{12.31}$$

12.10.2 Equilibrium Model and the Velocity of the Concentration Front

It is important to determine (even approximately) the velocity of propagation of the concentration front through the bed. This can be done using the experimental breakthrough data (see Section 12.8.2). A simple theoretical approach is described here based on the *local equilibrium model*. The model does not really help in the design of an adsorption column, but it helps in having an understanding and insight of the adsorption kinetics in a packed column. It is based on the following simplified assumptions:

(i) Isothermal equilibrium adsorption occurs at all points in the bed.

(ii) The solute concentration in the feed is small so that the fluid velocity remains fairly constant.

(iii) Plug flow of the gas occurs and there is no axial dispersion of the solute ($D_E = 0$).

The first assumption is characteristic of the equilibrium model. As the name implies, it is assumed that at each point in the bed, the adsorbent pellets are in equilibrium with the surrounding bulk fluid, i.e. $q = q(C)$. As such there is no diffusional resistance outside or inside a pellet.

Let us define the velocity of propagation of the concentration front as

$$u_c = \left(\frac{\partial z}{\partial t}\right)_{C=\text{constant}} \tag{12.32}$$

It will be in order to physically explain the quantity u_c. We refer to Figure 12.7. Let the dimensionless fluid-phase concentration of the solute in the bed at time t' and at the axial position $z = L_2$ be C'. The same concentration C' is found at an adjacent axial position, $z = L_3$, at a later time t''. So the concentration front moves through a distance $L_3 - L_2$ in time $t'' - t'$ for a constant solute concentration C' in the fluid. The velocity of propagation of the concentration front is therefore given by

$$u_c = \frac{L_3 - L_2}{t'' - t'} = \left(\frac{\partial z}{\partial t}\right)_{C'} \tag{12.33}$$

Since local equilibrium prevails, the solute concentration in the adsorbent is related to that in the fluid by an appropriate adsorption isotherm.

$$q = q(C) \tag{12.34}$$

Now we put $D_E = 0$ and $\partial q/\partial t = (\partial q/\partial C)(\partial C/\partial t)$ in Eq. (12.31),

$$\frac{\partial C}{\partial t} + u\frac{\partial C}{\partial z} + \frac{1-\varepsilon_b}{\varepsilon_b}\rho_p\frac{\partial q}{\partial C}\frac{\partial C}{\partial t} = 0$$

$$\Rightarrow \left[1 + \frac{1-\varepsilon_b}{\varepsilon_b}\rho_p\frac{\partial q}{\partial C}\right]\frac{\partial C}{\partial t} + u\frac{\partial C}{\partial z} = 0 \tag{12.35}$$

Further, the velocity of propagation of the concentration front defined in Eq. (12.32) can be expressed as

$$u_c = \left(\frac{\partial z}{\partial t}\right)_C = -\frac{(\partial C/\partial t)_z}{(\partial C/\partial z)_t} \tag{12.36}$$

The inclusion of a negative sign in the above equation deserves an explanation. If it is a case of adsorption, for example, the concentration of the solute in the fluid at a given axial position increases with time [i.e. $(\partial C/\partial t)_z > 0$]. On the other hand, at any time, the fluid-phase concentration decreases in the axial direction [i.e. $(\partial C/\partial z)_t < 0$]. But the wave velocity, $u_c = \left(\frac{\partial z}{\partial t}\right)_C > 0$. Hence the negative sign is included to make both sides of Eq. (12.36) consistent with respect to sign.

Combining Eqs. (12.35) and (12.36),

$$-u_c\left[1+\frac{1-\varepsilon_b}{\varepsilon_b}\,\rho_p\,\frac{dq}{dC}\right]\frac{\partial C}{\partial z}+u\left(\frac{\partial C}{\partial z}\right)=0$$

$$\Rightarrow \qquad u_c=\frac{u}{1+\dfrac{1-\varepsilon_b}{\varepsilon_b}\,\rho_p\,\dfrac{dq}{dC}} \qquad (12.37)$$

The above equation may be used to calculate the velocity of propagation of the concentration front u_c if local equilibrium exists. Since dq/dC is a function of C in the general case, the velocity u_c depends upon C. In the special case of *linear* equilibrium relation, $q = K_d C$, the velocity of propagation is constant (i.e. independent of C). In the case of two common types of isotherms, type I and type II (see Figure 12.3), the characteristics of the propagation velocity are described here.

(i) Let us first consider the case of *desorption* (or *elution*) of a solute from a bed initially in equilibrium (or saturated) with a fluid of concentration C_0. If the isotherm is favourable, dq/dC is always positive, but decreases at a higher value of C. Thus, the velocity of the concentration wave u_c is larger in the higher concentration region than in the lower concentration region in the bed. Since the solute concentration is more in the eluting carrier gas at larger z, the concentration wave becomes dispersive (i.e. gets broadened) as it moves through the bed. On the other hand, the concentration wave becomes compressive or *self-sharpening* in case of elution of a solute from a saturated bed if the isotherm is 'unfavourable' (type II), since dq/dC is larger and the velocity of propagation of the wave is smaller at a higher value of C for this kind of isotherm. Similarly, for adsorption of a gas with a 'favourable isotherm', the concentration wave-front becomes self-sharpening (Figure 12.14).

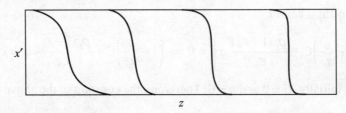

Figure 12.14 Self-sharpening wave-front in the bed (for a favourable isotherm) ($x' = q/q_o$).

(ii) Now let us consider the case of adsorption or loading of a bed with a step change in the feed concentration (say from $C = 0$ to $C = C_0$) at time $t = 0$. If the isotherm is 'unfavourable', the concentration front becomes dispersive because of the same reasoning given in (i) above. But for a favourable isotherm and a step increase in the feed concentration, the derivative dq/dC becomes undefined. The concentration wave moves through the bed as *shock wave* whose velocity can be obtained from the finite difference form of Eq. (12.35).

$$\left[1+\frac{1-\varepsilon_b}{\varepsilon_b}\,\rho_p\,\frac{\Delta q}{\Delta C}\right]\left[\frac{\Delta C}{\Delta t}\right]_z+u\left[\frac{\Delta C}{\Delta z}\right]_t=0 \qquad (12.38)$$

The velocity of the shock wave representing the concentration front is obtained from the above equation, i.e.

$$u_{sh} = \left[\frac{\Delta z}{\Delta t}\right]_C = -\frac{[\Delta C/\Delta t]_z}{[\Delta C/\Delta z]_t} = \frac{u}{1 + \frac{1-\varepsilon_b}{\varepsilon_b}\rho_p\frac{\Delta q}{\Delta C}} \qquad (12.39)$$

Here Δq is the step change in the equilibrium concentration of the adsorbed solute in response to a step change in the feed concentration from $C = 0$ to $C = C_0$ (i.e. $\Delta C = C_0 - 0 = C_0$).

The 'ideal breakthrough time' can be easily obtained as the time required for the shock wave to pass through the bed of length L [i.e. $(t_b)_{ideal} = L/u_{sh}$].

12.10.3   Constant Pattern Behaviour

It is explained before that as the concentration wave-front moves through the bed, the length of the mass transfer zone (MTZ) may change. For gas–solid systems exhibiting an unfavourable equilibrium relationship or if the effects of axial dispersion are significant, MTZ expands as it moves through the bed. But when the equilibrium relation is favourable (this occurs for Type-1 isotherm, Figure 12.3), and the axial dispersion effects are small, the MTZ may maintain a reasonably constant width and shape as it progresses through the bed. Under such conditions, the MTZ is called 'stable' and the system exhibits *constant pattern behaviour* (Sirkar and Kumar, 1983). The solute concentration in the bed can be expressed as a function of the single variable τ'

$$\tau' = t - z/u_c \qquad (12.40)$$

where z is the distance from the entrance end and u_c is the velocity of the centre of the wave. A change of variable from (z, t) to τ' gives

$$\frac{\partial C}{\partial t} = \frac{\partial C}{\partial \tau'}\frac{\partial \tau'}{\partial t} = \frac{\partial C}{\partial \tau'} \qquad \text{and} \qquad \frac{\partial C}{\partial z} = \frac{\partial C}{\partial \tau'}\frac{\partial \tau'}{\partial z} = -\frac{1}{u_c}\frac{\partial C}{\partial \tau'}$$

On substitution in Eq. (12.31),

$$\frac{d}{d\tau'}\left[\left(1-\frac{u}{u_c}\right)C + \frac{\rho_p(1-\varepsilon_b)}{\varepsilon_b}q\right] = 0 \Rightarrow \left(1-\frac{u}{u_c}\right)C + \frac{\rho_p(1-\varepsilon_b)}{\varepsilon_b}q = \text{constant} \quad (12.41)$$

If the bed is fresh initially, $C = 0$ and $q = 0$. Therefore, the constant in the above equation is zero.

Thus $\qquad \left(1-\frac{u}{u_c}\right)C = -\frac{\rho_p(1-\varepsilon_b)}{\varepsilon_b}q \qquad \text{and} \qquad \left(1-\frac{u}{u_c}\right)C_o = -\frac{\rho_p(1-\varepsilon_b)}{\varepsilon_b}q_o$

Further, if the solute concentration is low (i.e. interstitial fluid velocity = constant), dividing we get

$$\frac{C}{C_o} = \frac{q}{q_o} \qquad (12.42)$$

Here C_o is the solute concentration in the feed and q_o is the corresponding saturated bed concentration. The above equation is a condition for 'constant pattern behaviour'.

Now the local rate of adsorption can be expressed in terms of a mass transfer coefficient

$$(1-\varepsilon_b)\rho_p\frac{\partial q}{\partial t} = k_m\bar{a}(C - C^*) \qquad (12.43)$$

Here C is the solute concentration in the bulk fluid and C^* is the concentration that can remain in equilibrium with a solid having a solute concentration of q. We substitute q in terms of C from Eq. (12.42). Further, we assume that the adsorption equilibrium follows the Langmuir isotherm [a favourable isotherm, see Eq. (12.5)],

$$q = q_m \frac{KC^*}{1 + KC^*} \quad \Rightarrow \quad C^* = \frac{1}{K} \frac{q}{q_m - q} = \frac{1}{K} \frac{(q_o/C_o)C}{q_m - (q_o/C_o)C} \tag{12.44}$$

From Eqs. (12.43), (12.44) and (12.42),

$$C - C^* = C - \frac{C}{1 + K(C_o - C)} = C \frac{K(C_o - C)}{1 + K(C_o - C)}$$

$$\Rightarrow \qquad \frac{1}{C - C^*} = \frac{1 + K(C_o - C)}{K(C_o - C)C} = \frac{1 + KC_o}{KC_o} \frac{1}{C} + \frac{1}{KC_o} \frac{1}{C_o - C}$$

Substituting for $\dfrac{1}{C - C^*}$ in Eq. (12.43), putting $\dfrac{dq}{dt} = \left(\dfrac{q_o}{C_o}\right) \cdot \dfrac{dC}{dt}$ and rearranging,

$$\left[(1 - \varepsilon_b)\rho_p \frac{q_o}{C_o}\right] \frac{dC}{C - C^*} = k_m \bar{a}\, dt \quad \Rightarrow \quad \frac{1 + KC_o}{KC_o} \frac{dC}{C} + \frac{1}{KC_o} \frac{dC}{C_o - C} = \frac{k_m \bar{a} C_o}{(1 - \varepsilon_b)\rho_p q_o} dt$$

On integration from $t = t_1$, $C = C_1$ to $t = t$, $C = C$,

$$\frac{1 + KC_o}{KC_o} \ln \frac{C}{C_1} + \frac{1}{KC_o} \ln \frac{C_o - C_1}{C_o - C} = \frac{k_m \bar{a} C_o}{(1 - \varepsilon_b)\rho_p q_o}(t - t_1) \tag{12.45}$$

The above equation can be used to determine the concentration wave-front and hence the breakthrough for a given set of values of the parameters. This is illustrated in Example 12.5.

Here $k_m \bar{a}$ may be considered as the effective mass transfer coefficient expressible as a combination of mass transfer coefficients for external gas-film diffusion and pore diffusion (Wankat, 1994).

$$k_m \bar{a} = \left[\frac{1}{k_c \bar{a}} + \frac{r_o^2}{60 D_e m'(1 - \varepsilon_p)\rho_p}\right]^{-1} \tag{12.46}$$

Here m' is the slope of the adsorption isotherm. If a nonlinear isotherm (for example, the Langmuir isotherm) is used to describe the adsorption equilibrium, m' is the average slope of the isotherm over the concentration range of interest [i.e. $m' = (dq/dC)_{av.}$]. Among many correlations available for calculating the external gas-film mass transfer coefficient k_c, the Wakao and Funazaki (1978) correlation is fairly accurate.

$$\text{Sh} = 2.0 + 1.1(\text{Sc})^{1/3}(\text{Re})^{0.6}; \qquad 3 < \text{Re} < 10^4 \tag{12.47a}$$

$$\text{Sh} = k_c d_p/D; \qquad \text{Sc} = \mu_G/\rho_G D; \qquad \text{Re} = \rho_G u d_p/\mu_G$$

The second term in bracket on the right side of Eq. (12.46) stands for the pore diffusion resistance. Alternatively, the following equation (Sherwood and Pigford, 1975) for j_D may be used for the estimation of the mass transfer coefficient.

$$j_D = \left(\frac{k_c}{u}\right)(\text{Sc})^{0.667} = 1.17(\text{Re})^{-0.415} \tag{12.47b}$$

The 'effective diffusivity', D_e, to be used in Eq. (12.30) or (12.46) for the calculation of mass transfer within a pellet can be estimated from

$$D_e = \frac{\varepsilon_p}{\tau}\left[\frac{1}{(1/D)+(1/D_K)} + D_s\frac{\rho_p(K_H RT)}{\varepsilon_p}\right] \qquad (12.47c)$$

where

$K_H RT$ is the Henry's law constant [see Eq. (12.6)] if the adsorption equilibrium is linear $[q = K_H RT \cdot p/RT \Rightarrow q = K_H RT \cdot C]$

   τ = tortuosity factor
   D_K = Knudsen diffusivity
   D_s = surface diffusion coefficient.

EXAMPLE 12.5 (*Breakthrough for the constant pattern solution*) A gas stream containing 1.07×10^{-3} gmol/litre of a contaminant (mol. wt. = 60) flows through a bed of adsorbent at a superficial velocity of 0.3 m/s. The temperature is 300 K and the pressure is essentially atmospheric. Given the following data, calculate the breakthrough time and the velocity and length of the mass transfer wave-front. Calculate the same parameters again considering pore diffusion if the average pore diameter is 20 nm and its tortuosity $\tau = 2.3$.

Data: density of the adsorbent particles, $\rho_p = 850$ kg/m^3; bed porosity, $\varepsilon_b = 0.40$; specific surface area (external), $\bar{a} = 350$ m^2/m^3; particle diameter, $d_p = 0.5$ cm; internal porosity of a pellet, $\varepsilon_p = 0.42$; diffusivity of the contaminant in the gas, $D = 0.13$ cm^2/s; density of the gas stream, $\rho_G = 1.18$ kg/m^3, its viscosity, $\mu_G = 1.85 \times 10^{-5}$ kg/m·s. The adsorption equilibrium follows the Langmuir isotherm.

$$q = q_m\frac{KC}{1+KC}; \quad q = \text{gmol solute adsorbed/g solid}; \quad C = \text{gas concentration, gmol/litre};$$

$K = 126.8$ litre/gmol; $q_m = 0.00543$ gmol/g.

Solution

$$\text{Re} = \frac{d_p\rho_G u}{\mu_G} = \frac{(5\times10^{-3}\text{ m})(1.18\text{ kg/m}^3)(0.3/0.4\text{ m/s})}{1.85\times10^{-5}\text{ kg/m·s}} = 239 \quad (\text{since } u = u_o/\varepsilon_b = 0.3/0.4)$$

$$\text{Sc} = \frac{\mu_G}{\rho_G D} = \frac{1.85\times10^{-5}}{(1.18)(0.13\times10^{-4})} = 1.206$$

From the Wakao and Funazaki correlation, Eq. [12.47(a)]

$$\text{Sh} = 2 + 1.1(239)^{0.6}(1.206)^{1/3} = 33.3 \quad \Rightarrow \quad k_c = (33.3)(0.13\times10^{-4}/5\times10^{-3}) = 0.0866 \text{ m/s}$$

The adsorption isotherm, $\qquad q = (0.00543)\dfrac{126.8C}{1+126.8C}$

Feed concentration, $\qquad C_o = 1.07 \times 10^{-3}$ gmol/litre $= 1.07 \times 10^{-6}$ gmol/cm^3

$\Rightarrow \qquad \dfrac{q_o}{C_o} = \dfrac{(0.00543\text{ gmol/g})(126.8\text{ litre/gmol})}{1+(126.8\text{ litre/gmol})(1.07\times10^{-3}\text{ gmol/litre})} = 0.608$ m^3/kg

$$\frac{k_m \bar{a}}{(1-\varepsilon_p)\rho_p} \frac{C_o}{q_o} = \frac{(0.0866 \text{ m/s})(350 \text{ m}^2/\text{m}^3)}{(1-0.40)(850 \text{ kg/m}^3)(0.608 \text{ m}^3/\text{kg})} = 0.0977 \text{ s}^{-1}$$

(neglecting pore diffusion resistance, $k_m = k_c$)

The concentration front can be obtained from Eq. (12.45). Putting the values of the relevant quantities.

$$\frac{1+KC_o}{KC_o} \ln\left(\frac{C/C_o}{C_1/C_o}\right) - \frac{1}{KC_o} \ln\frac{1-C/C_o}{1-C_1/C_o} = 0.0977(t-t_1)$$

Put $KC_o = 0.1357$ and take $C_1/C_o = 0.02$ (arbitrarily selected breakthrough concentration) to get

$$\frac{1+0.1357}{0.1357} \ln\left(\frac{C/C_o}{0.02}\right) - \frac{1}{0.1357} \ln\frac{1-C/C_o}{1-0.02} = 0.0977(t-t_1) \qquad \text{(i)}$$

The above equation (i) is plotted in Figure 12.15 to obtain the constant pattern concentration front. The time required for the dimensionless concentration to change from 0.02 to 0.98 is

$$t_{\text{MTZ}} = 626 \text{ s} = 10.4 \text{ min}$$

We calculate the *approximate* velocity of the mass transfer wave-front from Eq. (12.39).

$$\left[\frac{\Delta q}{\Delta C}\right]_{C=C_o} = \frac{(0.00543)(126.8)}{1+(126.8)(1.07\times10^{-3})} = 0.607 \text{ m}^3/\text{kg}$$

$$u_s = \frac{0.3/0.4}{1+[(1-0.4)/0.4](850)(0.606)} = 0.097 \text{ cm/s}$$

length of the MTZ = (626 s)(0.097 cm/s) = 60.8 cm

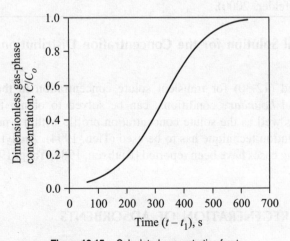

Figure 12.15 Calculated concentration front.

Breakthrough calculation considering pore diffusion (neglect surface diffusion)
First we estimate the Knudsen diffusivity (see Section 2.8.1).

$$D_K = 9700r_p(T/M)^{1/2} = (9700)(10 \times 10^{-7} \text{ cm})(300/60)^{1/2} = 0.0217 \text{ cm}^2/\text{s}$$

Effective diffusivity, Eq. [(12.47(c))], $D_e = \dfrac{0.42}{2.3}\left[\dfrac{1}{(1/0.13)+(1/0.0217)}\right] = 0.0034 \text{ cm}^2/\text{s}$

Effective mass transfer coefficient, Eq. (12.46),

$$k_m\bar{a} = \left[\frac{1}{k_c\bar{a}} + \frac{d_p^2}{60 D_e m'(1-\varepsilon_p)\rho_p}\right]^{-1}$$

$$= \left[\frac{1}{(0.0866)(350)} + \frac{(5\times10^{-3})^2}{(60)(3.4\times10^{-7})(0.61)(1-0.42)(850)}\right]^{-1}$$

$$= 27.03 \text{ s}^{-1}$$

From Eq. (12.45), $\dfrac{1+0.1357}{0.1357}\ln\left(\dfrac{C/C_o}{0.02}\right) - \dfrac{1}{0.1357}\ln\dfrac{1-C/C_o}{1-0.02} = 0.0871(t-t_1)$

The approximate velocity of the MTZ remains the same. The time for the movement of the MTZ through its own length (this corresponds to C/C_o from 0.02 to 0.98 selected arbitrarily) can be found to be $t_{MTZ} = 703$ s.

$$\text{Length of the MTZ} = (0.097 \text{ cm/s})(703 \text{ s}) = 68.2 \text{ cm}$$

[Since the effective volumetric mass transfer coefficient is less, the length of the MTZ is expectedly more.]

Adsorption breakthrough analysis has been largely used for the design of beds for purification of contaminated water. The BDST (bed depth service time) method, that uses data from a few laboratory scale columns of equal packing depth operated in series, is an important design technique (see Eckenfelder, 2000).

12.10.4 Analytical Solution for the Concentration Distribution Along the Bed

Equations (12.29) and (12.30) for transient solute concentration in the bed, subject to the appropriate *initial* and *boundary* conditions, can be solved to obtain the bed concentration profile, $C = C(z, t)$, as well as the solute concentration profile within a pellet [$c = c(r, z, t)$]. A suitable numerical solution technique has to be used (Tien, 1994). Analytical solutions in some approximate or limiting cases have been reported [Ruthven, 1984; Yang, 1987; Suzuki, 1990; and Tien, 1994].

12.11 THERMAL REGENERATION OF ADSORBENTS

Continuous separation of a mixture by adsorption is a cyclic process. When the breakthrough condition is attained, the feed flow to the adsorber stops and regeneration of the bed starts (Figure 12.1). This is the desorption or regeneration half-cycle. Higher temperature and lower pressure favour desorption. There are a few methods of bed regeneration.

Thermal swing

In gas purification applications, the adsorbate-loaded bed may be regenerated by passing a hot, relatively an inert gas (steam and air are common) to remove the adsorbed substance. The mass transfer phenomenon in regeneration is similar to that in adsorption. A desorption wave-front moves through the bed. The phenomenon would become more complex, nevertheless, since the bed does not reach the regeneration temperature very quickly. In fact, progress of a thermal front as well as of a concentration front occurs through the bed during thermal or temperature swing regeneration. The regeneration temperature is selected on the basis of the adsorption equilibrium or isotherm at different temperatures and also on the stability and characteristics of the adsorbent and of the adsorbate. This technique is called *temperature swing* since the bed temperature alternates between the adsorption and regeneration (or desorption) temperatures. Figure 12.16 shows the adsorption isotherms of a solute at two temperatures, T_a and T_d $(T_d > T_a)$. The partial pressure of the adsorbate in the feed is p_o. A bed in equilibrium with the feed has a concentration q_o in it. When regenerated at a temperature T_d, let us assume that the solute concentration in the bed is reduced to q_1, and the corresponding equilibrium partial pressure of the solute is p_1. Thus an amount $q_o - q_1$ of the solute per gram of the adsorbent is removed during regeneration. Countercurrent heating and cooling ensure a low residual solute retention in the bed. Heat requirement for regeneration is about 2.5 times the enthalpy of desorption. A hot regenerated bed needs to be cooled down before it goes for the next adsorption half-cycle.

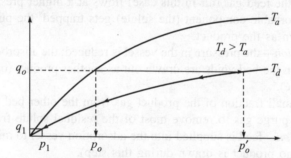

Figure 12.16 Adsorption isotherms in an ideal TSA cycle.

Purge-gas stripping

In this technique the bed loaded with the adsorbent is regenerated essentially at the same temperature and pressure by passing a relatively inert and non-adsorbable gas through the bed. Air is a common purge gas.

Pressure swing

This is based on reduction of the pressure in the adsorbent bed to nearly atmospheric or less when the bed gets stripped of the adsorbed solute. In fact, this is one of the steps of the technique of pressure swing adsorption (PSA) which has emerged as a very important strategy of gas separation (Ruthven et al., 1994; La Cava et al., 1998). It is described in the next section.

Regeneration of a bed in the case of liquid separation may be done by passing the solvent through the loaded bed or by chemical methods. This is sometimes called *concentration swing adsorption* (CSA).

12.12 PRESSURE SWING ADSORPTION

Pressure swing adsorption (PSA) has evolved as an alternative to the TSA process because of a few disadvantages of the latter like: (i) energy consumption for heating of the bed for regeneration; (ii) the solute is released as a dilute stream and may not be easy to recover; (iii) cooling of the bed should follow regeneration. The PSA technique was developed in 1960 by Skarstrom of Exxon Research for drying of gases by silica gel or alumina. It was called *heatless drying* at that time because of the particular application.

12.12.1 Basic Principles of PSA

Pressure swing adsorption depends on the fact that the adsorption capacity of a solid increases with increasing pressure of the solute. Thus in a PSA system adsorption occurs at a higher pressure of the feed gas when it is stripped of the solute. The flow of the feed stops at breakthrough and the bed is regenerated by reducing the pressure. At this stage the adsorbate is recovered in a relatively concentrated form. It is to be noted that a packed bed of adsorbent responds more rapidly to changes in pressure than to changes in temperature.[†] On the whole, the process requires less energy and is operationally simpler than TSA. The two-bed PSA system for air separation is shown in Figure 12.17. The four basic steps of the process according to the *Skarstrom cycle* are:

(a) *adsorption*—the feed gas (air in this case) flows at a higher pressure through the bed, the more adsorbable component (the solute) gets trapped; the purified gas is simultaneously drawn as the product.

(b) *depressurization*—the pressure in the vessel is reduced; the adsorbed component and the residual gas in the bed voids are drawn out as another product (or may be discarded if it is of no use).

(c) *purging*—a small fraction of the product gas from the other bed is passed through the vessel as the purge gas to remove most of the residual solute from the bed.

(d) *repressurization*—feed is supplied into the adsorption vessel to raise its pressure to that of the feed (no product is drawn during this step).

The process generally becomes more efficient if the flow of the gases during depressurization and purging occurs in the direction countercurrent to the direction of feed flow. Depressurization is also called *blowdown*. Upflow of the feed gas during adsorption, and downflow of the adsorbate-rich gas during depressurization and purging are the convenient flow configurations. A control system with interconnected pipes and valves is used to switch over the flows in a programmed manner. The beds operate under nearly isothermal condition. The heat liberated during adsorption remains in the bed and compensates for the heat of desorption during the regeneration step. A variation of PSA uses a vacuum pump to create a low pressure for regeneration of the bed. This is called *vacuum swing adsorption* (VSA). The Skarstrom cycle as described above works pretty well for gas drying but is not very efficient in the case of many mixtures. The other modified cycles using three or more beds were developed in later years (Cassidy and Holmes, 1984; Yang, 1987; Ruthven, 1994). The design of the PSA system has been discussed by White and Barkley (1989) and Ruthven et al. (1994).

[†] The cycle time for a PSA system varies from about 50 s to 6 min compared to about 1 to 15 h for a TSA system.

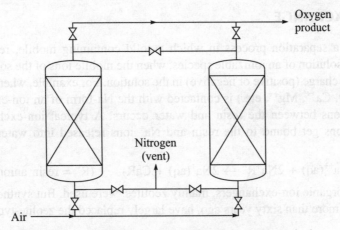

Figure 12.17 Schematic of a two-bed PSA unit for oxygen production.

12.12.2 Applications

So far the most important application of PSA (and also of VSA) has been for air separation to produce either oxygen or nitrogen. In the 1980s, small units (subatmospheric regeneration pressure of 0.35 bar absolute or a little higher) up to a capacity of 35 to 45 ton/day were developed and used in Japan to supply enriched oxygen of above 90% purity to steel plants. The oxygen-enriched gas has been used for many other purposes including biological degradation of wastewater. In the 1990s, Union Carbide patented lithium ion-exchanged zeolite-X with a reduced Si/Al ratio. This material offers a high selectivity of nitrogen over oxygen and is largely used for the production of oxygen by removing nitrogen by adsorption. Today, many producers of industrial gases offer VSA plants up to 120 ton/day capacity (Knaebel, 1999). The power consumption is 0.32 to 0.38 kWh/Nm^3 of oxygen. The major advantage of a PSA unit is the flexibility of scale of production and a high turndown ratio. A unit may run even at 10% of its rated capacity and is convenient and cost-effective for on-site gas generation. Cabinet-mounted small units are available. However, large air separation plants are still cryogenic and account for about 85% of total global production of oxygen and nitrogen.

Carbon molecular sieve (CMS) selectively adsorbs oxygen and is used for the production of nitrogen. A typical PSA plant for nitrogen operates between 5–7 bar for adsorption and at atmospheric pressure for depressurization and purging of the bed. A nitrogen capacity up to 50 ton/day with impurities varying from 1% to as low as 10 ppm is common. Oxygen is the major impurity.

PSA has many other applications besides air separation. One important application is hydrogen purification from steam reformer gases, refinery gases, etc. using activated carbon or zeolite adsorbent. Sirkar (1989) and Kumar and Van Sloun (1989) described a number of other applications of PSA developed by Air Products and Chemicals (Pennsylvania) like separation of CO_2 from methane, recovery of CO from waste gases of steel plants, separation of ammonia synthesis gases, helium purification, etc. UPO has a process of separation of *n*- and *iso*-paraffins by PSA using zeolite-5A. This is based on preferential adsorption of the straight-chain compound in zeolite. There are many global suppliers of PSA units like Air Linde, Praxair, etc.

12.13 ION-EXCHANGE

Ion-exchange is a separation process in which a solid containing mobile, replaceable ions is contacted with a solution of an ionizable species, when the mobile ions of the solid are exchanged by ions of similar charge (positive or negative) in the solution. For example, when water containing divalent ions (e.g. Ca^{++}, Mg^{++}, etc.) is contacted with the Na-form of an ion-exchange resin, an exchange of cations between the resin and water occurs. A typical ion-exchange reaction in which calcium ions get bound to the resin and Na^+ ions released into water in turn may be represented as

$$Ca^{++}(aq) + 2Na^+R^- \rightarrow 2Na^+(aq) + CaR_2 \qquad (R^- = \text{resin anion}) \qquad (12.48)$$

In early years, inorganic ion-exchangers, mainly zeolites, were used. But synthetic ion-exchange resins, developed more than sixty years ago, have largely replaced the zeolite-type ion-exchangers years ago.

12.13.1 Polymeric Ion-exchange Resins

Commercially used ion-exchange resins are mostly derived from organic polymers. Polystyrene, cross-linked with a small quantity of divinyl benzene (DVB), is the base material. A polymer with 10% DVA content is most common. Polymers prepared from methacrylic acid, acrylic acid or a condensation polymer of epichlorohydrin with a suitable amine are also used commercially (McNulty, 1997). The most important industrial use of ion-exchange resins is for softening and demineralization of water for boilers and chemical processes. Nevertheless these resins have also been used for:

(a) catalysis (example: esterification catalyst),
(b) high purity water production for semiconductor industries,
(c) separation of metal ions from wastewater (example: effluents from a metal finishing industry) for recovery as well as for pollution control, and
(d) membrane-based technologies like electrodialysis, etc.

Ionic sites—cationic or anionic—need to be incorporated in the polymer base for the preparation of a synthetic ion-exchange resin. A cationic site is incorporated by sulphonation of the benzene rings in polystyrene. An anion-exchange site is generated by chloromethylation of the benzene rings followed by amination. A few reactions in the preparation process are shown in Figure 12.18.

An ion-exchange resin swells in water. The amount of water uptake increases with the degree of substitution of ionic groups in the rings, but decreases with increase in crosslinking. Thus the degree of crosslinking should be controlled as to allow reasonable swelling of the resin. The more the crosslinking, the larger is the *elastic force* to resist water uptake or swelling. With increased swelling, the diffusivity of ions in the resin becomes larger causing a larger rate of ion transport in it as a result. The capacity of ion-exchange is also determined by the extent of substitution of the ionic groups. For common commercial resins, the ion-exchange capacity is about 5 milliequivalent per gram dry resin (it is about 2.5 meq per ml volume of the water-swelled resins).

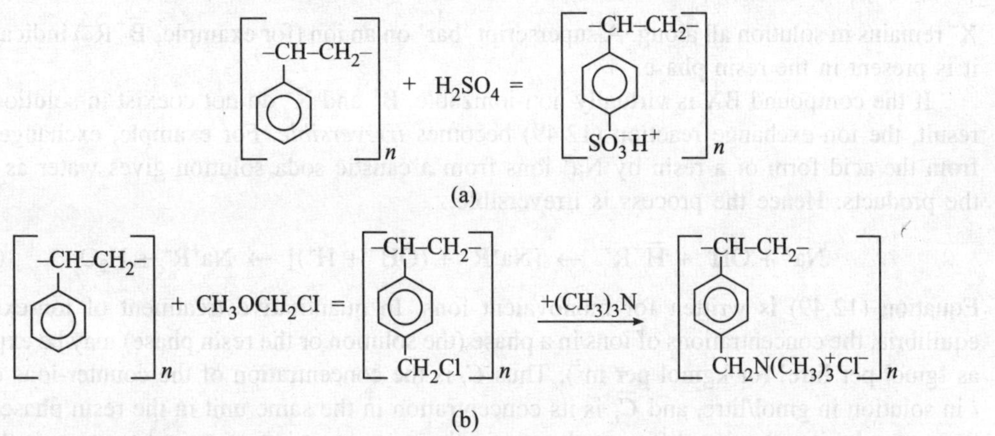

Figure 12.18 (a) Preparation of a strong-acid cation-exchange resin, and (b) preparation of a strong-base anion-exchange resin.

A cation-exchange resin has fixed negative charges in the matrix as $-SO_3^-$ (or $-COO^-$) groups. The cations (H^+ ions in the acid form, and Na^+ ions in the salt form) are mobile. These are called *counter-ions*. In R^-Na^+ (R is the basic unit of the polymer), Na^+ ions are the counter-ions. The strong base resins are in the form of quaternary ammonium ions (see Figure 12.18) and the anions are the counter-ions. An ion-exchange resin is capable of exchanging the counter-ions only because these are mobile. However, the counter-ions always balance the co-ions ($-SO_3^-$ is a co-ion in a cation-exchanger resin) in order to maintain electrical neutrality (also see Section 14.1.5). A copolymer of styrene and acrylic acid gives a 'weakly acid' ion-exchanger.

An ion-exchange resin may be prepared in two forms—'gel' and 'micro-reticular' (MR). Plain sulphonation of the polymer base gives a gel form resin. But if a third component, insoluble in the polymer, is incorporated during polymerization and leached out later, a macro-porous structure (called micro-reticular) is formed. Such a resin allows diffusion of larger molecules such as proteins into it.

'Amberlite', 'Duolite' (Rohm and Haas), 'Dowex' (Dow Chemicals), etc. are the trade names of a few common and widely used resins. These are available in the form of tiny beads, 40 μm to 1.2 mm in size. Water-swollen beads contain 40–65% water, with a density of 1.1 to 1.5 g/cm^3. Swelling depends upon the type of counter-ions (for example, the H^+ form resin swells more than the Na^+-form). A few other manufacturers of ion-exchange resins are Mitshubishi, Sybron Chemicals, Henkel India, etc.

12.13.2 Ion-exchange Equilibria

An ion-exchange 'reaction' can be expressed in the following form.

$$A^+ + \overline{B}^+R^- + X^- \rightarrow \overline{A}^+R^- + B^+ + X^- \tag{12.49}$$

Here the ions A^+ and X^- are formed in solution by dissociation of the compound AX; $\overline{B}^+R^-$ and $\overline{A}^+R^-$ stand for the cation-exchange resin. The resin changes from the B-form ($\overline{B}^+R^-$) to the A-form ($\overline{A}^+R^-$) on exchange of the cation B^+ in the resin by A^+ from the solution. The anion

X⁻ remains in solution all along. A superscript 'bar' on an ion (for example, $\overline{B}^+R^-$) indicates that it is present in the resin phase.

If the compound BX is virtually non-ionizable, B^+ and X^- do not coexist in solution. As a result, the ion-exchange reaction (12.49) becomes *irreversible*. For example, exchange of H^+ from the acid-form of a resin by Na^+ ions from a caustic soda solution gives water as one of the products. Hence the process is irreversible.

$$Na^+ + OH^- + \overline{H}^+R^- \rightarrow [Na^+R^- + (OH^- + H^+)] \rightarrow Na^+R^- + H_2O \qquad (12.50)$$

Equation (12.49) is written for monovalent ions. In quantitative treatment of ion-exchange equilibria, the concentrations of ions in a phase (the solution or the resin phase) may be expressed as 'gmol per litre' (or kgmol per m³). Thus C_i is the concentration of the counter-ions of type i in solution in gmol/litre, and $\overline{C}_i$ is its concentration in the same unit in the resin phase. Since there may be ions having different charges in the mixture, it is convenient to express the total concentration of the ions in gram-equivalent/litre. Thus the total ionic concentration in solution is C_e (eq./litre) and that in the resin phase is $\overline{C}_e$ (eq./litre). Also, the 'equivalent fraction' of the counter-ion i in solution is x_i, and that in the resin is y_i. If z_i is the charge of the ion i,

$$x_i = \frac{z_i C_i}{C_e} \quad \text{and} \quad y_i = \frac{z_i \overline{C}_i}{\overline{C}_e} \qquad (12.51)$$

The equilibrium constant, $K_{AB}{}^\dagger$, of the ion-exchange reaction, Eq. (12.49), involving *univalent* ions ($z_i = 1$) can be expressed as

$$K_{AB} = \frac{\overline{C}_A \, C_B}{C_A \, \overline{C}_B} = \frac{\overline{C}_e \, y_A \cdot C_e \, x_B}{C_e \, x_A \, \overline{C}_e \, y_B} = \frac{y_A \, x_B}{x_A \, y_B} \qquad (12.52)$$

The above expression for K_{AB} is an approximate one. Activities of the ions, rather than concentrations, should be used to get a thermodynamically correct expression. Since only two types of counter-ions, A and B, are involved,

$$y_A + y_B = 1 = x_A + x_B \qquad (12.53)$$

Equation (12.52) can now be re-written as

$$\frac{y_A}{y_B} = K_{AB} \frac{x_A}{x_B} \quad \Rightarrow \quad K_{AB} = \frac{y_A/(1-y_A)}{x_A/(1-x_A)} \qquad (12.54)$$

Thus the ion-exchange equilibrium constant, K_{AB}, is also the *selectivity coefficient* for the exchange process. Similarly, if we consider exchange of the monovalent counter-ions B by a divalent cation D in solution [Eq. (12.48) is a practical example], the ion-exchange 'reaction' becomes

$$D^{2+} + 2\overline{B}^- \rightarrow \overline{D}^{2+} + 2B^- \qquad (z_i = 1 \text{ for } B^-; \, z_i = 2 \text{ for } D^{2+}) \qquad (12.55)$$

In this case, $x_D = 2C_D/C_e; \quad x_B = C_B/C_e; \quad y_D = 2\overline{C}_D/\overline{C}_e; \quad y_B = \overline{C}_B/\overline{C}_e$

---

† The first subscript A of K_{AB} represents the ion in solution; the second subscript B is the replaceable ion in the resin.

The equilibrium constant is expressed as

$$K_{DB} = \frac{\overline{C}_D\, C_B^2}{C_D\, \overline{C}_B^2} = \frac{(\overline{C}_e\, y_D/2)(C_e\, x_B)^2}{(C_e\, x_D/2)(\overline{C}_e\, y_B)^2} = \frac{C_e}{\overline{C}_e}\frac{y_D\, x_B^2}{x_D\, y_B^2}$$

$$\Rightarrow \qquad \frac{y_D}{(1 - y_D)^2} = K_{DB}\,\frac{\overline{C}_e}{C_e}\,\frac{x_D}{(1 - x_D)^2} \qquad\qquad (12.56)$$

The equilibrium constant defined in Eq. (12.52) or (12.56) is also called the molar *selectivity coefficient* for the particular ion-exchange process. The maximum extent of ion-exchange under a given set of conditions can be calculated if the selectivity coefficient is known. The concentration of the ions in the resin and in the solution phase affects the molar selectivity coefficient, K_{DB}. The extent of ion exchange can thus be controlled by adjusting the solution concentration. The constant K for a resin depends upon the ions involved and the degree of crosslinking (and, therefore, the water content). The selectivity coefficient values of 8% DVB crosslinked polystyrene cation and anion exchange resins relative to Li^+ (for cation exchange) and Cl^- (for anion exchange) ions are given in Table 12.4. This coefficient for any pair of counterions can be obtained from the relative values given in the table. For example, the selectivity coefficient $K_{Ca^{2+}Mg^{2+}}$ is

$$K_{Ca^{2+}Mg^{2+}} = \frac{K_{Ca^{2+}Li^+}}{K_{Mg^{2+}Li^+}} = \frac{5.16}{3.29} = 1.57 \qquad\qquad (12.57)$$

Table 12.4 Selectivity scale for some cations and anions

Cations on 8% crosslinked strong-acid resin				Anions on strong-base resin			
Li^+	1.0	Zn^+	3.5	Cl^-	1.0	NO_3^-	4.0
H^+	1.3	Cu^{2+}	3.8	Br^-	3.0	SO_4^{2-}	0.15
Na^+	2.0	Mn^{2+}	4.1	HSO_4^-	1.6	CO_3^-	0.03
NH_4^+	2.6	Ni^{2+}	3.9	NO_2^-	1.3		
K^+	2.9	Ca^{2+}	5.2	CN^-	1.3		
Mg^{2+}	3.3	Pb^{2+}					

The selectivity value increases with the decreasing size of hydrated ions because it requires less space to be accommodated in the resin matrix, and also the stretching forces exerted on the polymer network are less. For the exchange of a monovalent ion A and a divalent ion D, the equilibrium constant is given by

$$K_{DA} = (K_{DLi^+})/(K_{ALi^+})^2 \qquad\qquad (12.58)$$

Details of the theory, applications and design of the ion-exchange processes have been discussed by Helfferich (1962), Streat (1991), and Anderson (1997).

EXAMPLE 12.6 (*Amount of resin for equilibrium batch separation*)   Water containing 120 ppm Ca^{++} is to be treated with an 8% DVB-crosslinked resin in the Na^+-form to remove 95% of the calcium ions. The resin has an exchange capacity of 2 eq./litre. Calculate the amount of resin required to treat 10 m^3 of the water.

Solution

For exchange of Ca^{++} ions by Na^+ ions, the equilibrium constant or selectivity is given by

$$K_{Ca^{++}/Na^+} = K'_{Ca^{++}}/K'_{Na^+} = 5.16/1.98 = 2.6 \qquad \text{(Table 12.4)}$$

For the resin phase, the total concentration of ion-exchange sites, $\overline{C}_e$ = 2 eq./litre

Total concentration of ions in solution (Ca^{++} and Na^+ ions after exchange) expressed as Ca^{++} ions

$$= 0.12 \text{ g/litre} = 0.12/40 \text{ gmol/litre} = 0.12/(40 \times 2) = 0.006 \text{ eq./litre} = C_e$$

95% of the Ca^{++} ions are removed at the end of the equilibrium contact.

Ca^{++} ions remaining in water = (0.05)(0.006) eq./litre = 0.0003 eq./litre.

Equivalent fraction of Ca^{++} in water at equilibrium, x_D = 0.0003/0.006 = 0.05

If y_D is the equivalent fractions of Ca^{++} in the resin phase, then from Eq. (12.56) we have

$$\frac{y_D}{(1 - y_D)^2} = (2.6) \left(\frac{2}{0.006} \right) \frac{x_D}{(1 - x_D)^2} = (866.7) \frac{0.05}{(1 - 0.05)^2} \quad \Rightarrow \quad y_D = 0.8657$$

Total amount of Ca^{++} ions in solution = (0.12 g/litre)(10^4 litre) = 1200 g = 60 g-equivalent Ca^{++} ions removed = (60)(0.95) = 57 g-equivalent

If m kg resin is used, quantity of exchange sites = $2m$ equivalent

A fraction of 0.8657 of the exchange sites are now occupied by Ca^{++} ions.

So, $(2m)(0.8657) = 57 \quad \Rightarrow \quad$ Quantity of resin, $m = \boxed{33 \text{ kg}}$

12.13.3   Isotherms and Separation Factors in Ion-exchange

The separation factor for the exchange of ions B in the resin by ions A present in a solution is expressed as

$$\alpha_{AB} = \frac{y_A/y_B}{x_A/x_B} = \frac{y_A x_B}{x_A y_B} \tag{12.59}$$

An ion-exchange process is called favourable if $\alpha_{AB} > 1$. For exchange between a pair of ions of the same valency or charge, the separation factor is identical to the selectivity coefficient. But for divalent-monovalent exchange, $\alpha_{DB} = K_{DB}(\overline{C}_e/C_e)$.

Equilibrium between two counter-ions undergoing mutual exchange can also be presented in the form of an ion-exchange isotherm. For a constant value of α_{AB}, the ion-exchange isotherm looks like the x–y diagram of a binary solution of constant relative volatility (Figure 12.19).

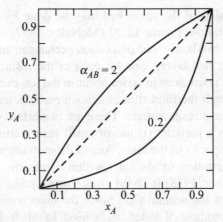

Figure 12.19   Ion-exchange isotherm for the reaction given by Eq. (12.59).

12.13.4   Ion-exchange in a Column

Ion-exchange may be carried out in a stirred vessel, in a packed bed of the resin, or even in a fluidized bed. The packed bed strategy is akin to the dual-bed gas adsorption technique. The solution is passed through a packed bed of resin till breakthrough occurs. The solution is then directed through the second bed while the first one goes for regeneration using a suitable regeneration medium.

As in the case of gas adsorption, a mass transfer zone (MTZ) forms in an ion-exchange column. The MTZ moves through the bed and at breakthrough the leading end of the front reaches the top of the bed. If the separation factor α_{AB} of A over B is larger than unity, the ion-exchange process is favourable and an S-shaped concentration distribution curve forms in the mass transfer zone which moves with a reasonably constant velocity. The larger the value of α, the thinner the ion-exchange or mass transfer zone. On the other hand, if the separation factor is less than unity, the ion-exchange zone appears pretty thick and spreads while it moves through the bed. For a favourable isotherm, an ion-exchange process is more efficient. But the regeneration process becomes unfavourable. The MTZ for regeneration spreads as it moves along the bed and a larger concentration/amount of the regenerating solution has to be used.

An ion-exchange vessel is shown in Figure 12.20. It is provided with a bed support at the bottom and a strainer for retaining the resin during countercurrent backwashing, and nozzles and

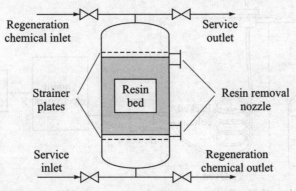

Figure 12.20   A bed of ion-exchanger employing countercurrent regeneration.

port connections. Regeneration of the spent bed may be done by cocurrent or countercurrent flow of the regenerating solution. Figure 12.20 (McNulty, 1997) shows countercurrent regeneration. For polishing water, two beds—one of a cation exchanger, another an anion-exchanger—are used. A mixed bed with two layers, one for each of the resins, is also used.

Broadly, two diffusional resistances in series occur in the ion-exchange process—the external resistance for diffusion through the fluid film on a resin particle, and the internal resistance for diffusion through the pores in a resin particle. There are two effective strategies of reducing the diffusional resistance within a particle: (i) use of small resin particles, and (ii) low fractional utilization of the exchange capacity of the resin. Any of these strategies reduces the diffusion path length or the depth of penetration of the ions within a particle. The Recoflo ion-exchange technique (Brown and Fletcher, 1988) is based on the above principle. The average size of the resin particles is one-tenth of the normal size. Since the mass transfer resistance is lowered, a thin resin bed and a high throughput of water can be used. In this technique, a bed depth of about 15 cm only is used which is somewhat larger than the length of the mass transfer zone. Only 20% of the exchange capacity of the resin is utilized in a demineralization half cycle.

The type of resin to be used for demineralization of boiler feed water depends upon the TDS of the feed water. For a high TDS feed (> 3000 mg/1), a weak acid cation exchange (WAC) resin is used. Use of the strong acid cation (SAC) resin is limited to low TDS feeds (< 3000 mg/1). Typical feed throughput is 2–24 gallons per minute/ft^2 for 400–800 mm bed using the Dowex resin (the Recoflo process claims to use a throughput of 100 gpm/ft^2). For boiler feed water, the hardness level should be preferably below 0.2 mg/1 or even less. Swelling of the resin by 10% to even 50% during generation of the acid form is a factor to be taken care of while designing an ion-exchange bed

12.14 CHROMATOGRAPHY

Chromatography is the most important and versatile technique for the separation of a mixture and is used primarily for analytical purposes. The technique is based on differences in affinities of the compounds in a mixture towards a suitable adsorbent. A chromatographic system consists of a number of parts (shown in Figure 12.21). The heart of the system is a column which is nothing but a narrow tubing generally packed with fine particles of an adsorbent called the *stationary phase*. A fluid (a gas or a liquid), called the *mobile phase*, flows through the adsorbent-

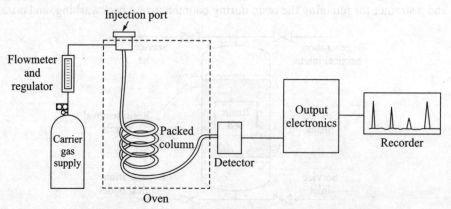

Figure 12.21 Basic components of a gas or gas–liquid chromatograph.

filled column. A sample of the mixture to be separated or analyzed is injected as a pulse at the inlet to the column. The mobile phase carries the components of the mixture through the stationary phase. Since individual components are reversibly adsorbed but have different affinities for the adsorbent, these are 'retarded' in the column to varying extents. A component that has a low affinity for the stationary phase is retarded less and moves faster than one having a stronger affinity for it. A compound that is not adsorbed moves with the velocity of the mobile phase. As a result, the components get separated while they are carried along at different velocities through the column. They emerge from the column at different times and their concentrations in the outlet mobile phase are measured as functions of time by a detector. The response of the detector, which is a measure of the concentration of a component, appears as distinct 'peaks' on a plot called the 'chromatogram'. Chromatographic separation of three species in a mixture is schematically shown in Figure 12.22.

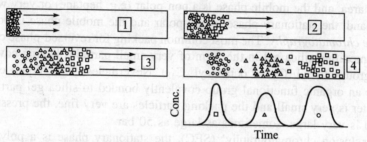

Figure 12.22 Schematic of movement and separation of three solutes in a sample in a chromatographic column. The three peaks correspond to the three solutes in the sample.

The chromatographic technique of separation was invented and developed by the Russian botanist M.S. Tswett in 1903. He separated the coloured plant pigments in a column packed with calcium carbonate using petroleum ether as the 'elutant' or mobile phase. The pigments were separated as distinct bands in the column depending upon differences in their affinity for the stationary phase (calcium carbonate). After a lapse of about forty years, A.J.P. Martin and R.L.M. Synge made very significant contributions towards development and use of various types of chromatographic techniques for which they were awarded Nobel Prize in Chemistry in 1952.

The common chromatographic techniques are shown in Figure 12.23. They differ in the types of stationary and mobile phases and the way the phases are used in the chromatographic

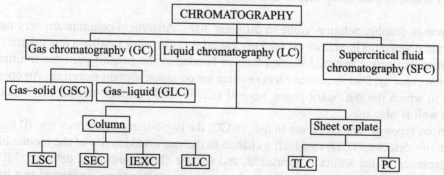

Figure 12.23 Classification of chromatographic techniques — SEC: size-exclusion chromatography; LSC: liquid–solid chromatography; IEXC: ion-exchange chromatography; LLC: liquid-liquid chromatography; TLC: thin-layer chromatography.

column. In gas chromatography, the mobile phase is a high purity light gas (N_2, Ar, CO_2 or He). The stationary phase may be porous solid adsorbent particles (in gas–solid chromatography, GSC) or a suitable liquid held in the pores of solid particles (GLC) as shown in Figure 12.24. A mixture having components that get vaporized at the temperature of the column can be separated by gas chromatography. If the mobile phase is a liquid, the technique is called *liquid chromatography* (LC). Liquid

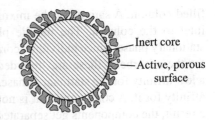

Figure 12.24 Pore structure of a particle (stationary phase).

chromatography again may be of a few types. Liquid–solid chromatography (LSC), that employs a solid stationary phase, is in common use as an analytical tool. It is called *adsorption chromatography* if the stationary phase is a relatively polar solid having a high surface area, and the mobile phase is a non-polar (e.g. heptane) or very weakly polar. If, on the other hand, the stationary phase is non-polar and the mobile phase is polar, it is called *reversed-phase chromatography*. The most common packing for reversed-phase chromatography is chemically modified silica gel in the form of very small particles having covalently bonded hydrophobic groups (octyl, C_8, or octadecyl, C_{18}). Nevertheless most liquid chromatography packings have an organic functional group covalently bonded to silica gel particles. Since the column diameter is very small and the packing particles are very fine, the pressure drop across an LC column is very large, sometimes as large as 50 bar.

In 'size-exclusion chromatography' (SEC), the stationary phase is a polymeric gel (e.g. polyacrylamide gel) having pores of a given size range. It is also called *gel-permeation chroma-tography*. Molecules (or their complexes with the solvent) are separated depending upon size. In 'ion-exchange chromatography', the stationary phase contains an ionic group (e.g. NO_3^-, SO_3^-) that interacts with an ionic compound in the sample and binds to it reversibly. Porous support particles loaded with a suitable liquid make the stationary phase in liquid–liquid chromatography (LLC). In supercritical fluid chromatography (SFC), the mobile phase is a supercritical fluid (such as supercritical CO_2). SFC has found applications in analysis of natural products, drugs, food, agrochemicals, etc.

In thin-layer chromatography (TLC), the stationary phase is coated on a glass or metal plate. A very small sample is applied on the plate which is then placed in a solvent-filled vessel, with the bottom end dipped in the solvent. The solvent flows up along the layer of stationary phase by capillary action and the components in the sample mixture are carried to different heights to form bands.

Chromatographic columns come in different sizes. Analytical columns are very narrow, up to 2 mm in diameter. The size of the packing particles is also very small—a few microns to about 50 microns. An active material is coated on or bonded to the support particles to impart it the adsorption capacity. Diatomaceous earth or silica are common support materials. An open tubular column in which the stationary phase, several micron thick, remains chemically bonded to the column wall is also used.

Various types of 'detectors' are in use. In GC, the two common detectors are: (i) the thermal conductivity detector (TCD) in which a change in thermal conductivity of the mobile phase due to the presence of the solute is measured, and (ii) the flame-ionization detector (FID) which measures the current due to the ions formed when an organic material is burned in a hydrogen-oxygen flame. A colourimetric detector working in both visible and UV range is common in liquid chromatography.

A typical chromatographic output or chromatogram for the separation of a mixture of two compounds is shown in Figure 12.25. Three peaks are seen. The small peak is due to a 'non-retained substance', which was there before the sample was injected. A 'non-retained substance' means one which does not have any affinity for the stationary phase and moves at the velocity of the mobile phase. The other two peaks are due to two components in the sample that get adsorbed to varying extent. If the volume of a sample injected is small and it is injected instantaneously, it is called a *perfect pulse*. Ideally, the peak corresponding to a component should be tall and very sharp. However, quite a few factors, including *axial dispersion* in the column, cause peak broadening. The peak width at the bottom is the time required for the compound to get desorbed at the end of the column. The area of a peak is proportional to the amount of the corresponding compound. A calibration graph can be prepared from the peak areas obtained for various samples of precisely known concentrations. The calibration graph can be used to determine the amount of a compound in an unknown sample. The time up to the middle of the peak since sample injection is called the *retention time*. In Figure 12.25, the retention time of compound 1 is t_{R1} and that of compound 2 is t_{R2}. The retention time is a measure of the affinity of a substance for the stationary phase. Here compound 2 has a greater affinity for the stationary phase and hence it is more retarded than compound 1. The time for the non-retained peak is t_m. It is the same as the time taken by the mobile phase to move through the column (i.e. the average residence time of the mobile phase or the breakthrough time).

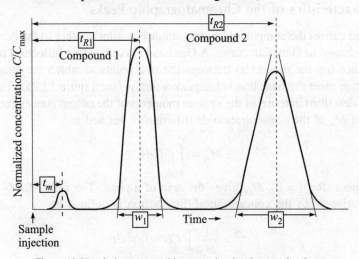

Figure 12.25 A chromatographic output showing the retention times.

12.14.1 Basic Theoretical Principles

Chromatographic separation of two compounds depends upon the difference in their affinity towards the stationary phase (Meyer, 1988), and a direct measure of the affinity is the adsorption equilibrium constant. Since chromatography involves low concentration of the solutes, a linear equilibrium relation is often applicable.

$$K_D = \frac{\text{solute concentration in the stationary phase}}{\text{solute concentration in the mobile phase}} \tag{12.60}$$

If a linear equilibrium relation is applicable, we call it 'linear chromatography'. A 'capacity factor' in chromatographic separation is defined as

$$k' = \frac{\text{total amount of solute in the stationary phase}}{\text{total amount of solute in the mobile phase}} \qquad (12.61)$$

If V_s and V_m are the volumes of the stationary and the mobile phases respectively, K_D and k' are related as

$$k' = K_D V_s / V_m \qquad (12.62)$$

The quantity k' can also be expressed in terms of the retention time as

$$k' = \frac{t_R - t_m}{t_m} \qquad (12.63)$$

where t_R and t_m are the times for the retained and unretained peaks respectively.

The selectivity of compound 2 over 1 is defined as

$$\alpha_{21} = \frac{t_{R2} - t_m}{t_{R1} - t_m} = \frac{K_{D2}}{K_{D1}} \qquad (12.64)$$

12.14.2   Characteristics of the Chromatographic Peaks

The mobile phase carries the compounds in the sample one after another to the detector. Normally, a peak is a bell-shaped or Gaussian curve. A Gaussian curve has two inflection points on its two arms. The distance (on the time axis) between the two points at which the tangents at the two points of inflection meet the base line is the peak width w (see Figure 12.25). The characteristic of a peak is best described in terms of the various moments of the output concentration distribution. The nth moment M_n of the concentration distribution is defined as

$$M_n = \int_0^\infty t^n C \, dt \qquad (12.65)$$

The zeroth moment (for $n = 0$), M_0, gives the area of a peak. The ratio M_1/M_0 is the retention time, t_R. The 'variance' of the concentration distribution is defined as

$$\sigma^2 = \frac{1}{M_0} \int_0^\infty C(t - t_R)^2 \, dt \qquad (12.66)$$

The 'resolution' of two neighbouring peaks is defined as

$$R' = \frac{t_{R2} - t_{R1}}{(w_1 + w_2)/2} = \frac{\text{difference in retention time}}{\text{average of the peak width at the base}} \qquad (12.67)$$

Two important quantities frequently used to describe the efficiency of a chromatographic column are the number of theoretical plates N_p, and the height of a theoretical plate (HETP) defined as follows if the peak is Gaussian.

$$N_p = 16(t_R/w)^2 \quad \text{and} \quad \text{HETP} = \sigma^2 L / t_R^2, \quad L = \text{column length} \qquad (12.68)$$

The resolution can be related to the selectivity α, capacity factor k' and the 'number of theoretical plates' N_p as

$$R' = \left(\frac{\alpha-1}{4}\right)\left(\frac{k'}{1+k'}\right)\sqrt{N_p}\,, \quad \text{where } k' = (k'_1 + k'_2)/2 \tag{12.69}$$

12.14.3 Peak Broadening and Tailing

If the mobile phase is in plug flow and the axial dispersion effects are small, a sharp peak is obtained for a compound in the sample. Dispersion effects make a peak broader and reduce its height. If too much peak broadening occurs, adjacent peaks may partially overlap. The operating conditions of the instrument have to be optimized in order to get sharp and nearly Gaussian peaks. In many cases, the rear end of a peak is found to spread out forming a tail. This is called *tailing*. Tailing reduces the plate number and hence the resolution. Tailing can be minimized by adjusting the operating parameters.

12.14.4 Gradient Method

In gas chromatography, the oven and column temperature is often programmed. This means that the column temperature is increased at a predetermined rate. A weakly adsorbed compound is eluted at a lower temperature and the strongly adsorbed ones are successively eluted as the column temperature rises. Similarly, in liquid chromatography, a solvent gradient is often used. This means that a mixed solvent, with its composition changing with time in a predetermined fashion, (done by automatically adjusting the flow rates of the individual solvents), is used as the mobile phase so that the eluting environment can be controlled to cause elution of the components in a controlled manner.

12.14.5 Process-scale Chromatography

Although chromatography is primarily used as an analytical tool, it is also used to separate high value commercial products (Jagschies, 1985). Major applications are in 'downstream bioseparation' and separation of pharmaceuticals when the conventional separation or purification techniques are not suitable. In adsorption, the objective is to capture the solute in the solid bed and then elute it in a concentrated form. In elution chromatography, the objective is to separate/purify the target compound even though it is diluted.

The two more important techniques for process-scale chromatography are 'affinity chromatography' and 'ion-exchange chromatography'. In the former technique, the stationary phase has an 'affinity ligand' attached to it. The affinity ligand binds the target biomolecules selectively. Such a process has a high selectivity and biomolecules can be concentrated from a very dilute solution by even 1000 times. After the undesired substances of the feed mixture are washed out, the bound target product is eluted by adjusting the pH and the ionic strength of the eluting medium. For biomolecules having a net charge, an alternative technique is ion-exchange chromatography. Separation occurs in contact with a stationary phase having ionic groups. Process chromatography is carried out in bigger diameter columns, although the detrimental effect of axial mixing becomes more important when the column diameter is increased.

EXAMPLE 12.7 (*Separation in a chromatographic column*)   A sample containing compounds *A* and *B* is analyzed in a chromatographic column, 30 cm long. The mobile phase velocity is 0.15 cm/s and the capacity factors are $k'_A = 9.0$ and $k'_B = 6.67$.

(a) Calculate the difference in the retention times of the compounds and the selectivity, α_{AB}.

(b) Calculate the HETP and the plate height of the column for separation of the mixture, if the peak width at the base of compound *A* is 150 s.

(c) Calculate the resolution between the peaks.

Solution

The dead time for the mobile phase, $t_m = L/v = (30 \text{ cm})/(0.15 \text{ cm/s}) = 200$ s.

(a) From Eq. (12.63),

$$k' = \frac{t_R - t_m}{t_m} \Rightarrow t_{RA} - t_{RB} = (k'_A - k'_B)t_m = (9.0 - 6.67)(200) = \boxed{7.8 \text{ min}}$$

Selectivity of *A* over *B*, $\alpha_{AB} = \dfrac{t_{RA} - t_m}{t_{RB} - t_m} = \dfrac{k'_A}{k'_B} = \dfrac{9.0}{6.67} = \boxed{1.35}$

(b) For component *A*, $t_{RA} = (k'_A + 1)t_m = (9.0 + 1)(200) = 2000$ s.

Peak width at the bottom, $w_A = 150$ s

Number of plates, $N_p = (16)(t_{RA}/w_A)^2 = (16)(2000/150)^2 = \boxed{2840}$

Height of a theoretical plate, HETP = 30 cm/2840 = $\boxed{1.06 \text{ mm}}$

(c) Resolution, $R' = \left(\dfrac{\alpha - 1}{4}\right)\left(\dfrac{k'}{1 + k'}\right)\sqrt{N_p}$

Putting $k' = (k'_A + k'_B)/2 = (9.0 + 6.67)/2 = 7.84$

$$R' = \left(\frac{1.35 - 1}{4}\right)\left(\frac{7.84}{7.84 + 1}\right)\sqrt{2840} = \boxed{4.14}$$

NOTATIONS

$\bar{a}$	: external surface area of the pellets, m^2/m^3
c	: gas-phase concentration of the adsorbate within the pores, mol/m^3
C	: gas-phase concentration of the adsorbate, mol/m^3
D_E	: axial dispersion coefficient, m^2/s
K	: adsorption equilibrium constant
K_H	: Henry's law constant for adsorption, gmol/(kg kPa)
K', K'', n	: adjustable parameters of isotherms
L	: bed length, m

L_s	:	effective length of the saturated bed, m
p	:	partial pressure of the adsorbate, kPa
P_v	:	vapour pressure of a liquid
q	:	solid-phase concentration, gmol/kg
q_o	:	solid-phase concentration in equilibrium with the feed gas of concentration C_o, gmol/kg
r', r_p	:	pore radius, m
r_o	:	radius of a pellet, m
t	:	time, s
t_b, t_e, t_s	:	breakthrough, equilibrium, and stoichiometric time respectively, s
T	:	temperature, K
u_c	:	velocity of propagation of the concentration front, m/s
u_s	:	velocity of the stoichiometric front (also of the MTZ), m/s or cm/s
u_{sh}	:	shock-wave velocity, m/s
u	:	interstitial fluid velocity, m/s
z	:	axial position
α_{12}	:	selectivity of species 1 over 2
$\varepsilon_b, \varepsilon_p$	:	porosity of the bed and of a particle respectively
σ^2	:	variance of exit concentration distribution
θ	:	contact angle, fractional surface coverage
ρ_b, ρ_p	:	density of the bed and the particle respectively
w	:	peak width at the base

SHORT AND MULTIPLE CHOICE QUESTIONS

1. Adsorption of a pure gas A on activated carbon follows the Langmuir isotherm.

$$q = \frac{6.4\,p}{1+1.53\,p}; \quad p \text{ in kPa and } q \text{ in mmol/g}$$

If the molecular weight of A is 65, what is the maximum quantity of gas (in kg adsorbate per kg carbon) that can be adsorbed?

(i) 0.712   (ii) 0.272   (iii) 0.523

2. Adsorption of CO_2 on BPL activated carbon at 30°C can be fitted by the Toth isotherm.

$$q = \frac{14.7\,p}{(11.2 + p^{0.424})^{2.36}}; \quad p \text{ in kPa and } q \text{ in mmol/g}$$

Calculate the Henry's law constant for this system applicable at low pressure of CO_2.

3. If adsorption of pure gases A and B follow the Langmuir isotherm equations, calculate the total loading of the adsorbates per gram of the solid in equilibrium with an equimolar mixture of A and B at a total pressure of 1 bar. Assume that the Langmuir isotherm is obeyed by the mixture as well.

$$q_A = q_{Am} \frac{K_A p_A}{1 + K_A p_A} = \frac{1.72\, p_A}{1 + 0.92\, p_A}$$

and

$$q_B = q_{Bm} \frac{K_B p_B}{1 + K_B p_B} = \frac{0.33\, p_B}{1 + 0.18\, p_B}$$

4. Calculate the adsorption separation factor α_{AB} in question 3 if a mixture of A and B (60% A, total pressure = 1 bar) is in equilibrium with the adsorbent.

5. Adsorbents of a small particle size are preferred for liquid separation compared to gas separation because
   (i) larger particles may be more porous and diffusional resistance is lower
   (ii) the adsorption capacity of smaller particles is larger
   (iii) the resistance to diffusion through the liquid-filled pores is greater than that in the case of a gas.

6. Entropy change for adsorption is
   (i) negative   (ii) zero   (iii) positive

7. An adsorption process is
   (i) always exothermic
   (ii) always endothermic
   (iii) either of these.

8. What is the size range of meso-pores?
   (i) 0–1 nm   (ii) 10–100 μm   (iii) 2–50 nm

9. A sample of activated alumina may have pores as small as 5 nm. What should be the minimum mercury pressure to ensure filling up these pores in a mercury porosimeter?
   (i) 100 bar   (ii) 1000 bar   (iii) 2000 bar

10. Select suitable adsorbents for the following purposes:
    (i) Final drying of air in an air liquefaction plant
    (ii) Drying of air for pneumatic instruments
    (iii) Removal of phenolic contaminants from wastewater
    (iv) Arresting benzene from storage tank emissions[#] during filling

11. Which of the following orientations of an adsorption vessel provides a satisfactory flow distribution of the feed?
    (i) Vertical bed
    (ii) Horizontal bed
    (iii) Bed of any orientation

[#] When an empty storage tank for a volatile liquid is filled, the vapour (often toxic) present in the tank gets vented out into the atmosphere. A bed of active carbon connected to the vent line of the tank arrests the volatiles. This prevents pollution as well as recovers the vapour.

12. How is breakthrough concentration defined for adsorption in a packed bed?
    (i) It is the minimum detectable or maximum allowable concentration in the effluent from the bed.
    (ii) It is approximately half of the solute concentration in the feed.
    (iii) It is the maximum solute concentration in the effluent.

13. The length of the unused bed (LUB) is more if the mass transfer zone is
    (i) wide   (ii) narrow   (iii) asymmetric

14. If the adsorption rate of the solute is infinitely fast and irreversible, the thickness of the MTZ would be
    (i) very large   (ii) about half of the bed length   (iii) zero.

15. Qualitatively, discuss the effects of the following on the thickness of the MTZ.
    (i) Particle size and porosity
    (ii) Feed stream velocity
    (iii) Axial dispersion of the solute
    (iv) Rate of adsorption

16. The velocity of the MTZ for adsorption of a solute in a packed bed is 5 cm/min. The length of the bed is 120 cm. The equilibrium time is 26 min. What is the thickness of the MTZ?
    (i) 10 cm   (ii) 40 cm   (iii) 0.2 cm

17. What percentage of the bed remains unused in Question 16 at breakthrough?
    (i) 8.3%   (ii) 26%   (iii) 84%

18. The water uptake or swelling of a styrene-DVB-based resin decreases with increased DVB content because
    (i) DVB is more water-repelling
    (ii) increased DVB content increases the degree of crosslinking, and the elastic force of the polymer chain to resist water uptake increases
    (iii) the pore-size in the resin decreases with increased DVB content.

19. A packed bed has a bulk density $\rho_b = 510$ kg/m^3, and the particles have a density $\rho_p = 770$ kg/m^3. The bed porosity ε is
    (i) 66%   (ii) 51%   (iii) 34%

20. What is the major use of carbon molecular sieve (CMS)?
    (i) Separation of lower hydro-carbons
    (ii) Adsorption of organics from drinking water
    (iii) Separation of air to produce N_2

21. Adsorption capacity of a regenerated bed compared to the fresh bed is generally
    (i) slightly less
    (ii) slightly more
    (iii) half of that of the fresh bed after the first regeneration.

22. How does the depth of the mass transfer zone (MTZ) change with increasing selectivity coefficient K_{AB} for mono-monovalent ion exchange?

    (i) Increases   (ii) Decreases   (iii) Remains almost the same

23. A cation-exchange resin in the Na-form is used to remove NH_4^+ from a 0.07 eq./litre solution of NH_4NO_3. The resin has a total capacity of 1.75 eq./litre. What is the limiting capacity of the resin for removal of NH_4^+?

24. If the mass transfer resistance is very small, the breakthrough line is

    (i) a vertical line
    (ii) a horizontal line
    (iii) a line of unit slope.

25. If the saturated zone of a bed expands at a rate u' (m/h) and the stoichiometric front moves at a constant velocity u_s (m/h), then

    (i) $u' = u_s$ (ii) $u' > u_s$ (iii) $u' < u_s$

26. An adsorbent-adsorbate pair exhibits an unfavourable isotherm. When such a bed, loaded with the adsorbent is regenerated, the depth of the MTZ will

    (i) increase with time
    (ii) decrease with time
    (iii) remain unchanged.

27. What are the assumptions underlying the LUB method of design of an adsorption bed?

28. If the mass transfer front or a part of it gets out of the bed during removal of an impurity by adsorption, the product purity will

    (i) increase   (ii) decrease   (iii) remain unchanged.

29. Depressurization of a loaded bed in PSA may be done in a cocurrent (the gases in the bed flow in the same direction as the feed flow) or countercurrent fashion. Which of these two leaves more of the adsorbed solute in the bed at the end of depressurization?

30. Air separation is done by liquefaction followed by cryogenic distillation or it is done by PSA. Which technique allows a higher turndown ratio?

31. Why does a straight-chain hydrocarbon get adsorbed more on a zeolite than a branched-chain one?

PROBLEMS

12.1 (*Adsorption calculation at equilibrium*)[1] Collela and Armenante (*J. Chem. Eng. Data*, *43*(1998) 573) reported adsorption equilibrium data of aqueous chlorophenols on powdered activated carbon which fitted the Freundlich isotherm [$q_e = K'(C_e)^{1/n}$] satisfactorily. The values of the parameters were found to be: 2,4-dichlorophenol (2,4-DCP), $K' = 502$ (mg/g)/(mg/litre)$^{1/n}$, $n = 7.87$; 2,6-dichlorophenol (2,6-DCP), $K' = 177$ (mg/g)/(mg/litre)$^{1/n}$, $n = 4.83$.

One thousand kilograms of an effluent containing 200 ppm of 2,4-DCP and 100 ppm of 2,6-DCP was treated with 1 kg of activated carbon in a batch contactor. Calculate the concentrations of the phenols in solution at equilibrium if the adsorption of the two compounds occur independently. (Note that the compounds, though close isomers, have substantially different values of the adsorption parameters. This occurs because of differences in forces of interaction of the compounds with the active sites.)

12.2 (*Fitting of adsorption equilibrium data using Freundlich isotherm*)[1] Gustafson et al. (*Ind. Eng. Chem. Prod. Res. Dev.*, 7(1968) 107) obtained the following data on equilibrium adsorption of glycine and of phenylalanine on Amberlite XAD. Fit the data to Freundlich isotherm and determine the adsorption parameters for the two amino acids. Comment on the goodness of fit by calculating the correlation coefficients.

Glycine		Phenylalanine	
Soln. conc. (mol/L)	Amt. adsorbed (mol/g solid)	Soln. conc. (mol/L)	Amt. adsorbed (mol/g solid)
0.0126	7.94×10^{-6}	0.0112	6.0×10^{-5}
0.0251	1.41×10^{-5}	0.0224	1.2×10^{-4}
0.10	5.62×10^{-5}	0.0302	1.58×10^{-4}
0.1995	1.12×10^{-4}	0.0355	1.78×10^{-4}

12.3 (*Fitting of Langmuir isotherm and determination of heat of adsorption*)[2] Equilibrium adsorption data for benzene vapour on silica gel at different temperatures are given below (Henley and Seader, *Separation Process Principles*, 1998, p. 874).

$p \times 10^3$, atm	$q \times 10^2$, mmol benzene adsorbed per g gel			
	70°C	90°C	110°C	130°C
0.5	14.0	6.7	2.6	1.13
1.0	22.0	11.2	4.5	2.0
2.0	34.0	18.0	7.8	3.9
5.0	68.0	33.0	17.0	8.6
10.0	88.0	51.0	27.0	16.0
20	—	78.0	42.0	26.0

(a) Fit the data to (i) Langmuir, (ii) Freundlich isotherms and obtain the isotherm equations. Which isotherm gives a better fit? (b) Draw the adsorption isosteres and calculate the heat of adsorption (prepare $\ln p$ vs $1/T$ plots for $q = 0.15$ and $q = 0.25$ mmol/g adsorbent).

12.4 (*Fitting of Langmuir isotherm and determination of heat of adsorption*)[2] Ray and Box (*Ind. Eng Chem.*, 42(1950) 1315) reported the following data on equilibrium adsorption of propane on activated carbon at three different temperatures.

T = 310.9 K		338.7 K		366.5 K	
p (kPa)	q (mmol/g)	p (kPa)	q (mmol/g)	p (kPa)	q (mmol/g)
15.6	2.819	27.2	2.469	21.07	1.677
31.74	3.48	53.2	3.078	45.33	2.386
59.6	3.97	99.97	3.635	93.34	2.954
99.97	4.342	244.8	4.188	279.2	3.584
293	4.94	424	4.475	461.9	3.922

(*Contd.*)

| 479.2 | 5.294 | 617.1 | 4.71 | 634.3 | 4.244 |
| 679.1 | 5.304 | 803.2 | 5.289 | | |

Fit the data using Langmuir isotherm and get the correlation coefficients. Determine the isosteric heat of adsorption.

12.5 (*Langmuir isotherm for two adsorbates in a mixture*)[3] Nakahara et al. (*J. Chem. Eng. Data*, *19*(1974) 310) obtained the following data for equilibrium adsorption of ethane and propane on MSC-5A carbon molecular sieve at 303.15 K.

Ethane		Propane	
p (kPa)	q (mmol/g)	p (kPa)	q (mmol/g)
3.067	0.858	0.227	0.565
5.733	1.081	0.893	0.955
9.733	1.310	1.653	1.238
15.13	1.493	4.000	1.463
21.47	1.649	8.000	1.612
27.87	1.746	13.60	1.723
36.13	1.862	24.00	1.803
45.13	1.939	39.47	1.859
58.53	2.025	57.67	1.900
83.00	2.128	84.00	1.955

Fit the data for the individual gases to Langmuir's isotherm. Calculate the amounts of ethane and propane adsorbed per kg adsorbent when in equilibrium with an equimolar mixture of ethane and propane at a total pressure of 1.0 bar.

12.6 (*Estimation of surface area from adsorption data*)[2] The following data on equilibrium adsorption of benzene on silica gel at 30°C were reported by Sirkar and Mayers (*AIChE J.*, *19*(1973) 159). Estimate the surface area of the adsorbent if no more than mono-molecular surface coverage occurs at a 'high pressure' of the adsorbate. (For benzene, $\rho_L = 0.875$ g/cm^3]

p (kPa)	1.193	2.373	4.733	7.36	8.81	13.43
q (mmol/g)	2.294	3.043	3.608	3.757	3.794	3.872

12.7 (*Batch adsorption from an aqueous solution*)[3] Adsorption equilibrium data of nitrobenzene (in an aqueous solution at low concentration) on a type of activated carbon fit in the Freundlich isotherm, $q_e = 68(C_e)^{0.43}$ [q_e in mg/g; C_e in mg/litre]. One m^3 of an aqueous solution containing 10 ppm of nitrobenzene is to be treated in a batch with activated carbon to reduce the concentration to 0.01 ppm. Calculate the minimum quantity of carbon required. If 1.3 times the minimum amount is used, determine the batch time. The adsorption kinetics is fast and the overall process is virtually 'diffusion-controlled'. The effective surface area of the adsorbent for transport of the solute from the bulk is 200 cm^2/g, and the external mass transfer coefficient is 1.8×10^{-5} m/s.

12.8 (*Two-step batch adsorption*)[2] Reconsider Example 12.3. Decolourization of 1000 kg of waste oil is done using the same quantity (24.72 kg) of adsorbent in two successive contacts. Half of the clay (12.36 kg) is added to the oil and a contact time of 30.6 min is allowed. The adsorbent is separated and the oil is further treated with the rest of the adsorbent for 12.2 min. Calculate the colour concentration in the oil after the two-stage contact. The mass-transfer coefficient remains the same (5.2×10^{-6} m/s). The loss of oil with the clay separated after the first stage contact may be neglected.

12.9 (*Adsorber design using breakthrough data*)[3]   Brosillon et al. (*Environ. Sci. Technol.*, *35*(2001) 3571) collected the following breakthrough data on adsorption of methyl ethyl ketone (MEK) from air using a packed bed of fine particles of silicalite (a type of zeolite).

Time, min	9.5	19	21	25.7	34.3	39	42	46.7	51.4
C/C_o in the effluent	0	0.018	0.037	0.083	0.287	0.435	0.491	0.620	0.713
Time, min	56.2	64.7	68.6	72.4	77.1	84.8	97.1	104.7	108.6
C/C_o in the effluent	0.768	0.852	0.935	0.972	0.963	0.970	0.981	0.991	1.0

The relevant parameters are: temperature = 20°C; pressure = essentially atmospheric; bed height = 0.2 m; superficial gas velocity = 0.29 m/s; C_o = 0.11 gmol/m³; bed density, ρ_b = 700 kg/m³.

(a) If the maximum permissible concentration of MEK in the effluent is specified at C/C_o = 0.03, determine the breakthrough time. What is the length of the MTZ?

(b) Using the above data, design a bed for treating 3000 m³/h of the same gas if an adsorption half cycle of 8 h is allowed. What is the average loading of the bed at the breakthrough time? Calculate the maximum solute loading at the given inlet concentration of MEK in the gas?

12.10 (*Adsorption bed parameters from breakthrough data*)[3]   Breakthrough data of acetone in air flowing through a bed of adsorbent are given below.

Time, min	180	187.5	191	195	205	210	215	220	225	230
C/C_o	0	0	0.005	0.018	0.091	0.143	0.210	0.285	0.372	0.46
Time, min	235	240	245	250	255	260	265	270		
C/C_o	0.553	0.655	0.743	0.825	0.892	0.948	0.98	0.992		

The experimental parameters are: superficial gas velocity = 0.25 m/s; C_o = 0.13 gmol/m³; bed height = 50 cm. Calculate (a) the breakthrough time if the breakthrough concentration is taken as 2.5% of the feed concentration, (b) the velocity of the stoichiometric front, and (c) fraction of the bed height utilized. Also calculate the LUB using the integration technique [see Eq. (12.26)].

12.11 (*Use of breakthrough data from two beds of different heights*)[3]   Collins reported the following breakthrough data on drying of nitrogen gas with 4A molecular sieve in two experimental columns (*AIChE Symp. Ser.*, *63*(74), 1967, 31).

Column-1: temperature = 26°C; pressure = 5.85 atm (absolute); gas mass flow rate = 3992 kg/(h m²); moisture in the feed = 1490 ppm(v/v); bed height = 0.44 m; adsorbent bulk density = 713 kg/m³; adsorption capacity of the bed under the given conditions = 0.215 kg moisture per kg adsorbent; initial moisture content of the bed = 0.01 kg/kg adsorbent; moisture content in the effluent at breakthrough = 1 ppm(v). Breakthrough data are given below.

Time (h)	< 15	15	15.3	15.4	15.6	15.8	16.0	16.2	16.4	16.6
Moisture (ppm)	< 1	1	4	5	26	74	145	260	430	610
Time (h)	16.8	17.0	17.2	17.4	17.6	17.8	18.0	18.3	18.5	
Moisture (ppm)	798	978	1125	1245	1355	1432	1465	1490	1490	

Column-2: temperature = 27°C; bed height = 0.27 m; other parameters as for column-1. Breakthorugh data are given below.

Time (h)	< 9.0	9.0	9.2	9.4	9.6	9.8	10.0	10.2	10.4	10.6
Moisture (ppm)	< 1	1	4	9	33	80	142	238	365	498
Time (h)	10.8	11.0	11.25	11.5	11.75	12.0	12.5	12.8	13.0	
Moisture (ppm)	650	808	980	1115	1235	1330	1410	1440	1440	

(a) Calculate the LUB for column-1. (b) Using the data for column-1, can you predict the breakthrough time for column-2? (c) Calculate the amount of moisture adsorbed by the bed till breakthrough in column-1. (d) Calculate the velocity of MTZ using the data from both the columns.

12.12 (*Packed bed adsorption*)[3]   Carbon dioxide is to be removed from a nitrogen stream by adsorption in a bed of NUXIT-AL activated carbon followed by thermal regeneration. Following data and information are given: temperature of adsorption = 20°C; total pressure = 10 bar; bed length = 2 m; LUB = 0.15 m at adsorption breakthrough; bed voidage = 0.42; bed bulk density = 500 kg/m^3; feed concentration = 3% CO_2 (v/v). The Toth isotherm given by Eq. (12.9) is suitable to describe the adsorption equilibrium of CO_2. The constants of the isotherm are: q_m = 7.935 gmol/kg; b = 22.87 in the kPa unit; n = 0.628; p in kPa. At the end of regeneration, the bed contains 1.0 gram residual CO_2 per kg adsorbent. Calculate the CO_2 removed per kg adsorbent in an adsorption cycle.

12.13 (*Estimation of external mass transfer coefficient and effective pore diffusivity*)[3]   A stream of N_2 containing 0.1% benzene flows through a packed bed of GAC of particle size, d_p = 3 mm (assumed spherical). Given the following data and information, calculate (a) the fluid-particle mass transfer coefficient, and (b) the effective diffusivity of benzene within a pellet (surface diffusion may be neglected). Temperature = 25°C; pressure = 1 atm; superficial gas velocity, u_o = 0.28 m/s; diffusivity of benzene in N_2 = 0.102 cm^2/s at 311.3 K; viscosity of the gas = 1.85 × 10^{-5} kg/(m·s); average pore diameter = 15 nm; bed porosity, ε_b = 0.43; particle porosity, ε_p = 0.45; pore tortuosity, τ = 2.8.

12.14 (*Calculation of the velocity and length of MTZ*)[3]   An experimental packed adsorption column of 0.5 m bed depth is used for breakthrough study of a dilute vent stream having 0.02 mole fraction of a volatile organic. The breakthrough curve is symmetric and the effluent concentration is 0.01 mole fraction at 60 min. It is also found that it takes 15 min for the effluent concentration to increase from y = 0.0004 to y = 0.0196 (i.e. 2% to 98% of the influent concentration). What are the length and velocity of the MTZ? What bed height would you recommend if 90% utilization of the bed is to be achieved under the same operating conditions? What is the breakthrough time for this bed?

12.15 (*MTZ calculation using the Langmuir model*)[3] A dilute vent stream with 2 vol% of a toxic vapour passes through a packed adsorption column at 26°C and 1.2 bar pressure. The adsorption equilibrium follows the Langmuir model and the parameters are $q_m = 6.2$ gmol/kg and $K = 0.12$ m^3/gmol. The volumetric mass transfer coefficient is estimated to be $k_m \bar{a} = 35$ s^{-1}. Calculate the velocity of the MTZ if the wave-front maintains a constant pattern. Also calculate the breakthrough concentration time if the bed height is 2 m. *Given:* adsorbent bulk density, $\rho_p = 700$ kg/m^3, $\varepsilon_b = 0.38$, and superficial gas velocity, $u_o = 0.32$ m/s. The breakthrough concentration may be taken to be $C/C_o = 0.025$.

12.16 (*Ion-exchange calculation*)[2] A solution of sodium acetate (110 g/litre) has 0.2% Ca^{++} in it. It is suggested to remove 90% of the Ca^{++} ions by a cation exchange resin in the sodium form having an exchange capacity of 2 eq./litre. Calculate the amount of resin required to treat 1 m^3 of the feed solution. Does the resin appear to be commercially attractive?

12.17 (*Kinetics of adsorption*)[3] Agricultural wastes have proven potential of adsorption of organic contaminants and even metal ions form effluents. An attempt to estimate the effectiveness of gram husk to remove textile dues from simulated wastewater has been reported by Chakraborty and Dutta (*Int. J. Env Pollution and Management*, 2006 in press). In a particular experiment, 0.9 g of washed and dried husk was contacted with 100 ml of methylene blue solution in a shaker bath at 30°C. The samples withdrawn from time to time analyzed as follows

Time, (min)	0	5	10	15	20	25	30	40	50	60	90
Dye conc. (mg/l)	488	328.5	247	175	127	100	79	52	40	32	32

Ho and McKay (*Process Biochem, 34*(1999) 451–465) suggested that kinetics of adsorption can often be interpreted as a pseudo-second order process.

$$\frac{dq_t}{dt} = k_2(q_e - q_t)^2$$

where q_t = amount of dye adsorbed per gram of solid at time t, q_e = amount of dye adsorbed per gram of solid at equilibrium, and k_2 = pseudo-second order lumped rate parameter.

Check if the above data on adsorption of methylene blue follows the Ho and McKay model. Find out the value of the rate parameter k_2, and calculate the correlation coefficient.

REFERENCES

Anderson, R.E., 'Ion-Exchange Separation' in *Handbook of Separation Techniques for Chemical Engineers*, P.A. Schweitzer (Ed.), McGraw-Hill, New York, 1997.

Braunauer, S., S. Emmett, and E. Teller, 'Adsorption of Gases in Multimolecular Layers', *J. Am. Chem. Soc.*, 60(1938) 309–319.

Braunauer, S. et al., *J. Am. Chem. Soc.*, 62(1940) 1723.

Brown, C.J., and C.J. Fletcher, 'The Recoffo short-bed ion-exchange process', in *Ion Exchange for Industry*, M. Streat (Ed.), Ellis Horwood, 1988.

Cassidy, R.T., and E.S. Holmes, *AIChE Symp. Ser.*, *80*(1984) 68–75.

Cooney, D.O., *Adsorption Design for Wastewater Treatment*, CRC Press, Boca Raton, 1999.

Do, D.D., *Adsorption Analysis: Equilibrium and Kinetics*, Imperial College, London, 1997.

Eckenfelder, W.W., *Industrial Water Pollution Control*, McGraw-Hill, New York, 2000.

Freundlich, H., *Colloid and Capillary Chemistry*, Methuen, London, 1926.

Gamane, N., and F. Lannoy, 'Estimate fixed-bed pressure drop', *Chem. Engg.*, August 1996, pp. 123–124.

Helfferich, F.G., *Ion Exchange*, McGraw-Hill, New York, 1962.

Ismadji, S., and S.K. Bhatia, 'Adsorption of flavor esters on granular activated carbon', *Canad. J. Chem. Eng.*, *78*(2000) 892–901.

Jagschies, G., 'Process-Scale Chromatograph' in *Ullmann's Encyclopedia* (*1985*), Vol. B-3, 10–44.

Johnston, V.A., 'Designing fixed-bed adsorption columns', *Chem. Engg.*, Nov. 27, 1972, 87–92.

Keller, G.E. et al., 'Adsorption' in *Handbook of Separation Processes*, R.W. Rousseau (Ed.), McGraw-Hill, New York, 1987.

Keller, G.E., 'Adsorption—building upon a solid foundation', *Chem. Eng. Prog.*, Oct. 1995, 56–67.

Knaebel, K.S., 'For your next separation consider adsorption', *Chem. Engg.*, Nov. 1995, pp. 92–101.

Knaebel, K.S., 'The basics of adsorber design', *Chem. Engg.*, April 1999, 92–101.

Kovach, J.L., 'Gas-phase Adsorption' in P.A. Schweitzer (Ed.) *Handbook of Separation Techniques for Chemical Engineers*, pp. 3–47.

Kumar, R., and J.K. Van Sloun, 'Purification by adsorptive separation', *Chem. Eng. Prog.*, Jan. 1989, 34–40

La Cava, A.I. et al., 'How to specify pressure swing adsorption systems', *Chem. Engg.*, June 1998, 110–117.

Langmuir, J., *J. Am. Chem. Soc.*, *40*(1981) 1361.

Lukchis, G.M., 'Adsorption systems', parts I and II, *Chem. Engg.*, June 11, 1973, 111–116; July 9, 1973, 83–90.

Metcalf and Eddy, *Waste Water Engineering*, 4th ed., McGraw-Hill, New York, 2003.

McNulty, J.T., 'The many faces of ion-exchange resins', *Chem. Engg.*, June 1997, 94–100.

Meyer, V.R., *Practical High Performance Liquid Chromatography*, John Wiley, New York, 1988.

Michaels, A.S., *Ind. Eng. Chem.*, *44*(1952) 1922.

Myers, A.L., and J.M. Prausnitz, 'Thermodynamics of mixed gas adsorption', *AIChE J.*, *11*(1965) 121–127.

Notaro, F. et al., 'Recover industrial gases via adsorption', *Chem. Engg.*, April 1999, 104–108.

Rosen, J.B., 'General numerical solution for solid diffusion in fixed beds', *Ind. Eng. Chem.*, *46*(1954) 1590–1594.

Ruthven, D.M., *Principles of Adsorption and Adsorption Processes*, John Wiley, New York, 1984.

Ruthven, D.M. et al., *Pressure Swing Adsorption*, VCH Wiley, New York, 1994.

Ruthven, D.M., *Encyclopedia of Separation Technology*, John Wiley, New York, 1997.

Shanley, A., 'Adsorbents corners green and niche markets', *Chem. Engg.*, Feb. 2000, 59–62.

Sherwood, T.K., and R.L. Pigford, *Mass Transfer*, McGraw-Hill, 1975.

Sirkar, S., and R. Kumar, 'Adiabatic analysis of bulk binary mixtures—constant pattern model', *Ind. Eng. Chem. PDD*, *22*(1983) 271–280.

Sirkar, S., 'Pressure Swing Adsorption Technology', in *Adsorption Science and Technology*, A. E. Rodrigues et al. (Ed.), Kluwer, 1989, 285–321.

Streat, M., *Principles of Ion Exchange Technology*, Butterworths, Oxford, 1991.

Suzuki, M., *Adsorption Engineering*, Elsevier, Amsterdam, 1990.

Tien, C., *Adsorption Calculations and Modeling*, Butterworths, Boston, 1994.

Valenzuela, D.P., and A.I. Myers, *Adsorption Equilibrium Data Handbook*, Prentice Hall, Engelwood Cliffs, NJ, 1989.

Wakao, N., and T. Funazakri, 'Effect of fluid dispersion coefficients on particle to fluid mass transfer coefficients in pocked beds: correlations of Sherwood numbers', *Chem Eng. Sci.*, *33*(1978) 1375–1384.

Wankat, P.C., *Rate-Controlled Separations*, Blackie, Glasgow, 1994.

White, D.H., and P.G. Barkley, 'The design of pressure swing adsorption systems', *Chem. Eng. Progr.*, January 1989, 25–33.

Yang, R.T., *Gas Separation by Adsorption Processes*, Butterworths, 1987.

Yoon, Y.H., and J.H. Nelson, 'Applications of gas adsorption kinetics', *Am. Ind. Hyg. Assoc. J.*, *45*(1984) 509–524.

Young, D.M., and A.D. Crowell, *Physical Adsorption of Gases*, Butterworths, London, 1962.

13 | Crystallization

Finished solid products of chemical process industries often come in the form of crystals. Examples are numerous—sugar, sodium chloride, sodium hydrogen phosphate, citric acid, ammonium sulphate, sodium chromate and a host of inorganic and organic compounds. Take the case of sugar which is an important component of our diet. The most important commercial sources of sugar are sugar-cane and sugar-beet. The first step in the process of manufacture of sugar is the extraction of juice from the crushed cane, followed by the removal of suspended and colloidal matters from the juice. The clear juice is then concentrated and cooled when the raw sugar crystallizes out. The raw sugar has to be refined to remove some residual colouring matters and impurities. The crystals are redissolved in a limited quantity of water; the impurities and the colouring matters are removed (the colouring matters are removed by adsorption). The clear and purified solution is again evaporated and cooled when snow-white crystals of sugar are obtained. The process of crystallization gives a product in an acceptable and granular form. The impurities present in a solution are mostly discarded when crystals are formed. An important quality parameter of a crystalline product is the crystal size distribution. For example, a sample of sugar having large crystals as well as fines will not be well accepted in the market. A crystalline product, in general, should have a narrow particle-size distribution (i.e. most of the crystals should have sizes within a narrow range).

A crystal is a solid body with plane faces in which the atoms are arranged in an orderly repetitive array. The atomic arrangements and interatomic distances remain constant for the crystals of a particular solid irrespective of its size. Crystals can be classified according to seven general systems (Figure 13.1). The relative sizes of the faces of the crystals of a substance can vary considerably. Such a variation is called a *modification of habit*. An elongated growth of the prismatic 'habit' gives a needle-shaped crystal. The relative growths of the faces of a crystal can be altered and often controlled by adjusting a number of factors such as the rate of cooling, presence of impurities, the type of solvent, etc. (Mullin, 2001). The study of geometry, properties and structure of crystals constitutes the branch of crystallography.

Most crystals are anisotropic; their mechanical, electrical, magnetic and optical properties are often different in different directions. Some liquids (for example, ammonium oleate) that exhibit anisotropy at temperatures just above their melting points are called *liquid crystals* because of

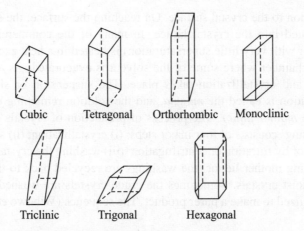

Cubic   Tetragonal   Orthorhombic   Monoclinic

Triclinic   Trigonal   Hexagonal

Figure 13.1 The seven general crystal systems (Mullin, 2001).

their similarity with crystalline solids (note that lattice formation cannot occur in a liquid). Two or more substances that crystallize in almost identical forms are called *isomorphous* (for example, K_2HPO_4 and $NH_4H_2PO_4$ are isomorphous; potassium and ammonium alums are also isomorphous). A substance capable of crystallizing into different but chemically identical crystalline forms is said to exhibit *polymorphism* (for example, graphite and diamond).

Crystalline materials generally have a high degree of purity even when obtained from a relatively impure solution. As stated before, the shape and size, particularly the size distribution, are important determinants of commercial acceptability of a crystalline product. Also, if the crystals are approximately uniform-sized (i.e. if the crystal size distribution is narrow), their separation from the liquor, washing, drying and packaging become more convenient.

The process of formation or production of crystals from a solution or a melt is called *crystallization*. When crystals are produced by cooling a saturated solution, the process is called *solution crystallization*. But in *melt crystallization*, crystals are generated by cooling a molten solid in the absence of any solvent. There is a commercial process of separation of xylene isomers (i.e. *o-* and *p*-xylene) by melt crystallization.

When the concentration of a liquid solution is increased (for example, by evaporation of the solvent, by cooling or by a combination of these), the solution gradually reaches the saturation level. On further evaporation or cooling, it attains a degree of 'supersaturation'. If the concentration of a solution is more than the solubility of the solid at a particular temperature, it is called 'supersaturated'. Supersaturation can be created and maintained for almost all systems. However, the level of supersaturation attainable not only depends upon the particular system but also on how calm and free from disturbances the system is. For example, a sugar solution can have a very high degree or level of supersaturation (the concentration may even be about 80% more than the saturation value), but in a solution of sodium chloride, the maximum attainable supersaturation is often too small to be measured. Spontaneous formation and growth of tiny crystals, called *nuclei*, take place in a supersaturated solution. Also, if a *nucleus* or a *seed* crystal is added to a supersaturated solution, it gradually grows to a larger size. These phenomena have some qualitative similarity with the formation and growth of vapour bubbles in a superheated liquid. The supersaturation in a solution provides the driving force for transport of the solute from the bulk of the solution to the crystal surface. On reaching the surface, the solute molecules get oriented and integrated into the crystal lattice. In many of the commercial crystallizers, the solution (saturated or with very little supersaturation) is heated in a heat exchanger and then led to a crystallization chamber where some of the solvent is evaporated. As a result, the solution gets supersaturated and crystallization takes place. The suspension or slurry containing the crystals and the solution is called the *magma*, and the solution remaining after removal of the crystals is called the *mother liquor*. The process of production of crystals from a solution and 'downstream processing' consists of four major steps: (i) crystallization; (ii) separation of crystals from the mother liquor by filtration or centrifugation; (iii) washing the crystals with fresh solvent to remove the adhering mother liquor (the washings are recycled back to the crystallizer); and (iv) drying of the moist crystals. Sometimes the crude crystals are washed, redissolved in the solvent and recrystallized to make a purer product. The sequence (Wibowo et al., 2001) is shown in Figure 13.2.

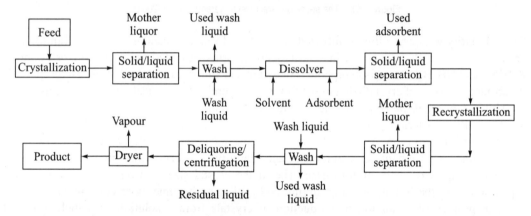

Figure 13.2   The major steps in the process of crystallization.

Besides separation and recovery of products from solutions, crystallization is an effective technique for concentration and purification. There are examples of concentration of solutions by partial removal of the solvent by crystallization. A fruit juice is sometimes concentrated in this way by cooling and removing the crystals of ice (an attempt to concentrate by evaporation destroys the vitamins, aroma, etc; alternatively, concentrating fruit juice and many other solutions is done by 'ultrafiltration', see Section 14.4.2). Improving the purity of a solid by dissolution and recrystallization is common in production of fine chemicals.

13.1 SOLID–LIQUID PHASE EQUILIBRIUM

Crystallization is opposite to dissolution of a solid in a liquid or solvent. Particles of a solid undergo dissolution so long as the solution concentration is less than the solubility of the solid at the given temperature. Conversely, if we have a supersaturated solution, and a few seed crystals are dropped into it, a driving force for transportation of the solute from the bulk of the solution to the crystal surface will come into play. Thus, the extent of supersaturation in a solution is the driving force for crystallization. It may be mentioned that the solubility of very small particles may be significantly larger than the normal solubility of a substance as given by Gibbs–Thompson equation (Mullin, 2001).

$$\ln\left(\frac{C}{C_s}\right) = \frac{2\sigma M_w}{RT\rho_c r} \tag{13.1}$$

where

C = solubility of a particle of radius r

C_s = normal solubility

σ = solid–liquid interfacial tension

M_w = molecular weight of the solid

T = absolute temperature

ρ_c = density of the particle.

Since the smaller particles have more than normal solubility, they dissolve even in a saturated solution and raise the concentration creating 'supersaturation'. The larger particles present in the suspension start growing. The overall process consists of dissolution of smaller particles making the larger particles grow. This phenomenon is called *Ostwald ripening*.

The solubility of a solid in a liquid at different temperatures is conveniently represented on a solid–liquid phase diagram. Some solutes form well-defined addition compounds with the solvents. Hydrates of inorganic salts such as $MgSO_4$ with varying number of water molecules of crystallization are common examples. Phase diagrams of such systems may sometimes be pretty complicated. To explain the characteristics of a phase diagram, we take the simple example of the naphthalene–benzene binary system shown in Figure 13.3.

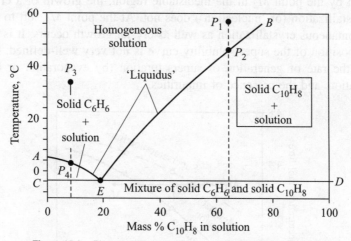

Figure 13.3 Phase equilibrium of the benzene–naphthalene system.

A point on the line *AEB* in Figure 13.3 represents the saturation concentration or solubility of naphthalene in the solvent (benzene) at different temperatures. In other words, *AEB* is the *solubility curve*. Any point in the region above *AEB* represents an unsaturated solution (a curve of this type is called 'liquidus'). If a solution of concentration and temperature represented by the point P_1 is cooled, it becomes saturated on reaching a temperature corresponding to the point

P_2 on the solubility curve vertically below P_1. On further cooling, naphthalene starts crystallizing out, and the state of the solution changes along the curve P_2E and eventually reaches the point E. Again, if we start with an unsaturated solution represented by the point P_3 and cool it, it reaches the saturation level at the point P_4. On further cooling, benzene crystallizes out and the solution concentration changes along P_4E, ultimately reaching E.

The point E is called the *eutectic point*; the corresponding temperature and composition are called the *eutectic temperature* and *eutectic composition*. When a solution of eutectic composition is cooled, the material solidifies completely at a particular temperature (the eutectic temperature). This is the lowest equilibrium solidification point possible for any system. For the naphthalene–benzene system too, complete solidification of the solution occurs when the solution represented by the point E is cooled. The region below *CED* represents solid mixtures of benzene and naphthalene. For any solution, the product of crystallization is determined by the state of the solution on the phase diagram.

A solution can very often be subcooled several degrees below the equilibrium temperature. At this condition, a *metastable region* is created near the crystal surface. The metastable region surrounding a particle appears like an envelope. The envelope theoretically extends up to a distance from the particle surface where $\partial^2 F/\partial x_{mf}^2 = 0$ (F = free energy of the solution; x_{mf} = mole fraction of the solute). The effective metastable zone is much thinner than that predicted theoretically by the above relation. The metastable region in solution crystallization is illustrated in Figure 13.4. The solid line is the equilibrium or 'solubility curve'; the upper broken line is the 'super-solubility curve' on the temperature–concentration plane. Let the state of a solution (given by its temperature and concentration) be described by the point M_1 on the right to the solid line in Figure 13.4. Crystallization cannot occur since the solution is unsaturated. If the state of the solution is given by the point M_2 in the metastable region, the growth of a crystal occurs but spontaneous crystallization (or 'nucleation') does not. At the point M_3, left to the broken line, uncontrolled spontaneous crystallization as well as crystal growth occurs. It is to be noted that the location or position of the super-solubility curve is not very well-defined. It depends upon factors such as the rate of generation of supersaturation (by evaporation or by cooling), the intensity of agitation, and the presence of impurities.

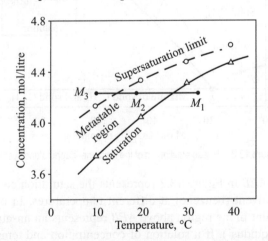

Figure 13.4   Metastable region on the temperature–concentration plane, KCl–water system (Myerson, 2002, p.17).

Solid–liquid equilibrium plays a vital role in the process design of a crystallizer as the vapour–liquid equilibrium does in distillation. This is especially true for practically important cases of crystallization of a substance from a multicomponent mixture. For a two solutes and one solvent system, phase equilibrium can be represented by surfaces in the three-dimensional space. If more components are present, equilibrium may be determined using a suitable thermodynamic model for the activity coefficients of the components. The use of phase equilibrium data for efficient crystallizer design has been discussed by Wibowo et al. (2001).

The process of crystallization has an associated thermal effect, called the *heat of crystallization*. It is equal in magnitude but opposite in sign to the differential heat of dissolution in a virtually saturated solution. In the absence of data, the heat of crystallization is approximately taken as the opposite of heat of solution in infinite dilution.

13.2 NUCLEATION AND CRYSTAL GROWTH

'Nucleation' means formation of tiny new crystals in a supersaturated solution. A new crystal thus formed is called a *nucleus*. Different types of nucleation are shown in Figure 13.5.

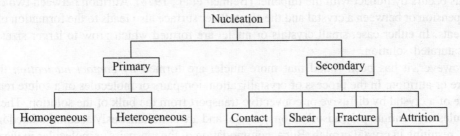

Figure 13.5 Important nucleation mechanisms.

13.2.1 Primary Nucleation

Primary nucleation is the phenomenon of formation of new crystals independent of the presence of other crystals in the medium. It may be of two types—'homogeneous' and 'heterogeneous'. Homogeneous nucleation has its origin in clusters of solute molecules or ions that form in a supersaturated solution. Such a cluster has some structural similarity with the solid state, but is too small to be regarded as a separate solid phase. A nucleus is formed if the cluster size exceeds a critical size. A theoretical analysis of the energetics of cluster formation shows that a high degree of supersaturation is necessary in order that a cluster of size larger than the critical size is formed. The theoretical rate of homogeneous nucleation can be derived from energy considerations (see Randolph and Larson, 1988; Myerson, 2002).

$$B^0 = A' \exp\left[-\frac{16\pi\sigma^3 v_M^2}{3k^3 T^3 [\ln(s+1)]^2}\right]; \qquad s = (C - C_s)/C_s \qquad (13.2)$$

Here A' = a constant; v_M = volume of a molecule; k = Boltzmann constant; T = absolute temperature; s = degree (or level) of supersaturation. At normal levels of supersaturation, homogeneous nucleation proceeds very slowly (in practice, it is faster than the rate predicted by the above equation). It increases rapidly if the supersaturation level is high. The formation of *clusters of small molecules* is slowed down if the solution viscosity is high. So, an increase in temperature has an additional positive effect on the nucleation rate because of the reduced viscosity. Primary nucleation (homogeneous nucleation, in paricular) does not have a substantial role in an industrial crystallizer.

The formation of crystals of a solute on tiny suspended foreign solid particles or on the surfaces of the crystallizer is called *heterogeneous nucleation*. The rate of heterogeneous nucleation depends not only on supersaturation but also on the availability of the 'active sites' for nucleation (Mullin, 2001). It has been found that if a solution is very pure and clean (i.e. foreign particles are absent), a very high degree of supersaturation is required for heterogeneous nucleation to occur.

13.2.2   Secondary Nucleation

The crystals present in a supersaturated solution are the most important source of generation of tiny new crystals. The phenomenon of formation of new crystals from the existing ones is called *secondary nucleation*. There are quite a few ways by which this can happen (see Figure 13.5); the two more important ways are: (i) fracture and attrition, and (ii) contact nucleation. If a suspension of crystals is vigorously agitated (or even pumped at a high velocity), fracture of crystals occurs by impact with the impeller (Bennett et al., 1973). Attrition between two crystals in suspension or between a crystal and the crystallizer surface also leads to the formation of small fragments. In either case, small crystals or nuclei are formed which grow to larger sizes in the supersaturated solution.

However, it has been found that more nuclei are formed by *contact nucleation* than by fracture or attrition. In the process of crystallization, ion-pairs or molecules of a solute reach the surface of a crystal by diffusive or convective transport from the bulk of the solution. The solute molecules are continuously adsorbed on a crystal and are simultaneously accommodated into the lattice, resulting in crystal growth. But accommodation of the ion-pairs or molecules in the crystal lattice does not occur instantaneously. Contact of a crystal with the agitator, pump or the pipe wall causes displacement of the adsorbed layer of solute on the crystal surface. Some of the 'cluster of molecules' or 'loosely ordered phase' in an adsorbed layer get displaced by the action of the agitator or pump or due to shear at the wall and give rise to a new crystal nucleus. At a high level of supersaturation, the adsorbed layer is thicker and more particles are formed by contact nucleation. When there is a high relative motion between a fluid and a crystal, the 'loosely ordered phase' near the crystal surface is carried into the bulk of the liquid (this is shear nucleation). Such a cluster of molecules acts as a secondary nucleus. Secondary nucleation is sometimes called *breeding*.

The formation of a secondary nucleus by *contact nucleation* involves three major steps: (i) the generation of a cluster of molecules near or at the crystal surface, (ii) the removal of the cluster, and (iii) the growth of the cluster to form a nucleus. The physical factors that affect the nucleation rate can be identified from the above steps. The degree or level of supersaturation (s) is a very important factor. Numerous evidences exist in this regard. For example, Garside et al. (1979) reported their experimental results on size distribution of potassium alum nuclei generated by contact nucleation [Figure 13.6(a)]. They conducted experiments at constant energy input but at varying levels of supersaturation. A qualitative comparison of the influence of supersaturation on the growth rate of nuclei is shown in Figure 13.6(b).

Another important factor, the intensity of agitation, relates to step (ii) mentioned above. An intense agitation or a high agitator speed helps in quickly dislodging an 'adsorbed' cluster of

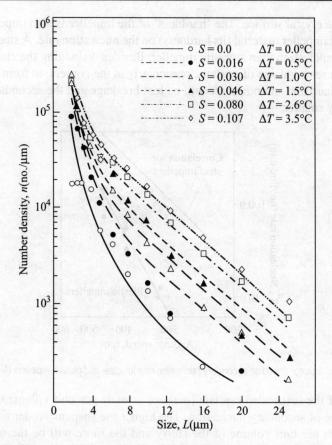

Figure 13.6(a) Size distribution of nuclei from contact nucleation at different levels of supersaturation (Garside, J. et al., *AIChE. J., 25* (1979) 57–64.).

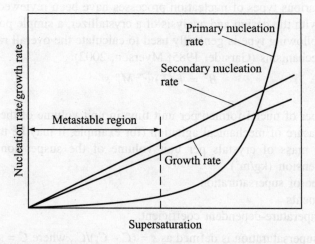

Figure 13.6(b) Influence of supersaturation on nucleation and growth rates.

molecules from the crystal surface. The 'hardness' of the impeller is also important. Figure 13.7 shows the effect of impeller material (its hardness) on the nucleation rate. A steel impeller is more effective to cause nucleation than a plastic impeller. Besides dislodging the cluster of molecules, a hard impeller causes breakage of crystals, particularly at the corners, to form secondary nuclei. If the crystals are hard and smooth, there will be less breakage and the secondary nucleation rate will be appreciably smaller.

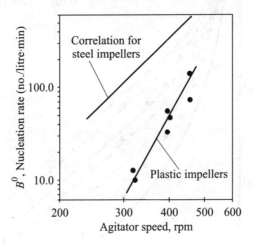

Figure 13.7   Effect of agitator speed on secondary nucleation rate for steel and plastic impellers (Myerson, 2002, p. 49).

The density of the suspended crystals (mass of crystals per unit volume of the suspension) also affects the rate of secondary nucleation. The higher the suspension density, the more is the crystal surface area per unit volume of the slurry and the more will be the number of 'cluster of molecules' formed near the surface. No definite trend regarding the effect of temperature on secondary nucleation rate has been reported (Myerson, 2002). The presence of impurities and foreign substances affects the nucleation rate. Experimental evidences, and theoretical analysis and modelling of various types of nucleation processes have been reviewed by Mullin (2001).

In connection with the design and analysis of a crystallizer, a simple power-law nucleation correlation of the following type is generally used to calculate the overall rate of nucleation by all of the above mechanisms (Garside, 1985; Myerson, 2002).

$$B^0 = \bar{k}(T) w^m M_T^n s^p \tag{13.3}$$

where

$\quad\quad B^0$ = number of nuclei formed per unit time in unit volume of the suspension

$\quad\quad w$ = a measure of mechanical agitation (for example, it may be the agitator speed)

$\quad\quad M_T$ = total mass of crystals per unit volume of the suspension or density of the suspension (kg/m^3)

$\quad\quad s$ = degree of supersaturation

$\quad m, n, p$ = exponents

$\quad\quad \bar{k}(T)$ = a temperature-dependent coefficient.

The degree of supersaturation is defined as $s = (C - C_s)/C_s$, where C = solute concentration in the supersaturated solution, and C_s = solubility of the solute at the given temperature.

The values of m, n, p and $\bar{k}$ have to be determined experimentally (the value of n is usually unity; p usually lies between 0.5 and 2.5) in a laboratory or using a pilot scale crystallizer. However, a suitable scaleup strategy has to be adopted to use such secondary nucleation kinetics to design an industrial crystallizer (Garside, 1985). The control of the secondary nucleation rate becomes necessary for the reduction of fines in the final product. A few steps that may be taken for this purpose are:

(a) adjustment of the speed of the stirrer tip and the clearance between the impeller tip and the wall,

(b) reduction in suspension density,

(c) maintaining a lower level of supersaturation, and

(d) coating the impeller with a soft material (for example, an elastomer).

13.3 CRYSTAL GROWTH

A few theories of crystal growth have been proposed by different workers. The two more important theories are:

(a) the adsorption theory, and

(b) the mass transfer theory (Mullin, 2001; Wankat, 1994).

The latter theory of crystal growth is discussed below.

13.3.1 Mass Transfer Theory of Crystal Growth

In this theory it is assumed that there are two steps in series in the growth of a crystal:

1. Convective transport of the solute from the bulk of the supersaturated solution to the surface of a crystal

2. Surface integration or accommodation of the solute molecules in the growing layers of a crystal.

The crystal growth rate is determined by taking into account the resistances offered by the above two steps. The second step is sometimes found to be a first order process, its rate depending upon the extent of supersaturation $(C - C_s)$ at the crystal surface. Thus, the mass transfer theory combines the diffusion and reaction processes and is sometimes called the *diffusion-reaction theory* of crystal growth. The rate of increase in the mass of a crystal can be written as

$$\frac{dm_c}{dx} = k_L A_c (C - C_i) = k_r A_c (C_i - C_s) \tag{13.4}$$

where

m_c = mass of a single crystal, and A_c = area of a single crystal

k_L = mass transfer coefficient at the crystal surface [for step 1 above]

C = bulk solute concentration

C_i = solute concentration at the solid–liquid interface

C_s = saturation concentration of the solute at the given temperature

k_r = the 'rate constant' for surface integration of the solute molecules.[†]

[†] Activation energy for 'surface integration', which is akin to a 'chemical reaction', is about 40–60 kJ/gmol whereas that for diffusion of a species lies in the range 10–20 kJ/gmol.

Eliminating C_i from Eq. (13.4),

$$\frac{dm_c}{dt} = K_L A_c (C - C_s); \qquad K_L = \frac{k_L k_r}{k_L + k_r} \tag{13.5}$$

Here K_L is the 'overall mass transfer coefficient' for the growth process which combines the two resistances. Equation (13.5) gives the growth rate of a crystal in terms of the rate of change of the mass of a particular crystal. Alternatively, the growth rate can be expressed as the rate of change of the 'characteristic size' of a crystal. The characteristic size (L) is related to the mass (m_c), area (A_c) and volume (v_c) of a crystal through a 'shape factor'.[tt]

$$m = \rho_c \phi_v L^3; \qquad A_c = \phi_a L^2; \qquad \text{and} \qquad v_c = \phi_v L^3 \tag{13.6}$$

where ρ_c = crystal density, ϕ_v = 'volume shape factor', and ϕ_a = 'area shape factor'. From Eqs. (13.5) and (13.6), we have

$$\frac{dm_c}{dt} = \frac{d}{dt}(\rho_c v_c) = \frac{d}{dt}(\rho_c \phi_v L^3) = K_L \phi_a L^2 (C - C_s) \Rightarrow 3\rho_c \phi_v L^2 \frac{dL}{dt} = K_L \phi_a L^2 (C - C_s) \tag{13.7}$$

$$\Rightarrow \qquad \frac{dL}{dt} = \frac{K_L \phi_a}{3\rho_c \phi_v}(C - C_s) = k\left(\frac{C - C_s}{C_s}\right) = ks \tag{13.8}$$

Here $dL/dt = G$ is a measure of the crystal growth rate (it is the time rate of increase in the characteristic size of the crystal), and $k = K_L \phi_a C_s / 3\rho_c \phi_v$. If the process of solute integration on the crystal surface [i.e. step 2 described before] is nonlinear, an empirical power-law expression for the growth rate given below may be conveniently used.

$$G = \frac{dL}{dt} = k'\left(\frac{C - C_s}{C_s}\right)^q = k' s^q \tag{13.9}$$

In general, the parameters k [Eq. (13.8)] and k' [Eq. (13.9)] depend upon (i) the temperature, (ii) the environment (i.e. agitation, geometry of the crystallizer, etc.), and (iii) the crystal size. The values of k or k' can be determined by experimental data fitting. Crystallization kinetics of a number of common systems have been reviewed by Garside and Shah (1980).

13.3.2   McCabe 'ΔL Law'

The experimental data on crystal growth of several substances presented by McCabe as early as in 1929 showed that the *crystal growth rate G is independent of crystal size L*, i.e. k or k' are independent of the characteristic size L, and

$$\frac{dG}{dL} = 0 \tag{13.10}$$

This is the well-known 'McCabe ΔL law'.

Not all systems obey McCabe ΔL law. Sometimes the growth rate of crystals has been found to depend upon the crystal size. This aspect is briefly discussed in Section 13.5.4.

[tt] Another quantity used to characterize the shape of a particle is called 'sphericity', ψ = (surface area of a sphere having the same volume as that of a crystal)/(actual surface area of the crystal).

Both nucleation and crystal growth rate depend upon the supersaturation in the solution. These two phenomena are competing in nature. Secondary nucleation and crystal growth rates are often found to be nearly linear in supersaturation. But the rate of primary nucleation is very slow at low supersaturations but increases very rapidly if the supersaturation is very high. The behaviour has been shown qualitatively in Figure 13.6(b).

At this point it is pertinent to differentiate between crystallization and precipitation. In contrast to crystallization, precipitation is the process of formation of a solid from a solution by very rapid and *simultaneous* nucleation, crystal growth and agglomeration of particles. Precipitation occurs for sparingly soluble solids at a very high level of supersaturation. For example, if a solution of NaCl is added to a solution of $AgNO_3$, an extremely high level of supersatuartion of AgCl is created in the solution and it precipitates out. In the process, nucleation (mostly primary nucleation) occurs at a very high rate, crystal growth occurs only to a limited extent, and all the supersaturation is lost very quickly. A huge number of small crystals are formed. Many substances are produced by liquid-phase reactions and product solids are separated by precipitation (examples: dyes, pigments, pharmaceuticals, 'precipitated ferric oxide', etc.). Precipitation processes have been discussed at some length by Karpinski and Wey (see Myerson, 2002). Controlled precipitation is a technique of preparation of nanoparticles.

13.4   CRYSTAL SIZE DISTRIBUTION

Supersaturation of a solution is 'lost' by the competing processes of nucleation and crystal growth; their relative rates depend upon a number of factors including supersaturation. In a continuous crystallizer, nuclei form (mostly by secondary nucleation) remain in the crystallizer for an average period of time (the average residence time) and then leave the crystallizer with the mother liquor. The crystals present in the apparatus at any time are of varying sizes as given by the *crystal size distribution* (CSD).

Crystal size distribution is an extremely important quantity in the design and analysis of crystallizers. A narrow size distribution is always preferred. Theoretical analysis of crystal size distribution is most conveniently done by using the *population balance technique* (Randolph and Larson, 1962). The following analysis of CSD is applicable to a *mixed suspension mixed product removal* (MSMPR) type crystallizer.

Most of the continuous crystallizers used in industrial practice are of the MSMPR type with suitable modifications. A schematic representation of such a crystallizer is shown in Figure 13.8. For a theoretical analysis of CSD, we make the following assumptions: (i) the particles remain uniformly distributed in the suspension; (ii) the feed enters continuously and the product is also continuously removed, keeping the volume of the suspension in the crystallizer constant; (iii) the suspension density and particle size distribution in the vessel and in the outlet stream are the same; (iv) negligible breakage of the crystals occurs; and (v) steady-state operation takes place.

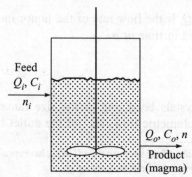

Figure 13.8   Schematic of an MSMPR crystallizer.

Let $n(L)$ be the crystal size distribution function defined on the basis of the characteristic length L of the crystals. Then $n(L)dL$ is the number of crystals of sizes in the infinitesimal range of L to $L + dL$ present in unit volume of the suspension[#]. The function $n(L)$ is also called the *population density function*. We now make a 'population balance' of the crystals on the following basis. Consider only those crystals of the arbitrary size range L_1 to L_2. The population density for the size L_1 is n_1; that for the size L_2 is n_2. The average population density $\bar{n}$, in the size range L_1 to L_2 is given by

$$\bar{n} = \frac{1}{L_2 - L_1} \int_{L_1}^{L_2} n(L)dL = \frac{1}{\Delta L} \int_{L_1}^{L_2} n(L)dL \Rightarrow \int_{L_1}^{L_2} n(L)dL = \bar{n}\Delta L; \ \Delta L = L_2 - L_1 \quad (13.11)$$

Over a small time dt, some crystals having size a little smaller than L_1 would grow and enter the size range $[L_1, L_2]$. Similarly, some other crystals that were a little smaller than L_2 in size, would become oversize after time dt and would leave this size range. The number of respective crystals in the volume V of the suspension are given as follows.

The number of crystals that crosses the size L_1 and now enters into the size range $[L_1, L_2]$ after an infinitesimal time dt is

$$= Vn_1 dL = Vn_1 \left[\frac{dL}{dt} \right]_{L=L_1} dt = Vn_1 G_1 dt \quad (13.12)$$

Similarly, the number of crystals that crosses the size L_2 and leaves the size range $[L_1, L_2]$ after the same time dt is

$$= Vn_2 dL = Vn_2 \left[\frac{dL}{dt} \right]_{L=L_2} dt = Vn_2 G_2 dt \quad (13.13)$$

Some crystals belonging to the size range $[L_1, L_2]$ may enter into the crystallizer with the feed. Similarly, the crystals of this size range leave the device with the suspension withdrawn as the product. Let n_i be the population density function of the crystals in the feed; the average value of the density function in the size range $[L_1, L_2]$ is given by $\bar{n}_i$.

$$\bar{n}_i = \frac{1}{L_2 - L_1} \int_{L_1}^{L_2} n_i(L)dL = \frac{1}{\Delta L} \int_{L_1}^{L_2} n_i(L)dL \Rightarrow \int_{L_1}^{L_2} n_i(L)dL = \bar{n}_i \Delta L$$

If Q_i is the flow rate of the liquor into the crystallizer, the number of crystals entering with the feed in time dt is

$$Q_i dt \int_{L_1}^{L_2} n_i(L)dL = Q_i dt \bar{n}_i \Delta L \quad (13.14)$$

Crystals belonging to the size range $[L_1, L_2]$ also leave the crystallizer with the suspension (volumetric flow rate[†] of the outlet stream = Q_o), and the number of these crystals is given by

---

[#] Sine dL is very small, $n(L)dL$ also represents the number of crystals in the size range $(L - dL)$ to L in unit volume of the suspension.

[†] It is to be noted that the rate of removal of the suspension from the crystallizer will not be equal to the feed rate because of evaporation of solvent from the vessel and the difference in density of the feed liquid and the suspension.

$$Q_o dt \int_{L_1}^{L_2} n(L)dL = Q_o dt\, \bar{n}\, \Delta L \tag{13.15}$$

We can now write down the following population balance equation using Eqs. (13.12) through (13.15) for the crystals of size range $[L_1, L_2]$ over a small time dt.

Number of particles within the vessel that grow and enter the given size range + Number of particles that enter into the vessel = Number of particles that grow larger than L_2 within the vessel + Number of particles that leave the vessel; i.e.

$$Vn_1 G_1 dt + Q_i dt\, \bar{n}_i\, \Delta L = Vn_2 G_2 dt + Q_o dt\, \bar{n}\, \Delta L \tag{13.16}$$

If the feed does not contain any crystal, we put $\bar{n}_i = 0$. Dividing both sides of Eq. (13.16) by $\Delta L.dt$ and taking the limit $\Delta L \to 0$,

$$V \lim_{\Delta L \to 0} \frac{n_1 G_1 - n_2 G_2}{\Delta L} = Q_o \bar{n} \tag{13.17}$$

As $\Delta L \to 0$, the average population density $\bar{n}$ reduces to n. Then

$$-V \frac{d(nG)}{dL} = Q_o n \Rightarrow \frac{d(nG)}{dL} + \frac{Q_o}{V} n = 0 \Rightarrow \frac{d(nG)}{dL} + \frac{n}{\tau} = 0 \tag{13.18}$$

Here $\tau = Q_o/V$ = the 'draw-down time' or 'holding time' or 'residence time'. Equation (13.18) is the basic *population balance equation* for an MSMPR crystallizer.

Size-independent growth: If the McCabe ΔL law given by Eq. (13.10) is valid (i.e. if the growth rate G does not depend upon L), the above equation reduces to

$$G \frac{dn}{dL} = -\frac{n}{\tau} \Rightarrow \frac{dn}{n} = -\frac{dL}{G\tau}; \quad \text{on integration,} \int_{n^0}^{n} \frac{dn}{n} = -\frac{1}{G\tau} \int_{0}^{L} dL$$

$$\Rightarrow \qquad\qquad n = n^0 \exp(-L/G\tau) \tag{13.19}$$

where n^0 is the population density of crystals having a *vanishingly small* size (i.e. $n = n^0$ as $L \to 0$). Equation (13.19) gives a 'two-parameter population density function' (n^0 and $G\tau$ are the two parameters). The crystal size distribution (CSD) or the population distribution in an MSMPR is similar to the residence time distribution of fluid elements in a continuous stirred tank reactor (CSTR). Different types of average particle sizes have been defined and can be derived if the particle size distribution is known. This is illustrated in Example 13.1.

EXAMPLE 13.1 (*Different types of average particle size*)   Derive the expressions for different types of average particle size on the basis of the exponential population density distribution function as given by Eq. (13.19).

Solution
Two types of averages should be defined—'ordinary average' and 'weighted average', both determined from the population density function.

Ordinary average: Three averages are of practical importance—length-, area- and mass-average sizes.

(i)   *Length-average size* $\bar{L}_L$ is the ratio of 'total length' (L_T) of all particles and the total number of particles (N_T) in a given volume, i.e.

$$L_T = \bar{L}_L N_T \qquad \text{or} \qquad \bar{L}_L = \frac{L_T}{N_T} \tag{i}$$

Considering unit volume of the suspension, the total length of all the particles is given by

$$L_T = \int_0^\infty L n(L) \, dL = \int_0^\infty L n^0 \exp(-L/G\tau) \, dL = n^0 (G\tau)^2 \int_0^\infty x e^{-x} \, dx = n^0 (G\tau)^2 \, \Gamma(2) = n^0 (G\tau)^2 \tag{ii}$$

$$N_T = \int_0^\infty n(L) \, dL = \int_0^\infty n^0 \exp(-L/G\tau) \, dL = n^0 G\tau \int_0^\infty e^{-x} \, dx = n^0 \, G\tau \tag{iii}$$

Here $x = \dfrac{L}{G\tau}$, and $\Gamma(\xi) = \displaystyle\int_0^\infty e^{-y} y^{\xi-1} \, dy$ = Gamma function. If ξ is an integer,

$$\Gamma(\xi + 1) = \xi! \tag{iv}$$

$$\text{Length-average particle size,} \ \bar{L}_L = \frac{L_T}{N_T} = \frac{n^0 (G\tau)^2}{n^0 (G\tau)} = \boxed{G\tau} \tag{v}$$

(ii)   The *area-average size* is the size of a particle that has an area equal to the average area of the particles in the sample. Thus, the area-average size $\bar{L}_a$ is given by

$$\phi_a (\bar{L}_a)^2 = \frac{A_T}{N_T}$$

where A_T is the 'total area' of the population and ϕ_a is the *area shape factor*. For unit volume of suspension, we have the following expression for A_T.

$$A_T = \int_0^\infty A_c n(L) \, dL = \int_0^\infty \phi_a L^2 \, n(L) \, dL = \phi_a \int_0^\infty L^2 \, n^0 \exp(-L/G\tau) \, dL = \phi_a n^0 (G\tau)^3 \int_0^\infty x^2 e^{-x} \, dx$$

$$= \phi_a n^0 (G\tau)^3 \, \Gamma(3) = 2\phi_a n^0 (G\tau)^3 \tag{vi}$$

$$\phi_a (\bar{L}_a)^2 = \frac{A_T}{N_T} = \frac{2\phi_a n^0 (G\tau)^3}{n^0 (G\tau)} = 2\phi_a (G\tau)^2$$

$$\Rightarrow \qquad \bar{L}_a = \boxed{\sqrt{2} \, (G\tau)} = \text{area-average particle size} \tag{vii}$$

(iii)   The *mass-average size* is the size of a particle that has a mass equal to the average mass of the particles in the sample. Thus the mass-average size $\bar{L}_m$ is given by

$$\phi_v (\bar{L}_m)^3 \rho_c = \frac{M_T}{N_T}$$

where M_T is the 'total mass' of the population per unit volume of suspension (suspension density) and ϕ_v is the *volume shape factor*. We have the following expression for M_T.

$$M_T = \int_0^\infty (\phi_v L^3 \rho_c) n(L) \, dL = 6\phi_v \, \rho_c n^0 (G\tau)^4 \tag{viii}$$

$$\Rightarrow \qquad \phi_v(\bar{L}_m)^3 \rho_c = \frac{6\phi_v \rho_c n^0 (G\tau)^4}{n^0 G\tau}$$

$$\Rightarrow \qquad \boxed{\bar{L}_m = \sqrt[3]{6}\,(G\tau)} = \textit{mass-average particle size} \qquad \text{(ix)}$$

The weighted average particle sizes are defined as below.

Population-weighted average particle size:

$$\bar{L}_{1,0} = \frac{\displaystyle\int_0^\infty Ln(L)\,dL}{\displaystyle\int_0^\infty n(L)\,dL} = \frac{\displaystyle\int_0^\infty Ln^0 \exp(-L/G\tau)\,dL}{\displaystyle\int_0^\infty n^0 \exp(-L/G\tau)\,dL} = \boxed{G\tau} \qquad \text{(x)}$$

Length-weighted average particle size:

$$\bar{L}_{2,1} = \frac{\displaystyle\int_0^\infty L[Ln(L)\,dL]}{\displaystyle\int_0^\infty Ln(L)\,dL} = \frac{\displaystyle\int_0^\infty L^2 n^0 \exp(-L/G\tau)\,dL}{\displaystyle\int_0^\infty Ln^0 \exp(-L/G\tau)\,dL} = \boxed{2G\tau} \qquad \text{(xi)}$$

Area-weighted average particle size:

$$\bar{L}_{3,2} = \frac{\displaystyle\int_0^\infty L[\phi_v L^2 n(L)\,dL]}{\displaystyle\int_0^\infty \phi_v L^2 n(L)\,dL} = \frac{\displaystyle\int_0^\infty L^3 n^0 \exp(-L/G\tau)\,dL}{\displaystyle\int_0^\infty L^2 n^0 \exp(-L/G\tau)\,dL} = \boxed{3G\tau} \qquad \text{(xii)}$$

Mass-weighted average particle size:

$$\bar{L}_{4,3} = \frac{\displaystyle\int_0^\infty L[\phi_v L^3 \rho_c n(L)\,dL]}{\displaystyle\int_0^\infty \phi_v L^3 \rho_c n(L)\,dL} = \frac{\displaystyle\int_0^\infty L^4 n^0 \exp(-L/G\tau)\,dL}{\displaystyle\int_0^\infty L^3 n^0 \exp(-L/G\tau)\,dL} = \boxed{4G\tau} \qquad \text{(xiii)}$$

The following points deserve attention:

- Length-average particle size $(\bar{L}_L)$ and population-weighted average particle size $(\bar{L}_{1,0})$ are the same.
- Each of the weighted averages defined above may be considered as the ratio of two consecutive moments of the population density function [see Section 13.5.1].

$$\bar{L}_{j+1,\,j} = \frac{\displaystyle\int L^{j+1} n(L)\,dL}{\displaystyle\int L^j n(L)\,dL} = \frac{(j+1)\text{th moment of } n(L)}{j\text{th moment of } n(L)}$$

The values of the parameters n^0 and τ in Eq. (13.19) can be determined from experimental data. If a sample of the suspension is drawn from a crystallizer, the crystals are separated and sieve-analyzed into different fractions, and the number of crystals belonging to a size range is plotted versus their average size on a semilog scale, a straight line should be obtained. Its intercept on the vertical axis is $\ln(n^0)$ and the slope is $-1/G\tau$ (see Example 13.2).

It is possible to calculate the nucleation rate B^0 from the parameters n^0 and $G\tau$. Let N be the total number of crystals of all sizes from $L = 0$ to $L = L$ $\left[\text{i.e.} \quad N = \int_{L=0}^{L} n \, dL \right]$ per unit volume of the suspension. The nucleation rate B^0 is the rate of formation of crystals of vanishingly small size. Therefore,

$$B^0 = \left[\frac{dN}{dt}\right]_{L \to 0} = \left[\frac{dN}{dL}\right]_{L \to 0} \left(\frac{dL}{dt}\right) = G\left[\frac{dN}{dL}\right]_{L \to 0} \qquad \text{(since } dL/dt = \text{growth rate, } G) \text{ (13.20)}$$

But
$$\left[\frac{dN}{dL}\right]_{L \to 0} = \left[\frac{d}{dL}\int_0^L n \, dL\right]_{L \to 0} = [n]_{L \to 0} = n^0 \quad \text{[from Eq. (13.19)]}$$

$$\Rightarrow \qquad B^0 = G\left[\frac{dN}{dL}\right]_{L \to 0} = Gn^0 \qquad \qquad \text{(13.21)}$$

It may be noted that the quantities n^0, G, and B^0 all depend upon the level of supersaturation (s). If experiments on measurement of CSD are repeated at different levels of supersaturation keeping other parameters (such as the holding time, τ; the intensity of agitation, etc.) constant, the values of B^0 and G for varying values of s can be obtained. The parameters of Eqs. (13.3) and (13.8) or (13.9) can be determined from these data. Both growth rate (G) and zero-size population density (n^0) are expected to depend upon the slurry density (M_T), the intensity of agitation and the level of supersaturation. Thus, Eq. (13.21) provides a theoretical support to Eq. (13.3) proposed on an intuitive and empirical basis.

The crystal size distribution (CSD) of an MSMPR unit depends upon a few interactive processes and factors. The supersaturation created in a crystallizer influences the rate of nucleation and crystal growth and hence the CSD and the surface area of the crystals. The surface area, in turn, influences supersaturation. The interactive phenomena in the entire process may be represented by a feedback loop shown in Figure 13.9.

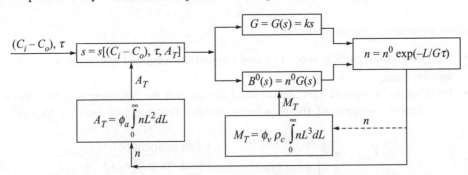

Figure 13.9   A feedback diagram illustrating the interaction among nucleation rate, growth rate, crystal size distribution and supersaturation.

EXAMPLE 13.2 (*Parameters of an MSMPR crystallizer from experimental data*) One litre suspension from an MSMPR crystallizer containing 161.07 g yielded the following results on sieve analysis. Determine the crystal size distribution function and the nucleation rate.

Tyler mesh	12/14	14/16	16/20	20/24	24/28	28/32	32/35	35/48	48/65	65/100	< 100
Mass	4.44	8.41	16.65	16.28	24.32	27.24	22.5	23.13	11.9	5.15	1.05

Given: solid density, $\rho_c = 2163$ kg/m^3; shape factor, $\phi_v = 2.0$; residence time, $\tau = 0.9$ h.

Solution

In order to determine the crystal size distribution [Eq. (13.19)], we have to calculate the number of particles n in each size range and prepare a plot of $\ln(n)$ versus the corresponding average size $\overline{L}$. If the number of crystals in the size range L to $L + \Delta L$ is $n\Delta L$, and ΔW is the mass of crystals per unit volume of the slurry in that size range (obtained by sieve analysis),

$$n\Delta L = \frac{\Delta W}{\rho_c \phi_v L^3} \quad \Rightarrow \quad n = \frac{\Delta W}{\rho_c \phi_v L^3 \Delta L} \tag{i}$$

The values of n corresponding to each size range (ΔL) are calculated from the given data using Eq. (i).

Mesh	Average opening, $\overline{L}$ (mm)		ΔL (mm)	ΔW (g/litre)	n, cm^{-4}	$\ln(n)$
12/14	(1.41 + 1.19)/2	= 1.3	0.22	4.44	21	3.055
14/16	(1.19 + 1.00)/2	= 1.095	0.19	8.41	78	4.360
16/20	(1.00 + 0.841)/2	= 0.92	0.159	16.65	311	5.700
20/24	(0.841 + 0.707)/2	= 0.774	0.134	16.28	606	6.407
24/28	(0.707 + 0.595)/2	= 0.651	0.112	24.32	1820	7.507
28/32	(0.595 + 0.5)/2	= 0.547	0.095	27.24	4050	8.306
32/35	(0.5 + 0.42)/2	= 0.46	0.12	22.5	4450	8.401
35/48	(0.42 + 0.297)/2	= 0.359	0.123	23.13	9397	9.148
48/65	(0.297 + 0.21)/2	= 0.253	0.087	11.9	19530	9.880
65/100	(0.21 + 0.149)/2	= 0.18	0.061	5.15	33470	10.418
< 100		0.0745	0.149	1.05		

Sample calculation: Take the size range 12/14; $\Delta W = 4.44$ g/litre; $\overline{L} = 0.13$ cm; $\Delta L = 0.022$ cm.

$$n = \frac{0.00444 \text{ g/cm}^3}{(2.163 \text{ g/cm}^3)(2.0)(0.13 \text{ cm})^3 (0.022 \text{ cm})} = 21 \text{ cm}^{-4}$$

From Eq. (13.19), $\ln(n) = \ln(n^0) - L/G\tau$. The mean particle size $\overline{L}$ of each fraction is calculated and given in the above table. We take $\overline{L}$ in place of L and prepare a plot of $\ln(n)$ versus $\overline{L}$ (Figure 13.10); n as number/cm^4, $\overline{L}$ in cm. The least square line fitted through the points has a slope = $-65.43 = -1/G\tau$. Since $\tau = 0.9$ h, $G = 1/(65.43)(0.9) = 0.017$ cm/h = 4.717×10^{-8} m/s; intercept = $11.564 = \ln(n^0) \Rightarrow n^0 = 1.052 \times 10^5$ number/cm^4.

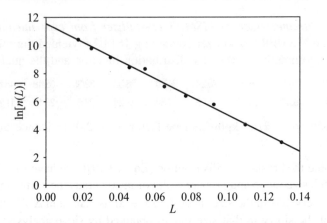

Figure 13.10 Example 13.2: The plot of $n(L)$ versus L.

The population distribution function: $\boxed{n = n^0 \exp\left(-65.43\,L\right),\ L \text{ in cm}}$

Nucleation rate [see Eq. (13.21)], $B^0 = Gn^0 = (4.717 \times 10^{-8}\ \text{m/s})(1.052 \times 10^5\ \text{cm}^{-4})$

$$= \boxed{4.96 \times 10^5\ \text{m}^{-3}\cdot\text{s}^{-1}}$$

13.5 CHARACTERISTICS OF CRYSTAL SIZE DISTRIBUTION

The population density function of an MSMPR crystallizer has quite a few important properties.

13.5.1 Moments of the Density Function

The pth moment of a distribution function, $\psi(\xi)$ $[0 \le \xi \le \infty]$ is defined as

$$\mu_p = \int_0^\infty \xi^p \psi(\xi)\, d\xi \tag{13.22}$$

The pth moment of $\psi(\xi)$ stands for the 'expected value' or the 'mean' value of ξ^p. The different moments of the distribution function relate to different 'means' of the properties of the crystals. For example, the 'mean value of the characteristic length' $\bar{L}_L$ or the 'length-average size' of the crystals is defined as follows [L_T = total length of the crystals; N_T = total number of crystals].

$$\bar{L}_L = \frac{L_T}{N_T} = \frac{\displaystyle\int_0^\infty L\,n(L)\,dL}{\displaystyle\int_0^\infty L^0\,n(L)\,dL} = \frac{\text{First moment of } n(L)}{\text{Zeroth moment of } n(L)} \tag{13.23}$$

Similarly, the *area-average* and *volume-average* sizes can be expressed in terms of the second and the third moments of the density function. The *mass-average* crystal size ($\bar{L}_m$) is also related to the third moment of $\psi(\xi)$. Determination of the different types of average sizes as well as weight-average sizes is illustrated in Example 13.3.

EXAMPLE 13.3 (*Crystal growth parameters*)   A laboratory MSMPR crystallizer has 0.05 m^3 suspension holdup. Measurements on a sample of suspension drawn from the crystallizer show a mass-weighted average particle size of 400 microns. Other data: the average holding time = 50 min; the suspension density, $M_T = 120$ kg crystals/m^3 of the suspension; true density of the crystals, $\rho_c = 2400$ kg/m^3; volume shape factor of a crystal, $\phi_v = 0.523$. Calculate (a) the crystal growth rate, (b) the zero-size nuclei density n^0, and (c) the nucleation rate.

Solution

(a) The expression for the mass-weighted average size is given by Eq. (xiii), Example 13.1, i.e.

$$\bar{L}_{4,3} = 4G\tau$$

Given in the problem: holding time, $\tau = 50$ min; size, $\bar{L}_{4,3} = 400$ μm.

$\Rightarrow$ Crystal growth rate, $G = \bar{L}_{4,3}/4\tau = 400/(4)(50) = 2$ μm/min $= \boxed{3.33 \times 10^{-8} \text{ m/s}}$

(b) The total mass of crystals per unit suspension volume is given by Eq. (viii), Example 13.1, i.e.

$$M_T = 6\phi_v\,\rho_c\,n^0\,(G\tau)^4$$

Given: $M_T = 120$ kg/m^3; $\phi_v = 0.523$; $\rho_c = 2400$ kg/m^3; $G\tau = (2$ μm/min$)(50$ min$) = 100$ μm

Substituting in the above equation,

$$120 = (6)(0.523)(2400)n^0(100 \text{ μm})^4 \quad \Rightarrow \quad n^0 = \boxed{1.6 \times 10^8 \text{ nuclei/(m}^3)(\text{μm})}$$

(c) The nucleation rate is given by Eq. (13.21),

$$B^0 = Gn^0 = (2 \text{ μm/min})[1.6 \times 10^8 \text{nuclei/(m}^3)(\text{μm})] = \boxed{3.2 \times 10^8 \text{ nuclei/(m}^3)(\text{min})}$$

EXAMPLE 13.4 (*Resistances in the process of crystal growth*)   Reconsider Example 13.3. The crystal growth rate (G) is found to be linear in the degree of supersaturation (s). *Given:* the fractional supersaturation is $s = 0.1$ at steady state; the area shape factor, $\phi_a = 3.14$; volume shape factor, $\phi_v = 0.523$; the solubility of the solute, $C_s = 0.2$ g/cm^3. If the mass transfer coefficient for the transport of solute from the bulk of the solution to the crystal surface, $k_L = 0.002$ cm/s, calculate the rate constant k_r for surface integration of the solute molecules and the fractional diffusional resistance.

Solution

Given: $G = 2$ μm/min; $s = 0.1$; $k_L = 0.002$ cm/s; $\phi_a = 3.14$; $\phi_v = 0.523$; $\rho_c = 2400$ kg/m$^3 = 2.4$ g/cm^3; $C_s = 200$ kg/m^3; $dL/dt = G = ks \Rightarrow k = (2$ μm/min$)/(0.1) = 20$ μm/min $= 3.33 \times 10^{-7}$ m/s. From Section 13.3.1

$$K_L = \frac{3\rho_c\phi_v k}{\phi_a C_s} = \frac{(3)(2400)(0.523)(3.33 \times 10^{-7})}{(3.14)(200)} = 2 \times 10^{-6} \text{ m/s} = 2 \times 10^{-4} \text{ cm/s}$$

Using Eq. (13.5),

$$K_L = \frac{k_L k_r}{k_L + k_r} \Rightarrow 2 \times 10^{-4} \text{ cm/s} = \frac{(0.002 \text{ cm/s}) \, k_r}{(0.002 + k_r) \text{ cm/s}} \Rightarrow k_r = \boxed{2.22 \times 10^{-4} \text{cm/s}}$$

Fractional diffusional resistance $= \dfrac{1/k_L}{1/K_L} = \dfrac{2 \times 10^{-4}}{0.002} = \boxed{10\%}$

(*Note:* The growth rate seems to be kinetically controlled.)

13.5.2 The Weight Distribution Function

Although the crystal-size distribution function given by Eq. (13.19) is the fundamental number distribution of the crystal size, it is practically much more important to use a 'cumulative mass or weight distribution function' $W(x)$, which represents the cumulative mass fraction of crystals having a dimensionless size 0 to x ($x = L/G\tau$ = dimensionless crystal size). The function $W(x)$ can be derived from the number distribution function [Eq. (13.19)] as shown below.

The mass of a single crystal of characteristic size L is given by Eq. (13.6). So the mass of the crystals having sizes ranging from L to $L + dL$ is

$$mn\,dL = \rho_c \phi_v L^3 n^0 \exp\left(-\frac{L}{G\tau}\right) dL = \rho_c \phi_v n^0 (G\tau)^4 \exp\left(-\frac{L}{G\tau}\right) d(L/G\tau) \qquad (13.24)$$

$$= \rho_c \phi_v n^0 (G\tau)^4 x^3 e^{-x} dx$$

where $x = L/G\tau$ is the dimensionless crystal size. The cumulative weight fraction $W(x)$ is the ratio of the weight of crystals in the size range 0 to x (i.e. 0 to L in terms of the dimensionless size, L) to the weight of all crystals in the entire size range 0 to ∞. From the above equation,

$$W(x) = \frac{\displaystyle\int_0^L mn\,dL}{\displaystyle\int_0^\infty mn\,dL} = \frac{\rho_c \phi_v n^0 (G\tau)^4 \displaystyle\int_0^x x^3 e^{-x} dx}{\rho_c \phi_v n^0 (G\tau)^4 \displaystyle\int_0^\infty x^3 e^{-x} dx} = \frac{\displaystyle\int_0^x x^3 e^{-x} dx}{\displaystyle\int_0^\infty x^3 e^{-x} dx} \qquad (13.25a)$$

The denominator $= \displaystyle\int_0^\infty x^3 e^{-x} dx = \Gamma(4) = 6$, where Γ denotes the Gamma function. Therefore,

$$W(x) = \frac{1}{6}\int_0^x x^3 e^{-x} dx = 1 - \left(1 + x + \frac{1}{2}x^2 + \frac{1}{6}x^3\right) e^{-x} \qquad (13.25b)$$

Equation [13.25(b)] gives the cumulative distribution of the weight fraction of the crystals with respect to the dimensionless crystal size, $x = L/G\tau$, in an MSMPR crystallizer.

The distribution of weight fraction of crystals (i.e. weight fraction of crystals having dimensionless size in the range x to $x + dx$ (or belonging to the dimensional size range L to $L + dL$) is given by

$$w(x) = \frac{dW}{dx} = \frac{1}{6}x^3 e^{-x} \qquad (13.26)$$

The maximum of $w(x)$ occurs at $L = L_D$ and is given by

$$\frac{dw(x)}{dx} = \frac{3}{6}x^2e^{-x} - \frac{1}{6}x^3e^{-x} = 0 \Rightarrow x = 3 \Rightarrow \frac{L}{G\tau} = 3 \Rightarrow L_D = 3G\tau \qquad (13.27)$$

L_D is called the *dominant* (or *modal*) *particle size* and is equal to the area-weighted average particle size (see Example 13.3). The *median size* L_M of the cumulative mass distribution is the value of x that corresponds to the 50 mass% of the crystals (L_D and L_M are two important crystal-size distribution parameters). To find out the median size, we put

$$W(x) = 1 - [1 + x + (x^2/2) + (x^3/6)]e^{-x} = 0.5 \Rightarrow x = 3.67 \Rightarrow L_M = 3.67G\tau \qquad (13.28)$$

It has been mentioned before that the crystal growth rate G depends upon supersaturation s and the suspension density or the magma density M_T. Taking these factors into account, the nucleation rate given by Eq. (13.3) may be recast as

$$B^0 = KM_T^iG^j \qquad (13.29)$$

Putting $n^0 = B^0/G$ [see Eq. (13.21)] in the expression for M_T given by Eq. (viii), Example 13.1, we have

$$M_T = 6\phi_v\rho_c(B^0/G)(G\tau)^4 \qquad (13.30)$$

In the simplest case, let us take $i = 1$. From Eqs. (13.29) and (13.30), we get

$$M_T = 6\phi_v\rho_c(KM_TG^{j-1})(G\tau)^4 \Rightarrow G = \left[\frac{1}{6\phi_v\rho_cK(G\tau)^4}\right]^{1/(j-1)} \qquad (13.31)$$

or, in terms of the dominant size L_D, or the median size L_M, the growth rate G may be expressed as

$$G = \left[\frac{27}{2\phi_v\rho_cKL_D^4}\right]^{1/(j-1)} = \left[\frac{30.3}{\phi_v\rho_cKL_M^4}\right]^{1/(j-1)} \qquad [K = \text{constant, Eq. (13.29)}] \qquad (13.32)$$

In many situations the desired dominant size or the median size of the crystals is given. If so, the necessary growth rate can be calculated from the above equation provided the nucleation kinetics [Eq. (13.29)] is known. Once G is determined, the required holding time and hence the crystallizer volume can be estimated.

EXAMPLE 13.5 (*Interrelations among crystallization parameters*)   An MSMPR crystallizer of working volume 5.5 m³ receives 6 m³/h of feed. The experimental nucleation rate (B^0) under the given conditions is linear in the magma density (M_T) but increases with the square of the growth rate (G). The magma density is 100 kg/m³; the median crystal size is 0.7 mm.
   (a) If the crystallizer is operated at a feed rate of 4 m³/h but the magma density remains unchanged, what would be the median crystal size? (b) If the crystallizer is operated at the same feed rate of 6 m³/h but at a higher magma density of 120 kg/m³, what would be the median crystal size?

Solution

The nucleation rate, $B^0 = KM_TG^2$. Magma density, $M_T = 6\phi_v\rho_cn^0(G\tau)^4$, see Eq. (viii), Example 13.1

Since $B^0 = n^0 G$, we have $n^0 = K M_T G$.

(a) Case I: $M_{T1} = 6 \phi_v \rho_c (n^0)_1 (G_1 \tau_1)^4$;   Case II: $M_{T2} = 6 \phi_v \rho_c (n^0)_2 (G_2 \tau_2)^4$

The suspension density is the same $\Rightarrow M_{T1} = M_{T2} \Rightarrow 6 \phi_v \rho_c (n^0)_1 (G_1 \tau_1)^4 = 6 \phi_v \rho_c (n^0)_2 (G_2 \tau_2)^4$

$$\Rightarrow \quad \frac{(n^0)_1}{(n^0)_2} = \left(\frac{G_2 \tau_2}{G_1 \tau_1} \right)^4 \quad \Rightarrow \quad \frac{K M_{T1} G_1}{K M_{T2} G_2} = \left(\frac{G_2 \tau_2}{G_1 \tau_1} \right)^4 \quad \Rightarrow \quad \frac{G_1^5}{G_2^5} = \frac{\tau_2^4}{\tau_1^4}$$

$$\Rightarrow \quad \frac{G_1 \tau_1}{G_2 \tau_2} = \left(\frac{\tau_1}{\tau_2} \right)^{1/5} \quad \Rightarrow \quad \frac{(L_M)_1}{(L_M)_2} = \left(\frac{\tau_1}{\tau_2} \right)^{1/5} \quad \text{[From Eq. (13.28)]}$$

Given: $\tau_1 = 5.5/6 \text{ h} = 55 \text{ min}; \; \tau_2 = 5.5/4 \text{ h} = 82.5 \text{ min}; \; (L_M)_1 = 0.7 \text{ mm}$

$$\Rightarrow \quad (L_M)_2 = (L_M)_1 (\tau_2/\tau_1)^{1/5} = (0.7)(82.5/55)^{1/5} = \boxed{0.76 \text{ mm}}$$

(b) For the same holding time, $\tau_1 = \tau_2$, but at different magma densities in the above two cases,

$$\frac{M_{T2}}{M_{T1}} = \frac{6 \phi_v \rho_c (n^0)_2 (G_2 \tau_2)^4}{6 \phi_v \rho_c (n^0)_1 (G_1 \tau_1)^4} = \frac{6 \phi_v \rho_c K M_{T2} G_2 (G_2 \tau_2)^4}{6 \phi_v \rho_c K M_{T1} G_1 (G_1 \tau_1)^4} \quad \Rightarrow \quad \left(\frac{G_2}{G_1} \right)^5 = 1$$

Since $\tau_1 = \tau_2$, $\dfrac{G_2 \tau_2}{G_1 \tau_1} = 1 \quad \Rightarrow \quad \dfrac{(L_M)_2}{(L_M)_1} = 1$

It appears that even though the magma densities are different, the median size remains the same in the two cases. This is because the nucleation rate is linear in the magma density. Otherwise the median size would be influenced by M_T.

13.5.3   Coefficient of Variation

The coefficient of variation (CV) of the crystal size is a measure of the spread of the size about the dominant crystal size. It is an important quality parameter of crystals and is defined as

$$\text{CV} = 100 \frac{L_{84\%} - L_{16\%}}{2 L_{50\%}} \tag{13.33}$$

If 84 mass% of the crystals have a length size up to L, we say $L = L_{84\%}$; $L_{16\%}$ and $L_{50\%}$ have similar significances. If the cumulative mass distribution function of the crystals is known, the coefficient of variation can be easily calculated. The larger the CV, the more is the 'spread' of the size distribution. Crystals from an MSMPR unit should not exceed a CV of about 50%. For mono- or uniform-sized crystals, CV = 0. Industrial crystallizers have CV values between 30% and 50%.

If the cumulative mass fraction distribution function is known in the form of an algebraic function or tabulated data, it is rather easy to determine the coefficient of variation, CV. For example, if we consider the cumulative weight fraction distribution of an MSMPR crystallizer given by Eq. [13.25(b)], $W(x) = 0.5 \Rightarrow x = 3.67$; $W(x) = 0.84 \Rightarrow x = 5.9$; and $W(x) = 0.16 \Rightarrow x = 2.1$. Since $x = L/G\tau$,

$$\text{CV} = 100 \frac{5.9 - 2.1}{(2)(3.67)} = 52\%$$

The length-average crystal size, $L_{1,0}$ [see Eqs. (v) and (x), Example 13.1], and the CV are the two important quantities used to describe the quality of a crystallizer product so far as the size and its uniformity are concerned.

13.5.4 Size-dependent Growth

If a system does not obey the McCabe ΔL law (such a system is said to exhibit *anomalous growth*), we have to integrate the population balance equation, Eq. (13.18), after substituting for the growth rate function applicable. Using a simple growth rate function, $G = G_0(1 + \gamma L)^b$, we have

$$\frac{d}{dL}[nG_0(1 + \gamma L)^b] + \frac{n}{\tau} = 0 \tag{13.34}$$

Integrating this equation from 0 to L, we have

$$n(L) = \beta n^0 (1 + \gamma L)^{-b} \exp\left[-\frac{(1 + \gamma L)^{1-b}}{G_0 \tau \gamma (1 - b)}\right]$$

$$n^0 = [n(L)]_{L \to 0}; \qquad \beta = \exp\left[\frac{1}{G_0 \tau \gamma (1 - b)}\right]; \; b < 1 \tag{13.35}$$

The data from an MSMPR crystallizer can be used to determine the size-dependent growth parameters and the population density parameters for a particular system from the above equation.

13.5.5 Growth Rate Dispersion

There are experimental evidences that show that crystals do not always grow at the same rate even when placed in the same environment (i.e. at the same level of supersaturation, suspension density, turbulence, temperature, etc.; see, for example, Garside (1985)). Wide variations in the growth rate of very small crystals is a frequent phenomenon. Such a variation in the growth rate of crystals is called the *growth rate dispersion*. One of the mechanisms put forward to explain the phenomenon is the random fluctuation model (Randolph and White, 1977) that attributes the growth rate dispersion to local fluctuations in flow and fluid velocity.

13.5.6 Crystal-size Control

An 'ideal' MSMPR crystallizer gives a product of wide size distribution. However, a few modifications of its operation become very effective to produce crystals of a narrow size range. The theoretical principle underlying any such strategy is to control the residence time of the crystals. If the smaller particles are not allowed to remain in the vessel for long but the larger ones are, the product will contain more of bigger crystals and less of fines. This is because the fines do not get sufficient time to grow and the population distribution changes in favour of larger crystals. Three common options, that can be used singly or in combination, are: (i) 'double draw-off' (DDO), also called 'clear liquid overflow' (CLO) or 'clear liquid advance' (CLA); (ii) fines removal with destruction; and (iii) classified product removal.

In the 'double draw-off strategy' (Figure 13.11), as the name implies, two streams are drawn from the crystallizer—(i) a 'clear' liquid stream having only a few fine crystals from near the top of the vessel at a point where a calming baffle is fixed near the wall to ensure relatively clear liquid, and (ii) a slurry or suspension from a lower level (this may be called 'underflow'). Since the crystallizer is operating at steady state, the total volumetric rate of output (overflow and underflow) must be the same as the rate of input. If the rate of withdrawal of the 'underflow' is reduced, that of the overflow will be more. The average residence time of the crystals is thus increased and so is the average crystal size. However, the spread of the crystal size cannot be regulated by the DDO strategy.

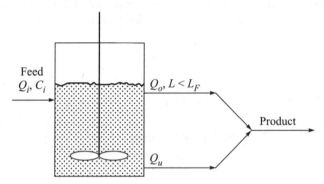

Figure 13.11   Schematic of the double draw-off (DDO) strategy.

If some of the small crystals or 'fines' are continuously removed from the crystallizer by a suitable technique, the concentration of the fines can be reduced. This helps in increased growth of the larger crystals. The stream containing the fines can be heated to dissolve the crystals and fed back to the crystallizer. Product crystals are drawn from the bottom of the vessel.

A crystallizer with fines removal and destruction

An industrial draft-tube baffle (DTB) crystallizer is often provided with a fines removal and destruction (FD crystallizer) arrangement. The construction and working principle of this type will be described later in Section 13.7.1 (Figure 13.14). Here we use a simple schematic (Figure 13.12) of a similar device for the analysis of crystal size distribution. A stream containing small crystals ($L \leq L_F$; the suffix 'F' stands for fines) is withdrawn from the top at a volumetric rate Q_o, the crystals are dissolved by heating in a heat exchanger and the solution is recycled back into the crystallizer vessel of working volume, V. The product stream

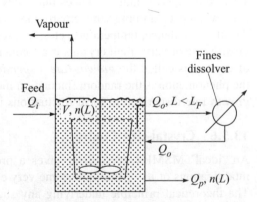

Figure 13.12   A crystallizer with fines removal and destruction.

is withdrawn at a volumetric rate of Q_p from a lower level. It may be noted that the bulk suspension is well-mixed and the population density is the same as that in the product stream. The population balance Eq. (13.16) may be extended to this case by taking into account the rate of removal of the fines (having $L \leq L_F$).

$$\text{Rate of removal of the fines in the overflow} = Q_o \bar{n} [1 - H(L_F - L)] \qquad (13.36)$$

where $H(L_F - L)$ is the Heaviside function defined as

$$H(\zeta) = 0 \text{ for } \zeta < 0 \qquad \text{and} \qquad H(\zeta) = 1 \text{ for } \zeta > 0.$$

Following Eq. (13.16), the population balance equation for this case may be written as (see Figure 13.12).

$$V \bar{n}_1 G_1 + Q_i \bar{n}_i \Delta L = V \bar{n}_2 G_2 + Q_p \bar{n} \, \Delta L + Q_o \bar{n} [1 - H(L_F - L)] \tag{13.37}$$

Putting $\bar{n}_i = 0$ (no crystal in the feed), letting $\Delta L \to 0$ and assuming that G is independent of L, we have

$$-VG \frac{dn}{dL} = Q_p n + Q_o n [1 - H(L_F - L)] \tag{13.38}$$

We can solve the above equation separately for the interval $[0, L_F]$ and for $L \geq L_F$. For $0 \leq L \leq L_F$,

$$-VG \frac{dn}{dL} = (Q_p + Q_o)n = R'nQ_p; \qquad R' = \frac{Q_p + Q_o}{Q_p} \tag{13.39}$$

$$\Rightarrow \qquad n = n^0 \exp\left[-\frac{R'Q_p}{VG}L\right] = n^0 \exp\left[-\frac{R'L}{G\tau_p}\right] \tag{13.40}$$

Here, $\tau_p = V/Q_p$ = average residence of the product or underflow, and R' is the ratio of the total volumetric rate of withdrawal $(Q_p + Q_o)$ to the volumetric rate of product withdrawal (Q_p).

For $L \geq L_F$, $\qquad -VG \frac{dn}{dL} = Q_p n \quad \Rightarrow \quad n = C_1 \exp\left[-\frac{L}{G\tau_p}\right] \tag{13.41}$

The integration constant C_1 can be determined by equating the distribution functions given by Eqs. (13.40) and (13.41) at $L = L_F$ (since the distribution must be continuous at $L = L_F$). Thus,

$$C_1 = n^0 \exp\left[-\frac{(R'-1)L_F}{G\tau_p}\right]$$

and $\qquad n = n^0 \exp\left[-\frac{(R'-1)L_F}{G\tau_p}\right] \exp\left[-\frac{L}{G\tau_p}\right] \qquad \text{for } L \geq L_F \tag{13.42a}$

$$\Rightarrow \qquad n = n^0 \exp\left[-\frac{L_F}{G\tau_F}\right] \exp\left[-\frac{L}{G\tau_p}\right]; \qquad \tau_F = \frac{V}{Q_o} \tag{13.42b}$$

The cumulative weight fraction distribution of the crystals having the above number density distribution is given by [compare with [Eq. 13.25(b)] for an MSMPR crystallizer] the following expression. It is assumed that the mass fraction of crystals having size $L < L_F$ is small.

$$W(x) = \frac{6\phi_v n^0 \exp(-L_F/G\tau_F)}{M_T}\left[1 - e^{-x}\left(1 + x + \frac{x^2}{2} + \frac{x^3}{6}\right)\right]; \quad \tau_F = \frac{V}{Q_o}; \quad M_T = \int_0^\infty \phi_v L^3 \rho_c n(L) dL$$

$$\tag{13.43}$$

The application of the above population distribution and the benefit of the fine dissolution strategy are illustrated by Example 13.6.

A common method of inducing crystallization is to inoculate or 'seed' a supersaturated solution with small particles of the solute. Seeding is often used as a technique of controlling the product size in an industrial crystallizer. The seed crystals also affect the rate of secondary nucleation.

EXAMPLE 13.6 (*A crystallizer with fine removal and destruction*)   This example illustrates the benefit of having a fine removal and dissolution arrangement in an MSMPR. Consider an 'ideal' MSMPR crystallizer that operates with a holding time $\tau_p = 90$ min and produces crystals of dominant size $L_{D1} = 0.5$ mm. A simple secondary nucleation kinetics, $B^0 = \bar{k} \, G_1^{2.8}$, is known for the given conditions and environment. The rate of withdrawal of the fines is such that $R' = 9.0$. Fines up to size of $L_F = 60$ micron are withdrawn in the overflow and dissolved before the stream is returned to the tank. Calculate the required growth rate of this crystallizer with fine dissolver if the same feed flow rate and production rate as in the 'ideal' MSMPR are to be maintained. Also calculate the corresponding dominant size of the product.

Solution

Case 1:   The *ideal* MSMPR crystallizer. *Given:* $B_1^0 = \bar{k} \, G_1^{2.8} \Rightarrow n_1^0 = B_1^0/G_1 = \bar{k} \, G_1^{1.8}$. Holdup time, $\tau_p = 90$ min; $L_{D1} = 0.5$ mm $= 500$ μm $= 3G_1\tau_p$ ($\tau_p = V/Q_p$, $Q_p =$ product withdrawal rate). Growth rate, $G_1 = 500$ μm$/(3)(90\text{min}) = 1.85$ μm/min; magma density, $M_{T1} = 6\phi_v \rho_c \, n_1^0 \, (G_1\tau_p)^4$.

Case 2:   Crystallizer with fine dissolver. The population density distribution is given by Eqs. (13.40) and (13.42). The magma density (mass of crystals per unit volume of suspension) is given by

$$M_{T2} = \int_0^{L_F} \phi_v L^3 \rho_c n_2^0 \exp\left[-\frac{R'L}{G_2\tau_p}\right] dL + \int_{L_F}^{\infty} \phi_v L^3 \rho_c n_2^0 \exp\left[-\frac{(R'-1)L_F}{G_2\tau_p}\right] \exp\left[-\frac{L}{G_2\tau_p}\right] dL$$

The mass of fines in the suspension is generally a small fraction of the total mass of crystals. So we can neglect the first integral. Therefore,

$$M_{T2} \approx 6\phi_v\rho_c n_2^0 \exp\left[-\frac{(R'-1)L_F}{G_2\tau_p}\right](G_2\tau_p)^4 \int_0^{\infty} \xi^3 e^{-x}\, d\xi = 6\phi_v\rho_c n_2^0 \exp\left[-\frac{(R'-1)L_F}{G_2\tau_p}\right](G_2\tau_p)^4$$

(i)

In the above integral, $\xi = L/G_2\tau_p$. Since the feed rate and the production rate remain the same for the 'ideal' and the fine dissolver crystallizer, the suspension density should be equal, i.e.

$$M_{T1} = M_{T2} \quad \Rightarrow \quad 6\phi_v\rho_c n_1^0(G_1\tau_p)^4 = 6\phi_v\rho_c n_2^0 \exp\left[-\frac{(R'-1)L_F}{G_2\tau_p}\right](G_2\tau_p)^4$$

Put $n_1^0 = \bar{k} \, G_1^{1.8}$ and $n_2^0 = \bar{k} \, G_2^{1.8}$ to get $G_1^{5.8} = G_2^{5.8} \exp\left[-\frac{(R'-1)\,L_F}{G_2\tau_p}\right]$

Given: $R' = 9.0$; $L_F = 60$ μm; $\tau_p = 90$ min; $G_1 = 1.85$ μm/min

$$\Rightarrow 5.8 \ln \frac{G_2}{G_1} = \frac{(R'-1)L_F}{G_2\tau_p} = \frac{(9.0-1)\,(60\,\mu m)}{(G_2)\,(90\,\text{min})} = \frac{G_1}{G_2}\frac{(9.0-1)\,(60\,\mu m)}{(1.85\,\mu m/\text{min})\,(90\,\text{min})} \quad \Rightarrow \quad \frac{G_2}{G_1} = 1.42$$

The required growth rate in the fine dissolver unit, $G_2 = 1.42G_1 = (1.42)(1.85$ μm$)$

$$= \boxed{2.63 \, \text{μm/min}}$$

Dominant size: Since the mass fraction of fines smaller than $L_F = 60$ μm is rather small, Eq. (13.27) can be used to calculate the dominant size without sacrificing much accuracy.

$$L_{D2} = 3G_2\tau_p = (3)(2.63 \text{ μm/min})(90 \text{ min}) = 710 \text{ μm} = \boxed{0.71 \, \text{mm}}$$

Thus the dominant size is increased by about 40% by incorporating the fines withdrawal and dissolution arrangement.

The fines constitute a small fraction of the total mass of the crystals in the vessel. Hence withdrawal of fines (DDO mode) or fines dissolution and recycling of the solution do not virtually influence the cumulative distribution of mass fraction. However, if the solution is not recirculated the overall yield is reduced.

A crystallizer with fine destruction and classified product removal

As compared with the fine dissolver unit, a crystallizer provided with an arrangement for removal of fines ($L < L_F$) as well as 'classified' product removal is still a better configuration to achieve larger crystals with a narrower size distribution. The overflow from such a unit removes the fines followed by dissolution and recirculation. The underflow passes through an 'elutriation leg' or a 'hydrocyclone' for recycling particles of size $L < L_c$ while withdrawing crystals larger than L_c as the product stream. The population distribution function of this crystallizer can be obtained using the techniques described before. The term 'classified' product removal means that the elutriating leg of the crystallizer separates or 'classifies' the particles of sizes below and above L_c to give a product of a smaller size range.

13.6 BATCH CRYSTALLIZATION

Batch crystallizers are commonly used for the production of fine chemicals, pharmaceuticals, and specialty chemicals. The capacity of batch crystallizers may vary from as low as 100 kg to as high as 15 tons of product a day. The large capacity units are generally run in the continuous mode (a sugar crystallizer is an exception).

In a batch crystallizer, the feed solution is pumped into the crystallization vessel and the necessary supersaturation is created by evaporation of the solvent. 'Seed crystals' are added in requisite quantity and the growth of the crystals begins. In order to sustain the growth rate, a suitable level of supersaturation has to be maintained till the batch operation is stopped and the product crystals are then harvested. This can be done in a number of ways.

- Evaporation of the solvent
- Cooling of the content in the crystallizer
- Addition of an anti-solvent (*salting out*)

Evaporation or cooling may be done under vacuum, if necessary. Before we go for a theoretical analysis of the evaporation or cooling strategy, it will be useful to look into the various physical factors that influence the operation of a batch crystallizer.

Formation of tiny crystals by secondary nucleation occurs simultaneously with the growth of the added seeds. The nuclei formed also grow alongside. This ultimately leads to a 'bimodal' or even 'multimodal' size distribution of the final product. A narrow crystal size distribution can be achieved if there is little or no nucleation, so that the final product is the result of growth of the seeds only. The common methods of reducing the rate of nucleation follow from Eq. (13.3): (i) to control the supersaturation level, (ii) to keep a low level of turbulence or mixing, (iii) to keep the slurry density low. The level of supersaturation can be controlled by controlling the evaporation or the cooling rate such that the solution concentration remains within the metastable region (the primary nucleation rate is very slow in this region). Controlled evaporation or cooling may be achieved by keeping a low temperature difference in the heat exchanger and providing a rather larger area to compensate for the small driving force. Fouling of the heat exchanger tubes by deposition also affects smooth operation directly and indirectly. The intensity of agitation should be enough to keep the solid particles in suspension but must not cause particle breakage (tiny fragments formed by particle breakage act as nuclei).

13.6.1 Theoretical Analysis of a Batch Evaporative Crystallizer

We consider a batch crystallizer operating at a constant level of supersaturation by evaporation of the solvent. Other relevant parameters (agitation, temperature, etc.) also remain unchanged. The crystallizer is initially fed with seed crystals of uniform size, L_s. We want to determine the required rate of evaporation of the solvent in order to maintain a constant level of supersaturation for producing crystals of average size, L_p. The crystal growth rate G remains constant. If we add N number of seeds, then at time t

$$\text{Crystal size, } L = L_s + Gt; \quad \text{mass of the crystals, } M = N\phi_v L^3 \rho_c$$

The rate of change of mass of the crystals,

$$\frac{dM}{dt} = \frac{d}{dt}(N\phi_v L^3 \rho_c) = 3N\phi_v L^2 \rho_c \frac{dL}{dt} = 3N\phi_v L^2 \rho_c G$$

This must be equal to the rate of change of the mass of solute in solution having a concentration, C.

$$3N\phi_v L^2 \rho_c G = -\frac{d}{dt}(VC); \quad V = \text{volume of the solution, } C = \text{concentration}$$

The equation may be rearranged to

$$-\frac{d}{dt}\left[\frac{VC}{3N\phi_v \rho_c L_s^3}\right] = \frac{L^2}{L_s^3}G = \left[\frac{L_s + Gt}{L_s}\right]^2 \frac{G}{L_s} \tag{13.44}$$

Let us now define, $\xi = \dfrac{VC}{3N\phi_v \rho_c L_s^3} = \dfrac{VC}{3M_s}$; $z = \dfrac{Gt}{L_s}$; M_s = mass of the seed crystals added.

$$-\frac{d\xi}{dz} = \left(\frac{L_s + Gt}{L_s}\right)^2 = \left(1 + \frac{Gt}{L_s}\right)^2 = (1 + z)^2 \tag{13.45}$$

The above equation can be used to calculate the required evaporation rate to achieve a final crystal size L_p in a batch time t. Since the solution concentration remains constant (only the volume changes),

$$-\frac{d\xi}{dz} = -\frac{C}{3M_s}\frac{dV}{dz} = (1+z)^2 \Rightarrow -\frac{C}{3M_s}\frac{dV}{dt}\frac{dt}{dz} = (1+z)^2$$

$$\Rightarrow \qquad -\frac{dV}{dt} = \frac{3M_s}{C}\frac{G}{L_s}\left(1+\frac{Gt}{L_s}\right)^2 \qquad \left(\text{since } \frac{dt}{dz} = \frac{L_s}{G}\right) \tag{13.46}$$

The above equation can be used to determine the evaporation program of a batch crystallizer. It is simple but very approximate, since it ignores many realities such as nucleation and resulting crystal size distribution. The strategy is illustrated in Example 13.7.

13.6.2 Theoretical Analysis of a Batch Cooling Crystallizer

An equation similar to the above can be developed for a batch cooling crystallizer. As the growth of the seed crystals proceeds, the solution is cooled so as to maintain the desired level of supersaturation. For simplicity we assume that the solubility is a linear function of temperature T, i.e. $C_s = a_1 + a_2 T$. If a constant but small degree of supersaturation s is maintained,

$$s = \frac{C-C_s}{C_s} \quad \Rightarrow \quad C = (s+1)C_s \quad \Rightarrow \quad \frac{dC}{dt} = (s+1)\frac{dC_s}{dt} \approx a_2\frac{dT}{dt} \tag{13.47}$$

In a cooling crystallizer, the liquid volume $V = $ constant. Following Eq. (13.46), we may write

$$-\frac{d}{dz}\left(\frac{VC}{3M_s}\right) = (1+z)^2 \quad \Rightarrow \quad -\frac{V}{3M_s}\frac{dC}{dz} = \frac{Va_2}{3M_s}\frac{dT}{dz} = (1+z)^2 \tag{13.48}$$

The above equation can be used to determine the cooling strategy of a batch crystallizer. A modified technique called *induction seeding* has been suggested by Moore (1994) for improving the product quality of batch crystallization.

EXAMPLE 13.7 (*Evaporation strategy in a batch evaporative crystallizer*)   Potassium chloride crystals of 1.1 mm average size are to be produced at a rate of 800 kg per batch in an evaporative crystallizer operating under vacuum at 40°C. At the start, the crystallizer is filled with a saturated solution of KCl and is seeded with reasonably uniform-sized crystals of $L_s = 80$ μm. The solubility of KCl at 40°C is 400 kg/m^3 and the density of the solution is 1300 kg/m^3. A maximum slurry density of 150 kg crystals/m^3 of slurry is allowed. The density of the crystals is 1990 kg/m^3; the crystal shape factor is taken as $\phi_v = 1.0$. The crystal growth rate can be assumed to remain constant at 3×10^{-8} m/s. Determine (a) the crystallizer volume, (b) the mass of seeds used, (c) the batch time, (d) the evaporation profile, and (e) the initial and final evaporation rate to be used.

Solution

(a) *Crystallizer volume*
In a batch crystallizer, the maximum slurry concentration ($M_T = 150$ kg/m^3) occurs at the end of the batch time.

Total mass of crystals at the end is W = 800 kg

Final slurry volume, V_f = 800 kg/(150 kg/m^3) = 5.333 m^3

Concentration of the solute (KCl) in the solution, C_s = 400 kg/m^3

Therefore, 800 kg of crystals are produced from 2 m^3 (= 2600 kg) solution, i.e. the total quantity of solvent evaporated, V_s = 2600 – 800 = 1800 kg.

Total volume of the solution at the start = 5.333 + 2 = 7.333 m^3

Assume the vessel to be 70% filled at the beginning;

volume of the crystallization tank = 7.333/0.7 = $\boxed{10.5\,\text{m}^3}$

(Any change in solution density because of supersaturation is assumed to be small.)

(b) *Mass of seeds used*

Final mass of the product crystals, W = 800 kg; size, L = 1.1 mm = 1.1 × 10^{-3} m; density, ρ_c = 1990 kg/m^3; size of a seed crystal, L_s = 80 × 10^{-6} m; growth rate, G = 3 × 10^{-8} m/s; ϕ_v = 1.0.

Mass of a single crystal, $m = \phi_v L^3 \rho_c$ = (1)(1.1 × 10^{-3})^3(1990) kg = 2.649 × 10^{-6} kg

Number of crystals, 800/(2.649 × 10^{-6}) = 3.02 × 10^8 = N = number of seeds

Mass of a seed crystal, $m_s = \phi_v L_s^3 \rho_c$ = (1)(80 × 10^{-6})^3(1990) = 1.019 × 10^{-9} kg

Mass of seeds, $M_s = N m_s$ = (3.02 × 10^8)(1.019 × 10^{-9}) = $\boxed{0.308\,\text{kg}}$

(c) *Batch time*

If t is the batch time, and G (= 3.0 × 10^{-8} m/s) is the constant growth rate,

$$L = L_s + Gt \implies t = (L - L_s)/G = \frac{1.1 \times 10^{-3} - 80 \times 10^{-6}}{3.0 \times 10^{-8}} = 3.4 \times 10^4 \text{ s} = \boxed{9.44\,\text{h}}$$

(d) *Evaporation profile* [Use Eq. (13.46)]

$$-\frac{dV}{dt} = \frac{3M_s}{C}\frac{G}{L_s}\left(1 + \frac{Gt}{L_s}\right)^2$$

Given: M_s= 0.308 kg, C = 400 kg/m^3, G/L_s= 3.75 × 10^{-4} s^{-1}

$$\implies \quad -\frac{dV}{dt} = \frac{(3)(0.308)}{400}(3.75 \times 10^{-4})(1 + 3.75 \times 10^{-4}\,t)^2$$

$$\implies \quad -\frac{dV}{dt} = 8.66 \times 10^{-7}(1 + 3.75 \times 10^{-4}\,t)^2 \text{ m}^3/\text{s}$$

(e) Initial rate of evaporation (at t = 0) = 8.66 × 10^{-7} m^3/s = $\boxed{0.0519\,\text{litre/min}}$

Final rate of evaporation, $-\dfrac{dV}{dt}$ = 8.66 × 10^{-7}[1 + (3.75 × 10^{-4})(3.4 × 10^4)]^2 m^3/s

$$= \boxed{0.714\,\text{litre/min}}$$

It appears that the required vaporization rate is pretty low at the beginning but should be much larger at the end. Since the crystal growth rate is assumed to be constant (independent of size), the initial rate of increase of mass of the crystals is small, the rate of loss of supersaturation is small and the required evaporation rate is also small.

EXAMPLE 13.8 (*Cooling strategy in a batch crystallizer*)   Reconsider the previous problem. The batch crystallizer is initially filled with a saturated solution of KCl at 80°C and 0.308 kg of seed crystals (L_s = 80 μm). A coolant is passed through the coil in the stirred crystallization tank. The solubility of KCl is approximately linear in temperature, $C_s = 287 + 2.82\theta \, \text{kg/m}^3$ where θ is the temperature in °C. The average density of the saturated solution, $\rho = 1280 \, \text{kg/m}^3$. The final temperature is 40°C, and the average rate of crystal growth is $G = 3.5 \times 10^{-8}$ m/s. Determine the cooling strategy for the unit.

Solution

We assume that the level of supersaturation is small and the solution concentration remains almost at the saturation value.

Initial concentration (θ = 80°C), C_{si} = 287 + (2.82)(80) = 512.6 kg/m^3

Final concentration (θ = 40°C), C_{sf} = 287 + (2.82)(40) = 400 kg/m^3

Solution density, ρ = 1280 kg/m^3

Initial concentration (w/w) = (512.6)/(1280 – 512.6) = 0.668 kg KCl per kg solvent (water)

Final concentration (w/w) = 400/(1280 – 400) = 0.454 kg KCl per kg solvent (water)

Crystals produced = 0.668 – 0.454 = 0.214 kg crystal per kg solvent

Total mass of crystals produced = 800 kg $\Rightarrow$ amount of solvent = 800/0.214 = 3738 kg water

Mass of the feed = (3738)(1 + 0.668) = 6236 kg; volume of the feed = 6236/1280 = 4.87 m^3

Final volume of slurry

$$\text{Mass of crystals = 800 kg; volume = 800/1990 = 0.402 m}^3$$

$$\text{Mass of solution left = 3738(1 + 0.454) = 5435 kg}$$

$\Rightarrow \qquad$ Volume of the solution = 5435/1280 = 4.25 m^3

Final volume of the slurry = volume of solids + volume of solution = 0.402 + 4.25 = 4.652 m^3. The initial volume (4.87 m^3) is larger.

Assume that the tank is 60% full initially. Tank volume = 4.87/0.6 = 8.12 m^3.

Use the average volume [V = (4.87 + 4.65)/2 = 4.76 m^3] to determine the cooling strategy.

Equation (13.48): $-\dfrac{dT}{dt} = \dfrac{3M_s}{a_2 V} \dfrac{G}{L_s}(z+1)^2 = \dfrac{(3)(0.308)(3.5 \times 10^{-8})}{(2.82)(4.76)(80 \times 10^{-6})}(z+1)^2$

$$= 3.01 \times 10^{-5}(z + 1)^2 \text{ °C/s}$$

$1 + z = 1 + (Gt)/L_s = L/L_s = (1.1 \times 10^{-3})/(80 \times 10^{-6}) = 13.75$ at the end, and $1 + z = 0$ at the start

Initial cooling rate (L/L_s = 1, and z = 0) = 3.01 × 10^{-5} °C/s

Final cooling rate = (3.01 × 10^{-5})(13.75)^2 = 5.7 × 10^{-3} °C/s = 0.34 °C/min

13.7   CRYSTALLIZATION EQUIPMENT

Satisfactory operation of a crystallizer depends upon quite a few factors. The rates of nucleation and crystal growth both depend upon the extent of supersaturation of the solution. At a high supersaturation level, the rate of nucleation is high. So there is a possibility of a higher fraction of fines in the product. At a low level of supersaturation, the rate of nucleation is slow. So it is likely that the product will contain a higher fraction of larger size crystals. The rate of secondary nucleation can be reduced (thereby reducing the fraction of fines in the product) by maintaining a low mechanical energy input [the nucleation rate depends upon the mechanical energy input, see Eq. (13.3)]. A high magma density (i.e. a high concentration of the suspended solid in the crystallizer) is conducive to achieving larger average crystal size. The construction and operating features of a few common crystallizers are discussed below.

13.7.1   Mixed Suspension Mixed Product Removal (MSMPR) Crystallizers or Circulating Magma Crystallizers

These are the most important class of industrial crystallizers. The growing crystals are kept in suspension by agitation; 20–40% solids in suspension is common. The basic principles and theory discussed before apply reasonably well to this kind of crystallizer. Two types of crystallizers of this class are described here.

Forced-circulation (evaporative) crystallizer

A forced circulation (FC) crystallizer shown in Figure 13.13 has four major components. The slurry is pumped through an external steam-heated vertical heat exchanger to raise its temperature

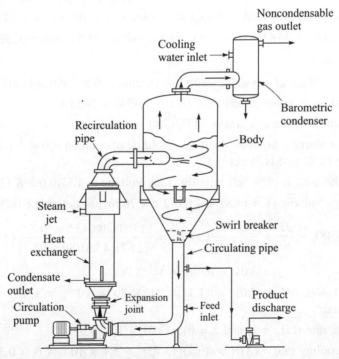

Figure 13.13   Forced circulation evaporative crystallizer.

by 2 to 6°C. Heat exchanger tube size of 1¼ to 1¾ inch is common; the liquid velocity is maintained at 2–3 m/s. No boiling occurs in the heat exchanger. The hot liquid is thrown into the crystallizer body when evaporation of the liquid occurs. This raises the solution concentration, reduces its temperature (because of evaporation of some liquid) and generates the supersaturation required for crystal growth. A condenser at the top removes the vapour generated. The equipment may be put under vacuum by coupling a barometric leg to the condenser. The product is withdrawn from the circulating pipe. The feed also enters the crystallizer through this pipe, but at a lower level as shown in Figure 13.13. An axial flow pump is preferred; the pump speed should be low in order to reduce the mechanical energy input so that the secondary nucleation rate by contact or attrition remains small. Many inorganic salts such as ammonium sulphate, sodium chloride, trisodium phosphate, potassium nitrate, citric acid, sugar, etc. are crystallized in an FC crystallizer. Crystals typically of the size range 30–60 mesh are produced.

Draft-tube-baffle (DTB) crystallizer

The body of a DTB crystallizer, shown in Figure 13.14, is provided with an inner baffle tube and also a skirt baffle. A long-shaft slow-moving impeller throws the liquid upwards through the baffle tube towards the boiling surface. This causes circulation of the magma in the crystallizer body; more circulation than in an FC unit is achieved at the same power input. Fouling is also less than that in an FC. The magma also flows out of the body through an annular zone between the skirt baffle and the wall, enters a steam-heated exchanger (the liquid flow path is shown by arrows) and recycles back to the crystallizer vessel. Some of the fines may dissolve in the heat exchanger. Thus the crystallizer has a fine destruction feature. Settling of large crystals occurs

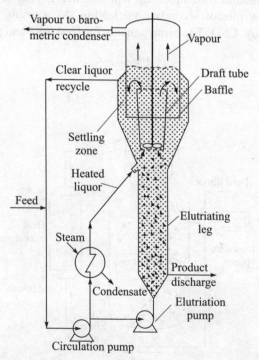

Figure 13.14 Draft-tube baffle crystallizer with an elutriating leg for product classification.

in the annular region so that only the fines leave with the recirculating slurry. However, this happens only when the mother liquor and the crystals have sufficiently different densities. An elutriating leg can be fitted to the conical bottom to achieve further classification of the product. A DTB crystallizer controls the solution superheating at the boiling surface to within 2°F, and thereby controls the bulk liquid supersaturation within a range which is attained in an FC crystallizer. A close control of crystal size is thus possible. Crystals ranging from 8–30 mesh may be produced by controlling the process conditions. Typical applications are for crystallization of adipic acid, KCl, K_2SO_4, etc.

Other common crystallizers belonging to the MSMPR class are conispherical magma crystallizer, forced circulation baffle surface-cooled crystallizer, etc. (Myerson, 2002; Rousseau, 1987).

13.7.2   Circulating Liquor Crystallizer

In circulating liquor crystallizers, the crystals are retained in the crystallizer vessel and only the liquor is circulated through an external heat exchanger in which the liquor is either heated by steam or cooled by a suitable cooling medium to generate supersaturation. Vacuum is also sometimes provided to enhance evaporation. Crystals are kept in suspension in the vessel by the upflowing liquid. The liquid velocity is so maintained that there is hardly any crystal present in the top region of the liquid in the vessel. Virtually, clear liquid from this region enters the circulating pipe. Figure 13.15 shows three 'Oslo-krystal' crystallizers belonging to this category. The speciality of this equipment is that supersaturation is created in a separate region before the liquor flows into the crystal suspension vessel. The level of supersaturation drops down as the liquor from the supersaturation zone mixes up with the slurry. This helps to achieve a uniform crystal growth and a low rate of secondary nucleation. As a result, this type of crystallizer produces crystals of narrow CSD. The arrangements for feed inlet and product removal are also

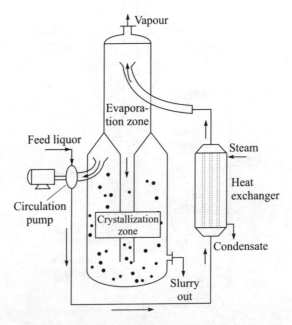

Figure 13.15   Oslo circulating liquor evaporator crystallizer.

shown in Figure 13.15. These are used for crystallization of inorganic compounds like ammonium nitrate, sodium nitrate, ammonium sulphate, dichromate, etc.

13.7.3 Tank Crystallizers

A tank crystallizer, as the name suggests, consists of a cylindrical tank provided with a cooling jacket or a cooling coil. The hot feed is pumped into the tank and the cooling liquid is passed through the jacket or the coil at a predetermined rate. The temperature differential between the liquor and the cooling fluid should be low in order to reduce deposition on the cooling surface. Use of an agitator to keep the crystals in suspension and to prevent excessive fouling of the heat transfer surface is pretty common. Seeding may be done at an appropriate time. A tank crystallizer is preferred if the production capacity is low (as in pharmaceutical and fine chemical industries).

13.7.4 Other Types of Crystallizers

Besides the above types of crystallizers, many other designs of the equipment are in use. For viscous and fouling solutions, 'scraped-surface crystallizers', having a coaxial double-pipe construction and provided with a screw-type internal surface scrapper, are convenient. Supersaturation is generated by cooling. These crystallizers are usually of small capacity because of the limited heat transfer area. The crystal size distribution is generally wide. Common examples of scrapped-surface crystallizers are the Votator and Armstrong crystallizer and the Swenson-Walker crystallizer. These crystallizers are mainly used for crystallizing organic compounds like fatty acids, dyes, *p*-xylene, chlorobenzene, naphthalene, etc. and also for some inorganic materials that have a tendency to form scale on surfaces. Fluidized bed crystallizers, surface-cooled crystallizers, direct-contact refrigeration crystallizers are a few other types in use (Myerson, 2002). Application of ultrasound has been found to be effective for controlled nucleation and has the potential of improving CSD and product quality of industrial crystallizers (McCausland, et al., 2001).

13.7.5 A Few Common Operational Problems

Industrial crystallization is a complex process with associated operational problems. The more common problems are low yield, more fines and a wide size distribution, and fouling of the vessel and the heat transfer surface. Some of these problems can be solved by properly controlling the supersaturation and magma density and by adjusting the average residence time of the crystals. Besides deteriorating the product quality, a larger fraction of fines is likely to cause deposition on the surfaces leading to 'incrustation'. If the yield is poor, a part of the mother liquor is recycled after separation of the crystals. A high crystal growth rate may adversely affect the purity since some of the foreign substances may get entrapped within the crystals. Price (1997) and Sutradhar (2004) reviewed many of these aspects of industrial crystallization.

13.8 DESIGN CONSIDERATIONS

The function of a crystallizer is to produce crystals of a given size specification from a feed at a specified rate. A suitable and adequate supersaturation is created by cooling the feed or by partial evaporation of the solvent. The second method is more common in industrial practice. It has been mentioned before that a narrow particle size distribution of the product is desired to maintain a good product quality. Besides the correct supersaturation and environment (i.e. agitation, pumping rate, etc.), techniques like fine redissolution or classified product removal are helpful to achieve a better product quality. Batch crystallizers require seeding (i.e. addition of fine crystals that act as nuclei). Secondary nucleation occurs continuously in a continuous crystallizer and seeding is not generally necessary.

The more important parameters and quantities involved in the design of a crystallizer are stated below.

- *The feed rate and state* (*concentration, temperature, pressure, etc.*). These are specified in the design problem.
- *The desired crystal size distribution* (*CSD*) *and yield.*   These are also generally given. The percentage theoretical yield is defined as

$$\text{Yield } (\%) = \frac{100(Q_i C_{\text{in}} - Q_o C_s)}{Q_i C_{\text{in}}} \tag{13.49}$$

where Q_i = feed rate, Q_o = rate of outflow of mother liquor, C_{in} = feed concentration, and C_s = solubility of the solid at the exit temperature. In the expression for 'theoretical yield', the exit liquid is assumed to have lost the supersaturation. If the temperature in the crystallizer is fixed, C_s can be obtained from the solubility data. From the specified yield (%), Q_o is calculated using Eq. (13.49). The required rate of evaporation is determined by a solvent balance.

- *Solvent evaporation rate and the heat transfer area required.*   These are to be calculated. The evaporation rate is calculated from material balance. A heat balance over the crystallizer gives the required rate of heat input. Heat of crystallization should be included in the heat balance. The steam or the heating fluid rate and the heat transfer area are then calculated.
- *Crystallizer volume.* This is to be calculated. For this purpose, experimental data on nucleation (B^0) and the growth rate (G) are required. These data can be obtained from a laboratory crystallizer. Data collected from a pilot plant crystallizer of volume around 50 litres or more can be more reliably used. If the product quality (in terms of the weight% of the crystals above a particular size) is specified in the design problem, Eq. (13.28) may be solved for the dimensionless cut-off size, x. From the known values of G and L, the holdup time and volume can be calculated. The diameter of a crystallizer is frequently determined on the basis of possible entrainment of liquid with the vapour generated.
- *Crystallizer dimension and recirculation rate.* These are to be calculated and checked. The recirculation rate of the slurry though the heat exchanger (see Figure 13.13) is important in heat transfer area calculation. The selected crystallizer diameter and recirculation rate should be checked so that adequate velocity is maintained to avoid settling of solid depending upon the type of crystallizer.

EXAMPLE 13.9 (*Working volume of a crystallizer*)   It is required to produce potassium sulphate crystals of dominant size $L_D = 0.6$ mm at a rate of 1000 kg/h in an MSMPR crystallizer. The nucleation rate has been experimentally obtained: $B^0 = 4 \times 10^{18} M_T G^2$ per m³ per second. Calculate the crystallizer volume. *Given:* magma density, $M_T = 240$ kg/m³ slurry; area shape factor of the crystals, $\phi_a = 3.8$; density of the crystals, $\rho_c = 2660$ kg/m³.

Solution

Volume shape factor of the crystals, $\phi_v = (\phi_a/\pi)^{3/2}(\pi/6) = 0.696$.

The required crystal growth rate can be calculated using Eq. (13.32). Put $\rho_c = 2660$ kg/m³; $K = 4 \times 10^{18}$; $L_D = 0.6$ mm $= 6 \times 10^{-4}$ m; $j = 2$. Then

$$G = \left[\frac{27}{(2)(0.696)(2660)(4 \times 10^{18})(6 \times 10^{-4})^4}\right]^{1/(2-1)} = 1.41 \times 10^{-8} \text{ m/s}$$

From Eq. (13.27), $\tau = L_D/3G = (6 \times 10^{-4})/(3)(1.41 \times 10^{-8}) = 14180$ s $= 3.94$ h

Production rate $= 1000$ kg/h; magma density $= 240$ kg/m³

Rate of withdrawal of the suspension, $Q_p = (1000 \text{ kg})/(240 \text{ kg/m}^3) = \boxed{4.17 \text{ m}^3/\text{h}}$

Working volume of the crystallizer, $V = Q_p\tau = (4.17 \text{m}^3/\text{h})(3.94 \text{ h}) = \boxed{16.43 \text{ m}^3}$

EXAMPLE 13.10 (*Sizing of a crystallizer*) Given the following data and information, it is required to design a forced circulation crystallizer of the type shown in Figure 13.13 operating under vacuum.

Feed (an aqueous solution) rate, $Q_i = 15$ m³/h; feed concentration, $C_i = 200$ kg/m³ solution; feed temperature $= 55°C$; average density of the solution $= 1100$ kg/m³ and average specific heat $= 0.90$ kcal/kg°C; operating pressure $= 100$ mm Hg (660 mm Hg vacuum); boiling point elevation of the saturated solution $= 13°C$; saturation concentration at the crystallization temperature $= 250$ kg/m³; magma density allowed, $M_T = 350$ kg crystal/m³ solution; crystal growth rate determined experimentally under the conditions of the crystallizer, $G = 4.67 \times 10^{-8}$ m/s; crystal density, $\rho_c = 1700$ kg/m³; desired dominant crystal size, $L_D = 0.8$ mm; heat of crystallization, $(\Delta H)_c = 30$ kcal/kg (absorption of heat occurs during crystallization); latent heat of vaporization of water at the temperature of the crystallizer $= 570$ kcal/kg; superheat allowed in the heat exchanger $= 3°C$; overall heat transfer coefficient in the heat exchanger, $U = 1000$ kcal/m²·h·°C; low pressure steam is available for the heat exchanger at 3 kg/cm² gauge, latent heat of condensation $= 510$ kcal/kg.

Solution

Material balance (basis 1 hour operation)

Solution in $= 15$ m³; solute in $= (15 \text{ m}^3)(200 \text{ kg/m}^3) = 3000$ kg

Water in $= (15)(1100 - 200) = 13,500$ kg

Magma density $= 350$ kg crystal per m³ solution

$\Rightarrow$ 350 kg crystal per 250 kg solute in the solution.

Crystals produced $= \dfrac{350}{350 + 250} \times 3000$ kg $= 1750$ kg. Solute leaving with mother liquor $= 1250$ kg

Volume of solution (clear mother liquor) leaving $= 1250$ kg/(250 kg/m³, solubility) $= 5$ m³

Mass of solvent (water) leaving $= (5\text{m}^3)(1100 - 250)$ kg/m³ $= 4250$ kg

Mass of water evaporated $=$ water in with feed water out with mother liquor

$= 13,500 - 4250 = 9250$ kg

Volume of slurry leaving per hour = volume of solution + volume of crystals leaving

$$= 5 \text{ m}^3 + [1750 \text{ kg}/(1700 \text{ kg/m}^3)] = 6.03 \text{ m}^3 \text{ per hour}$$

Crystallizer volume

Dominant size of the product, L_D = 0.8 mm = $3G\tau$; G = 4.67 × 10^{-8} m/s (given).

Required holding time, $\tau = L_D/3G = (8 \times 10^{-4} \text{ m})/(3)(4.67 \times 10^{-8} \text{ m/s}) = 5710 \text{ s} = 1.6 \text{ h}$

Volume of suspension in the crystallizer at any time = (6.03 m^3/h)(1.6 h) = 9.65 m^3

This is the 'working volume' of the crystallizer (note that the suspension holdup in the pipe line and in the heat exchanger tubes has been neglected). Add 60% to account for vapour bubbles and froth.

Effective suspension volume in the crystallizer = (9.65 m^3)(1.6) = 15.44 m^3

Select a $\boxed{3 \text{ m}}$ diameter vessel (this value is to be checked and changed if necessary) with a conical bottom. Take a cone angle of 45° for the conical bottom.

Volume of the conical part (radius = depth = 1.5 m) of the tank = $(\pi/3)(1.5)^2(1.5) = \boxed{3.53 \text{ m}^3}$

Volume of the cylindrical part = 15.44 − 3.53 = 11.91 m^3; height = $11.91/(\pi)(1.5)^2 = \boxed{1.68 \text{ m}}$

Add 1.25 m space above the boiling liquid for disengagement of the entrained droplets.

Total length of the cylindrical part of the tank = 1.68 m + 1.25 m = $\boxed{2.93 \text{ m, say 3 m}}$

Now check the assumed diameter of the tank.

Absolute pressure in the vapour space = 760 − 660 = 100 mm Hg = 0.1316 atm.

B.P. of water = 52°C. Boiling point elevation = 13°C ⇒ B.P of the solution = 52°C + 13°C = 65°C = 338 K.

Density of vapour (steam) at this temperature and pressure, $\rho_v = \dfrac{(18)(0.1316)}{(0.0821)(338)}$

$$= 0.0854 \text{ kg/m}^3$$

Volumetric rate of vapour generation = (9250 kg/h)/(0.0854 kg/m^3) = $\boxed{1.083 \times 10^5 \text{ m}^3/\text{h}}$

A Souders–Brown type equation [Eq. (5.4)] is used to determine the allowable velocity of the vapour without risking entrainment.

$$u_v = C_v \left(\frac{\rho_l - \rho_v}{\rho_v}\right)^{1/2} \approx C_v \left(\frac{\rho_l}{\rho_v}\right)^{1/2}$$

For evaporation under vacuum with a demister, a conservative value of C_v = 0.04 m/s is used.

$$\text{Allowable velocity, } u_v = 0.04 \left(\frac{1100 \text{ kg/m}^3}{0.0854 \text{ kg/m}^3}\right)^{1/2} = 4.54 \text{ m/s}$$

$$\text{Area required for evaporation} = \frac{1.083 \times 10^5 \text{ m}^3/\text{h}}{(3600)(4.54 \text{ m/s})} = 6.63 \text{ m}^2$$

Cross-section of the tank = 7.07 m². Hence a tank of 3 m diameter is suitable.

Energy balance and heat exchanger area

The feed liquor enters at 55°C; feed rate = 15 m³/h

$\Rightarrow$ (15 m³/h)(1100 kg/m³) = 1.65×10^4 kg/h

Take the BP of the liquor, 65°C, as the reference temperature.

Required heat input to raise the liquor temperature to 65°C,

$$= (1.65 \times 10^4)(0.9)(65 - 55)$$
$$= 148{,}500 \text{ kcal}$$

Heat required for evaporation of water = (9250 kg/h)(510 kcal/kg) = 5.272×10^6 kcal/h
(Superheat of the vapour produced is neglected.)

Heat of crystallization = (1750 kg/h)(30 kcal/kg) = 5.25×10^4 kcal/h (absorption)

Total heat input required, Q_h = $1.485 \times 10^5 + 5.272 \times 10^6 + 5.25 \times 10^4$ kcal/h
$$= 5.473 \times 10^6 \text{ kcal/h}$$

Heating steam supplied at 3 kg/cm² gauge (saturated) $\Rightarrow$ steam temperature = 143°C

Latent heat = 510 kcal/kg $\Rightarrow$ steam rate = (5.473×10^6 kcal/h)/(510 kcal/kg) = 10,730 kg/h

Heat exchange area

Temperature driving force, $(\Delta T)_1 = 143 - 65 = 78°C$; $(\Delta T)_2 = 143 - 68 = 75°C$; $(\Delta T)_m = 76.5°C$.

$$\text{Area of the heat exchanger} = \frac{Q_h}{U \cdot (\Delta T)_m} = \frac{5.473 \times 10^6}{(1000)\,(76.5)} = \boxed{71.5 \text{ m}^2}$$

An outline diagram of the crystallizer in given in Figure 13.16.

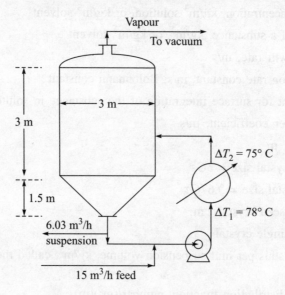

Figure 13.16   An outline diagram of the crystallizer.

13.9   MELT CRYSTALLIZATION

Melt crystallization (Wynn, 1997) is the technique of separation of a compound in an acceptably pure form from a mixture with undesired substances without using a solvent. The impure molten material is cooled to its freezing temperature when the target product crystallizes out. The technique is widely used for separation of many bulk organic products such as *p*-xylene from other isomers (separation by distillation is too difficult since the relative volatility is low), naphthalene from coal tar, acrylic acid (it may be produced by oxidation of propylene; cannot be separated by distillation because of the tendency of polymerization), monochloroacetic acid (from a mixture with acetic acid and its higher chlorinated derivatives), Bisphenol A (an important starting material for making polycarbonates).

Since melt crystallization does not need a solvent, it is a clean and non-polluting technique. This is especially true for separation and purification of non-polar organics for which water cannot be used as a solvent for crystallization. The technique is also used to separate and purify products having a low thermal stability. Melt crystallization may be carried out in suspension ('suspension crystallization') where crystal growth occurs in a supersaturated stirred medium. Alternatively, the melt may be passed through cooled tubes when the product deposits on the cold surface (this is called the 'layered growth process').

NOTATIONS

A_c : area of a single crystal, m^2

A_T : total area of m kg crystals, m^2

B^0 : nucleation rate, (number of nuclei formed)/(m^3)(s)

C : solution concentration, kg/m^3 solution, or kg/m^3 solvent

C_s : solubility of a substance, kg/m^3, or kg/m^3 solvent

G : crystal growth rate, m/s

k : crystallization rate constant, m/s; Boltzmann constant

k_r : rate constant for surface integration of the substance in solution, m/s

k_L ·: mass transfer coefficient, m/s

L : crystal size, m

L_D : dominant crystal size = $3G\tau$

L_M : median crystal size = $3.67G\tau$

L_s : size of the seed crystals, m

m_c : mass of a single crystal

M_T : mass of crystals per unit suspension volume, kg/m^3, called the suspension or slurry density

n : population distribution function, number/(m^3)(m)

n^0 : density of population of vanishingly small size

$n\Delta L$	: number of crystals per m^3 suspension in the size range L to $L + \Delta L$
N, N_T	: number of crystals in the size range 0 to L , total number of crystals
Q	: flow rate, m^3/s
R'	: $(Q_p + Q_o)/Q_p$, Eq. (13.39)
s	: fractional supersaturation, Eq. (13.2)
t	: time, s
V	: suspension volume, working volume of a crystallizer, m^3
$W(x)$	: cumulative weight fraction
x	: $L/G\tau$, dimensionless crystal size
z	: $G\tau/L_s$
ϕ_a	: area shape factor (A_c/L^2)
ϕ_v	: volume shape factor ($m/\rho_c L^3$, m = mass of a single crystal)
μ_p	: pth moment of a distribution, Eq. (13.22)
ρ_c	: crystal density, kg/m^3
ρ_s	: suspension density, kg/m^3
τ	: hold-up time or residence time, V/Q in s or h (suffixes have been used)

SHORT AND MULTIPLE CHOICE QUESTIONS

1. Define/explain the following terms:
   (i) crystal   (ii) magma   (iii) mother liquor   (iv) eutectic mixture
2. What is the difference between precipitation and crystallization?
3. Do crystals always form spontaneously in a supersaturated solution?
4. Give an example of melt crystallization.
5. What is a 'metastable region' in a phase diagram? Why is it so called?
6. What do you mean by nucleation? What are the different types of nucleation? What are the important factors that influence the rate of nucleation?
7. Do the crystals of a substance of size 1 mm have the same solubility in a solvent like the 1 μm particles? Can you give a qualitative explanation of any difference?
8. Which of the following is a unit of nucleation rate B^0?
   (i) s^{-1} (ii) m^{-3}·h^{-1} (iii) m^{-1}·h^{-1}
9. What is the ratio of ϕ_a/ϕ_v for a cubical particle?
   (i) 6   (ii) 1.6   (iii) 1/6
10. In an experiment on the growth of a sample of fairly uniform-size particles ($L = 1$ mm) in a supersaturated solution, it is found that the volume of a particle increases at a rate of $dv_p/dt = 5.2 \times 10^{-14}$ m^3/s. Determine the growth rate G, if the volume shape factor is given, $\phi_v = 0.42$.

11. The volume shape factor ϕ_v of a sphere is given by
    (i) 1.0   (ii) 0.523   (iii) 4.5

12. The area shape factor ϕ_a of a cube is given by
    (i) 1/6   (ii) 1.6   (iii) 6

13. The characteristic length of a particle increases from 1 mm to 1.1 mm when kept suspended in a solution of supersaturation level $s = 1.05$ for 2 h. If a particle of 0.8 mm size is allowed to grow in the same solution under similar conditions for 4 h, what would be its final size?
    (i) 1.2   (ii) 0.9   (iii) 1 mm

14. Heat of solution of A in water is $\Delta H_s = 10.3$ kcal/gmol (endothermic). The solubility of A is low. What is the heat absorbed for the formation of 1 gmol crystal of the substance?
    (i) –10.3 kcal   (ii) 10.3 kcal   (iii) No appreciable heat effect

15. The solubility of copper sulphate in water at 80°C is 55 g $CuSO_4$ per 100 g water, that at 30°C is 25 g per 100 g water. One ton of the saturated solution at 80°C is slowly cooled down to 30°C. What is the mass of the crystals ($CuSO_4$, $5H_2O$) produced? About 1% of water is lost by evaporation during cooling.

16. Which of the following types of nucleation is predominant in a continuous industrial crystallizer?
    (i) Homogeneous nucleation
    (ii) Nucleation by attrition
    (iii) Contact nucleation

17. How do the following factors govern the rate of (a) primary and (b) secondary nucleation?
    (i) Level of supersaturation
    (ii) Agitator speed
    (iii) Interfacial tension
    (iv) Temperature
    (v) Molar volume of the solid
    (vi) Slurry density
    (vii) The clearance between the impeller tip and the wall

18. The crystal size distribution of the product from an MSMPR crystallizer has been determined by particle size analysis: $n = 5.543 \times 10^{12 - 4.63L}$ number/m^4, L in mm. The holdup time is 200 min.
    (a) The dominant size of the crystals is
        (i) 0.94 mm   (ii) 0.28 mm   (iii) 0.45 mm
    (b) The crystal growth rate (cm/s) is
        (i) 7.82×10^{-7} (ii) 1.05×10^{-6} (iii) 3×10^{-9}
    (c) The rate of nucleation (m^{-3}·h^{-1}) is
        (i) 1.6×10^{10} (ii) 7.8×10^{9} (iii) 1.56×10^{8}

19. Which of the following may be used as a unit of the population density of nuclei (i.e. population density of crystals of vanishingly small size)?
    (i) m^{-3}·h^{-1} (ii) cm^{-1}·m^{-3} (iii) m^{-2}·s^{-1}

20. The population density function of the crystals from an MSMPR crystallizer is $n = 8.23 \times 10^{11} \exp(-9.58L)$ number/m^4; L in mm.
    (a) What is the mass average particle size?
        (i) 0.505   (ii) 0.278   (iii) 0.19 mm
    (b) What is the median size of mass distribution?
        (i) 3.6   (ii) 1.02   (iii) 0.38 mm
    (c) What is the coefficient of variation of the crystal size distribution?
        (i) 38%   (ii) 64%   (iii) 52%

21. Which of the following is most suited to produce larger crystals?
    (i) FC   (ii) DTB   (iii) Circulating liquor crystallizer

22. The size-dependent growth rate of the crystals of a substance has been found to be $G(L) = 9.85 \times 10^{-7}(1 + 0.16L)^{0.55}$ m/s; L in mm. What is the average growth rate of the crystals of size range 0 to 1 mm?
    (i) 9.85×10^{-7} (ii) 2×10^{-9} (iii) 1.03×10^{-6} m/s

23. Crystal growth for a system is known to be diffusion-controlled. Should the growth rate depend upon particle size?
    (i) Yes   (ii) No   (iii) No conclusion

24. The 'McCabe ΔL law' is found to be valid for the crystallization of a certain substance. Which resistance is likely to control the growth rate?
    (i) Diffusional   (ii) Surface reaction   (iii) Both of these

25. Which of the following is a probable value of the linear crystal growth rate ($G = dL/dt$)?
    (i) 10 m/day   (ii) 10^{-8} m/h   (iii) 10^{-6} m/min

26. Which of the following conditions favours formation of large crystals?
    (i) A high degree of supersatuartion
    (ii) A low nucleation rate
    (iii) A high magma density

27. Which heat transfer surface is more prone to fouling during crystallization?
    (i) A cooling surface
    (ii) A heating surface

28. All other conditions remaining the same, which of the following impeller material will cause the highest secondary nucleation rate?
    (i) An engineering plastic like nylon
    (ii) Aluminium
    (iii) Steel

29. (i) What is polymorphism? (ii) Explain qualitatively how the magma density affects the nucleation rate. (iii) What are the important auxiliary equipment required in a crystallization unit?

30. For which of the following an evaporative crystallizer is used? A substance
    (i) having a relatively flat solubility curve
    (ii) with solubility rapidly increasing with temperature
    (iii) having an inverse solubility relation.

31. The cumulative mass fraction of crystals up to a size of 200 μm in the product leaving an ideal MSMPR unit is 0.1. Calculate the mass fraction of crystals in the size range 0.4 to 0.6 mm.

32. A cubical crystal of size 0.5 mm grows in a solution of supersaturation, $s = 0.07$. *Given:* $\rho_c = 1800$ kg/m^3, $C_s = 150$ kg/m^3, and $k_L = 2.5 \times 10^{-3}$ cm/s, calculate the rate of crystal growth if it is known to be diffusion-limited.

33. The clear 'overflow' stream from a DDO crystallizer is drawn at a rate of 2 gallon/min, and the slurry leaves at the bottom at a rate of 1 gallon/min. The working volume of the crystallizer is 50 gallon. What is the average residence time of the crystals?
    (i) 16.7 min   (ii) 25 min   (iii) 50 min

PROBLEMS

13.1 (*A use of Gibbs–Thomson equation*)[1] Calculate the maximum diameter of a crystal of KCl that will not grow in a solution of having 5% supersaturation ($C/C_s = 1.05$) at 20°C. *Given:* density of solid KCl = 1990 kg/m^3; molecular weight = 74.5 g/gmol; solid–liquid interfacial tension = 0.030 J/m^2.

13.2 (*Derivation of the equation for primary nucleation rate*)[3] The classical theory of homogeneous nucleation (see Myerson, 2002) assumes that a cluster of molecules forms a nucleus when it attains a critical minimum free energy. The rate of formation of nuclei can be represented by an Arrhenius-type relation, $B^0 = A' \exp(-\Delta G_{cr}/kT)$, where ΔG_{cr} is the 'critical free energy' change for the formation of a nucleus, k = Boltzmann constant, and T = absolute temperature. The free energy change has two components—the surface free energy and the free energy of phase transformation. On the basis of this approach and using the Gibbs–Thomson Eq. (13.1), derive Eq. (13.2) for the rate of homogeneous nucleation.

Calculate the percent increase in the homogeneous nucleation rate if the supersaturation increases from (i) $s = 1.20$ to 1.21, and (ii) $s = 1.25$ to 1.26 for constant values of the other parameters. What do the results indicate?

13.3 (*Population density parameters from sieve analysis data*)[2] One hundred fifty grams of crystals separated from one litre of suspension from an MSMPR crystallizer is subjected to screen analysis to get the following data:

Tyler mesh	12/14	14/20	20/28	28/35	35/48	below 48 mesh
Mass(g)	28.5	29.2	37.5	27	24.7	3.1

Mesh no./ screen opening(μm) data: 12/1410 μm; 14/1190; 20/841; 28/595; 35/420; 48/297.

The working volume of the crystallizer is 200 litres, and the rate of withdrawal of the slurry is 250 litre per hour. Given $\rho_c = 1400$ kg/m^3 and volume shape factor $\phi_v = 0.42$, determine the crystal growth rate and the zero-size population density of the crystals. What is the rate of nucleation, B^0?

13.4 (*Population density parameters from sieve analysis data*)[2]   (a) A 4-litre laboratory MSMPR crystallizer receives a solution of potash alum at the rate of 8 litre/h. One hundred grams of the product crystals (volume shape factor, $\phi_v = 0.471$) is sieve analyzed to obtain the mass in different size ranges as given below. The true density of the solid is $\rho_c = 1770$ kg/m^3, and a suspension density of 142 g crystals per litre is maintained. Determine the rate of secondary nucleation (B^0) and of crystal growth (G).

Size range (mm)	0.71/0.5	0.5/0.355	0.355/0.25	0.25/0.18	0.18/0.125
	0.125/0.090	0.09/0.063	< 0.063		
Mass (g)	8.46	19.18	30.11	22.21	11.92
	5.29	1.87	0.85		

(b) The following values of n^0, G, and B^0 were obtained from the sieve analysis data of the crystals by operating the same crystallizer at the two other feed rates.

Feed rate (litre/h)	n^0 (m^{-4})	G (m/s)	B^0 (m^{-3}·s^{-1})
16	8.2×10^{14}	8.6×10^{-8}	7.1×10^7
24	1.1×10^{15}	1.3×10^{-7}	1.4×10^8

Do the values of B^0 and G for the three feed rates indicate any nonlinear relation between B^0 and G? How are they related? [Mullin, 2002]

13.5 (*Rate of secondary nucleation and crystal growth*)[1]   An MSMPR crystallizer of 5 m^3 working volume produces crystals of mass average particle size 1.0 mm. If the product stream is withdrawn at a rate of 4 m^3/h, calculate the crystal growth rate and the rate of secondary nucleation, B^0. The magma density is 150 kg/m^3, and the true density of the crystals is 1900 kg/m^3. The volume shape factor is 0.6.

13.6 (*Use of some basic parameters*)[1]   An MSMPR crystallizer yields crystals of median size $L_M = 0.8$ mm when a holding time of 1.8 h is maintained. The working volume of the equipment is 5 m^3, and the suspension density is 150 kg crystals per cubic metre. The crystals have a density of $\rho_c = 2500$ kg/m^3 and the volume shape factor is $\phi_v = 0.65$. What is the production rate of crystals? Calculate the secondary nucleation rate B^0, and the zero-size population density n^0. Also calculate the mass fraction and the number fraction of the crystals smaller than 0.2 mm in the product.

13.7 (*Use of some basic parameters*)[2]   The following size distribution function of the crystals from an MSMPR has been obtained by sieve analysis data of a sample.

$$n = n^0 \exp(-\, L/G\tau); \quad n^0 = 4.52 \times 10^7 \; (\text{m}^{-3}) \, (\mu\text{m})^{-1}; \quad G = 2.31 \times 10^{-8} \; \text{m/s}$$

(a)   For an average residence time of 2 h, determine the cumulative mass distribution function, the dominant size L_D and the median size L_M of the crystals.

(b)   The working volume of the crystallizer is 2 m^3. Calculate the volumetric rate of withdrawal of the product if the dominant size of the product crystals should be 0.6 mm. What mass fraction of the crystals will have a size below 0.2 mm?

13.8 (*Size-dependent crystal growth*)[3] (a) Determine the population density distribution function in an MSMPR crystallizer if the crystals have a size-dependent growth rate, $G = G_0(1 + \gamma L)^b$, $0 < b < 1$.

(b) The following size-dependent growth rate was derived from the results of laboratory experiments [Abegg et al., *AIChE J.*, *14* (1968) 118–122] on crystallization of Glauber's salt (Na_2SO_4, $10H_2O$). A few other data are also given.

$$G = G_0(1 + \gamma L)^b; \quad G_0 = 2.22 \times 10^{-9} \text{ m/s}; \quad \gamma = 1.25 \times 10^4 \text{ m}^{-1}; \quad b = 0.2; \quad \tau = 1 \text{ h};$$
$$n^0 = 8 \times 10^{14} \text{ m}^{-4}; \quad \phi_v = 0.48; \quad \rho_c = 1460 \text{ kg/m}^3.$$

Determine the population density distribution function, the magma density, and the dominant size of the crystals. What mass fraction of the crystals have sizes below 0.5 mm?

13.9 (*Use of some basic parameters*)[2] The crystal growth rate in an MSMPR crystallizer under a given set of conditions is 5×10^{-8} m/s. The holdup volume of the suspension is 10 m^3 and the suspension withdrawal rate is 4 m^3/h. The zero-size population density is 5×10^{10}/(cm)(litre). (a) Calculate the total number of crystals in the vessel at any time. (b) What is the mass fraction of crystals in the size range 0.5 to 1mm? (c) What is the coefficient of variation of the crystal size?

13.10 (*Use of some basic parameters*)[1] The secondary nucleation rate of potassium dichromate crystals in a solution was reported by Desai et al., *AIChE J.*, *20* (1974) 43 as follows:

$$B^0 = (7.33 \times 10^7) \, M_T^{0.8} G^{0.5} \text{ number/(m}^3\text{)(s)}$$

where M_T is in kg/m^3 and G is in m/s.

If the zero-size population density is $n^0 = 9.2 \times 10^{12}$/m^4 at a suspension density of 20 kg/m^3, calculate the rate of increase of the mass of a 0.5 mm crystal.
Given: $\phi_v = 0.6$, $\rho_c = 2700$ kg/m^3.

13.11 (*Benefit of a DDO strategy*)[3] It is planned to operate the crystallizer described in Problem 13.7 [volume = 2 m^3; crystal growth rate = 2.31×10^{-8} m/s; $Q_i = 1$ m^3/h] in the double draw-off mode (DDO) mode with 'clear liquid advance'. (a) Calculate the rate of overflow if 80 mass% of the crystals must be larger than 0.8 mm. (b) Calculate the same rate if the stream contains fines up to 60 μm size which are dissolved and returned into the vessel. The volume shape factor of the crystals is 0.72.

13.12 (*Benefit of a FD crystallizer*)[2] An MSMPR crystallizer of working volume 3.5 m^3 having the provision for fines removal and destruction is used for producing KCl crystals. The volume of the crystallizer is 3.5 m^3. The rate of overflow is 10 m^3/h and that of the underflow is 2 m^3/h. The fines trap removes particles up to a size of 70 μm and the liquid is returned after fines dissolution. A magma density of 150 kg/m^3 is maintained. If the crystal growth rate is 1.45 mm/h and the shape factor is $\phi_v = 0.55$, determine (a) the secondary nucleation rate, (b) the mass fraction of the crystals removed through the fines trap, and (c) the modal size of the product crystals.

13.13 (*Population density function if fine destruction and classified product removal are done*)[3] A DTB crystallizer of volume V with fines destruction and classified product removal is schematically shown in Figure 13.17(a). Following the procedure used in Section 13.5.6, develop the population density function.

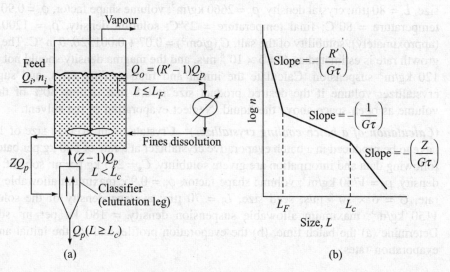

Figure 13.17 A mixed suspension crystallizer with fines destruction and classified product removal: (a) the basis of $R'–Z$ model, and (b) the population density plots.

Hints: The population balance equation becomes

$$-VG\frac{dn}{dL} = ZQ_pn + (R'-1)Q_pn[1 - H(L_F - L)] - (Z-1)Q_pn[1 - H(L - L_F)]$$

Separate equations for the three ranges $[0, L_F]$, $[L_F, L_c]$, and $[L \geq L_c]$ can be written and integrated. The integration constants can be found from the condition of continuity of the distribution at $L = L_F$ and $L = L_c$. The population density functions are

$$L \leq L_F: \qquad n = n^0 \exp\left(-\frac{R'L}{G\tau}\right)$$

$$L_F < L < L_c: \qquad n = n^0 \exp\left[-\frac{(R'-1)L_F}{G\tau}\right]\exp\left(-\frac{L}{G\tau}\right)$$

$$L \geq L_c: \qquad n = n^0 \exp\left[-\frac{(R'-1)L_F}{G\tau}\right]\exp\left[-\frac{(Z-1)L_c}{G\tau}\right]\exp\left(-\frac{L}{G\tau}\right)$$

Figure 13.17(b) shows typical plots of $\ln(n)$ versus the particle size L, for the three ranges. Randolph and Larson (1988) called it an $R'–Z$ crystallizer.

13.14 (*Calculation of a batch crystallizer*)[2] A batch crystallizer receives 2500 kg of a saturated solution of sodium chromate at 80°C. The solution is seeded with 1.2 kg of the crystals ($Na_2CrO_4, 10H_2O$) of 70 µm average size and cooled to 30°C. About 3% of the water present in the solution evaporates out during the cooling process. What are the quantity and average size of the product crystals? If the crystallization process takes 6 h, calculate the average growth rate. *Given:* $\rho_c = 1480$ kg/m³; $\phi_v = 0.45$; $C_s = 125$ g salt (anhydrous) per 1000 g water at 80°C, and 88.7 g per 1000 g water at 30°C.

13.15   *(Calculation of a batch cooling crystallizer)*[2]   Crystals of K_2SO_4 are to be produced at a rate of 400 kg per batch in a cooling crystallizer. The following data are given: seed size, $L_s = 80$ μm; crystal density, $\rho_c = 2660$ kg/m³; volume shape factor, $\phi_v = 0.90$; initial temperature = 80°C; final temperature = 25°C; solution density, $\rho_l = 1200$ kg/m³ (approximately); solubility of the salt, $C_s(g/cm^3) = 0.07 + 0.001320\theta$, θ in °C. The crystal growth rate is estimated as $G = 5 \times 10^{-8}$ m/s, and the magma density should not exceed 120 kg/m³ suspension. Calculate the initial and final cooling rates, and suggest a crystallizer volume if the desired product size is 0.8 mm. Allow 30% of the tank volume as open space above the liquid. Neglect evaporation of the solvent.

13.16   *(Calculation of a batch cooling crystallizer)*[2]   Crystals of an average size of 1.1 mm have to be produced in a batch evaporative crystallizer at a rate of 500 kg per batch. The following data and information are given: solubility, $C_s = 275$ kg per m³ solvent; crystal density, $\rho_c = 1750$ kg/m³; volume shape factor, $\phi_v = 0.95$; maximum allowable growth rate, $G = 6 \times 10^{-8}$ m/s; seed size, $L_s = 70$ μm; average density of the solution = 1150 kg/m³; maximum allowable suspension density = 180 kg per m³ solution. Determine (a) the batch time, (b) the evaporation profile, and (c) the initial and final evaporation rates.

REFERENCES

Abegg, C.E. et al., 'Crystal size distributions in continuous crystallizers when growth rate is dependent', *AIChE J.*, *14*(1968) 112–118.

Bennett, R.C. et al., 'Crystallizer influenced nucleation', *Chem Eng. Progr.*, *69*(July 1973) 86–93.

Bennett, R.C., 'Making big crystals', *Chem. Engg.*, October 1997, 90–93.

Garside, J., and M.B. Shah, 'Crystallization kinetics from MSMPR crystallizers', *Ind. Eng. Chem. PDD*, *19*(1980) 509–514.

Garside, J., 'Industrial crystallization from solutions', *Chem. Engg. Sci.*, *40*, No. 1 (1985), 3–26.

Genck, W.J., 'Crystallization from solutions', in *Handbook of Separation Process Technology*, Schweitzer, P.A. (Ed.), McGraw-Hill, New York, 1997.

Genck, W.J., 'Crystallization's forgotten facts', *Chem. Engg.*, October 1997, 94–100.

Genck, W.J., 'Better growth in batch crystallizers', *Chem. Engg.*, August 2000, 90–95.

McCausland, L.J., et al., 'Use the power of sonocrystallization for improved properties', *Chem. Eng. Progr.*, July 2001, 56–61.

Mersmann, A.B., et al., 'Current State of Crystallizer Design', *Ger. Chem. Engg.*, *2*(1979) 1–13.

Moore, W.P., 'Optimizing batch crystallization', *Chem. Eng. Progr.*, Sept. 1994, 73–79.

Myers, C.G., and R.W. Rousseau, 'Crystallization Operations', in *Handbook of Separation Processes*, R.W. Rousseau (Ed.), 578–643, McGraw-Hill, New York, 1987.

Myerson, A.S., *Handbook of Industrial Crystallization*, 2nd ed., Butterworths, London, 2002.

Mullin, J.W., *Crystallization*, 4th ed., Butterworth-Heinemann, Boston, 2001.

Price, C.J., 'Take some solid steps to improve crystallization', *Chem. Engg.*, Sept. 1997, 34–43.

Randolph, A.D., and M.A. Larson, 'Transient and steady state size distribution in continuous mixed suspension crystallizers', *AIChE J.*, 8(1962) 639–645.

Randolph, A.D., and M.A. Larson, *Theory of Particulate Processes*, 2nd ed., Academic Press, New York, 1988.

Randolph, A.D., and E.T. White, *Chem. Engg. Sci.*, 32(1977) 1067.

Sutradhar, B.C., 'Coping with crystallization problems', *Chem. Engg.*, March 2004, 46–52.

Tavare, N.S., and J. Garside, 'Analysis of batch crystallizers', *I&EC. Proc. Des. Dev. 19*(1980) 653–665.

Wankat, P.C., *Rate Controlled Separations*, Blackie, Glasgow, 1994.

Wibowo, C., et al., 'Design of integrated crystallization systems', *AIChE J.*, *47*(Nov. 2001) 2474–2492.

Wibowo, C. et al., 'Streamlining crystallization process design', *Chem. Eng. Progr.*, Jan. 2004, 30–39.

Wynn, N. 'Melt crystallization', in *Handbook of Separation Process Technology*, Schweitzer, P.A. (Ed.), McGraw-Hill, New York, 1997.

14 | Membrane Separation

Membrane separation has emerged as the most important and practically useful 'modern separation technique' in chemical process industries and many other fields. It has now attained considerable maturity to successfully compete with some of the traditional separation processes. The definition of a membrane has been a matter of debate.[†] A working definition of a membrane can be formulated as: 'a membrane is a thin barrier, placed between two phases or mediums, which allows one or more constituents to selectively pass from one medium to the other in the presence of an appropriate driving force while retaining the rest.' This is why a membrane used for separation of a mixture is called 'semipermeable'. Contrary to the conventional mass transfer operations, the two phases between which transfer of one or more species occurs are not in direct contact in membrane separation. Figure 14.1 is a schematic of a very simple arrangement for membrane separation wherein the membrane is placed on a rigid and highly porous support plate and then securely held between the flanges of a two-compartment cell. The feed enters into one of the compartments and flows over the membrane. One or more of the components in the feed diffuse or pass through the membrane and is/are collected from the other compartment of the cell as the *permeate*. The stream leaving the feed compartment of the cell is called the *retentate* because some of the substances in it have been 'retained'. The membrane may be porous or non-porous. A non-porous membrane is also called a 'dense membrane'.

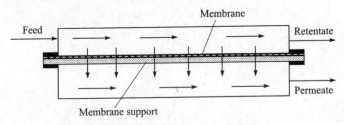

Figure 14.1 Schematic of a membrane separation unit.

[†] The question "What is a membrane?" was thrown open by Dr. H.K. Lonsdale, Editor of the *Journal of Membrane Science*, in an editorial in 1987 [*J. Membr. Sci.*, 34 (1987) 125–126]. The more important responses were reproduced in the editorial of a subsequent issue [*J. Membr. Sci.*, 43 (1989) 1–2].

Like other separation processes, membrane separation also requires a driving force. A membrane having fine pores is used for separating tiny particles in a suspension or large molecules in a solution. Separation occurs basically by a sieving mechanism. The solvent (along with small molecules, if any) passes through the pores of the membrane (Figure 14.2). Such a membrane separation process is called *microfiltration* (MF), *ultrafiltartion* (UF), or *nanofiltration* (NF), depending upon the range of membrane pore size or the size of the species separated. Here the driving force is the difference of pressure between the feed and the permeate sides. If separation of small molecules from a solution is required, a dense or non-porous membrane is generally used. In the case of separation of salt from brackish water, for example, the transport of the solvent (water) occurs under the effect of a pressure difference and potable water with only traces of salts is obtained as the permeate. The process is called *reverse osmosis* or RO [Figure 14.2(c)].

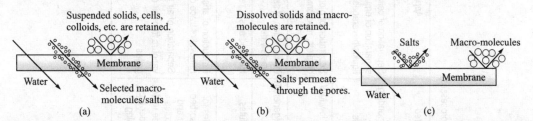

Figure 14.2 Schematic representation of common membrane separation techniques: (a) microfiltration, (b) ultrafiltration, and (c) reverse osmosis.

A similar process for the separation of one or more components from a mixture of liquids by preferential 'sorption' in and diffusion through a *dense* membrane is called *pervaporation* (PV). Here the permeate stream leaves as a vapour under vacuum and is condensed. For example, if rectified spirit is passed through the feed side of a cell fitted with a 'cross-linked polyvinyl acetate' membrane and vacuum is applied on the permeate side, water preferentially 'dissolves' in the membrane, diffuses through it and vaporizes at the permeate side causing dehydration of the feed alcohol [will be discussed later with reference to Figure 14.30(a)]. This happens because water has a higher 'affinity' for this membrane than alcohol and 'selective transport' of water through the membrane occurs. A difference of concentration across the membrane, created by maintaining the permeate side under vacuum, acts as the driving force. Separation of a gas mixture using a suitable dense membrane occurs by a similar mechanism called the *solution diffusion mechanism*. A component having a higher affinity for the membrane material gets dissolved or 'sorbed' at the feed side. Thus oxygen has a higher 'solubility' than nitrogen in an aromatic polyimide. A membrane of this material can separate oxygen from nitrogen in air if a pressure difference between the feed and the permeate sides is maintained. Oxygen is preferentially sorbed and then diffuses through the membrane and gets 'desorbed' at the other side, giving an oxygen-rich product gas. In 'dialysis', which is another important membrane separation process, there exists a difference in concentration of the target species in the solutions on the two sides of a 'semipermeable' membrane. A solute of smaller size diffuses faster and gets separated from the slower moving larger molecules under the influence of a concentration difference. In a variation of this process, called the *electrodialysis*, an electrical potential difference across the membrane causes faster transport and separation of charged species in solution. The more common membrane separation processes, the types of membranes used, the driving force that causes separation in each case, the mechanism of separation, and typical applications are listed in Table 14.1 (Koros, 1995). The ranges of pore-sizes of membranes (Ruthven, 1997) used in some of the above membrane processes are given in Figure 14.3.[†] Several other applications

Table 14.1 Common membrane separation processes

Membrane process	Separation mechanism	Feed	Driving force	Rejected species	Permeated species	Applications
Microfiltration	Sieving	Liquid/gas containing suspended particulates	Pressure difference $\Delta P < 2$ bar	0.1 μm to 20 μm	The suspending medium, liquid/gas	Separation of cells, sterilization of liquid/gas streams, separation of emulsified oil from water, clarification of liquids/beverages in food industries.
Ultrafiltration	Sieving	Liquid	Pressure difference $\Delta P = 2$ to 3.5 bar	Relatively large molecules (1-100 nm)	Solvent, low MW solute	Separation of biomolecules, proteins, emulsions, dispersed droplets, macromolecules, auto-paints from solutions.
Reverse osmosis	Solution-diffusion	Salt solutions, sea water	$\Delta P = 10$ to 100 bar or more	Low MW solutes, hydrated ions	Solvent (generally water)	Desalination of sea water, brackish water, treatment of wastewater.
Dialysis	Sieving, solution-diffusion	Solutions	Concentration difference	Larger molecules (5-50 Å) MW 50 to 10^4 dalton	Microsolutes, solvent	Haemodialysis, recovery of selected solutes
Pervaporation	Solution-diffusion	Liquid mixtures	Activity difference	Molecules that have higher affinities for the membrane are preferentially sorbed on the feed side of the membrane and then diffuse through it. The molecules get desorbed on the permeate side under vacuum (for pervaporation) or under the effect of pressure difference causing enrichment.		Production of absolute alcohol, dehydration of solvents, removal of trace organics from water.
Gas separation	Sorption-diffusion	Gas mixtures	Difference of fugacity, or Δp			Separation of air (O_2/N_2), CO_2 from methane, organic vapours from air or a carrier gas, H_2 from other light gases

of membrane separation will be highlighted in the following sections. Besides conventional uses, membranes have established potential of use in clean energy generation devices (for example, fuel cells), greenhouse gas separation, microelectronics and other cutting-edge technologies.

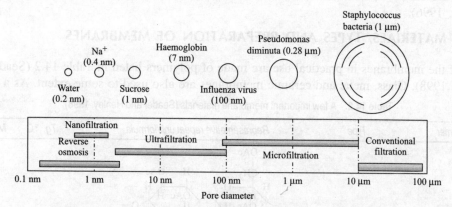

Figure 14.3 Pore size range in microfiltration, ultrafiltration, and reverse osmosis.

Membrane separation technology is attractive for many applications. The major advantages are: (i) it is inherently simple; (ii) modular design of the membrane device, a number of modules may be used in parallel if the feed rate is large; (iii) moderate operating temperature suitable for high-value heat-sensitive substances; (iv) no change of phase occurs (except in pervaporation), and this makes it energy-efficient (Koros, 2004); (v) the same basic principles apply to most membrane processes. Its disadvantages are: (i) membrane fouling and resultant flux decline; (ii) polymeric membranes have limited chemical resistance to organic solvents and to a wide range of pH; (iii) a high degree of separation may not be possible for many mixtures. The state of technological maturity and use maturity of a few membrane separation processes compared to the conventional ones is presented in Figure 14.4. Details of the developments in membrane

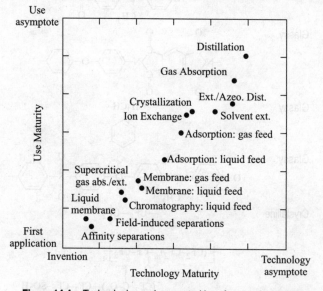

Figure 14.4 Technologies and use maturities of separation techniques.

[†] For a more comprehensive chart of size ranges of particles in a number of other separation processes, see Porter (1997).

technology during the last few decades are available in a number of monographs (Baker, 2004; Ho and Sirkar, 1992; Kesting, 1985; Kesting and Fritzche, 1993; Mulder, 1991; Noble and Stern, 1995; Paul and Yampolskii, 1994; Schafer et al., 2005; Scott and Hughes, 1996; Zeman and Zydney, 1996).

14.1 MATERIALS, TYPES AND PREPARATION OF MEMBRANES

Most of the membranes in practical use are made of polymers listed in Table 14.2 (Seader and Henley, 1998). Glass, metal and ceramic membranes are also used to some extent. As a matter

Table 14.2   A few important membrane materials (Seader and Henley, 1998)

Polymer	Type	Representative repeat unit/formula	T_g, °C	M.P., °C
Cellulose triacetate	Crystalline	[structure]		300
Polyisoprene (natural rubber)	Rubbery	$-\!\!\left[CH_2CH\!=\!C\!-\!CH_2\right]_n\!-$ with CH_3	–70	
Aromatic polyamide	Crystalline	[structure]		275
Polycarbonate	Glassy	[structure]	150	
Polyimide	Glassy	[structure]	310–365	
Polystyrene	Glassy	$-CH_2CH-$ (phenyl)	74–110	
Polysulphone	Glassy	[structure]	190	
Polytetrafluoro-ethylene (Teflon)	Crystalline	$-CF_2\!-\!CF_2$		327
Perfluorosulphonic acid ionomer, *Nafion*		$-\!\left[(CF_2\!-\!CF_2)_m\!-\!CF\!-\!CF_2\right]_n\!-$ O $(CF_2\!-\!\underset{CF_3}{C}\!-\!O_p)\!-\!CF_2\!-\!CF_2\!-\!SO_3H$		

of fact, use of porous ceramic membranes is growing significantly because of certain advantages described in Section 14.1.6. The more important polymers for preparation of membranes (Li and Sirkar, 1992) are cellulose di- or tri-acetate (CA), aromatic polyamides and polyimides, polysulphone (PSF), polyethersulphone, polyvinylpyrrolidone (PVP), polyacrylonitrile (PAN), polycarbonate, polytertrafluoroethylene (PTFE). Cellulose has glucose anhydride as its repeat units with two -OH and one -CH$_2$OH groups in each unit. If all the alcohol groups are acetylated, we get cellulose triacetate. However, the permeation property of the polymer depends upon the 'degree of acetylation' which is the fraction of hydroxyl groups esterified. Acetylation may be done with acetic anhydride or acetic acid in the presence of a catalyst like sulphuric acid.

Cellulose acetate used for UF, RO or gas separation applications is a blend of di- and tri-acetates having an overall degree of substitution (D.S.) of about 2.5. For use in processing of food and beverages, the membrane material should be an 'approved' one. The more important attributes of a good membrane material are: (i) good permeability; (ii) high selectivity; (iii) chemical stability and compatibility, and mechanical strength in the environment and conditions of application; (iv) resistance to fouling and adsorption; (v) amenability to casting of a thin film; (vi) suitability for fabrication of a module. Many novel polymers with excellent separation properties have been prepared in recent years (Stern, 1994). The more important membrane types (Figure 14.5) and the fabrication techniques are described below.

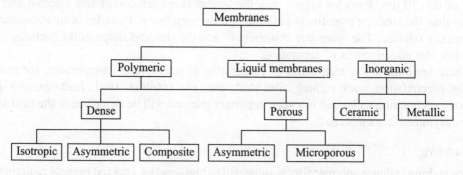

Figure 14.5   Types of membranes.

14.1.1   Dense Membranes

A dense or non-porous membrane is a thin film of a suitable material that allows selective passage of one or more components of a mixture. There are no pores in the physical sense. The permeating component 'dissolves' at the surface of the membrane, diffuses through the intermolecular spaces or 'free volume' within the membrane material and leaves at the opposite surface as the permeate or the product. Dense membranes are used for reverse osmosis, most gas separation processes, and for pervaporation.

It should be noted that a dense membrane may have an 'asymmetric' or even a 'composite' structure. An asymmetric dense membrane has a thin dense or non-porous permselective layer on a porous substructure. The ultrathin dense layer allows selective permeation (this is why it is called 'permselective'); the porous substructure offers the necessary mechanical strength to the membrane. Such a membrane predictably allows a high permeate flux since the flux is inversely proportional to the membrane thickness.

Symmetric dense polymeric films may be prepared by 'solution casting' or 'melt processing'. If a suitable solvent for the polymer is available, a casting solution is first prepared, usually at 15–20% concentration. The solvent should be non-toxic and volatile. The casting solution is spread by a casting blade on a suitable surface (a glass or a PTFE-laminated surface, for example). The thickness of the layer depends upon the clearance between the casting surface and the casting blade. Evaporation of the solvent is done under controlled conditions. The membrane is carefully pulled off after the solvent is expelled.

Polymers like polyethylene, polypropylene, nylon, etc. do not usually dissolve. The films of such materials are made by extrusion of the molten polymer through a slit. The thickness is regulated by stretching the film while soft, and then passing it through a series of closely spaced rolls.

14.1.2 Symmetric or Isotropic Microporous Membranes

Symmetric microporous membranes are functionally similar to conventional filters but differ in pore size and thickness. While filters separate relatively coarse particles in suspension and have pore sizes suitable for that purpose, the porous membranes separate very fine particles and colloidal or even dissolved solutes. Membranes are much thinner than filters. Microporous symmetric membranes have interconnected pores and a high porosity, and are used for microfiltration.[†] The pores are rarely of the same diameter. Isotropic membranes have pore sizes distributed in the range of 0.1–10 μm. Particles bigger than the largest pores are completely rejected and those smaller than the smallest pore freely pass through the membrane. Particles of intermediate sizes are partially rejected. The 'pore-size distribution' and the size and shape of the particles mainly determine the effectiveness of separation.

There are quite a few techniques of preparation of microporous membranes, for example, solution-precipitation, track etching, film stretching, etc. (Mulder, 1991; Ruthven, 1997). The solution-precipitation technique is a very important one and will be described in the next section under 'asymmetric membranes'.

Track etching

In track etching, a dense polymer film is subjected to high-energy, charged particle radiation from a suitable source. On hitting the film, the charged particles break the polymer chains creating 'tracks'. The film is then passed through an etching solution (an acidic or an alkaline solution) when the polymer dissolves along the tracks forming pores (Figure 14.6). In a track-etched

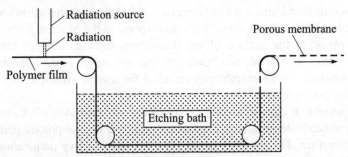

Figure 14.6 Preparation of a porous membrane by track etching.

[†] The term 'microfiltration' originates from the initial use of finely porous membranes for filtering microbes and bacteria from water and air.

membrane, the pores are nearly straight and have a narrow size distribution. This is the greatest advantage of such membranes. However, the etching process is quite expensive. The open area of the membrane is low (about 5–10%) and the solvent flux also remains low. Track-etched polycarbonate membranes are more common.

Film stretching

Film stretching is another important technique of generation of small openings in a dense film of a crystalline or a semi-crystalline polymer like PTFE or polypropylene (PP). The film is first made by extrusion and stretching at a temperature near the melting point of the polymer. It is then stretched again, but this time at right angle to the original stretching direction, when a very large number of slit-like voids or pores (20 to 250 nm) are formed. The porosity of this kind of membrane is very high (sometimes as high as 90%). Hoechst-Celanese makes microporous poly-propylene membranes (called *Celgard*) by this technique and W. L. Gore makes PTFE membranes called *Gore-Tex* (Figure 14.7). Microporous 'hollow-fiber membranes' are also made by a similar technique.

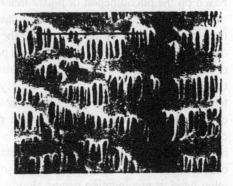

Figure 14.7 SEM picture of a stretched film.

14.1.3 Asymmetric Membranes

A membrane should be as thin as possible if a high permeation flux is to be achieved. Membrane separation may not be economical if the flux is low. But for all practical purposes, a membrane must have reasonable mechanical strength and should be 'defect-free' (large-size pores and fissures in a membrane are called *membrane defects*; defects may appear during fabrication of a membrane). If the membrane is too thin and mechanically weak, it becomes difficult to handle it and to fabricate a membrane separation module. It is practically impossible to cast a membrane less than about 20 μm in thickness. But an isotropic porous membrane of this thickness (for ultrafiltration, for example) offers too much resistance to solvent flow, and the flux does not become acceptable.

This seemingly formidable problem was solved by fabrication of the 'asymmetric membrane', which is probably the greatest breakthrough in membrane research and development. An asymmetric membrane has a thin (0.1 to 1 μm) permselective[†] layer supported on a highly porous substructure (Figure 14.8). The thin layer may be non-porous (for use as an RO membrane) or may have very fine pores (for use as a UF membrane). But the entire membrane is an integral piece of the same material. The thick,

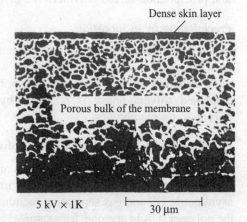

Figure 14.8 Scanning electron micrograph of an asymmetric flat membrane.

[†] This is another name for a semi-permeable membrane since it allows selective permeation of a solute.

highly porous substructure offers necessary mechanical strength but does not offer any appreciable resistance to permeation since it has much larger pores and a high porosity.

Preparation of an asymmetric membrane

The principle of preparation of an asymmetric polymeric membrane is apparently simple. It is based on the phenomenon of *phase inversion*—i.e. precipitation of the polymer from a layer of the casting solution by suitably manipulating the environment. Precipitation involves a change of the 'solution phase' of the polymer to the 'solid phase'. Hence the name. Phase inversion can be done by a number of techniques based on partial removal of the solvent or reduction of the solubility of the polymer in the solvent thus separating out the polymer as a solid 'polymer-rich phase' from the solution. The other phase is a polymer-lean or solvent-rich liquid phase. The common techniques of precipitation of a polymer are: (i) cooling of the casting solution, (ii) evaporation of the solvent, and (iii) immersion in a non-solvent like water. The most important factor that controls the membrane 'morphology' is the kinetics or rate of phase inversion. If the phase inversion process is fast, both the precipitated solid phase and the solvent form very small particles or droplets so that after removal of the solvent, a film with very small pores is obtained. On the other hand, if precipitation occurs slowly, the liquid droplets become large by agglomeration and the resulting membrane contains larger pores (Ruthven, 1997) suitable for microfiltration applications.

Precipitation by cooling

In this technique the polymer is dissolved in a solvent at an elevated temperature and then spread in a layer on the casting plate or surface. As the layer cools, the solubility of the polymer decreases and phase inversion occurs, forming a polymer matrix with interspersed regions of the solvent having a low concentration of the polymer. If the solvent is washed out, a porous membrane is left behind. This technique is useful to produce microfiltration membranes having rather large pores. Small pore membranes may, however, be made by rapid cooling of the layer and precipitation of the polymer.

Precipitation by evaporation

In this technique the polymer is dissolved in a mixed solvent—one solvent more volatile (e.g. acetone) and the other less volatile (e.g. water or alcohol). After casting on a plate, much of the more volatile solvent is allowed to evaporate, thereby precipitating the polymer. The remaining dispersed solvent phase is removed by washing as usual. This technique also produces microporous membranes.

Precipitation by immersion in a non-solvent

This technique was developed by Loeb and Sourirajan (1963) to prepare asymmetric cellulose acetate RO membranes. This extremely important and useful technique is now used for making asymmetric UF and gas separation membranes as well. For laboratory preparation, a solution of the polymer (CA in acetone, for example) is cast on a glass plate and then immersed in cold water. The polymer is not soluble in water—i.e. water is a 'non-solvent'. Some of the solvent (acetone) gets extracted in the water and the polymer precipitates at the exposed top surface of the film forming a dense ultrathin 'skin'. This skin slows down the rate of loss of solvent from inside the film. As a result, precipitation in the bulk of the film becomes slow and the pores therein become large, and an asymmetric membrane consisting of an ultrathin permselective layer on a highly porous substructure is formed.

For commercial membrane production, the film is cast on a non-woven fabric moving on a rotating drum. The thickness of the film is regulated by a 'doctor blade'. The fabric with the film on it moves through a gelation tank containing a non-solvent, where phase inversion and formation of the ultrathin top layer occur. Next, it passes through a rinse tank where all the solvent is washed out and the membrane is wound on a take-up roll. The arrangement is shown in Figure 14.9. Some defects in the form of 'pinholes' may occur in the membrane because of dust particles, tiny gas bubbles or imperfection in the support fabric. It is almost impossible to eliminate membrane defects completely. An asymmetric membrane is 'annealed' by immersion in water or by heating for a short time in order to enhance its performance.

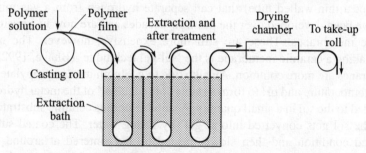

Figure 14.9   Schematic of a set-up for preparation of microporous membranes by the polymer precipitation technique.

The other important techniques of membrane preparation are interfacial polymerization and casting on a porous support or backing to form a composite membrane.

14.1.4   Composite Membranes

Composite membranes are functionally similar to asymmetric membranes. A composite membrane consists of a porous or dense, thin permselective upper layer cast on a thick mechanically strong 'backing' or support. The thin layer and the backing are often made from different materials. Composite polymeric membranes may be made by applying a polymer coating on a porous polysulphone or PTFE film or any other suitable backing. The technique of interfacial polymerization (Mulder, 1991) has often been used to prepare such membranes. Ceramic membranes (ZrO_2 or γ-Al_2O_3 permselective layer on a microporous alumina backing) have been largely reported and used. Like the substructure of an asymmetric membrane, the support layer of a composite membrane offers the requisite mechanical strength but very little resistance to permeation.

14.1.5   Electrically Charged Membranes

An electrically charged membrane material has ionic groups that give the membrane fixed charged sites. For example, the perfluoro ion exchange membrane (*Nafion* of Du Pont) has SO_3^- groups on a PTFE backbone (Table 14.2). The presence of this group gives negatively charged fixed sites. The cation (H^+ in the acid form, or a metal ion like Na^+ in the salt form of the ion-exchange polymer) can move freely within the membrane matrix and hence the membrane is called a *cation-exchange membrane*. Since the fixed charged sites repel negative charges, the membrane does not allow anions, called co-ions, to pass through it (rejection of ions because of electrical repulsion is called *Donnan exclusion*). But cations, called *counter-ions*, can permeate through the membrane without electrical repulsion. If the fixed charges are positive, the membrane is called an *anion-exchange membrane*. A very common type of cation-exchange membrane is made by sulphonation of a copolymer of styrene and divinylbenzene (Noble and Stern, 1995). A common application of a cation-exchange membrane is a cell-separator in electrolysis of brine.

14.1.6 Inorganic and Ceramic Membranes

Inorganic membranes have broadly two classes—metallic membranes and ceramic membranes (Figure 14.5). An important example of the former type is the palladium membrane (in the form of a thin film or a thin-walled tube) that can separate hydrogen from a gas mixture. Ceramic membranes have been developed over the past few decades and are now in a position to compete with polymeric membranes. These are still more expensive, however. The most important technique of making a ceramic membrane is the 'sol-gel technique' (Bhave, 1992). Alumina and zirconia membranes are more common. An alkoxide (e.g. aluminum *iso*-propylate) is hydrolyzed at a controlled temperature and pH to form a stable colloidal 'sol' of the metal hydroxide. A binder like PVA is added to the sol in a small quantity. A suitable porous ceramic substrate is coated with the sol when the sol gets converted into a 'gel' by losing water. The coated substrate is dried under controlled condition and then slowly heated to and sintered at around 500°C. A thin permselective layer of alumina or zirconia forms on the substrate. Ceramic membranes on tubular substrates are commercially more useful because of the convenience of fabrication of a module.

14.1.7 Hollow-fibre Membranes

As the name implies, a 'hollow-fibre' means a very narrow tubular membrane. It has an internal diameter ranging from 25 μm to about 2 mm and a wall thickness between 15 and 50 μm or more. Since 1960s, a lot of emphasis has been put on the development of hollow-fibres with an objective of using it for RO applications.

A hollow-fibre may be: (i) asymmetric having a dense permselective layer on either the inner or the outer side of a highly porous wall—for use in RO, (ii) asymmetric having a permselective skin with fine pores—for use in ultrafiltration, (iii) symmetric and microporous—for use in microfiltration, or (iv) it may have a dense wall—for use in pervaporation or gas separation. The common technique of spinning a hollow-fibre uses a filtered and de-gassed polymer solution (20–40%) which is forced through a coaxial jet spinneret (Figure 14.10). A pressurized 'bore fluid' (a non-solvent liquid or a gas) issues through an axial capillary. The polymer solution emerges in the form of a narrow hollow cylinder which next passes through a coagulation bath. It is stabilized by the bore fluid on the inside and also by an outer liquid medium kept in the coagulation bath. The polymer is precipitated in contact with the non-solvent in the bath, and a permselective outer skin on a highly porous wall is formed. The fibre then passes through a set of rolls and finally is wound on a take-up roll. The spinning rate (m/s), the polymer concentration and the temperature should be properly adjusted and regulated to prepare a fibre of desired morphology (Ruthven, 1997). Since the diameter of a hollow-fibre is small, the Reynolds number

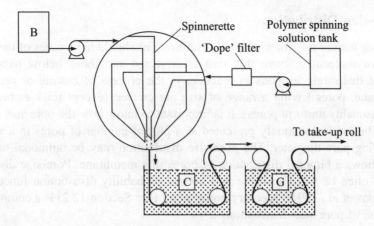

Figure 14.10 Schematic of a set-up for wet-spinning of hollow fibres (B: bore injection medium, liquid or gas; C: coagulation bath; G: quench bath).

for flow through it remains pretty small. The mass transfer coefficient also remains small as a result. Figure 14.11 gives the SEM picture of the cross-section of an asymmetric hollow-fibre membrane.

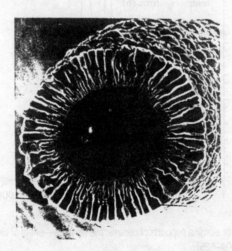

Figure 14.11 SEM picture of the cross-section of an asymmetric hollow fibre (the highly magnified pores on the wall are also shown).

14.2 MEMBRANE CHARACTERIZATION

The selection of a membrane for a particular separation application depends upon the membrane characteristics as well as the membrane material that can stand the prevailing environment (pH, temperature, solvent, etc.). Besides the membrane material and its morphology (surface structure, porosity, pore structure and pore-size distribution), the membrane thickness (or the thickness of the dense skin in case of an asymmetric or a composite membrane) is the most important characteristic for the selection of a membrane. Quite a few other characteristics are important for a porous membrane.

14.2.1 Pore-size Distribution

Ideally, a sieving membrane (for micro- or ultrafiltration) should have pores of the same size so that particles or molecules above that size are rejected and those below pass through the membrane. But this rarely happens in practice. In the process of casting or preparation of a porous membrane, pores having a range of size are created (except track-etched membranes which have reasonably uniform pores). It is important to know how the pore size is distributed. Pore-size distribution is commonly presented as a plot of number of pores in a sample versus the corresponding pore diameter. The pore-size distribution may be unimodal or multimodal. Figure 14.12 shows a bimodal distribution of pores in a membrane. Pore-size distribution of a membrane can often be fitted with the 'log-normal probability distribution function' (see, for example, Filippov et al., 1994). Mercury porosimetry (see Section 12.2) is a common technique of determination of pore-size distribution.

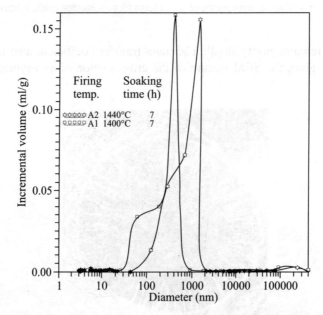

Figure 14.12 Pore-size distribution of alumina supports of ceramic membranes—effect of sintering temperature [Das and Dutta, *Sep, Sci Technol*, 34, No 4 (1999) 609–625].

Thickness of the permselective layer of a membrane and the pore structure can be determined by scanning electronic microscopy (SEM) of the cross-section and of the surface of a small piece of membrane. It is possible to have a clear, highly magnified photograph of the surface and pore structure by SEM (Figure 14.8).

14.2.2 Bubble Point Method

The bubble point method is a simple technique of characterizing the size of the largest pore in a membrane. The basic principle (Mulder, 1991) is to measure the minimum pressure necessary for forcing a gas through a membrane with liquid-filled pores. A suitable test cell is used for the purpose. The pore diameter is calculated from the Laplace equation.

$$\Delta P = 2\gamma_s/d \tag{14.1}$$

Since the liquid in the largest pore is displaced first, the pore size can be determined from the minimum pressure difference required for displacing the liquid and to form a bubble (this is why the name 'bubble point method'). The technique is also useful for detection of 'imperfections' in a membrane.

14.2.3 Water Permeability

Water permeability of a porous membrane can be determined by measuring pure water flux through the membrane at a given pressure gradient in a test cell. The resistance to solvent flow offered by the membrane can be determined by this experiment.

14.2.4 Perporometry

Not all the pores of a filtration membrane allow permeation of the solvent. Pores which have a dead end are inactive. 'Perporometry' is a useful and convenient technique for the determination of the size distribution of the 'active pores' in a membrane in the size range of 1.5 nm to 100 nm. It is based on the controlled blockage of the pores by capillary condensation and simultaneous measurement of gas diffusional flux through the remaining open pores.

Let us consider a porous solid in contact with a vapour at a pressure p. As the relative vapour pressure (p/P_v; $p < P_v$) is gradually increased, first a monomolecular layer is formed on the inner surface of the pores. With increasing relative vapour pressure, a multimolecular adsorbed layer forms followed by capillary condensation of the vapour within some of the pores causing pore blockage. Capillary condensation follows the Kelvin equation

$$\ln \frac{p}{P_v} = - \frac{\zeta \, \gamma_s \, V_m \cos\theta}{r_k \, RT} \tag{14.2}$$

where

ζ = a process parameter
γ_s = liquid–solid interfacial tension, in J/m^2
V_m = molar volume of the condensable vapour, in m^3/mol
θ = contact angle
r_k = kelvin radius, in m, which is the curvature of the gas–liquid interface.

The larger pores get filled only when the relative vapour pressure is high, and when $p/P_v = 1$, all the pores are filled.

Perporometry experiments are done in a two-compartment cell separated by the membrane. One compartment is filled with the vapour and the other with an inert gas at the same pressure. Only diffusion of the vapour occurs through the pores. With increasing pressure of the vapour, more and more pores get filled and the open area for diffusion of the vapour decreases. The data on decreasing diffusional flux with increasing pressure in the cell is used for the determination of size distribution of active pores (Cao et al., 1993).

Another practically useful characteristic of a UF membrane is the 'molecular weight cut-off' (MWCO). This will be described in Section 14.4.3.

14.3   MEMBRANE MODULES

A 'membrane module' is a compact unit housing the membrane as a barrier between the feed and permeate flow regions, and fitted with the inlet and outlet nozzles on both feed and permeate sides. Compared with conventional separation devices, a membrane module has a small size but a large packing density (the membrane area per unit volume of a module is called *packing density*). A number of modules can be used in parallel if the feed rate is large. It is never built as a big unit because of practical limitations. Four types of modules are in common use: (i) plate-and-frame, (ii) spiral-wound, (iii) hollow-fibre, and (iv) tubular.

14.3.1   Plate-and-frame Module

The plate-and-frame module is the earliest membrane module and somewhat resembles a plate-and-frame filtration unit. It consists of a number of 'plates', each having a frame around its perimeter. The plates are placed one after another maintaining a spacing and using sealing gaskets between two adjacent frames. A plate has two parallel perforated membrane supports with a gap in between. A flat membrane is fitted on each perforated support sheet. Every plate has an opening near the perimeter. Such openings lead to the permeate channel. Thus the module consists of a number of alternate channels between the support plates. The feed flows over each membrane, and the permeate passes through the membranes and leaves through the permeate channel. There are alternate feed and permeate regions separated by polymeric 'spacers'. Cross-flow (Figure 14.13) of the feed over the membranes reduces 'fouling'. An adequate number of plates or compartments are stacked together with seals and bolts. The packing density of such a module is about 100–400 m^2/m^3.

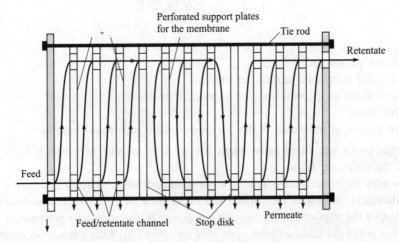

Figure 14.13   Schematic of a plate-and-frame membrane module.

14.3.2 Spiral-wound Module

The spiral-wound module resembles a spiral heat exchanger in construction. It is a compact device that uses flat membranes. The spiral element is a sandwich consisting of a porous backing sheet and a permeate side spacer placed between the two pieces of the membrane. Three edges of the element are sealed with epoxy leaving one edge open. This open edge is joined longitudinally to a central tube having holes. The membrane leaf together with a feed-side spacer is wound spirally around the central tube. It is rather difficult to prepare long membrane sheets. For this reason, a number of such leaves are wound simultaneously. A polypropylene or polyethylene net, 0.2 to 2 mm thick, may be used as the feed spacer, whereas a polyester cloth, 0.2 to 1 mm thick, may be used as the permeate spacer. The feed enters at one end of the spiral, moves longitudinally and leaves at the other end. The permeate flows spirally through the permeate passage, enters the central pipe through the holes on it and leaves through an end of the pipe (Figure 14.14). A spiral-wound module has a packing density of about 300 ft²/ft³. The diameter may be up to 12 inch, usual length 1 m, and membrane surface area up to 60 m². Modules up to 8 inch (0.2 m) dia are common. These are used for UF, NF and RO applications. The life of the membrane is 2–3 years in a well-maintained plant.

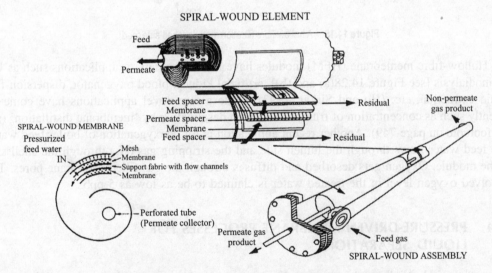

Figure 14.14 Schematic of a spirally wound membrane module.

14.3.3 Hollow-fibre Module

A hollow-fibre module has a shell-and-tube type construction. A bundle of a large number of fibres is inserted into a pipe of suitable diameter and provided with end flanges. The pipe acts as the 'shell' that should be fitted with inlet and outlet nozzles. The bundle of fibres is potted at the ends with epoxy (Figure 14.15). The feed may be supplied to either the shell or the tube side. A large number of fibres can be accommodated in a given volume offering a large area density. For example, a 0.04 m³ hollow-fibre module packed with 90 μm diameter fibres can offer 575 m² of effective area, whereas a spiral-wound flat-sheet module of the same volume offers only about

30 m^2 of area. Since the fibre diameter is small, it can withstand a substantially high internal or external pressure without any support. The shell-side feed arrangement is used for high pressure applications (up to 1000 psig); tube-side feed modules are used up to 150 psig. While it has a high packing density of the order of 10,000 ft^2/ft^3, the main disadvantage of a hollow-fibre module is its sensitivity to 'fouling' since the fibres form a bundle and there is little free space in between the fibres. The problem may be substantially overcome by a pretreatment of the feed to make it free from suspended particles. Also, the shell-side liquid is never properly distributed. For UF and MF applications, fibres of 1–2 mm diameter are used. An 8-inch dia module may contain about 2500 fibres of 2 mm diameter. About 20% of the module volume is filled with fibres (Baker, 2004).

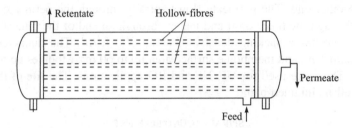

Figure 14.15   A hollow-fibre filtration module (shell-side feed).

Hollow-fibre memebrane (HFM) modules have found a variety of applications such as UF, haemodialysis [see Figure 14.28(a) and (b)], artificial kidney, blood oxygenator, dispersion-free liquid extraction, etc. (Ho and Sirkar, 1992). Quite a few novel applications have come up recently such as concentration of fruit juice or even desalination by 'membrane distillation' (see the footnote on page 749). Another recent application is for deoxygenation of boiler feed water. The feed water flows through the lumen side and the stripping gas (N$_2$) through the shell side of the module. Oxygen gets desorbed and diffuses through the gas-filled membrane pores. The dissolved oxygen level in the treated water is claimed to be as low as 5 ppb.

14.4   PRESSURE-DRIVEN MEMBRANE PROCESSES FOR LIQUID SEPARATION

Many of the industrial membrane separation processes are pressure-driven, i.e. a difference in pressure between the feed and the permeate sides acts as the driving force for permeation. The more important pressure-driven processes are microfiltration, ultrafiltration and reverse osmosis (also called 'hyperfiltration').

14.4.1   Microfiltration

Microfiltration refers to separation of fine particles and colloids from a liquid or of particulates from a gas using a porous membrane having pore sizes in the range 100 to 10^4 nm (0.1 to 10 μm). 'Microfiltration' (MF) is an old membrane separation process; MF membranes were first prepared in the 1920s (Noble and Stern, 1995). One of its traditional uses has been for separation of microorganisms, for example, separation of yeast from a fermentation broth. The first generation microfiltration membranes were made from nitrocellulose. Separation in microfiltration occurs by a simple sieving mechanism at a rather low pressure differential, normally within 2 bar. Broadly, two types of flow and filtration arrangements may be identified—'cross-flow filtration' and 'dead-end filtration' (Figure 14.16). In the former arrangement the feed flows parallel to the membrane surface. Most of the particles or solute retained are swept away with the flowing feed-side liquid. A part of the liquid is recirculated if the desired concentration of the retentate is not attained in a single pass. In the dead-end filtration arrangement, the feed flow is normal to the membrane surface. The retained particles or the solute remain on the membrane forming a cake or a gel layer. Particle accumulation on the membrane increases the filtration resistance. The applied pressure may be gradually increased to overcome the resistance and to maintain the flow. The cross-flow arrangement involves less accumulation of solid particles on the membrane and is preferred. The solvent and all dissolved molecules pass through a microfiltration membrane since it has relatively large pores. Some basic information about microfiltration and the membrane materials is given in Table 14.3. Of the total membrane market, the share of microfiltration membranes is next only to that of haemodialysis membranes.

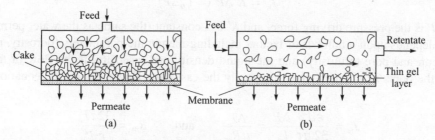

Figure 14.16 (a) 'Dead-end' filtration, and (b) 'cross-flow' filtration.

Table 14.3 Some basic information on microfiltration

Membrane type	Porous, mostly symmetric; asymmetric membranes are used in some cases.
Thickness and pore size	10–150 μm; pore size: 0.1–10 μm; the membrane porosity may be as high as 70% in some cases.
Pressure differential	Less than 2 bar
Mechanism of separation	Sieving or size exclusion
Membrane materials	Hydrophilic and partially hydrophilic polymers — cellulose acetate, polycarbonate, polysulphone (and polyether sulphone), polyimide (and polyetherimide), polyamide; hydrophobic polymers[†]— polypropylene, PTFE, poly-vinylidene fluoride; inorganic membranes — alumina, zirconia and titania membrane, glass membrane.

Applications

(i) Making small-scale laboratory separations for microbiological analysis of soft drinks, wines, pharmaceutical products; (ii) making sterile products like intravenous (IV) fluids, tissue culture media, antibiotics, vaccines, serum, plasma, etc.; (iii) sterilization and clarification in food and

---

[†] A hydrophobic membrane such as polypropylene or PTFE does not wet in water under normal conditions. These are first wetted in alcohol and then put into water when alcohol gradually diffuses out and the pores get filled with water. The membrane now allows water to pass through it.

beverages (biological stabilization of beer, wine and soft drinks), clarification of cheese whey, clarification of dextrose solutions; (iv) harvesting of cells from a fermentation broth; (v) detection and analysis of particulate contaminants in air; (vi) sterilization of gases, including air, for use in fermentation processes in pharmaceutical industries and for maintaining a sterile environment in pharmaceutical production and packaging (a huge fraction of microfilter membranes is used for disposable services like sterile filtration in the pharmaceutical industries); (vii) as a step in the preparation of ultrapure water for electronic fabrication industries; (viii) wastewater treatment and separation of emulsified oil droplets from wastewater.

Theoretical principles

In microfiltration, the objective is to concentrate a suspension by forcing the liquid through the pores of the membrane. Further processing of the concentrated product or retentate may follow if necessary. Calculation of the solvent flux in the membrane module under the prevailing conditions is essential for sizing of a microfiltration device. The flux may be expressed by the Darcy's law

$$J_w = K'\Delta P \ (= L_p \Delta P) \tag{14.3}$$

where ΔP is the pressure driving force, and K' is a constant (the same as the water permeability, L_p) that depends upon a number of factors including membrane parameters (porosity, pore-size distribution and pore tortuosity) and the liquid density and viscosity. If the flow of the liquid through the pores is laminar (which is usually the case), the Hagen–Poiseuille equation can be used.

$$J_w = \frac{\varepsilon d^2}{32\,\mu\tau} \frac{\Delta P}{l_m} = \frac{\Delta P}{\mu R_m} \quad \text{and} \quad R_m = \frac{32\,\tau\,l_m}{\varepsilon d^2} \tag{14.4}$$

where

ε = membrane porosity (which is taken as the fractional open area of the membrane surface)
d = pore diameter
τ = tortuosity of the pores (it is explained in Section 2.9)
l_m = membrane thickness
μ = liquid viscosity
ΔP = applied pressure driving force
$R_m{}^{\dagger}$ = flow resistance of the membrane of unit area.

Sometimes the membrane structure or morphology resembles more like an *assembly of particles with void spaces* which is similar to a very thin 'packed bed'. The pressure drop–flow relation (Noble and Stern, 1995) for such a membrane is given by the well-known Kozeny–Karman equation.

$$J_w = \frac{d_s^2\,\varepsilon^3}{180\,\mu(1-\varepsilon)^2} \frac{\Delta P}{l_m} \qquad (d_s \text{ is the 'equivalent particle diameter'}) \tag{14.5}$$

The initial solvent flux through a porous membrane can be calculated using one of the above equations. However, as the filtration proceeds, formation of a cake or a gel layer on the membrane surface may take place. Such a layer offers substantial resistance to flow. Since the flow

---

† The product μR_m has sometimes been used to represent the resistance to flow through the membrane [see, for example, Eykamp, 1995].

passages through a cake or a gel layer are very narrow, such a layer has a sieving capability and is called a *dynamic membrane*.

EXAMPLE 14.1 (*Flow of water through a porous membrane*)   A 75 μm thick polysulphone microporous membrane has an average porosity of $\varepsilon = 0.35$. Pure water flux through the membrane is 25 m³/m²h at a pressure drop of 1.2 bar at 25°C. The average pore size is estimated to be 1 μm. Calculate the tortuosity factor of the pores, the resistance to flow offered by the membrane and its water permeability. The viscosity of water at 25°C is 0.9 cP.

Solution

Use Eq. (14.4) to calculate the pure water flux through the membrane. The following quantities are given: $d = 1$ μm $= 10^{-6}$ m; $\Delta P = 1.2$ bar $= 1.2 \times 10^5$ Pa; $\mu = 0.9$ cP $= 9 \times 10^{-4}$ kg/m·s; $l_m = 75$ μm $= 75 \times 10^{-6}$ m; the fractional open area is taken to be the same as the average porosity, i.e. $\varepsilon = 0.35$; and $J_w = 25/3600$ m³/m²·s.

$$J_w = \frac{\varepsilon d^2}{32\mu\tau} \frac{\Delta P}{l_m} = \frac{(0.35)(10^{-6})^2}{(32) \times (9 \times 10^{-4})\tau} \frac{1.2 \times 10^5}{75 \times 10^{-6}} = \frac{25}{3600} \text{ m}^3/\text{m}^2 \cdot \text{s}$$

$\Rightarrow$ tortuosity, $\tau = \boxed{2.8}$

The resistance to flow R_m is also given by Eq. (14.4), i.e.

$$J_w = \frac{\Delta P}{\mu R_m} \quad \Rightarrow \quad R_m = \frac{\Delta P}{\mu J_w} = \frac{1.2 \times 10^5}{(9 \times 10^{-4})(25/3600)} = \boxed{1.92 \times 10^{10} \text{ m}^{-1}}$$

Water permeability L_p [see Eq. (14.3)] is given by

$$J_w = L_p \Delta P \quad \Rightarrow \quad L_p = \frac{J_w}{\Delta P} = \frac{25}{3600} \frac{\text{m}^3}{\text{m}^2 \cdot \text{s}} \bigg/ (1.2 \times 10^5 \text{ Pa}) = \boxed{5.79 \times 10^{-8} \frac{\text{m}^3}{\text{m}^2 \cdot \text{s} \cdot \text{Pa}}}$$

Laminar flow through the pores has been assumed in the above calculation. This may be easily established by calculating the Reynolds number. Take $u = 25/3600$ m/s; $\rho = 998$ kg/m³.

$$\text{Re} = \frac{du\rho}{\mu} = \frac{(1 \times 10^{-6})(25/3600)(998)}{9 \times 10^{-4}} = \boxed{7.7 \times 10^{-3}}. \text{ So the flow is definitely laminar.}$$

14.4.2   Ultrafiltration

Ultrafiltration (UF) is the process of separation or concentration of a large molecular weight solute (the approximate range of mol. wt. is from 1000 to 80,000 dalton[†]) or a colloidal suspension by using a membrane having pores in the size range 1 to 100 nm. It lies between MF and RO in the context of membrane pore size or particle size. Like microfiltration, the driving force for separation by UF is the pressure difference between the feed and the permeate sides. The basic characteristics of ultrafiltration, the membranes used and the applications are given in Table 14.4. Ultrafiltration can be used to separate relatively large molecules from smaller ones that can pass through the pores. Separation occurs by a sieving mechanism. But the molecules often get adsorbed or deposited on the membrane surface, particularly at the pore mouth, thereby reducing

---

[†] In membrane filtration literature, the molecular weight is customarily expressed as 'dalton'.

the effective pore size significantly. Thus the molecules retained by a UF membrane may be smaller than the pore size. One common but not very reliable criterion of separation capability or selectivity of a UF membrane is called the *molecular weight cutoff*.

Table 14.4 Some basic information on ultrafiltration

Membrane type	Asymmetric or composite
Thickness and pore dia	Up to 150 µm; pore dia—1–100 nm
Pressure difference	1–10 bar
Flux	1–10 m^3/m^2 day bar
Separation mechanism	Sieving (or size exclusion)
Membrane material	Polymeric—polysulphone, polyacrylonitrile, cellulose acetate, aromatic polyamides, polycarbonate. Ceramic—alumina, zirconia and titania
Module type	Spiral-wound and tubular modules. Hollow-fibre modules are not preferred because these are prone to fouling.

Applications

Ultrafiltration has many uses. A few important uses are described here.

(a) *Paint recovery:* In the 'electrocoat' paint industry, water-based paints are applied on items like automobile parts and bodies, appliances, furniture, etc. The excess paint (about 50%) gets removed or washed in the step of rinsing the surface by water before curing. The paint leaving with the rinse water cannot be disposed of since (i) it creates pollution, and (ii) the paint recovered by ultrafiltration can be reused and the permeate water can be recycled. Thus dual objectives are served by recovery of the paint from wash water.

(b) *Latex recovery:* Polymerization reactors are periodically cleaned. The 'wash-down' of a reactor contains partially polymerized material (latex) that cannot be thrown away in the sewer or the wastewater treatment unit since it is not readily biodegradable and causes pollution as well as blocking of the lines. Ultrafiltration is a suitable technique for separation of the latex from the wash-down liquid. The permeate water can be reused.

(c) *PVA recovery:* PVA (polyvinyl acetate) is a substitute 'sizing agent' used in the processing of synthetic fibres. It replaces the conventional sizing agents like starch or natural gum. But PVA is more expensive and does not undergo ready biodegradation. The excess PVA is removed in the de-sizing bath and then recovered by ultrafiltration. Since a PVA solution is highly viscous, the solution is heated to 80–90°C to increase the filtration rate. The retentate is reused, and the permeate water is recycled.

(d) *Separation of oil–water emulsion:* Oil–water emulsions are used or generated in a number of industrial operations like metalworking and metal finishing. Oil-in-water emulsions (about 2% oil) are routinely used for cooling and lubrication of tools and dies during cutting, forming and grinding of metals. Cleaning of metals before metal finishing (for example, electroplating) is done using surfactants. The waste water from these operations contains oil droplets up to submicron size. The oil can be concentrated in an ultrafiltration unit to about 10% and reused. Waste oil in refinery effluents may be concentrated to even 50% and can be disposed of by incineration.

(e) *Food industry:* Separation by UF is pretty common in: (i) concentration of milk and recovery of protein from cheese whey (CA, polysulphone or polyamide membranes are suitable);

(ii) separation of proteins and potato starch; (iii) bioseparation—recovery of proteins, enzymes and high-value products; (iv) clarification of fruit juice and alcoholic beverages where small solute molecules must not be retained (e.g. ultrafiltration of apple juice to remove colloidal matters—this has replaced the traditionally used diatomaceous earth). Polyvinylidene membrane is in common use for fruit juice clarification by batch ultrafiltration; about 95% of the juice is recovered leaving a retentate with as high as 40% solids[†].

(f) *Paper industry:*   Recovery of lignosulphates from spent sulphite liquor; reduction of colour in caustic bleach effluent in pulp and paper industries.

(g) *Water treatment:*   Ultrafiltration is now an accepted technology for filtration of drinking water. The world's biggest installation using UF is reported to be the Twin Oaks Valley Water Treatment Plant in San Diego having a capacity of 100 million gallons per day. It is also a very useful technique of 'pretreatment' of municipal wastewater before it is subjected to reverse osmosis. An example is a unit for pretreatment of 11.3 million gallons per day of wastewater in Singapore.

Configuration of a UF unit

Since a single membrane module does not accommodate a large area, a number of modules are used in parallel depending upon the feed rate. Also, the required degree of separation is hardly achieved in a single pass through a module. Two configurations of a UF unit are common—the 'recycle configuration' and the 'tapered configuration' (Scott and Hughes, 1996). In the recycle configuration [Figure 14.17(a)], a part of the retentate is recycled back to the inlet of the module to achieve a higher concentration of the retentate. The strategy also increases the cross-flow velocity and thereby reduces membrane fouling. In the other configuration, the modules are arranged in a parallel-series pattern [Figure 14.17(b)]. Since the retentate volume decreases after the liquid passes through a module, a lesser number of modules are provided in successive stages.

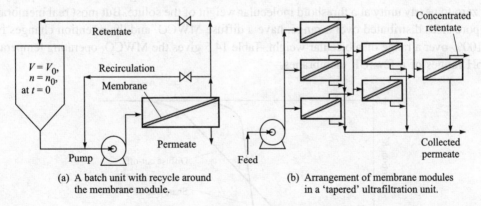

(a) A batch unit with recycle around the membrane module.

(b) Arrangement of membrane modules in a 'tapered' ultrafiltration unit.

Figure 14.17   Configuration of ultrafiltration modules.

[†] An alternative recent technique to concentrate fruit juice is 'membrane distillation'. The liquid flows through hydrophobic microporous hollow fibres (consider Figure 14.15) and cold water flows through the shell side at a considerably lower temperature. Water in the feed vaporizes, the vapour diffuses through the pores in the membrane and gets condensed by direct contact with cold water on the outer surface of the membrane. Since the membrane is hydrophobic, the membrane pores are not filled with either the aqueous feed or the cold water. This technique is also suggested to have the potential of use for desalination [Gujit et al., 'Air gap membrane distillation', *Separation Purification Tech.*, *43* (2005) 233–244.]

14.4.3   Molecular Weight Cut-off (MWCO)

This is an empirical method of characterization of a UF membrane. The ability of a membrane to reject solutes is conveniently expressed in terms of MWCO which refers to the molecular weight of a soluble macromolecule that can be separated from a solution (Noble and Stern, 1995). According to the generally accepted definition, MWCO is the molecular weight of 'globular protein' or any other standard 'monodisperse' solute (dextran, PVA or polyvinylpyrrolidone), 90% of which is rejected by the membrane [fractional rejection or retention of a solute is defined in Eq. (14.9)]. However, there are quite a few factors to be recognized in this connection. The molecular weight of a solute alone does not govern its retentivity. In fact, the shape and flexibility of the chain of a macromolecule, in addition to its molecular weight, are important factors. A straight chain polymer (for example, polyacrylic acid) of molecular weight substantially larger than the MWCO of a membrane may pass through it. Some branched chain but easily deformable molecules have also been found to behave similarly. The other important factors that affect rejection of a solute are adsorption of the solute at the pore mouth and the formation of a gel layer because of 'concentration polarization' (see the next Section 14.4.4). Adsorption depends upon the interaction of a solute with the membrane material (for example, a protein is prone to adsorption on a hydrophobic membrane), the pH, the ionic strength of the solution and the temperature. Adsorption at the pore mouth reduces the effective pore size. Further, if a layer of the rejected solute accumulates on the feed-side surface of the membrane (*gel layer*), an additional resistance to flow of the solvent occurs. But a better performance in respect of MWCO may be expected since the gel layer has a sieving effect.

Membranes generally do not exhibit a sharp MWCO. This is illustrated in Figure 14.18, that shows the comparison between the sharp cut-off membranes and diffuse cut-off membranes. For a sharp or steep cut-off membrane, the fractional retention changes almost as a step function from zero to nearly unity at a threshold molecular weight of the solute. But most real membranes, with pore sizes distributed over a range, have a diffuse MWCO, and the retention changes from 0 to 100% over a range of molecular weight. Table 14.5 gives the MWCO, operating temperature and pH ranges of a few UF membranes.

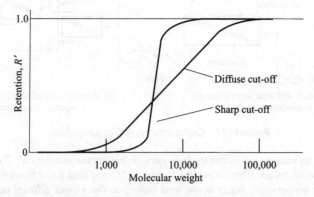

Figure 14.18   Comparison between sharp cut-off membranes and diffuse cut-off membranes [$R' = 1 - (C_p/C_m)$].

Table 14.5 Molecular weight cut-off (MWCO) of a few common polymeric membranes (Belfort, 1984)

Membrane material	Typical MWCO	Operating pH range	Max. oper. temperature	Cl_2 resistance	Membrane configuration
Cellulose acetate	1,000–50,000	3.5–7	35°C	Good	Flat sheets, tubes
Polysulphone	5,000–50,000	0–14	100°C	Good	Flat sheets, tubes, hollow-fibres
Aromatic polyamides	1,000–50,000	2–12	80°C	Poor	Flat sheets, tubes, hollow-fibre
Polyacrylonitrile	30,000–100,000	2–12	50°C	Fair	Flat sheets, tubes, hollow-fibre

14.4.4 Concentration Polarization and Other Resistances to Solvent Flow

In most membrane separation processes the membrane itself offers a substantial resistance to permeation. This resistance has to be overcome by application of the appropriate driving force. However, other resistances to transport frequently appear, particularly for separation of a suspension (by microfiltration) or a solution (by UF, RO, NF, or by pervaporation, for example). The more significant resistances are due to: (i) concentration polarization, (ii) gel formation, (iii) adsorption, and (iv) pore blockage. In some cases, one or more of them may control the flux.

Concentration polarization (Noble and Stern, 1995) is the reversible accumulation of the rejected solute in the fluid phase at the membrane–fluid interface as the solvent passes through the membrane. When the solvent (water) flows through the pores of a membrane, the solutes or the fine particles in suspension are left behind at the feed-side surface of the membrane. This increases the concentration of the solute in close vicinity of the membrane over that of the bulk solution. However, if steady state prevails, the solute retained will be transported back into the bulk solution through the boundary layer because of the concentration difference. This phenomenon is called *concentration polarization* since the solute concentration is 'polarized' or enhanced at the membrane surface. The polarization phenomenon offers a resistance to flow. If the solute is of a higher molecular weight (such as a protein or a macromolecule), its concentration at the membrane surface may be pretty large and a gel may form at the surface offering an additional resistance to flow.

Membrane pore blockage also offers resistance to filtration. The pores are not of uniform size. They are not cylindrical, but generally resemble fissures or cracks. The molecules separated are not spherical either. As a result, some solute molecules get stuck into some of the pores during the filtration process. This is called *pore blockage*. A blocked pore may allow little or no flow of the liquid through it. In reverse osmosis, the solutes are small molecules (salts in most cases), and the membrane used is a dense membrane. Adsorption is not important, and pore blockage cannot occur. Only concentration polarization can offer a substantial resistance in addition to the diffusional resistance offered by the membrane. Similar is the case of pervaporation. In gas separation, none of the above factors appear to be significant; the resistance offered by the membrane itself becomes controlling.

A severe decline of the initial flux of the solvent may occur because of the above resistances singly or in combination. For example, under normal pressure difference and with commercial membranes, 'pure water flux' is over 500 litre/$m^2 \cdot h \cdot bar$ for microfiltration, and 100–500 litre/$m^2 \cdot h \cdot bar$ for UF membranes. But for separation of a solution, the flux may be as low as 5% of the pure water flux.

Theoretical analysis of concentration polarization

The effect of concentration polarization on solvent flux can be quantified by a simple theoretical analysis. At steady state, a balance of the convective flux of the solute with the solvent towards the membrane, that through the membrane[†] and the flux due to back diffusion of the solute into the bulk of the solution through a 'stagnant film' of thickness δ can be written as follows (Figure 14.19).

$$\underset{\substack{\text{Solute flux through}\\\text{the membrane}}}{J_w C_p} \quad = \quad \underset{\substack{\text{Convective flux towards}\\\text{the membrane surface}}}{J_w C} \quad - \quad \underset{\substack{\text{Flux of back diffusion of}\\\text{the solute to the bulk of the liquid}}}{\left(-D\dfrac{dC}{dz}\right)} \qquad (14.6)$$

where

J_w = solvent flux
C_p = solute concentration in the permeate
D = diffusivity of the solute
C = local concentration of the solute in the film.

The following boundary conditions may be specified.

$$z = 0, \qquad C = C_m \qquad\qquad\qquad (14.7a)$$
$$z = \delta, \qquad C = C_b \qquad\qquad\qquad (14.7b)$$

where

δ = film or 'boundary layer thickness' at the membrane surface
C_b = solute concentration in the bulk solution
C_m = solute concentration in the liquid at the membrane surface.

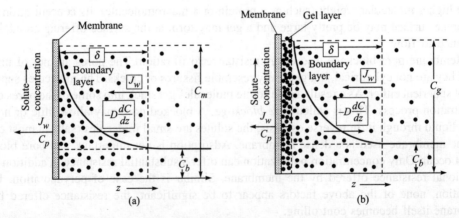

Figure 14.19   (a) Concentration profile of the solute in the boundary layer—the solvent is selectively permeated (MF, UF, NF, RO). (The black dots • are the species being separated.) (b) Concentration profile of the solute in the boundary layer—the solvent is selectively permeated (MF, UF, NF); a gel layer has formed on the membrane. (The black dots • are the species being separated.)

[†] It is assumed that a small part of the solute passes through the membrane since no real membrane is strictly semipermeable.

Integration of Eq. (14.6) using the boundary conditions, Eqs. [14.7(a)] and [14.7(b)], yields

$$\ln\frac{C_m - C_p}{C_b - C_p} = \frac{J_w \delta}{D} \quad \Rightarrow \quad \frac{C_m - C_p}{C_b - C_p} = \exp\left(\frac{J_w}{k_L}\right) \tag{14.8}$$

where k_L ($= D/\delta$) is the liquid-phase mass transfer coefficient at the membrane surface. If we define the 'rejection coefficient' (also called the 'fractional rejection' or 'fractional retention') of the solute as

$$R' = 1 - (C_p/C_m) \tag{14.9}$$

we may write

$$\frac{1 - (C_p/C_m)}{(C_b/C_m) - (C_p/C_m)} = \exp(J_w/k_L) \quad \Rightarrow \quad \frac{R'}{(C_b/C_m) - (1 - R')} = \exp(J_w/k_L)$$

$$\Rightarrow \quad R' = \frac{C_b}{C_m}\exp(J_w/k_L) - (1 - R')\exp(J_w/k_L) \quad \Rightarrow \quad \frac{C_m}{C_b} = \frac{\exp(J_w/k_L)}{R' + (1 - R')\exp(J_w/k_L)} \tag{14.10}$$

The ratio C_m/C_b is called the *concentration polarization modulus*. The quantity increases with flux, with increasing retention R' and decreasing mass transfer coefficient, k_L. For complete retention,

$$R' = 1 \quad \text{and} \quad C_m/C_b = \exp(J_w/k_L) \tag{14.11}$$

Mass transfer correlations

Mass transfer for flow in a hollow-fibre module (flow through a fibre; parallel or cross-flow outside the fibres) was extensively investigated by Wickramasinghe et al. (1992) and a set of correlations was proposed. The following correlations were suggested for flow through a fibre.

$$\text{Sh} = 1.62(\text{Gr})^{1/3}; \quad \text{Gr(Graetz number)} = \frac{d^2 u}{DL} > 4 \quad (d = \text{fibre diameter, } L = \text{length}) \tag{14.12}$$

For cross-flow ultrafiltration, the Leveque solution given below for heat transfer has been adapted to calculate the mass transfer coefficient (Porter, 1997).

$$\text{Sh} = \frac{k_L d_h}{D} = 1.62\left(\text{Re.Sc.}\frac{d_h}{L}\right)^{0.33}; \quad \text{Re} = \frac{u d_h}{v} \tag{14.13}$$

where d_h = equivalent hydraulic diameter (for a flat rectangular channel, $d_h = 2b$; b = channel height).

For turbulent flow through a conduit or a channel, the Dittus–Boelter equation given below can be adapted

$$\text{Sh} = 0.023(\text{Re})^{0.8}(\text{Sc})^{0.33} \tag{14.14}$$

In many applications of the microporous hollow-fibre modules the shell-side mass transfer resistance becomes an important factor and the corresponding coefficient needs to be determined. The current status of shell-side mass transfer correlations has been discussed recently by Liang and Long (2005).

14.4.5 Simple Models for Solvent Flux

Pure water flux through a membrane increases linearly with the applied pressure difference (ΔP). In the case of ultrafiltration, however, the increase of flux with pressure drop is slower and the flux levels off to a constant or plateau value at a high ΔP. This constant flux, which is virtually independent of the resistance to flow offered by the membrane, is called the *limiting flux*. The limiting flux, qualitatively shown in Figure 14.20, increases with increasing cross-flow velocity or decreasing bulk concentration of the solute. Increasing cross-flow velocity enhances the mass transfer coefficient and reduces the solute concentration C_m in the vicinity of the membrane. A lower solute concentration in the bulk has a similar effect on the limiting flux. Described below are the important models (Wijmans et al., 1984) to interpret flux behaviour in ultrafiltration.

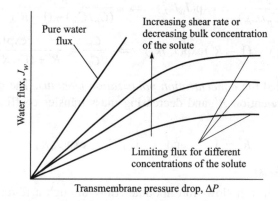

Figure 14.20   Flux behaviour in ultrafiltration (qualitative).

Resistance model

If substantial concentration polarization occurs in micro- or ultrafiltration, the retained high molecular weight solute (or the fine particles in suspension) may form a thin cake at the membrane surface. This cake layer offers a resistance to solvent transport. If we consider the two resistances—that of the membrane (R_m) and of the cake (R_c) in series—the solvent flux can be written as [compare with Eq. (14.4)].

$$J_w = \frac{\Delta P}{\mu (R_m + R_c)} \tag{14.15}$$

The resistance to flow through the cake can be estimated from the Kozeny–Karman relation

$$R_c = \frac{180(1-\varepsilon)^2 l_c}{d_s^2 \varepsilon^3} = r_c l_c \tag{14.16}$$

where

ε = porosity of the cake layer
l_c = its thickness
d_s = diameter of the particles (assumed spherical) forming the cake
r_c = resistance to flow offered by unit thickness of the cake, called the 'specific cake resistance'.

The resistance model can be further extended to describe the flux behaviour in 'dead-end filtration'. Let us consider batch filtration of a liquid using a membrane of area a_m and flow resistance R_m. If C_b = solute concentration in the feed and R' = rejection coefficient, the cake thickness at any time t after start is given by

$$C_b V R' = \rho_c l_c a_m \quad \Rightarrow \quad l_c = \frac{C_b V R'}{\rho_c a_m} \tag{14.17}$$

Here ρ_c = density of the cake layer, and V = volume of filtrate collected after time t. The solvent flux can be expressed as

$$J_w = \frac{1}{a_m} \frac{dV}{dt} \tag{14.18}$$

From Eqs. (14.15) to (14.18),

$$J_w = \frac{1}{a_m} \frac{dV}{dt} = \frac{\Delta P}{\mu} \left[R_m + \frac{r_c C_b R'}{\rho_c a_m} V \right]^{-1} \tag{14.19}$$

The above equation may be integrated to obtain a relation for flux decline with time in batch ultrafiltration (Cudacek and Fane, 1984). The initial condition is: $V = 0$ at $t = 0$.

$$R_m V + \frac{r_c C_b R'}{2 a_m \rho_c} V^2 = \frac{a_m \Delta P}{\mu} t \tag{14.20}$$

Combining Eqs. (14.19) and (14.20),

$$\frac{1}{J_w^2} = \frac{R_m^2 \mu^2}{(\Delta P)^2} + \frac{2 \mu C_b r_c R'}{\rho_c \Delta P} t \tag{14.21}$$

So a plot of $1/J_w^2$ versus t for dead-end batch filtration should be linear (Cudacek and Fane, 1984). The membrane resistance R_m and the specific cake resistance r_c can be determined from its slope and intercept (see Problem 14.7).

Gel polarization model

Under the effect of concentration polarization, the solute concentration at the membrane surface may be even an order of magnitude larger than that in the bulk liquid. Solutes like a polymer or a protein may form a slimy layer called 'gel' if a limiting concentration C_g is reached. At steady state, a constant thickness of the gel and a limiting flux J_∞ are attained. Convective transport of the macromolecules to the boundary of the gel and its back diffusion under the driving force $(C_g - C_b)$ occur simultaneously as discussed before. If k_L is the mass transfer coefficient, the total resistance can be expressed as the sum of the resistances offered by the membrane and the gel. Then the limiting flux becomes [see Eq. (14.8)]

$$J_\infty = \frac{\Delta P}{\mu (R_m + R_g)} = k_L \ln \left(\frac{C_g - C_p}{C_b - C_p} \right) \tag{14.22a}$$

If the solute rejection is high (i.e. $C_p \ll C_b$ and C_s),

$$J_\infty = k_L (\ln C_g - \ln C_b) \tag{14.22b}$$

If the model is valid, a plot of ln C_b versus J_∞ is expected to be linear, and the gel concentration C_g can be obtained from the intercept on the horizontal axis. Figure 14.21 shows a set of such plots for varying recirculation rates of the liquid in ultrafiltration of human albumin. The plots indicate the applicability of the gel polarization model for protein ultrafiltration. Since a larger rate of liquid recirculation increases the cross-flow velocity and the mass transfer coefficient k_L, the plot becomes steeper as the recirulation rate increases.

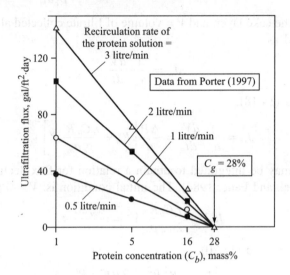

Figure 14.21 The water flux in ultrafiltration of human albumin as a function of the protein concentration at different rates of recirculation of the solution.

Osmotic pressure model

The concentration polarization phenomenon creates a much larger concentration of the solute in the vicinity of the membrane compared to that in the bulk solution. The osmotic pressure at the higher concentration of the solute near the membrane surface reduces the effective pressure differential for solvent flow through the membrane. The osmotic pressure model quantifies the effect of concentration polarization in terms of osmotic pressure. Osmotic pressure is a 'colligative property' and is determined by the molar concentration of the species in solution (see Section 14.4.7). At the same mass fraction concentration, a low molecular weight solute exerts a much larger osmotic pressure than a high molecular weight species. As a result, the effect of osmotic pressure is not very prominent in micro- or ultrafiltration since the solutes are generally of high molecular weight. However, at a high mass concentration, a solution of a macromolecule can also exert a substantial osmotic pressure. This affects the filtration rate (Wijmans et al., 1984). If $\Delta\Pi$ is the osmotic pressure of the solute at the concentration existing at the membrane surface *relative to* that at the permeate concentration, the flux may be expressed as

$$J_w = \frac{\Delta P - \Delta \Pi}{\mu R_m}$$

(14.23)

Here $\Delta P - \Delta \Pi$ may be considered as an 'effective pressure driving force' for solvent flow. The simplest method of calculation of osmotic pressure uses the vant Hoff equation

$$\Pi = CRT \qquad (C = \text{concentration in gmol/litre}) \qquad (14.24\text{a})$$

The osmotic pressure of a macromolecule may be satisfactorily described by a power-law dependence on concentration.

$$\Pi = \zeta C^n \qquad (14.24\text{b})$$

where ζ = constant; n = an exponential factor ($n = 1$ for small molecules, $n \approx 2$ for certain macromolecules).

The applicability of the osmotic pressure model to interpret limiting flux is illustrated here. Let us assume that the membrane rejects nearly 100% of the macromolecules in a solution ($C_p = 0$, $R' = 1$). Then from Eqs. (14.23), (14.24) and (14.11), we can write

$$J_w = \frac{\Delta P - \Delta \Pi}{\mu R_m} = \frac{\Delta P - \zeta C_m^n}{\mu R_m} = \frac{\Delta P - \zeta C_b^n \exp(n J_w / k_L)}{\mu R_m} \qquad (14.25)$$

A plot of J_w versus ΔP for a set of typical values of the parameters of the above equation is shown in Figure 14.22. It is seen that the solvent flux levels off at higher values of the applied pressure difference. The plateau value of the flux is the 'limiting flux'.

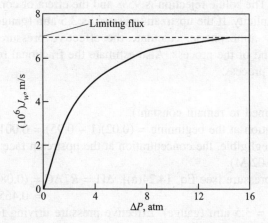

Figure 14.22 Limiting flux according to the osmotic pressure model, Eq. (14.25) [$n = 2$; $\zeta = 100$; $\mu R_m = 5 \times 10^5$ atm·s/m; $k_L = 2 \times 10^{-6}$ m/s; $C_b = 1\%$].

14.4.6 Membrane Fouling and Cleaning

Membrane fouling is defined as the deposition of retained particles, colloids, macromolecules, salts, etc. at the membrane surface, pore mouth or pore wall causing flux decline. Fouling does not normally occur in gas separation and pervaporation. It is not significant in RO if proper *pretreatment* of the feed water is done. Fouling can be caused by broadly three kinds of substances: organic (macromolecules, biological substances like proteins, enzymes etc.), inorganic (metal hydroxides, calcium salts, etc.), and particulates. It is to be noted that one of the important applications of ultrafiltration is in downstream processing[†] in microbial biotechnology and that some of the substances in the fermentation broth cause fouling of the membrane. Fouling is a complex phenomenon and depends upon the particular system (the solute and the membrane material, pH, temperature, ionic strength of the solution, etc.)

Proteins are strongly adsorbed on hydrophobic or less hydrophilic surfaces (e.g. polysulphones) but less on hydrophilic surfaces (e.g. cellulose acetate). Polysulphone, polyethersulphone, polyvinylidine fluoride can be made hydrophilic by surface modification (plasma treatment of the surface, grafting a hydrophilic group on the surface by UV or chemical initiation). The tendency of protein adsorption at the pore mouth, and hence membrane fouling, can thus be reduced by surface modification.

Since membrane fouling causes a severe decline of the solvent flux, it becomes necessary to clean the membrane periodically. The common cleaning methods are: hydraulic, mechanical, chemical, electrical, etc. Hydraulic cleaning is based on 'back-shock treatment' (i.e. back-flushing for a fraction of a second) by forcing the solvent to flow through the membrane in the reverse direction to dislodge the adhered foulants. Chemical cleaning is the most important cleaning method. It uses acids (like H_3PO_4, citric acid), alkalis, detergents (alkaline or non-ionic), and complexing agents like EDTA.

EXAMPLE 14.2 (*Ultrafiltration—the effect of osmotic pressure*)   A 0.02 molar feed solution containing a macromolecular solute is to be concentrated to 0.1 molar concentration by batch ultrafiltration at 25°C. The solute rejection is 95% and the effect of concentration polarization can be ignored for simplicity. If the upstream pressure is 3.5 atm (gauge) and the downstream pressure is essentially atmospheric, calculate the effective pressure driving force at the beginning and at the end of the process. Also estimate the fractional reduction in the solvent flux at the end of the process.

Solution
Rejection = 95% (assumed to remain constant).

Permeate concentration at the beginning = (0.02)(1 – 0.95) = 0.001(M); since the concentration polarization is negligible, the concentration at the upstream face of the membrane = the bulk concentration = 0.02(M).

Effective osmotic pressure [see Eq. 14.24(a)], $\Delta\Pi = RT\Delta C$ = (0.0821)(298)(0.02 – 0.001)
$$= 0.465 \text{ atm}$$

Feed side pressure = 3.5 atm (gauge). Effective pressure driving force = 3.5 – 0.465
$$= \boxed{3.035 \text{ atm}}$$

Similarly, at the end of the process, when the bulk concentration is 0.1 molar, the effective pressure driving force = 3.5 – (0.0821)(298)(0.1)(0.95) = 3.5 – 2.324 = $\boxed{1.176 \text{ atm}}$

The solvent flux is proportional to the pressure difference.

Hence the fractional reduction in solvent flux = (3.035 – 1.176)/3.035 = $\boxed{0.61}$

---

[*] A variety of high-values products in crude form are prepared in bioreactors. Separation and recovery of these products in a reasonably pure form pose a tough challenge. In fact, bioseparation accounts for 80–90% of the cost of production of high-value bio-products.

So, 61% reduction in the initial flux occurs because of osmotic reduction in the 'effective pressure difference'. It is to be noted that the solvent flux will be reduced much more in practice because of concentration polarization and membrane fouling and adsorption. The absence of concentration polarization is a drastically simplifying assumption.

EXAMPLE 14.3 (*Concentration polarization in UF*) An enzyme is being concentrated in an ultrafiltration module with the feed in cross-flow. Under the given flow condition the mass transfer coefficient at the membrane surface is estimated to be 3×10^{-5} cm/s. The bulk concentration is 0.3 mass%. If the water flux is 0.41 m^3/m^2·h, calculate the polarization modulus and the concentration of the enzyme in the liquid at the membrane surface. The membrane has a distribution of pore size and 95% rejection of the solute is achieved. If the diffusivity of the enzyme is 8×10^{-7} cm^2/s, calculate the thickness of the mass transfer 'film'.

Solution

Water flux, $J_w = 0.41$ m^3/m^2·h $= 0.41/3600 = 1.139 \times 10^{-4}$ m^3/m^2·s. Solute rejection, $R' = 0.95$.
From Eq. (14.10), the concentration polarization modulus is

$$\frac{C_m}{C_b} = \frac{\exp(J_w/k_L)}{R' + (1 - R')\exp(J_w/k_L)} = \frac{\exp[(1.139 \times 10^{-4})/(3 \times 10^{-5})]}{(0.95) + (1 - 0.95)\exp[(1.139 \times 10^{-4})/(3 \times 10^{-5})]} = \boxed{14.02}$$

Solute concentration at the membrane surface, $C_m = (14.02)(C_b) = (14.02)(0.3) = \boxed{4.2 \text{ mass\%}}$

Thickness of the 'mass transfer film', $\delta = D/k_L = (8 \times 10^{-7}$ cm^2/s$)/(3 \times 10^{-5}$ cm/s$) = 0.0267$ cm

EXAMPLE 14.4 (*Batch ultrafiltration*) A feed containing 60 lb protein (mol. wt. = 1510) in a 2000 gal solution is to be concentrated to 400 gal by batch ultrafiltration at 25°C using a ceramic membrane module. The initial flux is 2 gal/ft^2·h at a pressure differential of 44 psi across the membrane. Calculate the membrane area to be provided if the job is to be done in 3 h. Any reduction in the driving force due to osmotic pressure is to be taken into account. Complete rejection of the solute can be assumed. Concentration polarization and membrane fouling may be ignored.

Solution

Let V be the volume of solution in the tank at any time t, and n_0 be the total number of moles of solute present [see Figure 14.17(a)]. Solution concentration $= n_0/V$. Since 100% rejection of the solute occurs, the osmotic pressure difference at time t is $\Delta\Pi = RTn_0/V$, and the effective pressure driving force $= \Delta P - \Delta\Pi = \Delta P - (RTn_0/V)$. If L_p is the water permeability of the membrane and a_m the membrane area, the solvent flux is given by

$$J_w = -\frac{1}{a_m}\frac{dV}{dt} = L_p\left(\Delta P - \frac{RTn_0}{V}\right) = L_p\Delta P\left(1 - \frac{RTn_0}{\Delta P \cdot V}\right); \text{ at time } t = 0, \text{ volume, } V = V_0.$$

On integration and rearrangement, we get the following expression for the membrane area.

$$a_m = \frac{1}{L_p\Delta Pt}\left[(V_0 - V) + \frac{RTn_0}{\Delta P}\ln\frac{V_0 - (RTn_0/\Delta P)}{V - (RTn_0/\Delta P)}\right] \tag{i}$$

The following quantities are given or known: Mol. wt. of the protein = 1510; n_0 = (60)/(2.205)(1510) = 0.01802 kmol; R = 0.0821 $m^3 \cdot atm/(kmol \cdot K)$; T = 298 K; initial volume, V_0 = 2000 gal = (2000)(3.78) litre = 7.56 m^3; final volume, V = 400 gal = 1.512 m^3; ΔP = 44 psi = 44/14.7 = 3 atm; initial flux, J_{w0} = 2 $gal/(ft^2 \cdot h)$ = $(2 \times 3.78 \times 10^{-3})/(0.3048)^2 \Rightarrow 0.0814$ $m^3/(m^2 \cdot h)$; RTn_0 = 0.441.

The value of the quantity $L_p \Delta P$ can be calculated from the initial flux.

$$J_{w0} = L_p \Delta P \left(1 - \frac{RTn_0}{V_0 \Delta P}\right) \Rightarrow 0.0814 = L_p \Delta P \left(1 - \frac{0.441}{(7.56)(3)}\right)$$

$$\Rightarrow \qquad L_p \Delta P = \boxed{0.083 \ m^3/m^2 \cdot h}$$

The membrane area can now be calculated from Eq. (i) above taking t = 3 h.

$$a_m = \frac{1}{(3)(0.083)} \left[(7.56 - 1.512) + \frac{0.441}{3} \ln \frac{7.56 - (0.441/3)}{1.512 - (0.441/3)}\right] \Rightarrow \text{Area, } a_m = \boxed{25.3 \ m^2}.$$

EXAMPLE 14.5 (*Concentration polarization in UF*)   A macromolecular solution (mol. wt. = 6000; concentration = 1 mass%) is passed through a tubular ceramic UF membrane of 1 cm internal diameter and 1 m long at 27°C. The membrane admits of a pure water permeability of 2.11 $gal/(ft^2)(day)(psi)$. Given the following data, calculate the flow velocity to be maintained in the tube in order to prevent formation of a gel layer on the membrane surface. Rejection coefficient, R' = 0.995; applied pressure difference, ΔP = 1.5 bar; diffusivity of the solute, D = 8×10^{-7} cm^2/s; viscosity of the solution = 3 cP; concentration at which the solute forms a gel, C_g = 10.5%. Pore leakage and fouling may be ignored.

Solution
Take $C_m = C_g$ = 0.105 (mass fraction); this is the concentration of incipient gelation.
The other relevant concentrations (mass fractions) are:

C_b = 0.01; C_p = (1 − 0.995)C_m = (0.005)(0.105) = 0.0005 (since the solute rejection is 99.5%).

It is assumed that no fouling of the membrane occurs, i.e. the solvent permeability is the same as that of pure water. At the beginning of gelation [see Eq. 14.22(a)],

$$\frac{C_m - C_p}{C_b - C_p} = \frac{C_g - C_p}{C_b - C_p} = \frac{0.105 - 0.0005}{0.01 - 0.0005} = 10.6 \Rightarrow \exp\left(\frac{J_w}{k_L}\right) = 10.6 \Rightarrow \frac{J_w}{k_L} = 2.40$$

Calculation of the effective pressure driving force
Concentration at the membrane surface at incipient gelation, $C_m = C_g$ = 105/6000 = 0.0175 gmol/litre

Concentration difference between the feed and the permeate sides, $\Delta C = C_g - C_p \approx$ 0.0175 gmol/litre.

$$\Delta \Pi = (\Delta C)RT = (0.0175)(0.0821)(300) = 0.431 \text{ atm} = 6.34 \text{ psi}$$

$$\text{Applied pressure difference} = 1.5 \text{ bar} = (1.5/1.013)(14.7) = 21.77 \text{ psi}$$

$$\text{Effective pressure driving force, } \Delta P - \Delta \Pi = 21.77 - 6.34 = 15.43 \text{ psi}$$

Water flux, $J_w = [(2.11 \text{ gal/(ft}^2)(\text{day})(\text{psi})](15.43 \text{ psi}) = 32.56 \text{ gal/(ft}^2)(\text{day})$

$$= 1.535 \times 10^{-5} \text{ m}^3/\text{m}^2 \cdot \text{s}$$

$$k_L = J_w/2.40 = 1.535 \times 10^{-5}/2.40 = 6.4 \times 10^{-6} \text{ m/s}$$

Calculation of the minimum liquid velocity

Tube diameter, $d = 1 \text{ cm} = 0.01 \text{ m}$; solution viscosity, $\mu = 3 \text{ cP} = 3 \times 10^{-3} \text{ kg/m} \cdot \text{s}$; solution density, $\rho = 1000 \text{ kg/m}^3$; diffusivity of the solute, $D = 8 \times 10^{-11} \text{ m}^2/\text{s}$.

$$\text{Schmidt number, Sc} = \frac{\mu}{\rho D} = \frac{(3 \times 10^{-3})}{(8 \times 10^{-11})(1000)} = 3.75 \times 10^4$$

$$\text{Sherwood number, Sh} = \frac{k_L d}{D} = \frac{(6.4 \times 10^{-6})(0.01)}{8 \times 10^{-11}} = 800$$

Use this correlation for the mass transfer coefficient: $\text{Sh} = 0.023(\text{Re})^{0.8} (\text{Sc})^{1/3}$. Putting the values, $800 = (0.023)(\text{Re})^{0.8} (3.75 \times 10^4)^{1/3} \Rightarrow \text{Re} = 5930$ (the flow is turbulent and the correlation is applicable) $\Rightarrow \text{Re} = 5930 = d u \rho / \mu = (0.01)(u)(1000)/(3 \times 10^{-3}) \Rightarrow u = \boxed{1.78 \text{ m/s}}$

This is the minimum velocity to be maintained so that the wall mass transfer coefficient is high enough to prevent attainment of gelling concentration and formation of gel at the wall.

(A simple calculation shows that for a tube length of 1 m, only 0.1% of the water in the feed permeates through the wall. So the bulk solution concentration remains practically unchanged.)

14.4.7 Reverse Osmosis

Osmosis is a well-known phenomenon. When an aqueous solution of a substance is kept separated from water by a 'semi-permeable' membrane in a two-compartment cell, water diffuses through the membrane into the higher concentration compartment [Figure 14.23(a)]. This occurs because of a difference of chemical potential of water between the two compartments. The chemical

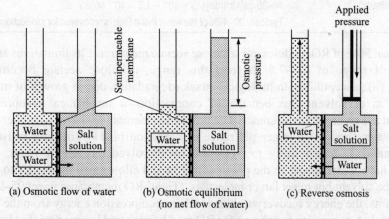

Figure 14.23 Osmosis and reverse osmosis illustrated.

potential of pure water is larger than that of water containing a dissolved solute. If the level of the solution is maintained at a certain elevated position, depending upon the concentration of the solute, the flow of water through the membrane to the higher concentration side stops. This condition is called *osmotic equilibrium* [Figure 14.23(b)] and the extra pressure due to the elevated level of the solution is called the *osmotic pressure* (here we denote it by Π). The chemical potential of water in a solution increases if it is subjected to an elevated pressure. Thus, on application of an extra pressure higher than the osmotic pressure, the chemical potential of water in the solution becomes larger than that of pure water. Under such a condition [Figure 14.23(c)] the flow of water through the membrane from the solution side to the water side occurs. This is 'reverse osmosis'. The driving force for water transport is its difference of chemical potential between the two sides. It is to be noted that there is hardly any membrane which is truly 'semipermeable'. As a result, a diffusional flux of the solute, driven by its own concentration difference, always occurs. A summary of the reverse osmosis process is given in Table 14.6.

Table 14.6 Some basic information on reverse osmosis

Membrane type	Asymmetric or composite (flat sheet or hollow-fibre)
Thickness	50–150 μm; active layer thickness ≈ 0.1 μm
Pore size	Less than 2 nm (this is *notional* and there are no pores in the physical sense; passage of the solvent and solute molecules occurs through the spaces or free volume in the polymer matrix)
Driving force	Pressure difference (more specifically the difference of chemical potential) for solvent flow; concentration difference for solute transport
Separation mechanism	Solution-diffusion
Membrane materials	Hydrophilic materials such as cellulose di- and triacetate (frequently a blend of these two is used); linear and cross-linked polyamides; alkyl-aryl polyether urea. Membrane life is 2–3 years.
Membrane module	Spiral-wound (up to about 8-inch diameter) and hollow-fibre modules
Pressure differential	10 to 100 bar or more; with improved membranes brackish water desalination is commercially done at 150–400 psi pressure differential.
Typical flux (in commercial installation)	10–30 gal/(ft^2)(day) [$5 \times 10^{-6} - 1.5 \times 10^{-5}$ (m^3/m$^2 \cdot$ s)]
Water recovery	Typically 20–40% of the water in the feed is recovered for production of potable water.

More than 50% of RO modules use cellulose acetate membrane. Its limitations are: (i) smaller allowable pH range of 4.5–7.5 (beyond this range, cellulose acetate becomes prone to hydrolysis), (ii) susceptibility to biological attack (degradation due to growth of microbes), and (iii) reduction of solvent flux because of compaction or mechanical compression of the membrane at a high pressure difference. The polyamide membranes have: (i) higher salt rejection but lower water flux, (ii) a larger pH range of operation (4–11), (iii) less resistance to free chlorine, and (iv) susceptibility to oxidation by dissolved oxygen in water. 'Loose' RO membranes have wider spaces in the polymer matrix and allow small molecules to pass through along with the solvent but reject larger molecules. 'Tight' RO membranes reject 95–99% of NaCl. In big RO units, the energy recovery turbines reclaim compression energy from the reject stream before disposal. A composite membrane for RO may be prepared by interfacial polymerization to create a permselective layer on a suitable UF membrane that acts as the substrate or backing.

Reverse osmosis is the most important technique of desalination of brackish (1000–5000 ppm salt) or sea water (about 35,000 ppm or 3.5% salt). Its potential was identified in the 1950s. But commercial exploitation was not possible until the 1960s. The development of high flux asymmetric cellulose acetate membrane by the phase inversion technique of Loeb and Sourirajan (1963) opened up commercial exploitation of this very important strategy of desalination. Currently, over 12,500 industrial scale desalination plants are operating worldwide with an average production rate of about 23 million m^3 per day of potable water (less than 200 TDS). A majority of these plants are RO units and the rest are based on 'thermal desalination'.

Admittedly, thermal desalination produces better quality water compared to RO (the permeate salinity is 30–150 ppm). The cost of an RO membrane module ranges from $500 to $1000 for a capacity of 50–100 m^3/day. A spiral wound module, 0.2 m in dia and 1 m long, may yield 8000–10,000 gal/day of water. The unit cost of desalinated water produced by RO is about $0.55 to $1.2/$m^3$. This is less than the cost of thermally desalinated water (Ettouney et al., 2002). Because of concentration polarization, salt concentration, particularly of low-solubility salts like $CaSO_4$, at the membrane surface during reverse osmosis may exceed the saturation level. Precipitation of salt on the membrane surface ('scaling') may occur causing membrane fouling and dramatic reduction of flux. In order to avoid this problem, the feed water to an RO unit should be adequately pretreated to remove the suspended and dissolved membrane fouling agents. An adjustment of the pH is also necessary. The schematic of an RO plant is shown in Figure 14.24.

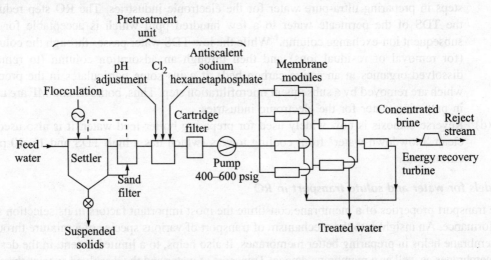

Figure 14.24 A simplified flow diagram of an RO plant.

Applications

The largest desalination plant purifies brackish water to produce 275,000 m^3/day potable water. The TDS is reduced from 3100 ppm to about 200 ppm. The largest sea-water desalination plant is in Jeddah, Saudi Arabia, having a capacity of 56,800 m^3/day of potable water. Water scarcity is predicted to appear as a big problem in many countries in the near future and RO is an effective strategy to combat this problem. Besides desalination, the other applications of RO are:

(a) Treatment of wastewater, particularly industrial waste water, to produce polished water for reuse. The retentate stream is 'concentrated wastewater' of much lesser volume and can be treated at a lower cost. The waste water from electroplating and metal finishing industries can be treated in an RO unit and the metals may be recovered with less difficulty from the concentrated retentate. There are quite a few RO installations for treatment of municipal wastewater as well. The technique is also used for the treatment of waste water/liquor from pulp and paper and textile industries. Reverse osmosis is indispensable to recover water from water streams and to achieve the target of 'zero discharge'. There are examples of successful application of municipal wastewater reclamation by RO—such as in the Orange County in the USA followed by many more (the Bedok NEWater plant and the Kranji plants in Singapore and similar units in the Middle East). The major problem in such an application is membrane fouling (colloidal fouling, biofouling, organic fouling, and scaling by silica, calcium phosphate and carbonate). This problem has been largely overcome by pretreatment of the wastewater by micro- or ultrafiltration. Examples of industrial wasterwater treatment by RO are numerous.

(b) In food and dairy industries: concentration of whey (for the recovery of protein); concentration of whole milk, fruit juice, etc.

(c) Membrane processes now play the major role in preparing 'ultra-pure' water (resistivity not less than 18 $M\Omega$-cm) for electronic fabrication industries. Rinsing with such water is necessary in almost every step of manufacture of integrated circuits (IC). Even multiple distillation steps fail to attain the quality target. Reverse osmosis is one of the steps in preparing ultra-pure water for the electronic industries. The RO step reduces the TDS of the permeate water to a few hundred ppm which is acceptable for the subsequent ion-exchange column.[†] While the low TDS water passes through the column (for removal of residual ions) and then through an adsorption column (to remove dissolved organics in an active carbon bed), it gains some particulates in the process which are removed by a subsequent microfiltration step. Thus, both RO and MF are used in preparing water for the electronic industries.

(d) Reverse osmosis is now widely used for preparing boiler-feed water. It is also used to clean 'blowdown water' from cooling towers (which has a high TDS and 15–20 ppm chromates).

Models for water and solute transport in RO

The transport properties of a membrane constitute the most important factors in its selection and performance. An insight into the mechanism of transport of various species of a mixture through a membrane helps in preparing better membranes. It also helps, to a limited extent, in the design of membranes as well as a membrane device. Transport of water and the dissolved species through an osmotic membrane is not a very simple phenomenon. Many attempts have nevertheless been made towards modeling of the reverse osmosis process. The more important models rely on either of two approaches. The first category of models is derived on the basis of irreversible thermodynamics where the membrane is treated as a 'blackbox' (Soltanieh and Gill, 1981); the 'flux' of a species is expressed as a linear function of the pertinent 'forces'. No attempt is made to visualize or identify the mechanism of transport. The other class of models assumes a reasonable transport mechanism to arrive at a relation between the flux and the forces.

[†] An ion-exchange column is meant for fine polishing and should not be overloaded by using high TDS water. An overloaded ion-exchange column needs frequent regeneration by using polluting chemicals.

Kedem–Katchalsky model

The earliest and most important model based on irreversible thermodynamics was proposed by Kedem and Katchalsky (1958). It starts with the Onsager reciprocal relationship among fluxes and forces (DeGroot and Mazur, 1962) and an 'energy dissipation' (or 'entropy generation') function. The model includes 'cross-coefficients' in the flux equation. In the case of reverse osmosis, the readily measurable forces that cause transport of the solvent and of the solute through a membrane are the transmembrane pressure drop (ΔP) and the osmotic pressure difference $(\Delta \Pi)$ between the solution and the permeate sides. According to the basic laws of irreversible thermodynamics, both these forces govern the fluxes of the solvent and the solute. The Kedem–Katchalsky model leads to the following equations relating the 'fluxes' $(J_w$ and $J_s)$ and 'conjugate forces' $(\Delta P$ and $\Delta \Pi)$.

Solvent flux: $$J_w = L_p \Delta P + L_{pD} \Delta \Pi \tag{14.26}$$

Solute flux: $$J_s = L_{Dp} \Delta P + L_D \Delta \Pi \tag{14.27}$$

Here L_p, L_D, L_{pD} and L_{Dp} are phenomenological coefficients; L_p stands for the permeability of the solvent and is called the *filtration coefficient*. The quantities L_{pD} and L_{Dp} are cross-coefficients and following the 'Onsager reciprocal relationship', these may set equal to each other (i.e. $L_{pD} = L_{Dp}$). By further theoretical manipulation, the above equations may be written in the following more convenient forms.

Solvent flux: $$J_w = L_p(\Delta P - \sigma \Delta \Pi) \tag{14.28}$$

Solute flux: $$J_s = J_w(1 - \sigma)C_{s,lm} + \omega \Delta \Pi \tag{14.28a}$$

Here $C_{s,lm}$ = 'log mean' solute concentration on the upstream and downstream sides of the membrane; $\sigma(= -L_{pD}/L_p)$ = reflection coefficient; $\omega = C_{s,lm}(L_D L_p - L_{pD}^2)/L_p$ = solute permeability at zero solvent flux, i.e. $\omega = [J_s/\Delta \Pi]_{J_w = 0}$. The second term of the solute flux in Eq. [14.28(a)] has sometimes been expressed as

$$\omega \Delta \Pi = P_s(C_R - C_p) \tag{14.28b}$$

where P_s is the 'salt permeability' (m/s), and C_R and C_p are the salt concentrations on the reject and the permeate sides respectively.

The 'phenomenological coefficients' $(L_p, L_D,$ and $L_{Dp})$ show dependence on solute concentration if the pressure drop and solute concentration are large. Spiegler and Kedem (1966) modified the above model to remove its deficiencies. A few other models based on irreversible thermodynamics have also been proposed. A good review was given by Soltanieh and Gill (1981). All these models are suitable near equilibrium conditions[†] and show deviations if the system is far away from equilibrium. Recently Hwang (2004) has given an overview of the application of the equations of irreversible thermodynamics to different membrane separation processes including RO.

Solution–Diffusion model

The solution–diffusion model is probably the most important model of the second category. The model proposed by Lonsdale et al. (1965) assumes that sorption of both the solvent and the solute

---

[†] In fact, the laws of irreversible thermodynamics are not applicable if a system is far away from equilibrium.

occurs at the upstream surface of the membrane, followed by diffusion through the non-porous and homogeneous permselective layer under chemical potential gradients of individual species. No coupling effect or cross-coefficient appears in the model. The diffusional flux of the solvent is given by

$$J_w = D_w \frac{dC_w}{dz} \qquad (14.29)$$

The change in chemical potential of the solvent is given by

$$d\mu_w \approx -RT d\ln C_w = -RT \frac{dC_w}{C_w} \qquad (14.30)$$

$$\Rightarrow \qquad J_w = -\frac{D_w C_w}{RT} \frac{d\mu_w}{dz} \approx \frac{D_w C_w}{RT} \frac{\Delta\mu_w}{l_m} \qquad (14.31)$$

where $\Delta\mu_w$ is the difference of chemical potential of the solvent across the homogeneous skin layer of thickness l_m. It is more convenient to express the driving force in terms of directly measurable quantities rather than the chemical potential difference. We may write

$$\Delta\mu_w = \int \left(\frac{\partial\mu_w}{\partial C_w}\right)_{T,P} dC_w + \int \left(\frac{\partial\mu_w}{\partial P}\right)_{T,C} dP = \int \left(\frac{\partial\mu_w}{\partial C_w}\right)_{T,P} dC_w + \overline{V}_w \Delta P^\dagger \qquad (14.32)$$

Here $\overline{V}_w$ is the partial molar volume of water in solution. Using the limiting condition, i.e. if $\Delta\mu_w = 0$, then $\Delta P = \Delta\Pi$, we may write

$$\int \left(\frac{\partial\mu_w}{\partial C_w}\right)_{T,P} dC_w = -\overline{V}_w \Delta\Pi \qquad (14.33)$$

$$\Rightarrow \qquad \Delta\mu_w = \overline{V}_w (\Delta P - \Delta\Pi) \qquad (14.33a)$$

From Eqs. (14.32) and (14.33),

$$J_w = \frac{D_w C_w}{RT l_m} \overline{V}_w (\Delta P - \Delta\Pi) = \tilde{P}_w (\Delta P - \Delta\Pi) \qquad (14.34)$$

where $\tilde{P}_w (= D_w C_w \overline{V}_w / RT)$ is the permeability coefficient of water according to this model.

For the salt, the contribution of pressure towards the chemical potential difference is negligible. So the salt flux is viewed as diffusive and is expressed as follows

$$J_s = -D_s \frac{dC_s}{dz} \approx -D_s \frac{\Delta C_s}{l_m} \qquad (14.35)$$

where D_s is the diffusivity of salt in the membrane. The salt rejection can be calculated from the flux Eqs. (14.34) and (14.35).

The solution–diffusion model gives a rather simple representation of the phenomena of solvent and salt transport. In fact, this model is more appropriate for a 'tight' membrane. Salt rejection in practice is often less than that predicted by the model. This happens because of 'imperfections' or pinholes in a membrane that allow leakage of the salt solution. Such leakages do not substantially contribute to solvent flux, but adversely affect salt rejection.

---

† This follows from the relation $d\mu = VdP - SdT$

There are quite a few other models to describe transport of water and salt in reverse osmosis. The preferential sorption-capillary diffusion (or 'surface–force pore flow') model of Sourirajan and his school (Sourirajan, 1970, 1977) assumes that the permselective layer of the membrane has very fine 'pores' through which capillary flow of water occurs. The size of the hypothetical pores calculated by them is less than 1 nanometre. Water is preferentially adsorbed on the pore wall. Sorption of the solute at the upstream membrane surface occurs according to a distribution coefficient and is transported by diffusion through the pores. The feed-side mass transfer resistance is taken into account to determine the salt concentration at the membrane surface and the effective pressure driving force is determined by subtracting the osmotic pressure from the applied pressure difference. Spiegler and Kedem (1966) proposed a frictional model according to which the driving force for transport of a species is balanced by the frictional forces exerted on it by the membrane as well as other components moving at a lower velocity. A brief description of the various models is available in Soltanieh and Gill (1981).

EXAMPLE 14.6 (*Concentration polarization in RO*) A cellulose acetate membrane admits of a pure water flux of 100 litre/m^2·h at a pressure differential of 100 bar. (a) Calculate the water and salt flux if a module fitted with this membrane is used to desalinate a 4% NaCl solution at an operating pressure difference of 90 bar. The salt rejection is nearly 100% and the osmotic pressure of 3% NaCl is 17.62 bar. The polarization modulus can be taken to be unity. (b) The same module is used to desalinate a 3.5% solution of *another salt*. The polarization modulus is estimated to be $M = 3.0$, and the salt rejection is $R' = 0.99$. If the osmotic pressure of the solution is 18 bar, calculate the water and salt flux at an applied pressure difference of 75 bar.

For simplicity, the salt rejection may be assumed to be independent of pressure.

Solution
(a) Pure water flux, $J_w = L_p \Delta P \Rightarrow 0.1 \text{ m}^3/\text{m}^2 \cdot \text{h} = L_p (100 \text{ bar})$

$$\Rightarrow \qquad L_p = \boxed{10^{-3} \text{ m}^3/\text{m}^2 \cdot \text{h} \cdot \text{bar}}$$

Water flux for the 4% NaCl *solution*
Concentration polarization modulus, $M = C_m/C_b = 1 \Rightarrow C_m = C_b \ (= 4\% \text{ solution})$
Salt rejection coefficient, $R' = 1 \Rightarrow$ Salt concentration in the permeate, $C_p = 0$.
Osmotic pressure difference between the feed and the permeate,

$$\Delta\Pi = \Pi \text{ of } 4\% \text{ solution} = (17.62)(4/3) = 23.5 \text{ bar [from Eq. 14.24(a)]}$$

Water flux, $J_w = L_p(\Delta P - \Pi) = (10^{-3})(90 - 23.5) = \boxed{0.0665 \text{ m}^3/\text{m}^2 \cdot \text{h}}$ [$= 39.2$ gal/ft^2·day]

Salt flux, $J_s = 0$ (since the salt rejection is about 100%).

(b) *Water and salt flux for the* 3.5% *salt solution*

Concentration polarization modulus, $M = C_m/C_b = 3.0 \Rightarrow C_m = (3.0)C_b = (3.0)(3.5) = 10.5\%$.
Salt rejection coefficient, $R' = 0.99 \Rightarrow$ Salt concentration in the permeate,

$$C_p = (0.01)(10.5\%) = 0.105\%$$

Given, $\Pi = 18$ bar for a 3.5% solution, the osmotic pressure difference between the feed and the permeate,

$$\Delta\Pi = (C_m - C_p)(18/3.5) = (10.5 - 0.105)(18/3.5) = 53.46 \text{ bar}$$

$$\text{Water flux, } J_w = L_p(\Delta P - \Pi) = (10^{-3})(75 - 53.46) = 0.0215 \text{ m}^3/\text{m}^2\cdot\text{h}$$

$$\text{Salt flux} = J_w C_m(1 - R') = (0.0215)(105 \text{ kg/m}^3)(1 - 0.99) = 22.6 \text{ g/m}^2\cdot\text{h}$$

The feed side mass transfer coefficient can be calculated using the given information.

$$\frac{C_m - C_p}{C_b - C_p} = \exp\left(\frac{J_w}{k_L}\right) \quad\Rightarrow\quad \frac{10.5 - 0.105}{3.5 - 0.105} = \exp\left(\frac{J_w}{k_L}\right) \quad\Rightarrow\quad \frac{J_w}{k_L} = 1.12$$

The mass transfer coefficient, $k_L = J_w/1.12 = 0.0215/1.12 \text{ m/h} = \boxed{5.33 \times 10^{-6} \text{ m/s}}$

EXAMPLE 14.7 (*Estimation of Kedem–Katchalsky model parameters*) The following laboratory test data were obtained for water flux and rejection of NaCl of a new RO membrane at different pressures.

Feed concentration (molar)	0.1	0.2	0.3	0.4	0.5	0.6
Feed side pressure (atm)	88.2	59.7	40.1	30	54.8	46.7
Water flux, J_w (m³/m²·h)	0.0525	0.0308	0.017	0.0082	0.0203	0.012
NaCl conc. in the permeate (molar)	0.0033	0.0069	0.0114	0.018	0.0183	0.0243

Given the following data, calculate the parameters (L_p, σ, $\overline{\omega}$) of the Kedem–Katchalsy model: permeate-side pressure = 1.1 atm; osmotic pressure of NaCl = 7.63 atm for a 0.165 molar solution which is linear in concentration.

Solution
The following equation is based on the Kedem–Katchalsy model:

$$J_w = L_p(\Delta P - \sigma\Delta\Pi) \tag{i}$$

$$J_s = J_w(1 - \sigma)C_{s,lm} + \overline{\omega}\,\Delta\Pi \tag{ii}$$

The salt flux can also be written as $J_s = J_w C_p$, (iii)
where C_p = salt concentration in the permeate. From Eqs. (ii) and (iii),

$$J_w C_p = J_w(1 - \sigma)C_{s,lm} + \overline{\omega}\,\Delta\Pi \tag{iv}$$

For simplicity and without incurring much error, we replace $C_{s,lm}$ by the arithmetic mean concentration (see Pusch, 1986).

$$C_{s,lm} \approx (C_f + C_p)/2. \text{ Also putting } \Delta\Pi = \xi(C_f - C_p)$$

$$J_w C_p = J_w(1 - \sigma)(C_f + C_p)/2 + \overline{\omega}'(C_f - C_p); \qquad \overline{\omega}' = \overline{\omega}\,\xi$$

The above equation can be rearranged to

$$\frac{C_p}{C_f - C_p} = \frac{1 - \sigma}{2\sigma} + \frac{\overline{\omega}'}{\sigma}\frac{1}{J_w}$$

Hence a plot of $C_p/(C_f - C_p)$ versus $1/J_w$ should give a straight line of slope $\overline{\omega}'/\sigma$ and an intercept of $(1 - \sigma)/2\sigma$. From the given data, we calculate the following:

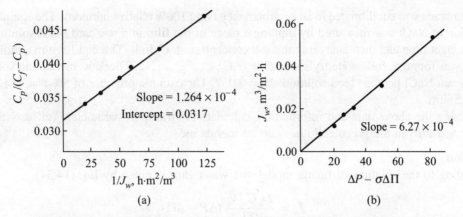

Figure 14.25 (a) Graphical determination of σ and ω', and (b) graphical determination of L_p.

C_f	0.1	0.2	0.3	0.4	0.5	0.6
$\dfrac{C_p}{C_f - C_p}$	0.0341	0.0357	0.0395	0.0471	0.038	0.0422
$1/J_w$	19.05	32.5	58.8	122	49.26	83.3

The plot is shown in Figure 14.25(a). Slope = 1.264×10^{-4}; intercept = 0.0317. Therefore,

$$(1 - \sigma)/2\sigma = 0.0317 \Rightarrow \sigma = 0.94; \qquad \overline{\omega}'/\sigma = 1.264 \times 10^{-4} \Rightarrow \overline{\omega}' = 1.19 \times 10^{-4}.$$

In order to determine L_p, the following calculated data are used.

C_f	0.1	0.2	0.3	0.4	0.5	0.6
$\Delta\Pi$	4.47	8.93	13.34	17.66	22.27	26.6
ΔP	87.1	58.6	39	28.9	53.7	45.6
$(\Delta P - \sigma\Delta\Pi)$	82.9	50.2	26.46	12.3	32.7	20.58
J_w	0.0525	0.0308	0.017	0.0082	0.0203	0.012

L_p is calculated from the slope of the plot [Figure 14.25(b)] of J_w versus $(\Delta P - \sigma\Delta\Pi)$, see Eq. (i) above.

$$L_p = \boxed{6.27 \times 10^{-4} \text{ m}^3/\text{m}^2 \cdot \text{h} \cdot \text{atm}}$$

EXAMPLE 14.8 (*Lonsdale's solution-diffusion model of RO*)   Lonsdale (1965) reported measurements on water and salt fluxes as well as other membrane parameters using a small laboratory RO apparatus. On the feed, there was a 5% solution of NaCl. The permeate-side was continuously flushed with distilled water so that the salt concentration on the permeate side remained zero. In a particular run using a 13 μm thick cellulose acetate membrane (39.5% acetyl content) the water flux J_w was 6.3 μg/cm$^2\cdot$s, and the salt flux J_s was 0.017 μg/cm$^2\cdot$s at 25°C, the transmembrane pressure difference being 80 atm. In order to determine the transport parameters, the equilibrium sorption data of water and NaCl in the membrane material was separately collected. The water sorption C_w was 0.156 g per cm^3 of the polymer when a piece of membrane was equilibriated in an environment having 100% relative humidity. The equilibrium sorption of NaCl was measured by dipping a piece of the film in a standard NaCl solution for a sufficient time and then analyzing the salt concentration C_s in it. The equilibrium sorption of NaCl was found to follow Henry's law, $C_s = H_s C_f$; C_s = gram NaCl per cm^3 membrane volume; C_f = gram NaCl per cm^3 feed solution; $H_s = 0.037$. The osmotic pressure of 5% NaCl solution is 39.5 atm.

Using the above data and information, calculate the transport parameters (diffusivities of water and salt) in the given cellulose acetate membrane.

Solution

According to the solution–diffusion model, the water flux is given by Eq. (14.34).

$$J_w = \frac{D_w C_w \overline{V_1}}{RT l_m}(\Delta P - \Delta \Pi)$$

Since the salt concentration on the permeate side is zero (i.e. osmotic pressure is zero), the osmotic pressure difference between the feed and the permeate sides is $\Delta \Pi = 39.5 - 0 = 39.5$ atm.

The effective pressure driving force is

$$(\Delta P - \Delta \Pi) = 80 - 39.5 = 40.5 \text{ atm}$$

Given: $C_w = 0.156$ g/cm^3 = 156 kg/m^3; for a dilute solution, the partial molar volume of water $\approx$ molar volume of water = 18 cm^3/gmol = 0.018 m^3/kmol; water flux, $J_w = 6.3 \times 10^{-5}$ kg/$m^2\cdot$s; membrane thickness, $l_m = 13$ μm = 1.3×10^{-5} m; $R = 0.0821$ ($m^3\cdot$atm)/(K·kmol); $T = 25°C = 298$ K.

Substituting these values in Eq. (14.34),

$$6.3 \times 10^{-5} \; \frac{\text{kg}}{m^2\cdot\text{s}} = \frac{D_w \, (156 \text{ kg}/m^3)(0.018 \text{ m}^3/\text{kmol})}{(0.0821)(298)(1.3 \times 10^{-5})}(80 - 39.5) \text{ atm}$$

$$\Rightarrow \qquad D_w = \boxed{1.762 \times 10^{-10} \text{ m}^2/\text{s}}$$

Diffusivity of NaCl in the membrane

Using Eq. (14.35), $\qquad\qquad J_s = -D_s(\Delta C_s/l_m)$

Salt concentration on the feed side of the membrane (neglecting the concentration polarization)

$$C_{s1} = H_s C_f = (0.037)(5/100) = 1.85 \times 10^{-3} \text{ g/cm}^3 = 1.85 \text{ kg/m}^3;$$

and on the permeate side, $C_{s2} = 0$.

Salt flux, $J_s = 0.017$ μg/$cm^2\cdot$s $\Rightarrow 1.7 \times 10^{-7}$ kg/$m^2\cdot$s $= D_s(1.85/1.3 \times 10^{-5})$

$$\Rightarrow \qquad \text{Diffusivity of salt in the membrane, } D_s = \boxed{1.2 \times 10^{-12} \text{ m}^2/\text{s}}$$

Design of an RO module

In a spiral wound reverse osmosis module, the feed flows over one side of the membrane and the product water (with a small concentration of salt/solute in it) is drawn from the other side. In the case of a hollow-fibre module, the feed may flow through either the lumen-side or the shell-side and the product water is drawn from the other side. A fraction of the water in the feed is recovered as the product and most of the salt leaves the unit with the reject stream. As the feed-side liquid moves through the module, its flow rate decreases but the concentration of salt in it increases. On the other hand, the flow rate of the product water increases along the flow channel. Since both water and salt flux change along the flow direction (mainly as a result of increasing salt concentration in the flow direction), the salt concentration in the product water also changes along with.

In the design of a module, the flow rate Q_{fi}, the concentration C_{fi} of the feed, and the allowable salt concentration in the product as well as the desired fractional recovery of the water as product are specified. The designer has to select the membrane, the module type and the operating pressure, and should determine the required membrane area to be calculated. The basic transport parameters of the membrane should be known. A simple procedure of calculation of membrane area is described below (Saltonstall and Lawrence, 1982). Alternative design techniques considering concentration polarization were suggested by Sirkar and Rao (1983). Ohya et al. (1987) discussed a design procedure of tapered RO modules based on modified Spiegler–Kedem equations and taking into account compaction of the membrane under pressure.

Since the salt concentration on the feed side changes along the flow channel, the permeation flux of both water and salt change simultaneously. Use of the average salt concentration on the feed side yields erroneous results if the change of concentration is substantial. If Q_f and C_f are the flow rate and concentration of the feed-side liquid at any section of the channel, and Q_p and C_p are those on the product or the permeate-side, the following material balance equations may be written (Figure 14.26):

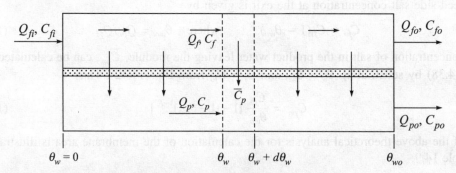

Figure 14.26 Flow rates and concentrations in an RO unit.

Total material balance:

$$Q_{fi} = Q_f + Q_p \qquad (14.36)$$

Salt balance:

$$Q_{fi}C_{fi} = Q_f C_f + Q_p \overline{C}_p \qquad (14.36a)$$

Here $\overline{C}_p$ is the salt concentration in the product water leaving the section, i.e. the average salt concentration in the product in the section under consideration.

If $\theta_w = Q_p/Q_{fi}$ is the local 'fractional recovery' of the water,

$$C_{fi} = \frac{Q_f}{Q_{fi}} C_f + \frac{Q_p}{Q_{fi}} \overline{C}_p = \frac{Q_{fi} - Q_p}{Q_{fi}} C_f + \theta_w \overline{C}_p \qquad (14.37)$$

$$\Rightarrow \qquad C_{fi} = (1 - \theta_w)C_f + \theta_w \overline{C}_p \quad \Rightarrow \quad C_f = \frac{C_{fi} - \theta_w \overline{C}_p}{1 - \theta_w} \qquad (14.38)$$

If R' is the fractional rejection of salt, the concentration in the local permeate C_p is given by

$$C_p = (1 - R')C_f$$

The bulk or average concentration of the salt in the permeate at the section is

$$\overline{C}_p = \frac{1}{\theta_w} \int_0^{\theta_w} (1 - R')C_f \, d\theta_w \qquad (14.39)$$

Substituting Eq. (14.39) in (14.38), the local salt concentration on the feed side is given by

$$C_f = \frac{1}{1 - \theta_w}\left[C_{fi} - \int_0^{\theta_w} (1 - R')C_f \, d\theta_w \right] \qquad (14.40)$$

Multiplying both sides with $(1 - \theta_w)$ and differentiating with respect to θ_w,

$$(1 - \theta_w)\frac{dC_f}{d\theta_w} - C_f = -(1 - R')C_f \;\Rightarrow\; (1 - \theta_w)\frac{dC_f}{d\theta_w} = R'C_f \;\Rightarrow\; \frac{dC_f}{C_f} = \frac{R' \, d\theta_w}{1 - \theta_w}$$

Integrating, we have, $C_f = K''(1 - \theta_w)^{-R'}$, where K'' is the integration constant.

Using the boundary condition, $\theta_w = 0$, $C_f = C_{fi}$, we get $K'' = C_{fi}$. Therefore,

$$C_f = C_{fi}(1 - \theta_w)^{-R'} \qquad (14.41)$$

The feed-side salt concentration at the exit is given by

$$C_{fo} = C_{fi}(1 - \theta_{wo})^{-R'} \qquad \text{where} \quad \theta_{wo} = Q_{po}/Q_{fi} \qquad (14.42)$$

The concentration of salt in the product water leaving the module, $\overline{C}_{po}$, can be calculated from Eq. (14.38) by substituting $\theta_w = \theta_{wo}$ and $C_f = C_{fo}$ from Eq. (14.42). Thus

$$\overline{C}_{po} = \frac{C_{fo}}{\theta_{wo}}[1 - (1 - \theta_{wo})^{1-R'}] \qquad (14.43)$$

Use of the above theoretical analysis for the calculation of the membrane area is illustrated in Example 14.9.

EXAMPLE 14.9 (*Design of an RO module*) It is required to design an RO module for production of 1500 m³/day potable water containing not more than 250 ppm salt from sea water containing 34 g salt per litre. A proprietary asymmetric cellulose acetate membrane with an inherent salt rejection ability of 98% is to be used. The water permeation coefficient is 0.043 m³/m²·day·atm. The recovery of the feed water should be 35% and an operating pressure of 70 atm gauge is suggested. The permeate side is at essentially atmospheric pressure. If spiral wound modules of 5 m² effective membrane area each is used, how many modules in parallel are required? What fraction of the input power can be recovered from the retentate if a turbine of 70% efficiency is used for energy recovery? The osmotic pressure of 5% brine (linear in salt concentration) is 39.5 atm.

Solution

Given: $Q_p/Q_{fi} = 0.35 = \theta_{wo}$; rejection, $R' = 0.98$; salt concentration in the feed, $C_{fi} = 3.4\%$.

Retentate concentration, $C_{fo} = C_{fi}(1 - \theta_{wo})^{-R} = 3.4(1 - 0.35)^{-0.98} = 5.186\%$

Exit concentration of the mixed permeate water, $\overline{C}_p = 250$ ppm $= 0.025\%$; its osmotic pressure $= 0.2$ atm.

Osmotic pressure of the feed brine (3.4%) = (39.5/5)(3.4) = 27.8 atm. (see Example 14.8); that of exit brine (5.186%) = 42.08 atm.

Take the average $\Delta\Pi$ value to calculate the effective pressure driving force (neglect the osmotic pressure of the permeate)

$$(\Delta\Pi)_{av} = (27.8 + 42.08)/2 = 34.94 \text{ atm}$$

$\Rightarrow \qquad (\Delta P - \Delta\Pi)_{av} \approx (70 - 34.94) = 35.06 \text{ atm}$

$$\text{Water flux} = (0.043)(35.06) = 1.51 \text{ m}^3/\text{m}^2 \cdot \text{day}$$

$$\text{Total membrane area required} = 1500/1.51 = 993 \text{ m}^2$$

$$\text{Number of modules} = 993/5 = 199, \boxed{\text{say } 200}$$

Calculation of power recovery: Given $Q_{fi} = Q_{fo} + Q_p$, $Q_p = 1500$ m^3/day. Now make a salt balance,

$$(Q_{fo} + 1500)(0.034) = (Q_{fo})(0.05186) + (1500)(0.00025) \Rightarrow Q_{fo} = 2835 \text{ m}^3/\text{day}$$

Power recovery (efficiency, $\eta = 0.7$) = $(Q_{fo}.\Delta P).\eta = (2835 \text{ m}^3/\text{day})(70 \text{ atm})(0.7)$

$$= \frac{2835}{(24)(3600)} \frac{\text{m}^3}{\text{s}} \cdot [(70)(1.013)(10^5) \text{ N/m}^2](0.7) = 1.629 \times 10^5 \text{ (Nm)/s}$$

$$= 1.629 \times 10^5 \text{ J/s} = \boxed{163 \text{ kW}}$$

14.4.8 Nanofiltration

Nanofiltration is placed midway between UF and RO; an NF membrane may be considered as a very 'tight' UF or a very 'loose' RO membrane. As the name implies, the size of the solutes excluded is of the order of 1 nanometre. The pore size range of NF membranes is roughly 0.5–2 nm, the MWCO lies between 150 and 300 or a little larger, and the operating pressure drop is 100–1000 psi (which is considerably smaller than that in RO). The most distinctive feature of NF membranes is nearly complete rejection of ions with two or more negative charge. The maximum rejection of NaCl may be about 70% but is much smaller in most cases. The permeation flux ranges from 0.1–1 m^3/m$^2 \cdot$ day.

Because of its capability of separating relatively small molecules at an operating pressure less than that in RO, nanofiltration has already found a lot of practical applications (Schafer, 2005). The major use areas are: water reclamation (both industrial and municipal), softening of brackish water, food industries (concentration of dextrose syrup, concentration and demineralization of UF-whey permeate, degumming of edible oils), chemical and other industries (metal recovery, recovery of textile dyes, cleaning paper mill effluents, solvent dewaxing).

An early successful attempt to prepare an NF membrane was based on interfacial polymerization of piperazine with a hydrophobic aromatic cross-linking agent on a UF polysulphone support. Cellulose acetate and acetate-butyrate, polyamides, polyimides, sulphonated polysulphone are a few important materials for making NF membranes. A few manufacturers of UF, NF and RO membranes are: Dow Filmtec, Hydranautics, Osmonics, Koch Membrane Systems, and PCI Membranes.

14.5 CONCENTRATION-DRIVEN PROCESSES

There are a number of membrane separation processes based on selective transport of a target species under a concentration driving force. The more important ones are dialysis, haemodialysis, pervaporation and liquid membrane separation.

14.5.1 Dialysis

Dialysis, the oldest membrane separation process, is the diffusional transport of one or more dissolved species through a thin permselective barrier placed between two aqueous solutions at different concentrations (Figure 14.27). Thus the separation is concentration-driven; there is no bulk flow of the solvent or of the solution through the membrane. Since smaller molecules diffuse faster than larger ones, the technique of dialysis separates such molecules from a solution. For example, sodium hydroxide (17–20%) in the viscose liquor containing colloidal hemicellulose can be

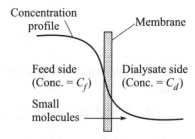

Figure 14.27   Separation by dialysis.

recovered as 9–10% caustic solution by dialysis. The other impurities which are of high molecular weight cannot diffuse through the membranes in any appreciable quantity. A dialysis unit is called a *dialyser*. The feed-side liquid leaving the unit is called *dialysate* (the same as retentate), and that leaving the permeate side is called *diffusate*. Since the process involves diffusional transport through a dense membrane, a membrane material that swells substantially in contact with the solvent is selected. Swelling of a polymer increases the spaces between the polymer chains and thereby facilitates diffusional motion of molecules through it. Table 14.7 gives a summary of the basic information on dialysis.

Table.14.7   Some basic information on dialysis

Membrane	Thin dense film; asymmetric membranes are preferred.
Thickness	10–100 μ; pore diameter: 0–10 nm
Separation mechanism	Solution–diffusion; difference in diffusivities of larger and smaller molecules
Membrane materials	Hydrophilic highly swelling materials like 'regenerated cellulose' (cellophane or cuprophan)[†], cross-linked vinyl acetate; copolymer of ethylene and vinyl acetate, etc.

[†] Cellulose, a natural polymer, can be solubilized in a suitable medium and then de-solubilized by changing the process conditions. The product is cellulose of lower average molecular weight, lesser crystallinity and of considerably different properties. This is 'regenerated cellulose', classically called rayon. There are two methods of solubilizing cellulose—the xanthate method ($NaOH + CS_2$), and the cuprammonium process ($NH_4OH + CuO$). Cuprophan is regenerated cellulose made by the latter process. Cellophane [*Cellu*lose + Dia*phane* (French: transparent)] film is made from regenerated cellulose.

Since a substantial concentration difference between the feed and the permeate side liquids must be maintained (this acts as the driving force for transport), the dialyzate has a lesser concentration of the solute than that in the feed. The feed side may have to be maintained at a higher pressure if the osmotic flow of water from the permeate side is to be prevented.

Applications

Dialysis offers a passive environment for transport since the solutions are not in direct contact and no pressure is applied as in RO. Its most important application is for medical purposes (see Section 14.5.2 on Haemodialysis). One commercially important application is adjustment of alcohol content in beer. Many breweries use dialysis to reduce the alcohol content of beer. Another application is for removal of salts from heat sensitive or mechanically labile compounds such as vaccines, hormones and enzymes.

Theoretical principles

Dialysis is a diffusional process and the resistances offered by the membrane as well as by the liquid boundary layers on both sides of it need to be taken into account for the calculation of the solute flux. If k_{Lf} and k_{Lp} are the liquid film mass transport coefficients on the feed and the permeate side respectively, D is the diffusivity of the solute in the membrane of thickness l_m, the flux of a species can be expressed in terms of an overall mass transfer coefficient defined as

$$J_i = K_L(C_f - C_p) \tag{14.44}$$

where

$$\frac{1}{K_L} = \frac{1}{k_{Kf}} + \frac{l_m}{\beta D_M} + \frac{1}{k_{Lp}} \tag{14.45}$$

Here β is a distribution coefficient defined as $C = \beta C_M$, C = conc. of the solute in the liquid and C_M is the equilibrium concentration in the membrane. The product, $\beta D_M = \hat{P}_s$, is called the permeability of the solute in the membrane. The following points need to be noted: (i) if the membrane is tubular with a thickness comparable to the radius, a log mean radius term appears in the membrane resistance term (the second term) in Eq. (14.45); (ii) if the boundary layer mass transfer coefficients k_{Lf} and k_{Lp} are high, the membrane may offer the controlling resistance to mass transfer; (iii) if the membrane is thin and has a high permeability of the solute, the boundary layer resistances will control.

14.5.2   Haemodialysis

Transport of small molecules routinely occur in living systems. Typical examples are absorption of oxygen and desorption of carbon dioxide in the lungs, removal of waste products (urea, creatinine, uric acid, etc.) from blood in the kidney, diffusion of a variety of substances through the cell wall, supply of oxygen from blood to muscles. Synthetic membranes and membrane devices play a very important role in mimicking the functions of bio-organs such as lungs and kidney. In fact, novel membrane-based bio-artificial organs such as blood oxygenator, haemodialyser, bio-artificial lever ('extra-corporeal devices') as well as intra-vascular devices for drug delivery have revolutionized the healthcare system to a considerable extent.

Removal of toxic low molecular weight compounds from blood using a membrane device is known as *haemodialysis*. This is *maintenance dialysis* for patients suffering from kidney failure. The first successful haemodialyser (artificial kidney) was constructed in 1945 by Kolf and Berk (see Baker, 2004) who used a cellophane membrane for the purpose. A common device presently used for haemodialysis [Figure 14.28(a)] consists of a bundle of hollow-fibre membranes 'potted' with a polyurethane epoxy resin at the two ends and fitted in an outer polycarbonate housing. The device has a shell-and-tube type construction and is fitted with nozzle connections. The blood drawn from an artery of a patient's body is passed through a PVC tube by a peristaltic pump to enter the lumen side of the haemodialyser. Heparin, an anticoagulent, is added to the blood. An 'isotonic aqueous solution' containing glucose and electrolytes flows through the shell-side (dialysate side) so that the osmotic flow of water through the membrane wall is eliminated. Countercurrent flow of blood and the dialysate is usually maintained. Purified blood flows back to a vein of the patient's body. A positive pressure differential of 100 to 500 mm Hg is maintained on the blood side to reject some water from the blood into the dialysate (this means that ultrafiltration occurs at a low rate simultaneously). A computer-controlled dialysis unit with a number of sensors is schematically shown in Figure 14.28(b).

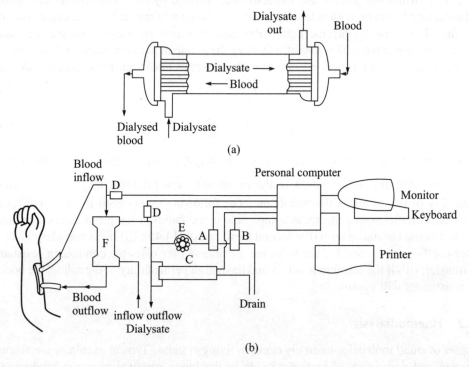

Figure 14.28 (a) and (b)   (a) Schematic of a haemodialyser. (b) A computer-controlled dialysis unit (Furusaki et al., *The Emerging World of Chemical Engineering*, 2002). [A: Urea sensor; B: Creatinine sensor; C: Middle-molecule sensor; D: Pressure sensor; E: Micropump; F: Dialyser].

The hollow-fibres typically have 200 μm i.d. and 10–25 μm wall thickness. The common membrane materials are: regenerated cellulose (Cellophane, or Cuprophan of Azco Fraser AG, made by the 'cuprammonium process'), cellulose acetate, polysulphone, polyacrylonitrile, polyacrylamide, polyamide. Although nearly half of the dialysers in use have cellophane membrane, microporous and asymmetric hollow fibres (skin layer on the inner side, in contact with blood) are being preferred because of higher permeability. The molecular weight cut-off is around 1000 so that substances such as urea (mol. wt. = 60), uric acid (mol. wt. = 168), creatinine (mol. wt. = 113) diffuse through the pores on the membrane wall but not the higher molecular weight substances. It is desirable that the hollow-fibre bundle is discarded after use. A typical haemodialyser has a surface area of 1–1.5 m^2; length = 25 cm; dia = 5 cm; number of fibres = 6000–10,000. About 60–100 ml blood fills the dialyser. The unit cost is around \$15. Haemodialysers are produced in huge quantities (over 70 million annually) and account for the largest share of the membrane market.

Theoretical analysis of solute transport in a haemodialyser

Transport of a solute in a haemodialyser is akin to heat transfer in a shell-and-tube heat exchanger. The flow arrangement of blood and the dialyzate may be cocurrent or countercurrent, the latter being more common. A unit with cocurrent flow is schematically shown in Figure 14.28(c) for the purpose of a simple theoretical analysis. The steady-state mass balance equations for solute transport from blood to the dialysate fluid are given below.

$$Q_b C_b\big|_z - Q_b C_b\big|_{z+\Delta z} = K_L(B'\Delta z)(C_b - C_d) \quad \Rightarrow \quad -Q_b \frac{dC_b}{dz} = K_L B'(C_b - C_d) \qquad (14.46a)$$

$$Q_d C_d\big|_z - Q_d C_d\big|_{z+\Delta z} = -K_L(B'\Delta z)(C_b - C_d) \quad \Rightarrow \quad -Q_d \frac{dC_d}{dz} = -K_L B'(C_b - C_d) \quad (14.46b)$$

Here Q_b and Q_d are the flow rates (assumed constant) of blood and of the fluid, and C_b and C_d are the local concentrations of the solute in the respective streams; K_L is the overall mass transfer coefficient; B' is the perimeter of the tubes, so that $B'\Delta z$ is the differential area for transport. Adding the equations, we get

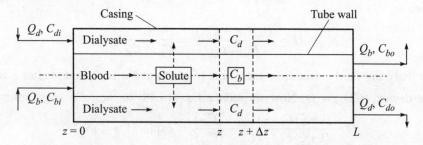

Figure 14.28(c)   Differential mass balance diagram for a cocurrent haemodialyser.

$$Q_b \frac{dC_b}{dz} + Q_d \frac{dC_d}{dz} = 0 \quad \Rightarrow \quad Q_b C_b + Q_d C_d = \text{constant} = Q_b C_{bi} + Q_d C_{di}$$

$$\Rightarrow \qquad C_d(z) = C_{di} + (Q_b/Q_d)(C_{bi} - C_b) = C_{di} + \zeta(C_{bi} - C_b); \quad \zeta = Q_b/Q_d \qquad (14.47)$$

From Eqs. [14.46(a)] and (14.47),

$$-Q_b \frac{dC_b}{dz} = K_L B' \left[C_b - \left(C_{di} + \frac{Q_b}{Q_d}(C_{bi} - C_b) \right) \right] = K_L B'[(1 + \zeta)C_b - (C_{di} + \zeta C_{bi})]$$

Integrating from $z = 0$, $C_b = C_{bi}$ to $z = L$, $C_b = C_{bo}$,

$$-\int_{C_{bi}}^{C_{bo}} \frac{dC_b}{(1+\zeta)C_b - (C_{di} + \zeta C_{bi})} = \int_0^L \frac{K_L B'}{Q_b} \, dz\,; \qquad \zeta = Q_b/Q_d$$

$$\Rightarrow \;\; \ln \frac{(1+\zeta)C_{bo} - (C_{di} + \zeta C_{bi})}{(1+\zeta)C_{bi} - (C_{di} + \zeta C_{bi})} = -\frac{(1+\zeta)K_L(B'L)}{Q_b} = -(1+\zeta)N_T; \quad N_T = \frac{K_L \, a_m}{Q_b} \quad (14.48)$$

The above equation gives the outlet concentration of the concerned species in the blood leaving the dialyser in terms of the 'number of transfer units' N_T, and other parameters ($a_m = B'L$ = area of the dialyser). The performance of a dialyser is expressed in terms of two quantities, the *clearance* and the *dialysance*.

The amount of solute transported to the dialysate as the blood flows through the dialyser at a rate Q_b is

$$\hat{m} = Q_b(C_{bi} - C_{bo}) \qquad \cdot\cdot$$

The input blood is only partly cleaned, the solute concentration changes from C_{bi} to C_{bo}. The equivalent flow rate of blood that will be totally free from the solute for the rate of transfer $\hat{m}$ of the solute is given by

$$(CL)_D(C_{bi} - 0) = \hat{m} \quad \Rightarrow \quad (CL)_D = \hat{m}/C_{bi} = Q_b(C_{bi} - C_{bo})/C_{bi} \qquad (14.49)$$

The quantity $(CL)_D$, in ml/min or a similar unit, is called the 'clearance' of the dialyser. Physically, it indicates the effective rate at which the dialyzer is capable of *fully* cleaning the blood. A typical dialyser has a clearance of 50–100 ml/min for a low molecular weight solute like urea or creatinin.

Dialysance is another indicator of the performance or solute removal capability of a dialyser. It is defined as

$$\hat{D} = \frac{Q_b(C_{bi} - C_{bo})}{C_{bi} - C_{di}} = \frac{\hat{m}}{C_{bi} - C_{di}} \qquad (14.50)$$

If the inlet dialysing fluid is free from the solute ($C_{di} = 0$) and it is discarded after a single pass though the device, $(CL)_D = \hat{D}$. Now we reduce Eq. (14.48) to the following form:

$$1 - \frac{(1+\zeta)C_{bo} - (C_{di} + \zeta C_{bi})}{(1+\zeta)C_{bi} - (C_{di} + \zeta C_{bi})} = \exp[-(1+\zeta)N_T]$$

$$\Rightarrow \qquad \frac{C_{bi} - C_{bo}}{C_{bi} - C_{di}} = \frac{1 - \exp[-(1+\zeta)N_T]}{1+\zeta} = \frac{\hat{D}}{Q_b} \qquad (14.51)$$

The ratio $\hat{D}/Q_b$ has sometimes been called the *extraction ratio*, $\hat{E}$. Then, from the above equation,

$$\frac{\hat{D}}{Q_b} = \frac{C_{bi} - C_{bo}}{C_{bi} - C_{di}} = \frac{1 - \exp[-(1+\zeta)N_T]}{1+\zeta} = \hat{E} \qquad (14.52)$$

Equation (14.51) or (14.52) gives the performance equation of a cocurrent haemodialyser. For the countercurrent flow configuration, the performance equation can be found to be

$$\hat{E} = \frac{C_{bi} - C_{bo}}{C_{bi} - C_{di}} = \frac{1 - \exp[(1-\zeta)N_T]}{\zeta - \exp[(1-\zeta)N_T]} \tag{14.53}$$

The above theoretical analysis of transport in a haemodialyser is a simplified one and does not take into account quite a few important factors. More elaborate treatment is available in the literature (see Fournier, 1999, and the references therein).

EXAMPLE 14.10 (*Time of dialysis using a hollow-fibre haemodialyser*)   Blood from a patient's body is pumped through a cocurrent haemodialyser at a rate of 280 ml/min to reduce the urea concentration from 200 mg% to 20 mg%. The other undesirable substances are removed as well. The available membrane area is 1.15 m², and the overall mass transfer coefficient is estimated to be 1.2×10^{-6} m/s. The volume of blood in a normal human body is about 5 litre. If the flow rate of the dialysate fluid is maintained high ($Q_d >> Q_b$), estimate the time of dialysis. Also the dialysate fluid is solute-free.

Solution

Since $Q_b << Q_d$, $\zeta = Q_b/Q_d \approx 0$. The dialysate fluid is solute-free, i.e. $C_{di} = 0 \approx C_{do}$.

Using Eq. (14.52), $\hat{E} = \dfrac{C_{bi} - C_{bo}}{C_{bi}} = 1 - e^{-N_T} \Rightarrow (C_{bi} - C_{bo}) = C_{bi}(1 - e^{-N_T})$

Let V_L be the volume of blood to be cleared of the urea. At any time t, the urea concentration in blood is C_{bi}. It enters the haemodialyser at this concentration which gets reduced to C_{bo} across the device. Thus the change in the urea concentration in the blood in time dt is given by

$$-V_L dC_{bi} = Q_b dt(C_{bi} - C_{bo}) \Rightarrow -V_L \frac{dC_{bi}}{dt} = Q_b C_{bi}(1 - e^{-N_T})$$

In order to estimate the time for change of the urea concentration from C_1 to C_2, we integrate the above equation to get

$$-\int_{C_1}^{C_2} \frac{dC_{bi}}{C_{bi}} = \int_0^t \frac{Q_b}{V_L}(1 - e^{-N_T})dt \Rightarrow \ln\frac{C_1}{C_2} = \frac{Q_b}{V_L}(1 - e^{-N_T})t$$

Given: $V_L = 5$ litre $= 5 \times 10^{-3}$ m³; $C_1/C_2 = 200/20 = 10$;

$K_L = 1.2 \times 10^{-6}$ m/s, $a_m = 1.15$ m²; $Q_b = 280$ ml/min $= 4.667 \times 10^{-6}$ m³/s

$\Rightarrow$ Number of transfer units, $N_T = (1.2 \times 10^{-6}$ m/s$)(1.15$ m²$)/(4.667 \times 10^{-6}$ m³/s$) = 0.296$

Estimated time, $t = \dfrac{V_L}{Q_b} \cdot \ln\dfrac{C_1}{C_2} \cdot (1 - e^{-N_T})^{-1}$

$$= \frac{5 \times 10^{-3}\,\text{m}^3}{4.667 \times 10^{-6}\,\text{m}^3/\text{s}}\,(\ln 10)\,(1 - e^{-0.296})^{-1}$$

$$= 9630\,\text{s} = \boxed{2\,\text{h}\,40\,\text{min}}$$

Although the above analysis is a simplified one, the estimated time is fairly realistic.

14.5.3   Electrodialysis

Electrodialysis (ED) is a process of removal of salts from an aqueous solution by transport through an electrically charged membrane. The basic principle is illustrated in Figure 14.29 which shows an ED cell. The cell is divided into a number of compartments by placing pieces of a cation exchange membrane and an anion exchange membrane alternately. At the two ends are placed a cathode and an anode connected to a dc power source. The feed solution containing a salt—NaCl, for example—flows through the compartments as shown in Figure 14.29. Let us consider one of

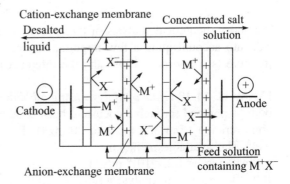

Figure 14.29   Basic principle of electrodialysis illustrated.

the compartments. The cations (Na^+) pass through the cation-exchange membrane that has fixed negative charges but the anions are retained. The other membrane partition of the compartment being an anion-exchange membrane, allows the anions (Cl^-) to pass through. Thus the solution flowing through this compartment gets depleted of the salt (i.e. both Na^+ and Cl^- ions through the membrane on two sides of a compartment), while the adjacent compartments get enriched in the salt. The concentration of the salt decreases in alternate compartments and increases in the rest. Desalinated water and concentrated brine leave from adjacent compartments. The applied electrical potential provides the driving force for transport of the ions through the membrane[†].

Electrodialysis is widely used for desalination of brackish water as an alternative to RO or thermal desalination to produce potable water. In Japan, the technique is used to concentrate sea water to about 200 g/litre salt prior to evaporation and crystallization for the production of table salt. The recovery of nickel salts by concentrating the electroplating rinse water is another commercial application of ED. The technique is used in food industries to demineralize, i.e. to remove salts from cheese whey that contains about 6% salt and 0.5% lactic acid that has to be removed before recovery of substances like proteins from it or for using it for the production of certain foods. A recent application of ED, in combination with mixed-bed ion-exchanger, has been the production of ultrapure water for the semiconductor industry.

Besides being simple in construction of the cell, ED is also attractive for its energy efficiency. It is particularly attractive if the salt concentration is low. The electrical current requirement is directly proportional to the amount of ions transported through the membranes and is given by

$$I = zFQ\Delta C/\xi \tag{14.54}$$

Here z = charge on an ion; F = Faraday's constant; Q = feed solution flow rate; ΔC = change in concentration of the solute; ξ = current utilization factor that accounts for the energy efficiency of the process. The electrical power consumption is given by

$$E = I^2(nR) \tag{14.55}$$

[†] This is an example where mass transfer occurs by an electrical potential driving force.

Electrical energy consumption in ED units is about 1.6–2.6 kWh/m^3 of product water from a feed having 1500–2000 mg salt/litre. Potable water produced by ED needs chlorination for disinfection but RO water does not.

14.5.4 Pervaporation

The technique of pervaporation (PV) combines, in a single operation, selective permeation of one or more species in a volatile liquid mixture and its subsequent vaporization (*permeation* + *evaporation*). The membrane—flat or tubular—separates the feed and the permeate sides. A component in the feed (which is a volatile liquid mixture) that has a larger affinity for the membrane material gets preferentially sorbed on the feed-side of the membrane. The solute then diffuses through the membrane and vaporizes at the product side of the membrane, which is maintained under vacuum. The vapour product, having the target compound at a much larger concentration than in the

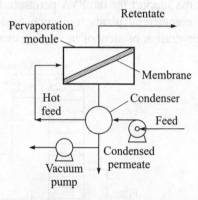

Figure 14.30(a) Schematic of a pervaporation unit.

feed, moves into a condenser where it is condensed and recovered as a liquid [Figure 14.30(a)]. Alternatively, the vapour product may be carried away from the downstream side by a sweep gas. This technique, rarely used in practice, is called *sweep-gas pervaporation*. For some mixtures, the retentate liquid is the product (for example, dehydration of alcohol) and the vapour is discarded or subjected to further separation.

Pervaporation cannot be considered a common alternative to conventional processes of separation of liquid mixtures like distillation and liquid extraction. The diffusional flux through a membrane is generally low. Also the right membrane that would provide high flux and a satisfactory separation factor is not always available. As a result, the practical application of this potentially important technique has so far been limited to the separation of some typical mixtures that are not easily amenable to treatment by conventional techniques (Dutta and Sikdar, 1997).

Industrial applications

A few more important industrial applications of pervaporation are: (i) preparation of absolute alcohol from a concentrated, near azeotropic, mixture of alcohol and water; (ii) dehydration of solvents; (iii) removal of organics from aqueous solutions at low concentrations. The world's largest pervaporation plant operates in Bethenville, France, to produce 150,000 litre ethanol (~99.95%) per day using 2400 m^2 membrane area. The traditional method of producing absolute alcohol (absolute alcohol is used in large quantities in pharmaceutical and fine chemical industries) by azetropic distillation using benzene as the third component is not only capital intensive (two distillation columns with reboilers, condensers and accessories are required) but is also undesirable because benzene itself is carcinogenic. As a result, the pervaporation technique which was developed by GFT in Germany in mid-1970s has been an attractive and economic alternative. A simplified, integrated distillation-pervaporation 'hybrid plant' that receives dilute alcohol from the fermentor (5–7% alcohol) and first produces 80–90% (nearly azeotropic) alcohol by distillation is shown in Figure 14.30(b). Water is then separated from the concentrated alcohol to yield a high purity product. GFT uses an asymmetric composite membrane consisting of three layers. There is a 'non-woven' polyester support on which a polyacrylonitrile (PAN) or polysulphone UF membrane is cast. On the top of the UF membrane layer is cast an ultrathin (0.1 μm) layer of cross-linked polyvinyl alcohol (PVA). The hydrophilic PVA layer allows preferential permeation of water through it and leaves dehydrated alcohol as the retentate. The lower two layers serve as the support for the PVA permselective film. Three pervaporation modules are used in series in commercial plants [only one is shown in Figure 14.30(b)]. Nearly one hundred units for dehydration of alcohol in varying quantities are now operating in different parts of the world.

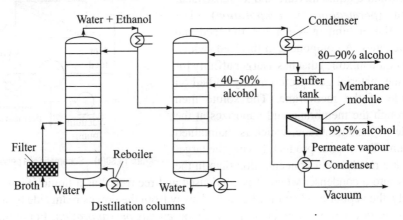

Figure 14.30 (b)   Integrated distillation-pervaporation plant for absolute alcohol.

Quite a few plants for dehydration of solvents and organics [for example, *iso*-propanol, ethyl acetate, ethers (tetrahydrofuran, dimethyl ether of ethylene glycol, etc.) and ketones] based on the GFT technology are in operation. These plants also use PVA membrane. On the other hand, a hydrophobic membrane prepared from polydimethylsiloxane (PDMS) is used for the separation of organics from water. Typical applications are for reducing the alcohol content of beer, removal of chlorinated hydrocarbons from waste water, removal and recovery of aroma compounds from aqueous extracts. Several commercial plants are in operation. Membrane modules for pervaporation are of plate-and-frame, tubular or spiral-wound design. A few modules in series are frequently used. The heat of vaporization is absorbed from the feed-side liquid only. So, intermittent heating of the liquid between two modules has to be done. The vapour product may be condensed by heat exchange with the feed which gets preheated.

Theoretical principles

The overall process consists of the following five steps in series (Gonzales and Utribe, 2001): (i) transfer of a species from the bulk of the feed solution to the membrane surface, (ii) selective sorption of the component at the membrane surface, (iii) diffusional transport of the component through the membrane, (iv) desorption of the component at the permeate side of the membrane, and (v) transfer of the component from the membrane surface to the bulk of the permeate. Although step (iii) is generally slow, the upstream and downstream diffusional resistances may sometimes play a significant, even controlling role (for example, separation of nonpolar organics from water) in the overall process.

Sorption equilibrium at the membrane surface: As in most other mass transfer processes, equilibrium sorption of the permeating component at the membrane surface is assumed. A simple description of sorption equilibrium in terms of the Henry's law does not apply to many membrane-solute systems because of a strong interaction between the solute and the membrane material. For simplicity, let us consider separation of a binary mixture only. Interfacial equilibrium at the membrane surface (upstream or downstream) demands equality of the chemical potential.

In general, the chemical potential of a species in solution is expressed as

$$\mu_i = \mu_{i,0} + RT \ln a_i = \mu_{i,0} + RT \ln(\gamma_i x_i) \tag{14.56}$$

where x_i = mole fraction of component i in solution and γ_i is its activity coefficient.

For sorption equilibrium,

$$\mu_{i,1}^m = \mu_{i,1}^l \quad \Rightarrow \quad a_{i,1}^m = \gamma_i x_{i,1} \tag{14.57}$$

where i = ith component; l = bulk liquid phase; v = vapour phase; m = membrane phase; 1 = upstream side; and 2 = downstream side.

The activity of a component in the feed-side solution can be obtained by using a standard equation (for example, the Wilson equation or the UNIFAC equation); that of a component sorbed in the membrane is related to its concentration or volume fraction. Again a suitable thermodynamic model for the polymer-solute system—for example, the Flory–Huggin's equation—has to be used to estimate the activity of the species in the membrane phase.

Now consider equilibrium at the permeate side of the membrane which is at a low pressure. The chemical potential of component i in the vapour can be expressed as

$$\mu_{i,2}^v = \mu_i^0[P_i^v, T] + RT \ln a_{i,2}^v; \quad a_{i,2}^v = \frac{P_2 y_{i,2}}{P_i^v} \quad [P_i^v = \text{vapour pressure}; V_i = \text{molar volume}] \tag{14.58}$$

The chemical potential of the solute in the membrane at the surface on the permeate side is

$$\mu_{i,2}^m = \mu_i^0[P_i^v, T] + V_i[P_1 - P_i^v] + RT \ln a_{i,2}^m; \quad a_{i,2}^m = \frac{P_2 y_{i,2}}{P_i^v} \tag{14.59}$$

Equating Eqs. (14.58) and (14.59) at equilibrium,

$$\mu_{i,2}^v = \mu_{i,2}^m \quad \Rightarrow \quad a_{i,2}^m = \frac{P_2 y_{i,2}}{P_i^v} \exp\left[\frac{V_i(P_i^v - P_1)}{RT}\right] \tag{14.60}$$

Equations (14.57) and (14.60) provide the boundary conditions for the solute activity at the two surfaces of the membrane. Because of the higher affinity of the membrane for a species in a mixture, the sorption equilibrium may be totally different from the normal vapour–liquid equilibrium. In the case of separation of a mixture of alcohol and water using a PVA membrane, for example, water is preferentially sorbed and permeated. Figure 14.31 shows the typical composition of the permeate, richer in water, compared to that of the vapour in ordinary distillation.

Permeation through the membrane: When a polymer is in contact with a solution, the diffusion phenomenon is highly non-ideal and a modified form of Fick's law with the gradient of chemical potential as the driving force is appropriate (Mulder and Smolders, 1984).

$$J_i = -C_i B_i \frac{d\mu_i^m}{dz} \tag{14.61}$$

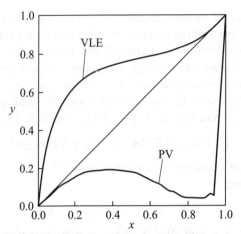

Figure 14.31   Separation of aqueous ethanol by pervaporation; VLE: ethanol mole fraction (y) in vapour for equilibrium vaporization, PV: ethanol mole fraction in the permeate through a PVA membrane.

Putting $d\mu_i^m = RT\, d\ln a_i^m$,

$$J_i = -C_i B_i RT \frac{d\ln a_i^m}{dz} = -C_i \overline{D}_i \frac{d\ln a_i^m}{dz} \tag{14.62}$$

where $B_i RT = \overline{D}_i$ is called the *thermodynamic diffusion coefficient* of species i in a frame of reference stationary with respect to the polymer. Also in a highly swollen polymer such as a pervaporation membrane, the diffusivity of a solute becomes strongly dependent upon the concentrations in the polymer. The more the extent of swelling, the more are the concentrations of the sorbed components and the higher are the diffusion coefficients. Equation (14.62) may be recast as

$$J_i = -\overline{D}_i(C_1, C_2) \frac{d\ln a_i^m}{d\ln C_i} \frac{dC_i}{dz} \tag{14.63}$$

For the components in a binary,

$$J_1 = -\overline{D}_1(C_1, C_2) \frac{d\ln a_1^m}{d\ln C_1} \frac{dC_1}{dz} \tag{14.64}$$

$$J_2 = -\overline{D}_2(C_1, C_2) \frac{d\ln a_2^m}{d\ln C_2} \frac{dC_2}{dz} \tag{14.65}$$

The integration of the above two equations over the membrane thickness using the equilibrium concentrations at the membrane surfaces at upstream and downstream sides from Eqs. (14.57) and (14.60) gives the fluxes of the two components as well as the separation factors. The equations are highly nonlinear because of the concentration-dependence of the diffusivities as well as the nonlinear dependence of the component activities on concentrations. As a result, the analytical solution is practically impossible and the numerical solution has to be done.

A simplified approach to calculation of the flux through the membrane is based on the Fick's law in the usual form and on concentration-dependent diffusivity.

$$J_1 = -D_1 \frac{dC_1}{dz} \quad \text{and} \quad J_2 = -D_2 \frac{dC_2}{dz} \tag{14.66}$$

The above two equations for the fluxes of the components in a binary mixture can be integrated over the membrane thickness if the surface concentrations of the solutes in the membrane phase on the upstream and the downstream sides and also the nature of dependence of diffusivities of the two species on concentrations are known. One common form of concentration-dependence of the diffusivities, D_1 and D_2, used for many systems is given below.

$$D_1 = D_{10} \exp(A_{11}C_1 + A_{12}C_2) \quad \text{and} \quad D_2 = D_{20} \exp(A_{21}C_1 + A_{22}C_2) \quad (14.67)$$

The above expressions (Brun et al., 1985) involve six parameters—D_{10} and D_{20} (diffusivities at 'zero concentration') and four coefficients (A_{ij}'s).

The liquid- and vapour-phase resistances at the upstream and downstream surfaces may also play an important role in specific cases. A typical example is the separation of trace organics from aqueous solutions or wastewater by using a hydrophobic membrane like PDMS which is now a commercial reality. Since such nonpolar or weakly polar organics have a strong affinity towards hydrophobic membranes, the feed-side mass transfer resistance cannot be ignored. In fact, in some cases the continuous phase mass transfer resistance may even control the overall rate of transport (Lipsy and Cote, 1990).

14.5.5 Liquid Membranes

The material for the preparation of a membrane need not be a solid only. A liquid may also act as a separation barrier between two phases or mediums where the transport occurs by the 'solution-diffusion mechanism'. Since a liquid film lacks mechanical strength as such, an appropriate technique has to be adopted to *stabilize* the liquid membrane so that it does not get ruptured during use. There are two common types of liquid membranes.

Immobilized liquid membrane (ILM)

An ILM, also called *supported liquid membrane* (SLM), is made by impregnating a thin porous film of a suitable solid substance with a liquid. The porous film only supports the liquid within the pores; it does not have any role in transport of the solute. If a solute is to be separated from an aqueous solution, the feed flows on one side of the liquid membrane and water on the other. The solute dissolves in the membrane liquid, diffuses through it and is taken up by the water on the other side. Also, if the feed is a gas mixture, the desired compound passes through the membrane by 'solution-diffusion' mechanism and is received by a carrier gas on the other side of the membrane. Transport through an immobilized liquid membrane is schematically shown in Figure 14.32(a).

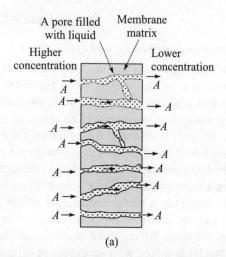

Figure 14.32(a) Transport through an immobilized liquid membrane (ILM); molecules of *A* diffuse through the liquid in the pores.

Emulsion liquid membrane (ELM)

An ELM is a liquid droplet which contains a number of very small globules of another liquid within it, suspended in a liquid medium. Transport through such a membrane separating two phases is schematically shown in Figure 14.32(b). The method of preparation of an ELM is rather simple. Two immiscible phases, an oil and water, for example, and a small quantity of a surfactant are mixed vigorously when an emulsion is formed. A water-in-oil emulsion, in which oil is the continuous phase, is more common. It is formed when the oil is in excess. If such an emulsion is poured into a large quantity of water or an aqueous solution, droplets of oil with fine globules of water in them form. This type of ELM is most common and is called 'water-oil-water emulsion liquid membrane'. The preparation procedure is schematically shown in Figure 14.33.

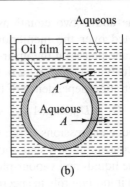

Figure 14.32(b) Transport through an ELM.

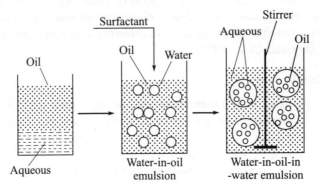

Figure 14.33 Preparation of ELM.

Separation mechanism and applications

The separation of a substance by ELM follows the same mechanism as in an ILM. Normally, a solute at a low concentration in the outer aqueous is recovered by permeation into the inner aqueous globules through the oil in the form of a liquid membrane. Thus the solute is recovered in a much smaller volume. The solute in the outer water phase gets dissolved at the water-oil (membrane) interface, diffuses through the membrane and reaches the inner aqueous globules. However, if the inner globules contain water only, the recovery of the solute will be very small. A high concentration of the solute in the aqueous globules can be obtained if it contains a reagent which reacts with the target solute. Thus an aqueous solution of a suitable reagent (rather than pure water) is used for preparation of the water-in-oil emulsion.

Let us consider the case of recovery of phenol from an aqueous solution at a low concentration. We may take an alkali, say NaOH, as a reagent within the globules. Thus a solution of NaOH is mixed with an excess of oil and a surfactant. The emulsion is now poured into the feed liquid (which has phenol in it at a low concentration). Phenol molecules dissolve at the water-oil interface, diffuse through the liquid membrane and get released and consumed by the alkali within the globules. Phenol continues to be transported till the alkali is depleted. Thus a much higher concentration of phenol in the inner phase can be attained. After a reasonable contact time, the oil droplets are separated from the feed liquid, and the water-in-oil emulsion is 'broken'. The aqueous phase containing the recovered phenol in a reacted form (sodium phenoxide) can be acidified for separating phenol from this liquid.

14.5.6 Facilitated (or Carrier-mediated) Transport, Coulped Transport and Active Transport

Transport of a species through a membrane or a fluid film driven by its concentration gradient is sometimes called *passive transport*. The term 'passive' is used to differentiate it from three other kinds of transport named above—facilitated (or carrier-mediated) transport, coupled transport, and active transport.

Facilitated transport

'Facilitated' or 'carrier-mediated' transport is the process of movement of a species A through a membrane that has in it a reactive reagent C, called the *carrier*. The carrier is a 'mobile' species that reversibly reacts with or binds to A at the feed-side of the membrane to form a permeate-carrier complex, CA. The complex CA diffuses through the membrane, reaches the permeate side of its surface and releases the permeant A by decomposition of the complex. The carrier C gets freed and diffuses back towards the feed side in order to pick up a fresh load of the permeant, A. Thus the carrier C acts as a 'shuttle' within the membrane. The concentration of the complex CA decreases along the membrane as illustrated in Figure 14.34(a); that of the carrier has a concentration gradient in the opposite direction. Both CA and C diffuse under their respective concentration driving force and keep on ferrying the permeant A across the membrane. A functional group in the polymer matrix can also act as a carrier, but only as a 'fixed carrier'. In such a case, the solute is transported by a 'hopping mechanism' similar to the one visualized for surface diffusion. Carrier-mediated transport of a species is much faster than passive transport since the (reversible) reaction with C greatly increases its effective solubility in the membrane.

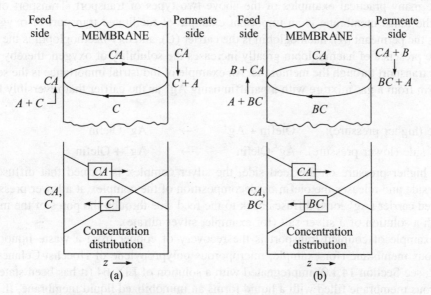

Figure 14.34   (a) Facilitated transport of A, and (b) coupled transport of A and B.

Sometimes the fluid on the permeate side may contain another species B that reacts with the complex CA and relieves it of A. However, the species BA does not diffuse through the membrane. Such a phenomenon further increases the flux of CA.

Feed side: $A + C \rightarrow AC$

Permeate side: $AC + B \rightarrow BA + C$

The permeate leaving the unit is processed or treated to decompose the complex BA to recover A while B is recycled back to the permeate-side fluid. The concentration of A in the combined form (i.e. as BA) in the permeate may be larger than that of A on the feed side. In such a case, the facilitated transport of A occurs against its 'apparent' concentration gradient.

Coupled transport

'Coupled transport' resembles facilitated transport except that a complex BC forms on the downstream surface of the membrane by reaction with a species present in the permeate-side liquid. This species diffuses through the membrane, reaches the upstream surface, reacts with A and releases C.

Feed side: $A + BC \rightarrow AC + B$

Permeate side: $AC + B \rightarrow BC + A$

Thus the species CA and BC diffuse in the opposite directions through the membrane [Figure 14.34(b)]. The second reaction above is the reverse of the first, and can be made to happen by maintaining a different 'environment' conducive to this reaction. In effect, A is transported from the feed side to the permeate side, and B from the permeate side to the feed side. This is why the phenomenon is called 'coupled transport'.

Examples

There are many practical examples of the above two types of transport. Transport of oxygen through the lungs membrane is an important example of facilitated transport of oxygen. Here oxygen is the permeant (A), haemoglobin is the carrier (C), and oxy-haemoglobin is the complex (CA). The presence of haemoglobin greatly increases the solubility of oxygen, thereby boosting its rate of transport through the membrane. An example of industrial importance is the separation of an olefin from a gas mixture with a paraffin using Ag^+ as the carrier that reversibly binds the olefin.

Feed side (higher pressure): $\quad$ Olefin + Ag^+ $\quad \rightarrow \quad$ Ag^+·Olefin

Permeate side (lower pressure): Ag^+·Olefin $\quad \rightarrow \quad$ Ag^+ + Olefin

At a higher pressure on the feed side, the silver complex is formed that diffuses to the permeate side and releases the olefin by decomposition of the complex at a lower pressure. The regenerated carrier (Ag^+ ions) diffuses back to the feed side through the pores of the membrane filled with a solution of a silver salt (for example, silver nitrate).

An example of coupled transport is the recovery of copper from a waste liquor using a microporous membrane (for example, microporous polypropylene of Hoechst-Celanese called 'Celgard'; see Section 14.1.2) impregnated with a solution of LIX-64 (it has been stated before that a porous membrane filled with a liquid forms an immobilized liquid membrane, ILM). This substance, LIX-64, contains an oxime dissolved in an organic medium immiscible with water. The feed side liquor has a pH of about 2.5 at which the oxime (C) forms a complex(CA) with Cu^{++} (A). The complex diffuses to the downstream side through the liquid-filled pores of the membrane. The solution on that side has a lower pH of about 1. At this pH, the complex reacts with H^+ ions (B) forming protonated oxime (BC) and releasing Cu^{++} ions. The species BC diffuses back towards the feed side and releases H^+ ions (B) at the higher pH, and the freed oxime now binds with Cu^{++} (A). Thus maintaining different environments (in this case, pH), Cu^{++} ions (A) and H^+ ions (B) can be subjected to coupled transport assisted by the carrier oxime (C).

Feed side (higher pH): $Cu^{++} + Oxime \cdot H^+ \quad \rightarrow \quad Cu^{++} \cdot Oxime + H^+$

Permeate side (lower pH): $Cu^{++} \cdot Oxime + H^+ \quad \rightarrow \quad Oxime.H^+ + Cu^{++}$

Active transport

'Active transport' is an extremely imporatnt phenomenon in biological systems. Here the species A is transported against its concentration gradient through a cell membrane. Since the process is not spontaneous, it requires an input of energy to happen. Typical examples of active transport are: (i) movement of Na^+ and K^+ ions through the cell membrane of red blood cells (RBC), both against respective concentration gradients, (ii) transport of glucose from blood (lower concentration) into liver cells (higher concentration), transport of minerals in soils (lower concentration) into the tissues of the roots of a plant (Avila, 1992). The mechanisms are expectedly complex. It has been suggested that the species to be transported bind to the 'transport protein' in the cell membrane. The protein squeezes and 'pumps' the species out. The mechanism may be roughly compared to pumping of a liquid by squeezing of the silicone tubing of a peristaltic pump by its rollers. Energy required for squeezing the transport protein and 'pumping' out the ions or molecules for active transport is supplied by ATP (adenosin triphosphate).

14.6 MEMBRANE GAS SEPARATION

Separation of light gases using a membrane as the separation barrier has been one of the major applications of membrane technology. The gas sorption and permeation properties of rubber were well known even in the nineteenth century. Sustained efforts to develop membrane-based gas separation started in the 1950s. The major hurdle was the preparation of thin and 'defect-free' membranes. Membrane defects such as 'pinholes' create more problems in gas separation than in liquid separation. The major breakthrough, as stated before, was achieved in 1962 by Loeb and Sourirajan who prepared asymmetric integrally skinned cellulose acetate membrane by the *phase inversion* technique. Since permeability of gases in a polymer (or any other membrane material) is generally low, a module with a large surface area is necessary for making membrane gas separation practically feasible. A hollow-fibre module could be suitable for the purpose. In the late 1970s, du Pont produced melt-spun polyester hollow fibres for hydrogen separation and a few other applications. A novel module was built that accommodated a huge number of hollow fibres giving a very high specific membrane surface area (area density as high as 10,000 ft^2/ft^3).

A second breakthrough was the preparation of the asymmetric polysulphone hollow fibre gas separation membrane by Monsanto in the early 1980s. The membrane still had pinholes. An ingenious strategy was adopted by Henis and Tripodi (1980) of Monsanto to overcome this problem. They applied a very thin layer of poly-dimethylsiloxane (PDMS) to plug the pinholes. Since this rubbery material admits of a high gas permeability, additional diffusional resistance due to this layer is only marginal. Monsanto made hollow-fibre modules, called PRISM separator using PDMS-coated membranes for the separation of a number of light gas mixtures including separation of O_2 from air, CO_2 from CH_4 and H_2 from ammonia plant purge gas (Fritzsche and

Narayan, 1987; Kesting and Fritzsche, 1993). Various other flat-sheet and hollow-fibre membranes have been developed thereafter leading to significant growth in the application to a variety of gas separation problems.

14.6.1   Gas Sorption and Permeation in a Polymer

Membranes used for gas separation are mostly polymeric, although the potential of ceramic membranes to separate gases, depending upon their differences in molecular size is quite high. Many properties of a polymer are determined by its degree of crystallinity. Glassy or amorphous polymers are characterized by a parameter called the *glass transition temperature* (T_g) above which a glassy polymer becomes rubbery. Glassy polymers and crystalline polymers are hard and brittle but the rubbbery polymers are readily distensible. Polymers such as polysulphones, aromatic polyimides, cellulose acetate, used for membrane preparation have been mentioned in Table 14.2.

The basic mechanism

A gaseous substance has some 'solubility' in a polymeric membrane. The solubility depends upon the particular gas-polymer pair (as in the case of dissolution of a gas in a liquid). If we consider a gas A on one side of a two-compartment vessel separated by a polymeric membrane or film while maintaining a lower partial pressure of A on the other side, sorption followed by diffusional transport of the gas from one side of the membrane to the other occurs. Dissolution of a gas in a polymer is called *sorption* and is different from *adsorption* in the sense that the latter phenomenon involves the formation of a mono- or multi-molecular layer of the solute near the surface as discussed in Chapter 12. The process involves the following steps.

- Sorption of the gas A at the upstream boundary of the film
- Diffusion of A through the film
- Desorption of A at the downstream boundary.

This is the well known *solution-diffusion mechanism* described before in connection with liquid separation. The pressures (or partial pressures) of A are different in the two compartments and, as a result, the solid-phase concentrations of the gas at the upstream and the downstream boundaries of the membrane are different. This causes a concentration driving force across the membrane and the gas molecules diffuse through the polymer under the influence of this driving force.

Gas solubility in a polymer—the Henry's law model

A simple way to express the solubility of a gas in a polymer is to apply the *Henry's law*.

$$C_A = S_A p_A, \qquad S_A \text{ in cm}^3 \text{ (STP)/(cm}^3 \text{ polymer)(cm Hg)} \qquad (14.68)$$

where

  p_A = (partial) pressure of A in the gas, in mm Hg

  C_A = equilibrium solubility of the gas in the polymer

  S_A = the solubility constant (Henry's law constant) for the particular gas–polymer pair.

The rate of transport

The permeation flux of a gas can be written following the Fick's law of diffusion, neglecting the 'bulk flow term'.

$$J_A = -D_A \frac{dC_A}{dz} \tag{14.69}$$

For steady-state transport through a constant area,

$$J_A(z_2 - z_1) = D_A(C_{A1} - C_{A2})$$

$$\Rightarrow \qquad J_A = \frac{D_A(C_{A1} - C_{A2})}{z_2 - z_1} = \frac{D_A S_A(p_{A1} - p_{A2})}{l_m} = \frac{\hat{P}_A(p_{A1} - p_{A2})}{l_m} \tag{14.70}$$

Here, l_m ($= z_2 - z_1$) is the membrane thickness and $D_A S_A$ is the *permeability* of the gas in the polymer.

$$\text{Permeability, } \hat{P} = D_A S_A \tag{14.71}$$

The unit of permeability is barrer, 1 barrer $= 10^{-10} \dfrac{cm^3 \text{ (STP) cm}}{(cm^2 \text{ polymer})(cm \text{ Hg})(s)}$

The quantity $\tilde{P}_A = \dfrac{\hat{P}_A}{l_m} = \dfrac{\text{permeability}}{\text{membrane thickness}}$ is called the *permeance* of A.

The two more important quantities that dictate the performance of a membrane device are the *flux* and the *separation factor* or *selectivity*. If x is the mole fraction of A in the feed side and y that in the permeate side for a binary mixture of A and B (the component A has a higher permeability), the separation factor is then given by (note that the corresponding mole fractions of component B are $1 - x$ and $1 - y$ respectively)

$$\alpha_{AB} = \frac{y/(1-y)}{x/(1-x)} \tag{14.72a}$$

$$\Rightarrow \qquad y = \frac{\alpha x}{1 + (1-\alpha)x} \tag{14.72b}$$

The ratio of the permeabilities of A and B, $\alpha_{AB}^* = \hat{P}_A/\hat{P}_B$ is called the 'ideal separation factor' [see Eq. (14.81)]. The permeability of a gas through a membrane is substantially influenced by the presence of other gases. Pure gas permeability is higher than that obtainable in a mixture.

EXAMPLE 14.11 (*Gas permeation through a membrane*) Selective permeation of CO_2 from a mixture of 10% CO_2 (A) and 90% CH_4 (B) occurs at 35°C and 10 atm total pressure in a small apparatus with a well-mixed feed compartment. An asymmetric polysulphone membrane of 1 micron skin layer thickness is used. The permeate side is continuously swept with nitrogen gas. Given the following data, calculate (a) the flux of CO_2, (b) the average diffusivity of CO_2 in polysulphone, and (c) the permeance of CH_4 in polysulphone. Permeation of the sweep gas (N_2) through the membrane may be neglected.

   Given: Ideal separation factor of CO_2 over CH_4, $\alpha_{AB}^* = 22$; Henry's law constant for solubility of CO_2 at 35°C in polysulphone, $S_A = 2.1$ cm^3(STP)/(cm^3)(atm); permeability of CO_2, $\hat{P}_A = 5.6$ barrer.

Solution

Partial pressure of CO_2 on the feed side, $p_{A1} = (0.1)(10 \text{ atm}) = 1 \text{ atm} (= 76 \text{ cm Hg})$; that on the permeate side, $p_{A2} = 0$ (since the compartment is swept with nitrogen).

(a) Flux of CO_2 [see Eq. (14.70)], $J_A = \dfrac{\hat{P}_A(p_{A1} - p_{A2})}{l_m}$

$$= \dfrac{5.6 \times 10^{-10} \dfrac{\text{cm}^3 (\text{STP}) \text{ cm}}{(\text{cm}^2)(\text{s})(\text{cm Hg})} (76 \text{ cm Hg} - 0)}{1 \times 10^{-4} \text{ cm}}$$

$$= 4.26 \times 10^{-4} \text{ cm}^3 (\text{STP})/(\text{cm}^2 \cdot \text{s}) = \boxed{1.9 \times 10^{-4} \text{ gmol}/(\text{m}^2 \cdot \text{s})}$$

(b) The diffusivity of CO_2 (D_A) is related to the permeability $\hat{P}_A$ and the Henry's law constant S_A by

$$\hat{P}_A = S_A D_A \quad \Rightarrow \quad 5.6 \times 10^{-10} \dfrac{\text{cm}^3 (\text{STP}) \text{ cm}}{(\text{cm}^2)(\text{s})(\text{cm Hg})} = 2.1 \dfrac{\text{cm}^3 (\text{STP})}{(\text{cm}^3)(\text{atm})} D_A$$

$$\Rightarrow \qquad\qquad D_A = \boxed{2.02 \times 10^{-8} \text{ cm}^2/\text{s}}$$

(c) Ideal separation factor, $\alpha^*_{AB} = 22 = \hat{P}_A/\hat{P}_B \Rightarrow \hat{P}_B = \hat{P}_A/22 = 5.6/22 = 0.254$ barrer. Permeance of $CH_4(B)$,

$$\tilde{P}_B = \hat{P}_B/l_m = (0.254 \times 10^{-10})/10^{-4} = \boxed{2.54 \times 10^{-7} \text{ cm}^3 (\text{STP})/(\text{cm}^2)(\text{s})(\text{cm Hg})}$$

The well-known 'resistances-in-series' model is also applicable to diffusion through a membrane. Equation (14.70) may be extended to express the flux of A as the ratio of the driving force and the permeation resistance.

$$J_A = \dfrac{p_{A1} - p_{A2}}{l_m/\hat{P}_A} = \dfrac{p_{A1} - p_{A2}}{\hat{R}_m} \qquad\qquad (14.73)$$

Here $\hat{R}_m = l_m/\hat{P}_A$ is the resistance to permeation offered by the membrane. If there are more than one resistances in series (for example, in a membrane containing more than one layer), the permeation flux is given by

$$J_A = \dfrac{p_{A1} - p_{A2}}{\sum_m \hat{R}_m} \qquad\qquad (14.74)$$

EXAMPLE 14.12 (*Transport through a composite membrane*)   An asymmetric polysulphone gas separation membrane has a skin thickness of $l_m = 0.15 \text{ µm}$. Since it has pinholes, a PDMS coating of thickness $l_c = 0.3 \text{ µm}$ is applied on it. The coating also fills the pinholes as shown in Figure 14.35. The cross-section of the pinholes occupies a fraction $\xi = 5 \times 10^{-6}$ of the membrane surface. Oxygen-enriched air is to be prepared using this membrane. Permeabilities of oxygen (A) and nitrogen (B) in the membrane material are $\hat{P}_{mA} = 1.2$, and $\hat{P}_{mB} = 0.19$; those in the coating are $\hat{P}_{cA} = 781$ and $\hat{P}_{cB} = 351$ (all in barrer). Determine the overall permeability and the ideal separation factor of O_2 in the composite membrane.

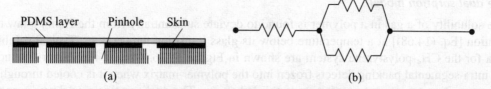

Figure 14.35 (a) The asymmetric membrane with a coating of PDMS, and (b) the equivalent 'resistances in series and parallel' model.

Solution

In the given membrane configuration, the resistances offered by the PDMS within the pores and the polysulfone membrane are in parallel. The resistance offered by the PDMS layer on the top acts in series with the above combination. The combined resistance to transport of the components A and B based on unit area of the membrane are [see the series-parallel combination of resistances, Figure 14.35(b)]:

$$\hat{R}_A = \frac{l_c}{\hat{P}_{cA}} + \frac{1}{\dfrac{(1-\xi)\hat{P}_{mA}}{l_m} + \dfrac{\xi\hat{P}_{cA}}{l_m}} = \frac{l_c}{\hat{P}_{cA}} + \frac{l_m}{(1-\xi)\hat{P}_{mA} + \xi\hat{P}_{cA}}$$

$$\hat{R}_B = \frac{l_c}{\hat{P}_{cB}} + \frac{1}{\dfrac{(1-\xi)\hat{P}_{mB}}{l_m} + \dfrac{\xi\hat{P}_{cB}}{l_m}} = \frac{l_c}{\hat{P}_{cB}} + \frac{l_m}{(1-\xi)\hat{P}_{mB} + \xi\hat{P}_{cB}}$$

Given: $l_c = 3 \times 10^{-7}$ m; $\quad l_m = 1.5 \times 10^{-7}$ m; $\quad \xi = 5 \times 10^{-6}$. Put $(1 - \xi) \approx 1$.

$$\hat{R}_A = \frac{3 \times 10^{-7}}{781 \times 10^{-10}} + \frac{1.5 \times 10^{-7}}{(1.2 \times 10^{-10}) + (5 \times 10^{-6})(781 \times 10^{-10})} = 1.25 \times 10^3 \ (\text{cm}^2)(\text{s})(\text{cm Hg})/\text{cm}^3$$

Similarly, $\qquad \hat{R}_B = 7.74 \times 10^3 \ (\text{cm}^2)(\text{s})(\text{cm Hg})/\text{cm}^3$

Overall permeabilities of A and B through the composite membrane

$$\hat{P}_A = \frac{l_m + l_c}{\hat{R}_A} = \frac{(0.3 + 0.15)10^{-6}}{1.25 \times 10^3} = 3.6 \times 10^{-10} = \boxed{3.6 \text{ barrer}} \ ; \quad \hat{P}_B = \frac{l_m + l_c}{\hat{R}_B} = \boxed{0.581 \text{ barrer}}$$

Ideal separation factor, $\qquad \alpha^*_{AB} = \dfrac{\hat{P}_A}{\hat{P}_B} = \dfrac{\hat{R}_B}{\hat{R}_A} = \dfrac{7.74 \times 10^3}{1.25 \times 10^3} = \boxed{6.2}$

Note 1: It has been assumed that the permeabilities of A and B are mutually independent.

Note 2: Ideal separation factor for a 'defect-free' PSF membrane = 1.2/0.19 = 6.3. So the application of the silicone coating does not effectively change the separation factor (or even the flux), but prevents *leakage*.

The dual sorption model

The solubility of a gas in a polymer is found to deviate substantially from the Henry's law type relation [Eq. (14.68)] at a temperature below its glass transition temperature. Typical solubility data for the CH_4-polystyrene system are shown in Figure 14.36. Quite a few factors including the intra-segmental packing defects frozen into the polymer matrix when it is cooled through the glass transition temperature contribute to this behaviour. The dual sorption model was proposed in the mid-1970s (Veith et al., 1976) to interpret deviation from the Henry's law.

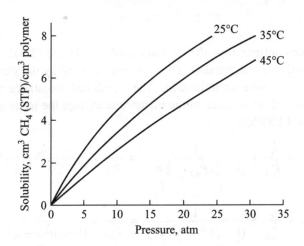

Figure 14.36   Solubility of methane in polystyrene.

The dual sorption model postulates the existence of two types of sorption sites in a glassy polymer. One type of site is the same as that in a rubbery polymer which involves dilation of the polymer matrix to accommodate the sorbed molecules. The other type of sorption site contains microvoids formed by intra-segmental packing defects. The model proposes that this second type of site is of 'Langmuir type' and sorption in these sites follows the Langmuir adsorption law. The total sorption is the arithmetic sum of the contributions of both.

$$C = C_D + C_H = Sp + \frac{C'_H bp}{1 + bp} \tag{14.75}$$

where C is the total solubility; C_D is the solubility in the Henry-type sites and C_H is that in the Langmuir-type sites; C'_H is called the 'hole saturation constant' and b is the 'hole affinity constant'.

At low pressure, $bp \ll 1$ and

$$C = (S + C'_H b)p \tag{14.76}$$

At high pressure, $bp \gg 1$ and

$$C = Sp + C'_H \tag{14.77}$$

Thus the solubility in the polymer is linear in the pressure of the solute gas at both low and high pressures. In the intermediate pressure range, the variation is nonlinear and is explained by the dual sorption model. The model interprets the sorption data for many gas–polymer pairs below the glass transition temperature (see, for example, Nadakatti, et al., 1995).

Both the above two models are macroscopic or continuum models; these are phenomenological in nature and involve one or more adjustable parameters to be estimated by fitting experimental sorption data.

Microscopic models

A number of microscopic models have been proposed over the years to describe the mechanism of gas sorption and transport in a polymer. The success has been partial, particularly because of the fact that gas transport in a polymer occurs by markedly different mechanisms above and below the glass transition temperature. Quite a few of the models for gas transport in rubbery polymers are based on the *free volume concept* (Fujita, 1960, see Kesting and Fritzsche, 1993). In the glassy state, the mobility of the chain segments of a polymer is extensively limited but above it, that is in the rubbery state, the mobility of the chain segments greatly increases. A number of physical parameters change at the glass transition temperature and one of these is the density (or the specific volume).

The *free volume*, V_f, is defined as the volume generated by thermal expansion of the initially close-packed molecules at absolute zero temperature, $V_f = V_T - V_0$; V_0 and V_T are molar volumes at temperatures absolute zero and T respectively. The *fractional free volume* is defined as $v_f = V_f/V_T$. The free volume concept has proved to be useful to describe and understand transport of small molecules through a polymer. The basic concept is that a molecule can diffuse from one point to another in a polymer if there is sufficient empty space or free volume. The following equation has been developed for the diffusivity D_T of a species in a polymer at temperature T K.

$$D_T = RT\alpha_f \exp(-\beta'/v_f) \qquad (14.78)$$

where α_f is a parameter dependent upon the size and shape of the penetrant molecule, and β' is the minimum local volume necessary to allow displacement of a solute molecule.

Structure-permeability relation of polymers

Despite the availability of a large volume of data on solubility and diffusivity of gases and vapours in glassy and rubbery polymers, the relationships between the polymer structure and the solubility and transport parameters were not properly understood for many years. The selection and modification of polymers for gas separation were mainly based on experience and experimental data. A set of data given in Table 14.8 shows the following characteristics:

Table 14.8 Gas permeabilities and separation factors for light gases in some rubbery and glassy polymers (Stern, 1995), at 35°C.

Polymer	Permeability (barrer)					Selectivity, α^*		
	He	N_2	O_2	CH_4	CO_2	He/N_2	O_2/N_2	CO_2/CH_4
Poly[1-(trimethylsilyl)-1-propyne]	5080	4970	7730	13,000	28,000	1.0	1.5	2.2
Poly(dimethylsiloxane)	590	351	781	1430	4550	1.7	2.2	3.2
Poly(*cis*-isoprene)	43.4	14.5	37.5	47.4	191	3.0	2.6	4.0
Poly(butadiene-styrene)	32.9	10.3	32.9	34.2	171	3.2	2.6	5.0
Ethyl cellulose	39.8	3.4	12.4	6.8	75	12	3.6	11
Bisphenol-A polycarbonate	13.0	0.38	1.6	0.36	7.01	72	5.8	20
Cellulose acetate	16.0	0.15	0.82	0.15	4.75	107	5.5	32
Bisphenol-A-polysulphone	10.8	0.19	1.2	0.18	4.6	57	6.3	26

- As the gas permeability in a polymer decreases, the selectivity increases. This is the well-known *inverse permeability/selectivity* behaviour.
- Rubbery polymers exhibit high permeability and low selectivity. Glassy polymers behave the opposite way. A remarkable exception is an alkyl silicon substituted polyacetylene, first prepared in 1983, called poly[1-(trimethylsilyl)-1-propyne]$_n$, [-(CH$_3$)C=C(Si(CH$_3$)$_3$)-]$_n$. This is a glassy polymer but has a tremendously high gas solubility because of a very high free volume of more than 20%.

During the last three decades there has been a sustained effort to develop new polymers and to modify the existing ones (by introducing side chains, for example) for achieving a better gas separation performance (Stern, 1994). A very important question in this connection has been whether it is possible to synthesize new polymers that would exhibit a high permeability as well as a high selectivity. Robeson (1991) prepared a plot (Figure 14.37) showing a hypothetical upper bound for O$_2$/N$_2$ selectivity/permeability on the 'selectivity-permeability plane' for both glassy and rubbery polymers. However, a few modified or substituted polymers have been developed recently that tend to contradict the inverse permeability vs. selectivity behaviour. For example, a membrane prepared from poly(trifluoropropyl methyl siloxane), i.e. [-(CF$_3$C$_2$H$_4$)CH$_3$SiO-]$_n$ shows significantly a higher selectivity for CO$_2$ in the CO$_2$/CH$_4$ system than that of other silicone polymers with similar permeability (Stern, 1994). Quite a few other polymers have been prepared that do not show the inverse permeability/selectivity behaviour. Recently, Koros and Mahajan (2000) discussed different aspects of exploitation of membranes for gas separation. They also mapped the regions of commercial interest of a few gas mixtures on the selectivity–permeability plane.

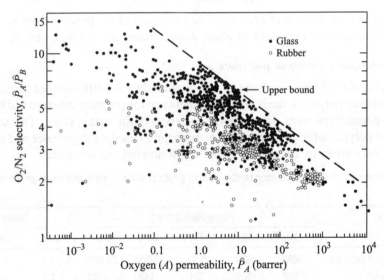

Figure 14.37   Hypothetical upper bound in O$_2$/N$_2$ selectivity versus O$_2$ permeability for various rubbery and glassy polymers (Robeson, 1991).

14.6.2   Module Design for the Separation of a Gas Mixture

Different types of flow arrangements and configurations are possible for modules used in gas separation. The common and simple flow arrangements are: perfect mixing, crossflow, cocurrent flow, and countercurrent flow.

A permeator with well-mixed compartments

This is the simplest flow arrangement. A method of determination of the membrane surface area necessary to achieve a desired degree of separation of A (more permeating) from B in a single membrane permeator is given below.

It is assumed that the permeabilities of the species are the same as those of the pure gases. The difference in partial pressures of a component in the two compartments is the driving force for its permeation. A schematic diagram of the module is shown in Figure 14.38(a). If Q_p is the permeate flow rate, the fluxes of A and B through the membrane can be written as

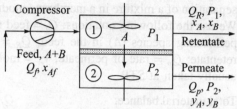

Figure 14.38(a) A 'well-mixed' permeator.

$$J_A = \frac{Q_p}{a_m} y_A = \frac{\hat{P}_A}{l_m}(P_1 x_A - P_2 y_A); \quad J_B = \frac{Q_p}{a_m} y_B = \frac{\hat{P}_B}{l_m}(P_1 x_B - P_2 y_B) \tag{14.79}$$

$$\Rightarrow \qquad \frac{(Q_p/a_m) y_A}{(Q_p/a_m) y_B} = \frac{J_A}{J_B}$$

$$\Rightarrow \qquad \frac{y_A}{y_B} = \frac{\hat{P}_A}{\hat{P}_B} \frac{P_1 x_A - P_2 y_A}{P_1 x_B - P_2 y_B} = \frac{\hat{P}_A}{\hat{P}_B} \frac{x_A - r y_A}{(1 - x_A) - r(1 - y_A)} \tag{14.80}$$

Here x and y are the mole fractions of a component in the feed and in the permeate compartment respectively; $r = P_2/P_1$ is the ratio of total pressures in the two compartments. The two most important factors that govern the performance of a membrane device are flux and separation factor (also called selectivity). The separation factor has been defined in Eq. [14.72(a)]. If the downstream (permeate) pressure is much smaller than the upstream (retentate) pressure, i.e.

$$P_2 y_A \ll P_1 x_A \qquad \text{and} \qquad P_2 y_B \ll P_1 x_B$$

then from Eq. (14.80), we get

$$\frac{y_A}{y_B} = \frac{\hat{P}_A}{\hat{P}_B} \frac{P_1 x_A}{P_1 x_B} \qquad \text{i.e.} \qquad \alpha_{AB}^* = \frac{y_A/y_B}{x_A/x_B} = \frac{\hat{P}_A}{\hat{P}_B} \tag{14.81}$$

The quantity α_{AB}^* is the *ideal separation factor* of A with respect to B as defined before.

If the downstream pressure cannot be neglected in comparison with the upstream pressure, the expression for the separation factor [see Eq. (14.80)] may be written as follows.

$$\alpha_{AB} = \frac{y_A/y_B}{x_A/x_B} = \alpha_{AB}^* \left(\frac{x_B}{x_A}\right) \frac{x_A - r y_A}{x_B - r y_B} = \alpha_{AB}^* \frac{(x_B/y_B) - r(y_A/y_B)(x_B/x_A)}{(x_B/y_B) - r} \tag{14.82}$$

Putting $x_B = x_B(y_A + y_B)$,

$$\frac{x_B}{y_B} = x_B \left(\frac{y_A}{y_B} + 1\right) = x_B \left(\alpha_{AB} \frac{x_A}{x_B} + 1\right) = \alpha_{AB} x_A + x_B = x_A(\alpha_{AB} - 1) + 1$$

Substituting the above result in Eq. (14.82),

$$\alpha_{AB} = \alpha_{AB}^* \frac{x_A(\alpha_{AB} - 1) + 1 - r\alpha_{AB}}{x_A(\alpha_{AB} - 1) + 1 - r} \tag{14.83}$$

The above quadratic equation can be solved to get the value of the separation factor which is a function of (i) the feed side concentration, (ii) the pressure ratio ($r = P_1/P_2$), and (iii) the ideal separation factor (α_{AB}^*). Example 14.13 illustrates the use of this relation.

Now we proceed to develop equations for the calculation of membrane area required for separation of a mixture in a membrane module with well-mixed compartments [Figure 14.38(a)]. We use the following notations: Q_f = feed rate (m³/s or mol/s); x_{Af} = mole fraction of the more permeating species (A) in the feed; Q_R = flow rate of retentate; x_A = mole fraction of A in retentate; Q_p = rate of permeate; y_A = mole fraction of A in permeate. Volume flow rates are usually taken at STP.

Total material balance: $Q_f = Q_R + Q_p$

Component A balance: $Q_f x_{Af} = Q_R x_A + Q_p y_A$

We define a term *stage-cut* as $\theta = Q_p/Q_f$ (which is the fraction of the feed that permeates and is obtained as the product), $Q_R/Q_f = 1 - \theta$. The component A balance equation reduces to

$$x_A = \frac{Q_f x_{Af} - Q_p y_A}{Q_R} = \frac{x_{Af} - (Q_p/Q_f) y_A}{(Q_f - Q_p)/Q_f} = \frac{x_{Af} - \theta y_A}{1 - \theta} \tag{14.84}$$

Permeation rate of A at steady state,

$$= Q_p y_A = (\text{flux})(\text{area}) = \frac{a_m \hat{P}_A}{l_m} (P_1 x_A - P_2 y_A) \tag{14.85}$$

Permeation rate of B at steady state,

$$= Q_p y_B = Q_p(1 - y_A) = (\text{flux})(\text{area}) = \frac{a_m \hat{P}_B}{l_m} (P_1 x_B - P_2 y_B) \tag{14.86}$$

Dividing Eq. (14.85) by (14.86),

$$\frac{y_A}{1 - y_A} = \frac{\hat{P}_A}{\hat{P}_B} \frac{P_1 x_A - P_2 y_A}{P_1 x_B - P_2 y_B} = \alpha_{AB}^* \frac{x_A - r y_A}{(1 - x_A) - r(1 - y_A)} \tag{14.87}$$

For the design of a permeator, the feed concentration x_{Af} should be given and the pressure ratio r should be given or selected. Then, for the given values of the stage-cut θ and the retentate concentration x_A, the permeate concentration y_A and the membrane area can be calculated (see Example 14.13). Sometimes a part of the permeate is recycled into the feed stream to increase the feed-side concentration of the target component [Figure 14.38(b)]. A purer product is obtained by this strategy. Example 14.14 deals with such a case.

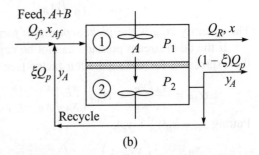

Figure 14.38(b)   A permeator with partial recycle of permeate.

EXAMPLE 14.13 (*Separation of a binary gas mixture; well-mixed compartments*) A mixture of 8% $CO_2(A)$ and 92% $CH_4(B)$ is to be separated at a rate of 100 m³/h (STP) in a membrane permeator with well-mixed compartments to reduce the CO_2 content to 2.5%. An asymmetric CA membrane with 0.15 micron skin layer is to be used. Given the following data, calculate the product rate, the mean product composition (%CO_2) and the membrane area: upstream pressure, $P_1 = 25$ atm; downstream pressure, $P_2 = 1.2$ atm; ideal separation factor, $\alpha^*_{AB} = 31.7$; permeability of CO_2 in the membrane; $\hat{P}_A = 4.75$ barrer; temperature = 35°C.

Solution

Since the compartments are well-mixed, the mole fraction of CO_2 in the retentate is the same as that in the upstream compartments, i.e. $x_A = 0.025$. Feed concentration, $x_{Af} = 8\%$, i.e. 0.08.

Use Eq. (14.87). Put $r = P_2/P_1 = 1.2/25 = 0.048$; $\alpha^*_{AB} = 31.7$.

$$\Rightarrow \qquad \frac{y_A}{1-y_A} = (31.7)\frac{0.025-(0.048)y_A}{(1-0.025)-(0.048)(1-y_A)}$$

$$\Rightarrow \qquad y_A = \boxed{0.28} = \text{permeate concentration}$$

The stage-cut may be obtained from Eq. (14.84).

$$x_A = \frac{x_{Af}-\theta y_A}{1-\theta} \quad \Rightarrow \quad 0.025 = \frac{0.08-\theta(0.28)}{1-\theta} \quad \Rightarrow \quad \text{stage-cut}, \ \theta = \boxed{0.216}$$

Given $Q_f = 100$ m³/h, permeate rate, $Q_p = \theta Q_f = (0.216)(100) = \boxed{21.6 \text{ m}^3/\text{h (STP)}}$

Also given, $l_m = 0.15 \times 10^{-4}$ cm; $\hat{P}_A = 4.75$ barrer. The membrane area may be calculated from Eq. (14.85).

$$a_m = \frac{Q_p y_A}{(P_1 x_A - P_2 y_A)} \cdot \frac{l_m}{\hat{P}_A}$$

$$= \frac{(21.6 \times 10^6 \text{ cm}^3/\text{s})(0.28)}{(3600)[(25)(0.08)-(1.2)(0.28)](76 \text{ cm Hg})} \cdot \frac{0.15 \times 10^{-4} \text{ cm}}{4.75 \times 10^{-10} \dfrac{\text{cm}^3.\text{cm}}{(\text{cm}^2)\,(\text{s})\,(\text{cm Hg})}}$$

$$\Rightarrow \qquad a_m = \boxed{240 \text{ m}^2}$$

EXAMPLE 14.14 (*Membrane area in a recycle permeator*) A small membrane module uses a novel membrane to separate 300 m³ (STP) of air per hour to yield a permeate stream containing 25% oxygen. The stage cut is 50%, and 60% of the permeate is to be recycled into the feed stream. Permeability of N_2 in the 0.1 μm thick dense layer of the membrane is 32 barrer. The ideal separation factor is 6.2. The feed-side pressure is 12 bar; that on the permeate side is 1.2 bar. Calculate the membrane area if both the feed and permeate sides are well-mixed.

Solution

The basic equations for the separation of a binary gas mixture ($A + B$) in a membrane device with well-mixed feed and permeate chambers and partial recycle of the permeate will be developed first. The notations are shown in Figure 14.38(b); Q_R = rate of flow of the retentate and ξ = fraction of the permeate recycled; P_1, P_2 = total pressures in the feed and permeate chambers.

$$\text{Total material balance:}\quad Q_f = Q_R + (1 - \xi)Q_p \tag{i}$$

$$\text{Component } A \text{ balance:}\quad Q_f x_{Af} = Q_R x_A + (1 - \xi)Q_p y_A \tag{ii}$$

$$\text{Stage-cut,}\quad \theta = Q_p/(Q_f + \xi Q_p) \Rightarrow Q_p = \theta Q_f/(1 - \theta \xi)$$

Put $Q_f = 300$, $\theta = 0.5$; $\xi = 0.6 \Rightarrow Q_p = 214.3$.

Given: permeate concentration,

$$y_A = 0.25;\ P_1 = 12 \text{ bar};\ P_2 = 1.2 \text{ bar};\ r = 1.2/12 = 0.1;\ \alpha^*_{AB} = 6.2$$

Use Eq. (14.87) to calculate x_A.

$$\frac{y_A}{1 - y_A} = \alpha^*_{AB}\frac{x_A - r y_A}{(1 - x_A) - r(1 - y_A)} \quad\Rightarrow\quad \frac{0.25}{1 - 0.25} = 6.2\frac{x_A - (0.1)(0.25)}{(1 - x_A) - (0.1)(1 - 0.25\,y_A)}$$

$$\Rightarrow \qquad\qquad\qquad x_A = \boxed{0.0709}$$

Permeability of O_2, $\hat{P}_A = \alpha^*_{AB}\hat{P}_B = (6.2)(32) = 198.4$ barrer

For calculating the membrane area, use Eq. (14.85) and put $l_m = 0.1\ \mu\text{m} = 10^{-5}$ cm and other values.

$$a_m = \frac{Q_p y_A l_m}{\hat{P}_A(P_1 x_A - P_2 y_A)} = \frac{(214.3 \times 10^6/3600)(0.25)(10^{-5})}{(198.4 \times 10^{-8})[(0.0709)(12) - (0.25)(1.2)](76/1.013)}\ \text{cm}^2 = 18\ \text{m}^2$$

Analysis of a permeator with crossflow

There may be two simple crossflow patterns. In both types, the feed side is assumed to be in plug flow without any axial mixing. However, the flow arrangements on the permeate side are different. In the following analysis (see Figure 14.39) of separation of a binary gas mixture of A and B, it is assumed that the permeate concentration also varies along the membrane depending upon the local concentration on the feed side. The permeate gets mixed up *only* at the exit. It is further assumed that the pressures on each side remain constant all through and that the steady-state condition prevails.

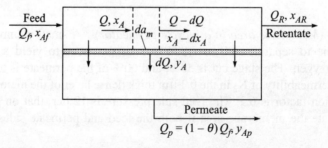

Figure 14.39   Flow rates and concentrations in a crossflow permeator.

We consider a differential element of the membrane area da_m and dQ mole (or m³ at STP) of permeate that diffuses from the feed to the retentate side through this differential area in unit time.

A differential mass balance over the small area is written below. Note that the quantities dQ and dx_A are taken as inherently positive.

$$y_A \, dQ = d(Q x_A) = Q \, dx_A + x_A \, dQ \quad \Rightarrow \quad (y_A - x_A) dQ = Q \, dx_A$$

$$\Rightarrow \qquad \frac{dQ}{Q} = \frac{dx_A}{y_A - x_A} \tag{14.88}$$

Substituting $\quad y_A = \dfrac{\alpha x_A}{1 + (\alpha - 1) x_A} \quad$ in Eq. (14.88), where α is the 'local selectivity',

$$\frac{dQ}{Q} = \frac{dx_A}{\dfrac{\alpha x_A}{1 + (\alpha - 1) x_A} - x_A} = \left[\frac{1 + (\alpha - 1) x_A}{x_A (\alpha - 1)(1 - x_A)} \right] dx_A \tag{14.89}$$

If we assume α to remain approximately constant, and integrate the above equation from any intermediate position where the feed side flow rate and concentration are Q and x_A to the end (Q_R, x_{AR}),

$$\int_Q^{Q_R} \frac{dQ}{Q} = \int_{x_A}^{x_{AR}} \frac{1 + (\alpha - 1) x_A}{x_A (\alpha - 1)(1 - x_A)} \, dx_A = \frac{1}{\alpha - 1} \int_{x_A}^{x_{AR}} \frac{dx_A}{x_A} + \frac{\alpha}{\alpha - 1} \int_{x_A}^{x_{AR}} \frac{dx_A}{1 - x_A}$$

$$\Rightarrow \qquad \ln \frac{Q_R}{Q} = \ln \left[\left(\frac{x_{AR}}{x_A} \right)^{1/(\alpha - 1)} \left(\frac{1 - x_A}{1 - x_{AR}} \right)^{\alpha/(\alpha - 1)} \right]$$

$$\Rightarrow \qquad Q = Q_R \left(\frac{x_A}{x_{AR}} \right)^{1/(\alpha - 1)} \left(\frac{1 - x_{AR}}{1 - x_A} \right)^{\alpha/(\alpha - 1)} \tag{14.90}$$

The local differential rate of permeation is given by

$$y_A \, dQ = \frac{\hat{P}_A \, da_m}{l_m} (P_1 x_A - P_2 y_A) \tag{14.91}$$

where P_2 and P_1 are the permeate and the feed side pressures respectively.

The required area of permeation is obtained by integration of the above equation as

$$a_m = \frac{l_m}{\hat{P}} \int_{x_R}^{x_f} \frac{y_A \, dQ}{x_A P_1 - y_A P_2} \tag{14.92}$$

The above integral can be evaluated to obtain the membrane area for a crossflow permeator (Example 14.15). An alternative solution of the design equations was given by Weller and Steiner (1950).

EXAMPLE 14.15 (*Calculation of the area of a crossflow permeator*)   A gas mixture having 20% A and 80% B is to be separated in a crossflow permeator using an asymmetric membrane of 0.2 micron active layer. The permeability of A is $\hat{P}_A = 7.2$ barrer and its ideal separation factor with respect to B is $\alpha^*_{AB} = 5.0$. The gas on the feed side is in crossflow; the permeate flows normal to the membrane surface and gets mixed up at the exit only (Figure 14.39). A stage-cut of 30% is suggested. The feed rate is 200 m³/h (STP) and the (constant) upstream and downstream pressures are $P_1 = 22$ atm and $P_2 = 1.1$ atm. Calculate the average permeate composition and the membrane area required.

Solution
The preceding theoretical analysis can be directly used to solve this problem if the separation factor, α, remains reasonably constant. The 'theoretical' separation factor is $\alpha^*_{AB} = 5.0$. Let us first calculate α for two gas concentrations, $x_f = 0.2$ (feed concentration of A), and an assumed retentate concentration, x_R (subscript A omitted) $= 0.01$. Putting $\alpha^*_{AB} = 5.0$, $x = 0.2$ and $r = P_2/P_1 = 1.1/22 = 0.05$ in Eq. (14.83), we get $\alpha = 4.47$. For $x = 0.01$ (other parameters remaining the same), $\alpha = 4.2$. Take the average value $\alpha = 4.33$ in the calculation. Now let us calculate the retentate concentration x_R from Eq. (14.90). Putting stage-cut, $\theta = 0.3$, $Q = Q_f$,

$$Q_R = Q_f(1 - \theta), \quad x_{Af} = x_f = 0.2, \text{ and } \alpha = 4.2, \text{ we get } x_R = \boxed{0.104}.$$

This calculated value of x_R is significantly larger than 0.01 taken as the trial retentate concentration. Now for $x = 0.104$, we get $\alpha = 4.33$ from Eq. (14.90). Take the revised averaged value of $\alpha = (4.47 + 4.33)/2 = 4.4$. Putting the values of the relevant quantities in Eq. (14.90),

$$Q_f = Q_f(1 - \theta)\left(\frac{x_A}{x_R}\right)^{1/(\alpha-1)}\left(\frac{1 - x_R}{1 - x_A}\right)^{\alpha/(\alpha-1)} \qquad [\text{since } Q_R = Q_F(1 - \theta)]$$

$$\Rightarrow \qquad 1 = (1 - 0.3)\left(\frac{0.2}{x_R}\right)^{1/(4.4-1)}\left(\frac{1 - x_R}{1 - 0.2}\right)^{4.4/(4.4-1)} \Rightarrow x_R = \boxed{0.1}$$

Material balance over the permeator will give the concentration of the *mixed permeate*.

$$Q_f x_f = Q_p x_p + Q_R x_R \Rightarrow x_f = \theta x_p + (1 - \theta)x_R$$

$$\Rightarrow \qquad 0.2 = (0.3)y_p + (1 - 0.3)(0.1) \Rightarrow y_p = \boxed{0.433}$$

[Simple calculations using Eq. (14.87) and putting $\alpha^*_{AB} = 5.0$, $r = 0.05$, and $x = 0.2$ (inlet to the permeator), we get $y = 0.528$. At the retentate outlet, $x = x_R = 0.1$, and $y = 0.326$. The average of these values is a little different from the mixed permeate concentration, y_p, calculated above.]

The membrane area is to be calculated by evaluating the integral in Eq. (14.92). Using Eqs. (14.89) and (14.90), we get (omit suffix A)

$$a_m = \frac{l_m}{\hat{P}} \int_{x_R}^{x_f} \frac{y\,dQ}{x P_1 - y P_2}$$

$$= \frac{l_m}{\hat{P}} \int_{x_R}^{x_f} \frac{\alpha x}{1 + (\alpha - 1)x} \frac{Q_f(1 - \theta)\left(\dfrac{x}{x_R}\right)^{1/(\alpha-1)}\left(\dfrac{1 - x_R}{1 - x}\right)^{\alpha/(\alpha-1)}}{P_1 x - P_2 y} \frac{1 + (\alpha - 1)x}{x(\alpha - 1)(1 - x)}\,dx$$

$$\Rightarrow \quad a_m = \frac{l_m}{\hat{P}} \frac{Q_f(1-\theta)\alpha}{P_1(\alpha-1)} (x_R)^{1/(1-\alpha)}(1-x_R)^{\alpha/(\alpha-1)} \int_{x_R}^{x_f} \frac{(x)^{1/(\alpha-1)}(1-x)^{(1-2\alpha)/(\alpha-1)}}{x-ry} dx \quad \text{(i)}$$

The integral has to be evaluated numerically; Eq. [14.72(b)] gives y as a function of x.

For $x_f = 0.2$, $x_R = 0.1$, $\alpha = 4.4$ and $r = 0.05$, the value of the integral is 0.686. The membrane area is

$$a_m = \frac{2 \times 10^{-5} \text{ cm}}{7.2 \text{ barrer}} \cdot \frac{200 \times 10^6}{3600} \frac{\text{cm}^3}{\text{s}} \frac{(1-0.3)}{(22 \text{ atm})(76 \text{ cm Hg/atm})} \frac{4.4}{3.4} \frac{(1-0.1)^{4.4/3.4}}{(0.1)^{1/3.4}} (0.686)$$

$$= \boxed{98.5 \text{ m}^2}$$

A countercurrent plug flow permeator

A countercurrent membrane permeator for separation of a binary mixture of A and B is schematically shown in Figure 14.40. We use a little different notations than before; Q_f, Q_p = local flow rates of the feed and the permeate streams; x, y = local concentrations of the more permeating component, A (the subscript A is dropped).

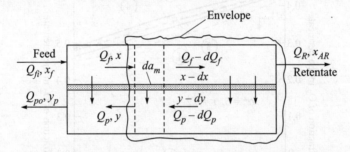

Figure 14.40   A countercurrent permeator—both feed and permeate sides are in plug flow.

Total material balance over the envelope: $Q_f = Q_p + Q_R$ (14.93)

Component A balance: $Q_f x = Q_p y + Q_R x_R$ (14.94)

The fractional-cut θ is given as $Q_R = (1 - \theta)Q_{fi}$ (i = inlet)   (14.95)

Combining the above equations,

$$Q_f x = (Q_f - Q_R)y + Q_R x_R \quad \Rightarrow \quad y = \frac{Q_f x - Q_R x_R}{Q_f - Q_R} \quad \Rightarrow \quad y = \frac{Q_f x - (1-\theta)Q_{fi} x_R}{Q_f - (1-\theta)Q_R} \quad (14.96)$$

Differential mass balance of A over a small section of the module having a differential area, da_m, is

$$- dQ_f = \frac{da_m}{l_m} [\hat{P}_A(P_1 x - P_2 y) + \hat{P}_B\{P_1(1-x) - P_2(1-y)\}] \quad (14.97)$$

$$\Rightarrow \quad - dQ_f = \frac{P_1 da_m}{l_m} [\hat{P}_A(x - ry) + \hat{P}_B\{(1-x) - r(1-y)\}] \quad (14.98)$$

The inlet condition is: $a_m = 0$; $Q_f = Q_{fi}$, $x = x_f$ and $y = y_p$.   (14.99)

Equations (14.98) and (14.95) can be solved by iteration subject to the inlet conditions (14.99). Given the feed and permeate side pressures (P_1 and P_2), the stage-cut (θ), and other quantities, computation starts with a guess value of x_R. Techniques for the solution of the design equations for a few configurations for the separation of binary and multicomponent mixtures are available (see, for example, Walawender and Stern, 1972; Sengupta and Sirkar *in* Noble and Stern, 1995; Li et al., 1990).

14.6.3 Configurations of Membrane Permeators

The degree of separation of a binary mixture attainable in a membrane module for well-mixed, cocurrent, countercurrent or crosscurrent flow of the feed and the permeate streams can be computed numerically by integration of the relevant differential mass balance equations. Figure 14.41 shows a typical plot of enrichment of A in the permeate that can be achieved for different flow arrangements of the feed and the permeate (perfect mixing, cocurrent, crosscurrent and countercurrent flow) versus the stage-cut. Expectedly, the best results are obtained for the countercurrent flow arrangement.

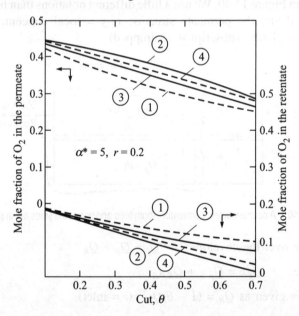

Figure 14.41 Effect of flow arrangement on separation of air in a membrane module—1: well-mixed permeate and retentate sides; 2: countercurrent flow on the two sides; 3: cocurrent flow; 4: crossflow.

It is now established that the extent to which a feed can be separated in a single permeator unit is severely restricted. A number of membrane permeators connected in parallel increase the treatment capacity of a unit, but when put in series, the performance, in terms of the degree of separation, is enhanced. A parallel-series arrangement enhances both capacity and degree of separation. Several innovative configurations in place of the parallel or series arrangements have been suggested for better performance and competitiveness based on the idea of cascades in traditional separation of gas mixtures or solutions. Figure 14.42 shows a countercurrent permeator cascade akin to a countercurrent distillation column. The feed to a permeator in the cascade is a mixture of the permeate and the retentate streams from two adjacent permeators as shown in the figure.

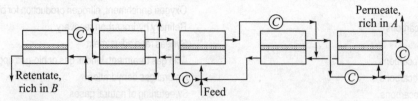

Figure 14.42 A multi-stage countercurrent permeator cascade with recycle. *C*: compressor.

Another flow configuration that has drawn much attention is the recycle permeator. It enhances separation by recycling of a fraction of the permeate stream into the feed, thereby increasing the feed concentration and hence the permeate concentration (Example 14.14). The concept is illustrated in Figure 14.43. The improvement in the purity of the permeate by this design is shown in Figure 14.44 as a function of the overall stage-cut and the increasing recycle fraction.

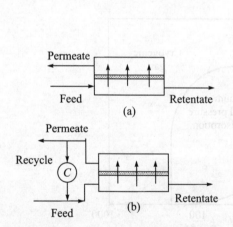

Figure 14.43 Permeator configuration: (a) without recycle, and (b) with recycle. *C*: recycle compressor.

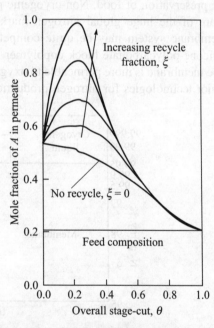

Figure 14.44 The effect of permeate stage-cut and recycle fraction on product concentration.

A few other configurations of the recycle membrane cascade have been proposed for better economy and purer products depending upon the concentration of the selectively permeating component in the feed. Some details are available in Kesting and Fritzsche (1993).

14.6.4 Industrial Applications of Membrane-based Gas Separation

Because of the success of the membrane process, more emphasis has been placed in several selected areas of gas separation. Several current application areas as well as a few potential applications are listed in Table 14.9. A few of them are discussed as follows.

Table 14.9   Application areas of membrane gas separation (Spillman, *CEP*, Jan. 1989, 41–62)

Gas mixture	Application areas
Air	Oxygen enrichment, nitrogen production for blanketing
H_2/Hydrocarbons	Refinery hydrocarbon recovery
H_2/CO	Syngas ratio adjustment
CO_2/Hydrocarbons	Acid gas treatment, landfill gas or bio-gas upgrading
H_2O/Hydrocarbons	Natural gas dehydration
H_2S/Hydrocarbons	Sweetening of natural gases
He-containing gases	Helium recovery
H_2O/Air	Air dehydration

Oxygen/Nitrogen separation

Among the major uses of nitrogen are nitrogen blanketing (blanketing cargo), purging pipelines, inerting applications on the offshore production platform, and for creating controlled atmosphere for preservation of food. Non-cryogenic processes (membranes and PSA) have more than 30% share of the huge global nitrogen market. Depending upon the capacity of production, the membrane system may be quite competitive to produce nitrogen of 95% to 99.95% purity. Silicone-polycarbonate block copolymer is a typical membrane material used for this purpose. The membrane is more permeable to oxygen and moisture. The dominant application areas of the major technologies for nitrogen production are mapped in Figure 14.45.

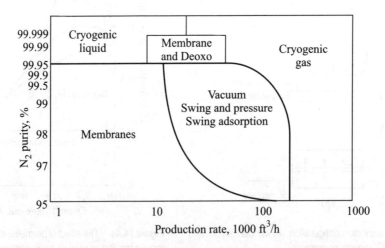

Figure 14.45   Mapping of the areas of application of membranes, PSA/VSA and the cryogenic process for nitrogen production (Courtesy: *Praxair*)

Oxygen enrichment

Relatively high purity oxygen (> 90%) and oxygen-enriched air (30% to 40% O_2) have a sizable market. The product having 40% oxygen can be directly delivered to patients. The membrane process is definitely attractive for the generation of oxygen-enriched air up to about 30% O_2, compared to pressure swing (PSA), volume swing (VSA) and the cryogenic process. However, the picture is not so bright for the production of an enriched stream with >30% oxygen. This is because the currently available membranes do not offer the required combination of O_2/N_2 permeability and selectivity. Commercial membranes have O_2/N_2 selectivities in the range of 3.5–5.5.

Separation of CO_2 from natural gas

This is an important gas separation problem where the application of membranes may be more attractive than the amine absorption process. Membranes can reduce CO_2 of natural gas to less than 2% and H_2S to 4 ppm. Polysulfone is a good candidate for the membrane material.

Hydrogen separation

Hydrogen separation from other light gases is one of the early application areas of membranes (PRISM separator). This includes cases like recovery of hydrogen from an ammonia purge stream, separation/recovery of hydrogen from various refinery streams or separation of hydrogen from CO–H_2 syngas in order to adjust the composition for a particular use. In many situations the membrane process has proved to be more economical than the conventional processes including the cryogenic processes. In the ammonia synthesis process, a purge stream continuously removes inert gases such as argon. The purge stream typically contains about 2% NH_3 and is water-scrubbed to recover this gas. The scrubbed gas contains about 60% H_2. The Monsanto Prism separator was successfully used to recover hydrogen from this stream in a two-stage unit. The average composition of the recovered hydrogen streams was 89% H_2, 6% N_2, and 5% inerts. The membrane used in the Prism separator was a bundle of asymmetric polysulphone hollow-fibres having an ultrathin coating of PDMS for sealing the defects and pinholes in the membrane.

Many of the hydrogen separation applications work at high pressure (for example in hydrotreating and hydrocracking processes). Membrane separator systems have been developed for 85% recovery of the hydrogen to 95% purity. The recovered hydrogen is recycled depending upon the process requirements and the retentate with about 25% hydrogen in it is added to the refinery fuel system. Similarly, the hydrocracker purge gas can be treated for selective recovery of hydrogen.

14.6.5 Biomedical Applications—The Blood Oxygenator

A blood oxygenator is an extra-corporeal device (called 'Extra-Corporeal Membrane Oxygenator', ECMO) used for supplying oxygen to blood during an open-heart surgery. A variety of devices, such as falling film absorber, bubble oxygenator and membrane oxygenator—has been used for the purpose since the first successful open-heart surgery on a human patient in 1953. Only the membrane oxygenators are in use now. Earlier, dense silicone tubing, that has a high permeability for oxygen, was used to make the device. This has mostly given way to microporous hollow fibres such as polypropylene hollow fibres (pore dia ~ 0.1 μm) for the construction of shell-and-tube type blood oxygenator. It is basically similar to the dialysis module. Oxygen/air, saturated with moisture at 37°C, flows through the lumen side and the blood through the shell side so that it is not subjected to a high shear stress. Since the fibres (200 to 500 μm diameter) are hydrophobic, blood does not enter into the micropores. Oxygen diffuses through the pores and gets absorbed into the blood at the outside surface of the fibres. Carbon dioxide is simultaneously desorbed. Since oxygen has a low solubility in blood, the gas-phase resistance is low (see Problem 14.28) and the mass transfer rate is controlled by the liquid-phase resistance. The reaction between haemoglobin and oxygen has to be taken into consideartion for a theoretical analysis of the process. The problem has been addressed by many researchers and a number of models have been suggested (Fournier, 1999). A comprehensive account of blood oxygenators of various designs has been given by Galletti and Colton (1995). In some of the designs cross-flow of blood over the hollow-fibres occurs since this flow configuration reduces the shear stress on blood. Development of an *implantable* artificial lung made of polypropylene hollow fibres has been described by Vaslef et al. (1994).

The unit cost of a blood oxygenator is $500 to $600, and the world-wide use is about 1 million per year. A good heart-lung machine must deliver about 250 cm^3 (STP) O$_2$/min and remove about 200 cm^3 (STP) CO$_2$. A blood flow rate of 2–4 litre/min through an oxygenator is maintained, which is about ten times the blood flow through an artificial kidney (haemodialyser, see Section 14.5.2). This is also much larger than the rate at which the heart pumps blood through the lungs. Since the lung membrane, through which oxygen from air is absorbed in blood, is very thin (~ 5 μm) and the area of blood capillaries in the lungs is large (~ 80 m^2), the lungs act as a much more efficient oxygenator than an artificial one.

NOTATIONS

a_m : membrane area, m^2

C, C_s : solute/salt concentration, kmol/m^3 (or kg/m^3)

C_b : solute concentration in the bulk solution, kmol/m^3

C_f : solute concentration in the feed, kmol/m^3 (or kg/m^3)

C_m : solute concentration at the membrane surface, kmol/m^3

C_p : solute concentration in the permeate, kmol/m^3

C_g : gel point concentration, kg/m^3

d : pore diameter or fibre diameter, m

D : diffusivity, m^2/s

J_w : water flux, m^3/(m^2·s), kg/(m^2·s)

J_∞ : limiting solvent flux, m^3/(m^2·s), kg/(m^2·s)

k_L : mass transfer coefficient, m/s

l_c : cake thickness, m

l_m : membrane thickness, m

L_D, L_{DP} : phenomenological coefficients, Eqs. (14.26) and (14.27)

L_p : water permeability, phenomenological coefficient

$p. p_A$: partial pressure of a component; Pa, atm

ΔP : pressure drop (across a membrane); Pa, atm

$\widetilde{P}_A$: permeance of the gas A ($= \hat{P}_A/l_m$)

$\hat{P}_A$: permeability of A

Q_{fi} : feed rate at the inlet, m^3/s

Q_p : rate of permeate, m^3/s

r : pressure ratio

r_c : specific cake resistance

R_c : cake resistance

R_m : resistance to flow offered by the membrane, m^{-1}

R' : fractional rejection, Eq. (14.9)

S_A : solubility constant, Eq. (14.63)

V : volume of solution, m^3

x_A, x_R : mole fraction of the solute in the feed side/in the retentate

y, y_p : mole fraction of the solute on the permeate side/in the permeate

α : separation factor

ε : porosity or fractional pore volume

Π : osmotic pressure, Pa, atm

σ : reflection coefficient, Eq. (14.28)

τ : tortuosity factor

ω : solute permeability at zero solvent flux

ρ_c : cake bulk density, kg/m^3

SHORT AND MULTIPLE CHOICE QUESTIONS

1. A membrane for reverse osmosis is
   (i) microporous
   (ii) dense
   (iii) porous with a dense skin.

2. Which of the following is a good polymeric material for the preparation of an asymmetric UF membrane and why?
   (i) Polysulphone   (ii) Polydimethylsiloxane (PDMS)   (iii) PTFE

3. The permeability of a gas through a polymer film is often expressed in 'barrer'. What is 1 barrer?

4. The term 'phase inversion' in the context of membrane preparation means
   (i) the dissolution of a polymer in a suitable low-viscosity solvent
   (ii) the transformation of a polymer from the solution phase to the solid state in a controlled manner
   (iii) the rapid evaporation of the solvent from a solution cast on a support.

5. Which of the following membranes is used for dehydration of alcohol?
   (i)   Cross-linked PVA
   (ii) Polycarbonate
   (iii) Cellulose acetate

6. In which of the following membrane processes the effect of concentration polarization is least important?
   (i) Gas separation   (ii) Haemodialysis   (iii) RO

7. A hollow-fibre membrane with *isotropic* dense wall is suitable for
   (i) microfiltration   (ii) RO   (iii) pervaporation.

8. A polymer solution for membrane casting should be degassed and freed from particles in order to
   (i)   avoid defects in the membrane formed
   (ii) improve the flow properties of the casting solution
   (iii) prepare a microporous membrane.

9. If the 'polarization modulus' in an RO module is unity, the feed-side mass transfer coefficient of the solute is
   (i)   very large
   (ii) very small
   (iii) is equal to the diffusional resistance of the membrane.

10. If the reflection coefficient σ is zero, an osmotic membrane is
    (i)   fully permeable
    (ii) impermeable
    (iii) partially permeable to the solute.

11. How does the selectivity of separation change with the increasing membrane thickness?
    (i)   Increases
    (ii) Decreases
    (iii) Remains unchanged

12. Which of the following techniques yields a membrane of narrow pore-size distribution?
    (i)   Film stretching
    (ii) Phase inversion
    (iii) Track etching

13. An asymmetric CA membrane is to be cast from a solution of the polymer in acetone. Which of the following liquids may be used as a non-solvent during membrane preparation by phase inversion?
    (i)   Water
    (ii) Dimethylformamide
    (iii) Acetic acid

14. Which of the following is a counterion for transport through a perfluorosulphonic ion-exchange polymer?
    (i) Na^+ (ii) Cl^- (iii) HSO_4^-

15. A UF membrane has a pore-size range of
   (i) 1–100 Å   (ii) 1–100 µm   (iii) 1–100 nm

16. What is the accepted definition of molecular weight cut-off (MWCO)?

17. Which of the following is an important common cause of flux reduction in ultrafiltration of a protein using a relatively hydrophobic membrane?
   (i) Pore-mouth adsorption
   (ii) Narrowing of pores because of membrane swelling
   (iii) Osmotic pressure of the protein solution

18. Here are three concentration figures in a module for ultrafiltration of a solution of a macromolecule: (a) bulk concentration = 1.5%; (b) permeate concentration = 0.32%; (c) concentration at the membrane surface = 8%. What is the rejection coefficient of the protein?
   (i) 0.0048   (ii) 0.04   (iii) 0.96

19. The following concentration figures are given for reverse osmosis of a salt solution: $C_b = 4\%$; $C_p = 0.03\%$; $C_w = 8\%$. What is the polarization modulus?
   (i) 2   (ii) 0.5   (iii) 0.24

20. A UF membrane offers a steady-state solvent flux of 0.052 $\text{m}^3/(\text{m}^2 \cdot \text{s})$ under gel polarization. The applied pressure drop is 4 bar and the resistance offered by the membrane is 2.4×10^9 m^{-1}. What is the resistance offered by the gel layer? (The viscosity of water may be taken as 0.9 cp)
   (i) 6.1×10^9 m^{-1} (ii) 6.5×10^{10} m^{-1} (iii) 1.25×10^8 m^{-1}

21. Which of the following is a possible value of the area density in a microporous hollow-fibre module?
   (i) 10 cm^2/cm^3 (ii) 500 ft^2/ft^3 (iii) 12,000 m^2/m^3

22. Which of the following membrane processes uses the largest quantity of microporous hollow-fibre membrane?
   (i) Microfiltration   (ii) Haemodialysis   (iii) Pervaporation

23. How does the swelling of a membrane affect diffusion of molecules through it?
   (i) Increases   (ii) Decreases   (iii) No influence

24. Which of the following membrane processes may be suitable for removing traces of moisture from the solvent MIBK?
   (i) Microfiltration   (ii) Reverse osmosis   (iii) Pervaporation

25. Which of the following is a likely value of permeability of O_2 in a polysulphone membrane?
   (i) 1.2 barrer   (ii) 25,500 barrer   (iii) 203,000 barrer

26. In which of the following states a polymer sorbs more of a gas?
   (i) Crystalline   (ii) Melt   (iii) Rubbery

27. According to the 'dual sorption model', the total amount of gas sorbed by unit volume of a polymer is the sum of ( ) and ( ):
   (i) Amount sorbed according to Henry's law

(ii)   Amount adsorbed according to Langmuir equation

(iii)   Amount chemisorbed on the polymer surface

(iv)   Amount sorbed according to Raoult's law

(v)   Amount occupying the free volume of the polymer

28.   The ideal separation factor of B over A for diffusion through a polymer film is $\alpha^*_{BA} = 4.5$. The permeability of A is $\hat{P}_A = 3$ barrer. What is the permeability of B?

   (i) 1.5   (ii) 7.5   (iii) 13.5

29.   The limiting flux through a UF membrane is 0.042 m³/m²·h and the membrane surface mass transfer coefficient is estimated as 5×10^{-6} m/s. If the membrane rejects the solute completely, the polarization modulus is

   (i) 8.03   (ii) 10.03   (iii) 25.3

30.   Identify the mixtures that may be separated by a membrane process commercially: (i) CH_4 from C_2H_6; (ii) O_2 from N_2; (iii) CO_2 from CH_4; (iv) H_2 from CH_4; (v) recovery/reclamation of water from the wastewater stream in a paper mill; (vi) aniline from nitrobenzene; (vii) dehydration of 'rectified spirit'; (viii) clarification of apple juice; (ix) concentration of nitric acid; (x) reduction of alcohol content of beer; (xi) separation of H_2O_2 from an aqueous solution; (xii) separation of aromatics from kerosene; (xiii) removal of emulsified oil from water; (xiv) drying of air.

   Suggest a suitable membrane/membrane material in each case.

31.   Ultrafiltration of a protein from an aqueous solution is being done in the gel polarization regime. What happens to the thickness of the gel with increasing pressure drop across the membrane? The gel thickness

   (i) increases   (ii) decreases   (iii) remains unchanged.

32.   In membrane filtration, the solute molecules are carried to the membrane surface by

   (i) Knudsen diffusion   (ii) Fickian diffusion   (iii) convection.

33.   The permeability of carbon monoxide in a polysulphone film at 25°C is 0.3 barrer. What is the permeability value in (gmol·m)/m²·s·Pa?

   (i) 1.0×10^{-16} (ii) 2.9×10^{-15} (iii) 4.8×10^{-13}

34.   Which of the following is a unit of 'resistance to solvent flow through a gel layer'?

   (i) kg/m²   (ii) m⁻¹·s⁻¹   (iii) m⁻¹

35.   With increased concentration polarization on an RO membrane at a constant applied pressure difference, the solvent flux decreases. What happens to the solute flux?

   (i) Increases   (ii) Decreases   (iii) Remains unchanged

36.   How does the rejection coefficient of a solute change in UF and in RO as the solvent flux is increased by applying a larger pressure on the feed side?

   (i)   Increases

   (ii)   Decreases

   (iii)   Remains unchanged if the membrane is asymmetric

37.   According to the 'film theory' (see Chapter 3), the transport of a solute across a phase boundary occurs through a stagnant film and the solute concentration distribution in the

film is linear. But in membrane separation, the concentration distribution of the solute in the film is often nonlinear. Explain this difference.

38. Mention the three major negative effects of concentration polarization on desalination by RO.

39. In a spiral-wound ultrafiltration module for protein separation, the bulk concentration on the feed side is known to be 2 mass%, and the apparent rejection coefficient is 0.975. The flux is 1.8×10^{-5} m^3/m$^2\cdot$s, and the feed-side mass transfer coefficient is 4.4×10^{-5} m/s. What is the true rejection coefficient?

40. Which of the following problems are typical of CA membranes used for RO?
  (i) Concentration polarization
  (ii) Biological attack
  (iii) Hydrolysis under acidic or alkaline condition
  (iv) Attack by free chlorine that may be present in water

41. In a well-stirred continuous gas permeator, $J_A = J_B$. The more permeating component A that diffuses into the downstream compartment is continuously swept out by a stream at B at 1.5 atm pressure. If the ideal separation factor is 3.15, and the total upstream pressure is 12.5 atm, calculate the composition of the mixture on the upstream side.

42. If the ideal separation factor of a mixture of A and B is $\alpha_{AB}^* = 1$, the actual separation factor should be:
  (i) $\alpha_{AB} = 1$ (ii) $\alpha_{AB} < 1$ (iii) $\alpha_{AB} > 1$

43. With increasing solute concentration in the bulk solution, the ultrafiltration flux
  (i) increases   (ii) decreases   (iii) remains unchanged.

44. Figure 14.46(a) gives a very simple sketch of the arrangement of brine electrolysis to produce caustic and chlorine in a membrane cell using a cation exchange membrane (e.g. Nafion). Sodium ions are counterions and pass through the membrane but chloride ions do not. Chlorine gas is generated at the anode, and hydrogen at the cathode. The cation-exchange membrane separates the cell into two compartments. Brine is fed into the anode compartment and NaOH is produced in the cathode compartment.

An alternative scheme, shown in Figure 14.46(b), proposes to use an anion exchange membrane (for which Cl$^-$ ions are the counterions) and brine is fed into the cathode compartment. Do you see any practical difficulty with this alternative arrangement?

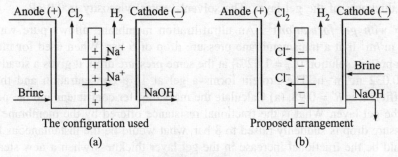

Figure 14.46

45. The following data are available on a dialyser: area = 1.2 m²; fibre diameter = 300 μm; number of fibres = 5,000; overall mass transfer coefficient, $K_L = 1.3 \times 10^{-6}$ m/s. The wall thickness of the fibre is rather small, and the flow rate of the dialysate is much larger than that of blood. If an extraction ratio of $\hat{E} = 0.85$ is achieved in the dialyser, calculate its HTU.

PROBLEMS

14.1 (*Calculation of tortuosity from flux data*)[1] The flux data for the flow of pure water through a microporous membrane, 100 μm thick, at 25°C at different applied pressures are given below. If the average pore size is 1 μm and the average void volume of the membrane is $\varepsilon = 0.32$, estimate the tortuosity factor of the membrane.

ΔP, kPa	40	60	80	100	120
Flux, kg/(m²·h)	496	755	1020	1225	1500

14.2 (*Driving force and concentration polarization in UF*)[1] A macromolecular solute is ultrafiltered using a polycarbonate membrane at 25°C. The solution concentration is 0.015 molar, and 96% solute rejection is achieved. If the feed side pressure is 4 bar and the downstream pressure is 1.1 bar (absolute), calculate the effective pressure driving force. Neglect concentration polarization. Calculate the same if the concentration polarization modulus is 5.5.

14.3 (*Membrane area for batch UF*)[2] It is required to concentrate a protein solution (MW = 1213) by batch ultrafiltration from 14 kg/m³ to 84 kg/m³ concentration. The feed volume is 800 gallon and the batch time is two hours. Membrane fouling and the effect of concentration polarization can be ignored for simplicity. Calculate the required membrane area. The osmotic pressure may be calculated using the equation $\Pi = CRT$. The unit is to operate at $\Delta P = 3$ bar and a rejection coefficient of 0.97 can be achieved. The membrane admits of a pure water flux of 11.5 gal/ft²·h at this pressure difference.

14.4 (*Gel resistance in UF*)[2] A protein solution is being ultrafiltered using an asymmetric membrane having 0.3 μm active layer, 35% fractional open area, and 15 nm average pore diameter. The tortuosity of the pores is 2.7. A major part of the resistance to solvent flow is offered by a gel layer which has an estimated voidage of 50%. The solvent flux is 1.2 m³/m²·h at $\Delta P = 4$ bar. If the diameter of the protein molecules is 30 nm, calculate the thickness of the gel layer. The solvent (water) viscosity is 0.9 cP.

14.5 (*UF with gel formation*)[2] An ultrafiltration membrane allows pure water flux of 0.8 m³/m²·h at a transmembrane pressure drop of 6 bar. When used for ultrafiltration of a protein solution ($C_b = 1.52\%$) at the same pressure drop, it gives a steady-state flux of 0.032 m³/m²·h. The protein forms a gel at 15% concentration and the rejection coefficient is $R' = 0.98$. (a) Calculate the mass transfer coefficient and the permeability of the gel layer. What is the fractional resistance offered by the membrane? (b) If the pressure drop is suddenly raised to 8 bar, what would be the instantaneous flux? What would be the fractional increase in the gel layer thickness when a new steady state is attained? The osmotic effects may be neglected.

14.6 (*Batch UF with concentration polarization*)[3] Consider *batch* ultrafiltration of a solution. As filtration proceeds, the solute concentration in the retentate increases which influences transport in the boundary layer as well as the osmotic pressure. Assuming (i) pseudo-steady state behaviour in respect of solvent flux, and (ii) 100% solute rejection, develope equations for the calculation of the time required to concentrate the feed from C_i to C_f.

14.7 (*Estimation of resistance to flow from laboratory data*)[2] The following time-varying flux data were collected at 25°C for unstirred batch ultrafiltration of 2% bovine serum albumin (BSA, mol. wt. = 69,000 dalton) using Amicon PM-10 membrane of 10,000 dalton MWCO. The applied pressure difference was maintained constant at 30 kPa. Calculate the membrane resistance R_m and the cake resistance (as r_c/ρ_c). Assume complete rejection. The viscosity of water is 0.9 cP.

Time, s	10	20	30	40	50	60	70	80
$10^2 J_w$, litre/m²·h	6.58	5.18	4.45	3.89	3.52	3.27	3.07	2.86

14.8 (*Membrane area for batch UF*)[1] Experimental data on batch ultrafiltration of milk using a proprietory asymmetric membrane could be correlated to express the permeate flux as a function of permeate volume at a constant ΔP [Tekic et al., *J. Membrane Sci.*, *61*(1996) 157].

$$J_w = 2.5 \times 10^{-5} V_p^{-0.2}; \qquad J_w \text{ in m}^3/\text{m}^2\cdot\text{s}; \qquad V_p = \text{permeate volume in m}^3.$$

Calculate the membrane area if 1 m³ of milk is to be ultrafiltered to half the volume in 1 hour per batch.

14.9 (*Limiting flux for the osmotic pressure model*)[2] Use Eq. (14.25) together with the following data to prepare a plot of the flux curves for ultrafiltration of a macromolecular solute at a bulk concentration, $C_b = 0.006$ and 0.04 kmol/m³. *Given: n = 2*; $\zeta = 120$ atm; $\mu R_m = 6 \times 10^5$ atm·(S/m) and $k_L = 3.0 \times 10^{-6}$ m/s. What is the limiting flux?

14.10 (*Gel layer thickness in crossflow UF*)[2] An aqueous macromolecular solution is being ultrafiltered under cross-flow over an asymmetric membrane of average pore size 20 nm (tortuosity, $\tau = 1.7$), open area of 35%, and a permselective skin thickness of 0.45 μm. A plate-and-frame module of 7 mm channel depth is used. The following data are given: Reynolds number of the liquid, Re = 6500; bulk solute concentration, $C_b = 1.3\%$; solution viscosity, $\mu_l = 9.5 \times 10^{-3}$ N·s/m², density = 1030 kg/m³; solvent (water) viscosity, $\mu_s = 8.8 \times 10^{-4}$ N·s/m²; diffusivity of the solute, $D = 3.5 \times 10^{-7}$ cm²/s; transmembrane pressure drop, $\Delta P = 3$ bar; temperature = 27°C; mol. wt. of the solute = 5000; rejection, $R' = 0.99$.

It is known that gelation of the solute occurs at a concentration of 12%. Diameter of the particles in the gel, $d_p = 20$ nm, and the average porosity of the gel is 50%. The mass transfer coefficient can be calculated from the correlation: Sh = 0.025(Re)$^{0.75}$(Sc)$^{1/3}$. Take the channel depth as the characteristic length in the mass transfer correlation. Calculate (a) the thickness of the gel layer, and (b) the pressure drop ΔP at which the formation of a gel layer on the membrane starts.

14.11 (*Time of batch UF*)[1] It is required to concentrate a 1.4% protein (mol. wt. = 2020) solution to a final concentration of 10.5% by batch ultrafiltration at 27°C. A module having 50 ft² filtration area is available and the rejection is almost 100%. Pure water flux through the membrane is 9.5 gallon/(h ft^2) at $\Delta P = 3$ bar. Calculate the time required to process a 600 gallon batch of the feed. Effects of concentration polarization and membrane fouling may be neglected. However, the reduction in the effective transmembrane pressure drop because of osmotic pressure of the solution has to be taken into consideration.

14.12 (*Concentration polarization in RO*)[1]   A spirally wound RO module operates at an upstream pressure of 70 atm (absolute) to produce potable water at a rate of 300 litre/h. The permeate side pressure is essentially atmospheric. The average salt concentration on the feed side is 5.2%. The area of membrane is 20 m^2 and its water permeability is $L_p = 7.5 \times 10^{-4}$ m^3/m^2·h·atm. Do the given data suggest any concentration polarization? If so, what is the polarization modulus?

14.13 (*RO calculation*)[2]   An RO unit uses an asymmetric cellulose acetate membrane having a water permeability coefficient, $L_p = 9 \times 10^{-4}$ m^3/m^2·h·atm, and a salt permeability [see Eq. 14.29(b)], $\hat{P}_s = 3.2 \times 10^{-8}$ m/s. The other relevant data are: feed-side salt concentration = 32 g/litre; feed-side pressure = 40 atm; permeate-side pressure = 1.5 atm; friction coefficient for salt transport, $\sigma = 1$. Calculate the permeate flux and its quality. If the allowable limit of salinity in the permeate is 200 ppm, what is the minimum operating pressure required to maintain this quality? Use the osmotic pressure data given in Example 14.6.

14.14 (*Design of an RO unit*)[3]   It is required to produce 20,000 m^3 per day of potable water having a salt concentration not more than 300 ppm from sea water containing 3.3% salt. An asymmetric cellulose acetate membrane (thickness = 0.8 micron) having a water permeability of 70 l/m^2·h·MPa and salt rejection of 98% is used. The feed-side pressure is 75 atm, that on the permeate side is 1 atm. If 30% of the feed water permeates through the membrane, calculate the required membrane area. The polarization modulus is 1.2.

14.15 (*Desalting by dialysis*)[2]   A solution having 3% sodium acetate and 8% of a target substance of molecular weight 520 is obtained from a pharmaceutical process at a rate of 200 litre/h. A dialyser fitted with a microporous cellophane membrane (thickness, l_m = 100 μm, pore volume = 40%, average pore diameter = 4 nm) is to be designed to reduce the salt concentration to 500 ppm. The dialysate is pure water and a flow rate much larger than that of the fluid is to be maintained. The combined mass transfer resistance of the fluid and the water side may be taken as 2.5×10^5 s/m. Given the diffusivity of sodium acetate, $D = 1.2 \times 10^{-5}$ cm^2/s [estimated using the Nernst–Haskell equation, see Poling et al. (2001), cited in Chapter 2; the equation uses ionic conductance and charge on the ions to estimate its diffusivity in water.], calculate the membrane area required. If the target substance diffuses ten times slower than sodium acetate, estimate its loss in the dialysis process.

14.16 (*Design equation for a countercurrent haemodialyser*)[3]   Following the procedure given in Section 14.5.2, develop equation (14.53) for the 'extraction ratio' $\hat{E}$, in a countercurrent haemodialyser.

14.17 (*Time of haemodialysis*)[3]   A countercurrent haemodialyser has a membrane area of 1.2 m^2, and the overall mass transfer coefficient is estimated to be $K_L = 1.05 \times 10^{-6}$ m/s. (a) Calculate the extraction ratio if the blood flow rate is 300 ml/min, and the dialysate flow rate is ten times as high. (b) Calculate the time of reduction of blood urea from 220 mg% to 20 mg% if the blood volume in the patient's body is 5.5 litre.

14.18 (*Moisture loss through a food wrap*)[1]   One kilogram of a sterilized foodstuff is wrapped leakproof in a cellophane film, 30 μm thick. The moisture content of the freshly packed material is 20% and must not go below 12% (moist basis) during storage. The area of the wrap is 1000 cm². How long can it be stored at room temperature (25°C) without excessive loss of moisture? Permeability of moisture through cellophane is 1.4 barrer. The vapour pressure of water at 25°C is 24 mm Hg. The average relative humidity of ambient air is 60%.

14.19 (*Gas permeation through a composite membrane*)[2]   An equimolar mixture of CO_2 and N_2 permeates through a composite membrane consisting of a 5 μm thick layer of PDMS on a 0.2 μm thick skin of an asymmetric cellulose acetate membrane. Given the following data (Stern, 1994), calculate the ideal separation factor of CO_2 over N_2 at 35°C for the composite membrane. Permeability (barrer) in PDMS is: 4550 for CO_2, 351 for N_2; and in CA: 4.75 for CO_2, 0.15 for N_2.

14.20 (*Gas permeation, concentration-dependent diffusivity*)[2]   Kumazawa and Bae [*J. Appl. Polymer Sci.*, 60(1996) 115–121] studied sorption and permeation of CO_2 through poly-4-methyl-1-pentene at 20°C. The solubility of the gas in the polymer follows the Henry's law, $C = 8.33p$ [C is in m^3(STP)/m^3 polymer; p in MPa]. The diffusivity of the gas through the polymer was found to depend upon its concentration exponentially. i.e.

$$D = D_0 \exp(\beta C); \quad D_0 = 4.53 \times 10^{-17} \ m^2/s; \quad \beta = 0.07 \ m^3/m^3 (STP)$$

Calculate the permeation flux of the gas through a 20 μm thick film of the polymer and its average permeability if the upstream and downstream pressures of CO_2 are 2.3 and 1.5 MPa respectively.

14.21 (*Gas permeation through a composite membrane*)[3]   Pinnau et al. [*J. Membrane Sci*, 37(1988) 81–87] studied the applicability of the 'resistances-in-series model' for gas permeation through composite membranes. In a particular experiment, a composite membrane made of a PDMS layer on a microporous polysulphone backing is used to separate an equimolar mixture of $O_2(A)$ and $N_2(B)$. Permeation of the gases through the microporous backing occurs by a combination of Poiseuille and Knudsen flow and is non-selective. The normalized permeability or permeance ($\hat{P}_A/l_m$) of both the gases through the backing is 10^{-3} cm^3(STP)/(cm^2)(s)(cm Hg). The ideal separation factor for O_2-N_2-PDMS is $\alpha_{AB}^* = 2.2$, and the permeability of N_2 in the PDMS layer is 270 barrer. What should be the thickness of the PDMS layer in the composite if the flux of O_2 has to be twice that of N_2? The pressure on the permeate side is much smaller than that on the feed side.

14.22 (*Permeation of a binary gas mixture*)[1]   The feed-side of a membrane gas separator has an equimolar mixture of $H_2(A)$ and $CH_4(B)$ at 30 bar total pressure. The product side is at 1.1 bar. (a) If the downstream pressure is considered to be much smaller than that of the feed-side, calculate the product flux and its composition. (b) Compare the 'ideal separation factor' with the actual calculated without neglecting the permeate-side pressure. *Given:* membrane (asymmetric) thickness = 0.2 μm; permeability, $\hat{P}_A = 30$ barrer $\hat{P}_B = 0.12$ barrer.

14.23 (*Membrane area in a well-mixed permeator*)[1]   A membrane gas separation unit is to be designed for separating air at a rate of 100 m^3/(h) (STP) to yield an enriched permeate stream having 25% O$_2$ at 35°C. The feed air is compressed, cooled and freed from moisture and oil particles (the compressed gas from a compressor is likely to have some very fine suspended oil particles) before it is fed to the membrane unit. A composite polysulfone membrane having 0.15 μm thick active layer is used. The operating pressures are 10 bar on the feed side and 1 bar on the permeate side. A product-cut of $\theta = 0.25$ is suggested. The gas-phase mass transfer resistance on either side of the membrane is small. Given the permeability of oxygen, $\hat{P}_A = 1.7$ barrer and the ideal separation factor, $\alpha_{AB}^* = 5.2$, calculate the membrane area.

14.24 (*A well-mixed permeator*)[1]   The well-stirred feed compartment of a membrane permeator has 20% CO$_2$(A) and 80% CH$_4$(B) at a total pressure of 12.5 atm. The permeate side is continuously flushed with pure CH$_4$ at 1.5 atm so that the CO$_2$ concentration in it is virtually zero. A 300 μm thick PDMS film is used as the membrane. The following data are given: the ideal separation factor, $\alpha_{AB}^* = 3.15$; permeability of CO$_2$ in PDMS at the given condition, $\hat{P}_A = 4570$ barrer; solubility coefficient of CH$_4$ in PDMS, $S_B = 0.0059$ cm^3(STP)/cm^3(polymer)-mm Hg. Calculate (a) the flux of CO$_2$ and of CH$_4$ through the film, (b) the permeance of CO$_2$ in PDMS, and (c) the diffusivity of CH$_4$ in the membrane.

14.25 (*Calculation of permeability from flux data*)[1]   Air is passed at a high rate through the feed chamber of a membrane permeator at 15 atm pressure. The 'well-stirred' downstream chamber has a pressure of 1.5 atm. An integrally skinned high free volume membrane with 0.2 μm thick permselective layer separates the chambers. At steady-state condition and at 35°C, the flux of O$_2$(A) and N$_2$(B) are found to be 1.245 × 10^{-3} and 1.06 × 10^{-3} cm^3(STP)/cm^2·s respectively. What is the separation factor? Calculate the permeability of the gases in the membrane.

In a separate experiment, 10.5 g of the polymer is found to sorb 10.4 cm^3(STP) oxygen when equilibrated with pure O$_2$ at 5 atm. What is the Henry's law constant (S_A) for oxygen and the average diffusivity of O$_2$ in the membrane? The density of the polymer is 1.02 g/cm^3.

14.26 (*A two-stage permeator with well-mixed compartments*)[3]   A modified asymmetric polyphenylene oxide membrane having a skin thickness of 0.5 micron is used for producing 96% N$_2$ for blanketing at a rate of 100 m^3(STP)/h. Separation is to be done in a *two-stage* device having well-mixed feed and permeate compartments (Figure 14.47). Compressed air is fed to the first stage at 11.5 bar. The retentate from this stage enters the feed chamber of the second stage at the same pressure. The permeate compartments of both the stages are at essentially atmospheric pressure. Permeability of O$_2$ in the polymer is 48 barrer and the ideal separation factor is 4.3. If the stage-cut is the same for both the stages, calculate the permeate rates and compositions, and the membrane areas.

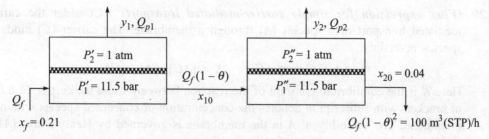

y_1, Q_{p1} y_2, Q_{p2}

$P_2' = 1$ atm $P_2'' = 1$ atm

$P_1' = 11.5$ bar $Q_f(1-\theta)$ $P_1'' = 11.5$ bar $x_{20} = 0.04$

Q_f x_{10}

$x_f = 0.21$ $Q_f(1-\theta)^2 = 100$ m³(STP)/h

Figure 14.47 A two-stage gas permeator.

14.27 (***Area of a cross-flow permeator***)[3] It is required to separate air at a rate of 300 m³/h (STP) in a membrane permeator fitted with a novel ultrathin membrane (0.1 μm) offering an ideal separation factor of $\alpha_{AB}^* = 4.5$ for oxygen. The crossflow configuration on the permeate side is selected and a stage-cut of 30% is suggested. The upstream pressure is 18 atm and the downstream pressure is essentially atmospheric. The permeability of A is 12 barrer. If the permeate gets mixed up only at the exit, calculate the oxygen concentration in the permeate and the membrane area.

14.28 (***A membrane blood oxygenator***)[3] A common type of blood-oxygenator consists of a microporous hollow-fibre module with blood flowing through the shell-side and the oxygen-rich gas through the lumen-side. In order to simulate the performance of a blood-oxygenator, the experimental work on oxygen absorption in water in a hollow-fibre module has been reported in numerous publications [see, for example, Lund et al., *J. Membrane Sci.*, *117*(1996) 207–219].

An experimental set-up consisting of a bundle of 500 microporous polypropylene fibres (length = 0.25 m; o.d. = 175 μm; wall thickness = 40 μm; void fraction of the fibre wall = 0.40; tortuosity of the pores = 2.55). The pores are very fine and Knudsen diffusion of O_2 through the pores occurs. Two hundred ml of water is continuously recirculated through the shell-side of the unit at 30°C. The liquid-side mass transfer coefficient is estimated to be 0.005 cm/s. If the water is oxygen-free initially, calculate the time required for the oxygen concentration in the water to reach 5 ppm. The solubility of oxygen in water, 37.4 ppm at 1 atm O_2 pressure at 30°C, follows the Henry's law. The Knudsen diffusivity of O_2 is 0.05 cm²/s. How important is the gas-phase diffusional resistance? Since polypropylene is hydrophobic, water does not enter into the membrane pores which remain filled with gas only (Figure 14.48).

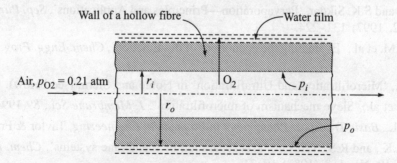

Wall of a hollow fibre   Water film

Air, $p_{O2} = 0.21$ atm r_i O_2 p_i

r_o

p_o

Figure 14.48 Oxygen transport through the wall of a hollow fibre.

14.29 (*Flux expression for simple carrier-mediated transport*)[3]   Consider the carrier-mediated transport of a species (A) through a membrane. The carrier (C) binds the species reversibly.

$$A + C \rightleftharpoons AC; \qquad K = [AC]_m/[A]_m \cdot [C]_m$$

Here K is the equilibrium constant of the reaction between A and the carrier C; a term in brackets with subscript m denotes the concentration of concerned species within the membrane. The solubility of A in the membrane is governed by Henry's law, $[A]_m = \beta[A]$, $[A]$ is the concentration of A in the fluid.

Develop an expression for the carrier-madiated flux of A through the membrane. The contribution of 'passive transport' may be neglected.

14.30 (*Water flux through a membrane having a size distribution of the pores*)[3]   The pore diameter d in a microporous membrane has a size-distribution [Filipov et al., *J. Membrane Sci.*, 89(1994) 199] that follows the log-normal function.

$f(d) = \exp[-\ln(d - e_m)^2/2\sigma_m^2]/\sqrt{2\pi\sigma_m d}$; d is in μm; e_m and σ_m are parameters of the distribution.

(a)   Show that the average pore size is given by $E_m = \exp[(\sigma_m^2/2) + e_m]$.
(b)   If, for the particular membrane, $e_m = 0.01$ and $\sigma_m = 0.1$, calculate the pure water flux through the membrane at $\Delta P = 20$ kPa. The average free area of the membrane is 30%, and the tortuosity of the pores is estimated to be 2.5.

REFERENCES

Avila, V.L., *Biology*, Bookmark Publishers, San Diego, 1992.

Baker, R.W., *Membrane Technology and Applications*, 2nd ed., Wiley VCH, 2004.

Bhabe, R., *Inorganic Membranes*, van Nostrand Reinheld, 1991.

Cao, G.Z., et al., 'Perporometry study on the size distribution of active pores in porous ceramic membranes', *J. Membrane Sci.*, 83(1993) 221–235.

Cudacek, M.W., and A.G. Fane, 'The dynamics of polarization in unstirred and stirred ultra-filtration', *J. Membrane Sci.*, 21(1984) 145–160.

DeGroot, S.R., and P. Mazur, *Nonequilibrium Thermodynamics*, Wiley Interscience, New York, 1962.

Dutta, B.K., and S.K. Sikdar, 'Pervaporation—Principles and Applications', *Sep. Purif. Methods*, 25(no. 2, 1997) 131–224.

Ettouney, H.M. et al., 'Evaluating the economics of desalination', *Chem. Engg. Prog.*, Dec. 2002, 32–39.

Eykamp, W., 'Microfiltration and Ultrafiltration' in Noble and Stern, (see below).

Filippov, A. et al., 'Sieve mechanism of microfiltration', *J. Membrane Sci.*, 89(1994) 199–213.

Fournier, R.L., *Basic Transport Phenomena in Biomedical Engineering*, Taylor & Francis, 1999.

Fritzsche, A.K., and R.S. Narayan, 'Gas separation by membrane systems', *Chem. Econ. Engg. Review*, 19, No. 1–3 (1987) 19–31.

Galletti, P.M., and C.K. Colton, 'Artificial lung and blood-gas exchange devices' in *The Biomedical Engineering Handbook,* CRC Press, 1995.

Gonzales, B.G., and I.O. Utribe, 'Mathematical modeling of the pervaporative separation of methanol-methyl-terbutyl ether mixtures', *Ind. Eng. Chem. Res.*, *40*(2001) 1720–1731.

Ho, W.S.W., and K.K. Sirkar, *Membrane Handbook*, Chapman & Hall, New York, 1992.

Hwang, S.T., Non-equilibrium thermodynamics of membrane transport, *AIChE J.*, *50*(2004) 862–870.

Kedem, O., and A. Katchalsky, 'The physical interpretation of phenomenological coefficients of membrane permeability', *Biochem. Et Biophys. Acta*, *27*(1958) 229.

Kesting, R.E., *Synthetic Polymeric Membranes*, 2nd ed., Wiley Interscience, New York, 1985.

Kesting, R.E., and A.K. Fritzsch, *Polymeric Gas Separation Membranes*, John Wiley, New York, 1993.

Koros, W.J., 'Membranes—Learning a lesson from nature', *Chem. Eng. Prog.*, October 1995, 68–81.

Koros, W.J., 'Evolving beyond the thermal age of separation processes: membranes can lead the way', *AIChE J.*, *50*(2004) 2326–2334.

Koros, W.J., and R. Mahajan, 'Pushing the limits on possibilities for large scale gas separation: which strategies', *J. Membrane Sci.*, *175*(2000) 181–196.

Li, K., et al., 'Mathematical modeling of multicomponent membrane permeators', *J. Membrane Sci.*, *52*(1990) 205–219.

Liang, T., and R. L. Long, 'Corrections to correlations for shell-side mass transfer coefficients in the hollow-fibre membrane (HFM) modules', *Ind. Eng. Chem. Res.*, *44*(2005) 7838–7843.

Loeb, S., and S. Sourirajan, 'Advances in Chemistry Series', Vol. 38—Saline Water Conversion II, *American Chemical Society*, 1963.

Lonsdale, H.K. et al., 'Transport properties of cellulose acetate osmotic membranes', *J. Appl. Poly. Sci.*, *9*(1965) 1341–1362.

Mulder, M., *Basic Principles of Membrane Technology*, Kluwer Academic Publ., Amsterdam, 1991.

Nadakatti, S.M., J.H. Kim, and S.A. Stern, 'Solubility of light gases in poly(n-methylacrylate) at elevated pressures', *J. Membrane Sci.*, *108*(1995) 279–291.

Noble, R.D., and S.A. Stern, *Membrane Separations Technology*, Elsevier, Amsterdam, 1995.

Ohiya, H. et al., 'Design of reverse osmosis process', *Desalination*, *63*(1987) 119–133.

Paul, D.R., and Y.P. Yampolskii, *Polymeric Gas Separation Membranes*, CRC Press, Florida, 1994.

Porter, M.C., 'Membrane filtration' in *Handbook of Separation Process Technology*, 2nd ed., P.A. Schweitzer (Ed.), McGraw-Hill, New York, 1997.

Robeson, L.M., 'Correlation of separation factors versus permeability of polymeric membranes', *J. Membrane Sci.*, *62*(1991) 165–185.

Ruthven, D.M. (Ed.), *Encyclopedia of Separation Technology*, John Wiley, New York, 1997.

Saltonstall, C.W., and R.W. Lawrence, 'Calculation of expected performance of reverse osmosis plants', *Desalination*, *42*(1982) 247–253.

Schafer, A.I., A.G. Fane, and T.D. Waite, *Nanofiltration—Principles and Applications*, Elsevier, London, 2005.

Scott, K., and R. Hughes, *Industrial Membrane Separation Technology*, Blackie, London, 1996.

Seader, J.D., and E.J. Henley, *Separation Process Principles*, John Wiley, New York, 1998.

Sirkar, K.K., and G.H. Rao, 'Shortcut design methods for reverse osmosis separation with tubular modules', *Desalination*, *48*(1983) 25–42.

Soltanieh, M., and W.N. Gill, 'Review of reverse osmosis membranes and transport models', *Chem. Engg. Commun.*, *12*(1981) 247–253.

Sourirajan, S. (Ed.), *Reverse Osmosis and Synthetic Membranes: Theory, Technology, Engineering*, National Research Council, Canada, 1977.

Sourirajan, S., *Reverse Osmosis*, Academic Press, New York, 1970.

Spiegler, K.S., and O. Kedem, 'Thermodynamics of hyperfiltration (reverse osmosis): criteria for efficient membranes', *Desalination*, *1*(1966) 311–326.

Stern, S. A., 'Polymers for gas separation—the next decade', *J. Membrane Sci.*, *94*(1994) 1–65.

Vaslef, S.N. et al. 'Design and evaluation of a new, low pressure loss, implantable artificial lung', *ASAIO J.*, 1994, M522–M526.

Veith, W.R., J.M. Howell, and H.J. Hsieh, 'Dual sorption theory', *J. Membrane Sci.*, *1*(1976) 177–220.

Walawender, W.P., and S.A. Stern, *Separation Sci.*, *7*(1972) 553–584.

Weller, S., and Steiner, W.A., *Chem Eng. Progr.*, *46*(1950) 585.

Wijmans, S., S. Nakao, and C.A. Smolders, 'Flux limitation in ultrafiltration osmotic pressure model and gel layer model', *J. Membrane Sci.*, *20*(1984) 115–124.

Wickramasinghe, S.R. et al., 'Mass transfer in various hollow-fiber geometries', *J. Membrane Sci.*, *69*(1992) 235–250.

Zeman, L.J., and A.L. Zydney, *Microfiltration and Ultrafiltration*, Marcel Dekkar, Boston, 1996.

Multicomponent Distillation

The analytical and graphical techniques of separation calculation for gas absorption and distillation discussed and illustrated in Chapters 6 and 7 deal with binary mixtures. However, a majority of fluid mixtures in chemical process and allied industries contain more than two components. These are called *multicomponent mixtures*. In this chapter we shall briefly introduce the topic of multicomponent distillation.

15.1 DEGREES OF FREEDOM IN MULTICOMPONENT DISTILLATION

A single column cannot separate more than one component in a reasonably pure form from a multicomponent mixture. If we have $\underline{C}$ number of components[†], then in principle, we must have $\underline{C}$ – 1 number of columns to separate all of them. Thus we may separate the most volatile component, say A, as the top product from a ternary mixture of A, B and C. The remaining components leaving as the bottom product may be further fractionated in a second column to yield B and C in reasonably pure forms (Figure 15.1). It is to be remembered that all the product streams will, in general, contain small quantities of the other components and the required purity of the streams have to be specified in the design problem.

The complete statement of a multicomponent distillation problem is associated with its 'degrees of freedom'. As it will be elaborated in Section 15.5, all the relevant variables in a distillation problem are related by a set of independent equations. The same is true for other separation processes as well. Examples of such equations are mass and energy balances, equilibrium relations, etc. (see Section 7.6 for such equations for the case of continuous distillation of a binary mixture). However, the number of variables happens to be more than the number of independent equations. The difference between the number of variables and the number of independent equations is called the 'degrees of freedom'. If a set of suitable variables equal to the number of degrees of freedom is specified or known, the others can be calculated from the available equations.

If we maintain a constant pressure in the column and neglect heat loss or gain by it, the variables that should be specified to describe separation of a ternary distillation system completely

---

[†] We use the notation $\underline{C}$ to denote the number of components and it should not be confused with concentration or a component called C.

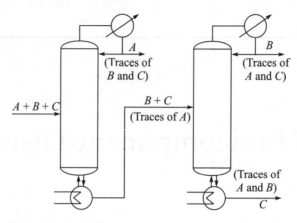

Figure 15.1 Two columns in series to separate a ternary mixture.

and unambiguously are given in Table 15.1. The number of degrees of freedom of a system is found to be 9. In fact, it is $\underline{C}$ + 6 (see Section 15.5) where $\underline{C}$ is the number of components. If there are four components in the mixture, the degrees of freedom is ten (note that three mole fractions describe the feed concentration of a four-component mixture).

Table 15.1 Degrees of freedom in a ternary system ($\underline{C}$ = 3)

Variables	Number to be specified
Feed rate (F)	1
Feed composition (z_1, z_2)	2
Quality of the feed (in terms of enthalpy H_F, or temperature T_F)	1
Distillate (composition $x_{1,D}$, or amount D)	1
Bottom product (composition $x_{2,W}$, or amount W)	1
Reflux ratio (R)	1
Reflux condition (T_o)	1
Optimum feed plate	1
	Total 9 (= $\underline{C}$ + 6)

The selection of one degree of freedom for each of the top and the bottom products needs justification. The amounts and compositions of these two streams (D, W, $x_{i,D}$, $x_{i,W}$) are related by the following material balance equations [Eq. (15.1)] and mole fraction constraints [Eq. (15.2)] for the ternary.

$$Fz_i = Dx_{i,D} + Wx_{i,W}, \qquad i = 1, 2, 3 \tag{15.1}$$

$$\sum_{i=1}^{3} x_{i,D} = 1 \quad \text{and} \quad \sum_{i=1}^{3} x_{i,W} = 1 \tag{15.2}$$

In Table 15.1, we have specified the mole fraction of only one component in the top product ($x_{1,D}$) and of another ($x_{2,W}$) in the bottom product. Let us see what happens if we specify the mole fraction of one more component, say $x_{2,D}$, in the distillate. Since the mole fractions sum up to unity [Eq. (15.2)], the composition of any ternary mixture becomes completely defined if two mole fraction values are fixed. Once the distillate composition is known, it is possible to perform tray-by-tray calculation (see Example 15.6) beginning at the top and eventually reaching a liquid composition in which $x_{2,W}$ *nearly* attains the value specified in the problem. This is the bottom liquid. But the set of specified distillate composition and the calculated bottom composition may not satisfy the material balance equation, i.e. Eq. (15.1). So we cannot specify the mole fraction of more than one component each in the distillate and in the bottoms. We should rather proceed as follows:

(a) Assume reasonable values of the mole fractions of the other components in either the distillate or in the bottoms.
(b) Use the balance Eqs. (15.1) and (15.2) to calculate the composition of the other stream.
(c) Perform tray-to-tray calculations (see Example 15.6) beginning at one end to arrive at the composition at the other terminal.
(d) If this composition does not match the values (in all probability, it will not) calculated from the balance equations in step (a), the entire sequence of calculations has to be repeated with assumed *revised* values of the mole fractions. It is important to find out an efficient numerical technique to obtain revised values. Multicomponent distillation calculation is essentially one of 'trial-and-error' type and the number of cycles of calculation required to arrive at matching values of mole fractions depends upon the accuracy of the *initial guess values* of the mole fractions.

15.2 KEY COMPONENTS

The two components of the feed whose concentrations are specified in the distillate and in the bottom product are called the *key components*. A column separates the key components to the desired extent. The more volatile of the two keys that concentrates in the distillate is the *light key* (LK); the less volatile one is the *heavy key* (HK). All other components which get *distributed automatically* between the distillate and the bottoms are *non-keys*. A non-key more volatile than the light key is a *light non-key* (LNK); a non-key less volatile than the heavy key is a *heavy non-key* (HNK). In some separation problems, there may be one or more components having volatilities intermediate between the LK and the HK. These are called 'intermediate keys' or 'distributed keys' since they get distributed between the top and the bottom products satisfying Eqs. (15.1), (15.2) and the equilibrium relations. Example 15.1 illustrates how we can calculate the compositions of the top and the bottom products *assuming* the values of one or more non-keys in the products.

EXAMPLE 15.1 (*Distribution of the keys and non-keys*)   It is required to separate a saturated quaternary mixture containing propane (component 1, $z_1 = 0.06$), n-butane (component 2, $z_2 = 0.33$), n-pentane (component 3, $z_3 = 0.45$), and n-hexane (component 4, $z_4 = 0.16$) at a rate of 1000 kmol/h. The total pressure is assumed constant at 1 atm. The reflux ratio is $R = 3.0$, and the reflux is at its bubble point. It is desired to recover 99% of the butane in the distillate and 99.5% of the pentane in the bottoms. Calculate (a) the flow rates and compositions of the distillate and the bottom product, and (b) the condensation rate and the boilup rate.

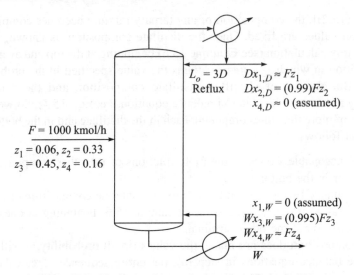

Figure 15.2   The feed and the product streams of Example 15.1.

Solution

There are four component mass balance equations from Eq. (15.1) for $i = 1, 2, 3,$ and 4 (in fact, one of the equations is essentially the total mass balance equation, $F = D + W$), and two conditions from Eq. (15.2). Fractional recoveries of components 2 and 3 are given. These are the light and the heavy keys respectively. There are eight unknowns, namely D, W, $x_{1,D}$, $x_{2,D}$, $x_{3,D}$, $x_{1,W}$, $x_{2,W}$, and $x_{3,W}$. The number of available equations is six. So there are *two more unknowns* than the number of equations (in fact, this is a major difference from the case of distillation of a binary mixture in which the number of such unknowns is the same as the number of equations). There is one light non-key (propane), and one heavy non-key (hexane). We have to make reasonable assumptions ('guess values') of the concentrations of these components in the distillate or in the bottoms in order to solve for the remaining six unknowns.

Since a high recovery of the keys is stipulated, it is reasonable to assume that all the LNKs get into the top product, and all the HNKs remain in the bottoms—i.e. $x_{4,D} = 0$, and $x_{1,W} = 0$. *Given:* 99 mol% of component 2 (LK) is recovered at the top and 99.5% of component 3 (HK) at the bottom. Therefore,

$$\frac{Dx_{2,D}}{Fz_2} = 0.99 \Rightarrow Dx_{2,D} = (0.99)(1000)(0.33) = 326.7 \text{ kmol/h} \tag{i}$$

and $\qquad\qquad Wx_{2,W} = Fz_2 - Dx_{2,D} = (1000)(0.33) - 326.7 = 3.3 \text{ kmol/h} \tag{ii}$

Similarly, for component 3,

$$\frac{Wx_{3,W}}{Fz_3} = 0.995$$

or $\qquad\qquad Wx_{3,W} = (0.995)(1000)(0.45) = 447.75 \text{ kmol/h} \quad \text{and} \quad Dx_{3,D} = 2.25 \tag{iii}$

Now we can write down the following equations:

$$Fz_1 = Dx_{1,D} + Wx_{1,W} \Rightarrow Dx_{1,D} = (1000)(0.06) - 0 = 60 \tag{iv}$$

$$D(x_{1,D} + x_{2,D} + x_{3,D} + x_{4,D}) = D \Rightarrow D = 60 + 326.7 + 2.25 + 0 = \boxed{388.95} \qquad \text{(v)}$$

$$W = F - D = 1000 - 388.95 \Rightarrow W = \boxed{611.05} \qquad \text{(vi)}$$

and $\qquad x_{1,W} + x_{2,W} + x_{3,W} + x_{4,W} = 1.0 \Rightarrow x_{2,W} + x_{3,W} + x_{4,W} = 1.0 \qquad$ (vii)

All the unknown variables can be obtained as tabulated below by solving the above equations.

Component (i)	Feed (z_i)	Distillate ($x_{i,D}$)	Bottom product ($x_{i,W}$)
Propane (1)	0.06	0.1543	0.0000
n-Butane (2)	0.33	0.8400	0.0055
n-Pentane (3)	0.45	0.0057	0.7327
n-Hexane (4)	0.16	0.0000	0.2618

The rate condensation in the reboiler = RD = (3)(388.95) = $\boxed{1166.85 \text{ kmol/h}}$

Since the feed is liquid at its bubble point, the vaporization rate in the reboiler = $\boxed{1166.85 \text{ kmol/h}}$

Note: In some problems the concentrations of the LK and the HK, rather than the fractional recoveries, are specified. The above calculations are very approximate. Better results may be obtained using the Fenske equation (see Example 15.5).

15.3 COLUMN OPERATING CONDITIONS

The top and bottom compositions as well as the operating conditions (temperature and pressure) need to be ascertained before the calculation of the number of ideal stages can start. The *trial* compositions at the top and at the bottom are determined from the desired concentrations or fractional recoveries of the key components as discussed above and illustrated in Example 15.1. The common technique of determination of the top temperature and pressure is based on the coolant temperature. For example, if water from a cooling tower is the coolant in the overhead condenser, its *maximum* outlet temperature should not exceed 120°F[†] (49°C), but is normally limited to 40–45°C. The bubble point of the condensate may remain around 50°C so that a temperature driving force of 5–10°C is available in the condenser. The condenser pressure is now easy to calculate. A reasonable pressure drop in the column including the condenser is assumed to calculate the reboiler pressure. Since the trial liquid composition in the reboiler is already known, the reboiler temperature can be calculated. The calculation of bubble point and dew point is necessary for the determination of the temperature on a tray and that at the top and the bottom. The procedure of this calculation has been shown in Chapter 7 and is also outlined in the Appendix.

[†] Normally the temperature of the cooling water leaving a condenser is limited to about 45°C in order to reduce fouling of the tubes. Very often it is less than this value.

15.4   APPROXIMATE METHODS OF DISTILLATION CALCULATION—THE *FUG* TECHNIQUE

Once the *trial* compositions and operating conditions at the top and at the bottom are fixed, the number of ideal stages for the separation can be calculated using a suitable *exact method*. Before we go for a brief description of it, we will outline below the most important approximate methods of calculation collectively called the Fenske–Underwood–Gilliland (FUG) method (van Winkle, 1967; Wankat, 1988; Seader and Henley, 2006). A few other techniques are given in Ludwig (1997).

15.4.1   Fenske Equation

The Fenske equation for the minimum number of ideal trays in a column operating under total reflux for a binary mixture has been discussed in Section 7.6. Equation (7.85) can be extended to separation of the two key components, A(LK) and B(HK), of a multicomponent mixture.

$$N_{min} = \frac{\log\left[(x_{A,D} \cdot x_{B,W})/(x_{B,D} \cdot x_{A,W})\right]}{\log(\alpha_{AB})_{av}} \tag{15.3}$$

Here N_{min} is the minimum number of trays (*including* the reboiler which also acts as an equilibrium stage), and $(\alpha_{AB})_{av}$ is the average relative volatility of A(LK) with respect to B(HK). It is customary to take $(\alpha_{AB})_{av}$ as the geometric mean of the α's at the conditions at the top and the bottom.

If the fractional recoveries of the key components (instead of concentrations) are given, Eq. (15.3) can be expressed as

$$N_{min} = \frac{\log\left[\dfrac{f_{A,D} \cdot f_{B,W}}{(1 - f_{A,D})(1 - f_{B,W})}\right]}{\log(\alpha_{AB})_{av}} \tag{15.4}$$

Here $f_{A,D}$ is the fractional energy of component A in the distillate, and $f_{B,W}$ is that of the component B in the bottom product.

$$f_{A,D} = \frac{D x_{A,D}}{F z_A} \quad \Rightarrow \quad x_{A,D} = \frac{F z_A \cdot f_{A,D}}{D};$$

$$x_{A,W} = \frac{F z_A(1 - f_{A,D})}{W}; \quad f_{B,W} = \frac{W x_{B,W}}{F z_B} \tag{15.5}$$

Once the minimum number of stages (N_{min}) is determined, it is easy to calculate the distribution of a non-key (or an intermediate key) between the top and the bottom products. For any component J (heavier than A), we can write down the following equation for separation between A and J.

$$N_{min} = \frac{\log\left[\dfrac{f_{A,D} \cdot f_{J,W}}{(1 - f_{A,D})(1 - f_{J,W})}\right]}{\log(\alpha_{AJ})_{av}} \tag{15.6}$$

Example 15.2 illustrates the procedure.

EXAMPLE 15.2 (*The minimum number of trays and the distribution of the non-keys*)   A feed mixture containing six components ($z_1 = 0.032$, $z_2 = 0.068$, $z_3 = 0.17$, $z_4 = 0.30$, $z_5 = 0.32$, and $z_6 = 0.11$) is to be separated by distillation so that 98.5% of component 3 goes to the distillate and 98% of component 5 goes to the bottom product. Determine the minimum number of trays required and the composition of the top and the bottom products. The average relative volatility values are: $\alpha_{15} = 3.15$, $\alpha_{25} = 2.75$, $\alpha_{35} = 2.35$, $\alpha_{45} = 1.40$, $\alpha_{55} = 1$, $\alpha_{65} = 0.75$.

Solution

Take the basis, $F = 1000$ kmol/h. Component $3 \rightarrow$ light key (LK), component $5 \rightarrow$ heavy key (HK).

98.5% of component 3 (LK) goes to the distillate.

$\Rightarrow$ $\qquad\qquad Dx_{3,D} = (0.985)Fz_3 = (0.985)(1000)(0.17) = 167.45$

$\Rightarrow$ $\qquad\qquad Wx_{3,W} = Fz_3 - 167.45 = 170 - 167.45 = 2.55$ kmol/h

98% of component 5 (HK) goes to the bottom.

$\Rightarrow$ $\quad Wx_{5,W} = (0.98)Fz_5 = (0.98)(1000)(0.32) = 313.6$; $Dx_{5,D} = 320 - 313.6 = 6.4$

Obtain the minimum number of trays from the Fenske equation, Eq (15.3).

$$N_{min} = \frac{\log\left[(x_{3,D} \cdot x_{5,W})/(x_{5,D} \cdot x_{3,W})\right]}{\log \alpha_{35}} = \frac{\log\left[(Dx_{3,D} \cdot Wx_{5,W})/(Dx_{5,D} \cdot Wx_{3,W})\right]}{\log \alpha_{35}}$$

$\Rightarrow$ $\quad N_{min} = \dfrac{\log\left[(167.45 \times 313.6)/(6.4 \times 2.55)\right]}{\log 2.35} = \boxed{9.45}$

The minimum number of trays required can also be directly calculated from Eq. (15.4) by putting $f_{3,D} = 0.985$ and $f_{5,W} = 0.98$. Therefore,

$$N_{min} = \frac{\log\left[(0.985 \times 0.98)/(1 - 0.985)(1 - 0.98)\right]}{\log 2.35} = \boxed{9.45}$$

Now we find out the distribution of component 1 between the top and the bottom products. Consider the pair 1–3 and using the Fenske equation for this pair, we have

$$N_{min} = \frac{\log\left[(x_{1,D} \cdot x_{3,W})/(x_{3,D} \cdot x_{1,W})\right]}{\log \alpha_{13}} \Rightarrow 9.45 = \frac{\log\left[(Dx_{1,D} \times 2.55)/(Wx_{1,W} \times 167.45)\right]}{\log(3.15/2.35)}$$

$\Rightarrow$ $\qquad\qquad \dfrac{Dx_{1,D}}{Wx_{1,W}}(0.015228) = (1.340425)^{9.45} \Rightarrow \dfrac{Dx_{1,D}}{Wx_{1,W}} = 1046.6$ $\qquad\qquad$ (i)

From material balance,

$$Fz_1 = Dx_{1,D} + Wx_{1,W} \Rightarrow Dx_{1,D} + Wx_{1,W} = (1000)(0.032) = 32 \qquad\qquad \text{(ii)}$$

Solving (i) and (ii), $Dx_{1,D} = 31.9695$; $Wx_{1,W} = 0.0305$

Similarly, considering the pairs 2–5, 4–5, and 6–3 and using the Fenske equation,

$$Dx_{2,D} = 67.766, \; Wx_{2,W} = 0.2342; \qquad Dx_{4,D} = 98.74, \; Wx_{4,W} = 201.26;$$
$$Dx_{6,D} = 3.224 \times 10^{-5}, \; Wx_{6,W} = 109.99966 \approx 110$$

The amount of distillate,

$$D = \sum_{i=1}^{6} Dx_{i,D} = 31.9695 + 67.766 + 167.45 + 98.74 + 6.4 + 3.442 \times 10^{-5} = 372.325$$

$$W = 1000 - 372.325 = 627.675 \text{ kmol/h}$$

The compositions of the top and the bottom products are given below:

Component	$\alpha_{i,5}$	z_i	$Dx_{i,D}$	$Wx_{i,W}$	$x_{i,D}$	$x_{i,W}$
1	3.15	0.032	31.9695	0.0305	0.08586	4.86×10^{-5}
2	2.75	0.068	67.766	0.2342	0.182	3.73×10^{-4}
3	2.35	0.17	167.45	2.55	0.4497	4.06×10^{-3}
4	1.4	0.30	98.74	201.26	0.2652	0.3206
5	1.0	0.32	6.4	313.6	0.01719	0.4996
6	0.75	0.11	3.442×10^{-5}	110	9.2×10^{-8}	0.1752
		1.0	372.325	627.675	0.99995	0.99988

15.4.2   The Underwood Equation for Minimum Reflux

In a column for distillation of a binary mixture with minimum reflux, the pinch point occurs at the feed tray if the solution is ideal or nearly ideal. For a multicomponent system too, the pinch point appears at the feed tray if all the components are distributed between the top and the bottom products. However, if one or more of the non-keys appear in only one of the products, separate pinch points in the rectifying and the stripping sections may occur.

Let us consider an envelope in the rectifying section of a multicomponent distillation column shown in Figure 15.3. A steady state mass balance of component i at total reflux is

$$V_{n+1}y_{i,n+1} = L_n x_{i,n} + Dx_{i,D}$$

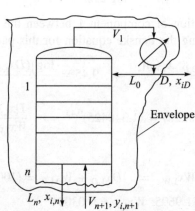

Figure 15.3   Mass balance envelope in the rectifying section of a multicomponent distillation column.

If constant molar overflow (CMO) occurs and if the column operates at minimum reflux (i.e. $V_{n+1} = V = V_{\min}$, and $L_n = L = L_{\min}$),

$$V_{\min}y_{i,n+1} = L_{\min}x_{i,n} + Dx_{i,D} \tag{15.7}$$

Since the compositions are essentially constant near a pinch point,

$$y_{i,n-1} = y_{i,n} = y_{i,n+1} \quad \text{and} \quad x_{i,n-1} = x_{i,n} = x_{i,n+1} \tag{15.8}$$

Further, we assume a linear equilibrium relation,

$$y_{i,n} = K_i x_{i,n} \tag{15.9}$$

Combining Eqs. (15.7), (15.8) and (15.9),

$$V_{min}\, y_{i,n+1} = L_{min}(y_{i,n+1}/K_i) + Dx_{i,D} \tag{15.10}$$

Define the relative volatility of component i with respect to the heavy key as

$$\alpha_i = \frac{y_{i,n}/x_{i,n}}{y_{HK,n}/x_{HK,n}} = \frac{K_i}{K_{HK}} \tag{15.11}$$

Equation (15.10) can be rearranged as

$$V_{min}\, y_{i,n+1}\left(1 - \frac{L_{min}}{V_{min}\,\alpha_i\, K_{HK}}\right) = Dx_{i,D} \;\Rightarrow\; V_{min}\, y_{i,n+1} = \frac{\alpha_i\, Dx_{i,D}}{\alpha_i - \dfrac{L_{min}}{V_{min}\, K_{HK}}} \tag{15.12}$$

Now we sum up the above equation for all the components.

$$\sum_i V_{min}\, y_{i,n+1} = V_{min} = \sum_i \frac{\alpha_i\, Dx_{i,D}}{\alpha_i - \dfrac{L_{min}}{V_{min}\, K_{HK}}} = \sum_i \frac{\alpha_i\, Dx_{i,D}}{\alpha_i - \phi} \tag{15.13}$$

A similar equation can be written from a mass balance over an envelope in the stripping section including the reboiler.

$$-\overline{V}_{min} = \sum_i \frac{\alpha_i\, Wx_{i,W}}{\alpha_i - \dfrac{\overline{L}_{min}}{\overline{V}_{min}\, K_{HK}}} = \sum_i \frac{\alpha_i\, Wx_{i,W}}{\alpha_i - \overline{\phi}} \tag{15.14}$$

where
$$\phi = \frac{L_{min}}{V_{min}K_{HK}}; \quad \overline{\phi} = \frac{\overline{L}_{min}}{\overline{V}_{min}K_{HK}}$$

The quantities $\overline{V}$, $\overline{L}$ and $\overline{\phi}$ refer to the stripping section. Further assumptions behind the Underwood equation are (i) constant relative volatility, and (ii) $\phi = \overline{\phi}$. The relative volatility of a component is likely to vary along the column. As stated before, the geometric mean of the values at the top and at the bottom, $\alpha_i = (\alpha_{i,top}/\alpha_{i,bottom})^{1/2}$, is used.

With these assumptions, the addition of Eqs. (15.13) and (15.14) will yield

$$\Delta V_f = V_{min} - \overline{V}_{min} = \sum_i \left(\frac{\alpha_i Dx_{i,D}}{\alpha_i - \phi} + \frac{\alpha_i Wx_{i,W}}{\alpha_i - \phi}\right) \tag{15.15}$$

Putting $\Delta V_f = F(1 - q)$ where q is the fraction liquid in the feed and putting $Dx_{i,D} + Wx_{i,W} = Fz_i$, Eq. (15.15) reduces to

$$1 - q = \sum_i \frac{\alpha_i z_i}{\alpha_i - \phi} \tag{15.16}$$

Equation (15.16), known as 'Underwood equation', can be solved for ϕ. Putting the value of ϕ in Eq. (15.13), we can calculate the minimum vapour rate, V_{min}. The minimum liquid rate, and hence the minimum reflux ratio, can be obtained from

$$L_{min} = V_{min} - D \tag{15.17}$$

It is to be noted that the distribution of the non-keys and the intermediate key (if any) can be calculated using the Underwood method as well. So far as the roots of Eq. (15.16) are concerned, the following cases deserve attention.

Case 1

The non-keys are either too light or too heavy to distribute, i.e. all the LNKs go to the top, all the HNKs go to the bottom. Also there is no intermediate key.

Solve Eq. (15.16) for the root lying between the relative volatilities of the two key components, i.e. $\alpha_{LK} < \phi < \alpha_{HK}$. Calculate V_{min} from Eq. (15.13) and then calculate

$$D = \sum_i Dx_{i,D}$$

Case 1 is illustrated in Example 15.3.

Case 2

The distribution of the non-keys follows Fenske equation [see Example 15.3]; there is no intermediate key.

Follow Case 1 to obtain the root $\alpha_{LK} < \phi < \alpha_{HK}$. Calculate $Dx_{i,D}$ for a non-key from the Fenske equation and $Dx_{i,D}$ for a key from the required degree of separation stated in the problem. This case is also illustrated in Example 15.3.

Case 3

Assume that all the components distribute but no use of Fenske equation is made. There are $\underline{C}$ number of components, and $\underline{C} - 1$ roots lying between α_1 to $\alpha_{\underline{C}}$ are found out such that $\alpha_1 < \phi_1 < \alpha_2 < \phi_2 < \cdots < \phi_{(\underline{C}-1)} < \alpha_{\underline{C}}$.

Now Eq. (15.13) is written for each ϕ value to get $\underline{C} - 1$ equations which are solved for V_{min} and $Dx_{j,D}$ where j is a non-key. Note that there are just $\underline{C} - 1$ unknowns [including V_{min}] to be found out from $\underline{C} - 1$ algebraic equations. The cases are illustrated in Examples 15.3 and 15.4.

If all the components of a multicomponent mixture distribute between the distillate and the bottom products, and if the mixture is *nearly ideal*, the pinch point occurs at the feed plate. However, if some of the components do not distribute (i.e. if a component goes either to the top or to the bottom *almost totally*), two pinch points occur—one above the feed tray and the other below it. While using the Underwood technique to determine the minimum reflux ratio, care should be taken to check if some of the components do not distribute. Only those roots of Eq. (15.16) are to be considered to calculate $Dx_{i,D}$ values that lie between the relative volatility values of the distributing components. Thus, use of Case 3 without judgement may lead to absurd results (see Example 15.3).

EXAMPLE 15.3 (*The minimum reflux ratio*) A saturated liquid feed containing 35 mole% benzene(1), 35 mole% toluene(2) and 30% mole% ethylbenzene(3) is to be fractionated to recover 97% of the benzene at the top and 98% of the toluene in the bottom product. The total pressure is essentially atmospheric and the reflux returned to the tower is at its bubble point. Determine the minimum number of trays using the Fenske equation and the minimum reflux ratio using the Underwood equation. The average relative volatilities with respect to toluene(2) are: $\alpha_{12} = 2.4$ and $\alpha_{32} = 0.48$

Solution

Given: $f_{1,D} = 0.97, f_{2,W} = 0.95, \alpha_{12} = 2.4$. Use Eq. (15.4) to determine the minimum number of trays.

$$N_{min} = \frac{\log\left[(0.97 \times 0.95)/(1 - 0.97)(1 - 0.95)\right]}{\log(2.4)} = \boxed{7.33}$$

To calculate the fraction of ethylbenzene removed at the bottoms, apply Fenske equation to the 1–3 pair.

$$N_{min} = \frac{\log\left[\dfrac{f_{1,D} \cdot f_{3,W}}{(1 - f_{1,D})(1 - f_{3,W})}\right]}{\log \alpha_{13}} \Rightarrow 7.33 = \frac{\log\left[\dfrac{(0.97) \cdot f_{3,W}}{(1 - 0.97)(1 - f_{3,W})}\right]}{\log 5}$$

$$\Rightarrow \quad f_{3,W} = \boxed{0.99976}$$

Calculation of R_{min} (the minimum reflux ratio):

We will apply both Case 1 and Case 2 strategies.

Case 1 strategy: Since most of the ethylbenzene goes to the bottoms (see the value of $f_{3,W}$ above), we assume that it does not distribute. Use Eq. (15.16), take $q = 1$ (saturated liquid).

$$1 - 1 = \frac{\alpha_1 z_1}{\alpha_1 - \phi} + \frac{\alpha_2 z_2}{\alpha_2 - \phi} + \frac{\alpha_3 z_3}{\alpha_3 - \phi} \Rightarrow 0 = \frac{(2.4)(0.35)}{2.4 - \phi} + \frac{(1)(0.35)}{1 - \phi} + \frac{(0.48)(0.3)}{0.48 - \phi}$$

$$\Rightarrow \quad \phi = 1.4652, 0.5894$$

Since component 3 does not go to the distillate, choose $\phi = 1.4652$.

$$Dx_{1,D} = (0.97)(Fz_1) = (0.97)(100)(0.35) = 33.95$$

$$Dx_{2,D} = Fz_2 - (0.95)(Fz_2) = (0.05)(100)(0.35) = 1.75; \; Dx_{3,D} = 0$$

$$\Rightarrow \quad V_{min} = \frac{(2.4)(33.95)}{2.4 - 1.4652} + \frac{(1)(1.75)}{1 - 1.4652} + \frac{(0.48)(0)}{0.48 - 1.4652} = 83.4$$

Distillate, $D = Dx_{1,D} + Dx_{2,D} + Dx_{3,D} = 33.95 + 1.75 + 0 = 35.70$

Since $(R_{min} + 1)D = V_{min}$, $R_{min} = (83.4)/(35.7) - 1 = \boxed{1.336}$

Case 2 strategy: The values of the quantities $Dx_{1,D}$ and $Dx_{2,D}$ are known. We put the values of ϕ obtained before in Eq. (15.13) and solve for V_{min} and $Dx_{3,D}$.

$$\phi = 1.4652 \Rightarrow V_{min} = \frac{(2.4)(33.95)}{2.4 - 1.4652} + \frac{(1)(1.75)}{1 - 1.4652} + \frac{(0.48)(Dx_{3,D})}{0.48 - 1.4652} \qquad \text{(i)}$$

$$\phi = 0.5894 \quad \Rightarrow \quad V_{\min} = \frac{(2.4)(33.95)}{2.4 - 0.5894} + \frac{(1)(1.75)}{1 - 0.5894} + \frac{(0.48)(Dx_{3,D})}{0.48 - 0.5894} \tag{ii}$$

The solution of the above two equations (i) and (ii) yields a *negative value* of $Dx_{3,D}$. This occurs since the component 3 practically does not distribute—it appears almost entirely in the bottoms. So the minimum reflux ratio, $R_{\min}$, should be calculated using Case 1 strategy only.

EXAMPLE 15.4 (*Distribution of the intermediate key using Underwood equation*)   A saturated liquid feed containing 38 mole% benzene(1), 17 mole% toluene(2) and 45 mole% cumene(3) is to be separated to recover 99.7% benzene in the distillate and 99.9% of the cumene in the bottoms. Calculate the minimum reflux ratio and the distribution of the intermediate key (toluene) using the Underwood method. The following average relative volatilities with respect to toluene are given: $\alpha_{12} = 2.28$, $\alpha_{22} = 1$, $\alpha_{32} = 0.22$.

Solution

Take $F = 100$ kmol/h at its bubble point. *Given:* $z_1 = 0.38$, $z_2 = 0.17$, $z_3 = 0.55$.

99.7% of the benzene goes to the distillate $\quad \Rightarrow \quad Dx_{1,D} = (0.997)Fz_1 = 37.886$

99.9% of the cumene goes to the bottoms $\quad \Rightarrow \quad Dx_{3,D} = (1 - 0.999)Fz_3 = 0.055$

Substituting the values of α and z in the Underwood equation, Eq (15.16), we have

$$q - 1 = 1 - 1 = 0 = \frac{(2.28)(0.38)}{2.28 - \phi} + \frac{(1)(0.17)}{1 - \phi} + \frac{(0.22)(0.55)}{0.22 - \phi}$$

$$\Rightarrow \qquad \phi_1 = 1.233, \ \phi_2 = 0.358 \qquad (\text{Note that } \alpha_1 > \phi_1 > \alpha_2 > \phi_2 > \phi_3)$$

Substituting the values of α, ϕ, $Dx_{1,D}$ and $Dx_{3,D}$ in Eq. (15.13), we have

$$\phi = 1.233 \quad \Rightarrow \quad V_{\min} = \frac{(2.28)(37.886)}{2.28 - 1.233} + \frac{(1)(Dx_{2,D})}{1 - 1.233} + \frac{(0.22)(0.055)}{0.22 - 1.233} \tag{i}$$

$$\phi = 0.358 \quad \Rightarrow \quad V_{\min} = \frac{(2.28)(37.886)}{2.28 - 0.358} + \frac{(1)(Dx_{2,D})}{1 - 0.358} + \frac{(0.22)(0.055)}{0.22 - 0.358} \tag{ii}$$

Solving the above two equations, $V_{\min} = 54.877$ and $Dx_{2,D} = 6.4337$

Using the above values it is easy to calculate $R_{\min} = \boxed{0.237}$ and $D = \boxed{44.375}$ kmol/h.

15.4.3   Gilliland Correlation for the Number of Trays

Gilliland made tray-by-tray calculation to determine the number of ideal stages (N, the reboiler included) required for the separation of a series of multicomponent mixtures and could correlate it with the reflux ratio (R), the minimum reflux ratio ($R_{\min}$) and the minimum number of stages ($N_{\min}$) at total reflux. He proposed the correlation in a graphical form in terms of two new variables, $\underline{X}$ and $\underline{Y}$. The correlation was later expressed in terms of the following empirical equation (see Seader and Henley, 2006).

$$\underline{Y} = 1 - \exp\left[\left(\frac{1 + 54.4\,\underline{X}}{11 + 117.2\,\underline{X}}\right)\left(\frac{\underline{X} - 1}{\underline{X}^{0.5}}\right)\right] \tag{15.18}$$

$$Y = \frac{N - N_{min}}{N + 1} \quad \text{and} \quad X = \frac{R - R_{min}}{R + 1}$$

Figure 15.4 shows a comparison of some reported computed data and the correlation, Eq. (15.18). Recently Rusche (*Hydrocarbon Proc.*, Feb 1999) suggested the following equation correlating X and Y.

$$Y = 0.2788 - 1.3154X + 0.4114X^{0.291} + 0.8268 \ln X + 0.9020 \ln [X + (1/X)] \quad (15.19)$$

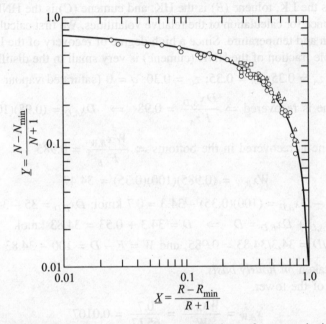

Figure 15.4 Relation between reflux ratio and the number of theoretical trays. [○ computed values from the literature—Eq. (15.18).

Also the optimal feed stage location could be expressed by the Kirkbride equation

$$\frac{N_R}{N_S} = \left[\left(\frac{z_{HK}}{z_{LK}} \right) \left(\frac{x_{LK,W}}{x_{HK,D}} \right)^2 \frac{W}{D} \right]^{0.206} \quad (15.20)$$

Here N_R is the number of trays in the rectifying section, and N_S that in the stripping section; the uppermost tray in the latter section is the feed tray. Akashah et al. (1979) suggested that the number of ideal stages *above* the feed tray, N_R', can be better calculated from the equation,

$$N_R' = N_R - 0.5 \log N \quad (N = \text{total number of ideal stages}) \quad (15.21)$$

EXAMPLE 15.5 (*Minimum number of trays and minimum reflux ratio*) A feed mixture containing 35% benzene, 35% toluene and 30% cumene (all mole%) is to be fractionated at a rate of 100 kmol/h to recover 98% of the benzene in the distillate and 98.5% of the toluene in the bottom product. The feed is a saturated vapour and the reflux is at its bubble point. Constant molar overflow and ideal solution behaviour may be assumed. Calculate (a) the minimum number of equilibrium stages using the Fenske equation, (b) the minimum reflux ratio using the Underwood equation, and (c) the number of ideal stages if a reflux ratio 1.3 times the minimum is used.

The vapour pressure equations for benzene and toluene are given under Example 7.14. That for cumene is $\ln P^v$ (mm Hg) = $17.9232 - 4802/T$, where T is in K. The total pressure is essentially 1 atm.

Solution

Here benzene (A) is the LK, toluene (B) is the HK, and cumene (C) is the HNK. Take toluene as the reference substance for calculation of the relative volatilities. We first calculate the top and the bottom composition and temperature. Since a high degree of recovery of the LK is required, we assume that the mole fraction of the HNK (cumene) is very small in the distillate (i.e. $x_{C,D} \approx 0$).

Given: $F = 100$; $z_A = 0.35$; $z_B = 0.35$; $z_C = 0.30$; $q = 0$ (saturated vapour feed).

98% of the benzene is recovered $\Rightarrow \dfrac{Dx_{A,D}}{Fz_A} = 0.98 \Rightarrow Dx_{A,D} = (0.98)(100)(0.35) = 34.3$

98.5% of the toluene is recovered in the bottoms $\Rightarrow \dfrac{Wx_{B,W}}{Fz_B} = 0.985$

$\Rightarrow \qquad\qquad\qquad Wx_{B,W} = (0.985)(100)(0.35) = 34.47$

Also, $Wx_{A,W} = Fz_A - Dx_{A,D} = (100)(0.35) - 34.3 = 0.7$ kmol; $Dx_{B,D} = 35 - 34.47 = 0.53$ kmol.

Since $x_{C,D} \approx 0$, $Dx_{A,D} + Dx_{B,D} = D \Rightarrow D = 34.3 + 0.53 = 34.83$ kmol.

Also, $x_{A,D} = Dx_{A,D}/D = 34.3/34.83 = 0.985$; and $W = F - D = 100 - 34.83 = 65.17$ kmol.

All flow rates are taken *on hourly basis.*

At the bottom of the tower,

$$x_{A,W} = \frac{Wx_{A,W}}{W} = \frac{0.7}{65.17} = 0.0107$$

Temperatures at the top and at the bottom

Since there is a total condenser and the condensate is at its bubble point, the temperature of the vapour at the top is estimated to be 80.5°C; that at the bottom is 124°C (see Sections 7.1.3 and 7.1.6). These values are arrived at assuming ideal behaviour, 1 atm total pressure, and using the values of vapour pressures obtained from the given equations.

Vapour pressures and relative volatilities

Temperture (°C)	P_A^v (mm Hg)	P_B^v	P_C^v	α_{AB}	α_{CB}
80.5 (top)	768.5	301	76.6	2.55	0.254
124 (bottom)	2495	1109	344.7	2.25	0.311

(a) *Total reflux condition—minimum number of ideal trays*

Use Eq. (15.4). Fractional recoveries: $f_{A,D} = 0.98$; $f_{B,W} = 0.985$;

$$(\alpha_{AB})_{av} = (2.55 \times 2.25)^{1/2} = 2.4; \quad (\alpha_{CB})_{av} = (0.254 \times 0.311)^{1/2} = 0.281$$

$$N_{min} = \frac{\log\left[\dfrac{(0.98)(0.985)}{(1-0.98)(1-0.985)}\right]}{\log (2.4)} = \boxed{9.2} \quad \text{[8.2 ideal trays } plus \text{ the reboiler]}$$

Our assumption that practically there is no C (cumene) in the distillate can be cross checked by using Eq. (15.6).

(b) *Calculation of the minimum reflux ratio*

Since the feed is a vapour at its dew point, $q = 0$, and $\Delta V_f = F(1 - q) \Rightarrow \Delta V_f = F = 100$ kmol.

Take the average values of the α's. From Eq. (15.16),

$$1 = \frac{z_A \, \alpha_{AB}}{\alpha_{AB} - \phi} + \frac{z_B \, \alpha_{BB}}{\alpha_{BB} - \phi} + \frac{z_C \, \alpha_{CB}}{\alpha_{CB} - \phi} = \frac{(0.35)(2.4)}{2.4 - \phi} + \frac{(0.35)(1.0)}{1.0 - \phi} + \frac{(0.30)(0.281)}{0.281 - \phi}$$

The solution of the above equation lying between the α-values of the keys (the HNK is non-distributing) is $\phi = 1.44$.

Calculate V_{min} from Eq. (15.13) as

$$V_{min} = \frac{\alpha_{AB} \, D x_{A,D}}{\alpha_{AB} - \phi} + \frac{\alpha_{BB} \, D x_{B,D}}{\alpha_{BB} - \phi} + \frac{\alpha_{CB} \, D x_{C,D}}{\alpha_{CB} - \phi} = \frac{(2.4)(34.3)}{2.4 - 1.44} + \frac{(1.0)(0.53)}{1.0 - 1.44} + 0$$

$$= 84.54 \text{ kmol}$$

$$L_{min} = V_{min} - D = 84.54 - 34.83 = 49.71 \text{ kmol}$$

Minimum reflux ratio, $\qquad R_{min} = \dfrac{L_{min}}{D} = \dfrac{49.71}{34.83} = \boxed{1.43}$

(c) *Number of ideal trays from Gilliland correlation*

Reflux ratio used, $R = 1.3 R_{min} = (1.3)(1.43) = 1.86$

$$\underline{X} = \frac{R - R_{min}}{R + 1} = \frac{1.86 - 1.43}{1.86 + 1} = 0.1503; \quad N_{min} = 9.2$$

$$\underline{Y} = 1 - \exp\left[\left(\frac{1 + (54.4)(0.1503)}{11 + (117.2)(0.1503)}\right)\left(\frac{0.1503 - 1}{(0.1503)^{0.5}}\right)\right] = 1 - \exp(-0.703) = 0.505 = \frac{N - N_{min}}{N + 1}$$

$$\Rightarrow \qquad N = \boxed{19.6} = \text{number of ideal stages}$$

Feed plate location

Using Eq. (15.20),

$$\frac{N_R}{N_S} = \left[\left(\frac{z_{HK}}{z_{LK}}\right)\left(\frac{x_{LK,W}}{x_{HK,D}}\right)^2 \left(\frac{W}{D}\right)\right]^{0.206} = \left[\left(\frac{0.35}{0.35}\right)\left(\frac{0.0107}{0.015}\right)^2 \left(\frac{65.17}{34.83}\right)\right]^{0.206}$$

$$= 0.99$$

Also,

$$N_R + N_S = 19.6$$

$$\Rightarrow \qquad N_R = 9.85$$

Add feed to the 10th ideal tray from the top.

In order to use an *exact method* for the determination of the number of trays for a given reflux ratio, it is necessary to begin with an initial guess of the terminal concentrations. Also a prior knowledge of the approximate number of trays provides a useful check of the 'exact' calculation. The FUG method gives such useful information (product distribution and the approximate number of trays) necessary for the calculation. It is to be noted that the product (nonkey) distribution obtained from Fenske equation is often found to be a better approximation than that calculated from the Underwood equation.

15.5 RIGOROUS METHODS OF DISTILLATION CALCULATION

Rigorous multicomponent distillation calculation methods may be of two broad categories — the 'equilibrium methods' and the 'rate-based method'. In a distillation column operating at steady state, four types of basic relations or balance equations are available. A rigorous 'equilibrium method' of calculation (see, for example, Wankat, 1988; Seader and Henley, 2006) attempts to solve these balance equations sequentially or simultaneously in order to determine the number of stages as well as the temperature and composition of the liquid and vapour phases at each tray in the column. The basic relations associated with a tray are the MESH equations — (i) mass balance (**M**); (ii) equilibrium relationship (**E**); (iii) sum relations (**S**); and (iv) heat balance (**H**). The total pressure increases in the column downwards from the top because of the pressure drop across every stage. Preliminary estimate of pressures at each stage is used in the rigorous calculations in order to estimate the vapour–liquid equilibria. Figure 15.5 shows a tray and the input and output streams, including a feed stream and two side-stream withdrawals. The balance equations are:

M—*Material balance equations*
Total material balance:

$$L_{n-1} + V_{n+1} + F_n - (L_{sn} + L_n) - (V_{sn} + V_n) = 0; \qquad n = 1, 2, ..., N \qquad (15.22)$$

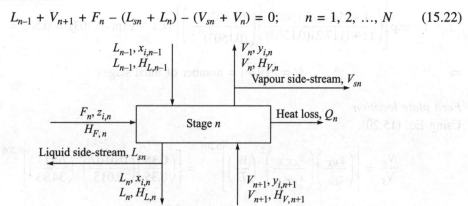

Figure 15.5 Input and output streams at the stage *n*.

Component *i* balance:

$$L_{n-1} \cdot x_{i,n-1} + V_{n+1} \cdot y_{i,n+1} + F_n \cdot z_{i,n} - (L_{sn} + L_n) \cdot x_{i,n} - (V_{sn} + V_n) \cdot y_{i,n} = 0 \qquad (15.23)$$

The subscript '*n*' denotes the *n*th stage, *i* denotes the *i*th component, and *s* denotes a side stream; *N* is the number of stages, and $\underline{C}$ is the number of components. It is to be noted that Eq. (15.23) summed up over all the components (i.e. $i = 1, 2, ..., \underline{C}$) yields Eq. (15.22).

E—*Equilibrium relations*

If the trays are 'non-ideal' and the Murphree tray efficiency (E_{MG}) is given, the following relation between the liquid and vapour composition on the nth tray can be written.

$$E_{MG,i-n} \cdot K_{i,n} \cdot x_{i,n} - y_{i,n} + (1 - E_{MG,i-n})y_{i,n+1} = 0 \tag{15.24}$$

S—*Summation of mole fractions*

$$\sum_i y_{i,n} = 1 \quad \text{and} \quad \sum_i x_{i,n} = 1 \tag{15.25}$$

H—*Heat (enthalpy) balance*

$$L_{n-1} \cdot H_{L,n-1} + V_{n+1} \cdot H_{V,n+1} + F_n \cdot H_{F,n} - (L_n + L_{sn}) \cdot H_{L,n} - (V_n + V_{sn}) \cdot H_{V,n} - Q_n = 0 \tag{15.26}$$

Table 15.2 Equations and variables in a multicomponent distillation problem

Equations	Number
• Total mass balance on each tray, Eq. (15.22)	N
• Component balance on each of the N trays. [Since the mole fractions in a stream sum up to unity, i varies from 1 to $C-1$ on each tray, see Eq. (15.23)]	$(C-1)N$
• Equilibrium relations [There are C number of equilibrium relations (one for each component) at the temperature and pressure of each tray, Eq. (15.24)]	CN
• Sum relations [Two equations (one for the vapour, and another for the liquid) for each tray, see Eq. (15.25)]	$2N$
• Enthalpy balance [One equation for each tray, Eq. (15.26)]	N
Total:	$(2C+3)N$
Variables	
• Total pressure (P) and temperature (T) on each tray	$2N$
• Liquid and vapour flow rates (L_n and V_n) at each tray	$2N$
• Liquid and vapour side-streams (L_{sn}, V_{sn}) withdrawn from each tray	$2N$
• Heat loss (or supply) to each tray (Q_n)	N
• Feed composition [In general, assume that there is a feed to each of the N trays; C mole fractions for each feed stream.]	CN
• Feed enthalpy (H_{Fn}) and flow rate (F_n) at each tray	$2N$
• Liquid composition on each of the N trays	CN
• Vapour composition on each of the N trays	CN
Total:	$(3C+9)N$

Degrees of freedom = $(3C + 9)N - (2C + 3)N = (C + 6)N$

The design of a multicomponent distillation column requires solution of the above set of simultaneous nonlinear equations (these may be linear under special cases). There are $(2\underline{C} + 3)N$ number of equations and $(3\underline{C} + 9)N$ number of variables (see Table 15.2 for the details) leaving $(\underline{C} + 6)N$ degrees of freedom. Thus, in general, a total of $(\underline{C} + 6)N$ variables should be specified in order to find solution to the MESH equations.

All the early rigorous methods were based on tray-by-tray calculation beginning at one end and repeating the calculations till a satisfactory match between the *assumed* or *estimated* terminal compositions and the calculated ones could be achieved. Two well-known classical methods are the 'Lewis-Matheson' and the 'Thiele-Geddes' methods.

15.5.1 The Lewis–Matheson Method

The method, in its simplest form, is based on the following considerations (Schweitzer, 1997).

(a) If the composition of a stream leaving a tray and the pressure (or temperature) are known, the composition of the other stream leaving the tray can be determined using the equilibrium relations. For example, if the liquid composition on a tray and the pressure are given, the bubble point and the corresponding equilibrium vapour composition can be calculated. Similarly, if a vapour composition is given, its dew point and equilibrium liquid composition can be calculated.

(b) The material balance (and also enthalpy balance, if necessary) equations over an envelope including one end (the top or the bottom) of the tower can be used to calculate an unknown flow rate or rates entering or leaving the envelope.

To outline the Lewis–Matheson method, we assume 'constant molar overflow' as a simplification and neglect heat exchange at the wall so that enthalpy balance is not necessary except for the calculation of condenser and reboiler heat duties. Neglecting the side-stream withdrawal, the material balance equation for the ith component in the *rectifying section* can be written as follows.

$$Vy_{i,n+1} = Lx_{i,n} + Dx_{i,D} \tag{15.27}$$

Since V and L remain constant over a section, no suffix is used. If R is the reflux ratio, we may write

$$y_{i,n+1} = \frac{R}{R+1}x_{i,n} + \frac{x_{i,D}}{R+1} \tag{15.28}$$

The above equation is the operating line for the ith component and is comparable to Eq. (7.73) for a binary mixture. Together with the equilibrium relations, it can be used to calculate the compositions of the phases on the trays starting from the top. A similar equation, the *stripping section* operating line for the ith component, is given by

$$y_{i,m+1} = \frac{\bar{L}}{\bar{V}}x_{i,m} - \frac{W}{\bar{L}-W}x_{i,W} \tag{15.29}$$

On the basis of the problem statement (feed flow rate, fractional recovery of the kep components) and the chosen flux ratio, the liquid and vapour flow rates in both the rectifying and stripping sections are calculated and the operating line equations are found out. The calculation may now start at one end of the column, say the reboiler, that acts as an ideal tray. From the 'known' composition of the bottom liquid, the temperature at the reboiler, which is the bubble point of the liquid at the specified pressure (supplied or assumed), and the vapour composition can be calculated. The composition of the liquid from the $(N-1)$th entering the reboiler can be calculated from the stripping section operating line, Eq. (15.29). Now the same procedure has to be followed to determine the bubble point and the vapour composition at the $(N-1)$th tray. The calculation proceeds till the liquid composition reasonably matches that of the feed. The calculation for the trays above proceeds the same way except that now the rectifying section operating line equation has to be used.

If the 'assumed' bottom composition $(x_{i,W})$ is 'correct', the calculated composition should match the feed composition at the feed tray. This will not happen except by coincidence since the concentrations of some of the species $(x_{i,W})$ are only *guess values* (recall the discussion in Section 15.1). However, there are techniques to revise the guess values in a suitable way before beginning the second round of calculation that will aim at reducing the mismatch so that the solution converges. The following example shows tray-by-tray calculation for the separation of a ternary liquid system. Ideal behaviour is assumed in order to make the illustration simple and easy to follow.

EXAMPLE 15.6 (*Tray-by-tray calculation, constant molar overflow*)   Determine the number of trays for the separation of a ternary mixture of components 1, 2 and 3 using the Lewis–Matheson method. Use Rault's law to calculate VLE. Constant molar overflow may be assumed. Following data and information are given.

$F = 100$ kmol/h; feed composition: $z_1 = 0.4$, $z_2 = 0.45$, and $z_3 = 0.15$ (mole fraction); condition of the feed: saturated liquid; total pressure, $P = 2$ atm (1520 mm Hg, assumed constant; pressure drop along the column is neglected); 98% of component 1 is to be distilled out in the top product and not more than 2% of component 2 should go to the distillate. A reflux ratio of 3.0 is suggested. Constants of the Antoine equation and the boiling points (at 1520 mm Hg) are:

	Comp., i	A_i	B_i	C_i	BP, °C
$\ln P_i^y$ (mm Hg) $= A_i - B_i/(\theta + C_i)$	1	15.8365	2477.07	233.21	58
(θ in °C)	2	15.9155	2778	223.14	100.3
	3	15.877	2911.32	226.65	113.8

Solution

Take component 1 as the light key (LK), component 2 as the heavy key (HK), i.e. component 3 is the HNK. Since component 3 has a low volatility and also a low concentration in the feed, we *assume* that its concentration in the distillate is small, i.e. $x_{3,D} \approx 0$.

Given: 98% of 1 goes to the distillate $\Rightarrow Dx_{1,D} = (0.98)(z_1F) = (0.98)(0.4)(100) = 39.2$

2% of component 2 goes to the distillate $\Rightarrow Dx_{2,D} = (0.02)(z_2F) = (0.02)(0.45)(100) = 0.9$

Since $x_{3,D} \approx 0$ (assumed), $Dx_{1,D} + Dx_{2,D} = 39.2 + 0.9 = D \Rightarrow D = 40.1$ kmol/h.

Also $W = 100 - 40.1 = 59.9$ kmol/h; $x_{1,D} = Dx_{1,D}/D = 39.2/40.1 = 0.9775$; $x_{2,D} = 0.9/40.1 = 0.0225$.

The bottom composition can also be obtained by material balance. The material balance results are:

Feed, $F = 100$ kmol/h   Distillate, $D = 40.1$ kmol/h   Bottom product, $W = 59.9$ kmol/h

$z_1 = 0.4$ $x_{1,D} = 0.9775$ $x_{1,W} = 0.0134$

$z_2 = 0.45$ $x_{2,D} = 0.0225$ $x_{2,W} = 0.7362$

$z_3 = 0.15$ $x_{3,D} = 0.00$ $x_{3,W} = 0.2504$

Reflux ratio, $R = 3.0 \Rightarrow V = D(R + 1) = (40.1)(3 + 1) = 160.4$; $L = DR = (40.1)(3)$
$$= 120.3 \text{ kmol/h}$$

In the stripping section, $\overline{V} = V = 160.4$; $\overline{L} = L + F = 120.3 + 100 = 220.3$ kmol/h

Operating line equations for the rectifying and the stripping sections

Rectifying [Eq. (15.28)]: $y_{i,n+1} = \dfrac{R}{R+1} x_{i,n} + \dfrac{x_{i,D}}{R+1}$

$$= \frac{3}{4} x_{i,n} + \frac{1}{4} x_{i,D} = 0.75 x_{i,n} + 0.25 x_{i,D} \qquad \text{(i)}$$

Stripping [Eq. (15.29)]:

$$y_{i,m+1} = \frac{\overline{L}}{\overline{V}} x_{i,m} - \frac{W}{\overline{V}} x_{i,W} = \frac{220.3}{160.4} x_{i,m} - \frac{59.9}{160.4} x_{i,W} = 1.3734 x_{i,m} - 0.3734 x_{i,W} \qquad \text{(ii)}$$

Since all the components are present in the bottom product, we begin tray-by-tray calculation from the reboiler. The calculation can, however, start from the top if we assume a *small concentration* (rather than zero) of the heavy non-key in the distillate. Let the reboiler be the Nth tray. In order to calculate the composition of the vapour leaving the reboiler, we have to determine the bubble point of the reboiler liquid first. This can be done by following the procedure given in Chapter 7. Let us do it by a simple trial-and-error procedure. [Note that $x_{i,W} \equiv x_{i,N}$].

$$\text{Try } \theta = 100°C \Rightarrow P_1^v = 4458.4; \ P_2^v = 1508.1;$$

$$P_3^v = 1058.2 \text{ mm Hg (from the vapour pressure equations)}.$$

Total pressure,
$$P = P_1^v x_{1,W} + P_2^v x_{2,W} + P_3^v x_{3,W}$$

$$= (4458.4)(0.0134) + (1508.1)(0.7362) + (1058.2)(0.2504) = 1435 \text{ mm}$$

Since this is smaller than the given total pressure of 1520 mm Hg, try a larger trial temperature,

$$\theta = 102°C \Rightarrow P_1^v = 4661; \ P_2^v = 1590; \ P_3^v = 1117.2 \text{ mm Hg},$$

and the total pressure is

$$P = (4661)(0.0134) + (1590)(0.7362) + (1117.2)(0.2504) = 1510 \text{ mm Hg}$$

This is also smaller than the given value of 1520 mm Hg. The correct bubble point can now be obtained by *extrapolation*:

$$\theta = 102°C + \frac{1520 - 1510}{1510 - 1435} \cdot (2°C) = 102.2°C. \text{ (In some cases, } \textit{interpolation}^\dagger \text{ may have to be done.)}$$

[†] If the calculated total pressure, P, in the second trial was larger than the stipulated value of 1520 mm Hg, the bubble point might be determined by interpolation between the two values.

The vapour pressures of the components at this temperature are: $P_1^v = 4681$, $P_2^v = 1598$, and $P_3^v = 1123$ mm Hg, and the total pressure is found to be $P = 1520.4$ mm Hg which is acceptable[††]. The vapour mole fractions are:

$$y_{1,N} = \frac{4681}{1520.4} (0.0134) = 0.0413$$

$$y_{2,N} = \frac{1598}{1520.4}(0.7362) = 0.7738$$

$$y_{3,N} = \frac{1123}{1520.4} (0.2504) = 0.1849$$

Now the liquid composition on the $(N - 1)$th tray has to be calculated from the operating line, Eq. (ii) above.

$$0.0413 = (1.3734)x_{1,(N-1)} - (0.3734)(0.0134) \quad \Rightarrow \quad x_{1,(N-1)} = 0.0337$$

$$0.7738 = (1.3734)x_{2,(N-1)} - (0.3734)(0.7362)$$

$$\Rightarrow \qquad x_{2,(N-1)} = 0.7634 \qquad \text{and} \qquad x_{3,(N-1)} = 0.2027$$

The next step is the calculation of the bubble point of the liquid on the $(N - 1)$th tray following the trial-and-error procedure given above. The sequential procedure in this particular case may be represented as:

Bubble point of liquid at a tray $\longrightarrow$ vapour composition at the given total pressure $\longrightarrow$ liquid composition on the next upper tray from the operating line equation $\longrightarrow$ reach the feed tray and change to the other operating line $\longrightarrow$ continue calculation, proceed to the top tray and check with the specified distillate composition.

The calculation is to be continued till the feed tray is reached. An approximate method of identification of the feed tray will be described later. The results of tray-by-tray calculation for a few trays are given below.

Tray no.	N(Reboiler)	N − 1	N − 2	N − 3	N − 4	N − 5
Temperature, °C	102.2	100	96.8	91.5	84.5	77.8
x_1	0.0134	0.0337	0.0756	0.1537	0.2735	0.4094
x_2	0.7362	0.7634	0.7523	0.6983	0.5994	0.4812
x_3	0.2504	0.2027	0.1721	0.1479	0.1271	0.1090
y_1	0.0413	0.0988	0.2061	0.3706	0.5573	0.7067
y_2	0.7738	0.7584	0.6842	0.5483	0.3860	0.2536
y_3	0.1849	0.1406	0.1096	0.0810	0.0567	0.0397

The liquid composition on the $(N - 5)$th tray is 'close' to the feed composition and we take it as the feed tray (a revised calculation may be done to get more accurate values and a better match). Since we have started computation from the bottom, the rectifying section operating line equations have to be used beginning the feed tray. So the composition of the liquid *entering* the $(N - 5)$th tray (or the feed tray) from tray number $(N - 6)$ is calculated from Eq. (i) above. The

---

[††] A flowchart for bubble point calculation is given in the Appendix.

distillate composition necessary for the calculation has been obtained before by material balance calculations.

$$y_{1,N-5} = 0.75x_{1,N-6} + 0.25x_{1,D} \quad \Rightarrow \quad 0.7067 = 0.75x_{1,N-6} + (0.25)(0.9775)$$

$$\Rightarrow \qquad\qquad\qquad\qquad x_{1,N-6} = 0.6164$$

Similarly, $x_{2,N-6} = 0.3306$, and $x_{3,N-6} = 0.0529$. The calculated values of the liquid and vapour compositions and the temperatures at the trays above the feed tray are given below.

Tray no.	N – 6	N – 7	N – 8
Temp., θ (°C)	69.4	63	59.8
x_1	0.6164	0.8101	0.9275
x_2	0.3306	0.1704	0.0667
x_3	0.0529	0.0195	0.0058
y_1	0.8520	0.9400	0.9798
y_2	0.1334	0.0557	0.0195
y_3	0.0146	0.0043	0.0010

Since a total condenser is used at the top, the composition of the vapour from the top tray is equal to that of the distillate. The distillate composition matches approximately at the 8th tray from the top.

So, the number of ideal stages = 9 (8 trays + reboiler)

The feed tray is supplied to the 4th tray from the top.

It will be interesting to calculate the number of trays by the short-cut method [Eq. (15.17)] for comparison. The minimum number of trays (at total reflux), the minimum reflux ratio and the actual reflux ratio are needed.

The minimum number of stages: It is calculated from the Fenske equation and is found to be $N_{min} = 6.6$ (calculations not shown; left as an exercise).

The minimum reflux ratio: It is calculated using the Underwood method, Eq. (15.16). The average relative volatility values of components 1 and 3 with respect to component 2 (selected as the reference component) are calculated first. Since ideal behaviour has been assumed, $\alpha_{ij} = P_i^v/P_j^v$.

At the top tray (59.8°C),

$$P_1^v = 1607.8, \qquad P_2^v = 444.6, \qquad P_3^v = 303 \text{ mm Hg}$$

and $\qquad\qquad \alpha_{12} = 1607.8/444.6 = 3.616, \qquad \alpha_{32} = 303/444.6 = 0.6815$

At the bottom (102.2°C) the vapour pressures are as given before,

$$\alpha_{12} = 2.928, \qquad \alpha_{32} = 0.703$$

Taking the geometric mean value

$$\Rightarrow \qquad \alpha_{12} = (3.616 \times 2.928)^{0.5} = 3.254; \qquad \alpha_{32} = (0.703 \times 0.6815)^{0.5} = 0.692$$

The feed is a saturated liquid $\Rightarrow q = 1$. Putting the feed composition and α-values in Eq. (15.16),

$$0 = \frac{(0.4)(3.254)}{3.254 - \phi} + \frac{(0.45)(1)}{1 - \phi} + \frac{(0.15)(0.692)}{0.692 - \phi} \qquad \Rightarrow \qquad \phi = 1.634, \ 0.7387$$

It can be seen by using the Fenske equation that very little of the component 3 appears in the distillate ($Dx_{3,D} \approx 0$) and it is essentially *non-distributing*. So we have to use the root $\phi = 1.634$ only (which lies between α_{12} and α_{22}) in order to calculate V_{min} from Eq. (15.13).

$$V_{min} = \sum_i \frac{\alpha_i D x_{i,D}}{\alpha_i - \phi} = \left[\frac{(3.254)(39.2)}{3.254 - 1.634} + \frac{(1)(0.9)}{1 - 1.634} + \frac{(0.692)(0)}{0.692 - 1.634} \right] = 77.78$$

Minimum reflux ratio,

$$R_{min} = \frac{V_{min} - D}{D} = \frac{77.78 - 40.1}{40.1} = 0.94$$

The number of ideal stages calculated from the Gilliland correlation, Eq. (15.17), for $R = 3.0$ is $N = 9$.

The location of the feed tray calculated from Eq. (15.21) shows that the feed is to be introduced to the fifth tray from the top (there are four trays in the rectifying section; calculation not shown here). This also approximately matches the feed tray location obtained from tray-by-tray calculation. The calculated temperature and the concentration profiles along the column are presented in Figure 15.6. The mole fraction of component 2 shows a maximum.

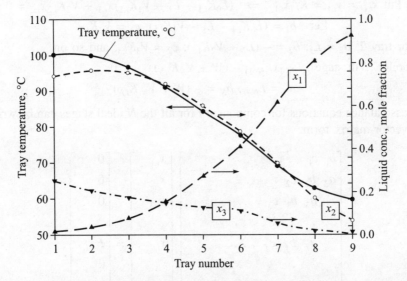

Figure 15.6 Temperature and liquid concentrations on the trays. (The mole fraction of component 2 shows a maximum.)

While the temperature profile in a multicomponent distillation column shows a monotonic decrease from the reboiler to the condenser, the concentration profiles are often complex. This is because in parts of the column the concentrations of one or more of the components may be very small and separation occurs among the remaining components. Existence of a plateau or an extremum in the concentration are frequently observed. A useful brief discussion on the concentration profile in a column separating a ternary mixture of benzene, toluene and cumene is given by Wankat (1988).

15.5.2 Matrix Method of Solution

Multicomponent distillation calculation basically involves the solution of a set of simultaneous algebraic equations (generally nonlinear) representing mass and enthalpy balance along with the equilibrium relations expressed by the MESH equations, (15.22) to (15.25). The set of equations for a particular component for N number of stages including the reboiler (and the partial condenser, if there is one) can be expressed in the vector-matrix form. We assume only one feed stream entering the fth tray and there is no side stream withdrawal. It is further assumed that the trays are ideal [$E_{MG} = 1$ in Eq. (15.24)] and the K-form of equilibrium relation ($y_{i,n} = K_{i,n} x_{i,n}$) is applicable. Equation (15.23) can be rearranged as follows.

$$L_{n-1}x_{i,n-1} - (L_n + V_nK_{i,n})x_{i,n} + V_{n+1}K_{i,n+1}x_{i,n+1} = -F_nz_{i,n} \tag{15.30}$$

$$\Rightarrow \qquad a_nx_{i,n-1} - b_nx_{i,n} + c_nx_{i,n+1} = -F_nz_{i,n} \tag{15.31}$$

$$[F_n = F \text{ for } n = f; \; F_n = 0 \text{ otherwise}]$$

Let there be a total condenser for the top vapour. Then for stage 1 (see Figure 15.3)

$$L_0x_{i,D} - (L_1 + V_1K_{i,1})x_{i,1} + V_2K_{i,2}\,x_{i,2} = 0 \tag{15.32}$$

$$\text{Put } x_{i,D} = y_{i,1} = K_{i,1}x_{i,1} \quad \Rightarrow \quad (L_0K_{i,1} - L_1 - V_1K_{i,1})x_{i,1} + V_2K_{i,2}x_{i,2} = 0$$

$$\text{Let} \quad b_1 = (L_0K_{i,1} - L_1 - V_1K_{i,1}); \; c_1 = V_2K_{i,2} \tag{15.33}$$

For stage or tray 2, $a_2 = L_1$; $b_2 = -(L_2 + V_2K_{i,2})$; $c_2 = V_3K_{i,3}$, and so on.

For the reboiler (Nth stage), $L_{N-1}x_{i,(N-1)} - (W + V_NK_{i,N})x_{i,N} = 0$

$$\Rightarrow \qquad a_N = L_{N-1}; \; b_N = -(W + V_N K_{i,N}) \tag{15.34}$$

The mass balance equations for component i for all the N ideal stages can be written in the following vector-matrix form.

$$
\begin{bmatrix}
b_1 & c_1 & \cdots & & & & \\
a_2 & b_2 & c_2 & \cdots & & & \\
& a_3 & b_3 & c_3 & \cdots & & \\
& \cdots & & & & & \\
& & a_f & b_f & c_f & \cdots & \\
& & & \cdots & & & \\
& & & \cdots & & & \\
& & & & a_{N-1} & b_{N-1} & c_{N-1} \\
& & & & & a_N & b_N
\end{bmatrix}
\begin{bmatrix}
x_{i,1} \\
x_{i,2} \\
x_{i,3} \\
\vdots \\
x_{i,f} \\
\vdots \\
\vdots \\
x_{i,N-1} \\
x_{i,N}
\end{bmatrix}
=
\begin{bmatrix}
0 \\
0 \\
0 \\
\vdots \\
Fx_{i,f} \\
0 \\
0 \\
0 \\
0
\end{bmatrix}
\tag{15.35}
$$

Another set of equations may be written by enthalpy balance. The coupled equations have to be solved by using a suitable numerical technique to find out the concentration and temperature on each tray. An excellent summary of the computational techniques have been given by Seader and Henley (2006). Several simulation software such as ASPEN PLUS[†], HYSIS[††], CHEMCAD, etc. are available for multicomponent distillaition design (also for design of many other process equipment).

15.6 THE RATE-BASED METHOD

A major limitation of the equilibrium method arises out of the fact that the efficiency of a real tray, generally expressed in terms of the Murphree efficiency, varies from tray to tray as well as from component to component. It is established both theoretically and experimentally that the rate of transport of a species in a multicomponent system does not depend upon its own driving force only. It depends upon the rates of transport of the other species in the mixture as well. The limitations of Murphree efficiency in this context were investigated by Krishna et al. (1977), who reported that the value of E_{MG} of a species in a multicomponent mixture can be negative to a few hundred per cent in extreme cases. These observations led to an altogether different strategy of separation calculation of multicomponent mixtures, not necessarily distillation alone. This strategy, called the *rate-based method*, has been discussed at length in the recent literature (for example, Taylor et al., 1994, 2003). The rates of exchange of mass as well as heat between the phases on a tray are written in terms of the available driving force and the heat and mass transfer coefficients. These equations are solved for all the trays to relate the extent of separation and the number of trays in a column. A simulation program RATEFRAC is available in the ASPEN PLUS package for rate-based separation calculations.

15.7 SEPARATION OF CLOSE-BOILING AND AZEOTROPIC MIXTURES

The separation of liquid mixtures having components which are close-boiling or form an azeotrope poses a difficult problem since the relative volatility is near unity or unity. If it is a mixture of close-boiling components, uneconomically large number of trays are required for the separation; if it is an azeotrope, separation by conventional distillation is impossible. There are quite a few strategies of separation of such mixtures, the more important ones being extractive distillation, azeotropic distillation or reactive distillation. These and other similar techniques have been called *enhanced distillation* by Stichlmair et al. (1989). A brief description of the techniques is given below.

15.7.1 Extractive Distillation

Let us consider a mixture of components A and B which are close-boiling. In order to separate the components by extractive distillation, a suitable non-volatile solvent, C, is introduced near the top of the column. The solvent preferentially associates with one of the components, say B, and thereby increases the relative volatility of the other component, A. A stream of relatively pure A

[†]ASPEN PLUS is a software for a variety of process simulation and design. Originally developed as a part of the **A**dvanced **S**ystem for **P**rocess **EN**gineering Project in the energy laboratory of MIT in the 1970s, it was commercialized with the foundation of Aspen Tech in 1981 by Dr. Larry Evans, a professor of chemical engineering at MIT. Since then there has been rapid enhancement of the scope and usefulness of the software as well as its market.

[††]Aspen Technology acquired **HY**protech **SYS**tem (a Canadian supplier of process simulation and engineering software for oil and gas industries) in 2002 and HYSYS became a part of the ASPEN package.

is obtained as the top product of the column. The mixture of *B* and *C* leaves at the bottom and is further processed to recover the solvent for recycle and to separate the product *B*. The solvent *C* is called an *entrainer* since it 'entrains' or 'extracts' one of the components. A few trays above the solvent entry point serve to remove the solvent from the vapour stream. The number of these trays depends upon the volatility of the solvent.

The most important factors in the selection of a solvent are 'solvent selectivity' and 'solvency' (Lee, 1998). Selectivity refers to the solvent's ability to enhance the separation of the 'key' component(s) in the mixture. It is expressed as the ratio of the distribution coefficients of the two components in the solvent. Solvency is the concentration ratio of the entrained component *B* in the solvent phase and the raffinate phase. In addition, the solvent should be low-cost, non-corrosive, non-toxic, non-reactive, and should have a low latent heat. The solvent should *not* form an azeotrope with any of the components but it should definitely have more affinity for the less volatile component. The difference in polarity of the light and the heavy keys is an important factor that dictates solvent selection. Compounds of a wide range of polarity—hydrocarbons to water—may be used as the solvent or entrainer. Some more details of solvent selection for extractive distillation are given by Schweitzer (1997).

There are many examples of commercial application of extractive distillation. An aqueous solution of thiophene is separated using concentrated sodium hydroxide as the entrainer that retains water. Thiophene with traces of water leaves at the top and can be purified further, if required. A classical example of use of extractive distillation is the concentration of nitric acid using sulphuric acid as the solvent that entrains water [Mg(NO$_3$)$_2$ is now preferred to H$_2$SO$_4$]. Separation of butadiene from a mixture with butane, butene and small quantities of other unsaturated hydrocarbons by extractive distillation is an industrial process developed by Union Carbide (Bannister and Buck, 1969). Low polarity solvents like furfural, dimethyl acetamide, N-methyl pyrrolidone are good entrainers for butadiene. Extractive distillation for the separation of 1-butene from *iso*-butane using furfural as the solvent is shown in Figure 15.7. The relative

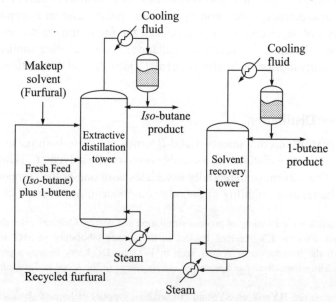

Figure 15.7   Separation of a mixture of *iso*-butane and 1-butene by extractive distillation (Humphrey and Keller, 1997).

volatility of *iso*-butane to 1-butene increases to 2.0 in the presence of furfural compared to the normal value of 1.2. This occurs because of the interaction between 1-butene and furfural.

15.7.2 Azeotropic Distillation

Equilibrium in an azeotropic system has been discussed in Chapter 7. An azeotrope may be heterogeneous or homogeneous. If the vapour mixture of *A* and *B* of azeotropic composition, upon condensation, forms two phases—one rich in *A* and the other rich in *B*—it is called a *heterogeneous azeotrope*. The butanol–water system is an example of this category. On the other hand, if the condensate is a single phase liquid, it is called a *homogeneous azeotrope*. The techniques for separation of these two types of azeotropes are predictably different.

Binary heterogeneous azeotrope: Separation of this type of azeotrope is not difficult and does not need the addition of a third component as the entrainer. Consider a partially miscible binary of 1-butanol and water. While distilling this mixture, the minimum-boiling azeotrope leaving the top of the column forms two phases after condensation (Wankat, 1988). Here water is 'self-entraining'. The butanol-rich phase is fed back to the column as reflux and the water-rich phase is distilled separately in a second column. Dehydrated butanol leaves the bottom of the first column and water from the second column. Open steam may be used for heating the second column (this is a practical example of the use of open steam for the distillation of an aqueous solution). Another example of separation of a mixture that forms a hetero-azeotrope is drying of an organic liquid such as dehydration of gasoline (this is particularly important in cold climate) or benzene. The hetero-azeotrope vapour leaving the top of the distillation column is phase-separated after condensation. Here again water is 'self-entraining'. The organic-rich phase is sent back to the column as reflux, and the water phase with traces of organic is discarded, possibly after stripping.

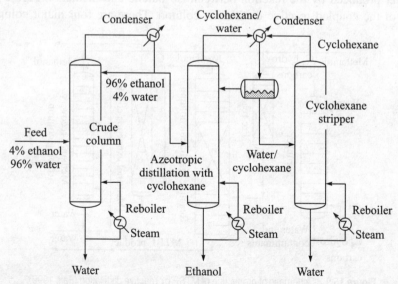

Figure 15.8 Traditional separation of ethanol–water by azeotropic distillation (Humphrey and Keller, 1997).

Homogeneous azeotrope: Such an azeotrope exists as a single liquid phase. The most common example is the ethanol–water system, the separation of which also requires an entrainer.

But, unlike in the case of extractive distillation, the entrainer forms a new lower boiling azeotrope with one or more of the components in the feed. This azeotrope exits as the overhead vapour (this is why it is called azeotropic distillation) and the other component(s) are left behind that form the bottom product.

Figure 15.8 gives the flow diagram of alcohol dehydration by azeotropic distillation using cyclohexane (or toluene) as the entrainer (use of benzene as the entrainer has been discontinued since it is a carcinogen). A minimum-boiling azeotrope of water and cyclohexane leaves as the overhead vapour. The condensate is phase-separated as usual and the cyclohexane phase is sent back as reflux. Dehydrated ethanol leaves the bottom of the column. The water-rich phase flows to a cyclohexane stripper. The recovered hydrocarbon is recycled.

15.7.3 Reactive Distillation

Reactive distillation involves a chemical reaction and product separation in the same column simultaneously. This is an example of process intensification (refer to Section 5.6). Although the concept is pretty old (its potential was known even in the 1920s), it has been exploited extensively only recently. There are two major classes of application of this technique.

Consider the separation of a mixture of A and B. If it is possible to find out a reagent (C) that reversibly reacts with a component (B) in a mixture, the relative volatility of the other component A increases. Thus A may be recovered as the top product. The combination of B and C leaves at the bottom and has to be separated using a suitable technique. This strategy is adopted satisfactorily for mixtures when the relative volatility is close to unity. The component C is, in fact, a 'reactive entrainer'.

Another class of reactive distillation involves a reaction that leads to a desired product. This will be illustrated by an example — production of methyl tertiary butyl ether (MTBE)[†], a synthetic octane-booster produced by the reaction between *iso*-butene and methanol. Figure 15.9 shows a schematic of the coupled reactive distillation column. There are four major columns besides

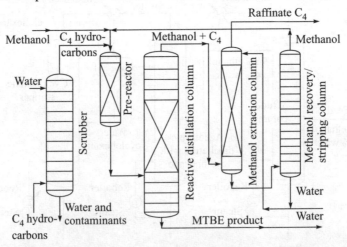

Figure 15.9   Schematic of production of MTBE by reactive distillation (Fair, 1999).

[†] MTBE has lost much of its initial attraction as an octane-booster because of environmental implications. In fact, it is now banned in parts of the USA.

a pre-reactor. The feed gas is *iso*-butene mixed with other hydrocarbons. Iso-butene reacts with methanol in the upper part of the column packed with the catalyst, and the product MTBE gets *purified* in the stripping section in the lower part of the column. A reasonably rich stream of MTBE leaves the bottom of the column which is separated in a second column.

Quite a few other esterification processes are commercially carried out in a reactive distillation column. Typical examples are production of methyl acetate and ethyl acetate. Selective hydrogenation of C_4 and C_5 streams coupled with product separation, hydration of ethylene oxide to ethylene glycol and many other applications of reactive distillation as well as the theoretical principles and column simulation have been discussed by Sundmacher and Kienle (2003).

15.8 DIVIDED-WALL COLUMNS

Before explaining the idea of a divided-wall column, let us have a look into the conventional process of separation of a ternary mixture of *A*, *B* and *C* using two columns in sequence (Figure 15.1). The concentration profiles of the component *B*, that has a volatility intermediate between *A* and *C*, in columns 1 and 2 are shown in Figure 15.10. In the upper part of the column, a split between *A* and *B* occurs and the mole fraction of *B* attains a maximum somewhere in the middle of the column. The components *B* and *C* are separated mainly in the lower part of the column and the concentration of *B* decreases towards the bottom. Thus the enrichment in the concentration of *B* achieved in the upper section is lost in the lower section. It has to be regained only in the second column that involves both capital and operating cost.

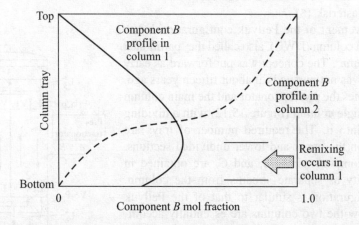

Figure 15.10 Concentration profiles of component *B* in the two columns of Figure 15.1.

Petlyuk et al. (1965) came forward with a novel alternative to the two-column configuration shown in Figure 15.1. His idea (Figure 15.11) was to use a 'prefractionator' that would receive three streams — (i) the feed mixture containing *A*, *B* and *C*, (ii) a liquid stream from the upper part of the main column, and (iii) a vapour stream from its lower part. Vapour, mainly containing *A* and *B*, goes from the prefractionator to the main column; liquid having mainly *B* and *C* flows into the lower part of it. With this configuration, the main column separates *A* and *B* more efficiently in the upper part, and *B* and *C* in the lower part. The peak concentration of *B* attains a much higher value in the middle of the main column than that in column 1 of Figure 15.1. As a result, B can be drawn at sufficient purity as a side stream from the main column of Figure 15.11. A substantial savings in the capital and operating costs to the tune of 10 to 30% is achieved since there are only one reboiler and one condenser in the Petlyuk configuration. The flow configuration of the liquid and vapour streams in the coupled columns is also shown in the figure. The main column is considered to consist of four 'sections' as shown. Liquid stream L3-P from section 3 (upper section) of the main column, and a vapour stream V6-P from section 6 (lower section) enter into the prefractionator. The vapour stream from the prefractionator which is a mixture of A and B with little C, V1-P, enters section 3 of the main column The liquid stream, L2-P, having mainly B and C enters the lower part of the main column. Splitting of both liquid and vapour streams occurs in the main column, one part flows to the prefractionator and the other part through it. A combined stream in Figure 15.11 is denoted by an asterisk (*).

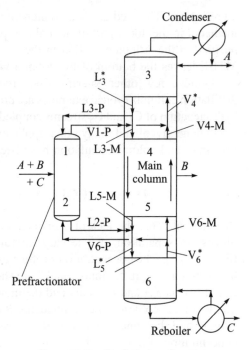

Figure 15.11 The Petlyuk configuration.

The improvement of the Petlyuk configuration led to the divided-wall column (DWC), also called the 'partitioned distillation column'. The concept was put forward as early as in 1949 but was not pursued till about fifteen years ago. A DWC combines the prefractionator and the main column together in a single column (Figure 15.12) with a dividing wall installed into it. The required number of trays are provided both in the upper and lower undivided sections. All the three components, A, B, and C, are obtained in acceptable purity as separate streams from the column. The flow configuration is similar to that of the Petlyuk column, but now the two columns are essentially accommodated in a single column. The dividing wall should not allow transmission of heat through it. Thus a DWC does the job of two columns (Sumitomo Co of Japan calls it a *column-in-column* system).

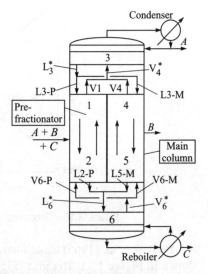

Figure 15.12 The divided-wall column.

DWCs are gradually gaining acceptance in the process industries. It should be remembered that there are a number of factors that determine the suitability of DWC for a particular operation. If a component B is present in high concentration (say, above 50%) and the other two components have nearly equal concentrations, a DWC works satisfactorily. The relative volatilities α_{AB} and α_{BC} should be comparable. Recent developments in DWCs have been reviewed by Lestak and Collins (1997), Hairston (1999), Schultz et al.

(2002), and Becker et al. (2001). A few practical applications of DWCs, both tray type and packed type, by BASF and UOP have been described by Jobson (2005).

NOTATIONS

A, B, C : components in a ternary mixture

$\underline{C}$: the number of components

F, D, W : rate of flow of feed, distillate and bottom product respectively, kmol/h

$K_{i,n}$: distribution coefficient of the ith species on the nth tray

$L, \bar{L}, L_{min}$: liquid rate, 'bar' means the stripping section, 'min' means minimum, kmol/h

N : Number of stages or trays (including the reboiler)

N_{min} : minimum number of trays

R : reflux ratio

R_{min} : minimum reflux ratio

$V, \bar{V}, V_{min}$: vapour rate, 'bar' means the stripping section, 'min' means minimum, kmol/h

$x_{i,n}, y_{i,n}, z_{i,n}$: mole fraction of component i at the nth tray for liquid, vapour or the feed

SHORT AND MULTIPLE CHOICE QUESTIONS

1. Make a list of the degrees of freedom for the separation of a binary mixture by distillation. Justify your selection.

2. A distillation column separates a mixture of propane (30 mole%), n-butane (20 mole%), n-pentane (31 mole%) and n-heptane (19 mole%). The top product should have 95 mole% propane in it. At least 96% of n-pentane should leave in the bottom product.

   (a) Which component is the heavy non-key (HNK)?

       (i) Propane   (ii) n-Butane   (iii) n-Heptane

   (b) Which component is the heavy key (HK)?

       (i) n-Butane   (ii) n-Pentane   (iii) n-Heptane

   (c) Which is the intermediate key?

       (i) Propane   (ii) n-Butane   (iii) n-Pentane

3. One hundred kmol of a feed ($z_1 = 0.3$, $z_2 = 0.4$ and $z_3 = 0.3$) enters a column per hour. Not less than 98% of component 1 should go to the distillate. If the distillate contains 2.5 kmol of component 2 and 0.1 kmol of component 3, what is the rate of withdrawal of the distillate?

   (i) 30 kmol/h   (ii) 32 kmol/h   (iii) 53 kmol/h

4. The cooling water temperature at the outlet of a condenser is normally limited to

   (i) 30–35°C   (ii) 40–45°C   (iii) 55–60°C

5. A mixture of A, B (LK), C (HK) and D is to be separated in a distillation column. The relative volatilities with respect to the HK are $\alpha_A = 6.2$, $\alpha_B = 2.1$, $\alpha_D = 0.8$. It is required

that about 95% of the light key should be distilled out. In order to calculate the minimum reflux ratio using the Underwood equation, which root for ϕ should possibly by ignored?

 (i) The largest root

 (ii) The intermediate root

 (iii) The smallest root

6. What do the MESH equations stand for?

7. In the distillation of a mixture of four components 1, 2, 3, and 4, it is estimated that the component 1 is virtually absent in the bottom product. But all the components are present in measurable concentrations in the distillate. At which terminal of the column it is convenient to begin tray-by-tray calculation?

 (i) The top end

 (ii) The bottom end

 (iii) Any of the two terminals

8. Name a few simulation softwares for the design of separation equipment.

9. Which of the following mixtures forms a hetero-azeotrope?

 (i) Methanol–Water

 (ii) Ethanol–Water

 (iii) Butanol–Water

10. Which of the following is used as an entrainer for breaking the ethanol-water azeotrope?

 (i) Ethylene oxide

 (ii) *n*-Butyl alcohol

 (iii) *Cyclo*-hexane

11. Which of the following functions does a 'divided wall column' perform in relation to distillation of a ternary mixture?

 (i) Separates *A*, *B* and *C* in reasonably pure forms in a single column.

 (ii) Performs separation of *A* and *B* on one side of the wall and that of *B* and *C* on the other side.

 (iii) Performs separation of the ternary mixture using the minimum number of trays.

12. Draw the typical concentration profiles of the components of a ternary mixture *A*, *B* and *C* in a tray tower if the component *C* (HNK) is practically absent in the distillate.

13. What do you mean by 'process intensification'? Give two examples.

14. For the separation of a gas mixture of *A* and *B* it is planned to use a 'reactive entrainer' D that reacts with B reversibly to form a compound B_2D. The column operates at a vacuum of 20 inch Hg, the entrainer, D, enters at the top and the compound B_2D leaves at the bottom. The stream B_2D is decomposed in another column to recover D and to separate B. Prepare a schematic flow diagram of the process.

15. In connection with the calculation of the number of ideal stages for separation of a multicomponent mixture, the following values of relative volatility of the light and of the heavy key at the conditions at the column top and at the bottom, are estimated. Top: α_{LH} = 2.24, α_{HH} = 1; bottom: α_{LH} = 1.29, α_{HH} = 1 [*L* = light key, *H* = heavy key]. What value of α should be taken for the determination of N_{min} by using Fenske equation?

 (i) 1.29   (ii) 1.5   (iii) 1.7

PROBLEMS

15.1 (*Number of ideal stages at total reflux*)[2] A saturated vapour feed containing 40 mol% benzene (A), 30 mol% toluene (B) and 30 mol% cumene (C) is to be separated in a distillation column provided with a total condenser and a partial reboiler. It is required to recover 95% of the toluene in the distillate and 95% of cumene should go to the bottoms. The reflux is a saturated liquid and the total pressure is 1 atm. The relative volatility of benzene (A) and of cumene (C) with respect to toluene (B) may be assumed to be independent of temperature: $\alpha_{AB} = 2.25$; $\alpha_{CB} = 0.21$. Determine the number of equilibrium stages at total reflux and the benzene concentration in the condensate.

15.2 (*The minimum number of stages and product distribution*)[2] A feed containing 30 mole% benzene (A), 25 mole% toluene (B) and 45 mole% ethylbenzene (C) is to be separated by distillation so that 98.5% of benzene and not more than 2% of the toluene should go to the distillate. Calculate the minimum number of ideal stages required. Also estimate the approximate distribution of ethylbenzene, the heavy non-key (HNK) between the distillate and the bottoms using the Fenske equation. The average relative volatilities are $\alpha_{AB} = 2.43$, and $\alpha_{AC} = 5.0$.

15.3 (*Application of the FUG method*)[2] A ternary mixture ($z_1 = 0.12$, $\alpha_1 = 3.8$; $z_2 = 0.5$, $\alpha_2 = 1.0$; $z_3 = 0.38$, $\alpha_3 = 0.70$) is to be separated in a column to recover 98.5% of component 2 (LK) in the distillate and 99% of component 3 (HK) in the bottom product. Using the FUG method, determine the number of ideal trays and the location of the feed tray if a reflux ratio of $R = 1.3R_{min}$ is used. The feed is liquid at its bubble point.

15.4 (*The number of ideal stages*)[3] A mixture of benzene ($z_1 = 0.4$, $\alpha_1 = 10.5$), toluene ($z_2 = 0.25$, $\alpha_2 = 4.54$) and cumene ($z_3 = 0.35$, $\alpha_3 = 1.0$) is to be fractionated to recover 99.9% of the benzene at the top and 99.5% of the cumene at the bottom. The reflux is a saturated liquid and the reflux ratio is $R = 1.25R_{min}$. If the feed is a mixture of 50% liquid and 50% vapour, determine the distribution of the intermediate key (toluene) and the number of ideal stages required for the separation.

15.5 (*Tray-by-tray calculation of binary distillation*)[2] Determine the number of ideal trays required for the following separation using *tray-by-tray* calculation.

Feed: 100 kmol/h, equimolar mixture of A and B, saturated liquid; relative volatility, $\alpha_{AB} = 2.1$; reflux ratio, $R = 2.5$; distillate composition, $x_D = 0.98$; bottom product, $x_w = 0.025$.

15.6 (*Determination of the number of ideal stages*)[2] We have a four component mixture of ethylbenzene ($z_1 = 0.06$, $\alpha_1 = 1.25$), p-xylene ($z_2 = 0.40$, $\alpha_2 = 1.15$), o-xylene ($z_3 = 0.30$, $\alpha_3 = 1.0$), and cumene ($z_4 = 0.24$, $\alpha_4 = 0.68$). The feed rate is 80 kmol/h (liquid at its bubble point). It is required that 99% of p-xylene should be recovered in the distillate and 96% of the o-xylene should go to the bottom product. Determine the number of ideal stages required if a reflux ratio three times the minimum is used.

15.7 (*Condenser heat duty*)[3] A quaternary mixture of propane ($z_1 = 0.1$), n-butane ($z_2 = 0.35$), iso-pentane ($z_3 = 0.4$) and n-hexane ($z_4 = 0.15$) is to be separated in a column at a rate of 100 kmol/h in order to recover 98.8% of the butane in the distillate and 99% of the pentane in the bottom product. The reflux is a saturated liquid and a reflux ratio of $R = 3.0$ is suggested. If the non-keys are 'non-distributing', calculate the flow rates and compositions of the distillate and the bottom product. Given the following values of the heats of vaporization of the components at the condenser temperature ($\lambda_1 = 410$, $\lambda_2 = 390$, $\lambda_3 = 350$, and $\lambda_4 = 290$ kJ/mole), calculate the condenser heat duty.

15.8 (*Degrees of freedom of a ternary mixture*)[2] The degrees of freedom of a mixture having $\underline{C}$ components (see Table 15.2) is found to be ($\underline{C}$ + 6). Under what conditions does it lead to nine degrees of freedom for a ternary mixture as given in Table 15.1?

REFERENCES

Bannister, R.R., and E. Buck, 'Butadiene recovery via extractive distillation', *Chem. Eng. Prog.*, Sept., 1969, 65–68.

Becker, H. et al., 'Partitioning distillation columns—why, when and how?' *Chem. Engg.*, Jan. 2001, 68–74.

Fair, R., and J.G. Stichlmair, *Distillation—Principles and Practice*, John Wiley, New York, 1998.

Fredenslund, A. et al., *Vapour-Liquid Equilibria Using UNIFAC*, Elsevier, Amsterdam, 1977.

Hairston, D., 'The divide in distillation', *Chem. Engg.*, April, 1999, 32–35.

Humphrey, J.L., and G.E. Keller, *Separation Process Technology*, McGraw-Hill, New York, 1997.

Jobson, M., 'Divided wall distillation comes of age', *The Chem. Engr.*, April, 2005.

Krishna, R. et al., *Trans. Inst. Chem. Engrs.*, 55(1977) 78.

Lee, Fu-Ming, 'Extractive distillation—separating close-boiling-point components', *Chem. Engg.*, Nov. 1998, 112–121.

Lestak, F., and C. Collins, 'Advanced distillation saves energy and capital', *Chem. Engg.*, July 1997, 72–76.

Ludwig, E., *Applied Process Design*, Vol 2, 3rd ed., Gulf Publishing, 1997.

Petlyuk, F.B. et al., 'Thermodynamically optimal method for separating multicomponent mixtures', *Intern. Chem Engg.*, 5(1965) 555–561.

Prausnitz, J.M. et al., *Molecular Thermodynamics of Fluid-Phase Equilibria*, Prentice Hall, New Jersey, 1986.

Schultz, M.A., 'Reduce costs with divided-wall columns', *Chem. Eng. Prog.*, May 2002, 64–72.

Schweitzer, P.A. (Ed.), *Handbook of Separation Techniques for Chemical Engineers*, 3rd ed., McGraw-Hill, 1997.

Seader, J.D., and E.J. Henley, *Separation Process Principles*, 2nd ed., John Wiley, New York, 2006.

Stichlmair, J. et al., 'Separation of azeotropic mixtures via advanced distillation', *Chem. Eng. Prog.*, Jan., 1989, 63–69.

Sundmacher, K., and A. Kienle (Eds.), *Reactive Distillation—Status and Future Directions*, Wiley VCH, Weinheim, 2003.

Taylor, R. et al., 'A 2nd generation nonequilibrium model for computer simulation of multicomponent separation processes', *Comput. Chem. Eng.*, *18*(1994) 205–217.

Taylor, R. et al., 'Real-world modeling of distillation', *Chem Eng. Prog.*, July 2003, 28–39.

van Winkle, M., *Distillation*, McGraw-Hill, New York, 1967.

Walas, S.M., *Phase Equilibria in Chemical Engineering*, Butterworths, New York, 1985.

Wankat, P.C., *Equilibrium Staged Separations*, Elsevier, New York, 1988.

16

Transient Diffusion and Mass Transfer with Chemical Reaction

A majority of mass transfer processes are carried out or intended to be carried out at steady state. For example, an absorption or a distillation column, a liquid extraction unit, or a water cooling tower is, in general, designed to operate at steady state. However, every piece of equipment passes through a period of unsteady state operation during startup and sometimes during shutdown. Also, there are examples of unsteady state operations which are considered to run at 'pseudo-steady state' for the sake of simplified theoretical analysis. A common example is batch distillation in a tray column. But there are a few mass transfer equipment which operate at truly unsteady state. Common examples are packed bed leaching or adsorption (see Figures 9.2 and 12.7), mass transfer in a bed of ion exchanger, drying of a bed of porous solid, etc. In each of these operations, a species (a solute in case of leaching or adsorption, and moisture in case of drying) diffuses through the particles and the rate of mass transfer can be followed by solution of the unsteady state diffusion equation concerned. In this chapter we shall deal with a few simple cases of unsteady state diffusion, formulation of the relevant equations, and their solutions and applications. This will be followed by a brief introduction to mass transfer accompanied by a chemical reaction at steady state or unsteady state.

16.1 TRANSIENT DIFFUSION IN THREE DIMENSIONS

The three common geometries encountered in engineering practice are planar, cylindrical, and spherical (Figure 16.1). The equation for transient diffusion in any of these geometries can be easily arrived at by mass balance over an appropriately selected differential volume element. It is to be noted that the transient diffusion equations in mass transfer are very similar to those in heat transfer. The procedure for obtaining the transient heat diffusion equations (see, for example, Dutta, 2001) is also applicable to mass diffusion phenomena in most cases.

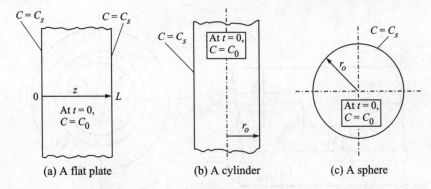

Figure 16.1   Diffusion in the three common geometries; the initial and surface concentrations are shown.

16.1.1   Transient Diffusion Equations and Solutions

Diffusion in a rectangular block: The mass diffusion equation, which is a partial differential equation, in the rectangular geometry can be obtained by mass balance over a small rectangular volume element.

$$\frac{\partial C}{\partial t} = D\left(\frac{\partial^2 C}{\partial x^2} + \frac{\partial^2 C}{\partial y^2} + \frac{\partial^2 C}{\partial z^2}\right) = D\nabla^2 C \tag{16.1}$$

where ∇^2 is the Laplacian operator, $\nabla^2 = \dfrac{\partial^2}{\partial x^2} + \dfrac{\partial^2}{\partial y^2} + \dfrac{\partial^2}{\partial z^2}$ (16.2)

In deriving Eq. (16.1) and similar unsteady state equations, the simplified form of Fick's law given by Eq. (2.17) is often used to express the mass flux. The diffusivity D is assumed to remain constant. Equation (16.1) can be solved subject to a given set of 'initial' and 'boundary conditions'.

Diffusion in a cylindrical solid: The equation for unsteady state diffusion in a right cylinder can be obtained by mass balance over a thin cylindrical shell [Figure 16.2(a)].

$$\frac{\partial C}{\partial t} = D\left(\frac{\partial^2 C}{\partial r^2} + \frac{1}{r}\frac{\partial C}{\partial r} + \frac{\partial^2 C}{\partial z^2}\right) \tag{16.3}$$

Here r is the radial coordinate and z is the axial coordinate in the cylindrical coordinate system. Appropriate initial and boundary conditions need to be specified for obtaining the solution of the above equation.

Diffusion in a spherical solid: The governing equation for unsteady state diffusion is developed below as a typical example. Let us make a mass balance over a thin spherical shell (often called 'shell balance') of thickness Δr at the radial position r as shown in Figure 16.2(b). It is assumed that diffusion occurs from inside the sphere to the medium outside.

Rate of input of the solute to the shell at $r = 4\pi r^2 N]_r$ (16.4a)

Rate of output of the solute from the shell at $r + \Delta r = 4\pi r^2 N]_{r+\Delta r}$. (16.4b)

Rate of accumulation in the shell $= \dfrac{\partial}{\partial t}(4\pi r^2 \Delta r\, C) = 4\pi r^2 \Delta r\, \dfrac{\partial C}{\partial t}$ (16.4c)

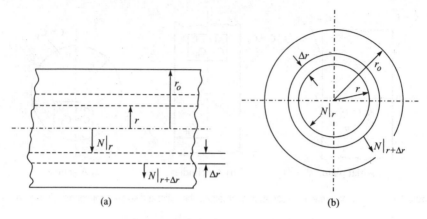

Figure 16.2   Shell balance in a (a) cylinder and (b) sphere.

Here N is the flux of the diffusant through the 'shell' at the radial position r. By mass balance over the shell, we have

$$\underbrace{4\pi r^2 \, N]_r}_{\text{Rate of input}} - \underbrace{4\pi r^2 \, N]_{r+\Delta r}}_{\text{Rate of output}} = \underbrace{4\pi r^2 \Delta r \frac{\partial C}{\partial t}}_{\text{Rate of accumulation}}$$

Dividing by $4\pi r^2 \Delta r$ throughout, putting $N = -D\partial C/\partial r$ and taking the limit $\Delta r \to 0$,

$$\frac{r^2 N]_r - r^2 N]_{r+\Delta r}}{r^2 \Delta r} = \frac{\partial C}{\partial t} \quad \Rightarrow \quad \frac{\partial C}{\partial t} = \frac{D}{r^2}\frac{\partial}{\partial r}\left(r^2 \frac{\partial C}{\partial r}\right) \tag{16.5}$$

Equations (16.1), (16.3) and (16.5) represent the unsteady state diffusion process in solids of three common geometries, namely, rectangular, cylindrical and spherical, respectively. Appropriate initial and boundary conditions [I.C. and B.C.] need to be specified for solving any of these equations. The techniques of solution and the solutions themselves are similar to those of corresponding heat diffusion problems (see, for example, Carslaw and Jaeger, 1959; Myers, 1971; Crank, 1974). Analytical solutions of the heat diffusion equations in several simple cases have been worked out in Dutta (2001) and are applicable for mass diffusion as well. The two common techniques applicable to relatively simple cases are called *separation of variables* and *combination of variables*. However, most practical unsteady state mass diffusion problems do not admit of analytical solutions, and numerical techniques have to be adopted instead. Here we cite analytical solutions for unsteady state diffusion in an 'infinite slab' (length and breadth are large; thickness is finite), in a 'long cylinder' (the length is much larger than the diameter), and in a sphere. It is interesting to note that for these three particular cases the diffusion equations can be combined into a single equation of the form

$$\frac{\partial C}{\partial t} = \frac{D}{\xi^p}\frac{\partial}{\partial \xi}\left(\xi^p \frac{\partial C}{\partial \xi}\right) \tag{16.6}$$

$[p = 0, \, \xi = x$ for a slab; $p = 1, \, \xi = r$ for a long cylinder; $p = 2, \, \xi = r$ for a sphere]

Flat plate [Figure 16.1(a), Eq. (16.1); For a 'large' slab, the concentration is independent of x and y; initial and boundary conditions: I.C.: $C(0, z) = C_0$; B.C.: $C(t, 0) = C(t, L) = C_s$; $C(t, z)$ is the concentration at a location distant z from the reference surface, $z = 0$, at any time, t].

Local concentration:

$$\frac{C - C_s}{C_0 - C_s} = \frac{4}{\pi} \sum_{m=0}^{\infty} \frac{1}{(2m+1)} \sin\left[\frac{(2m+1)\pi z}{L}\right] \cdot \exp\left[-\frac{(2m+1)^2 \pi^2 Dt}{L^2}\right] \qquad (16.7a)$$

Average concentration:

$$\frac{C_{av} - C_s}{C_0 - C_s} = \frac{8}{\pi^2} \sum_{m=0}^{\infty} \frac{1}{(2m+1)^2} \exp\left[-\frac{(2m+1)^2 \pi^2 Dt}{L^2}\right] \qquad (16.7b)$$

'Long' cylinder [Figure 16.1(b); Eq. (16.3); I.C.: $C(0, r) = C_0$; and B.C.: $C(t, r_o) = C_s$; $C(t, 0)$ = finite]

Local concentration:

$$\frac{C - C_s}{C_0 - C_s} = 2 \sum_{m=1}^{\infty} \frac{J_0(\lambda_m \bar{r})}{\lambda_m J_1(\lambda_m)} \exp\left(-\frac{\lambda_m^2 Dt}{r_o^2}\right); \qquad \bar{r} = \frac{r}{r_o} \qquad (16.8a)$$

Average concentration:

$$\frac{C_{av} - C_s}{C_0 - C_s} = 4 \sum_{m=1}^{\infty} \frac{1}{\lambda_m^2} \exp\left(-\frac{\lambda_m^2 Dt}{r_o^2}\right) \qquad (16.8b)$$

Sphere [Figure 16.1(c); Eq. (16.5); I.C.: $C(0, r) = C_0$; B.C.: $C(t, r_o) = C_s$; $C(t, 0)$ = finite, or $\partial C(t, 0)/\partial r = 0$]

Local concentration:

$$\frac{C - C_s}{C_0 - C_s} = \frac{2}{\pi \bar{r}} \sum_{n=1}^{\infty} \frac{(-1)^m}{m} \sin(m\pi \bar{r}) \exp\left(-\frac{m^2 \pi^2 Dt}{r_o^2}\right); \qquad \bar{r} = \frac{r}{r_o} \qquad (16.9a)$$

Average concentration:

$$\frac{C_{av} - C_s}{C_0 - C_s} = \frac{6}{\pi^2} \sum_{m=1}^{\infty} \frac{1}{m^2} \exp\left(-\frac{m^2 \pi^2 Dt}{r_o^2}\right) \qquad (16.9b)$$

Here $C = C(t, z)$ or $C = C(t, r)$ is the local concentration in the slab or in the cylinder or sphere of radius r_o; C_{av} is the average concentration in the solid as a function of time. In [Eq. 16.8(a), and (b)], λ_m ($m = 1, 2, \ldots$) are the roots of $J_0(\lambda) = 0$; $J_n(\zeta)$ is the Bessel function of first kind of order n. Figure 16.3 shows the spatial concentration distributions in the three geometries with Dt/L^2 (for a slab) and Dt/r_o^2 (for a cylinder or a sphere) as a parameter. The change in average concentration with time is presented in Figure 16.4.

The above solutions for the mean concentration of the diffusant can be expressed in much simpler forms for the limiting cases of 'short time' or 'long time' of exposure. In the case of diffusion in a sphere, for example, we have

$$\frac{C_{av} - C_s}{C_0 - C_s} = \frac{6}{r_o}\left(\frac{Dt}{\pi}\right)^{0.5}; \qquad \text{for a short time of exposure} \qquad (16.9c)$$

$$\frac{C_{av} - C_s}{C_0 - C_s} = \frac{6}{\pi^2} \cdot \exp\left(-\frac{\pi^2 Dt}{r_o^2}\right); \qquad \text{for a long time of exposure} \qquad (16.9d)$$

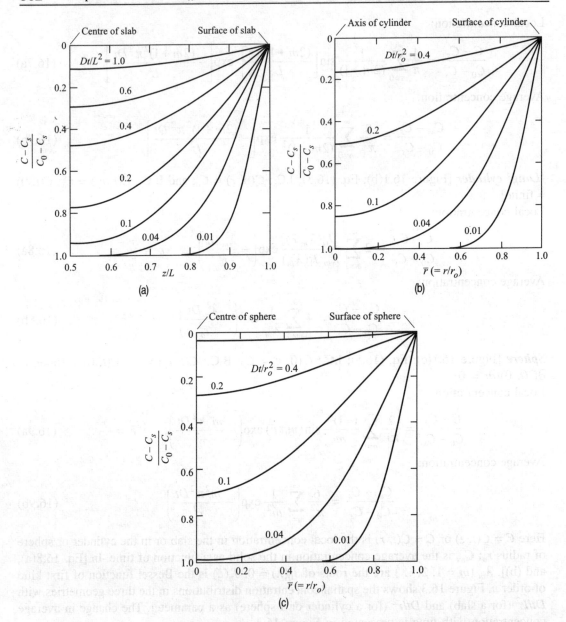

Figure 16.3   (a) Transient concentration profiles in (a) a slab, (b) a cylinder, and (c) a sphere.

Equations [16.9(c)] and [16.9(d)] can be directly used to determine the diffusivity of a solute from experimental uptake data in a spherical body under a given set of conditions. Similar simplified equations can be obtained for 'short time' and 'long time' diffusion in a slab and in a cylinder as well (Vergnaud, 1991).

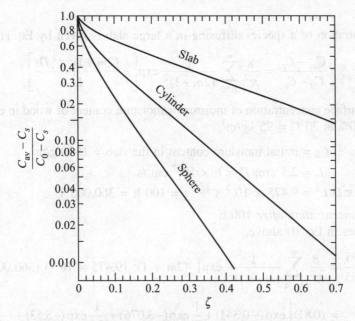

Figure 16.4 Transient average concentration in a slab ($\zeta = 4Dt/L^2$), a cylinder and a sphere ($\zeta = Dt/r_o^2$).

16.1.2 Applications

Diffusion of a species in a solid has numerous practical applications. However, in many cases the solid may not be a continuum—it may have pores or it may even be a composite. Drying of a solid is a typical example. Diffusion of moisture through a solid undergoing drying may occur by different mechanisms in different phases of drying or with varying moisture content in it. Diffusion through the pores of an adsorbent is often the controlling step to determine the rate of adsorption or desorption. Diffusion accompanied by adsorption and reaction is common to all gas–solid catalytic reactions. In many of the membrane separation processes, diffusion of the permeating species occurs through the membrane (see Chapter 14). Diffusion through a polymer film or beads is one real-life application area in connection with membrane separation—swelling of a polymer or removal of the unreacted monomer from the product polymer beads. Diffusion through polymers has been discussed in detail by Vergnaud 1991. Another relatively recent application is 'controlled release' of drugs, plant nutrients, etc. For example, a drug may be encapsulated in a permeable polymeric film or may be impregnated in a porous substrate so that the drug diffuses out over a prolonged period of time to suit the needs of a patient (Wise, 2000). The advantages are obvious. A few relevant illustrative examples on transient diffusion in a solid are given below.

EXAMPLE 16.1 (*Drying of a slab*)   A slab of wood, 2.5 cm thick, having 150 kg/m^3 moisture is exposed to a stream of air of relative humidity 60% at 30°C. The moisture content of wood in equilibrium with the bulk air is 95 kg/m^3. Average diffusivity of moisture in the sample of wood is 6×10^{-7} cm^2/s. (a) Calculate the average moisture content and the minimum local moisture content at the end of 100 hours. (b) What is the time required for the maximum local moisture content to drop down to 100 kg/m^3? The gas-phase diffusional resistance may be ignored.

Solution

Average concentration of a species diffusing in a large slab is given by Eq. [16.7(b)].

$$\frac{C_{av} - C_s}{C_0 - C_s} = \frac{8}{\pi^2} \sum_{m=0}^{\infty} \frac{1}{(2m+1)^2} \exp\left[-\frac{(2m+1)^2 \pi^2 Dt}{L^2}\right] \tag{i}$$

Given: C_s = surface concentration of moisture = moisture content of wood in equilibrium with air of R.H. = 60% at 30°C = 95 kg/m³.

$$C_0 = \text{initial moisture content in the slab} = 150 \text{ kg/m}^3$$

$$L = 2.5 \text{ cm}; \ D = 6 \times 10^{-7} \text{ cm}^2/\text{s}$$

$$\Rightarrow \qquad \pi^2 D/L^2 = 9.475 \times 10^{-7} \text{ s}^{-1}; \quad t = 100 \text{ h} = 360{,}000 \text{ s}$$

(a)   *Average concentration after* 100 h
We put the values in Eq. (i) above,

$$\frac{C_{av} - 95}{150 - 95} = \frac{8}{\pi^2} \sum_{m=0}^{\infty} \frac{1}{(2m+1)^2} \exp[-(2m+1)^2 (9.475 \times 10^{-7}) (360{,}000)]$$

$$= (0.81)\left[\exp(-0.341) + \frac{1}{9}\exp(-3.076) + \frac{1}{25}\exp(-8.53) + \cdots\right]$$

$$= (0.81)[0.711 + 0.00516 + 7.92 \times 10^{-6} + \cdots]$$

$$= 0.58 \qquad \text{[The higher-order terms decrease rapidly.]}$$

$$\Rightarrow \qquad C_{av} = 95 + (0.58)(55) = \boxed{127 \text{ kg/m}^3}$$

Alternatively, we can use Figure 16.4. For a slab,

$$\zeta = \frac{4Dt}{L^2} = \frac{(4)(6 \times 10^{-7})(360{,}000)}{(2.5)^2} = 0.138$$

$$\Rightarrow \qquad \frac{C_{av} - C_s}{C_0 - C_s} = 0.6$$

$$\Rightarrow \qquad C_{av} = 95 + (0.6)(55) = \boxed{128 \text{ kg/m}^3}$$

(b)   *Time to attain a maximum local moisture concentration,* $C = 100 \text{ kg/m}^3$
At any time, the maximum local concentration occurs at the centre plane of the slab, i.e. at $z = 1.25$ cm.

Use Eq. [16.7(a)] to calculate the time t to attain $C = 100 \text{ kg/m}^3$ at $z = 1.25$ cm, or $z/L = \frac{1}{2}$. Putting the values of different quantities,

$$\left(\frac{100 - 95}{150 - 95}\right)\left(\frac{\pi}{4}\right) = \sin\frac{\pi}{2}\exp(-9.475 \times 10^{-7}t) + \frac{1}{9}\sin\frac{3\pi}{2}\exp[(-9)(9.475 \times 10^{-7}t)] + \cdots$$

The second and higher-order terms are very small. It is sufficient to consider only the first term.

$$\Rightarrow \qquad t = \boxed{774 \text{ h}}$$

EXAMPLE 16.2 (*Determination of diffusivity from unsteady state mass transfer data*) Slices of potato, 4 mm thick, are dried in a stream of air under constant drying conditions and the 'free moisture' content is measured against time. The data collected in an experiment are given below [Mohr, K.H.: *International Chem. Eng.*, **34** (1994) 210].

Free moisture, kg/(kg dry solid)	3.2	2.0	1.3	0.95
Time, h	1.0	2.0	3.0	4.0

It is known that in such cases the gas-phase diffusional resistance to moisture loss remains small if a sufficiently high velocity of the gas is maintained. Neglecting shrinkage of a slice as well as the moisture loss from the edges (since the slices are thin), determine the average diffusivity of moisture in the sample.

Solution

Since (i) the gas-phase resistance to transport is small, (ii) shrinkage is neglected, and (iii) moisture loss from the edges is neglected, the problem reduces to that of unsteady state diffusion in a slab with constant surface concentration. We can use Eq. [16.7(b)] to express the average moisture content in a slice as a function of time. The surface concentration of moisture C_s, is in fact the equilibrium moisture under the given drying conditions. Since the data collected are for 'large time', we take into account only the first term of the series.

$$\frac{C_{av} - C_s}{C_0 - C_s} = \frac{8}{\pi^2} \exp\left(-\frac{\pi^2 Dt}{L^2}\right) \quad \Rightarrow \quad \ln(C_{av} - C_s) = \ln[8(C_0 - C_s)/\pi^2] - (\pi^2 Dt/L^2)$$

Here $(C_{av} - C_s)$ represents the average 'free moisture' concentration, kg/(kg dry solid). A plot of $\ln(C_{av} - C_s)$ versus t is expected to yield a straight line. The plot is shown in Figure 16.5 which is a straight line with a *correlation coefficient* above 0.99. The value of the diffusivity can be easily calculated from the slope of the line.

$$\text{Slope} = -0.407; \quad \text{thickness of the slice, } L = 4 \text{ mm} = 4 \times 10^{-3} \text{ m}$$

$$\Rightarrow \quad \text{Diffusivity, } D = \frac{(0.407)(4 \times 10^{-3})^2}{(\pi^2)(3600)} = \boxed{1.83 \times 10^{-10} \text{ m}^2/\text{s}}$$

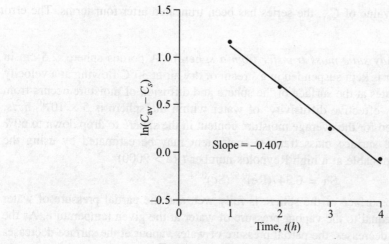

Figure 16.5 Plot of $\ln(C_{av} - C_s)$ versus time, t.

EXAMPLE 16.3 (*Transient mass transfer to rigid drops*)   Ozonation is now an attractive technique for disinfection of water since the traditional technique of chlorination produces halo-organics which are hazardous even in trace quantities. A stream of water is being ozonated at 1 atm total pressure and 25°C in a 2.5 m tall spray tower. The average diameter of the water droplets is 500 μm. The contact time is 0.8 second. The droplets may be assumed to behave as 'rigid spheres'. Concentration of ozone in the gas is $S_G = 200$ g/m^3, and the solubility of ozone in water may be calculated from the equation (Gottschalk et al., 2000).

$$\log S = -0.25 - 0.013T \ (°C); \quad S = S_G/S_L^*; \quad S_L^* = \text{solubility of ozone (g/m}^3)$$

Given the diffusivity of ozone in water = 1.3×10^{-5} cm^2/s at the given condition, calculate the average concentration of ozone in the exit water. Mention any specific assumptions made.

Solution

At $T = 25°C$, $\log S = -0.25 - (0.013)(25) = -0.575 \Rightarrow S = 0.266$

Given: $S_G = 200$ g/m^3, $S_L^* = 0.266 S_G = (0.266)(200) = 53.2$ g/m^3

Assume: (i) negligible gas-phase mass transfer resistance; (ii) mass transfer during formation of a droplet at the nozzle is not considered; (iii) ozone concentration in the droplets at the top of the tower is zero. Then the average concentration of ozone in a drop is given by Eq. [16.9(b)] or Figure 16.4.

Given: $\dfrac{Dt}{r_o^2} = \dfrac{(1.3 \times 10^{-9})(0.8)}{(500 \times 10^{-6})^2} \left[\dfrac{(\text{m}^2/\text{s})(\text{s})}{\text{m}^2} \right] = 0.00416$; take $C_0 = 0$, and $C_s = S_L^* = $ interfacial conc.

Since the value of Dt/r_o^2 is very small, it is difficult to use Eq. (16.4). We use Eq. [16.9(b)].

$$\frac{C_{av}}{C_s} = 1 - \frac{6}{\pi^2} \sum_{m=1}^{\infty} \frac{1}{m^2} \exp\left(\frac{-m^2 \pi^2 Dt}{r_o^2} \right) = 1 - \frac{6}{\pi^2} \sum_{m=1}^{\infty} \frac{1}{m^2} \exp\left(-0.00416 m^2 \pi^2 \right)$$

$$= 1 - (6/\pi^2)[0.96 + 0.212 + 0.0768 + 0.0324 + \cdots] = 1 - 0.78 = 0.22$$

$\Rightarrow \qquad C_{av} = (0.22)(C_s) = (0.22)(53.2 \text{ g/m}^3) = \boxed{11.7 \text{ g/m}^3}$

In the calculation of the value of C_{av}, the series has been truncated after four terms. The error involved is less than 2%.

EXAMPLE 16.4 (*Unsteady state mass transfer from a sphere*)   A porous sphere, 2.5 cm in diameter, soaked in water is kept suspended in a stream of dry air at 30°C flowing at a velocity of 10 m/s. Water evaporates at the surface of the sphere and diffusion of moisture occurs from inside the sphere. If the 'effective diffusivity' of water within the sphere is 5×10^{-10} m^2/s, calculate the time required for the average moisture content in the sphere to drop down to 60% of the initial value. The surface mass transfer coefficient may be estimated by using the following correlation applicable at a high Reynolds number (Re > 2000).

$$\text{Sh} = 0.347(\text{Re})^{0.62}(\text{Sc})^{0.31}$$

Assume that initially the surface of the sphere is fully wet, and the partial pressure of water vapour at the surface is equal to the vapour pressure of water at the given temperature. As the surface moisture content decreases, the partial pressure of water vapour at the surface decreases proportionally.

Solution

The governing partial differential equation for transient moisture distribution is [see Eq. (16.5)]

$$\frac{\partial C}{\partial t} = \frac{D}{r^2} \frac{\partial}{\partial r}\left(r^2 \frac{\partial C}{\partial r}\right) \tag{i}$$

Initial condition: $t = 0,$ $\quad C = C_0$ for all r (ii)

Boundary conditions: $r = 0, C = $ finite (alternatively, $\partial C/\partial r = 0$) for all t (iii)

$$r = r_o; \quad -D\left(\frac{\partial C}{\partial r}\right)_{r=r_o} = k_G(p - 0); \quad p = \frac{C}{C_0}p^* \tag{iv}$$

Here D = diffusivity of moisture within the sphere; r_o = outer radius of the sphere; p^* = vapour pressure of water at the given temperature; k_G = gas-phase mass transfer coefficient at the surface of the sphere; C_0 = initial moisture of the sphere.

It is convenient to rewrite Eq. (i) and the I.C. and B.C.'s in terms of dimensionless variables.

$$\overline{C} = C/C_0; \quad \overline{r} = r/r_o; \quad \theta = Dt/r_o^2, \text{ when}$$

$$\frac{\partial \overline{C}}{\partial \theta} = \frac{1}{\overline{r}^2} \frac{\partial}{\partial \overline{r}}\left(\overline{r}^2 \frac{\partial \overline{C}}{\partial \overline{r}}\right) \tag{v}$$

I.C.: $\theta = 0, \overline{C} = 1$; B.C.: $\overline{r} = 1, -\partial\overline{C}/\partial\overline{r} = \alpha\overline{C}, \alpha = k_G p^* r_o/DC_0$; $\overline{r} = 0, \overline{C} = $ finite (vi)

If we define a new concentration variable, $\hat{C} = \overline{r}\,\overline{C}$, Eq. (v) and the I.C. and B.C.'s given in Eq. (vi) reduce to

$$\frac{\partial \hat{C}}{\partial \theta} = \frac{\partial^2 \hat{C}}{\partial \overline{r}^2} \tag{vii}$$

I.C.: $\theta = 0, \hat{C} = \overline{r}\,\overline{C} = \overline{r}$; B.C.1: $\overline{r} = 0, \quad \hat{C} = \overline{r}\,\overline{C} = 0$;

B.C.2: $\overline{r} = 1, \quad \partial\hat{C}/\partial\overline{r} = (1 - \alpha)\hat{C}$ (viii)

The equations will now be solved by using the technique of 'separation of variables'. Following the usual procedure we assume that the solution is the product of two functions as shown below.

$$\hat{C} = R(\overline{r}) \cdot \Theta(\theta) \tag{ix}$$

where $R(\overline{r})$ is a function of $\overline{r}$ only and $\Theta(\theta)$ is a function of θ only. On substitution of Eq. (ix) in Eq. (vii) and with a little algebraic manipulation, we may write

$$\frac{d\Theta}{d\theta} = \frac{1}{R}\frac{dR}{d\overline{r}^2} = -\lambda^2 = \text{constant} \tag{x}$$

Solution for the function Θ: $\Theta = K_1 \exp(-\lambda_m^2 \theta)$ (xi)

Solution for the 'eigenfunctions', $R(\overline{r}) = K_2 \sin(\lambda_m \overline{r})$ (xii)

where λ_n are the roots of the equation: $\lambda \cot \lambda = 1 - \alpha$ (xiii)

The complete solution for transient concentration distribution in the sphere may be found to be

$$\overline{C} = \frac{C}{C_0} = \frac{2\alpha}{\overline{r}} \sum_{m=1}^{\infty} \frac{\sin\lambda_m}{\lambda_m^2 - (1-\alpha)\sin^2\lambda_m} \sin(\lambda_m \overline{r}) \exp(-\lambda_m^2 \theta) \qquad \text{(xiv)}$$

The numerical part is left as a piece of exercise for the student.

EXAMPLE 16.5 (*Higbie's penetration theory*)   Consider unsteady state absorption of a gas in a stagnant liquid element as conceptualized in Higbie's penetration theory. The one–dimensional diffusion equation applicable to the situation is given by Eq. (3.32); also see Section 16.2.2. The initial and boundary conditions are given in Eq. (3.33). Obtain (a) the solution for the concentration distribution of the dissolved gas in the liquid element (considered to have an 'infinite' depth), and (b) an expression for the mass transfer coefficient [see Eq. (3.38)].

Solution
(a)   The governing partial differential equation for the transient concentration distribution is

$$\frac{\partial C}{\partial t} = D\frac{\partial^2 C}{\partial z^2} \qquad \text{(i)}$$

I.C.: $C(0, z) = C_0$;   B.C.: $C(t, 0) = C_i$; $C(t, \infty) = C_0$ [i = gas–liquid interface]   (ii)

The problem admits of a 'similarity solution' (Dutta, 2001). We combine the two independent variables (z and t) to define a new variable η, and also to define a dimensionless concentration, $\overline{C}$.

$$\eta = \frac{z}{2\sqrt{Dt}} \qquad \text{and} \qquad \overline{C} = \frac{C - C_0}{C_i - C_0} \qquad \text{(iii)}$$

Substituting Eq. (iii) in Eqs. (i) and (ii) and doing a little algebra, the partial differential equation can be transformed into an ordinary differential equation

$$\frac{d^2\overline{C}}{d\eta^2} + 2\eta\frac{d\overline{C}}{d\eta} \qquad \text{(iv)}$$

The initial and boundary conditions are transformed to

$$\eta = 0, \ \overline{C} = 1, \quad \eta = \infty, \ \overline{C} = 0 \qquad \text{(v)}$$

Putting $d\overline{C}/d\eta = \zeta$ in Eq. (iv) and integrating

$$\frac{d\zeta}{d\eta} + 2\eta\zeta = 0 \ \Rightarrow \ \zeta = A'e^{-\eta^2} \ \Rightarrow \ \frac{d\overline{C}}{d\eta} = A'e^{-\eta^2} \ \Rightarrow \ \overline{C} = A'\int_0^\eta e^{-\eta^2}\,d\eta + B' \qquad \text{(vi)}$$

Using the boundary conditions we may evaluate the integration constants A' and B'.

At $\eta = 0$, $\overline{C} = 1$; $\Rightarrow B' = 1$, putting the value of B' and also putting $\overline{C} = 0$ at $\eta = \infty$ in Eq. (vi),

$$A'\int_0^\infty e^{-\eta^2}\,d\eta + 1 = 0 \qquad \Rightarrow \qquad A' = -\frac{2}{\sqrt{\pi}} \qquad \text{(vii)}$$

The final solution for the transient concentration distribution in the liquid element is given by

$$\bar{C} = \frac{C - C_0}{C_i - C_0} = 1 - \frac{2}{\sqrt{\pi}} \int_0^\eta e^{-\eta^2} d\eta = 1 - \mathrm{erf}(\eta) = \boxed{\mathrm{erfc}(\eta)} \tag{viii}$$

Here $\mathrm{erf}(\eta)$ is called the 'error function' and $\mathrm{erfc}(\eta)$ is the 'complimentary error function'.

(b) The absorption flux at time t is given by

$$N = -D\left[\frac{dC}{dz}\right]_{z=0} = -D\left[\frac{dC}{d\eta}\right]_{\eta=0}\left[\frac{\partial \eta}{\partial z}\right]_{z=0} = -D(C_i - C_0)\left(-\frac{2}{\sqrt{\pi}}\right)\frac{1}{2\sqrt{Dt}}$$

$$= (C_i - C_0)\sqrt{\frac{D}{\pi t}} \tag{ix}$$

The instantaneous mass transfer coefficient,

$$k_L(t) = \frac{N}{C_i - C_0} = \boxed{\sqrt{\frac{D}{\pi t}}} \tag{x}$$

The average mass transfer coefficient over a contact time t_c is

$$k_{L,\mathrm{av}} = \frac{1}{t_c}\int_0^{t_c} k_L(t)\,dt = \frac{1}{t_c}\int_0^{t_c}\sqrt{\frac{D}{\pi t}}\,dt = \boxed{2\sqrt{\frac{D}{\pi t_c}}} \tag{xi}$$

16.2 DIFFUSION ACCOMPANIED BY A CHEMICAL REACTION IN A LIQUID

Chemical reactions can be broadly considered to belong to either of two classes—homogeneous and heterogeneous. A homogeneous reaction between two reactants occurs in a single phase, but a heterogeneous reaction occurs at the interface between two phases. Catalytic gas–solid reactions belong to the second category. Such a reaction is preceded by diffusion of the reactants from the bulk gas to the active sites on the catalyst surface. Since most industrial catalysts have a porous structure, diffusion plays a vital role in the process. Gas–liquid reactions, on the other hand, are homogeneous reactions. The reactive component of the gas is absorbed at the gas–liquid interface and diffuses into the bulk of the liquid while undergoing a simultaneous chemical reaction possibly with a species present in solution. Diffusion plays an important role for transport in the gas as well as in the liquid phase.

Before dealing with the theoretical principles of gas absorption with a chemical reaction, it will be pertinent to cite a few industrially important processes involving gas–liquid reactions (Table 16.1). So far as the absorption capacity is concerned, the removal of CO_2 from synthesis gas in an ammonia plant tops the list. Hot potassium carbonate or ethanolamine solutions are the preferred solvents. Air oxidation of p-xylene to manufacture terephthalic acid is a gas–liquid reaction in which the oxygen of air is absorbed at 200°C and 25 atm pressure in a mixture of p-xylene and acetic acid containing Mn-acetate as the dissolved catalyst. Acetic acid acts as the diluent of p-xylene. Cyclohexanol and cyclohexanone, the starting materials for the manufacture of caprolactum (which is the precursor of nylon-6) are manufactured by liquid-phase air-oxidation of cyclohexane. Some of the examples of gas absorption cited in Table 6.1 involve a chemical reaction in the liquid-phase. There are cases of gas-liquid-solid reactions in which a dissolved gas and another reactant react on the surface of suspended catalyst particles. A common example is hydrogenation of vegetable oil using nickel catalyst.

Table 16.1   Some industrially important gas–liquid reactions

---

- *Liquid-phase air-oxidation of hydrocarbons*

   (i)   aliphatic hydrocarbons to fatty alcohols

   (ii)   *p*-xylene to terephthalic acid[#] (solvent: acetic acid; dissolved catalyst: manganous acetate)

   (iii)   cumene to cumene hydroperoxide in the process of manufacture of phenol and acetone.

- *Liquid-phase chlorination of aromatics*

   (i)   chlorination of benzene to mono- and dichlorobenzene

   (ii)   chlorination of toluene to benzyl chloride in the process of manufacture of benzyl alcohol.

- *Absorption of olefins in sulphuric acid for the conversion of*

   (i)   *iso*-butylene to *iso*-butyl alcohol

   (ii)   butelene to butyl alcohol.

- *Absorption and reaction of C_2H_4 and Cl_2 in dichloroethane medium. The product is also dichloroethane which is used for the manufacture of vinyl chloride.*

- *Absorption of H_2S and SO_2 in an aqueous medium to convert them to elemental sulphur.*

- *Absorption of ethylene and chlorine in an aqueous medium to make ethylene chlorohydrin (a precursor for the manufacture of ethylene glycol[##])*

- *Absorption of CO_2 in an aqueous suspension of lime*

- *Absorption of SO_2 in an aqueous solution of $NaNO_2$ containing suspended zinc powder for the manufacture of hydroxilamine.*

   Hydrogenation of unsaturated organic compounds by H_2 in liquid phase using Ni catalyst.

[#] Oxidation of *o*-xylene to phthalic acid is done in the vapour phase.

[##] This is the old route of making ethylene glycol. Now it is made by hydration of ethylene oxide.

    The reaction between the absorbed gas and a reactant already present in solution (for example, the reaction between CO_2 and mono-ethanolamine) occurs in the liquid-phase generally near the gas–liquid interface. Theoretical analyses of gas–liquid reactions have mostly been done on the basis of the three common theories of mass transfer—the film, the penetration or the surface renewal theory—duly taking into consideration the rate of depletion of the reactants because of the reaction. In fact, the analysis of gas–liquid reactions rather than 'physical absorption' are the major practical applications of these theories. Detailed treatment of the gas–liquid reactions is available in Astarita (1967), Danckwerts (1970) and Doraiswamy and Sharma (1984).

16.2.1   The Film Theory for Absorption Accompanied by a Reaction

Let us consider a rectangular liquid element of unit surface area (normal to the direction of diffusion) and of differential thickness Δz as shown in Figure 3.6(a). Let the absorbed species, A, undergo a chemical reaction with a dissolved species B given as

$$A + vB \rightarrow \text{Products} \tag{16.10}$$

The rate of consumption of A by reaction (moles reacting per unit volume per unit time) has to be taken into account while making a mass balance over the differential element. Since the film theory is a steady-state theory, there is no accumulation of the species and the mass balance equation is given by

$$N_A\big|_z \quad - \quad N_A\big|_{z+\Delta z} \quad = \quad (\Delta z)(1)R_A \tag{16.11}$$

$$\underbrace{\qquad}_{\text{Rate of input}} \quad \underbrace{\qquad}_{\text{Rate of output}} \quad \underbrace{\qquad}_{\text{Rate of depletion due to reaction}}$$

Dividing the above equation by Δz throughout, taking the limit $\Delta z \to 0$, and putting $N_A = -D_A(dC_A/dz)$,

$$D_A \frac{d^2 C_A}{dz^2} = R_A \tag{16.12}$$

A common and simple situation occurs if the dissolved species A is consumed by a first order ($R_A = k_1 C_A$) or a 'pseudo-first order' ($R_A = k_2 C_{Bo} C_A = k_1 C_A$) reaction. A gas–liquid reaction is considered 'pseudo-first order' if the concentration of the dissolved species B in the film remains nearly the same as in the bulk liquid (C_{Bb}).

$$D_A \frac{d^2 C_A}{dz^2} = k_1 C_A \tag{16.13}$$

The following 'boundary conditions' may be specified.

$C_A = C_{Ai}$ (concentration of A at the gas–liquid interface) at $z = 0$ $\qquad$ (16.14a)

$C_A = C_{Ab}$ (concentration of A in the bulk liquid) $\qquad$ at $z = \delta$ $\qquad$ (16.14b)

The solution of Eq. (16.13) subject to boundary conditions, Eqs. [16.14(a)] and [16.14(b)], can be written as

$$\frac{C_A}{C_{Ai}} = \frac{1}{\sinh\varphi}\left[\sinh\left(\varphi - z\sqrt{\frac{k_1}{D_A}}\right) + \frac{C_{Ab}}{C_{Ai}}\sinh\left(z\sqrt{\frac{k_1}{D_A}}\right)\right] \tag{16.15}$$

$$\varphi^2 = \delta^2[k_1/D_A] \tag{16.16}$$

The quantity φ has a physical significance as given below.

$$\varphi^2 = \frac{k_1 C_{Ai}\delta}{(D_A/\delta)(C_{Ai} - 0)}$$

$$= \frac{\textit{maximum rate} \text{ of reaction of } A \text{ in the film per unit interfacial area}}{\textit{maximum rate} \text{ of physical mass transfer per unit interfacial area}} \tag{16.17}$$

It is to be noted that according to the film theory, the 'physical mass transfer coefficient' (when no chemical reaction takes place) is given by [see Eq. (3.31)]

$$k_L = D_A/\delta \tag{16.18}$$

Equation (16.16) can therefore be written as

$$\varphi = \left(\frac{k_1 D_A}{(D_A/\delta)^2}\right)^{1/2} = \left(\frac{k_1 D_A}{k_L^2}\right)^{1/2} = \text{Ha} \tag{16.19}$$

The group φ is more frequently called the 'Hatta number'. The rate of absorption or flux of the species A at the interface in the presence of the reaction, $(J_A)_r$, can be obtained from Eq. (16.15).[†]

$$\text{Flux of } A = (J_A)_r = -D_A\left[\frac{dC_A}{dz}\right]_{z=0} = \frac{D_A}{\delta}\frac{\text{Ha}}{\tanh(\text{Ha})}\left[C_{Ai} - \frac{C_{Ab}}{\cosh(\text{Ha})}\right]$$

$$= k_L\frac{\text{Ha}}{\tanh(\text{Ha})}\left[C_{Ai} - \frac{C_{Ab}}{\cosh(\text{Ha})}\right] \qquad (16.20)$$

If there is no chemical reaction and the concentration of A in the bulk liquid remains the same (i.e. $C_A = C_{Ab}$), the steady-state physical mass transfer flux is

$$(J_A)_p = k_L(C_{Ai} - C_{Ab}) \qquad (16.21)$$

Typical concentration profiles of A in the liquid film for both physical absorption and absorption with reaction are shown in Figure 16.6. The effect of chemical reaction on increasing the rate of absorption of A compared to the rate of 'physical absorption' alone is expressed in terms of an 'enhancement factor', E_A.

$$E_A = \frac{(J_A)_r}{(J_A)_p} = \frac{\text{flux of } A \text{ at the interface with chemical reaction}}{\text{flux of } A \text{ at the interface without chemical reaction}} \qquad (16.22)$$

The enhancement factor can be calculated by taking the ratio of fluxes given by Eqs. (16.20) and (16.21) in the general case. However, there are a few limiting cases which are practically important and admit of simpler expressions for E_A. Two cases are mentioned below:

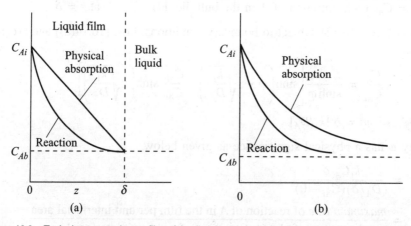

Figure 16.6   Typical concentration profiles of the dissolved gas: (a) film theory, and (b) penetration theory.

(i) *The reaction is fast* ($\varphi > 2$)
For $\varphi = 2$, $\tanh\varphi = 0.965 \Rightarrow$ for $\varphi > 2$, $\tanh\varphi \approx 1$. Also if the reaction is fast, the bulk concentration of A remains pretty small and practically all the solute absorbed reacts in the film. Putting $\tanh\varphi = 1$, and $C_{Ab}/\cosh\varphi \ll C_{Ai}$ in Eq. (16.20), we get

$$E_A = \frac{k_L C_{Ai}\varphi}{k_L C_{Ai}} = \varphi \qquad \text{where} \qquad \varphi > 2 \qquad (16.23)$$

[†] The subscript 'r' indicates reaction. However, the subscript has not always been used in the text.

(ii) *The reaction is slow* ($\varphi < 0.3$)

For $\varphi = 0.3$, $\tanh\varphi = 0.29$, and $\cosh\varphi = 1.04 \Rightarrow \varphi/\tanh\varphi \approx 1$, and $C_{Ab}/\cosh\varphi \approx C_{Ab}$, and

$$E_A = \frac{(k_L)(1)(C_{Ai} - C_{Ab})}{k_L(C_{Ai} - C_{Ab})} = 1 \qquad \text{where} \qquad \varphi < 0.3 \qquad (16.24)$$

Hence practically no reaction occurs in the film and the rate of absorption is *not enhanced* due to the chemical reaction. In the intermediate range of values of φ ($2 > \varphi > 0.3$), the roles of mass transfer and *resistances* due to mass transfer and chemical reaction both become important.

EXAMPLE 16.6 (*Determination of the rate constant from the absorption data*) 'Pure' chlorine gas is absorbed in water in a continuous stirred cell at 25°C and 1 atm pressure (see Figure 3.21). The gas–liquid contact area is 50 cm^2. The rate of absorption, measured from the difference in flow rate of the gas at the inlet and the outlet, is 4.02×10^{-3} gmol/min. The water flow rate is kept sufficiently high so that the concentration of dissolved chlorine in the bulk liquid remains pretty low. An independent measurement of the rate of absorption of CO_2 is done in the apparatus under identical hydrodynamic conditions and the 'physical mass transfer coefficient' for the CO_2–water system is found to be 2.3×10^{-3} cm/s. Assuming that the film theory is applicable, calculate the first order rate constant of the reaction between chlorine and water ($Cl_2 + H_2O = H^+ + Cl^- + HOCl$). The following data are available. Diffusivity in water: Cl_2—1.5×10^{-5} cm^2/s, CO_2—1.7×10^{-5} cm^2/s; solubility of chlorine in water under the given condition = 6.7 g/litre.

Solution

Absorption flux of chlorine, $N_A = \dfrac{(4.02 \times 10^{-3})}{(60)(50)} = 1.34 \times 10^{-6}$ (gmol)/(cm^2)(s)

Interfacial concentration (or solubility) of chlorine, $C_i = 6.7$ g/litre = 0.0944 gmol/litre; $C_b \approx 0$.

According to the film theory, the 'physical mass transfer coefficient' is proportional to the diffusivity. 'Diffusivity correction' of the mass transfer coefficient for absorption of CO_2 in water may be done to calculate the 'physical mass transfer coefficient' for absorption of chlorine in water.

$$(k_L)_{Cl_2-\text{water}} = (k_L)_{CO_2-\text{water}} \cdot \frac{D_{Cl_2}}{D_{CO_2}} = (2.3 \times 10^{-3})\left(\frac{1.5 \times 10^{-5}}{1.7 \times 10^{-5}}\right) = 2.03 \times 10^{-3} \text{ cm/s}$$

Using Eq. (16.20) for the mass transfer flux in the presence of a first-order reaction,

$$(J_A)_r = k_L \frac{\varphi}{\tanh\varphi} \cdot C_i \quad \Rightarrow \quad 1.34 \times 10^{-6} = (2.03 \times 10^{-3}) \frac{\varphi}{\tanh\varphi} (0.0944 \times 10^{-3})$$

$$\Rightarrow \qquad \frac{\varphi}{\tanh\varphi} = 7 \quad \Rightarrow \quad \varphi = 7 = \left(\frac{k_1 D_A}{k_L^2}\right)^{1/2}$$

Given, the diffusivity of chlorine, $D_A = 1.5 \times 10^{-5}$ cm^2/s, and $k_L = 2.03 \times 10^{-3}$ cm/s, $k_1 = \boxed{13.5 \text{ s}^{-1}}$

16.2.2   Penetration Theory of Absorption Accompanied by a Reaction

The basic assumptions underlying the 'penetration theory' have been laid down in Section 3.7.2. Here we further assume that the unsteady state diffusion of the dissolved gas is accompanied by a chemical reaction occurring in the liquid element at the surface. In order to make a mass balance over a differential liquid element of unit area and of thickness Δz, we have to consider an accumulation term in addition to the input, output and reaction terms in Eq. (16.11). This is required since, as stated in Section 3.7.2, the penetration model assumes that unsteady state mass transfer occurs in the small 'stagnant' liquid element during its stay at the gas–liquid contact surface.

Rate of accumulation of A in the differential volume [Figure 3.6(a)] $= \dfrac{\partial}{\partial t}[(\Delta z \cdot 1) \cdot C_A]$

The unsteady-state mass balance takes the form

$$\underbrace{\frac{\partial}{\partial t}(\Delta z . C_A)}_{\text{Rate of accumulation}} = \underbrace{N_A\big|_z}_{\text{Rate of input}} - \underbrace{N_A\big|_{z+\Delta z}}_{\text{Rate of output}} - \underbrace{R_A \cdot \Delta z}_{\text{Rate of consumption}} \qquad (16.25)$$

$$\Rightarrow \qquad \frac{\partial C_A}{\partial t} = D_A \frac{\partial^2 C_A}{\partial z^2} - R_A \quad \Rightarrow \quad \frac{\partial C_A}{\partial t} = D_A \frac{\partial^2 C_A}{\partial z^2} - k_1 C_A \qquad (16.26)$$

Again we assume that the rate of reaction is first order (or pseudo-first order) in the concentration of A. The same set of initial and boundary conditions given in Eq. (3.33) apply. If no chemical reaction occurs in the liquid, $R_A = 0$, and Eq. (16.26) reduces to Eq. (3.32).

If the concentration of the absorbed species A is zero in the bulk liquid ($C_{Ab} = 0$), the solution of Eq. (16.26) subject to initial and boundary conditions given by Eq. (3.33) may be obtained by using the Laplace transform technique (see, for example, Froment and Bischoff, 1990).

$$\frac{C_A}{C_{Ai}} = \frac{1}{2}\exp\left(-z\sqrt{\frac{k_1}{D_A}}\right)\text{erfc}\left(\frac{z}{2\sqrt{D_A t}} - \sqrt{k_1 t}\right) + \frac{1}{2}\exp\left(z\sqrt{\frac{k_1}{D_A}}\right)\text{erfc}\left(\frac{z}{2\sqrt{D_A t}} + \sqrt{k_1 t}\right) \qquad (16.27)$$

where erfc(ξ) is the complementary error function of ξ [see Eq. (viii), Example 16.5]. The instantaneous flux of absorption is given by

$$J_A = -D_A\left[\frac{\partial C_A}{\partial z}\right]_{z=0} = C_{Ai}\sqrt{k_1 D_A}\left[\text{erf}(\sqrt{k_1 t}) + \frac{e^{-k_1 t}}{\sqrt{\pi k_1 t}}\right] \qquad (16.28)$$

The average flux over a contact time t_c is

$$(J_A)_{\text{av}} = \frac{1}{t_c}\int_0^{t_c} J_A\,dt = C_{Ai}\sqrt{k_1 D_A}\left[\left(1 + \frac{1}{2k_1 t_c}\right)\text{erf}\sqrt{k_1 t_c} + \frac{e^{-k_1 t_c}}{\sqrt{\pi k_1 t_c}}\right] \qquad (16.29)$$

The above expression for the average flux can be considerably simplified in the following limiting cases.

(i) As the value of $k_1 t_c$ increases, the first term of Eq. (16.29) tends to unity and the second term decreases rapidly. When $k_1 t_c$ is 'large',

$$J_A = C_{Ai} \sqrt{D_A k_1} \qquad (16.30)$$

The error remains within 10% if $k_1 t_c > 5$, and within 5% if $k_1 t_c > 10$. Also when $k_1 t_c > 2$,

$$J_A = C_{Ai} \sqrt{D_A k_1} \left(1 + \frac{1}{2 k_1 t_c}\right) = C_{Ai} \sqrt{D_A k_1} \left(1 + \frac{\pi k_L^2}{8 D_A k_1}\right) = C_{Ai} \sqrt{D_A k_1} \left(1 + \frac{\pi}{8 \mathrm{Ha}^2}\right) \quad (16.31)$$

In getting the above expression we have used the relation, $k_L = 2\sqrt{D_A / \pi t_c}$. The enhancement factor is

$$E_A = \sqrt{\frac{D_A k_1}{k_L^2}} \left(1 + \frac{\pi}{8 \mathrm{Ha}^2}\right) \qquad (16.32)$$

(ii) When $k_1 t_c$ is rather small, say $k_1 t_c < 0.5$, Eq. (16.29) may be approximated as

$$J_A \approx 2 C_{Ai} \sqrt{\frac{D_A}{\pi t_c}} \left(1 + \frac{k_1 t_c}{3}\right) = C_{Ai} k_L \left(1 + \frac{k_1 t_c}{3}\right) \qquad \text{(error: within 5\%)} \qquad (16.33)$$

The enhancement factor is

$$E_A = \left(1 + \frac{k_1 t_c}{3}\right) \qquad (16.34)$$

If $k_1 t_c < 0.1$ (or Ha < 0.3),

$$J_A \approx k_L C_{Ai} \qquad \text{and} \qquad E_A \approx 1 \qquad (16.35)$$

Thus the enhancement factor ranges from $E_A = 1$ to that given in Eq. (16.32).

16.2.3 Surface Renewal Theory

The age distribution function of the liquid elements at the gas–liquid interface is (see Example 16.5)

$$\psi(t) = s e^{-st} \qquad (16.36)$$

Since the age of the tiny liquid elements varies from zero to infinity, the absorption flux can be obtained from Eqs. (16.28) and (16.36).

$$J_A = \int_0^\infty J_A(t) \psi(t)\, dt = \int_0^\infty C_{Ai} \sqrt{D_A k_1} \left[\mathrm{erf}\left(\sqrt{k_1 t}\right) + \frac{e^{-k_1 t}}{\sqrt{\pi k_1 t}}\right] s e^{-st}\, dt$$

$$= C_{Ai} \sqrt{D_A (k_1 + s)} = C_{Ai} \sqrt{D_A k_1 + k_L^2} \qquad (16.37)]$$

[since $k_L = \sqrt{D_A s}$; see Example 16.7, Eq. (iii)]

The enhancement factor E_A is given by

$$E_A = \frac{C_{Ai} \sqrt{D_A k_1 + k_L^2}}{k_L C_{Ai}} = \sqrt{1 + \frac{D_A k_1}{k_L^2}} = \sqrt{1 + \mathrm{Ha}^2} \qquad (16.38)$$

EXAMPLE 16.7 (*Danckwert's surface renewal model*)   Derive the expression for the 'physical mass transfer coefficient' of a gas given in Eq. (3.39) following the Danckwert's surface renewal model. Recall that according to this model the probability of a liquid element at the interface getting displaced by a fresh element from the bulk is independent of age. The constant fractional rate of surface renewal is s (s^{-1}).

Solution

We shall first derive the age distribution function of the liquid elements at the gas–liquid interface following the Danckwert's model. Let $\psi(t)$ be the age distribution function such that $\psi(t)dt$ is the fraction of the liquid elements belonging to the age group t to $(t + dt)$. This fraction of the elements may be equated to the fraction that passes from the previous age group of $(t - dt)$ to t into the present age group [i.e. t to $(t + dt)$] *less* the fraction replaced or renewed in time dt. If s is the 'fractional rate of surface renewal', the following 'population balance' equation may be written (compare with the derivation of crystal population density function in Section 13.4).

$$\underset{\substack{\text{Fraction of surface elements} \\ \text{in the age group } t \text{ to } (t + dt)}}{\psi(t)dt} \quad = \quad \underset{\substack{\text{Fraction in the previous} \\ \text{age group of } (t - dt) \text{ to } t}}{\psi(t - dt)dt} \quad - \quad \underset{\substack{\text{Fraction 'renewed'} \\ \text{in time } dt}}{(sdt)\psi(t - dt)dt}$$

$$\Rightarrow \quad \psi(t) = \left[\psi(t) - \frac{d\psi}{dt}dt \right] - sdt\left[\psi(t) - \frac{d\psi}{dt}dt \right] = \psi(t) - \frac{d\psi}{dt}dt - s\psi(t)dt + s\frac{d\psi}{dt}(dt)^2$$

Neglecting the second-order term containing $(dt)^2$ and simplifying, we get

$$\frac{d\psi}{dt} = -s\psi \quad \Rightarrow \quad \psi(t) = Ke^{-st} \text{ where } K \text{ is the integration constant.}$$

Since the total fraction of the surface of all age groups (i.e. from $t = 0$ to ∞) is unity,

$$1 = \int_0^\infty \psi(t)dt = K\int_0^\infty e^{-st}dt = \frac{K}{s} \quad \Rightarrow \quad K = s$$

So the 'surface age distribution function' is given as

$$\psi(t) = se^{-st} \tag{i}$$

The mass transfer coefficient at the surface that consists of liquid elements of age ranging from $t = 0$ to $t = \infty$ is given by

$$k_{L,av} = \int_0^\infty k_L(t)\psi(t)dt \tag{ii}$$

where $k_L(t)$ is the coefficient of mass transfer into an element of age t given by Eq. (x), Example 16.5. Hence

$$k_L = \int_0^\infty \sqrt{\frac{D}{\pi t}}\,se^{-st}dt = \sqrt{\frac{Ds}{\pi}}\int_0^\infty (st)^{-1/2}\,e^{-st}\,d(st)$$

$$= \sqrt{\frac{Ds}{\pi}} \int_0^\infty e^{-\tau} (\tau)^{-1/2} \, d\tau = \sqrt{\frac{Ds}{\pi}} \, \Gamma\left(\frac{1}{2}\right) = \sqrt{\frac{Ds}{\pi}} \, \sqrt{\pi}$$

$$\Rightarrow \qquad \boxed{k_L = \sqrt{Ds}} \qquad\qquad\qquad \text{(iii)}$$

Note: The improper integral $\Gamma(p) = \displaystyle\int_0^\infty e^{-\tau} (\tau)^{p-1} \, d\tau$ is called the 'Gamma function'; see Example 13.1.

16.3 IRREVERSIBLE SECOND-ORDER REACTION

In the previous section we analyzed absorption of a gas A in a liquid with a simultaneous first-order (or pseudo-first order) chemical reaction. Now we shall consider the case of absorption accompanied by a second-order reaction given by Eq. (16.10). In general, the concentration of A in the film decreases away from the gas–liquid interface, while that of B increases (qualitatively shown in Figure 16.7). Let the reaction be first order in the concentrations of both A and B. The local rate of consumption of A is $R_A = k_2 C_A C_B$, and that of B is $R_B = \nu k_2 C_A C_B$. Putting the expression for R_A in the film theory Eq. (16.12), we have

$$D_A \frac{d^2 C_A}{dz^2} - k_2 C_A C_B = 0 \qquad\qquad (16.39)$$

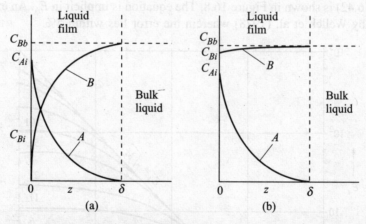

Figure 16.7 Typical concentration profiles of A and B in the liquid film: (a) second-order reaction (depletion of B in the film), and (b) pseudo-first order reaction (insignificant depletion of B in the film).

A similar equation may be written for the concentration distribution of B in the liquid film.

$$D_B \frac{d^2 C_B}{dz^2} - \nu k_2 C_A C_B = 0 \qquad\qquad (16.40)$$

The following boundary conditions apply.

$$C_A = C_{Ai} \qquad \qquad \text{at } z = 0 \qquad \qquad (16.41a)$$

$$C_A = C_{Ab} \quad \text{and} \quad C_B = C_{Bb} \qquad \text{at } z = \delta \qquad (16.41b)$$

$$dC_B/dz = 0 \qquad \qquad \text{at } z = 0 \qquad \qquad (16.41c)$$

Here C_{Ab} and C_{Bb} are the concentrations of A and B in the bulk liquid. Equation [16.41(c)] indicates that the reactant B is non-volatile and its flux (and therefore the concentration gradient) is zero at the gas–liquid interface ($z = 0$).

The simultaneous nonlinear ordinary equations (16.39) and (16.40), subject to the boundary conditions given by Eqs. [16.41(a), (b), and (c)], do not admit of analytical solutions. van Krevelen and Hoftijer (1948) obtained numerical solution for the enhancement factor E_A as a function of M ($= \varphi^2$) and E_i assuming that the concentration of A in the bulk liquid is negligibly small ($C_{Ab} \cong 0$). They further showed that the computed results could be correlated in the following form (the maximum error lies within 10%). Here E_i is the enhancement factor if the reaction between A and B is instantaneous, see Section 16.4.

$$E_A = \frac{\left(M \cdot \dfrac{E_i - E_A}{E_i - 1} \right)^{1/2}}{\tanh\left(M \cdot \dfrac{E_i - E_A}{E_i - 1} \right)^{1/2}} \qquad (16.42)$$

$$M = \frac{D_A k_2 C_{Bb}}{k_L^2} \qquad \text{and} \qquad E_i = 1 + \frac{D_B C_{Bb}}{v D_A C_{Ai}} \qquad (16.43)$$

A plot of Eq. (16.42) is shown in Figure 16.8. The equation is implicit in E_A. An explicit relation was suggested by Wellek et al. (1978) wherein the error lies within 5%.

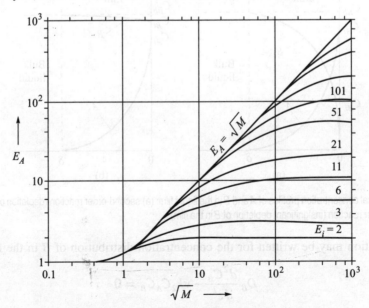

Figure 16.8   Enhancement factor for a second-order reaction.

$$(E_A - 1)^{-1.35} = (E_i - 1)^{-1.35} + \left[\frac{\sqrt{M}}{\tanh \sqrt{M}} - 1 \right]^{-1.35} \tag{16.44}$$

If there is no substantial depletion of the reactant B in the liquid film [Figure 16.7(b)], the reaction is considered to be pseudo-first order. This happens if the bulk concentration of B is sufficiently high (so that there is ample diffusion of B from the bulk into the liquid film) or the reaction rate is moderate. The following criterion (Danckwerts, 1970) may be used to decide if the reaction is pseudo-first order.

$$\sqrt{M} < E_i/2 \tag{16.45}$$

The enhancement factor for this case may be calculated by using the relations given in Section 16.2.1.

It may be noted that the numerical solution of the simultaneous partial differential equations for absorption with a second-order reaction based on the penetration model predicts enhancement factors to be close to that given by the film theory result, i.e. Eq. (16.43).

16.4 INSTANTANEOUS REACTION

There are some gas–liquid reactions which are instantaneous. For example, the reaction of an acidic gas such as H_2S with a strongly alkaline species is instantaneous. Let us refer to Figure 16.9 showing steady-state concentration profiles of A and B, if such a reaction occurs in a film of thickness δ. Since the reaction is instantaneous, it takes place at a 'reaction front' within the film. Let the reaction front be located at a distance δ' from the gas–liquid interface. The species A diffuses towards the front from the left, and B from the right. They react instantaneously on reaching the front where the concentrations of both A and B are virtually zero. There is no A in the region right to the reaction front, and there is no B in the region left to it. The concentration of B in the bulk liquid (i.e. beyond the liquid film) is C_{Bb}; that of A at the gas–liquid interface is C_{Ai}.

$$\text{Flux of } A \text{ (at steady state)} = \frac{D_A}{\delta'} C_{Ai} \tag{16.46}$$

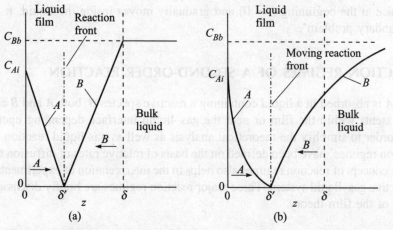

Figure 16.9 Typical concentration profiles of *A* and *B* for an instantaneous reaction: (a) film theory, and (b) penetration theory.

$$\text{Flux of } B \text{ (at steady state)} = \frac{D_B}{\delta - \delta'} C_{Bb} \tag{16.47}$$

Since the stoichiometric coefficient is ν, the fluxes are related as

$$\nu \frac{D_A}{\delta'} C_{Ai} = \frac{D_B}{\delta - \delta'} C_{Bb} \quad \Rightarrow \quad \frac{\delta'}{\delta - \delta'} = \frac{\nu D_A C_{Ai}}{D_B C_{Bb}} \quad \Rightarrow \quad \delta' = \delta \cdot \frac{\nu D_A C_{Ai}}{\nu D_A C_{Ai} + D_B C_{Bb}} \tag{16.48}$$

Hence the absorption flux of A is

$$J_A = \frac{D_A C_{Ai}}{\delta'} = \frac{D_A C_{Ai}}{\delta} \frac{\nu D_A C_{Ai} + D_B C_{Bb}}{\nu D_A C_{Ai}} = k_L C_{Ai} \left(1 + \frac{D_B C_{Bb}}{\nu D_A C_{Ai}} \right) \tag{16.49}$$

The enhancement factor for absorption of A with instantaneous reaction with dissolved B is

$$E_i = \left(1 + \frac{D_B C_{Bb}}{\nu D_A C_{Ai}} \right) \tag{16.50}$$

Theoretically, a reaction is called instantaneous if the reaction rate constant is infinite. In gas–liquid systems whether a reaction can be considered to be instantaneous depends upon the relative magnitudes of C_{Ai} and C_{Bb}, besides the physical mass transfer coefficient k_L (or the film thickness). The diffusivities of A and B have also a role to play. For practical purposes, a reaction may be considered instantaneous if the following criterion is satisfied.

$$\sqrt{M} > 10E_i \tag{16.51}$$

It may be noted that in the case of an instantaneous reaction too, the enhancement factor predicted by the penetration theory is closely comparable to that predicted by the film theory, i.e. Eq. (16.49). For example, when $E_i \gg 1$, the penetration theory results for the enhancement factor may be approximated by the equation

$$E_i = \sqrt{\frac{D_A}{D_B}} + \frac{C_{Bb}}{\nu C_{Ai}} \sqrt{\frac{D_B}{D_A}} \tag{16.52}$$

Since penetration theory is an unsteady state theory, the reaction front superimposes on the gas–liquid interface at the beginning ($t = 0$) and gradually moves inside the liquid. It constitutes a 'moving boundary problem'.

16.5 REACTION REGIMES OF A SECOND-ORDER REACTION

When a gas A is absorbed in a liquid containing a reactive species B, both A and B are consumed to varying extents within the film or near the gas–liquid interface depending upon the rate of reaction. In order to simplify the theoretical analysis as well as gas-liquid reaction calculations, a few 'reaction regimes' have been defined on the basis of relative rates of diffusion and chemical reaction. The concept of reaction regimes also helps in the interpretation of experimental absorption data in a reactive gas–liquid system. Three major reaction regimes are briefly discussed as follows on the basis of the film theory.

16.5.1 Slow Reaction Regime

If absorption occurs in the slow reaction regime, the absorbed species A does not undergo any appreciable depletion due to reaction in the liquid film. In other words, transport of A through the film occurs as in the case of physical absorption. The concentration of the dissolved reactive species B throughout the film thickness also remains the same as in the bulk liquid, C_{Bb}. However, the reaction between A and B occurs, though slowly, in the bulk liquid. This regime is identical to that for a first-order reaction with Ha < 0.3. In the slow reaction regime the Hatta number is given as

$$\text{Ha} = \sqrt{\frac{D_A k_2 C_{Bb}}{k_L^2}} = \sqrt{\frac{D_A k_1}{k_L^2}} < 0.3 \tag{16.53}$$

Here $k_1 = k_2 C_{Bb}$ is the pseudo-first order reaction rate constant.

16.5.2 The Fast Reaction Regime

In this regime the reaction rate is sufficiently high so that almost all the A absorbed at the gas–liquid interface reacts in the film and its concentration is virtually zero in the bulk liquid ($C_{Ab} \approx 0$). Some depletion of the dissolved reactant B may, however, occur in the film. If the depletion of B in the film is not significant, the reaction is called pseudo-first order [Figure 16.7(b)]. The criterion of a fast, pseudo-first order reaction is given as (see also Section 16.2.1)

$$\sqrt{\frac{D_A k_2 C_{Bb}}{k_L^2}} = \sqrt{\frac{D_A k_1}{k_L^2}} > 2 \tag{16.54}$$

EXAMPLE 16.8 (*Effect of liquid-phase chemical reaction on packed height*) Removal of oxides of nitrogen (NO_x) from waste gases is an important problem in air pollution control. Chen et al. [*Environmental Progr.*, 21(2002) 225–230] carried out experimental tests on absorption of NO_2 at low concentrations in an aqueous solution of sodium sulphite (Na_2SO_3). The gas NO_2 has a low solubility in water. As a result, the absorption of NO_2 in water is liquid-film resistance controlled. But the reaction with Na_2SO_3 [$2NO_2 + SO_3^{2-} + H_2O = 2NO_2^- + 2H^+ + SO_4^{2-}$] in the liquid-phase is expected to enhance the rate of absorption significantly. Compare the packed height necessary to absorb 95% of NO_2 from a waste gas of 200 ppm concentration using water to that using 0.25 molar Na_2SO_3 solution. The liquid rate is maintained sufficiently high so that the concentration of NO_2 in the bulk liquid remains very small.

Given: total pressure in the column = 1 atm; temperature = 25°C; gas-phase mass transfer coefficient, $k_y = 5 \times 10^{-4}$ kmol/(m^2)(s)(Δy); $k_L = 9.5 \times 10^{-5}$ m/s; diffusivity of NO_2 in water = 2×10^{-9} m^2/s; solubility of NO_2 in water at 25°C = 0.04 gmol/litre, and Henry's law is applicable; second-order rate constant for the reaction between dissolved NO_2 and Na_2SO_3, $k_2 = 11 \times 10^5$ litre/(gmol)(s).

Solution

Packed height to achieve a given degree of separation is given by Eq. (6.22). Since the gas is very dilute, we take $y^*_{BM} \approx 1$, $1 - y \approx 1$, $y^* \approx 0$, since the concentration of NO_2 in the bulk liquid is small.

$$\Rightarrow \qquad h_T = H_{tOG} \cdot N_{tOG} = \frac{G'}{K_y \bar{a}} \int\limits_{y_2}^{y_1} \frac{dy}{y - y^*} = \frac{G'}{K_y \bar{a}} \int\limits_{y_2}^{y_1} \frac{dy}{y} = \frac{G'}{K_y \bar{a}} \cdot \ln \frac{y_1}{y_2} \qquad \text{(i)}$$

Calculation of the 'overall gas-phase mass transfer coefficient', K_y

Case 1: Physical absorption. Total molar concentration of the liquid $\approx$ molar concentration of the medium (water), $C_m = 55.5$ kmol/m^3.

Given: $\qquad k_L = 9.5 \times 10^{-5}$ m/s $\Rightarrow k_x = k_L \cdot C_{av} = (9.5 \times 10^{-5}$ m/s$)(55.5$ kmol/m$^3)$

$$= 5.27 \times 10^{-3} \text{ kmol/(m}^2)(s)(\Delta x)$$

Solubility of $NO_2 = 0.04$ gmol/(litre)(atm) $= (0.04)/(55.5) = 7.21 \times 10^{-4}$ mole fraction/atm.

Henry's law $(y = mx)$ constant $\Rightarrow m = 1/(7.21 \times 10^{-4}) = 1387$.

Also given, $k_y = 5 \times 10^{-4}$ kmol/(m^2)(s)(Δy)

Overall mass transfer coefficient,

$$\frac{1}{K_y} = \frac{1}{k_y} + \frac{m}{k_x} = \frac{1}{5 \times 10^{-4}} + \frac{1387}{5.27 \times 10^{-3}} = 2000 + 263,190 = 265,190$$

$$\Rightarrow \qquad K_y = 3.77 \times 10^{-6} \text{ kmol/(m}^2)(s)(\Delta y)$$

Case 2: Absorption with reaction. We have to calculate the enhancement factor E first. We consider the reaction to be pseudo-first order since the concentration of Na_2SO_3 is much higher than that of NO_2.

$$\varphi = \left[\frac{k_2 C_{Bb} D_A}{k_L^2} \right]^{0.5} = \frac{[(11 \times 10^5)(0.25)(2 \times 10^{-9})]^{0.5}}{9.5 \times 10^{-5}} = 247 \quad \Rightarrow \quad E = \frac{\varphi}{\tanh \varphi} = 247$$

Overall mass transfer coefficient is given by

$$\frac{1}{K_y} = \frac{1}{k_y} + \frac{m}{E k_x} = \frac{1}{5 \times 10^{-4}} + \frac{1387}{(247)(5.27 \times 10^{-3})} = 3065$$

$$\Rightarrow \qquad K_y = 3.26 \times 10^{-4} \text{ kmol/(m}^2)(s)(\Delta y)$$

Since all other parameters (G', $\bar{a}$, y_1, y_2) remain the same the ratio of the packed heights in the two cases is

$$\frac{(h_T)_{\text{physical}}}{(h_T)_{\text{chemical}}} = \frac{(K_y)_{\text{chemical}}}{(K_y)_{\text{physical}}} = \frac{3.26 \times 10^{-4}}{3.77 \times 10^{-6}} = \boxed{87}$$

16.5.3   Instantaneous Reaction Regime

This regime has already been discussed in Section 16.4. The rate of absorption is completely diffusion-controlled. The criteria for the regimes of an *m-n* order reaction have been discussed by Danckwerts (1970).

EXAMPLE 16.9   The reaction of CO_2 with NaOH is first order in the concentration of each of CO_2 and the OH^-. The stoichiometric equation for the reaction is

$$CO_2 + 2OH^- = CO_3^{--} + H_2O \qquad \text{(i)}$$

If pure CO_2 is absorbed in 0.5 molar NaOH at 25°C, determine the regime of the reaction.

The following data are given: diffusivity of CO_2 in the solution, $D_A = 1.7 \times 10^{-5}$ cm²/s; diffusivity of OH^-, $D_B = 2.9 \times 10^{-5}$ cm²/s; Henry's law constant for CO_2 at the given temperature $= 1.63 \times 10^3$ atm/mol fraction; physical mass transfer coefficient, $k_L = 0.008$ cm/s; second-order reaction rate constant, $k_2 = 4000$ s⁻¹.

Solution

Solubility of CO_2 under the given condition is ($H_A = 1.63 \times 10^3$ atm/mol fraction)

$x_{Ai} = p_A/H_A = 1/(1.63 \times 10^3) \quad \Rightarrow \quad C_{Ai} = 3.41 \times 10^{-5}$ gmol/cm³. Also given, $C_{Bb} = 0.5$ molar.

From Eq. (16.43),

$$\sqrt{M} = \left[\frac{D_A k_2 C_{Bb}}{k_L^2} \right]^{1/2} = \left[\frac{(1.7 \times 10^{-5})(4000)(0.5)}{(0.008)^2} \right]^{1/2} = 23.0$$

$$E_i = \left(1 + \frac{D_B C_{Bb}}{\nu D_A C_{Ai}} \right) = \left(1 + \frac{(2.9 \times 10^{-5})(0.5 \, \text{mol/litre})}{(2)(1.7 \times 10^{-5})(3.41 \times 10^{-2} \, \text{mol/litre})} \right) = 13.5$$

For the reaction to be instantaneous, $\sqrt{M} > 10 E_i$ which is not true and hence the reaction is *not instantaneous*.

But the criterion $\sqrt{M} < E_i/2$ is valid. So the reaction is a fast pseudo-first order type. The value of the enhancement factor can be obtained from Figure 16.8.

For $\sqrt{M} = 23$ and $E_i = 13.5$, $E_A = 10.5$.

The value of E_A can be calculated from the Weller equation, Eq. (16.44), as well. This gives $E_A = 9.4$.

NOTATIONS

C	: concentration
C_{Ai}	: concentration of A at the gas–liquid interface (= physical solubility of A)
C_{Ab}, C_{Bb}	: concentration of A and of B in the bulk liquid
C_0	: initial concentration in the medium
C_s	: surface concentration
D, D_A, D_B	: diffusivity
E_A	: enhancement factor of A
E_i	: enhancement factor for an instantaneous reaction
Ha	: Hatta number, [Ha $= \varphi = (D_A k_1/k_L^2)^{1/2}$]

k_L	: physical mass transfer coefficient
k_1	: first-order reaction rate constant
k_2	: second-order reaction rate constant
M	: quantity defined in Eq. (16.43)
N	: molar flux
r	: radial position
r_o	: radius of a cylinder or sphere
R_A	: reaction rate of A
s	: fractional rate of surface renewal
t	: time
t_c	: contact time between the gas and a liquid element
z	: axial position, distance coordinate
δ	: liquid film thickness
ψ	: surface age distribution function
θ	: dimensionless time

SHORT AND MULTIPLE CHOICE QUESTIONS

1. If S_1 is the slope of the concentration distribution (C–z plot) at the interface for physical absorption of a gas, and S_2 is the same when the absorbed species undergoes a chemical reaction, then

   (i) $S_1 > S_2$ (ii) $S_1 = S_2$ (iii) $S_1 < S_2$

2. Which of the following represents the convective boundary condition for diffusion in a cylinder?

   (i) $C = C_0$ at $r = 0$

   (ii) $\partial C/\partial r = 0$ at $r = 0$

   (iii) $\partial C/\partial r = \xi(C - C_b)$ at $r = r_o$

3. Which of the following conditions is applicable at $z = 0$ for diffusion in a slab of thickness $2L$ ($-L \leq z \leq L$)?

   (i) $C = C_0$ at $z = 0$

   (ii) $\partial C/\partial z = $ infinite at $z = 0$

   (iii) $\partial C/\partial z = 0$ at $z = 0$

4. What is the approximate fraction of the absorbed gas that reacts in the liquid film if the slow reaction regime prevails?

   (i) 0%   (ii) 20%   (iii) 50%

5. Under which of the following conditions the enhancement factor is practically independent of the contact time of a liquid element with the solute gas?

   (i) $k_1 t_c \ll 1$ (ii) $k_1 t_c = 1$ (iii) $k_1 t_c \gg 1$

6. An absorbed gas A reacts with a dissolved solute B; the reaction is first-order in the concentrations of both A and B. The concentration of B in the bulk liquid is 1 molar and that at the gas–liquid interface is 0.95 molar. Then the reaction may be considered to be
   (i) zero order
   (ii) pseudo-first order
   (iii) instantaneous.

7. An absorbed gas A diffuses through a liquid film of thickness 0.1 mm and reacts with a dissolved solute B. The steady-state flux of A at the interface is 5×10^{-7} kmol/(m²·s). If the process corresponds to the slow reaction regime, the flux of A at the end of the film (i.e. at $z = \delta$) is
   (i) 5×10^{-7} (ii) 5×10^{-8} (iii) almost zero

8. If the film theory is applicable and an instantaneous reaction between the absorbed species (A) and the dissolved reactant (B) occurs in the film, the reaction front
   (i) is stationary
   (ii) moves towards the interface
   (iii) moves away from the interface.

9. The species A is absorbed in a liquid with a simultaneous first-order reaction, $R_A = k_1 C_A$, $k_1 = 65$ s^{-1}. Given, $D_A = 1.1 \times 10^{-5}$ cm²/s, and $k_L = 6.2 \times 10^{-3}$ cm/s, calculate the enhancement in the rate of absorption if the Danckwerts' surface renewal theory is applicable.

10. What is the expression for "Hatta number"?
    (i) $\sqrt{k_L/k_G}$ (ii) $\sqrt{D_A/k_1\delta^2}$ (iii) $\sqrt{D_A k_1/k_L^2}$

11. Briefly discuss the usefulness of the theories of mass transfer when a chemical reaction occurs.

12. What are the qualitative criteria of the major regimes of gas absorption with a chemical reaction?

13. Consider Eq. (16.50) for the enhancement factor E_i of an instantaneous reaction. If E_i increases with C_{Ab} but decreases with C_{Ai}, what is the qualitative explanation for this?

14. Identify a few cases of mass transfer with chemical reaction in living systems.

15. Given the following data and information, calculate the fractional increase in the absorption rate of the gas A because of a first-order reaction occurring in the liquid. The film theory is applicable. $k_y = 9.2 \times 10^{-4}$ kmol/(m²)(s)(Δy); $k_x = 3.95 \times 10^{-3}$ kmol/(m²)(s)(Δx); $m = 410$ (in $y = mx^*$); $D_A = 1.5 \times 10^{-9}$ m²/s; $k_1 = 1000$ s^{-1}; $C_{Ab} \approx 0$.

PROBLEMS

16.1 (***Derivation of the equations for a few cases of mass transfer with chemical reaction***)[2] Derive the governing partial differential equation for the concentration distribution of the diffusing species in each of the following cases. Write down the initial and boundary conditions.

(a) Transient diffusion of moisture in a 'finite' cylindrical piece of wood; the gas-phase mass transfer resistance *cannot* be ignored.

(b) A solution containing A is in laminar flow through a tube. The species A is consumed by a catalytic reaction at the tube wall. Consider the steady-state condition.

(c) A liquid is in steady-state laminar flow as a film along a vertical surface coated with a soluble substance, A. The contact time is small.

(d) Solvent extraction of oil from a flake (a thin slice) of oil seed.

16.2 (***Diffusion in a falling film***)[3] Obtain the solution for the concentration distribution in the case of Problem 16.1(c) in terms of error function.

16.3 (***Unsteady state diffusion in a slab***)[2] A slab of wood, 2.5 cm thick, having 15% moisture content is exposed to a stream of air of relative humidity of 60% at 30°C. The equilibrium moisture content of wood under this condition is 9.5%. The diffusivity of moisture in wood is 5.7×10^{-7} cm²/s. Calculate the time required for the (a) average moisture content to drop to 11%, and (b) the maximum local moisture content to drop down to 10%. The surface mass transfer resistance may be neglected.

16.4 (***Unsteady state diffusion in a sphere***)[2] A porous sphere, 2 cm in diameter, soaked in water is placed in a large volume of an aqueous solution of glucose at a concentration of 50 g/litre. The liquid is well-stirred. The sphere is taken out after 10 h and is found to contain 0.05 g glucose. If the porosity of the sphere is 0.25, estimate the diffusivity of glucose in water from the given data. The surface mass transfer coefficient is large.

16.5 (***Determination of diffusivity in a thin slab***)[2] Diethylhexyl phthalate (DEHP) is widely used as plasticizer of PVC. When a PVC container is used to store a liquid, some loss of the plasticizer by diffusion into the liquid occurs. Thus the determination of the diffusivity of a plasticizer in a polymer is practically important. In an experiment, a 5 cm dia thin disk of PVC containing 20% of DEHP is kept suspended in a large volume of ethanol for 100 hours and 50% loss of the plasticizer is found to occur. If the thickness of the disk is 3 mm, calculate the diffusivity of DEHP in PVC.

16.6 (***Unsteady diffusion in a semi-infinite medium***)[2] After intermittent rain for a few days, the moisture content in soil at a place has reached an essentially uniform value of 32% up to a depth of a few metres. What would be the moisture content 0.1 m below the surface and the rate of loss of moisture after three days if it does not rain any more? The equilibrium moisture content of soil at the average condition of ambient air is estimated to be 3.2%; the diffusivity of moisture in soil is 8×10^{-9} m²/s.

16.7 (***Unsteady state diffusion in a semi-infinite medium***)[2] Pure carbon dioxide gas is absorbed in a deep stagnant pool of 'pure' water. Calculate the thickness of the saturated layer of water that corresponds to the amount of CO_2 absorbed in 30 minutes. The diffusivity of CO_2 in water is 1.7×10^{-5} cm²/s.

16.8 (***Rate constant from absorption data in a laminar jet***)[3] A laminar jet apparatus (see Example 3.5) is a simple and useful device for the study of the kinetics of gas–liquid reactions. The hydrodynamics of flow is simple since the jet has a flat velocity profile (called 'rod-like' flow). In an experiment, a laminar jet of 0.2 molar solution of NaOH issues from a 3 mm diameter nozzle at a flow rate of 5 ml/s. The jet length is 6.5 cm.

The rate of absorption of pure CO_2 in the jet is found to be 5×10^{-6} gmol/(cm$^2 \cdot$s). If the reaction is pseudo-first order, calculate the reaction rate constant. The diffusivity of CO_2 in the solution is 1.45×10^{-5} cm^2/s, and the ratio of D_{OH^-} and D_{CO2} is 1.7. The chart given in Figure 16.8 is applicable without much error.

16.9 (*Importance of gas-phase mass transfer resistance*)[3] The solute A is being absorbed from a gas in a liquid with a simultaneous first-order reaction. Given the following data determine if the gas-phase mass transfer resistance is substantial. Partial pressure of A in the bulk gas, $p_{Ab} = 0.2$ atm; Henry's law constant for solubility of the gas ($C_A^* = H_A p_A$), $H_A = 0.05$ kmol/(m^3)(atm); liquid-phase diffusivity of A, $D_A = 1.1 \times 10^{-9}$ m^2/s; gas-phase mass transfer coefficient, $k_G = 4 \times 10^{-4}$ kmol/(m^2)(s)(atm); liquid-phase mass transfer coefficient, $k_L = 9.2 \times 10^{-6}$ m/s; the first-order reaction rate constant, $k_1 = 200$ s^{-1}; concentration of A in the bulk liquid is small.

16.10 (*Enhancement factor for a first-order reversible reaction*)[3] Develop an expression for the enhancement factor for absorption of A in a liquid with an accompanying first-order reversible reaction, $A \rightleftharpoons B$.

16.11 (*Rate of gas absorption for a pseudo-first order reaction*)[3] Chlorination of p-cresol is being done in a stirred gas-liquid contactor by passing chlorine gas (A), diluted with nitrogen, through a p-cresol (B) taken in an inert organic liquid ($C_{Bb} = 1$ kmol/m^3) at 100°C. The partial pressure of chlorine in the gas is 20 kPa; the Henry's law constant is 2.67×10^{-6} kmol/(m^3)(Pa); the reaction is second-order and the rate constant is $k_2 = 190$ m^3/(kmol$\cdot$s); diffusivity of chlorine in the liquid, $D_A = 3 \times 10^{-9}$ m^2/s; the diffusivity ratio, $D_A/D_B = 0.72$. Assuming that the film theory is applicable and the liquid-phase mass transfer coefficient, $k_L = 0.0095$ cm/s, calculate the rate of absorption of chlorine in the liquid.

16.12 (*Concentration profiles near the interface*)[2] Sketch the concentration profiles of A (the species being absorbed) and B (a dissolved reactant) near the gas–liquid interface (p_A, C_A and C_B versus z) for the following cases.

(a) The gas is a mixture of A and a carrier, the reaction of dissolved A with B is instantaneous and occurs at the gas–liquid interface only.

(b) A pure gas A is being absorbed, the reaction between A and B is pretty slow.

(c) A fast second-order reaction between A and B occurs in the film.

(d) A fast pseudo-first order reaction occurs in the film.

16.13 (*Diffusion with surface reaction on a non-porous catalyst particle*)[3] A dilute aqueous solution of A (concentration = 0.5 kmol/m^3) flows through a packed-bed catalytic reactor at a superficial velocity of 2 cm/s. The catalyst particles, 2 mm in diameter, are essentially non-porous. The species A undergoes a first-order chemical reaction ($A \rightarrow B$) at the catalyst surface, $N_A = k' C_A$ [N_A = flux of A to the catalyst surface at steady state, kmol/m$^2 \cdot$s; C_A = concentration of A at the catalyst surface; and k' = first-order reaction rate constant, m/s]. If the concentration of A in the effluent from the reactor is 0.021 kmol/m^3, calculate the reaction rate constant, k'. *Given*: height of the catalyst bed = 3.0 m; density of the solution = 1010 kg/m^3; diffusity of $A = 9 \times 10^{-10}$ m^2/s; viscosity of the solution = 0.9 cP. Use the correlation $j_D = 1.09(Re_p)^{-2/3}$ [see Table 3.3] in order to calculate the mass transfer coefficient.

16.14 (*Solution to the one-dimensional diffusion equation*)   A small amount of an impurity called 'dopant' is deliberately introduced into a semiconductor material during electronic processing in order to control its electrical conductivity (Middleman and Hochberg, 1993). An 'ideal technique' of doping is to deposit a thin layer of the dopant onto the surface of the semiconductor and then raise the temperature to a value suitable for diffusion of the dopant into the material. Consider the one-dimensional diffusion equation [say Eq. (i), Example 16.5]

$$\frac{\partial C}{\partial t} = D\frac{\partial^2 C}{\partial x^2}$$

The boundary conditions may be taken as $\partial C/\partial x = 0$ at $x = 0$ (it implies that the dopant concentration maintains a maximum at the surface at all time), and $C \to 0$ as $x \to \infty$ (i.e. the depth of penetration of the dopant remains small since the diffusivity in the solid phase is very low). The thin layer of dopant applied to the surface at time $t = 0$ contains a finite amount of the substance but presumably at a very high concentration that may be represented by the Dirac delta function, $\delta(x) = \infty$ at $x = 0$, and $\delta(x) = 0$ for $x \neq 0$. If the total amount of the dopant applied to a unit area of the semiconductor is S, the 'initial condition' may be expressed as

$$\int_{-\infty}^{+\infty} C(x).\delta(x)\, dx = S \qquad \text{at } t = 0$$

Show that the solution to the one-dimensional diffusion equation for the dopant concentration subject to the above boundary and initial conditions is given by

$$C = \frac{S}{\sqrt{\pi Dt}}\exp\left(-\frac{x^2}{4Dt}\right)$$

[Note the similarity between the above solution and the solution to the equation of dispersion of the emission from a stack given in the Appendix, Section A.3.]

REFERENCES

Astarita, G., *Mass Transfer with Chemical Reaction*, Elsevier, Amsterdam, 1967.

Carslaw, H.S., and J.C. Jaeger, *Conduction of Heat in Solids*, Oxford Univ. Press, Oxford, 1959.

Crank, J., *The Mathematics of Diffusion*, Claredon Press, Oxford, 1974.

Danckwerts, P.V., *Gas-Liquid Reactions*, McGraw-Hill, New York, 1970.

Doraiswamy, L.K., and M.M. Sharma, *Heterogeneous Reactions: Analysis, Examples and Reactor Design*, John Wiley, 1984.

Dutta, B.K., *Heat Transfer—Principles and Applications*, Prentice-Hall of India, New Delhi, 2001.

Froment, G.F., and K.B. Bischoff, *Chemical Reactor Design and Analysis*, 2nd ed., Wiley, New York, 1990.

Gottschalk, C. et al., *Ozonation of Water and Waste Water*, Wiley VCH, New York, 2000.

Middleman, S., and A.K. Hochberg, *Process Engineering Analysis in Semiconductor Device Fabrication*, McGraw-Hill, New York, 1993.

Myers, G.E., *Analytical Methods in Conduction Heat Transfer*, McGraw-Hill, New York, 1971.

Vergnaud, J.M., *Liquid Transport Processes in Polymeric Materials*, Prentice Hall, New Jersey, 1991.

Wellek, F.M. et al., *Can. J. Chem. Engg.*, 56(1978) 181.

Westerterp, K.R. et al., *Chemical Reactor Design and Operation*, Wiley, New York, 1984.

Wise, D.L., *Handbook of Pharmaceutical Controlled Release Technology*, Marcel Dekker, Boston, 2000.

A.1 VAPOUR–LIQUID EQUILIBRIA

A great majority of the mixtures and solutions processed or separated in industries are 'non-ideal'; the rest are nearly ideal. So far as design of separation processes is concerned, equilibrium data calculated by considering non-ideality of the solution or collected experimentally should be used. A few basic equations on vapour–liquid equilibrium in a non-ideal system have been given in Section 7.1.8. It is clear from Eqs. (7.15) and (7.16) that for a given liquid composition (x_i = mole fraction of the ith component) we have to calculate the fugacity of a species in the vapour phase (ϕ_i^v) and in the liquid phase (ϕ_i^l) in order to find out the equilibrium vapour composition from Eq. (7.15). Alternatively, we can calculate the activity coefficient γ_i and the fugacity coefficient ϕ_i^v for the ith component to determine y_i for a given set of values of x_i from Eq. (7.16). Since both ϕ_i^v and ϕ_i^l depend upon the compositions of the liquid and vapour phases, an iterative method of calculation needs to be adopted. The exercise becomes simpler if the pressure is low to moderate so that we can assume $\phi_i^v = 1$ (ideal vapour phase) and $f_i^0 = P_i^v =$ vapour pressure of component i at the concerned temperature (this is an approximation for the fugacity at 'standard state'). There are broadly two strategies for the calculation of the fugacity coefficients ϕ_i^v and ϕ_i^l and the activity coefficient γ_i. These are:

- Use of an equation of state (EOS), and
- Use of an activity coefficient model of the liquid mixture.

Equation of state approach

Development of an equation to describe the pressure–volume–temperature (P–V–T) relation of real fluids has been a challenge to physicists, physical chemists and chemical engineers since long. The first milestone of success was the van der Waals equation that has a theoretical foundation. It could describe the P–V–T behaviour of many gases reasonably well at low-to-moderate pressures. Its application could be extended to gas mixtures by using suitable mixing rules. A 'mixing rule' expresses the parameters for a mixture in terms of pure component parameters and composition. A rigorous general mixing rule does not exist. The most common choice of mixing rule for a 'molecular size parameter' is a linear combination. For example, the van der Waals constant b_{mix} for a mixture of gases is expressed as

$$b_{\text{mix}} = \sum_{i=1}^{C} y_i b_i; \quad (\underline{C} = \text{number of components in the mixture}) \qquad (1)$$

The 'force parameter' for a mixture, a_{mix}, is taken as quadratic expression.

$$a_{\text{mix}} = \sum_{i=1}^{C} \sum_{j=1}^{C} y_i y_j a_{ij} \quad \text{where } a_{ij} = \sqrt{a_i a_j} \qquad (2)$$

a_i and b_i being the van der Waals constants for the pure component i. A few other mixing rules have been described by Muhlbauer and Raal (1995) and by Prausnitz et al. (1999).

Table A.1   Common equations of state (Seader and Henley, 2006)

	Equation	Adjustable parameters
Ideal gas law	$P = \dfrac{RT}{v}$	None
Generalized equation	$P = \dfrac{ZRT}{v}$	$Z = Z(P_r, T_r, \omega)$
Redlich–Kwong (R–K)equation	$P = \dfrac{RT}{v-b} - \dfrac{a}{(v^2 + bv)\sqrt{T}}$;	$b = 0.08664 RT_c/P_c$ $a = 0.42748 R^2 T_c^{2.5}/P_c$
Soave–Redlich–Kwong (S–R–K equation)	$P = \dfrac{RT}{v-b} - \dfrac{a}{(v^2 + bv)\sqrt{T}}$	$b = 0.08664 RT_c/P_c$ $a = 0.42748\dfrac{R^2 T_c^{2.5}}{P_c}[1 + f_\omega (1 - T_r)^{0.5}]^2$
Peng–Robinson (P–R) equation	$P = \dfrac{RT}{v-b} - \dfrac{a}{v^2 + 2bv - b^2}$	$b = 0.07780 RT_c/P_c$ $a = 0.45724\dfrac{R^2 T_c^2}{P_c}[1 + f_\omega(1 - T_r)^{0.5}]^2$ $f_\omega = 0.37464 + 1.54226\omega - 0.26992\omega^2$

where
v = molar volume
P_c, T_c = critical pressure and temperature
Z = compressibility factor
P_r, T_r = reduced pressure (P/P_c) and temperature (T/T_c)
ω = eccentric factor.

Several equations of state that have much better accuracies (see Table A.1) than the van der Waals equation are now available. These are: the virial equation of state (as a power series in density or reciprocal of molar volume, or as a power series in pressure), the Benedict–Webb–Rubin (B–W–R) equation of state, and the cubic equations of state. A cubic equation of state expresses the molar volume as a cubic equation having coefficients that are functions of temperature and pressure. The first cubic equation of state is of course the van der Waals equation. Two other highly successful cubic equations of state for both gases and liquids are the Soave–Redlich–Kwong (S–R–K) equation (1972) and the Peng–Robinson (P–R) equation (1976).

The B–W–R equation, a modification of the virial equation, works quite well for both gases and liquids but has the disadvantage of having eight coefficients or adjustable constants[†] which are to be found out by experimental $P–V–T$ data fitting.

The S–R–K and P–R equations are successful in describing the $P–V–T$ behaviour of condensed phases (i.e. liquids or highly compressed gases) as well. These have found wide applications in the calculation of thermodynamic properties of fluids and fluid mixtures. A suitable mixing rule has to be used when applied to a mixture.

Fugacity of a component i (ϕ_i^v and ϕ_i^l) can be obtained from any of the above equations of state using the following thermodynamic relation.

$$\ln \phi_i^v = \frac{1}{RT} \int_{V_v}^{\infty} \left[\left(\frac{\partial P}{\partial n_i} \right)_{T,V,nj} - \frac{RT}{V} \right] dV - \ln \frac{PV_v}{nRT} \tag{3}$$

and

$$\ln \phi_i^l = \frac{1}{RT} \int_{V_l}^{\infty} \left[\left(\frac{\partial P}{\partial n_i} \right)_{T,V,nj} - \frac{RT}{V} \right] dV - \ln \frac{PV_l}{nRT} \tag{4}$$

where V = volume of $n \left(= \sum_i n_i \right)$ moles of the mixture (suffix v = vapour, l = liquid); n_i = moles of the component i in the mixture.

In the design of separation processes such as distillation, calculation of bubble point or dew point and, of course, equilibrium phase compositions, x_i and y_i, is routinely required. As stated before, the relation between the last two quantities is sometimes given in terms of the K-value ($K = x_i/y_i$). An iterative computational algorithm of the K-values of the components and the bubble point pressure of a liquid mixture of given composition x_i and temperature T using an equation of state is shown in Figure A.1 (Sandler, 1998).

Activity coefficient approach

In this approach, the activity coefficient γ_i of the species i in solution is calculated. Many liquid phase activity coefficient models and equations have been reported in the literature. A detailed account is available in the standard texts on chemical engineering thermodynamics (for example, Sandler, 1998; Prausnitz et al., 1999). The simplest one is perhaps the van Laar equation. One widely used equation is the Wilson equation which is based on the 'local composition model',

$$\ln \gamma_i = 1 - \ln \left(\sum_{j=1}^{C} x_j \Lambda_{ij} \right) - \sum_{k=1}^{C} \left(\frac{x_k \Lambda_{ki}}{\displaystyle\sum_{j=1}^{C} x_j \Lambda_{kj}} \right) \tag{5}$$

where Λ_{ij} is the Wilson's parameter for the i-j pair, $\Lambda_{ii} = 1$, and $\Lambda_{ij} \neq \Lambda_{ji}$. These are 'adjustable binary parameters' to be determined by fitting of experimental binary vapour–liquid equilibrium data.

[†] An adjustable constant is a parameter in an equation (for example, 'a' or 'b' in the van der Waals equation) whose value is determined by fitting experimental data. To obtain the best fit or to minimize the error, a suitable 'optimization' technique is used.

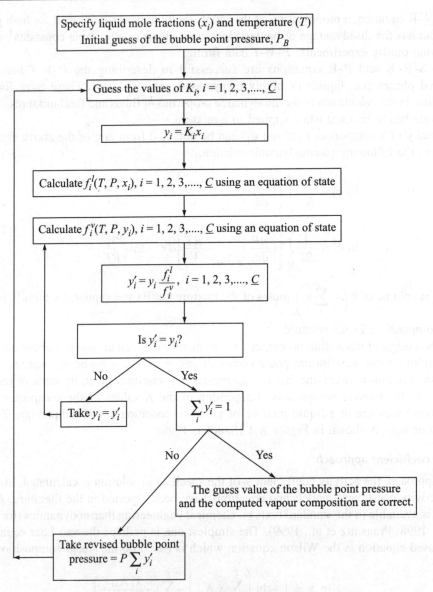

Figure A.1 A computational algorithm.

An extension of the Wilson model to describe equilibrium in a system that involves a partially miscible liquid phase (a partially miscible liquid system is pretty common in hydrocarbon processing when there is moisture in the gas; the condensate consists of a heterogeneous mixture of hydrocarbons and water) is the NRTL (Non-Random Two-Liquid) model. A theoretically sound model based on the principles of statistical mechanics is the UNIQUAC (UNIversal QUAsiChemical) model. It can predict the vapour–liquid equilibria of non-ideal mixtures but contains adjustable parameters that have to be estimated by experimental data fitting. A more convenient strategy of VLE calculation was developed later on that uses the group contribution method called UNIFAC method (UNIquac Functional group Activity Coefficient, Prausnitz et al., 1999). Experimental binary data are *not* required.

Computational algorithms for bubble point pressure (or temperature) and equilibrium composition using an activity coefficient model are available in the literature(Muhlbauer and Raal, 1995). These can also be calculated using a suitable software such as ASPEN or HYSYS. A simple example of bubble point and equilibrium calculation of a non-ideal binary mixture is given below.

EXAMPLE A.1 The activity coefficients of a mixture of water (1) and acetic acid (2) can be correlated by the following simple equations.

$$\ln \gamma_1 = 0.806\,x_2^2 \quad \text{and} \quad \gamma_2 = 0.533\,x_1^2$$

(a) Calculate the bubble point of and the vapour composition in equilibrium with an equimolar liquid mixture of water and acetic acid.

(b) One kilomole of the above mixture is flash-distilled at 1 atm total pressure to yield 0.3 kmol vapour and 0.7 kmol liquid product. Determine the compositions of the products.

The vapour phase may be assumed to be ideal. Vapour pressures of the compounds may be calculated using the Antoine equation (see Table 7.2).

Solution

Consider Eq. (7.16), $\phi_i^v y_i P = x_i \gamma_i P_i^v$. Since the vapour phase is ideal, we put $\phi_i^v = 1$. For the binary mixture,

$$x_1 \gamma_1 P_1^v = x_1 \exp(0.806\,x_2^2)P_1^v = y_1 P = p_1 \tag{i}$$
$$x_2 \gamma_2 P_2^v = x_2 \exp(0.533\,x_1^2)P_2^v = y_2 P = p_2 \tag{ii}$$
$$x_1 \exp(0.806\,x_2^2)P_1^v + x_2 \exp(0.533\,x_1^2)P_2^v = p_1 + p_2 = P \tag{iii}$$

The above equation can be used to calculate the *equilibrium data.*

(a) Take $x_1 = 0.5 = x_2$. Assume a temperature, calculate P_1^v and P_2^v and check if Eq. (iii) is satisfied.

From Table 7.2,

$$\ln P_1^v \text{ (mm Hg)} = 18.5882 - \frac{3984.92}{233.43 + \theta°C} \quad \text{and} \quad \ln P_2^v \text{ (mm Hg)} = 18.47233 - \frac{4457.83}{258.46 + \theta°C}$$

Trial temperature, $\theta°C$	P_1^v, mm Hg	P_2^v, mm Hg	p_1	p_2	$P = p_1 + p_2$
101°C	790.5	433.1	483.5	247.4	730.9
103°C	848.5	463.8	518.9	265	783.9

Calculate the bubble point ($P = 760$ mm Hg) by *interpolation* between the above two temperatures, 101° and 103°C.

$$\theta = 101 + \left(\frac{760 - 730.9}{783.9 - 730.9}\right)(103 - 101) = 102.01, \text{ say } \boxed{102°C}.$$

At 102°C, $P_1^v = 819.1$ mm Hg; $P_2^v = 448.2$ mm Hg. Partial pressures, $p_1 = 501$ mm Hg, $p_2 = 256.0$ mm Hg

Equilibrium vapour composition, $y_1^* = p_1/P = 501/760 = \boxed{0.66}$; $y_2^* = \boxed{0.34}$

(b) Flash vaporization of 30 mol% of an equimolar mixture of water and acetic acid.

Use Eq. (7.30), $\qquad -\dfrac{W}{D} = \dfrac{x_D - z_F}{x_W - z_F};\quad z_F = 0.5,\ D = 0.3,\ W = 0.7$ kmol.

x_D = mole fraction of the more volatile (water) in the distillate, x_W = mole fraction of the more volatile (water) in the bottom product. Call $x_D = y_1^*$, $x_W = x_1$

$$y_1^* = p_1/P = x_1\gamma_1 P_1^v/P = x_1 \exp(0.806\,x_2^2)P_1^v/P;\quad y_2^* = p_2/P = x_2 \exp(0.533 x_1^2)P_2^v/P$$

Find x_1 and x_2 by trial such that

$$-\frac{W}{D} = -\frac{0.7}{0.3} = \frac{[x_1 \exp(0.806\,x_2^2)P_1^v/P] - 0.5}{x_1 - 0.5} \tag{iv}$$

Calculation steps: Assume a value of x_1 and put the value of x_2 ($= 1 - x_1$) and P in Eq. (iv); calculate P_1^v from Eq. (iv); calculate the corresponding temperature, θ; calculate P_2^v; calculate y_1^* and y_2^* and check if $y_1^* + y_2^* = 1$.

x_1	x_2	P_1^v, mm Hg	$\theta°C$	P_2^v, mm Hg	y_1^*	y_2^*	$y = y_1^* + y_2^*$
0.4	0.6	771.7	100.3°C	423.1	0.543	0.364	0.907
0.35	0.65	871.7	103.8°C	476.1	0.564	0.435	0.999

Incidentally the trial value $x_1 = 0.35$ is found to be appropriate.

Composition of the vapour product, $y_1^* = \boxed{0.564}$, and that of the liquid, $x_1 = \boxed{0.435}$.

A.2 *K*-VALUES OF HYDROCARBONS

The equilibrium vaporization ratio or *K*-value of a hydrocarbon can be read from the DePriester Chart [Figures 7.8(a) and (b)]. An explicit expression for *K* as a function of temperature and

Table A.2 Coefficients of the McWilliams equation for *K*-values

Compound	a_1	a_2	a_3	b_1	b_2	b_3
Methane	−292860	0	8.2445	−0.8951	59.8465	0
Ethylene	−600076.87	0	7.90595	−0.84677	42.94594	0
Ethane	−687248.25	0	7.90694	−0.88600	49.02654	0
Propylene	−923484.687	0	7.71725	−0.87871	47.67624	0
Propane	−970688.562	0	7.15059	−0.76984	0	6.90224
iso-Butane	−1166846	0	7.72668	−0.92213	0	0
n-Butane	−1280557	0	7.94986	−0.96455	0	0
iso-Pentane	−1481583	0	7.58071	−0.93159	0	0
n-Pentane	−1524891	0	7.33129	−0.89143	0	0
n-Hexane	−1778901	0	6.96783	−0.84634	0	0
n-Heptane	−2013803	0	6.52914	−0.79543	0	0
n-Octane	0	−7646.816	12.4846	−0.73152	0	0
n-Nonane	−255194	0	5.68313	−0.67818	0	0
n-Decane	0	−9760.457	13.80354	−0.71470	0	0

pressure was developed by McWilliams (1973) by fitting the values obtained from the chart.

$$\ln K = \frac{a_1}{T^2} + \frac{a_2}{T} + a_3 + b_1 \ln P + \frac{b_2}{P^2} + \frac{b_3}{P} \tag{6}$$

where T = temperature in degree Rankine, and P = pressure in psia. The constants of the McWilliams equation are given in Table A.2. The error remains within 5% in most cases. It is convenient to use this equation for computer calculations of distillation problems.

Rachford–Rice equation for flash calculation

Although flash calculations can proceed by solution of Eqs. (7.34) to (7.36) using K-values, it is established that Eq. (7.40), called the Rachford–Rice equation, has excellent convergence characteristics (Wankat, 1988). In order to develop the equation, we recall the Newton's technique of solution of the algebraic equation, $\psi(\zeta) = 0$. If $\psi_j = \psi(\zeta_j)$ is the value of the function in the jth trial (when $\zeta = \zeta_j$), its value for the $(j + 1)$th trial can be obtained by the classical Newton convergence technique.

$$\psi_{j+1} - \psi_j = (\zeta_{j+1} - \zeta_j)\left[\frac{d\psi}{d\zeta}\right]_j \tag{7}$$

We want to select ζ_{j+1} such that $\psi_{j+1} = 0$, $\Rightarrow$ $\zeta_{j+1} = \zeta_j - \dfrac{\psi_j}{(d\psi/d\zeta)_j}$ \hfill (8)

Equation (7.40) is now differentiated w.r.t. ζ (the subscript F of z_{Fi} is dropped).

$$\psi = \sum_{i=1}^{C} \frac{(K_i - 1)z_i}{[1 + (K_i - 1)\zeta_j]} \qquad \Rightarrow \qquad \frac{d\psi}{d\zeta} = -\sum_{i=1}^{C} \frac{(K_i - 1)^2 z_i}{[1 + (K_i - 1)\zeta]^2}$$

Substituting in Eq. (8),

$$\zeta_{j+1} = \zeta_j + \frac{\displaystyle\sum_{i=1}^{C} \frac{(K_i - 1)z_i}{[1 + (K_i - 1)\zeta_j]}}{\displaystyle\sum_{i=1}^{C} \frac{(K_i - 1)^2 z_i}{[1 + (K_i - 1)\zeta_j]^2}} \tag{9}$$

The trial ends when the value of $\psi(\zeta)$ is sufficiently close to zero. Application of the technique is illustrated by the following example.

EXAMPLE A.2 Twenty kilomoles of a feed mixture consisting of 15 mol% ethane(1), 20 mol% propane(2), 40 mol% n-butane(3), and 25 mol% n-pentane(4) is flash-distilled at a temperature of 35°C and a pressure of 2.5 bar(gauge) in a flash drum. Calculate the moles of the vapour and liquid products and their composition.

Solution
Given: P = 2.5 bar gauge = 3.513 bar absolute = 351.3 kPa; T = 35°C.
From the De-Priester chart, Figure 7.8(a),

$$K_1 = 8.85; \qquad K_2 = 5.05; \qquad K_3 = 0.92; \quad \text{and} \quad K_4 = 0.3.$$

Put the K-values and the feed mole fractions ($z_1 = 0.15$, $z_2 = 0.2$, $z_3 = 0.4$, $z_4 = 0.25$) in Eq. (9) to get

$$\zeta_{j+1} = \zeta_j + \cfrac{\cfrac{(8.85-1)\,(0.15)}{1+(8.85-1)\zeta_j} + \cfrac{(5.05-1)\,(0.2)}{1+(5.05-1)\zeta_j} + \cfrac{(0.92-1)\,(0.4)}{1+(0.92-1)\zeta_j} + \cfrac{(0.3-1)\,(0.25)}{1+(0.3-1)\zeta_j}}{\cfrac{(8.85-1)^2\,(0.15)}{[1+(8.85-1)\zeta_j]^2} + \cfrac{(5.05-1)^2\,(0.2)}{[1+(5.05-1)\zeta_j]^2} + \cfrac{(0.92-1)^2\,(0.4)}{[1+(0.92-1)\zeta_j]^2} + \cfrac{(0.3-1)^2\,(0.25)}{[1+(0.3-1)\zeta_j]^2}}$$

Take $\zeta_j = \zeta_1 = 0.2$ as the initial guess. Putting $\zeta_j = \zeta_1 = 0.2$ in the above equation,

$$\zeta_2 = \zeta_1 + 0.261 = 0.2 + 0.261 = 0.461. \quad \text{For } \zeta = \zeta_2 = 0.461,\ \psi(\zeta_2) = 0.246.$$

$$\zeta_3 = \zeta_2 + \cfrac{\cfrac{(8.85-1)\,(0.15)}{1+(8.85-1)\zeta_2} + \cfrac{(5.05-1)\,(0.2)}{1+(5.05-1)\zeta_2} + \cfrac{(0.92-1)\,(0.4)}{1+(0.92-1)\zeta_2} + \cfrac{(0.3-1)\,(0.25)}{1+(0.3-1)\zeta_2}}{\cfrac{(8.85-1)^2\,(0.15)}{[1+(8.85-1)\zeta_2]^2} + \cfrac{(5.05-1)^2\,(0.2)}{[1+(5.05-1)\zeta_2]^2} + \cfrac{(0.92-1)^2\,(0.4)}{[1+(0.92-1)\zeta_2]^2} + \cfrac{(0.3-1)^2\,(0.25)}{[1+(0.3-1)\zeta_2]^2}}$$

$$= 0.684$$

After the next cycle of calculation, $\zeta_4 = 0.709$ and $\psi\,(0.709) = -0.007$ which is reasonable. The moles of vapour and liquid products can now be calculated.

Take $\qquad\qquad \zeta = D/(W+D) = 0.709, \qquad$ and $\qquad D+W = 20$

$\Rightarrow \qquad D = (0.709)(20) = 14.18, \qquad$ and $\qquad W = 5.82; \qquad$ and $\qquad W/D = 0.4104$

Use Eq. (7.34) to calculate the vapour composition, and Eq. (7.35) to calculate the liquid composition.

$$y_{D1} = 0.2022, \qquad y_{D2} = 0.2609, \qquad y_{D3} = 0.3901, \qquad y_{D4} = 0.1500; \quad \text{and} \quad \sum_i y_{Di} = 1.0032$$

$$x_{W1} = 0.0228, \qquad x_{W2} = 0.0516, \qquad x_{W3} = 0.4241, \qquad x_{W4} = 0.4963; \quad \text{and} \quad \sum_i x_{Wi} = 0.9948$$

There are two variables in the Rachford–Rice equation—the fraction vapour product ζ, and the K-values. The K-value of a component, in turn, depends upon temperature and pressure. If the temperature and pressure are known (as in the above problem), the K-values are fixed and the fraction vaporized, ζ, can be calculated as shown above. If, on the other hand, ζ and either temperature or pressure of the flush drum are given, an iterative method of calculation is required.

A.3 DISPERSION IN A FLOW FIELD

The phenomenon of spreading of a solute in a medium in motion (i.e. in a flow field) as a result of the combined effects of convection and molecular diffusion is called dispersion. The dispersion flux is expressed by a Fick's law type equation (flux $= -D_E dC/dz$). While we developed the differential mass balance equation for a packed bed [Section 6.4.1 for contact of a gas and a liquid; Section 6.82, Eq. (6.58), for vapour–liquid contact where the liquid is in axial flow and the vapour is in cross flow; or Section 12.10.1, Eq. (12.31), for flow of a solute-laden gas through a packed bed of adsorbent], the fluid phase was assumed to be in plug flow (or rod-like flow, i.e. the fluid has a flat velocity profile). Even when the fluid is in streamline flow (such as laminar flow through a pipe), the variation of the axial velocity over a cross-section itself causes a degree of mixing and dispersion. This occurs because the fluid elements near the centre-line move faster than those near the wall giving rise to mixing. More than fifty years ago, G. I. Taylor suggested in a seminal paper (Taylor, 1953) that the mixing in laminar flow can be expressed in terms of a Taylor dispersion coefficient that measures the dispersion relative to an observer moving with the average velocity of the fluid.

The phenomenon does not remain amenable to theoretical analysis when the flow is turbulent or the fluid passes through a packed bed of solids or through a fluidized bed, a bubble column, etc. unless drastic simplifying assumptions are made. If the average bulk velocity is one-dimensional, the mixing process is normally described by an empirical dispersion coefficient, D_E, that *lumps* into it the effects of molecular diffusion, turbulent or eddy diffusion, and the convective diffusion caused by non-uniformity of the velocity over the cross-section. The transport by dispersion is superimposed on convection by idealized plug flow of the fluid. In some situations there may be radial mixing as well. But the effect of radial mixing or dispersion becomes small if the ratio of bed diameter to length is small or the fluid velocity is large. Dispersion is a much faster process than molecular diffusion. The dispersion coefficient may be even 10^4 to 10^{10} times larger than molecular diffusivity.

One dimensional axial dispersion equation

A general one-dimensional model for axial dispersion in a packed bed of adsorbent has been developed in Section 12.10.1. The transient material balance equation, [Eq. (12.28)] is applicable in other situations as well with appropriate modifications. For example, if dissolution of a solid occurs in a packed bed or a species undergoes reaction in a packed bed of catalyst, the third term on the left side of Eq. (12.28) needs to be modified accordingly. One simple case is removal of a species by a first-order chemical reaction in a tubular reactor.

$$\frac{\partial C}{\partial t} = D_E \frac{\partial^2 C}{\partial z^2} - u \frac{\partial C}{\partial z} - k'C \tag{10}$$

The equation may be derived by making a differential mass balance over a thin slice of the reactor. While it is easy to set the initial condition (for example, at $t = 0$, $C = C_i$ for all values of z, i.e. the initial concentration is uniform throughout), the boundary conditions became a matter of controversy in the 1950s. The following boundary conditions, called the 'Danckwerts' boundary conditions' [Danckwerts, P. V., *Chem Eng. Sci*, 2 (1953) 1] are now well-accepted.

$$z = 0, \qquad uC_i = uC_{i,z\to 0+} - D_E\left(\frac{\partial C}{\partial z}\right)_{z\to 0+} \tag{11}$$

$$z = L, \qquad \left(\frac{\partial C}{\partial z}\right) = 0 \tag{12}$$

The first boundary condition, Eq. (11), means that at $z = 0$, rate of input = rate of convection + rate of dispersion. The second boundary condition implies that no more dispersion occurs at $z = L$, or dispersion flux is zero, $D_E\left(\frac{\partial C}{\partial z}\right) = 0 \Rightarrow \left(\frac{\partial C}{\partial z}\right) = 0$. Solutions to the above equation, Eq. (10), subject to the boundary conditions, Eq. (11) and (12), are available.

Dispersion plays an important role in separation equipment such as packed columns and tray towers as well. A large number of experimental and theoretical studies have been reported. Both axial and radial dispersion have been studied. It is to be noted that the fluid velocity in a packed tower has a temporal radial component that occurs because of randomness of the packing— although the average radial velocity is zero unless there is channelling. Dispersion, both axial and radial, significantly affects the performance and efficiency of a packed bed—whether it is used for absorption, adsorption, liquid extraction and distillation or a chemical reaction. A large volume of literature on theoretical and experimental investigations in a packed bed and in other flow geometries is available (see for example, Gunn, 1987; Rexwinkel, 1995).

Axial dispersion in the liquid on a distillation tray

An expression for the tray efficiency was developed in Chapter 6 assuming that the liquid is well-mixed. While this assumption is approximately true for a small diameter column, it is grossly inappropriate in a big column where the liquid flow path from the downcomer to the weir is large and the liquid concentration varies substantially. Axial dispersion in the liquid is an important factor to be considered in the determination of the efficiency of a tray. A simple illustration of how axial dispersion can be taken into account to relate the point efficiency with the Murphree tray efficiency is shown below.

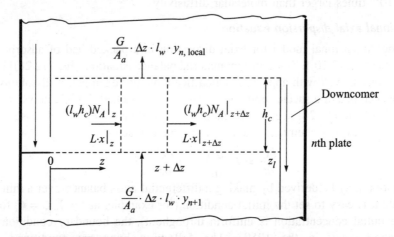

Figure A.2 Mass balance on a tray with axial dispersion.

Figure A.2 shows an elementary section of a tray in which the liquid is in crossflow. The element has a width of Δz and breadth l_w (assumed constant). We make a differential mass balance of the solute in the liquid phase considering convection, axial dispersion and absorption from the gas bubbling through the liquid. Let us use the following notations: L = molar flow rate of the liquid; G = molar flow rate of the gas; l_w = weir length; h_c = clear liquid height on the tray; x, y = mole fractions of the solute in the liquid and the gas respectively; A_a = active area of a tray; $l_w.h_c$ = area available for crossflow of the liquid on a tray. Let us write down the terms relating to solute transport on the tray.

$L \cdot x|_z$ and $L.x|_{z+\Delta z}$ = rates of input and output of the solute by convection at z and at $z + \Delta z$

$(h_c \cdot l_w) \cdot N_A|_z$ and $(h_c \cdot l_w) \cdot N_A|_{z+\Delta z}$ = rates of transport by axial dispersion at z and at $z + \Delta z$

$$\frac{G}{A_a}(l_w \cdot h_c)(y_{n+1} - y_{n,\text{local}}) = \text{net rate of absorption of the solute}$$

Now we make a steady state material balance of the solute over the element, divide throughout by Δz and take the limit $\Delta z \to 0$. Also the dispersion flux is expressed as $N_A = -D_E \dfrac{dC}{dz} = -D_E \overline{C} \dfrac{dx}{dz}$, where D_E is the axial dispersion coefficient and $\overline{C}$ is the total molar concentration of the liquid.

$$D_E \overline{C} \cdot (l_w \cdot h_c) \frac{d^2 x}{dz^2} - L \frac{dx}{dz} + \frac{G}{A_a} \cdot l_w (y_{n+1} - y_{n,\text{local}}) = 0$$

Let us define the following quantities: z_l = downcomer to weir distance (= length of the flow path of the liquid); u = linear velocity of the liquid = $(L/\overline{C})(1/l_w h_c)$; Pe = Peclet number = $z_l u/D_E$; $\overline{z} = z/z_l$; the point efficiency, $E_{OG} = (y_{n+1} - y_{n,\text{local}})/(y_{n+1} - y^*_{n,\text{local}})$. Further, a linear equilibrium relation, $y^* = mx$ is assumed and it is noted that $x_{n,\text{local}} = x$.

$$\Rightarrow \qquad \frac{1}{\text{Pe}} \frac{d^2 x}{d\overline{z}^2} - \frac{dx}{d\overline{z}} + \lambda \cdot E_{OG}(x^*_{n+1} - x) = 0; \qquad \lambda = mG/L \tag{13}$$

Final solution of the above equation subject to the boundary conditions: $\overline{z} = 1$, $x = x_n$, and $dx/d\overline{z} = 0$ can be expressed in the form

$$\frac{E_{MV}}{E_{OG}} = \frac{1 - \exp\left[-(\eta + \text{Pe})\right]}{(\eta + \text{Pe})\left[1 + (\eta + \text{Pe})/\eta\right]} + \frac{\exp(\eta) - 1}{\eta\left[1 + \eta/(\eta + \text{Pe})\right]}; \qquad \eta = \frac{\text{Pe}}{2}\left[\left(1 + \frac{4\lambda E_{OG}}{\text{Pe}}\right)^{0.5} - 1\right] \tag{14}$$

The above equation can be used to calculate the Murphree efficiency (E_{MV}) if the point efficiency (E_{OG}) and other parameters are known.

Atmospheric dispersion

Another important application of the theory of dispersion is in the spreading of pollutants discharged in air, natural water or ground water. A lot of theoretical and experimental work has been done in this area (Clark, 1996; Heinsohn and Kabel, 1999) and computational algorithms and softwares are now readily available to estimate the effects of discharge of a pollutant on the neighbouring regions. The equations of dispersion of a pollutant emitted at a stack are briefly discussed below.

Figure A.3 shows a buoyant stream of pollutant leaving a stack as a 'plume'. The stack height is h (the height H in the figure is called the 'effective stack height') and the wind velocity, $U = U(z)$, is assumed to be a function of elevation from the ground level, z. The emitted gas is transported downwind (x-direction) by the air with simultaneous dispersion in the y- and z-directions by molecular and eddy diffusion. Since the material is carried by the wind in the x-direction, dispersion effect in that direction is often neglected. The partial differential equation for the concentration distribution of the pollutant is given by

$$U(z)\frac{\partial C}{\partial x} = D_{Ey}\frac{\partial^2 C}{\partial y^2} + D_{Ez}\frac{\partial^2 C}{\partial z^2} \tag{15}$$

The following boundary conditions apply.

$C \to \infty$ at $x = 0$ (this means that the pollutant concentration is very high at the stack)
$C = 0$ at $x, y, z \to \infty$ (very low concentration at a large distance from the stack)

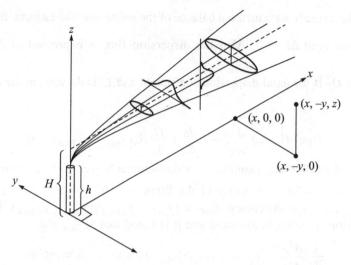

Figure A.3 Dispersion in a plume (*Source:* Masters, G.M., *Introduction to Environmental Engineering and Science*, 2nd ed., 1998)

$\dfrac{\partial C}{\partial z} = 0$ at $z = 0$ (no dispersion flux at the ground level)

The solution of Eq. (15) can be obtained in the flowing form for a constant wind velocity, U.

$$C(x, y, z) = \frac{\dot{m}}{2\pi x (D_{E_y} \cdot D_{E_z})^{1/2}} \exp\left[-\frac{U}{4x}\left(\frac{y^2}{D_{E_y}} + \frac{z^2}{D_{E_z}} \right) \right] \tag{16}$$

Here $\dot{m}$ is the rate of emission of the pollutant at the stack, kg/s.

The most important indicator of the effect of dispersion is the ground level concentration of a pollutant (i.e. at $z = 0$) in the neighbouring regions since this affects all the living organisms. This can be calculated from the above solution, Eq. (16). Standard techniques and charts are available for this purpose (Heinsohn and Kabel, 1999).

The dispersion phenomenon is also important in spreading of a pollutant or a solute in subsoil water (in the aquifer). A brief but comprehensive description is available in Domenico and Schwartz (1998).

REFERENCES

Clark, M. M., *Transport Modeling for Environmental Engineers and Scientists*, John Wiley, 1996.

Domenico, P. A., and F. W. Schwartz, *Physical and Chemical Hydrogeology*, John Wiley, 2nd ed., 1998.

Gunn, D.J., 'Axial and radial dispersion in fixed beds', *Chem. Eng. Sci.*, *42* (1987) 363–373.

Heinsohn, R. J., and R. L. Kabel, *Sources and Control of Air Pollution*, Prentice Hall, NJ, 1999

McWilliams, M. L., 'An equation to relate K-factors to pressure and temperature', *Chem. Eng.*, Oct 29, 1973, 138–141.

Muhlbauer, A.L., and J.D. Raal, 'Computational and thermodynamic interpretation of high pressure vapour–liquid equilibrium—a review', *Chem. Eng. J.*, *60* (1995) 1–29.

Peng, D.Y., and D.B. Robinson, 'A new two-constant equation of state', *Ind. Eng. Chem. Fundamentals*, *15* (1976) 59–64

Prausnitz, J. M. et al., *Molecular Thermodynamics of Fluid-Phase Equilibria*, Prentice Hall, NJ. 3rd ed., 1999.

Rexwinkel, G. et al., 'Mass transfer in packed beds at low Peclet numbers – wrong experiments or wrong interpretation?' *Chem Eng. Sci.*, *52* (1997) 3995–4003.

Sandler, S.I., *Chemical and Engineering Thermodynamics*, John Wiley, 3rd ed., 1998.

Soave, G., 'Equilibrium constants from a modified Redlich-Kwong equation of state', *Chem Eng. Sci.*, 27 (1972) 1197–1203.

Taylor, G.I., 'Dispersion of a soluble matter in solvent flowing slowly through a pipe', *Proc. Royal Soc. Lond.*, *A219* (1953) 186–203.

Wankat, P.C., *Equilibriun Staged Separations*, Butterworths, 1988.

Seader, J.D., and E.J. Henley, *Separation Process Principles*, 2nd ed., 2006, John Wiley, New York.

Answers/Hints to Selected Questions and Problems

CHAPTER 2

Short and Multiple Choice Questions

1. Diffusion of an ionic species in a bed of an ion-exchange resin, diffusion in the pores of a catalyst pellet, diffusion through a membrane for gas separation.
2. If the molecular weights of the components are equal.
8. At the liquid–gas interface.
9. At $z = z_2$.
11. Yes. It follows from the Cauchy's mean value theorem.
12. The flux for case (i) is larger, if all the parameters remain the same. *Reason*: molecules of B diffusing in the opposite direction offer more 'resistance' to diffusion of molecules of component A.
14. The flux will be very high; pseudo-steady state condition will not be applicable.
16. (a) (ii).   (b) (i).   (c) (iii).   (d) (i).   (e) (i).   (f) (i).   (g) (iii).
    (h) (iii).   (i) (iii).   (j) (ii).   (k) (ii).   (l) (ii). (m) (ii).   (n) (i).
    (o) (i).   (p) (iii).   (q) (iii).   (r) (iii).   (s) (ii).   (t) (iii).   (u) (i).
    (v) (ii).   (w) (ii).   (x) (i).   (y) (ii).   (z) (ii).

Problems

2.1 $N_A = 0.116$ kg/m^2·h

2.2 Stagnant air-film thickness = 5.4 mm

2.3 $9{\cdot}602 \times 10^{-2}$ kg/m^2·h

2.4 (a) $N_A = 4.488 \times 10^{-5}$ kmol/m^2·s

     (b) At 4 mm from the acid surface, take $z = 10 - 4 = 6$ mm = 0.006 m.

        Put $N_A = 4.488 \times 10^{-5}$, $z = 0.006$. $P = 400$ mm Hg, and

p_{A0} = 160 mm Hg in Eq. (2.28) to get p_A = 73.9 mm Hg.

Use Eq. (2.24) to calculate the partial pressure gradient (dp_A/dz) at the position where p_A = 73.9 mm Hg (use the steady-state flux, N_A, calculated before). Partial pressure gradient, dP_A/dz = −22.2 bar/m.

(c) At the acid surface, p_A = 0, and the flux due to 'bulk flow' = $(N_A + N_B)$. p_A/P = 0, and the entire flux (4.488 × 10⁻⁵ kmol/s²·s) occurs due to 'molecular diffusion'. At the gas-side end of the film, z = 0, p_A = 0.2133 bar; bulk flow term = 1.796 × 10⁻⁵ kmol/m²·s, and molecular diffusion term = 2.692 × 10⁻⁵ kmol/m²·s

2.5 Calculate the diffusivity of camphor(A) in air(B) using the Fuller's equation (2.57).

$$\left(\sum v\right)_A = 202.16, \qquad \left(\sum v\right)_B = 20.1$$

M_A = 152.13, M_B = 28.9, T = 298 K, P = 1 atm $\Rightarrow$ D = 5.644 × 10⁻⁶ m²/s

Flux = 2.685 × 10⁻⁷ kmol/m²·s; sublimation time = 5.4 h.

2.6 Flux of CO_2 midway in the film = −6.15 × 10⁻⁵ kmol/m²·s; diffusion velocity, v_d = −5.9 × 10⁻³ m/s.

2.7 (a) Molar flux of N_2 from vessel 1 to 2 w.r.t. a stationary observer, N_A = −7.824 × 10⁻⁶ kmol/m²·s. Velocity of the N_2 molecules at the vessel 1 end, u_{A1} = $\dfrac{N_A}{C_{A1}}$ = −0.00197 m/s; at the vessel 2 end, u_{A2} = −2.46 × 10⁻⁴ m/s; mean velocity of the nitrogen molecules = −0.00111 m/s = velocity of the observer (u_o). Molar flux of N_2 w.r.t. this observer

$$= (u_A - u_o)C_A = N_A - u_o \cdot p_A/RT; \ p_A = (p_{A1} + p_{A2})/2 = 0.45 \text{ bar}$$

midway in the film (since the partial pressure distribution is linear in equimolar counterdiffusion).

Required flux = 1.19 × 10⁻⁵ kmol/m²·s from vessel 1 to 2.

(b) Use Eq. (2.79) to calculate the rate of transport if the tube is tapered. r_1 = 0.005 m, r_2 = 0.01 m, rate of transport, W = −1.23 × 10⁻⁹ kmol/s.

(c) The same as in part (b).

(d) Use the theoretical approach of Section 2.5.1. Integrate Eq. (2.49) to get

$$\ln\left(\frac{p_{A10} - p_{A20}}{p'_{A1} - p'_{A2}}\right) = \frac{aD_{AB}}{l}\left(\frac{1}{v_1} + \frac{1}{v_2}\right) \cdot t$$

p_{A10} = 0.1 bar, p_{A20} = 0.8 bar (initial values); a = 7.853 × 10⁻⁵ m²; p'_{A1} = $2p_{A10}$ = 0.2 bar. Calculate p'_{A2} by material balance.

$V_1 C_{A10} + V_2 C_{A20} = V_1 C'_{A1} + V_2 C'_{A2}$ ($C = p/RT$) $\Rightarrow$ p'_{A2} = 0.633 bar.

Put the values in the integrated equation. Time, t = 11.3 h.

p_A midway of the tube after 20 h = 0.4 bar (with the same pseudo-steady state approximation).

2.8 The rate of reaction (per unit area of the catalyst surface):

(a) $\dfrac{D_{AB}}{RT\delta}(P - p_{B0})$;   (b) $\dfrac{2D_{AB}P}{RT\delta} \ln \dfrac{2P}{P + p_{B0}}$;   (c) $\dfrac{2D_{AB}P}{RT\delta} \ln \dfrac{3P - p_{B0}}{2P}$

2.9 Time required = 36.38 h

2.10 Reaction: $2CO(1) + O_2(2) \rightarrow 2CO_2(3)$

Flux relation: $N_1 = 2N_2 = -N_3$; C = total concentration = P/RT.

Use Eq. (2.37) to write the following flux equations.

$$-C \frac{dy_1}{dz} = N_1 \left(\frac{y_2}{D_{12}} + \frac{y_3}{D_{13}} \right) - y_1 N_1 \left(\frac{1}{2D_{12}} - \frac{1}{D_{13}} \right)$$

$$-C \frac{dy_2}{dz} = \frac{N_1}{2} \left(\frac{y_1}{D_{21}} + \frac{y_3}{D_{23}} \right) - y_2 N_1 \left(\frac{1}{D_{21}} - \frac{1}{D_{23}} \right)$$

Make 'temperature correction' to the given diffusivities.

At the given temperature, $D_{12} = 0.363$, $D_{23} = 0.368$ and $D_{12} = 0.49$ cm^2/s.

Assume $D_{ij} = D_{ji}$ and use the mole fraction relation $y_1 + y_2 + y_3 = 1$.

$$-\frac{C}{N_1} \cdot \frac{dy_1}{dz} = 2.755 - 1.02 y_1 - 0.714 y_2$$

and

$$-\frac{C}{N_1} \cdot \frac{dy_2}{dz} = 1.359 - 0.338 y_1 - 0.682 y_2$$

At $z = 0$ (bulk gas), $y_1 = 0.2$, $y_2 = 0.2$

At $z = \delta = 0.8$ mm (catalyst surface), $y_1 = 0$, $y_2 = ?$, $y_3 = ?$

Use the Laplace transform technique to solve the above pair of equation. Substitute $\xi = zN_1/C$.

Solution: $y_1(\xi) = 2 - 1.7436 \exp(1.3705\xi) - 0.0564 \exp(0.3315\xi)$

If the reaction is instantaneous, $y_1 = 0$ at the catalyst surface $\Rightarrow \xi = 0.0787 = \delta N_1/C$; $\delta = 0.008$ m, $C = 2.329 \times 10^{-5}$ gmol/cm^3 $\Rightarrow N_1 = 2.29 \times 10^{-5}$ gmol/cm^2·s = rate of formation of CO_2/cm^2 area.

2.11 Rate of reaction of $NH_3 = 8 \times 10^{-6}$ gmol/cm^2·s (use the procedure of Problem 2.10).

2.12 Use Eqs. (2.44) and (2.45). $N_1 = 8.8465 \times 10^{-5}$, $N_2 = 4.892 \times 10^{-5}$ kmol/m^2·s.

2.13 Effective diffusivity of CO_2 in the mixture, $D_{1m} = 8.54 \times 10^{-6}$ m^2/s.

Flux, $N_1 = 1.355 \times 10^{-4}$ kmol/m^2·s

2.14 $t' = 23.3$ h

2.15 $D_{AB} = 2.29 \times 10^{-5}$ m^2/s

2.16 (a) (i) $D_{AB} = 4.66 \times 10^{-5}$ m^2/s;   (ii) $D_{AB} = 1.9 \times 10^{-5}$ m^2/s;

(iii) $D_{AB} = 5.8 \times 10^{-5}$ m^2/s.

(b) $D_{AB} = 8.67 \times 10^{-6}$ m^2/s [experimental value = 9.7×10^{-6} m^2/s]

2.17 Flux = 8.4×10^{-10} kmol/m^2·s

2.18 (a) $N_A = \dfrac{l}{C}\left[(K_1 + K_2 C)\ln\left(\dfrac{C - C_{Al}}{C - C_{A0}}\right) - K_2(C_{A0} - C_{Al})\right]$

(b) $N_A = \dfrac{1}{l}\left[K_1(C_{A0} - C_{Al}) + \dfrac{K_2}{2}(C_{A0}^2 - C_{Al}^2)\right]$

2.19 (a) 1.65×10^{-9} m^2/s; (b) 1.136×10^{-9} m^2/s; (c) 1.484×10^{-9} m^2/s.

2.20 Calculate the cell constant using [Eq. (2.65(b))], $\beta = 1.5 \times 10^{-4}(\varepsilon/\tau)$. Put the diffusivity of KCl. KCl concentration in the larger compartment at the end of 44.5 h = 0.1965 molar (by KCl balance). Similarly, methanol concentration in the larger compartment at the end of 44.5 h = 0.1818 molar.

By comparing the results, $D_{AB} = 1.683 \times 10^{-9}$ m^2/s.

2.21 $\tau = 2.9$

2.22 (a) $\dfrac{4\pi D_{AB}}{RT}(P - p_{B0})\cdot\dfrac{r_s(r_s + \delta)}{\delta}$; (b) $\dfrac{8\pi D_{AB}P}{RT}\cdot\dfrac{r_s(r_s + \delta)}{\delta}\cdot\ln\dfrac{2P}{P + p_{B0}}$

2.23 (a) $W = 4.764 \times 10^{-4}$ gmol O$_2$/s [from Problem 2.22(a)];

(b) The change of size of the sphere is given by

$$-\dfrac{d}{dt}\left[\dfrac{4}{3}\pi r_s^3\cdot(\rho_s/M)\right] = \dfrac{4\pi D_{AB}p_{A0}}{RT}\cdot\dfrac{r_s(r_s + \delta)}{\delta} = \text{rate of diffusion of oxygen.}$$

Integrate from $t = 0$, $r_s = r_{s0}$ to $t = t$, $r_s = r_{sf}$

$$t = \dfrac{RT\delta}{D_{AB}p_{A0}}\cdot(\rho_s/M)\cdot\left[(r_{si} - r_{sf}) - \delta\ln\left(\dfrac{r_{si} + \delta}{r_{sf} + \delta}\right)\right] = 133 \text{ s}$$

[By putting $\rho_s = 0.9$ g/cm^3, $M = 12$, $p_{A0} = 0.8$ atm, $r_{si} = 0.6$ cm, $r_{sf} = 0.4$ cm]

2.24 This problem (like Example 2.15, Problems 2.23, 2.25 and 2.26) involves diffusion through a film having a radially varying area. $4\pi r^2 N_A = \text{constant} = W$,

$$N_A = -\dfrac{D_{AB}P}{RT(P - p_A)}\cdot\dfrac{dp_A}{dr}, \text{ Eq. (2.72). Integrate over the film thickness, i.e. } r = r_s,$$

$p_A = p_{As}$ (sublimation pressure) to $r = r_s + \delta$, $p_A = 0$ (bulk partial pressure).

This gives the pseudo-steady state rate of sublimation,

$$W = \dfrac{4\pi D_{AB}P}{RT\delta}\cdot r_s(r_s + \delta)\cdot\ln\dfrac{P}{P - p_{As}}$$

Rate of change of size of the sphere,

$$-\dfrac{d}{dt}\left[\dfrac{4}{3}\pi r_s^3(\rho_s/M_A)\right] = W$$

Integrate from r_{si} to r_{sf} to get

$$(r_{si} - r_{sf}) - \delta\ln\dfrac{r_{si} + \delta}{r_{sf} + \delta} = \dfrac{D_{AB}P}{RT\delta}\cdot\dfrac{M_A}{\rho_s}\cdot\ln\dfrac{P}{P - p_{As}}\cdot t$$

Put the values of the different quantities to get $t = 91.7$ h

2.25 171 s; 345 s.

2.26 Rate of condensation, $W = 7.17 \times 10^{-8}$ kmol/s

2.27 1.974×10^{-8} kmol/s

2.29 Take V = volume of the gas space in vessel 1, Q_V = flow rate of nitrogen ($\simeq$ flow rate of N_2 + ethanol leaving vessel 1 since the partial pressure of ethanol remains rather low), p_A = partial pressure of ethanol in the gas space at any time t, a = cross-section of vessel 1. Under pseudo-steady state condition,

$$-\frac{V}{RT}\frac{dp_A}{dt} = \frac{Q_V p_A}{RT} - a N_A = \frac{Q_V p_A}{RT} - \frac{a D_{AB}}{RT\delta} \cdot (p_{As} - p_A)$$

(a) Integrate from $t = 0$, $p_A = p_{As}$ (initially the N_2 in the vapour space is saturated with ethanol) to $t = t_f$, $p_A = p_{Af}$. Time, $t_f = 14$ s.

(b) At steady state, $\dfrac{Q_V p_A}{RT} = a N_A$. Solve to get, $p_A = 0.0325$ bar.

2.30 Assume that the flow rate of $(N_2 + NH_3)$ mixture through bulb 1 remains approximately constant.
The flux of ammonia becomes zero at $t = 969$ s
(when $p_{A1} = p_{A2} = 0.0456$ atm).
Before $t = 969$ s, NH_3 diffuses from bulb 2 to bulb 1. Then the direction of diffusion changes from bulb 1 to bulb 2.

2.31 Rate of formation of nickel carbonyl = 7.406×10^{-5} kmol/m^2·s

2.32 (a) The observer is stationary.

(b) velocity = 0.291 m/h towards vessel 1.

2.33 Time = 1143 days

CHAPTER 3

Short and Multiple Choice Questions

1. k_y depends upon concentration because of the term p_{BM} or y_{BM} (see Table 3.1); k_y' is independent of concentration.

2. $k_Y/k_{Y'} = p_{BM}/P$ (see Example 3.1).

7. Yes, at a point on the interface.

9. Colburn-Drew mass transfer coefficient,

$$k_y' = \frac{N_{A1}}{\Delta y} = \frac{5 \times 10^{-3}}{0.3 - 0.05} = 2 \times 10^{-2} \text{ kmol/(m}^2)(\text{s})(\Delta y)$$

Flux for diffusion through a stagnant film (1 mm),

$$N_{A2} = \frac{D_{AB} P}{RT\delta\, y_{BM}} \cdot \Delta y = \frac{k_y'}{y_{BM}} \cdot \Delta y = \frac{2 \times 10^{-2}}{0.8823}(0.2 - 0.03) = 3.85 \times 10^{-3} \text{ kmol/m}^2\cdot\text{s}$$

10. (a) (i) diffusivity, (iv) hydrodynamics, (v) viscosity.

(b) (ii). (c) (i). (d) (i). (e) (i). (f) (i). (g) (ii). (h) (ii).
(i) (i). (j) (ii). (k) (iii). (l) (iii). (m) (ii). (n) (ii). (o) (i).
(p) (iii). (r) (iii). (s) (ii). (t) (ii). (u) (i). (v) (iii). (w) (iii).
(x) (ii). (y) (iii). (z) (iii).

Problems

3.1 $N_A = 5.083 \times 10^{-5}$ kmol/m^2·s; $\quad k_G = 9.658 \times 10^{-4}$ kmol/(m^2)(s)(atm)

3.2 $k_y = 0.001176$ kmol/(m^2)(s)(Δy); $\quad k_c = 0.0251$ kmol/(m^2)(s)(kmol/m^3).

3.3 Instantaneous bubble radius = r; pressure of CO_2 = P.

$$-\frac{d}{dt}\left[\frac{4}{3}\pi r^3 \cdot \frac{P}{RT}\right] = k_L \cdot 4\pi r^2 (C_i - C_b) \Rightarrow r = r_0 - \frac{RT}{P} \cdot k_L (C_i - C_b)t$$

Saturation conc. or solubility of CO_2 = 1.45×10^{-3} mass fraction

$\simeq 1.45 \times 10^{-3}$ kg CO_2/kg solution = $(1.45 \times 10^{-3}/44)$ kmol CO_2/litre

$= 3.295 \times 10^{-2}$ kmol/m^3 = C_i. $\quad C_b = 0$.

$t = 0$, $r = r_0 = 0.004$ m; $t = 80$ s, $r = 0.001$ m $\Rightarrow k_L = 4.65 \times 10^{-5}$ m/s

3.4 (a) $\delta = 1.6$ mm

(b) $k_G' = 2.552 \times 10^{-4}$ kmol/(m^2)(s)(bar)

$k_y' = 3.828 \times 10^{-4}$ kmol/m^2·s

(c) 0.001 kmol/m^3

3.5 The area of the droplet and the transfer coefficient change with time as it descends through the air.

The instantaneous rate of evaporation can be written as

$$-\frac{d}{dt}\left[\frac{4}{3}\pi r^3 \cdot \rho_w / M_w\right] = k_G(P^v - p_b) \cdot 4\pi r^2 \Rightarrow -\frac{dr}{dt} = k_G(P^v - p_b) \cdot \frac{M_w}{\rho_w}$$

p_b = bulk partial pressure of moisture; k_G is given by the correlation; P^v = vapour pressure.

$$\text{Re} = \frac{2r \cdot v_t \cdot \rho_a}{\mu_a}; \text{ Sh} = \frac{k_G \cdot p_{BM} \cdot RT \cdot (2r)}{D_{AB} \cdot P}. \text{ Put in the correlation.}$$

$$k_G = \frac{1.532 \times 10^{-3}}{r}[6.854 \times 10^{-4} + (r^{3/2} - 2.935 \times 10^{-6})^{1/2}]$$

Substitute for k_G and integrate from $r = 4 \times 10^{-4}$ m to 3×10^{-4} m.
Numerical integration is necessary. Time = 63 s.

3.7 $H = 0.00337$ mass fraction/atm = 0.00176 mole fraction/bar.

$$x_i = 1.8 \times 10^{-5} \Rightarrow p_i = x_i/H = \frac{1.8 \times 10^{-5}}{0.00176} = 0.01023 \text{ bar}$$

$$p_b = (1.6)(0.15) = 0.24 \text{ bar. Flux} = k_c\left(\frac{p_b}{RT} - \frac{p_i}{RT}\right) = 0.0317 \text{ kmol/m}^2 \cdot \text{h}$$

3.8 $N_A = k_G(p_i - p_b) = 2.324 \times 10^{-4}$ kg $H_2O/m^2 \cdot s$

3.9 Make a mass balance over an elementary section of the column of length dz.
$2\pi r\delta \cdot v \cdot (dC) = k_L \cdot (2\pi r) \cdot dz(C^* - C)$; δ = film thickness ($\delta \ll r$), r = column radius, v = average film velocity; C_b = solute concentration in the film at any z; C^* = saturation concentration corresponding to the bulk gas concentration.
The gas flow rate is large $\Rightarrow$ bulb gas concentration remains constant.
$$k_L = 4.183 \times 10^{-5} \cdot (z)^{-1/2}, \text{ from the given correlation.}$$
Integrate from $C = 0$ to $C = 0.1C^*$. Tower height = 7 m.

3.10 Calculate $C^* = 36.3/(136.3/1300)$; $C_b = 39/(139/1300)$.
Calculate Re = 390, Sc = 549 $\Rightarrow$ Sh = 129.7; $k_L = 7.26 \times 10^{-5}$ m/s
$$(N_A)_{\text{theo.}} = k_L(C_b - C^*) = 1.343 \times 10^{-3} \text{ kg/m}^2 \cdot \text{s}$$
$$(N_A)_{\text{exp}} = \frac{1}{4\pi r^2} \cdot \frac{d}{dt}\left(\frac{4}{3}\pi r^3 \rho_s\right) \Rightarrow \rho_s \cdot \frac{dr}{dt} = 2.052 \times 10^{-4} \text{ kg/m}^2 \cdot \text{s}$$
Since the theoretical flux (assuming diffusion control) is significantly larger than the experimental flux, the process cannot be considered diffusion-controlled.

3.11 $k_L = 2.462 \times 10^{-4}$ m/s; rate of mass transfer = 4.747×10^{-12} kmol O_2/s.

3.12 Contact time, $t_c = 0.25$ s; mass transfer coefficient,
$$k_{L,\text{av}} = 9.89 \times 10^{-5} \text{ m/s; bubble area} = 4.85 \times 10^{-4} \text{ m}^2$$
$C^* = 1.5$ kg/m^3; $C_b = 0$; residence time of a bubble in the tube = tube length/bubble velocity = 3 s. CO_2 absorbed from a single bubble during passage through the tube = 2.158×10^{-7} kg CO_2/s. Number of bubbles entering = 3 per second.
Total rate of absorption = 38.8 mg CO_2/s; experimental $\rightarrow$ 40 mg/s
$\Rightarrow$ The penetration theory is applicable.

3.13 518 s

3.14 Use Eq. (3.41); $(k_L)_{\text{av}} = 4.786 \times 10^{-6}$ m/s; $N_A = 1.441 \times 10^{-5}$ kg/m$^2 \cdot$s
Equivalent stagnant film thickness, $\delta = 0.239$ mm.

3.15 Sh = 199.4; $k_G = 5.303 \times 10^{-4}$ kmol/(m^2)(s)(atm).
Evaporation rate = 0.0574 kg water/h

3.16 Use Eq. (3.41). Re = 2.344×10^5; Sc = 2.667; Sh = 446
(a) $C_i = P^v/RT = 1.255 \times 10^{-5}$ kmol/m^3
(b) $k_G = 4.346 \times 10^{-6}$ kmol/(m^2)(s)(atm) (take $p_{BM} \simeq P$)
(c) 3.36×10^{-8} kmol/s per unit breadth of the plate.

3.17 3.64 gmol/h

3.18 Contact time, $t_c = 0.0192$ s; (a) $(k_L)_{\text{av}} = 3.732 \times 10^{-4}$ m/s
(b) 175 s
(c) 1.27×10^{-6} kg $O_2/m^2 \cdot$s (occurs at the beginning). It is necessary to write an unsteady state mass balance equation: $V \cdot \dfrac{dC_b}{dt} = (k_L)_{\text{av}} \cdot a (C^* - C_b)$.

V = volume of water; a = total area of the bubble in the tank; C_b = oxygen concentration at any time t.

3.19 Air hold up fraction = 0.005

3.20 $k_y = 7.286 \times 10^{-4}$ kmol/(m^2)(s)(Δy)

3.21 Write an unsteady mass balance equation:

$$V\frac{dC_b}{dt} = k_L a(C^* - C_b) \text{ and integrate, } \ln\frac{C^* - C_i}{C^* - C_b} = \frac{k_L a}{V}t$$

Initial solute conc. $C_i = 0$; $V = 10^{-4}$ m^3; $C_b = 0.112$ mass% $\simeq 1.12$ kg/m^3 at time $t = 720$ s; $a = 3.15 \times 10^{-3}$ m^2.

Calculate $C^* = 1.49$ kg CO$_2$/m^3 $\Rightarrow k_L = 6.17 \times 10^{-5}$ m/s from the integrated equation.

$$\text{Rate of surface renewal, } s = \frac{k_L^2}{D} = 1.98 \text{ per second}$$

3.22 $k_y = 7.23 \times 10^{-4}$ kmol/(m^2)(s)(Δy)

3.23 Conversion = 91.7%

3.24 81 s

3.26 Make a mass balance over a differential section dz of the bed: $u \cdot dC_b = k_c(\bar{a}\,dz)(C^* - C_b)$; integrate and put the values of the parameters. $C_b = 0$ at $z = 0$ and $C_b = 0.0138$ mole % $= 5.74 \times 10^{-6}$ kmol/m^3. Bed height = 12.7 cm. k_c from the given correlation for $j_D = 0.0218$ m/s.

3.27 $t = 754$ s

3.28 $D = 1.82 \times 10^{-5}$ cm^2/s

3.29 Evaporation flux = 1.52×10^{-5} kmol/m^2·s. Time of evaporation = 0.86 h.

3.31 The transition Reynolds number reaches at $\frac{\mu \cdot z}{\nu} = 3 \times 10^5$, or $z = 0.884$ m.

From the given correlations for (Sh$_z$),

$$k_c = 0.00426(z)^{-1/2} \text{ m/s } \text{ for } 0 < z \le 0.884 \text{ (laminar zone)}$$
$$k_c = 0.1225(z)^{-0.2} \text{ m/s } \text{ for } 0.884 \le z \le 3 \text{ (turbulent zone)}$$

Calculate the average values of k_c for the respective zones—0.00906 m/s (laminar) and 0.0109 m/s (turbulent). Take 1 m breadth of the pan, $(a)_{lam} = 0.884$ m^2; $(a)_{turb} = 2.116$ m^2. Rate of evaporation of water = 4.319×10^{-5} kmol/s. Time of evaporation of the water = 10.72 h.

3.32 Calculate the contact time of a liquid element with air from the angular exposure of a disk and the rotational speed; $t_c = \frac{2\pi - \theta}{2\pi N_r} = \frac{360 - 120}{(360)(0.5)} = 1.33$ s.

$D_{AB} = 2.05 \times 10^{-9}$ m^2/s. Using the penetration theory, $(k_L)_{av} = 4.425 \times 10^{-4}$ m/s. Oxygen solubility (calculate),

$$C^* = 2.78 \times 10^{-4} \text{ kmol/m}^3; \quad C_b = 5 \text{ ppm} = 1.56 \times 10^{-4} \text{ kmol/m}^3.$$

Area of exposure (both sides of a disk) = 2.764 m^2.
Rate of oxygen desorption = 7.06×10^{-3} kg/h.

3.33 Dissolved oxygen concentration distribution (along the distance),

$$[DO] = \frac{k L_0}{k_m - k} e^{-kt} \left\{ [DO]_0 - \frac{kL_0}{k_m - k_1} \right\} e^{-k_m t}$$

where $t = z/u$; $k_m = k_L \cdot b/a'$. The maximum DO sag occurs at

$$z = \frac{u}{k_m - k_1} \ln \left[\frac{k_m}{k_1} \left\{ 1 - \frac{[DO]}{L_0} \left(\frac{k_m - k_1}{k_1} \right) \right\} \right]$$

3.34 $t_f = \dfrac{r_0^2}{6 C_{AB} D_{eff}} \rho_A / M_A$, when k_c is large.

3.35 Dissolution rate constant, $k' = \dfrac{k_L C_s}{r_0 \rho_s} = 0.016 \text{ s}^{-1}$

CHAPTER 4

Short and Multiple Choice Questions

1. (a) O_2—liquid-film resistance controlled, (i); CO_2—(ii); H_2S—major resistance in the liquid film; SO_2—major resistance in the liquid film; Cl_2—(iii) (moderately soluble in water); NH_3—(i) (very high solubility in water).
   (b) H_2S–NaOH and SO_2–NaOH are primarily gas-film resistance controlled; CO_2–NaOH—liquid film may offer significant resistance if the NaOH strength is not high.
   (c) All the three systems are gas-film resistance controlled.
   (d) Desorption of NH_3—gas film, benzene and TCA—liquid film resistance controlled.
   (e) Normally both gas and liquid phases offer comparable resistance.

2. $H = 5.5 \times 10^4$ kPa; 229 mg/litre.

3. Driving force at the top, $\Delta Y = Y_2 - Y_2^* = 0.00555$; $Y_2^* = 0 \Rightarrow Y_2 = 0.00555$; from overall material balance, $X_1 = 0.0831 \Rightarrow Y^* = \alpha X_1 = 0.0914$; $(\Delta Y)_{\text{bottom}} = Y_1 - Y_1^* = 0.0196$.

4. (a) Countercurrent absorption; (b) Countercurrent stripping; (c) Cocurrent absorption; (d) Cocurrent stripping.

6. (i).   7. (ii).   8. (i).   9. (iii).   10. (ii).   11. (ii).   12. (ii).
13. (ii).   14. (i).   15. (iii).   16. (i).   17. (iii).   18. (iii).
19. (a) (iii)   (b) (iii)   (c) (ii)   (d) (i).

22. No, since for $\bar{A} = 1$, the solution (4.38) is undefined.

Problems

4.1 (a) $y_A = 13.33 x_A$;   (b) $p_A = 1800 C_A$;   (c) $Y_A = \dfrac{13.33 X_A}{1 - 12.33 X_A}$

4.2 (a) $3.41 \text{ kmol/(m}^2)(\text{h})(\Delta x)$;   (b) $0.313 \text{ kmol/m}^2 \cdot \text{h}$;   (c) $y_i = 0.0637$.

4.3 $k_G = 0.2667$ kmol/(m^2)(h)(Δp,atm); $x_{Ai} = 0.0331$; $p_{Ai} = 0.827$ atm.

4.4 $N_A = k_y(y_{Ab} - y_{Ai}) = k_x(x_{Ai} - x_{Ab})$

$$\Rightarrow \quad \frac{D_{AB}^G P^2}{RT\delta_G p_{BM}}(y_{Ab} - y_{Ai}) = \frac{D_{AB}^L (\rho/M)_{av}}{\delta_L x_{BM}}(x_{Ai} - x_{Ab}), \; x_{BM} \approx 1$$

$$\Rightarrow \quad \frac{(1.76 \times 10^{-5})(1.0)^2}{(0.0821)(298)(2 \times 10^{-3})} \ln\frac{1 - p_{Ai}}{1 - 0.21} = \frac{(2.1 \times 10^{-9})(55.55)}{(2 \times 10^{-4})(1)}(2.3 \times 10^{-5} p_{Ai})$$

$\Rightarrow \qquad p_{Ai} \approx 0.21$. Calculate $k_y = 4.553 \times 10^{-4}$ kmol/(m^2)(s)(Δy),

$k_x = 5.833 \times 10^{-4}$ kmol/(m^2)(s)(Δx). Put these values and $m = 4.36 \times 10^4$.

$K_y = 1.338 \times 10^{-8}$ kmol/(m^2)(s)(Δy), $K_x = 5.833 \times 10^{-4}$ kmol/(m^2)(s)(Δx).

Using the penetration theory, $k_x = 2.872 \times 10^{-3}$ kmol/(m^2)(s)(Δx).

4.5 $K_y = 6.88 \times 10^{-6}$ kmol/(m^2)(s)(Δy); fractional resistance in the organic phase = 20%.

4.6 Fractional resistance offerred by the B-phase = 18.3%; neither phase offers the controlling resistance.

4.7 $k_c = 0.028$ m/s $\Rightarrow k_G = 1.145 \times 10^{-3}$ kmol/(m^2)(s)(Δp,atm);

$k_L = 8.333 \times 10^{-6}$ m/s; $p_A = H'C_A$, calculate $H' = 0.0099$ atm/(kmol/m^3).

(a) $\dfrac{1}{K_G} = \dfrac{1}{k_G} + \dfrac{H'}{k_L} \Rightarrow K_G = 8.356 \times 10^{-5}$ kmol/(m^2)(s)(Δp,atm).

$K_L = 8.273 \times 10^{-6}$ m/s; (b) Fractional gas-phase resistance = 7%;

(c) Flux of MIBK = 7.2×10^{-10} kmol/m$^2\cdot$s.

4.8 $k_y = 7.645$ kmol/(m^2)(h)(Δy); $k_x = 56.94$ kmol/(m^2)(h)(Δx)

(b) $K_x = 17.11$ kmol/(m^2)(h)(Δx);   (c) $K_G = 5.35$ kmol/(m^2)(h)(Δp,atm)

4.9 (a) $k_y = Pk_G = 6$ kmol/(m^2)(h)(Δy); $y_{Cb} = 0.15$, $x_{Cb} = 0.045$;

Flux, $N_C = 0.08$ kmol/m$^2\cdot$h $= k_y(y_{Cb} - y_{Ci}) \Rightarrow y_{Ci} = 0.1367$;

$x_{Ci} = y_{Ci}/m = 0.05468$; from $N_C = k_x(x_{Ci} - x_{Cb})$, calculate $k_x = 8.264$.

(b) Take $(k_y)_2 = 1.5k_y = 9$, $k_x = 8.264$ to calculate $(K_y)_2 = 2.35$ kmol/(m^2)(h)(Δy).

Flux, $(N_C)_2 = 0.0881$ kmol/h$\cdot$m^2.

4.10 One set of data: $(x_A, y_A) \rightarrow (0.21, 0.2987)$; $(C_A, y_A) \rightarrow (10.67, 0.2987)$

4.11 Use the given data and the overall mass balance Eq. (4.30) to have the following flow rates and terminal concentrations:

$$L_s = 700 \text{ kg/h}, \; G_s = 2953.2 \text{ kg/h}, \; X_2 = 0.4286 \text{ (kg water)/(kg H}_2\text{SO}_4),$$

$Y_2 = 0.00039$ (kg moisture)/(kg dry air), $Y_1 = 0.01584$, $X_1 = 0.4938$; at the intermediate section; $X = 0.46$ (kg H$_2$O)/(kg dry acid). Prepare the x-y plot using the given date. Bulk concentrations (in mole fraction) at the intermediate section, $(x, y) \rightarrow (0.714, 0.0078)$.

$$k_y = P\cdot k_G = 12.16 \text{ kmol/(h) (m}^2) \, (\Delta y), \; k_x = 0.96, \; -k_x/k_y = -0.079.$$

Prepare a diagram like Figure 4.5 to obtain $(x_i, y_i) \rightarrow (0.796, 0.006)$.
Concerned slope of the chord, $m' = 0.0624$.
Use Eq. (4.18) to calculate, $K_y = 6.8$ kmol/(h)(m^2)(Δy).

4.12 7.8

4.13 Use Kremser equation; $x_1 = 0.00601$

4.14 From the given data and the overall material balance, Eq. (4.32): $L_s = 3996$ kg/h, $G_s = 1500$ kg/h, $Y_{N+1} = 0$, $X_N = 5 \times 10^{-5}$, $X_0 = 0.001$, $Y_1 = 0.00253$. Also $\alpha = 4.35$, stripping factor, $\overline{S} = \alpha G_s/L_s = 1.633$, $\overline{A} = 0.6124$.

From Kremser equation, Eq. (4.44), $N = 4.5$.

Number of 'ideal trays' available $= (20)(0.5) = 10$.

So the available column is suitable for the job.

4.15 (a) Operating line, $Y = 0.941X + 0.00882$

    (b) The operating line in mole fraction unit, $\dfrac{y}{1-y} = \dfrac{0.941x}{1-x} + 0.00882$

    $\dfrac{dy}{dx} = 0.937$ at $x = 0.1$. Obtain the slopes at the two terminals. Maximum slope of the operating line occurs at the bottom terminal (gas inlet), $(dy/dx) = 0.9437$.

4.16 Operating line: $Y = 1.2289X + 0.001505$; required driving force, $\Delta y = y - y^* = 0.00306$.

4.17 (a) 82.17%, 90.6%;   (b) 4.27 kg, 0.82 kg.

4.19 98%

4.20 4135 kg

4.21 Using the given data and equilibrium relation, the following material equation may be written for the three stages:

$$1800(0.1111 - W_{l1}) = G_s(1.176W_{l1} - 0.001)$$
$$1800(W_{l1} - W_{l2}) = G_s(1.176W_{l2} - 0.001)$$
$$1800(W_{l2} - 0.0055) = G_s(0.00653 - 0.001)$$

Eliminate G_s and W_{l2} to get a cubic equation in W_{l1}:

$$W_{l1}^3 - 0.002556W_l^2 + 2.2 \times 10^{-6}W_{l1} - 5.73 \times 10^{-5} = 0$$

Solution: $W_{l1} = 0.0394$, $W_{l2} = 0.014\ 33$, $G_s = 284$ kg

Total solvent $= 3G_s = 2847$ kg.

4.22 'Theoretical' fractional removal:

    (a) cocurrent—57.1%;   (b) countercurrent—100%;   (c) crosscurrent—73.6%.

4.23 (a) 0.0115 kg;   (b) 3.08 mm Hg.

4.24 Make an unsteady state mass balance equation. $m_s \cdot \dfrac{dX}{dt} = k_Y a(Y_b - Y^*) =$ rate of moisture adsorption at any time t, $m_s =$ mass of the adsorbent sphere.

Take $Y^* = 0.1X$ (equilibrium concentration) and integrate from $t = 0$, $X = 0$ to $t = 3$ min, $X = 0.16$.

$$K_Y = 1.12 \times 10^{-3} \text{ kmol/(m}^2)(s)(\Delta Y)$$

4.25 Overall mass transfer driving force (aqueous or continuous phase basis):

top: $(\Delta x)_{\text{I}} = x_b - x_1^* = x_b - \dfrac{y_{1b}}{11.37} = 0.01607$

bottom: $(\Delta x)_{\text{II}} = 0.01425$; $(\Delta x)_{\text{av}} = 0.01516$

Use the given correlations to calculate K_x.

Continuous phase, $(k_L)_c = 1.095 \times 10^{-4}$ m/s; dispersed phase, $(k_L)_d = 1.46 \times 10^{-5}$ m/s; $k_x = (k_L)_c \cdot (\rho_c/M)_{av} = 5.816 \times 10^{-3}$ and $k_y = (k_L)_d \cdot (\rho_d/M)_{av} = 1.82 \times 10^{-4}$ kmol/$(m^2)(s)(\Delta y)$; M = average molecular weight of the respective phase.

Use the equation, $\dfrac{1}{K_x} = \dfrac{1}{k_x} + \dfrac{1}{mk_y}$ to calculate $K_x = 1.527 \times 10^{-3}$ kmol/$(m^2)(s)(\Delta x)$

Fractional resistance in the aqueous phase = 26.3%.

Assuming 'rigid drop', contact time = 0.06 s; mass transfer coefficient from Higbie's

theory, $(k_L)_c = 2\sqrt{\dfrac{D_c}{\pi t_c}} = 2.06 \times 10^{-4}$ m/s.

4.26 Fractional recovery using three ideal stages—countercurrent, 78.8%; crosscurrent (using the same amount of solvent in each stage), 61.1%.

4.27 $K_x = 3.318 \times 10^{-4}$ kmol/$(m^2)(s)(\Delta x)$; $K_y = 9.885 \times 10^{-5}$ kmol/$(m^2)(s)(\Delta y)$

Per cent of the resistance offered by the gas phase = 33.6%.

4.30 Thickness of the diffusion layer = 0.012 mm

4.31 'Effective diffusivity' of the solute through the cellophane membrane

$$= 1.662 \times 10^{-6} \text{ cm}^2/\text{s}$$

CHAPTER 5

Short and Multiple Choice Questions

1. Packed tower (ii);   Tray tower (i);   Spray tower (ii);
   Falling film absorber (iii);   Bubble column (i);   Agitated vessel (i).

2. (i).   3. (iii).   4. (iii).   5. (i).   6. (ii).   7. (iii).   8. (ii).

9. (i).   10. (i).   11. (iii).   12. (ii).   13. (ii).   14. (iii).   15. (ii).

16. (i).   17. (ii).   18. (iii).   19. (ii).   20. (ii).   21. (i).

22. (a) (ii);   b (i);   (c) (iii).   23. (i).   24. (ii).   25. (iii).   26. (i).

27. (ii).   28. (iii).   29. (i).   30. (i).   31. (i).   32. (i).   33. (ii).

34. (iii).   35. (i).   36. (iii).   37. (iii).   38. (iii).   39. (ii).   40. (iii).

41. (i).   42. (i).   43. (iii).   44. (iii).   45. (ii).   46. (i).   47. (ii).

48. (ii).   49. (ii).   50. (ii).   51. (i).   52. (iii).   53. (i).   54. (iii).

55. (iii).   56. (i).   57. (iii).   58. (iii).   59. (i).   60. (i).   61. (i).

62. (ii).   63. (ii).   64. (i).   65. (i).   66. (ii).   67. (iii).   68. (ii).

69. (i).   70. (ii).   71. (i).

Problems

5.1 An acceptable design: column dia = 1.5 m; downcomer area = 10% on one side; 3/8 inch dia holes, 1975 no. of holes; weir height = 2 inches; select tray thickness = 1/8 inch; dry tray pressure drop = 1.41 inches of liquid head; h_{ow} = 0.88 inch liquid; clear liquid height = 1.8 inches; total pressure drop across a tray = 7.47 inches of liquid; take the tray spacing = 20 inches; fractional liquid entrainment = 0.025.

5.4 (i) For 1.5 inch ceramic intalox saddles: tower diameter = 1 m; pressure drop across the packing = 0.13 psi; operating liquid holdup = 0.042.

(ii) For #50 IMTP: tower diameter = 0.95 m (taking $\Delta P/L$ = 0.2 inch water per foot packing).

5.5 (i) For #25 IMTP, diameter = 1.4 m

(ii) For 25 mm metal Pall ring, diameter = 1.53 m

(taking $\Delta P/L$ = 0.5 inch water per foot packing)

5.7 Equate the drag force on a droplet to its weight to derive Eq. (5.4).

$$C_D \cdot \frac{\pi d_p^2}{4} \cdot \frac{1}{2} \rho_G u_{fl}^2 = \frac{\pi}{6} d^3 p(\rho_L - \rho_G)g; \; C_D = \text{drag coefficient}; \; d_p = \text{diameter of a droplet}$$

$$\Rightarrow \qquad u_{fl} = C_{SB} \left(\frac{\rho_L - \rho_G}{\rho_G} \right)^{1/2}; \qquad C_{SB} = \left(\frac{4 d_p \cdot g}{3 C_D} \right)^{1/2}.$$

Eq. (5.19) → Equate the surface tension force for a hole of diameter d_H with the pressure of a liquid column of height h_σ.

CHAPTER 6

Short and Multiple Choice Questions

1. Since $N_A = k_G(p_{Ab} - p_{Ai}) = k_L(C_{Ai} - C_{Ab})$, slope of $PM = -k_L/k_G$, (ii).
2. Figures (a) and (d)—countercurrent; Figures (b) and (c)—cocurrent; Figure 6.16(b) represents an equilibrium cocurrent operation.
3. (iv), since the operating line cannot cross the equilibrium line.
4. A horizontal line segment from K to the equilibrium line represents the local overall liquid-phase driving force; a vertical line segment represents the same for the gas phase.
5. (a) → (iii); (b) → (iii).
6. (iii), since the available driving force over the latter 40% of the concentration range is actually larger than what the student assumed.
7. (iii), (iv) and (v) will help in reducing the required packed height.
8. (i). 9. (ii).
10. Option (iii) is the best, although option (i) may work in some cases.
11. (i). 12. (i). 13. (ii).
14. For the solute C, since the largest packed height is required for its separation.

15. (i) and (ii).

16. (iii).   17. (ii).   18. (ii).   19. (i), see Eq. [6.25(a)].

20. Eq. (6.23) $\rightarrow \dfrac{y_1 - y_2}{(y - y^*)_{av}} = N_{tOG} = 1 \Rightarrow (y_1 - y_2) = (y - y^*)_{av} = (0.014 + 0.0098)/2$

    $= 0.012$, (iii).

21. $L/G = m$, (iii).   22. (ii).   23. (iii).

24. Use Eq. [6.24(b)], take $y_{iBM} \approx x^*_{BM}$ and $x_{iBM} \approx x^*_{BM}$ for a dilute solution, (ii) 1.6 ft.

25. (i).   26. (i).   27. (iii).   28. (i).   29. (ii), use Eq. (6.49).

30. (iii).

31. Use Eq. (6.61), take the limit of E_O as $G'/L' \rightarrow 1$, $E_O = E_{MG} = 0.6$.

32. (iii).

33. Convex upwards for $m < 1$, convex downwards for $m > 1$; can be checked from the sign of the second derivative, d^2Y/dX^2.

34. From material balance and the equilibrium relation, $L_s/G_s = 2.742$; make another material balance including the section where $Y = 0.04$. $(X^* - X) = 0.00178$.

35. 0.8.

36. $H_{tOL} = \overline{A} H_{tG} + H_{tL}$.

38. More number of drip points on a packing causes frequent termination of the liquid film and more surface renewal. This enhances the mass transfer efficiency of the packing.

39. Ratio of the slopes of the equilibrium and operating lines.

40. (iii).   41. (ii).   42. (i).   43. (ii).

45. Yes; for example, for a 'dilute' gas-liquid system we can write

$$\frac{1}{K_y} = \frac{RT}{D_{AB}^G} \cdot \delta_g + \frac{1}{D_{AB}^L \, \overline{C}} \cdot \delta_l$$

47. Using the Schmidt number correction, Eq (6.37).

48. Yes; a packed bed may be simulated by a wetted-wall column, see Billet's channel model of a packed bed in Chapter 5.

51. (i) Concentrated H_2SO_4; (ii) water; (iii) di- or tri-ethylene glycol; (iv) concentrated H_2SO_4; (v) mono- or di-ethanol amine; (vi) water; (vii) as in case (v); (viii) a (non-volatile) absorption oil.

52. Yes, when $\overline{A}$ is very large.

Problems

6.1 (a) Calculated equilibrium data corresponding to $p_A = 19.3$ mm Hg;

    $(x_A, y_A, X_A, Y_A) \rightarrow (0.0207, 0.0245, 0.02118, 0.0251)$.

  (b) 3678 kmol/h

6.2 (a) If $\overset{*}{Y} = \dfrac{KX}{1 + (1 - K)X}$,

$$y = \frac{Y}{1+Y} = K \cdot \frac{X}{1+X} = Kx = 0.19x \Rightarrow \text{Raoult's law is followed.}$$

$K = 0.19 = P^v/P \Rightarrow$ vapour pressure of benzene, $P^v = 0.2033$ bar.

(b) Overall material balance, $G_s(Y_1 - Y_2) = L_s(X_1 - X_2)$; $G_s = 62.63$ kmol/h, $L_s = 20$, $Y_2 = 0.00502$, $Y_1 = 0.105$; $X_2 = 0$; $X_1 = 0.3125 \Rightarrow x_1 = 0.238$.

(c) Volumetric flow rate of the feed gas = 1655.6 m^3/h, superficial gas velocity = 0.32 m/s; tower dia = 1.353 m. Use Eq. (5.27) to calculate the flooding liquid rate. $\rho_G = 1.385$ kg/m^3, $\rho_L = 840$ kg/m^3, $F_{lv} = 0.082 \Rightarrow Y_{fl} = 0.1435$. Take $F_p = 94.5$ for 1½″ rings, calculate $G'_{fl} = 1334$ lb/h·ft^2. Actual $G' = 333$ lb/h·ft^2 (taken at the tower bottom); required ratio = $G'/G'_{fl} = 0.242$.

(d) Make stage construction on the X–Y plane. Number of ideal trays = 3.7; number of real trays = 3.7/0.35 = 11.

6.3 Equilibrium relation in mole ratio unit: $Y = \dfrac{4.23X}{1-3.23X}$. Lean oil leaving the tower, (50 ppm), $X_N = 1.486 \times 10^{-4}$, $Y_{N+1} = 0$, $X_0 = 0.0347$; the minimum steam rate can be found to be 63.7 kmol/h, actual steam rate = 82.8 kmol/h. Draw the equilibrium and operating lines on the X–Y plane, construct several trays in the high concentration region and then use the Kremser equation to calculate the number of ideal trays in the low concentration region. For example, if seven trays are constructed, $(X_7,\ Y_8) \rightarrow$ (0.007, 0.031). Below this concentration, the slope of the equilibrium line (approximately linear), $\alpha = 4.23$ and $\bar{A} = 0.869$. Using the Kremser equation to reach $(X_N,\ Y_{N+1}) \rightarrow$ $(1.486 \times 10^{-4}, 0)$, the number of ideal stages = 14.
Total number of ideal stages = 7 + 14 = 21

6.4 $(G')_{av} = 91.54$ kmol/m^2.h; $K_y = 3.52 \times 10^{-4}$ kmol/(m^2)(s)(Δy);
$H_{tOG} = 0.688$ m; $N_{tOG} = (y_1 - y_2)/(y - y^*)_M = 6.52$; $h = 4.5$ m.

6.5 (a) $m = 960$;   (b) 98%.

6.6 Minimum solvent rate = 24.85 kmol/m^2.h; actual solvent rate is more than the minimum; absorption factor, $L'/mG' = 1.161$; $(x_i, y_i) \rightarrow$ (0.0211, 0.05475) at the section where $x = 0.02$. Individual gas-phase driving force = $y - y_i = 0.00873$.

6.7 (a) 10 ideal trays;   (b) should be operated at 1.663 bar.

6.8 (a) $Y = 3.029X + 0.0008$;   (b) $N_{tOG} = 14.6$;   (c) 0.397.

6.9 It is convenient to prepare a sketch of the absorber–stripper assembly. Consider the absorber.
At 25°C, vapour pressure of benzene, $P^v = 100$ mm Hg; partial pressure in the feed = 90 mm Hg; $y_{N+1} = 0.1184$, $Y_{N+1} = 0.1343$; $G_{N+1} = 100$ kmol/h, $G_s = 88.16$ kmol/h; 2.5% of the feed benzene leaves the tower $\Rightarrow Y_1 = 0.00336$; $X_N = 0.3$ (given); make an overall material balance to get $L_s = 39.4$ kmol/h $\rightarrow$ (a). The X–Y data can be nicely fitted by a straight line, $Y = 0.25X$.

(b) Using the Kremser equation, number of ideal trays for absorption = 6.2.

(c) At 110°C, P^v = 1781.5 mm Hg; $y = \dfrac{1781.5}{760} x = 2.345x$

$$\Rightarrow \qquad Y = \frac{2.345\, X}{1 - 1.345\, X} \rightarrow \text{draw the equilibrium line.}$$

Given data for the stripping section (a 'prime' is used to indicate the stripping section): X'_0 = 0.3 (feed solution), X'_N = 0.007, Y'_{N+1} = 0 (stripping steam), L_s = 39.7 kmol/h. Draw a tangent to the equilibrium curve from the point $(X'_N, Y'_{N+1}) \rightarrow (0.007, 0)$; slope = $(L_s/G_s)_{max}$ = 2.733 $\Rightarrow (G_s)_{min}$ = 14.5 kmol/h. (d) Actual steam rate used = 1.5$(G_s)_{min}$ = 21.75 kmol/h, slope of the actual operating line = 1.83. Construct stages, N = 8.

(e) Draw the pseudo-equilibrium line midway between the operating line and the equilibrium line (since E_{MG} = 0.5). Construct stages. Number of real stages = 17.

6.10 (a) 1.138 kmol/h;   (b) $p = Hx$, given $p = x$ (p in bar) $\Rightarrow H$ = 1 bar;   (c) $y - y^*$ = 0.0101 – 0.00857 = 0.00153 (the values of x and y at the section are to be calculated from material balance;   (d) doubling the operating pressure will increase the driving force, result in more absorption of the gas and reduction of exit ammonia concentration. The ½″ size packing will offer larger interfacial area and, therefore, better removal of NH_3 (but the pressure drop across the column will be higher).

6.11 H_{tOG} = 0.51 m (using the mean gas rate); N_{tOG} = 8.6 m/0.51 m = 16.86 $\Rightarrow$ mean driving

force $(\Delta y)_M = \dfrac{y_1 - y_2}{N_{tOG}}$ = 2.046 × 10^{-3}. From this relation, calculate x_1 = 0.01172.

Calculate the liquid rate by material balance, L' = 352 kmol/m^2.h. Number of ideal trays (use Kremser equation; note that low concentration approximation can be used) = 15.6. HETP of the feed = 8.16 m/15.6 = 0.55 m.

6.13 Select solvent 1.

6.14 (a) L'_s = 104 kmol/m^2.h

(b) $y = 2.395x + 0.000363$ in the low concentration range

(c) Driving forces on gas-phase basis: $(\Delta y)_{top} = y_2 - y^*_2$ = 0.000363; $(\Delta y)_{bottom}$ = 0.00575; liquid phase basis: $(\Delta x)_{top}$ = 0.0000186, $(\Delta x)_{bottom}$ = 0.00295; (d) N_{tOG} = 16;

(e) H_{tOG} = 0.346 m, and packed height = 5.54 m.

6.15 The more concentrated feed gas enters at the bottom of the absorption tower, the less concentrated one at an intermediate position. The individual flow rates, the total flow rates and terminal concentrations can be calculated from the given data. Since the equilibrium line is linear (in mole ratio unit), the two operating lines will meet on the equilibrium line when the minimum liquid rate is used.

Minimum liquid rate = 152 kmol/h. Number of trays (if 1.25 times the minimum liquid rate is used) obtainable by graphical construction = 8; the low concentration gas stream should be supplied to the third tray from the bottom.

6.16 $H_{tOG} = 0.607$ m, $N_{tOG} = 13.9$ (can be obtained by analytical integration), packed height = 8.46 m. To remove 99.5% of the solute, the packed height should be increased by 58%.

6.17 The concentrations of the liquid and vapour streams below the third tray in the upper section are $(x_3, y_4) \rightarrow (0.00743, 0.01127)$. The required height of the packed section below the trays = 9.5 m.

6.18 (a) Use Eq. [6.24(c)] to calculate $H_{tOG} = 0.68$ m (take the geometric mean of the absorption factor to account for the change in the flow rates). (b) HETP = 0.75 m.

6.19 $k_c = 5.253 \times 10^{-2}$ m/s, $k_x = 0.006$ kmol/$(m^2)(s)(\Delta x)$, $\bar{a} = 68.95$ m^2/m^3, $H_{tL} = 0.512$ m, $H_{tG} = 0.453$ m, $H_{tOG} = 0.826$ m, height of packing required = 8.2 m.

6.20 $y_2/y_1 = \exp(-N_{tOG})$

6.21 $x_p = 0.055$, $y_p = 0.06648$.

6.22 $K_y \bar{a} = 171.4$ kmol/$(m^3)(h)(\Delta y)$

6.23 The terminal points: $(X_N, Y_{N+1}) \rightarrow (0.00174, 0)$ and $(Y_0, Y_{1,max}) = (0.087, 0.181)$. (b) $Y_n = 1.634 X_{n+1} - 0.00248$; (c) change of concentration, $Y_5 - Y_6 = 0.0123$.

6.24 0.961 m

6.25 *Case* 1: Feed at the top of the column—400 ppm TCE, i.e. $x_2 = \dfrac{400/119.4}{10^6/18} = 6.03 \times 10^{-5}$

[mol. wt: TCE — 119.4, water — 18; mol. wt. of the feed liquid $\approx$ 18]. $x_1 \rightarrow 3$ ppm TCE $= 4.523 \times 10^{-7}$. For the stripping air, $y_1 = 0$ (at the bottom of the packed section). For the minimum air flow rate, the pinch point will occur at the top of the packed section $\Rightarrow$ $(y_2)_{max} = mx_2 = (661.1)(6.03 \times 10^{-5}) = 3.986 \times 10^{-2}$. Material balance: $(G')_{min}[(y_2)_{max} - y_1] = L'(x_2 - x_1)$; G' and L' are virtually constant in dilute solution $\Rightarrow$ $(G')_{min}/L = 1.5 \times 10^{-3}$.

$(G'/L')_{actual} = 0.003$. By material balance, $y_2 = 0.02$. Overall driving forces: $(\Delta y)_2 = y_2^* - y_2 = mx_2 - y_2 = 0.03986 - 0.02 = 0.01986$; $(\Delta y)_1 = y_1^* - y_1 = mx_1 - y_1 = 0.0003$. Log mean driving force, $(\Delta y)_M = 4.665 \times 10^{-3}$; $N_{tOG} = 4.28$. $H_{tOG} = 3m/4.28 = 0.701$ m.

Case 2: Since the gas and liquid rates remain the same, H_{tOG} remains unchanged. TCE concentration at the bottom = 0.1 ppm $\Rightarrow x_1 = 1.5075 \times 10^{-8}$; x_2 is as in Case 1. By material balance, $y_2 = 0.03014$. Driving forces: $(\Delta y)_1 = 9.97 \times 10^{-6}$; $(\Delta y)_2 = 0.02966$; $(\Delta y)_M = 0.003707$. $N_{tOG} = 8.13$. Packed height necessary = $(8.13)(0.701)$ ft = 5.7 m.

6.26 $K_G = 3.75$ kmol/$(m^2)(h)(\Delta p$, atm$)$, $K_y = 4.875$ kmol/$(m^2)(h)(\Delta y)$. $H_{tOG} = 0.328$ m, $N_{tOG} = 0.61$. (a) Point efficiency = 0.457.

(b) Murphree efficiency, from Eq. (6.58), $E_{MG} = 0.556$; with entrainment, from Eq. (6.59), $E_{MG} = 0.537$; (c) $E_O = 0.533$.

6.27 Liquid rate = 170 kmol/h (to be determined by trial and error).

6.28 Liquid rate, $L_s = 155.4$ kmol/h; side stream, $S = 62.5$ kmol/h (to be determined by trial and error).

CHAPTER 7

Short and Multiple Choice Questions

1. (a) (ii); (b) (i), $\alpha_{AB} = K_A/K_B$. **2.** Yes.
3. Heat loss from the still causing rectification of the vapour; superheating of the boiling liquid; entrainment of liquid droplets in the vapour.
4. (a) (i), the total vapour pressure exerted by the liquid is less than the ambient pressure; (b) (ii), at this temperature $y_A/P_A^v + (1 - y_A)/P_B^v \approx 1$.
5. (i), (ii) and (iv).   **6.** (iii).   **7.** (i).
8. $z_F = 0.35$.   **9.** (ii).   **10.** (a) (i); (b) (ii); (c) (iii).
11. 1100 kcal/kmol; $x = 0.667$.   **12.** (i).   **13.** (a) No; (b) (i).
14. 70.5 mol steam.   **15.** Capacity and product purity.   **16.** 0.105 kmol/h
17. No; $y_{D,av} = 0.77$.   **18.** 0.069.
19. The minimum slope = 0.74, occurs at minimum reflux; for the stripping section operating line, the minimum slope occurs at total reflux.
20. (i).   **21.** (ii).   **22.** Flooding is a possibility.
23. (iii).   **24.** 1.8.   **25.** 9.4 ideal trays + reboiler.
26. 0.682.   **27.** (i).   **28.** 0.616; 0.325.
29. (a) $y = 0.687x + 0.306$; (b) $x = y$; the feed line reduces to a point, $x = y = z_F$.
30. (ii).
31. (a) (iii); (b) (ii); (c) Bulk vapour concentration at the point, $y = (0.6)(0.8) + 0.376 = 0.856$. Equating the rates of transport in the liquid and vapour phases at steady state, $k_x'\bar{a}(x - x_i) = k_y'\bar{a}(y_i - y) \Rightarrow 400(0.8 - x_i) = 170(y_i - 0.856)$. x_i and y_i are related as

$$y_i = \frac{\alpha\, x_i}{1 + (\alpha - 1)\, x_i} = \frac{2x_i}{1 + x_i}$$

Solving the equations, $x_i = 0.789$, $y_i = 0.882$.
32. At total reflux, $y_{n+1} = x_n \Rightarrow y_6 = x_5 = 0.4$; $y_5 = 0.545$.
33. At minimum reflux and saturated liquid feed ($z_F = 0.6$), the vertical feed line meets the equilibrium line at $y^* = 0.75$.
    Top product: $x_D = 0.98$. Slope of the rectifying section operating line at minimum reflux $= (0.98 - 0.75)/(0.98 - 0.6) = 0.605 = R_m/(R_m + 1) \Rightarrow R_m = 1.53$.
    So a reflux ratio of 1.5 suggested by the plant engineer is not practicable.
34. $[dy/dx]_{x=0} = \alpha$ and $[dy/dx]_{x=1} = 1/\alpha \Rightarrow$ Product = 1.
35. $x = 0.414$.
36. Intersection of the operating lines is $x = 0.5$, $y = 0.652$; the feed is an equimolar mixture ($x = 0.5$) $\Rightarrow$ the feed line is vertical $\Rightarrow$ the feed is a saturated liquid.
37. (i).
38. $y = x$ for both the operating lines.
40. $K_1 = \gamma_1 P_1^v/P = 1.971$; $K_2 = \gamma_2 P_2^v/P = 0.584$.

Problems

7.1 (b) $\alpha = 4.74$ at $x = 0.1$, $\alpha = 6.54$ at $x = 0.9$; (c) initial vapour, $y^* = 0.559$ at $x = 0.2$ and 1 atm; (d) if a vapour of composition $y = 0.518$ [c (ii)] is completely condensed, then $x = 0.518$ in the liquid and $y^* = 0.863$ for the initial vapour formed from this liquid.

7.2 Bubble point of the liquid = 78.9°C; dew point of the vapour = 96°C.

7.5 $x_{D1} = 0.475$, $x_{W1} = 0.287$; $x_{D2} = 0.35$, $x_{W2} = 0.193$.

7.6 6.9 mass%.   **7.7** 1207 kcal.

7.11 (a) 6.365 kmol;   (b) $D = 7.641$ kmol;   (c) $x_W = 0.516$;   (d) $x_W = 0.381$.

7.12 (a) 0.93;   (b) 23.3 kmol/h.   **7.13** 34.5 min.   **7.14** 0.923 kg/h

7.15 Feed line: $y = 0.9 - x$; rectifying section operating line for minimum reflux: $y = 0.608x + 0.376$; $R_m = 1.551$; for $R = 1.5R_m$, number of ideal trays = 10, the feed is to be supplied to the 6th tray from the top.

7.16 $D = 22.1$ and $W = 17.9$ kmol/h. (a) $R_m = 0.95$; (b) $R = 1.4R_m = 1.33$; (c) slope of the rectifying section operating line = 0.571, that of the stripping section operating line = 1.347; (d) slope of the rectifying section operating line for subcooled reflux = 0.5827; number of theoretical trays = 12.8, feed plate—6th from the top.

7.17 (a) $R_m = 3.45$. (b) Minimum number of trays = 30. (c) Take $R = R_m = 6.9$, draw the two operating lines and construct stages starting from an *arbitrarily* chosen concentration (at which the driving force is sufficient for reasonably accurate graphical construction). We start from $x = 0.915$ and end the graphical construction at $x = 0.1$. The number of ideal stages = 15. Next determine the number of stages in the concentration ranges $0.915 \leq x \leq 0.98$ and $0.005 \leq x \leq 0.1$ using the Kremser equation. Linearized equilibrium lines in these concentration ranges are $y = 0.7x + 0.3$ and $y = 1.5x$. Using the Kremser equation, number of ideal trays in the upper concentration range = 19, that in the lower concentration range = 13. The feed tray is 23rd tray from the top. (d) Condenser vapour load = 481.1 kmol/h.

7.18 Minimum reflux ratio, $R_m = 3.31$; boilup ratio = 0.412.

7.20 Rectifying section operating line [it passes through (0.96, 0.96) and (0.55, 0.63)]: $y_{n+1} = 0.805x_n + 0.187$; $x_W = 0.0463$; number of ideal trays = 10.3; feed is to be supplied to the 6th tray from the top.

7.22 (a) $y_5 = 0.747$. (b) The 5th tray belongs to the rectifying section. (c) Enrichment across the 4th tray = $y_4 - y_5 = 0.089$. (d) Boilup ratio = 1.316.

7.28 (a) $R = 3.75$ (obtained by construction by trial such that just 16 trays can be fitted between $x_D = 0.95$ and $x_W = 0.06$). (b) Location of the feed tray—6th from the top. (c) Minimum number of trays (using Fenske equation), $N_m = 10.6$

7.30 There will be three operating lines in total. Reflux ratio, $R = 1.5$; slope of the middle operating line = 0.494; the feed line and the side-stream line are both vertical. The total number of ideat trays = 7.6; feed tray—5th from the top; side stream withdrawal—4th ideal plate from the top.

CHAPTER 8

Short and Multiple Choice Questions

1. (i).   **2.** (ii).   **3.** (iii).   **4.** (iii).   **5.** (ii).   **6.** (i).   **7.** (v).

9. (iii).   **10.** (i).   **11.** (ii).

12. No, since the mutual miscibility will be more.

13. (iii).   **15.** (ii).   **16.** (ii).

17. No. Intersecting tie-lines mean multiplicity of equilibrium concentration which is unknown.

18. (i).   **19.** (ii).   **21.** (i).   **24.** (i).   **25.** (i).   **26.** (ii).   **27.** (ii).

29. (iii).

Problems

8.1 (a) $S_m = 3350$ kg/h; (b) 10 ideal stages (use Kremser equation); (c) 0.884; (d) 6466 kg/h; (e) 22,660 kg/h.

8.2 $(y_C)_E = 0.32$; $E = 623.5$ kg; 76.2%.

8.3 Stage 1: $(x_C)_{R_1} = 0.315$, $(y_C)_{E_1} = 0.42$, $R_1 = 381$ kg/h, $E_1 = 319$ kg/h;
Stage 2: $(x_C)_{R_2} = 0.18$, $(y_C)_{E_2} = 0.26$, $R_2 = 338.2$ kg/h, $E_2 = 242.8$ kg/h;
Stage 3: $(x_C)_{R_3} = 0.102$, $(y_C)_{E_3} = 0.15$, $R_3 = 330.2$ kg/h, $E_3 = 208$ kg/h.
Total amount of acetone removed from the feed = 216.3 kg/h, 0.865.

8.4 $(x_C)_{R_1} = 0.358$, $(y_C)_{E_1} = 0.47$, $R_1 = 781.3$, $E_1 = 468.7$;
$(x_C)_{R_2} = 0.22$, $(y_C)_{E_2} = 0.306$, $R_2 = 603.5$, $E_2 = 477.8$, etc.
Total solute recovered in four stages = 473.4 kg.

8.5 Use the mass ratio unit. Supply the solvent at rates $S_1, S_2,..., S_N$ to the N cross-current stages. Overall mass balance: $R_S(X_0 - X_N) = \sum_{n=1}^{N} S_n Y_n$. Total amount of solvent $= \sum_{n=1}^{N} S_n$.

Profit, p = price of extracted solute − cost of processing $= c_1 R_S(X_0 - X_N) - c_2 \Sigma S_n$

For the nth stage, $S_n = \dfrac{R_S(X_{n-1} - X_n)}{Y_n} = \dfrac{R_S(X_{n-1} - X_n)}{\psi(X_n)} = \dfrac{R_S(X_{n-1} - X_n)}{\alpha X_n}$

For a 4-stage cascade, $\bar{p} = \dfrac{p}{c_1 R_S} = (X_0 - X_4) - r \sum_{n=1}^{4} \left(\dfrac{X_{n-1}}{X_n} - 1 \right)$, $r = \dfrac{c_2}{c_1 \alpha}$

$\Rightarrow \qquad \bar{p} = X_0 - X_4 + 4r - r \left(\dfrac{X_0}{X_1} + \dfrac{X_1}{X_2} + \dfrac{X_2}{X_3} + \dfrac{X_3}{X_4} \right)$

To maximize the profit, put $\dfrac{\partial \bar{p}}{\partial X_1} = \dfrac{\partial \bar{p}}{\partial X_2} = \dfrac{\partial \bar{p}}{\partial X_3} = \dfrac{\partial \bar{p}}{\partial X_4} = 0$

when $X_1 = (r X_0^4)^{1/5}$, $X_2 = (r^2 X_0^3)^{1/5}$, $X_3 = (r^3 X_0^2)^{1/5}$, $X_4 = (r X_0)^{1/5}$.

Solvent rate to stage 1, $S_1 = \dfrac{R_S}{\alpha} [X_0(rX_0^4)^{1/5} - 1]$, etc.

8.6 $N = 5.9$ ideal stages; minimum solvent rate = 2018 kg/h; actual solvent rate is 2970/2018 = 1.47 times the minimum.

8.7 $N = 4$ ideal stages; minimum solvent rate = 617 kg/h.

8.8 $N = 3.4$ ideal stages; minimum solvent rate = 647.5 kg/h.

8.9 $R = 547.7$ kg/h, $E = 452.4$ kg/h, glycol extracted = 23.5 kg.

CHAPTER 9

Short and Multiple Choice Questions

1. (i) and (iii). **2.** (ii), (iv) and (vi).
3. (i) ethanol; (ii) water; (iii) ammonium cyanide; (iv) ammoniacal solution; (v) hexane; (vi) water.
4. (i) solid-phase diffusion; (ii) liquid-phase diffusion; (iii) liquid-phase diffusion.
5. (i). **6.** (i). **7.** (i). **8.** 90%. **9.** (i). **10.** (ii).
11. (ii), since the solution of higher density tends to move downwards.
13. (iii). **14.** (iii).
15. (i) Bollman, moving basket; (ii) moving belt; (iv) moving belt; (v) Rotocel.
16. (i), (iii), (v) and (vii).
19. Solution concentration = Y_C, solid-free basis; 1 kg solvent present in $1/(1 - Y_C)$ kg solution $\Rightarrow Z_V = 0.1Y_C/(1 - Y_C)$ kg solid per kg solution:
    Underflow: solids content = $0.35 - 0.4X_C^2$ mass fraction

    $$\text{Solids in the sludge} \Rightarrow Z_L = \frac{0.35 - 0.4X_C^2}{1 - (0.35 - 0.4X_C^2)} \frac{\text{kg solid}}{\text{kg solid-free solution}}$$

    The overflow and underflow curves can now be drawn.

Problems

9.2 (a) Mass of underflow = 1900 kg; overflow = 900 kg
    (b) fraction of oil removed = 0.47. For two-stage cross-current extraction, fractional recovery = 72.6%.

9.3 2241 kg/h wash water to be supplied; $N = 3$ ideal stages.

9.4 Mass fraction of oil in the extract = 0.56; number of ideal stages = 6.5.

9.5 $N = 2.8$

9.6 $N = \dfrac{\log\left(\dfrac{x_N - r}{x_0 - r}\right)}{\log a}$; $r = \dfrac{L'X_1 - \alpha X_0 V_0'}{L' - \alpha V_0'}$;

$$a = \cfrac{1}{1 - E_M \left(\cfrac{L'}{\alpha V_0'} - 1 \right)} \, ; L' = \text{constant underflow and } V_0' = \text{overflow rate.}$$

9.8 $N = 2.5$ **9.9** $N = 4$

CHAPTER 10

Short and Multiple Choice Questions

1. (ii).
2. (iii), this is the humidity of saturated air at 30°C and 1 atm—can be obtained from the chart or calculated using the vapour pressure equation for water.
3. (i), it is given by $c_{pL} \cdot \Delta T / \lambda_0$.
4. (ii).
5. (iii), can be calculated from the vapour pressure equation:

$$\frac{dY_s'}{dT} = \frac{d}{dT}\left[\frac{P^v}{P - P^v} \cdot \frac{18.02}{28.97} \right] = \frac{3984.92}{(T - 39.724)^2}$$

6. (i).   **7.** (ii).   **8.** (ii).   **9.** (iii).
10. (iii), $(h_L/k_{Y'}) = (H_i' - H')/(T_L - T_{Li})$, Eq. (10.27); $T_{Li} = 39$°C, $P^v = 0.0692$ bar, $Y_s' = 0.0456$ kg/(kg dry air), $H_i' = 156.5$ kJ/(kg dry air) at 39°C, Eq. (10.8); $H' = 135$,

$$T_L = 42°C \Rightarrow \frac{h_L}{k_{Y'}} = 7.17 \text{ kJ/kg} \cdot °C.$$

11. None of the quantities changes.
12. (iii).   **13.** (ii).   **14.** (ii).
15. Since the makeup water is supplied at a temperature $T_L < T_w$, the steady-state water temperature would be a little lower than T_w. The air temperature and humidity would follow the adiabatic saturation line on the psychrometric chart.
16. (i).   **17.** (ii).   **18.** (iii).   **19.** (i) and (ii).   **20.** (i).   **21.** (iii).
22. (ii).
23. (iii), since the fans are supported on an elevated structure.
24. (i).   **26.** No.
27. Items (ii), (iv) and (vi) will improve the capacity.   **28.** (i).
29. Power plants, metallurgical industries, rolling mills, refineries, etc.
30. (i).
33. As the 'approach' increases, the driving force becomes larger, and the required packed height decreases. If the 'cooling range' increases, the driving force becomes less, and the required packed height increases.
34. (iii).   **37.** (ii) and (iii).   **38.** (iii).   **39.** (ii).

40. Sketch (i) shows the correct orientation; for (ii) and (iii), water splash will occur; also (ii) will allow more light into the tower, promoting algal growth.

41. The V-shaped passage allows a gradually increasing flow area up the packing in order to accommodate increasing air flow rate.

Problems

10.1 (a) Humidity, $Y' = 0.014$ kg/(kg dry air); enthalpy, $H' = 69$ kJ/(kg dry air); dew point, $T_d = 16°C$; humid volume, $v_H = 0.886$ m³/(kg dry air); humid heat, $c_H = 1.031$ kJ/(kg dry air)(°C).

(b) 27°C.

(c) First check if the air becomes saturated in course of cooling from 33°C to 15°C.

$P^v = 0.0168$ bar at 15°C, corresponding saturation humidity $= \dfrac{0.0168}{1.013 - 0.0168} \times$

$\dfrac{18.02}{28.97} = 0.0105$, which is less than the humidity of the sample of air (0.014). Therefore condensation of moisture occurs — (0.014 − 0.0105) i.e. 0.0035 kg/(kg dry air).

Heat rejected on cooling $= (c_H)(\Delta T) + (\Delta Y')(\lambda)$

$\qquad = (1.031)(33 - 15) + (0.0035)(2500) = 27.3$ kJ/(kg dry air).

(d) Relative humidity = 36.5%; dew point = 31°C.

10.3 1419.5 kJ/min

10.4 Heat requirement = 5400 kJ/min; rate of steam condensation = 2.66 kg/min.

10.5 Humidity of the atmospheric air = 0.01723 kg/(kg dry air); the humidity increases to $Y'_{as} = 0.035$ on adiabatic saturation of this sample of air, and $T_{as} = 34°C$. Corresponding dry-bulb temperature = 78°C [part (a)]. This means that atmospheric air is first heated to 78°C and then adiabatically saturated when its temperature becomes 34°C [part (b)], and humidity 0.035. The air is then further heated to 80°C. (c) Psychrometric condition of this air: $T = 80°C$, $Y' = 0.035$, $H' = 173.2$ kJ/kg.

10.6 Moisture removed = 0.1243 kg/(kg dry air)

10.7 Inlet air: $T_{G1} = 32°C$, $T_{w1} = 22°C$, $Y'_1 = 0.013$ kg/(kg dry air); $H'_1 = 66.5$ kJ/kg. Water temperature at the bottom, $T_{L1} = 29°C$. Draw the 'equilibrium line' [T_L–H', corresponding to saturation condition, locate the lower terminal of the operating line, $Q(29, 66.5)$, and draw the tangent to this curve] from the point Q. Slope of the line is

$\dfrac{L\,c_{wL}}{G_{s,\,min}} = 9.37$ kJ/kg·°C; $L = 8500$ kg/h·m²; $G_{s,\,min} = 3800$ kg/m²·h, dry basis. Actual

gas rate = 6000/1.013 = 5923 kg/m²·h, which is 5923/3800 = 1.56 times the minimum. Actual slope of the operating time = 6.01. Upper terminal of the operating line (P) corresponds to $T_{L2} = 42°C$. Locate the operating line and make a plot of $1/[H'^* - H']$ against H'. By graphical integration, $N_{tOG} = 2.83$.

10.8 Slope of the operating line for the minimum air rate = 8.78; $G_{s, \, min}$ = 2623 kg/m^2·h; $G_{s, \, actual}$ = 3279 kg/m^2·h: Locate the operating line. N_{tOG} = 6.14. H_{tOG} = 1.312 m. Packed height = 8 m.

10.9 (a) Minimum water rate = 7450 kg/h.m^2; actual = 9330 kg/h.m^2; outlet water temperature = 41°C; (b) water condensed = 194 kg/h.m^2; (c) packed height = 6.57 m.

10.10 N_{tOG} = 3; makeup water = 88.4 kg/h.

10.11 Blowdown rate = 165 gallon/h; makeup water = 420 gallon/h.

10.12 Heat required for evaporation of water in the dryer = 7.11 × 10^5 kJ/h; heat duty = (1.15) (7.11 × 10^5) = 8.18 × 10^5 kJ/h. Feed air: T_G = 25°C, R.H. = 70%, Y_1' = 0.01373 kg/ (kg dry air). Exhaust air: T_G = 55°C, T_w = 40°C, Y_2' = 0.0297 kg/(kg dry air). Air Supply

$$= \frac{\text{evaporation rate}}{Y_2' - Y_1'} = 18785 \text{ kg/h, dry basis. Enthalpy of exhaust air} = 132.6 \text{ kJ/kg;}$$

temperature of hot air to the dryer = 137.5°C. Steam condensation rate = 391 kg/h; area of the heater = 115.5 m^2.

CHAPTER 11

Short and Multiple Choice Questions

1. (ii), since sand is totally nonhygroscopic, and all the moisture is "free".
2. (ii) and (iv).
3. (a) (iii), compared to a 5 cm thick bed, a 10 cm thick bed of the same material will have a higher critical moisture; (b) → (i), the transport resistance to water diffusion is less if the particle size is larger; (c) → (i).
4. (iii), which is the wet-bulb temperature of the drying gas.
6. (iii).   7. (i).

8. (iii), since X^* = 0, $t_1 = \dfrac{W_s}{a} \cdot \dfrac{X_c}{N_c} \cdot \ln \dfrac{X_c}{(X_c/10)}$ for linear falling rate, and

$$t_2 = \frac{W_s}{a} \cdot \frac{X_c^2}{N_c} \left[\frac{1}{(X_c/10)} - \frac{1}{X_c} \right] \Rightarrow t_1/t_2 = 0.256$$

9. (ii).   10. (i).   11. (ii).
12. (ii), since the temperature of the solid should remain low.
13. (iii).   14. Yes.   15. (ii).   16. (i).   17. (i).   18. (ii).
19. (i) spray dryer; (ii) drum dryer; (iii) direct heat rotary (hot air, *not* flue gas, may be used); (iv) rotary; (v) spray; (vi) belt or conveyer; (vii) belt or conveyer/tray; (viii) rotary; (ix) tunnel; (x) tunnel; (xi) indirect heat rotary.
20. If the surface is completely moist, constant rate drying flux, $N_c = k_{Y'} \Delta Y'$ = (120) (0.037 − 0.018) = 2.28 kg/h.m^2. Y_s' = 0.037 ⇒ the fraction of surfaces having wetted patches = 1.5/2.28 = 65.8%.

21. (ii). **22.** (iii). **23.** (iii).

24. A → unsaturated surface drying; B → two falling rate periods, one linear and another nonlinear; C → nonlinear falling rate, substantial resistance to liquid diffusion.

25. (c). **27.** (i). **28.** (a) → (i); (b) → (ii); (c) → (ii). **29.** (iii). **30.** (ii).

31. (ii) and (iii). **32.** (ii). **33.** (ii).

Problems

11.1 (i) 1.91 h; (ii) 2.2 kg/m^2.h.

11.2 $X \geq X_{c_1}$, constant drying rate, $N = N_c$; $X_{c_1} \geq X \geq X_{c_2}$, first falling rate, $N_{f_1} = \alpha_1 X + \alpha_2$; $X_{c_2} \geq X \geq 0$, second falling rate, $N_{f_2} = \beta X_{c_2}^2$. Assume continuity of flux at $X = X_{c_2} \Rightarrow$

$\dfrac{d}{dX}(N_{f_1}) = \dfrac{d}{dX}(N_{f_2})$ at $X = X_{c_2} \Rightarrow \alpha_1 = 2\beta X_{c_2}$. Equating drying rates at $X = X_{c_2}$,

$\alpha X_{c_2} + \alpha_2 = \beta X_{c2}^2$. Solving,

$$\alpha_1 = \frac{2N_c}{2X_{c_1} - X_{c_2}}; \ \alpha_2 = -\frac{N_c X_{c_2}}{2X_{c_1} - X_{c_2}}; \ \beta = \frac{N_c}{X_{c_2}(2X_{c_1} - X_{c_2})}.$$

Integrating the drying rate equation,

$$t_{f_1} = \frac{W_s}{a} \cdot \frac{(2X_{c_1} - X_{c_2})}{2N_c} \cdot \ln\frac{N_{c1}}{N_{c2}}; \ t_{f_2} = \frac{W_s}{a} \cdot \frac{X_{c_2}(2X_{c_1} - X_{c_2})}{N_c} \left(\frac{1}{X_f} - \frac{1}{X_{c_2}} \right).$$

$$t = t_c + t_{f_1} + t_{f_2} = 1.027 + 1.029 + 17.552 = 19.6 \text{ h}$$

11.3 $t = 8.7$ h; highest drying rate = 0.836 kg/m^2.h; the lowest drying rate = 0.088 kg/m^2.h.

11.4 $N_c = 2.15$ kg/m^2.h; drying time = 3.346 h.

11.5 Calculate the Reynolds number of the hot gas (on the basis of inlet condition since the exit condition is unknown). $\rho_G = 0.962$ kg/m^3, $\mu_G = 2.1 \times 10^{-5}$ N.s/m^2, $u = 0.8$ m/s, effective diameter of a pellet, $d_p = (d_c l_c + 0.5 d_c^2)^{1/2} = 6.124$ mm. Re = 224.4.
$h_c = 140$ W/m^2.°C [from Eq. (2.24)]; $k_Y = h_c/C_H = 0.1346$ kg/(m^2)(s)(ΔY).
$H_{tG} = G'/k_Y \bar{a} = 0.0143$ m; $N_{tG} = 0.03/0.0143 = 2.1$.
(i) Initial rate of drying (= constant rate of drying) = 56.58 kg/m^2.h;
(ii) Total drying time = 14 min; (iii) time required for heating the solid from the wet-bulb temperature (36.5°C) to 70°C is obtained from

$$l_s \rho_s c_{ps}(dT/dt) = (l_s \cdot 1)\, \bar{a}\, h_c (T_G - T)$$

$$\Rightarrow \quad t = \frac{\rho_s C_{ps}}{\bar{a}\, h_c} \cdot \ln \frac{T_G - T_1}{T_G - T_2} = 4.2 \text{ s}$$

11.6 $G' = 6777$ kg/m^2.h; h_c [from Eq. (11.1)] = 23.7 W/m^2.°C;
Solid temperature = $T_s = 35$°C; drying time, $t = t_c + t_f = 1.991$ h + 1.695 h = 3.7 h.

11.7 Use the results of Problem 11.2. $t_{f1}/t_{f2} = 0.061$.

11.8 $X_c = 0.108$

11.9 The convective heat flux to a tray bottom is equated to the sum of conduction heat flux to the solid and radiant heat flux to the open solid below $\Rightarrow h_c(T_G - T_b) = (k_s/l_s)(T_b - T_s) + \sigma(T_b^4 - T_s^4)$, T_s = solid surface temperature. Also total heat input by convection at the tray bottom and at the open solid surface goes for vaporization of moisture at steady state, i.e.,

$$h_c(T_G - T_b) + h_c(T_G - T_s) = k_Y(Y_s - Y_G)\lambda_w$$

Solving these equations, $T_s = 46°C$, $T_b = 84°C$, $Y_s = 0.069$.
Drying rate in the constant rate period, $N_c = k_Y(Y_S - Y_G) = 4.213$ kg/m^2.h
Constant rate drying time; $t_c = 1.965$ h
Falling rate drying time $t_f = 3.148$ h

11.10 3 h

11.11 $t_c = 0.952$ h; $t_{f_1} = 0.683$; $t_{f_2} = 3.214$ h.

11.12 2.9 h; 25%.

11.13 Since the solid on the belt is in 'plug flow', the drying time is the same as the batch drying time for through circulation through a bed of the same thickness.
For batch drying in through circulation (see Problem 11.5), mass flow rate of the gas, $G' = 3503$ kg/m^2.h, $h_c = 174$ W/m^2.°C from Eq. (11.24), $H_{tG} = 0.0118$ m; $N_{tG} = l_s/H_{tG}$ = 2.97; $N_c = 78.6$ kg/h.m^2; $t = 0.476$ h; belt length = 10 m, belt velocity = 0.35 m/min, breadth of the belt = 2 m. Production rate = 1306 kg solid/h (bone dry basis); So the dryer can perform the required job.

11.14 Follow Example 11.5. Area of the heater = 271 m^2.

11.15 3.26 h   **11.16** Drying time = 2.114 h   **11.17** Drum diameter = 0.35 m; rph = 37.

11.20 (a) $N = 10.17X - 0.215$ in the falling rate; (b) $k_G = 1.664$ kmol/(m^2)(h)(bar); (c) 42.3%;
(d) 10.38 h.

CHAPTER 12

Short and Multiple Choice Questions

1. Maximum adsorption occurs at large p, i.e. $q = q_m = 6.4/1.53 = 4.18$ mmol/g adsorbent = 0.272 kg/kg adsorbent.

2. Henry's law constant, $K_H = [dq/dp]_{p\to0} = 0.0491$ mmol/g.kPa.

3. Total loading = $q_A + q_B = 1.536 + 0.295$, mg/g.

4. $\alpha_{AB} = \dfrac{x_A/x_B}{y_A/y_B} = 5.23$.   5. (iii).

6. (i), since the absorbed phase is more orderly.

7. (i).   8. (iii).   9. (iii).

10. (i) molecular sieve; (ii) silica gel; (iii) active carbon; (iv) active carbon.

11. (i).   12. (i).   13. (i).   14. (iii).   16. (i).   17. (i).   18. (ii).

19. (iii).   20. (iii).   21. (i).   22. (ii).   24. (i).   25. (i).   26. (ii).

28. (ii).   30. PSA.

Problems

12.1 2, 4-DCP: $C_e = 7.15 \times 10^{-4}$ mg/litre; 2, 6-DCP: $C_e = 0.0632$ mg/litre

12.2 Glycine: $q_e = 5.2 \times 10^{-4}(C_e)^{0.9736}$, correlation coeff., $\gamma^2 = 0.999$;
Phenylalanine, $q_e = 4.37 \times 10^{-3}(C_e)^{0.952}$, correlation coeff., $\gamma^2 = 0.998$.

12.3 *Langmuir Isotherm*   *Freundlich Isotherm*

$$T = 70°C, \quad q = (1.591) \cdot \frac{0.137 \times 10^3 p}{1 + 0.137 \times 10^3 p} \qquad\qquad q = 17.74 \cdot p^{1/1.578}; \ p \text{ in atm.}$$

$$T = 110°C, \quad q = (0.861) \cdot \frac{0.052 \times 10^3 p}{1 + 0.052 \times 10^3 p} \qquad\qquad q = 8.893 \cdot p^{1/1.307}; \ p \text{ in atm.}$$

Heat of adsorption: $\Delta H = -12.13$ kcal/gmol for $q = 0.15$

$$\Delta H = -11.3 \text{ kcal/gmol for } q = 0.25$$

12.4 $\Delta H = -8.312$ kcal/gmol

12.5 At $p_1 = 50$ kPa and $p_2 = 50$ kPa, $q_{1, \text{mix}} = 0.351$ gmol ethane/kg,
$q_{2,\text{mix}} = 1.62$ gmol propane/kg adsorbent.

12.6 $S_g = 76.05$ m^2/g

12.7 Minimum carbon requirement = 1.064 kg
If 1.3 times this quantity ($m_s = 1.383$ kg) is used, we have the relation

$$\frac{(1000)(10 - C_e)}{1383} = 68(C_e')^{0.43} \Rightarrow C_e' = 2.575 \times 10^{-5} (10 - C)^{2.3256}$$

where C = concentration of nitrobenzene in aqueous solution, and C_e' = equilibrium concentration in the solution corresponding to the solute loading in the adsorbent.

Instantaneous balance: $-V_L \dfrac{dC}{dt} = k_L(m_s a')(C - C_e')$

Integrate, $C = 10$ to $C = 0.01$ to get $t = 4.3$ h

12.8 Use 24.72/2 = 12.36 kg clay in each stage. Contact time is $t_c = 30.6$ min = 1836 s. Use the technique of Problem 12.7 to calculate $Y_1 = 4.313$ colour unit/kg oil for the oil leaving stage 1. By the same technique, $Y_2 = 0.372$ unit/kg for stage 2.

12.9 (a) Draw the mass transfer wave front (it is not symmetric). Consider the portion of the curve from $C/C_o = 0.025$ to $C/C_o = 0.975$. Find $t_s = 46$ min by making the areas below the breakthrough curve (for $t < t_s$, $C/C_o \leq 0.025$) and that above it (for $t > t_s$, $C/C_o \leq 0.975$). For $C/C_o = 0.975$, $t \approx t_e = 86$ min; $u_s = L/t_s = 0.2/46 = 0.00435$ m/s; $t_b = 19.5$ min; LUB $= u_s(t_s - t_b) = 0.115$ m;

(b) Bed height = (8 h)(u_s) + LUB = 2.2 m.
Loading of solute (based on 1 m^2 of bed area) = 919 gmole

12.10 The mass transfer wave front is reasonably symmetric. $t_b = 196$ min; $t_m = 232$ min (for $C/C_o = 0.5$); $u_s = L/t_m = 0.215$ cm/min; LUB $= L(1 - t_b/t_s) = 7.6$ cm. Fraction of the bed utilized $= \dfrac{L - \text{LUB}}{L} = 84.5\%$.

LUB = 8.9 cm by using the integration technique [taking C/C_o = 0.005, t_b = 191 min; and C/C_o = 0.992, t_e = 270 min]

12.11 Column 1: t_{b1} = 15.5 h; t_{s1} = 16.75 h; LUB = 3.3 cm.

(b) Take $u_s = L_1/t_{s1}$ = 0.0438 cm/min; L_{s_2} = L_2 − LUB = 23.7 cm; $t_{b2} = L_{s_2}/u_s$ = 540 min.

(c) 58.67 kg; (d) $u_s = \dfrac{L_2 - L_1}{t_{s_2} - t_{s_1}} = \dfrac{0.44 - 0.27}{16.75 - 10.9}$ = 0.0484 cm/min.

12.12 39.24 kg

12.13 (a) Calculate Re = 121, Sc = 1.71, Sh = 25.37 [from Eq. 12.74(a)], k_c = 0.08 m/s.

(b) Effective diffusivity: D = 0.0945 cm^2/s (at 25°C), D_K = 0.0142 cm^2/s; D_e = 0.00198 cm^2/s from Eq. [12.74(c)].

12.14 u_s = 50 cm/60 min = 0.833 cm/min; length of the MTZ = 12.5 cm; For 90% bed utilization, L = 62.5 cm, t_b = 67.5 min.

12.15 Use Eq. (12.45). t_{MTZ} = 9.2 min; u_s = 0.0011 m/s; length of the MTZ = 0.61 m; L_s = 1.695 m; t_b = 25.7 min.

12.16 25.7 litre per litre solution.

12.17 Integrate the equation and rearrange in the form $1/q_t = 1/q_e + 1/(k_2q_e^2 t)$. The plot of $1/q_t$ against $1/t$ is linear (correlation coefficient = 0.997) $\Rightarrow$ the Ho and McKay modal is applicable. Slope of the line = $1/k_2q_e^2$ = 0.2073; intercept = $1/q_e$ = 0.0153. Estimated parameters: q_e = 65.36 mmol/g, k_2 = 1.13 × 10^{-3}.

CHAPTER 13

Short and Multiple Choice Questions

3. Needs a seed crystal or a very high supersaturation.

4. Crystallization of an organic compound such as *p*-xylene, naphthalene, bisphenol, etc.

7. A small crystal has a higher solubility (because of a larger surface energy).

8. (ii).   **9.** (i).

10. $G = \dfrac{dL}{dt} = \dfrac{1}{3L^2\phi_v} \cdot \dfrac{d}{dt}(v_p)$ = 4.13 × 10^{-8} m/s

11. For a sphere, $\phi_v = \pi/6$ = 0.523.

12. (i).   **13.** (iii).   **14.** (i).

15. 355 kg CuSO$_4$·5 H$_2$O.   **16.** (iii).

18. (a) (ii); (b) (iii); (c) (iii).   **19.** (ii).

20. $G\tau$ = 1/9.58 = 0.1044 mm $\Rightarrow$ (a) $\overline{L}_m = (\sqrt[3]{6})\cdot G\tau$ = 0.19 mm (iii); (b) (iii); (c) (iii).

21. (ii).   **22.** (iii).   **23.** (i).   **24.** (ii).   **25.** (iii).   **26.** (i).   **27.** (i).

28. (iii).   **30.** (i).

31. $W(x) = 1 - e^{-x}\left(1 + x + \dfrac{x^2}{2} + \dfrac{x^3}{6}\right)$; $W(x) = 0.1 \Rightarrow x = 1.74 = L/G\tau$.

$G\tau = 114.9$ μm. $L_1 = 400$ μm $\Rightarrow x_1 = 3.48$ and $W(x_1) = 0.46$; $W(x_2) = 0.764$

$$W(x_2) - W(x_1) = 0.304$$

32. $\dfrac{dm_c}{dt} = \rho_c \cdot 3L^2 \cdot \dfrac{dL}{dt} = k_L \cdot A_c \cdot \Delta C = k_L \cdot A_c \cdot \left[\dfrac{C - C_s}{C_s} \cdot C_s\right]$. Put the values to get

$G = dL/dt = 2.9 \times 10^{-7}$ m/s.

33. (iii).

Problems

13.1 $r = 19$ mm

13.2 $(\Delta G)_{cr} = 4\pi r_c^2 \cdot \sigma + \dfrac{4}{3}\pi r_c^3\left(-\dfrac{2a}{r_c}\right)$

Now consider Eq. (13.1). $\ln(C/C_s) = \ln S = \dfrac{2\sigma\, M_w}{RT \cdot r_c \cdot \rho_c} = \dfrac{2\sigma\, v_M}{kT\, r_c}$, v_M = volume of a

molecule. $(\Delta G)_{cr} = \dfrac{4}{3}\pi\sigma\, r_c^2 = \dfrac{16\pi\,\sigma^3\, v_M^2}{3\,(kT \ln S)^2}$ etc.; 300%.

13.3 Prepare a plot of $\ln(\eta)$ against L. Slope $= -6.005$, intercept on the ordinate $= 13.2 \Rightarrow$
$G = 5.74 \times 10^{-8}$ m/s; $B^0 = 3.09 \times 10^5$ nuclei/m³.s.

13.4 $B^0 = 3.04 \times 10^7$ nuclei/m³.s; $G = 4.34 \times 10^{-8}$ m/h.

13.5 $G = 1.222 \times 10^{-7}$ m/s; $B^0 = 2.933 \times 10^4$ nuclei/m³.s.

13.6 Production rate $= Q_p \cdot M_T = (V/\tau) \cdot M_T = (2.778$ m³/h$)(150$ kg/m³$) = 417$ kg/h.
$L_M = 0.8$ mm $= 3.67 G\tau \Rightarrow G = 3.364 \times 10^{-8}$ m/s.
$M_T = 6\phi_v \rho_c n^0 (G\tau)^4 \Rightarrow n^0 = 6.814 \times 10^{12}$ m⁻⁴.
$B^0 = G. \, n^0 = 2.292 \times 10^5$ nuclei/m³.s. If $L = 0.2$ mm, $x = 0.917$; $W(x) = 0.014 \Rightarrow 1.4\%$
of the total mass is due to crystals of size $L \le 2$ mm.
Number fraction of crystals lower than $L = 0.2$ mm size

$$= \frac{N}{N_T} = \left[\int_0^L n^0 e^{-L/G\tau}\, dL\right]\bigg/\left[\int_0^\infty n^0 e^{-L/G\tau}\, dL\right] = 0.6$$

13.7 (a) $W(x) = 1 - e^{-x}\left(1 + x + \dfrac{x^2}{2} + \dfrac{x^3}{6}\right)$, $x = 6.013 \times 10^3 L$, L in m; $L_D = 0.5$ mm;

$L_M = 0.61$ mm.
(b) $Q_p = 0.833$ m³/h; $W(x) = 0.019 \Rightarrow 1.9\%$.

13.8 (a) From Eq. (13.18), $\dfrac{d(nG)}{dL} = -\dfrac{nG}{\tau\, G_0\,(1 + \gamma_L)^b}$; $L = 0$, $n = n^0$, $G = G_0$

Integrate to get, $\ln\left(\dfrac{nG}{n^0 G_0}\right) = \dfrac{1-(1+\gamma L)^{1-b}}{\tau G_0 \cdot \gamma(1-b)}$

(b) Population density distribution function,

$n(L) = 8 \times 10^{14}\,(1 + 1.25 \times 10^4 L)^{-0.2}.\,\exp[1.25\{1 - (1 + 1.25 \times 10^4 L)^{0.8}\}]$; L in m.

$M_T = 288$ kg/m^3

13.9 (a) $N_T = 2.25 \times 10^{12}$ crystals/m^3; (b) 15.8%; (c) 52%.

13.10 $dm_c/dt = 2.18 \times 10^{-12}$ kg/s

13.11 (a) $Q_o = 0.52$ m^3/h

(b) $Q_o = 0.52$ m^3/h, since the fines removed constitute a small mass fraction of the crystals.

13.12 (a) $B^0 = 1280$ muclei/m^3.s; (b) $M_F = \displaystyle\int_0^{L_F} (\phi_v\,L^3\rho_c)\cdot n(L)\,dL = 2.323 \times 10^{-4}$ kg/m^3; mass fraction removed as fines = 5.16×10^{-6}.

13.13 Write down the population balance equations (see the Hints) for $L \le L_F$, $L_F \le L \le L_c$, and $L_c \le L$ and integrate. Use the condition of continuity of population density, i.e. $n(L_F) = n(L_c)$.

13.14 $G = 1.47 \times 10^{-8}$m/s

13.15 Initial cooling rate = 1.3×10^{-3} °C/s; final cooling rate = 0.13 °C/s.

13.16 (a) Batch time = 4.77 h; (b) evaporation profile, $-dV/dt = 1.206 \times 10^{-6}$ m^3/s at $t = 0$; 1.894×10^{-5} m^3/s at $t = 4.77$ h.

CHAPTER 14

Short and Multiple Choice Questions

1. (iii).

2. (i), the other two polymers are not soluble.

4. (ii). **5.** (i). **6.** (i). **7.** (iii). **8.** (i). **9.** (i). **10.** (i).

11. (i). **12.** (iii). **13.** (i). **14.** (i). **15.** (i). **17.** (i). **18.** (iii).

19. (i). **20.** (i). **21.** (iii). **22.** (ii). **23.** (i). **24.** (iii). **25.** (i).

26. (iii). **27.** (i) and (ii).

28. (iii). **29.** (ii).

30. (ii), CA, polyimide; (iii) PDMS; (iv) PDMS; (v) an asymmetric UF membrane; (vii) cross-linked PVA; (viii) asymmetric UF; (x) PDMS; (xiii) ceramic membrane; (xiv) CA.

31. (i). **32.** (iii). **33.** (i). **34.** (iii). **35.** (i).

39. Apparent rejection = $1 - C_p/C_b = 0.975 \Rightarrow C_p = 5 \times 10^{-4}$; $J_w(C_b - C_p) = k_L(C_m - C_b)$

$\Rightarrow C_m = 0.1$; true rejection = $1 - \dfrac{5 \times 10^{-4}}{0.1} = 0.995$.

40. (ii) and (iii).

41. $x_A = 0.212$; $x_B = 0.788$.

42. (i).   **43.** (ii).

44. The alternative arrangement will not work. (Brine is fed to the cathode compartment and the product NaOH is also to be withdrawn from the same compartment. The product will have a lot of NaCl in it.)

45. Use Eq. (14.52). Take $\zeta = 0 \Rightarrow 0.85 = 1 - e^{-N_T} \Rightarrow N_T = 1.9$; length of the hollow fibres, $L = a_m/n \cdot B' = 0.225$ m; HTU $= L/N_T = 0.134$ m.

Problems

14.1 Plot J_w (kg/m^2.h) against ΔP(kPa). Slope $= 0.0125$ m^3/(h)(m^2)(kPa)

$$\Rightarrow \frac{\varepsilon d^2}{32 \mu \, l_m \tau} = 0.0125 \Rightarrow \tau = 3.2.$$

14.2 2.543 bar; 0.937 bar.

14.3 3.47 m^2

14.4 Membrane resistance, $R_m = \dfrac{32\tau \, l_m}{\varepsilon d^2} = 3.3 \times 10^{11}$ m^{-1};

$$J_w = \frac{\Delta P}{(R_m + R_g)\mu} \Rightarrow R_m + R_g = 1.333 \times 10^{12} \text{ m}^{-1};$$

$$R_g = 1.003 \times 10^{12}, \; l_g = 2.507 \text{ μm}.$$

14.5 (a) Use Eq. (14.10) to get $k_L = 3.57 \times 10^{-6}$ m/s. Pure water flux, $J_w = \Delta P/\mu R_m \Rightarrow \mu R_m$

$= 7.5$ bar.m^{2}h/m^3; ultrafiltration flux $= 0.032$ m^3/m$^2 \cdot$h $= \dfrac{6 \text{ bar}}{\mu(R_m + R_g)}$

$\Rightarrow \mu R_g = 180$ (m^2)(h)(bar)/(m)^3.

Permeability of the gel layer $= \dfrac{1}{\mu R_g} = 5.55 \times 10^{-3}$ m^3/(m^2)(h)(bar).

(b) $J_w = (0.032) \left(\dfrac{8 \text{ bar}}{6 \text{ bar}}\right) = 0.0427$ m^3/m^2.h

Fractional increase in the gel layer thickness $= 33.3\%$ (assumed that the given flux is nearly the limiting flux).

14.7 Use Eq. (14.21). Plot $1/J_w^2$ against time. From the intercept (90.7 m^{4}s^2/(litre)^2), $R_m = 3.17 \times 10^{11}$ m^{-1}. From the slope (14.03 m^{4}s^2/(litre)^2.s), $r_c/\rho_c = 1.17 \times 10^{13}$.

14.8 $a_m = 4$m^2

14.9 Use Eq. (14.25). Limiting flux according to the osmotic pressure model

$$= 1.6 \times 10^{-5} \text{ m}^3/\text{m}^2.\text{s}$$

14.10 (a) $l_g = 90$ μm; (b) $\Delta P = 0.62$ bar.   **14.11** 1.28 h

14.12 Yes, polarization modulus = 1.2.

14.13 $\Delta\Pi$ = 25.3 atm for 32 g/litre salt solution; effective pressure differential = $\Delta P - \Delta\Pi$ = 13.2 atm. Water flux = $L_p \cdot (\Delta P)_{\text{eff}}$ = 1.188 × 10^{-2} m^3/m^2.h; salt flux = $\hat{P}_s(C_b - C_p)$ = 1.024 × 10^{-6} kg/m^2.s $\Rightarrow$ permeate concentration = 310 ppm, which is above the allowable limit of 200 ppm. In order to maintain 200 ppm salt in the permeate, the water flux should be (1.188 × 10^{-2})(310/200) = 1.841 × 10^{-2} m^3/m^2.h = $L_p(\Delta P - 25.3)$

$\Rightarrow$ ΔP = 45.8 atm. Feed side pressure = 45.8 + 1.5 = 47.3 atm.

14.14 Use Eq. (14.45); C_{fi} = 3.3, θ_{wo} = 0.3, R' = 0.98 $\Rightarrow$ C_{fo} = 4.68%. Exit concentration of the mixed permeate = 300 ppm = 0.03%. Polarization modulus = 1.2 $\Rightarrow$ C_{mi} = 1.2C_{fi} = 3.96%; C_{mo} = (4.68)(1.2) = 5.62%. $(\Delta C)_i$ = 3.96 – 0.03 = 3.93%; $(\Delta C)_o$ = 5.62 – 0.03

= 5.59%. $(\Delta\Pi)_i = \left(\dfrac{39.5}{5}\right)$(3.93) = 31.05 atm; $(\Delta\Pi)_o = \left(\dfrac{39.5}{5}\right)$(5.59) = 44.16 atm;

average, $\Delta\Pi$ = 37.6 atm. $(\Delta P)_{\text{eff}}$ = (75 – 1) – (37.6) = 36.4 atm; water flux = $L_p(\Delta P)_{\text{eff}}$

= 0.258 m^3/m^2.h. Membrane area = $\dfrac{20{,}000}{(24)(0.258)}$ = 3230 m^2

14.15 $(\Delta C)_{\text{inlet}}$ = 0.366 kmol/m^3, exit—500 ppm = 0.0061 kmol/m^3. Log mean ΔC = 0.088. Total resistance = 2.5 × 10^5 s/m + $l_m/D \cdot \varepsilon$ = 4.58 × 10^5 s/m

$\Rightarrow$ K_L = 1/(4.58 × 10^5) = 2.18 × 10^{-6} m/s

$Q_f(C_f - C_o) = K_L a_m(\Delta C)_m \Rightarrow a_m$ = 104 m^2. Loss in the dialysis process = 33.7%.

14.17 (a) $\hat{E}$ = 0.2202 from Eq. (14.53).   (b) 200 min.

14.18 Use Eq. (14.70) to calculate the moisture flux.

Time (for loss of 91 g moisture) = 55.5 years!

14.19 $R_A = R'_A + R''_A$ = 4.32 × 10^4 (cm^2)(s)(cm Hg)/cm^3(STP); $\hat{P}_A = \dfrac{l_m}{R_A}$ = 120.4 barrer

$R_B = R'_B + R''_B$ = 1.347 × 10^6; $\hat{P}_B$ = 3.86 barrer.

Ideal separation factor, $\alpha^*_{AB} = \hat{P}_A/\hat{P}_B = \dfrac{120.4}{3.86}$ = 31.2.

14.20 J_A = 2.057 × 10^{-12} kmol/m^2.s; $\hat{P}_A$ = 1.537 × 10^{-4} barrer.

14.21 3 micron

14.22 (a) J_A = 7.53 × 10^{-6} gmol/cm^2.s having 99.6% A;   (b) α = 232, α^* = 250.

14.23 a_m = 318 m^2

14.24 (a) J_A = 1.27 × 10^{-7} gmol/cm^2.s; J_B = 1.394 × 10^{-7} gmol/cm^2.s

(b) $\tilde{P}_A$ = 1.523 × 10^{-5} cm^3(STP)/(cm^2)(s)(cm Hg); (c) D_B = 2.46 × 10^{-6} cm^2/s.

14.25 $\alpha = 4.42$; $\hat{P}_A = 1.4$ barrer; $\alpha^*_{AB} = 5.6$; $\hat{P}_B = 0.25$ barrer.

$S_A = C_A/p_A = 0.962$ cm^3(STP)/(cm^3 polymer)(atm); $D_A = 1.1 \times 10^{-8}$ cm^2/s.

14.26 $a_{m_1} = 715$ m^2; $a_{m_2} = 280$ m^2.

14.27 Follow Example 14.15. $y_p = 0.44$; $Q_p = 90$ m^3/h; $a_m = 51.5$ m^2.

14.28 Time = 10 min. Virtually no gas-phase resistance.

CHAPTER 15

Short and Multiple Choice Questions

2. (a) (iii). (b)(ii). (c) (ii). **3.** (ii). **4.** (ii). **5.** (i). **6.** (i).

7. (i). **9.** (iii). **10.** (iii).

CHAPTER 16

Short and Multiple Choice Questions

1. $(N_A)_{\text{phys.}} < (N_A)_{\text{chem}} \Rightarrow -D_A\left(\dfrac{dC_A}{dz}\right)_{\text{phys}} < -D_A\left(\dfrac{dC_A}{dz}\right)_{\text{chem}}$

$$\Rightarrow \left(\frac{dC_A}{dz}\right)_{\text{phys}} > \left(\frac{dC_A}{dz}\right)_{\text{chem}} \Rightarrow S_1 > S_2 \text{ (i).} \left[\text{Note that } \left|\left(\frac{dC_A}{dz}\right)_{\text{phys}}\right| < \left|\left(\frac{dC_A}{dz}\right)_{\text{chem}}\right|\right]$$

2. (iii). **3.** (iii). **4.** (i). **5.** (iii).

6. (ii), since only little depletion of the dissolved reactant B occurs in the film.

7. (i). **8.** (i).

9. Use Eq. (16.37). $E = 4.43$. **10.** (iii).

Problems

16.3 (a) 328 h

16.4 6.77×10^{-6} cm^2/s

16.7 0.2 cm

16.8 $k_1 = k_2 C_{Bb} = 212.6$ s^{-1}

16.9 Gas-phase resistance is less than 10% of the liquid-phase resistance.

16.13 By a differential mass balance over a section of the bed, the inlet (C_{bi}) and the outlet (C_{bo}) concentrations of the reactant can be found to be

$$\ln \frac{C_{bi}}{C_{bo}} = \frac{\bar{a}}{v_L} \cdot \frac{k_L k'}{k_L + k'} \cdot h$$

Put the values of the different quantities to get $k' = 4.46 \times 10^{-5}$ m/s.

14.24 $D_p = 4.1 \times 10^{-5}$, $P_p = L^2$ butter $6_p = 5.6 \times 10^{-8}$ Å, $\theta = 0.25$ bar/m

$\S_p = C/C_0 = 0.907$ cm (STP)/cm^3 (mem. polymer)/atm, $D_p = 4.1 \times 10^{-5}$ cm^2/s

14.26 $m_p = 715$ m, $m_b = 291$ m/s

14.27 Follow Example 14.15, $\gamma_A = 0.41$, $Q_v = 0.09$ m/s, $m_p = 51.5$ m

14.28 Time = 10 min. Virtually no gas-phase resistance.

CHAPTER 15

Short and Multiple Choice Questions

1. (D)   4. (D)   6. (a)   8. (D)   a. (D)   9. (10)   e. (a. D)
b. c.   9. (D)   10. (m)

CHAPTER 16

Short and Multiple Choice Questions

1. $\left[\dfrac{dC_A}{dt}\right]_{\text{reaction}} = k\rho_b(C_A^{\,n} - \cdots) = -D_A\dfrac{d^2C_A}{dz^2}$

4. $\left[\dfrac{dC_A}{dt}\right]_{\text{reaction}} = \cdots = \Delta H_{RX}(-r_A)$ (F) triple bar

5. a. (D)   3. (10)   7. (a)   d. (D)

6. ... that the only time-dependence of the dissolved reactant B occurs in the film ...

7. a. (D)   8. (D) ...

8. line bar $\dfrac{(H_{RX})}{\cdots}$, $\Gamma = k \cdots$ 10. (D) ...

Problems

16.2 ($1) = 354$ s

16.4 4873, 162 m/s

16.7 A 2 cm

16.8 $t = k$, $C_{B_0} = 0.120$ ...

16.9 Our assumption is less than 10% of the liquid-phase resistance.

16.13 By a differential mass balance over a section of the bed of the interval C_{A} and the molar (C_A) concentrations of the reactant can be found to be

$$\ln\dfrac{C_{A_0}}{C_A} = \dfrac{-k_s A}{v + k_s A}$$

Putting the values of the different parameters to get $k' = 4.6 \times 10^{-4}$ m/s ...

Index